Contents

United Kingdom

Ireland

France

Spain

Portugal

Maps

The history of ACSI

From duplicated booklet to 674,500 guides

No more closed barriers

Teacher Ed van Reine set off with his family in the summer of 1965. The fervent camper steered his car towards the Spanish sun in good spirits. However the journey ended in disappointment, as there was no room for the family at the campsite they had so carefully selected. Situations like this could surely be prevented? Van Reine brainstormed on the spot with two teacher colleagues about a reservation system for popular European campsites. They called it 'Auto Camper Service International'. ACSI was thus born and the basis was formed for the familiar green ACSI campsite guides.

These three pioneers selected 55 campsites, collected information and distributed it in a duplicated booklet for the modest price of one Dutch guilder. No more closed barriers; from now on it was possible to contact the campsite in advance to reserve a pitch. During the sixties, when camping became something of a national sport, demand for the guide grew.

The way to the top

By the third year a number of campsites asked if it was possible to supplement their entry in the guide for a fee to include a piece of text and a photo. Inspectors were recruited and so the first team to travel around Europe to collect campsite details was created.

In the early eighties ACSI set its sights high when the company decided to publish the campsite guide itself. The number of campsites increased

Ed van Reine

to 7,500 and in 1985 the first group of Dutch campers went on holiday with ACSI Camping Tours: group tours offering individual freedom. These tours are now also organised for German and English-speaking campers. ACSI officially became a family business from the moment that Ed van Reine brought in his son Ramon, the current director of ACSI. From then on the company developed rapidly.

ACSI diversifies

In the nineties ACSI was involved with digitisation, product expansion and internationalisation. In 1999 ACSI was the first in Europe to launch a dynamic campsite search engine on the internet. The information on the website www.eurocampings.net could be accessed in four languages. Nowadays ▶ *www.EUROCAMPINGS.eu* ◀ is available in 14 languages and the visitor could already filter the amenities inspected.

Various new guides with different interests and themes have since appeared and these are also published in multiple languages. The introduction of CampingCard ACSI in 2004 put the campsite specialist on the record for good: the incredibly simple, user-friendly discount system for the low season proved to be immensely popular with campers!

Nowadays 180 permanent employees are occupied in optimising existing products and developing new ones. More than 300 enthusiastic inspectors travel throughout Europe in order to ensure that only campsites with the highest standards of quality appear in the ACSI campsite guides. The extensive and objective information that results from these annual inspections has for years been ACSI's strength.

Progressive since 1965

ACSI brings campers and campsites together throughout Europe by publishing campsite information, but ACSI does much more. ACSI Club ID members can go on holiday with a camping carnet, an alternative identity document, accepted at almost 9,000 campsites.

ACSI continues to listen to the wishes of both campers and campsites and react to them. The result is clear: over the years ACSI has grown to become the most progressive campsite specialist to receive more than 10 million visitors a year on www.eurocampings.eu, has sold more than 300,000 apps and this year will reach the record circulation of 674,500 campsite guides. You now have one of them. Thanks for your trust! ACSI wishes you lots of enjoyable camping in 2018.

Directions for use

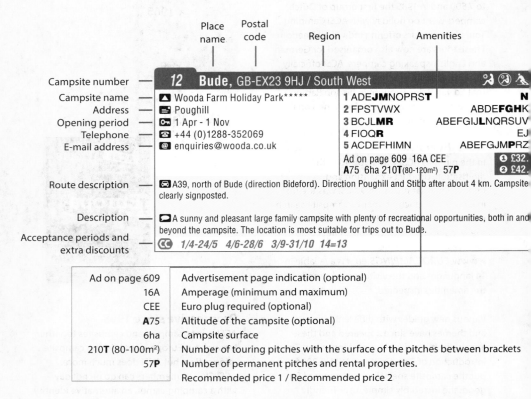

Campsite number	—	
Campsite name	—	
Address	—	
Opening period	—	
Telephone	—	
E-mail address	—	

12 **Bude,** GB-EX23 9HJ / South West

▲ Wooda Farm Holiday Park*****
▣ Poughill
▣ 1 Apr - 1 Nov
☎ +44 (0)1288-352069
@ enquiries@wooda.co.uk

1 ADE**JM**NOPRS**T**   **N**
2 FPSTVWX   ABDE**FGH**K
3 BCJL**MR**   ABEFGIJ**L**NQRSUV
4 FIOQ**R**   EJ
5 ACDEFHIMN   ABEFGJM**P**RZ

Ad on page 609 16A CEE   ❶ £32.
A75 6ha 210**T**(80-120m²) 57**P**   ❷ £42.

Route description — ▣A39, north of Bude (direction Bideford). Direction Poughill and Stibb after about 4 km. Campsite clearly signposted.

Description — ▣A sunny and pleasant large family campsite with plenty of recreational opportunities, both in and beyond the campsite. The location is most suitable for trips out to Bude.

Acceptance periods and extra discounts — ◖◗ 1/4-24/5 4/6-28/6 3/9-31/10 14=13

Place name · Postal code · Region · Amenities

Ad on page 609	Advertisement page indication (optional)
16A	Amperage (minimum and maximum)
CEE	Euro plug required (optional)
A75	Altitude of the campsite (optional)
6ha	Campsite surface
210**T** (80-100m²)	Number of touring pitches with the surface of the pitches between brackets
57**P**	Number of permanent pitches and rental properties.
	Recommended price 1 / Recommended price 2

The editorial entry
Above is an example of an editorial entry as they are used in the ACSI Campsite Guide. An editorial entry is a text block including all of the information about a campsite. These instructions for use indicate the meaning of the numbers, letters and symbols in the editorial entry. Page 10 explains how you can search for a campsite in this guide.

Campsite number
At the top left in the green bar is a campsite's sequence number. You can use this number to establish the location of the campsite on the maps in the back of the guide.

Place name, postal code and region
The place name and postal code of the campsite and the region in which it is located.

Special campsites
You will see a variety of symbols in the green bar. Whenever a campsite is suitable for the disabled, you will see this symbol: ♿

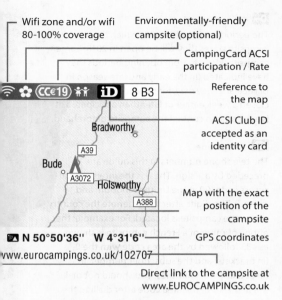

Wifi zone and/or wifi 80-100% coverage

Environmentally-friendly campsite (optional)

CampingCard ACSI participation / Rate

Reference to the map

ACSI Club ID accepted as an identity card

Map with the exact position of the campsite

GPS coordinates

Direct link to the campsite at www.EUROCAMPINGS.co.uk

If a campsite is a winter sports campsite, you will see the following symbol. Campsites with 🧖 are intended for naturists only and campsites with an area designated for naturists are indicated with 🧖

✿ Environmentally-friendly campsite
If a campsite has an eco-label, it indicates that a campsite is environmentally friendly.

🛜 Wifi zone and/or
🛜 Wifi 80-100% coverage
If there is a wifi zone on the campsite, then there is a location on the campsite where you can access wireless internet. You will see this symbol in the editorial entry for these campsites: 🛜
If there is 80-100% wifi coverage, then you can access wireless internet on at least 80% of the campsite. You will see this symbol in the editorial entry for these campsites: 🛜

CC CampingCard ACSI campsite
If this icon with the amount of €11, €13, €15, €17 or €19 is indicated for the campsite, the campsite participates in CampingCard ACSI. This means that your overnight accommodation is provided at this rate in the early and late season. Page 12 and further provide an extensive explanation.

🧒 Three children up to and including the age of 5 included (possible)
If (a maximum of) 3 children under 6 are included in the CampingCard ACSI rate, you will see the following symbol: 🧒 in the editorial entry. This applies only to campsites that participate in the CampingCard ACSI.

iD ACSI Club ID
You can use the ACSI Club ID Card at many campsites, this is a substitute identity card. Campsites indicate whether they accept the ACSI Club ID. Go to page 24 of this guide for more information about this Camping Carnet.

Reference to maps
At the top right in the green bar is the number of the map and the accompanying area on the map in which the campsite is located. On the map is a tent with the campsite's sequence number for easy reference to the campsite.

Take note: You can find the maps in the back of this guide and you can recognize them by the yellow bar on the side of the page. The campsite number in the editorial entry refers to the map number on the left or right side at the top of these pages.

▲ Campsite name and star ratings

Here you can see the campsite name and possibly the number of stars. ACSI does not give stars or other classifications to campsites. Star ratings or other types of classification are awarded to the campsite by local or national organisations and are shown after the campsite name. Stars do not always indicate the quality but more often the comfort that a campsite offers. The more stars there are, the more amenities. Whether a campsite is good or not and whether you think it deserves two stars or four is something you must decide for yourself.

▤ Address

The postal address of the campsite. You will find the postal address including the postal code in the uppermost block of the editorial entry. Sometimes, in France for example, you will see that there is no postal address. You will discover that you will usually be able to find the campsite yourself once you have arrived in the town. To make it easier to find the campsite, we have included a route description and the GPS coordinates in the editorial entry.

⚷ Opening period

The period or periods during which the campsite states they will be open in 2018. Some campsites deviate from opening periods they have indicated (in the early and late season in particular). They may, for instance, be opened or closed a week earlier or later than anticipated. It is advisable to contact the campsite beforehand.

☎ Telephone

The telephone numbers in this guide are preceded by a + sign. The + is the international access code (00 in the United Kingdom and Ireland). The digits after the + denote the country where the campsite is located. For example: the phone number of a French campsite is shown as +33 followed by the area code with the 0 (in brackets) and the subscriber number. In most European countries, you should not dial the first zero of the area code after dialling the international access code. So for France you dial 0033 and then the area code, without the zero, followed by the subscriber's number.

@ E-mail address

The campsite's e-mail address. The e-mail address is especially useful to make a reservations or enquiries in the low season, when the reception may be staffed less frequently.

Amenities

ACSI campsite inspectors annually visit all campsites. They collect information about over 200 amenities. Amenities are classified according to ten headings:

1. Regulations
2. Location, ground and shade
3. Sports and play
4. Recreation and wellness
5. Shops and restaurants

6 Water recreation
7 Washing up, laundry and cooking
8 Washing and toilet facilities
9 Rental facilities
10 Miscellaneous

The letters behind the figures correspond to the amenities, which you can find on the **fold-out flap** at the front of the guide. Heading 1 indicates for example whether mobile homes or pets are allowed, and headings 3 and 4 indicate whether there are any trails and bicycle routes and whether the campsite has playground equipment. Headings 7 and 8 indicate the bathroom amenities and 10 states possible Internet options and whether the paths and roads are illuminated.

You can compare the amenities list in the front of the guide with the campsite you have selected. You can also check whether surcharges apply for certain facilities. The facilities list indicates a star for facilities for which a surcharge may apply. If you see a **bold** letter at one of these facilities, this means that the facility is not included in the overnight rate. For instance: 3H means that pony riding is free of charge, and **3H** means you have to pay for this. If facilities do not include a star, the inspector does not check whether this facility is free or not. These facilities are never bold, but this does not necessarily mean that they are free.

Bear in mind that not all facilities indicated are available throughout the entire opening period. Some facilities under the sports and play, recreation and wellness, and purchase headings may be available only in the high season. Go to ▶ *www.EUROCAMPINGS.co.uk* ◀ for more information about the opening periods of the facilities.

Bringing your dog on your holiday
Many campsites allow pets; this is stated in heading 1. Some campsites apply a limit to the number of dogs per camper and/or some breeds are not permitted. It may also be that certain breeds or numbers of dogs are permitted in the low season only. Please contact the campsite if you have any doubts as to whether dogs are allowed.

Advertisement following this notification
If the campsite advertises, you can usually find the advertisement with additional information immediately following the editorial entry. It may be that an advertisement is on another page. The page on which the advertisement is shown is indicated here.

Available amperage of the electrical connection
For each campsite, we indicate the amperage available. When the campsite information mentions 6-10A, this means that at this campsite there are pitches with an amperage of minimum 6 and maximum 10.

CEE
This indication means that you will need a three pin euro-plug.

Surface area of the campsite
The surface area of the campsite is given in hectares. 1ha = 10,000 m² (square metres) or approximately 2.5 acres.

Altitude of the campsite
The altitude of the campsite is indicated in metres. It is stated only if the campsite is on an altitude of at least 50 metres.

Number of touring pitches / permanent pitches
The number that is stated for the T indicates the number of touring places on the campsite. Some campsites differentiate between touring pitches that are hired per overnight stay, and seasonal pitches reserved for guests who are on the campsite all season. The T thus stands for the number of touring pitches without any seasonal pitches.

The number before the P indicates the number of pitches that is not intended for tourist campers; the permanent pitches. These include the pitches intended for seasonal campers (seasonal pitches and low season pitches) as well as rental properties.

Smallest/largest touring pitch
Behind the number of touring pitches is an indication about their measurements. If it says (80-120 m²), you can assume that the smallest touring pitch is 80 m² and the largest 120 m².

Recommended price 1 / Recommended price 2
Two recommended prices are charged in the ACSI Campsite Guide: a recommended price without children (recommended price 1) and one with children (recommended price 2). Campers thus receive the best price indication. These are rates that are charged in the high season.

Recommended price
2 adults, 1 car, 1 caravan, front bell/awning, tourist tax (2 adults), environmental tax and electricity (lowest amperage).

Recommended price 2
This recommended price is calculated identically to recommended price 1, including 2 children aged 6 and 9.

For recommended price 1 and 2, these are rates for standard pitches in the high season. These are the most common pitches on the campsite. A surcharge applies for comfort pitches (pitches that commonly have and RTV connection, water supply and a water outlet). Prices are based on the price in the currency of the country concerned in September 2017. Refer to the 'Currency and financial affairs' heading on the pages with country information for the currency and exchange rate of a country.

The recommended prices are stated in the currency of the country concerned.

Take note: the guide states the rates that were applicable in 2017, when the inspector visited the campsite. Prices thus serve as an indication only.

Description
This block of text provides some concise information about the location of the campsite, the ambiance and the environs.

Route description
The written directions in this route description will assist you in finding your way during the last few miles to the campsite entrance and will advise you which motorway exit to take and which signs to follow.

Acceptance period and extra discount CampingCard ACSI
Each campsite decides its own acceptance period and so defines its own low season. For dates when the CampingCard ACSI discount is available, you will need to look at the acceptance periods in the lower block of the editorial entry for the campsite. If, for example a campsite shows '7=6' this means that you pay only 6 nights at the CampingCard ACSI rate for a 7 night stay.

Map
The map shows where the campsite is located in its immediate surroundings. The exact location of the campsite is indicated with a red tent.

GPS coordinates
If you use a navigation system, the GPS coordinates are almost indispensable. Our inspectors have measured the coordinates right next to the campsite barrier. Mind: not all navigation systems are configured for cars with a caravan, so always read the route description that is included with each campsite and don't forget to watch out for the signs. The GPS coordinates are shown in degrees, minutes and seconds. When you enter the data into your navigation system, check that it is also configured in degrees, minutes and seconds. The letter N is shown by the first number. Following the second number there is a letter E or W (right or left of the Greenwich meridian).

In some cases, your navigation system will not guide you to the campsite when following the coordinates to the barrier. If this is the case, ACSI has opted to navigate to the campsite access road. You will be guided to the campsite when you follow the signposts and/or directions from that point.

If you make use of the ACSI Campsites Europe app, you can easily navigate to the campsite using Google Maps or Apple Maps.

Website and campsite number
Each campsite indicates the direct link to ▶ *www.EUROCAMPINGS.co.uk* ◀, followed by a six-digit number; the campsite's unique number. When you enter the entire link, you are taken directly to the campsite page where you can see photos and read evaluations by co-campers.

How to find a campsite

Finding a campsite in the ACSI Campsite Guide is very simple. Each country starts with a map that is divided into regions. Each region indicates the page where the information about a region starts. You can start by reading more about the region concerned, after which the campsites in the area are listed in alphabetical order of city name. There are several possibilities to find a campsite:

In this campsite guide:
Search for a campsite by place. Go to the alphabetical list of cities on page 868 and further. Behind the city is the page number of the campsite(s) in this city.

On the maps:
Each campsite on the map has a number, which is indicated at the top left in the editorial entry of the ACSI Campsite Guide. The blue tents indicate that the campsite is included in the CampingCard ACSI. In addition, you can find the location of the campsite from the editorial entry. At the top right is the number of the map and the accompanying area on the page.

On the website:
Website ▶ *www.EUROCAMPINGS.co.uk* ◀.
See also page 29.

In the ACSI Campsite Europe app:
See also page 32.

CampingCard ACSI

The ultimate off-season discount card

As a user of the ACSI Campsite Guide, you receive your personal CampingCard ACSI discount card you can use in 2018 at 3,330 campsites.

What is the CampingCard ACSI?

You can use the CampingCard ACSI discount card to stay at quality campsites in Europe at one of the five following reasonable fixed rates: €11, €13, €15, €17 or €19.

The rates are below the lowest rate participating campsites charge in the early season, so you can count on a high discount per overnight stay! Discounts vary from a minimum of 10% to 50% of regular prices! The 3,330 participating CampingCard ACSI campsites are all ACSI-inspected and approved.

Take note: ACSI inspects a total of over 9,900 campsites throughout Europe. This Campsite Guide includes a selection of campsites in the United Kingdom, Ireland, France, Spain and Portugal, 1438 campsites of which accept the CampingCard ACSI. You will recognise these campsites by the blue CampingCard ACSI CC logo CC at the top right in the editorial entry. Campsites indicate their participation with the sticker with the blue CC logo or the large flag at reception. These are the campsites for which a discount applies.

All 3,330 campsites that accept the CampingCard ACSI are stated in the CampingCard ACSI guide 2018 and on ▶ *www.CAMPINGCARD.com* ◀

How does the CampingCard ACSI work?

- Fill in the back of your CampingCard ACSI. The personal card is valid for one calendar year.
- Show your discount card (valid for two adults) upon arrival at the campsite.
- During your stay, benefit from low rates (during the acceptance period only).
- When paying your bill, show your discount card again at the campsite reception. *
- Pay the reasonable CampingCard ACSI rate of only €11, €13, €15, €17 or €19 per overnight stay. **

* In principle, you can pay afterwards using your CampingCard ACSI. The payment method may be determined by campsite regulations, such as the time at which you are required to pay, or that a down payment is required. For instance, if you indicate that you will be staying for one night only or if you wish to book, the campsite may ask you to complete your payment immediately. The campsite reception will inform you about the campsite's policy concerning this.

** Refer to 'Not included in the overnight rate' for any additional costs. See page 15.

CampingCard ACSI acceptance periods

Each participating campsite has established the period in which the CampingCard ACSI is accepted. These include at least 9 weeks in May, June and September, but usually the acceptance period is longer and sometimes up to the entire calendar year, with a maximum of 15 days in July and August.

Participating campsites are committed to ensuring that the main facilities are present and functioning in the acceptance period of the discount card.

The opening and acceptance dates have been compiled with utmost care. Owing to circumstances, it may be that these dates are subject to change after the publication of this guide. Refer to ▶ *www.CAMPINGCARD.com/modifications* ◀ to see if any changes apply to the campsite of your choice.

Please refer to the acceptance periods in the bottom bar of the campsite's editorial entry for the dates on which the CampingCard ACSI discount applies. The last date specified in a period is always the last possible day of arrival in order to stay overnight with a CampingCard ACSI discount. An acceptance period of 1/1 - 30/6 means that the first night you are entitled to a discount is the night from 1 January to 2 January, and the last night you are entitled to a discount is the night from 30 June to 1 July. So, on the night from 1 July to 2 July, you will pay the normal rate.

Booking

Some campsites allow advance booking using the CampingCard ACSI. If this is the case, the campsite has stated facility point 10D in the editorial entry. In principle, a booking with CampingCard ACSI is treated as a regular booking, the only difference being that the overnight rate is much more advantageous. When booking, please state that you are a CampingCard ACSI holder. If you fail to do this, chances are that you will be obliged to pay the regular rate. In some cases, bookings require payment, and a down payment may be requested. The campsite may consider reservations made long before by a CampingCard ACSI holder to be inconvenient. If this is the case, a campsite might not accept the booking. In addition, booking is not possible for some campsites.

What do the participating campsites have to offer for the fixed CampingCard ACSI rate?

Participating campsites offer the following in the CampingCard ACSI rate on touring pitches:

- A camping pitch. *
- Overnight stay for 2 adults.
- Car & caravan & awning, or car & folding caravan, or car & tent, or motor home & awning.
- Electricity. A connection of maximum 6A or a consumption of maximum 4 kWh per day is included in the CampingCard ACSI rate. When a campsite only has pitches with a lower amperage, this lower amperage will apply. If you use excess, for example 5 kWh, you might have to pay extra. See also 'Available amperage of the electrical connection' on page 7.
- Hot showers. At campsites where showers are operated by tokens, CampingCard ACSI holders are entitled to one token per adult per day. **
- Maximum one dog staying on campsites that accept dogs. For a second (or additional) dog you might have to pay extra.
- VAT.

* Some campsites make a distinction between standard, luxury or comfort pitches. Luxury or comfort pitches are in general larger and equipped with their own water supply and drainage. CampingCard ACSI gives you the right to a standard pitch but it may occur that you are able to have a more expensive pitch at the CampingCard ACSI rate. The campsite has the right to decide this; you can NEVER insist on a luxury or comfort pitch.
Be aware also that some campsites have a different policy with regard to twin-axle caravans and mobile homes that are so large that they will not fit on a standard pitch.

** The campsite is required to allow the CampingCard ACSI holder one shower per day in accordance with the CampingCard ACSI conditions. Consequently each CampingCard ACSI holder has the right to one shower token per person per overnight stay. When a campsite operates a different 'shower system' such as coins, a key or a SEP key, the above conditions still apply, but the camper will need to make the necessary arrangements with the

campsite. Hot water in sinks is not included in the price. Unused shower tokens cannot be exchanged for money.

Not included in the overnight rate

In general the CampingCard ACSI rate is sufficient to pay for the overnight charge. The campsite may, however, impose extra charges for a number of items:

- Tourist taxes, environmental taxes, waste disposal charges or local authority requirements are not included in the CampingCard ACSI rate. These taxes can differ greatly by country and region.
- Reservation and administration charges are not included in the CampingCard ACSI rate. You can read more about reserving with CampingCard ACSI on page 13.
- A campsite may impose a surcharge for a luxury or comfort pitch (unless the campsite only has comfort pitches).
- Campsites make pitches available for two adults. The campsite may decide if more guests may stay on these pitches, apart from the two adults who can stay for the CampingCard ACSI rate (for example the guests' children or more adults), for payment of the regular rate per guest. If this is not allowed, then the camping group will be directed to pitches that are not meant for CampingCard ACSI users and for which the regular low season rates must be paid. However, at campsites which display the following symbol: 👨‍👦 (a maximum of) three children up to and including the age of 5 are included in the CampingCard ACSI rate. Items such as shower coins and tourist tax (if applicable) for these children are not included.
- A 6A power connection or consumption of 4 kWh is included in the price. Some campsites have pitches with 10A. If you require 10A, be

sure to clearly indicate this to the campsite owner; a surcharge may apply.
- Extra services such as facilities for which the campsite charges, such as a tennis court, can be charged to you at the applicable low season rate.

Additional discount

Many campsites have an additional discount for longer stays. For instance: if the guide states 7=6 for a certain campsite, this means that you only pay 6 times the CampingCard ACSI rate for a 7 night stay! Be sure to indicate the number of nights you intend to stay when registering or booking. The campsite will make a booking beforehand and applies the discount. The discount may not apply if you decide to stay longer during your stay and thereby reach the required number of days.

Take note! If a campsite has several of these discounts you are only entitled to one of these offers. For example: the special offers are 4=3, 7=6 and 14=12. If you stay for 13 nights you only have the right to one 7=6 discount and not to multiples of 4=3 or a combination of 4=3 and 7=6.

3 children free of charge

This guide includes 280 campsites where (no more than) 3 children under 6 are included in the CampingCard ACSI rate! These campsites are recognised by the following symbol: 👨‍👦

Take note: while a campsite displays this symbol they may still require you to pay tourist tax for children, as the campsite has to pay the tourist tax directly to the local authorities. Items such as shower tokens for children are not included.

Find a CampingCard ACSI campsite?

After reading the tips in this chapter, finding the campsite you are looking for will be easy.

Information per campsite in this guide

The campsites have been classified by country, region and city. The blue CampingCard ACSI logo in the extensive editorial entry demonstrates that the campsite accepts the CampingCard ACSI and which rate is charged (€11, €13, €15, €17 or €19).

Internet

You can find all participating CampingCard ACSI campsites on ▶ *www.CAMPINGCARD.com* ◀ The website is also suitable for tablets and mobile telephones. There are many ways to search for a campsite, such as:

- By map
- By city, region or country
- By campsite number
- By campsite name
- By holiday period (arrival and departure)
- By facilities
- By holiday theme

Take note: not all campsites in France that accept the CampingCard ACSI are included. Go to the website for a complete overview.

For 2018 only!

The CampingCard ACSI discount card applies for 2018 only, as does the information about the CampingCard ACSI campsites. Each calendar year, new campsites can register, campsites may modify the acceptance rate or charge a different overnight rate. The information in the guide will therefore be updated annually. Make sure you have the most recent guide when going on holiday. Before your departure, check

▶ *www.CAMPINGCARD.com/modifications* ◀ for updated information.

CampingCard ACSI guide 2018

You can also use the special 2018 CampingCard ACSI guide for the complete selection (in 21 countries) of CampingCard ACSI campsites. It includes more extensive information for each campsite, such as two photos of each campsite to give you an idea of the view and atmosphere. Order the CampingCard guide for €16.95 (shipping excluded), or subscribe to CampingCard ACSI from €11.95 per year (shipping excluded). You will be automatically sent the discount card and CampingCard ACSI guide at your home address. For more information, go to: ▶ *www.WEBSHOP.ACSI.eu* ◀

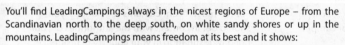

Prepare for your holiday

Rules and regulations

If you have decided to go on holiday abroad, it is wise to be properly prepared. Many formalities and agreements about matters such as necessary travel documents, car papers, requirements relating to your means of transport and accommodation, medical expenses and taking pets with you not only depend on the country you are travelling to, but also on your departure point and nationality. The length of your stay can also play a role here. It is not possible within the confines of this guide to guarantee the correct and most up-to-date information with regard to these matters.

We advise you to consult the relevant authorities before your departure about:
- which travel documents you will need for yourself and your fellow passengers
- which documents you need for your car
- which regulations your caravan or camper must meet

- which goods you may import and export
- how medical treatment will be arranged and paid for in your holiday destination in cases of accident or illness
- whether you can take pets. Contact your vet well in advance. They can give you information about the necessary vaccinations, proof thereof and obligations on return. It would also make sense to enquire whether any special regulations apply to your pet in public places at your holiday destination. In some countries for example, dogs must always be muzzled or transported in a cage.

You will find plenty of general information on ▶ *www.europa.eu* ◀ but make certain you select information that is relevant to your specific situation.

For the most recent customs regulations, you should get in contact with the authorities of your holiday destination in your country of residence.

The best
family campsites

Average rating 8.3

Suncamp holidays

Search for and book your campsite online

- Camping pitches, fully equipped tents, and holiday homes
- Plenty of swimming fun: at the pool or on the beach
- Secure booking and payment

Book easy on: **www.SUNCAMP.co.uk** or call: +44 (0) 845-22 50 931

Special campsites

Campsites suitable for the disabled

Every year ACSI checks to see which campsites are suitable for the disabled. The standards applied for this have been established in consultation with the Dutch Council for the Disabled. These campsites all have a bathroom and shower suitable for the disabled, or a combination of the two. We also indicate if a campsite has other facilities that are useful for the disabled. These campsites are indicated by the following symbol ♿ at the top of the editorial entry.

Winter sports campsites

Some campsites are designated 'winter sports campsites'. Various winter sports facilities are indicated for these campsites, such as 'ski storage', 'drying room' or 'ski bus stop by the campsite'. The winter sports campsites in this guide can be recognised by the following symbol ⛷ at the top of the editorial entry.

Naturist campsites

Various campsites in this guide are exclusively for naturists. We also indicate if a campsite has a designated area for naturists. Campsites intended exclusively for naturists are indicated by the following symbol 🧘 at the top of the editorial entry, and campsites with a designated area are indicated by the following symbol 🧘 .

Online searches

▶ *www.EUROCAMPINGS.co.uk* ◀ allows you to easily filter for the Campsites for disabled, Winter sports campsites and Campsites for naturists holiday themes, so you can immediately see the campsites that comply with your search criteria.

New: online booking!

Book directly with the campsite

Nothing is more irritating than finding a campsite, and then arriving there to find there's no space left. Anyone looking for a rental accommodation on a campsite knows that booking is almost a requirement, but it is also wise to book a pitch, certainly during holidays or for campsites in popular areas. This is now a thing of the past! You can reserve your campsite space or rental accommodation on an increasing number of campsites through ACSI.

You can do this from home or on the road, via *www.EUROCAMPINGS.co.uk*, or by using the ACSI Campsites Europe app. These bookable campsites have an extra red button. You book directly with the campsite and immediately make an online deposit. This will ensure the booking is definitive both for you and the campsite.

Booking a campsite

Once you've found a bookable campsite that suits, just click on the red button. Then select your preferred date of arrival and length of stay, click 'Book now' in the calendar, and follow the steps on the next page.

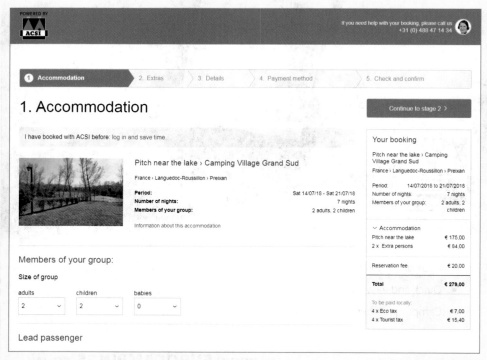

Sample booking form

1. Fill in the names of the people you're travelling with
2. Select any extras
3. Enter any other details, and the details of your camping vehicle
4. Choose your payment method
5. Check your details, and click on 'Confirm booking'

You are redirected to the payment page, and pay the requested down payment. When booking for a short-term stay, the full amount is usually requested. Your booking is final, and is made under the campsite's terms and conditions. If you cancel, this is also under the campsite's terms and conditions.

The advantages of booking online

· You can be sure that there will be space for you
· All costs will be clear in advance
· The price is the same as the price at the campsite

More and more campsites bookable via ACSI

The number of campsites that you can book via ACSI is increasing all the time. So keep an eye on the website, and check the app regularly. If you want to know more about booking a campsite pitch via ACSI, check out
▶ *www.EUROCAMPINGS.co.uk/bookonline* ◀

Advantages of the ACSI Club ID

The ACSI Club ID, the leading Camping Carnet for Europe, is indispensable for every camper. You will benefit from it both during your camping holiday and at home! Become a member right now and pay only €4.95 a year. We have listed all the advantages of the ACSI Club ID below:

Alternative identity card

You can hand in your Camping Carnet, the ACSI Club ID, at participating ACSI Club ID campsites instead of your passport or identity papers. Passport fraud is an ongoing issue in Europe and with the ACSI Club ID you remain in control of your valuable passport or ID card. You will not have to hand in your identity papers but can always keep them safely in your pocket.

Take note: It is possible that in some countries, including Spain, Italy and Croatia, you will still have to hand in your identity document at the campsite due to local regulations.

Liability insurance coverage

If you are in possession of the ACSI Club ID, you and your travelling companions (max 11 people) are insured against liability during your camping holiday or when staying in a hotel or rented accommodation. This insurance applies when you cause damage for third parties, for example if you accidentally drop your bicycle onto your neighbour's tent during your holiday.

Benefit from various offers

As an ACSI Club member, you'll always pay the lowest price in the ACSI Webshop.

Visit ▶ *www.ACSIclubID.eu* ◀ to stay informed about the latest developments concerning the ACSI Camping Carnet.

Accepted at almost 9,000 campsites in Europe

Almost 9,000 campsites in the ACSI campsite guides accept the ACSI Club ID. The amenity that shows that a campsite accepts the ACSI Club ID is mentioned in the list of amenities as 1A. You can also recognise these campsites by the 'ID' logo in the green bar above the editorial entry.

If you are camping in Scandinavia, there is a chance that you will need a special card that you must show at reception. You can purchase this card at the relevant campsite.

Take note: the ACSI Club ID does not entitle you to a discount at campsites.

Differences between ACSI Club ID and CampingCard ACSI

There are differences between ACSI Club ID and the CampingCard ACSI. We have put these differences in a table for your benefit.

ACSI Club ID	CampingCard ACSI
The Camping Carnet, a substitute means of identification	The discount card for camping in low season
A membership	A standalone product
Liability insurance and discounts on ACSI products in the ACSI webshop	Gives you the right to a fixed low overnight rate during low season
Accepted as alternative means of identification at almost 9,000 campsites in 29 countries	Accepted at 3,330 participating campsites in 21 countries
Valid for 1 year, until the expiration date	Valid for one calendar year, from 1 January until 31 December
€4.95 per year	From € 11.95 per year, including two-part guide
www.ACSIclubID.eu	www.CAMPINGCARD.com

Application

You can apply for the ACSI Club ID via ▶ *www.ACSIclubID.eu* ◀. Your card can be ordered in just a few steps. Be sure to have your identity papers handy when ordering.

The ACSI Club ID can be used by campers with any of the following nationalities: Dutch, Belgian, French, German, Austrian, Swiss, British (English, Scottish, Welsh and Northern Irish), Irish, Spanish, Italian, Norwegian, Swedish, Finnish and Danish.

Take note: campers with any of the nationalities above but not resident in the Netherlands, Germany, France, Belgium, Denmark, Switzerland, Austria, Ireland, the United Kingdom, Norway, Sweden, Finland, Portugal, Spain or Italy, cannot apply for the ACSI Club ID for insurance-related reasons.

The ACSI Inspection team

Reliable, objective and up-to-date

The ACSI Campsite Guides are a household word for camping fans and campsite owners, and for over fifty years have provided campers with any information required. The reason for the popularity of the ACSI guides is the fact that the information in them is correct. You might think that this is obvious, but that is not the case. Each year, new campsite facilities are started or terminated, and campsites change owners on a regular basis.

The quality of campsites can thus change considerably, both in a positive and a negative sense. A new owner may substantially invest in new facilities or hygiene or, conversely, devote

less attention to maintenance. As a camper, you benefit from reliable, objective and up-to-date campsite information, and ACSI is well aware of this.

For the ACSI Campsite Guide, in 2017 over 134 inspectors set out to visit, inspect and select over 2350 campsites. They do this based on a list of 220 facilities and many other points of interest.

Annual inspections

ACSI is one of the few campsite guides in Europe to annually revisit and reinspect each campsite that is included in the next campsite guide. The inspector personally puts the ACSI annual sticker under 'Last ACSI inspector inspection' at the reception. This demonstrates that the campsite has actually been visited by the ACSI inspector, unlike most other campsite guides that send the annual stickers with the notification that the campsite has been included in their guide. Something quite different! Some inspectors carry out inspections until early September, so if you visit a campsite before our inspector does, it may be that the most recent ACSI sticker is not present yet.

Explanation Eurocampings

Find the perfect campsite for you
Find the campsite that suits you, quickly and easily, at ▸ *www.EUROCAMPINGS.co.uk* ◂ This website lists all of the campsites that are visited and inspected annually by our inspectors. Currently, this concerns over 9,900 campsites in 31 European countries!

Booking online
From this year, you will have the option of booking a pitch or accommodation at various campsites from home or while underway, using our booking process! Go to page 22 in this guide for more information about this new option.

Honest descriptions
Our inspectors visit all campsites annually to check their quality and atmosphere. They do this based on a list of 220 amenities and many other points of interest. Our inspectors do not provide a value judgement, but instead describe the campsite in an objective and honest manner.

Photos and videos
Various photos or a video are available for most campsites to provide you with a proper and reliable image of your destination.

Campsite reviews by other campers
A total of 130,000 reviews have been placed by campers such as yourself. You are welcome to leave your opinion about a campsite to help others.

Compare campsites
If you find it difficult to make a choice, simply select two or three campsites and compare them!

Interactive maps
Zoom in and out to view campsites nearby.

Over 200 amenities
Filter according to over 200 amenities; indicate your personal preferences and find out which campsite suits you best.

Everything we know about the campsite is shown on ▸ *www.EUROCAMPINGS.co.uk* ◂ and you can make a good choice based on this information.

The website adapts itself to the size of your screen, so you can use it on a tablet or smartphone.

If you are looking for inspiration, register for the ACSI Eurocampings newsletter. You can do this on any page on the website. After registering, you will receive no more than one newsletter a week with campsite tips, special offers from ACSI, and carefully selected partners.

Did you have a fun time camping?
We would love to hear about it!

Your experience
Most campers like to prepare for their journey, and you can help them with a review. Because although everything is usually great, there can be occasional disappointments.

Your campsite
Go to www.EUROCAMPINGS.co.uk to find the campsite you were staying at. You can do this quickly and easily via the search box on the homepage.

Your review
The campsite page shows the 'Reviews' tab. Open it and click on the 'Add a review' button to let us and others know what you thought about the campsite. This way, we can work with a complete picture of each campsite!

ACSI Campsites Europe app

Added convenience with the ACSI Campsites Europe app

This handy app for smartphones, tablets, laptops and computers ensures you have all campsite information available at all times. Filters allow you to find a campsite easily and quickly, even without an Internet connection. And from now on, you can buy country packages that provide campsite information and motorhome location information!

Free trial
Try the app for free with various campsites around Lake Garda. If you are happy with it, you can buy one or several country packages in the app. Packages are available from €0.99 a year.

Search for name 1
You can search for countries, regions and names. The database has over 500,000 search terms! Enter a search term and view the campsite(s) or motorhome location(s) on the map.

In the vicinity 2
Have you enabled location determination on your device? If so, the app will recognise your current position and show the campsites and motorhome locations nearby. If you are looking for overnight accommodation elsewhere, simply enter the location manually.

Extensive information 3
For each campsite, you will find extensive information about the grounds and amenities.

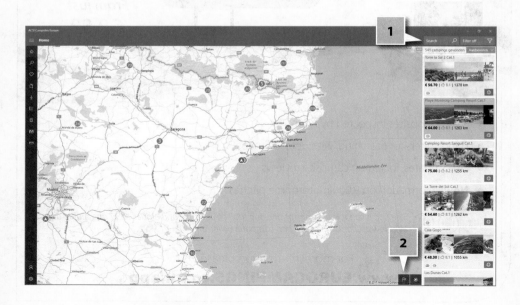

Reviews by other campers will help you to decide on a campsite, and you can leave your own campsite reviews using the app!

Favourites

Once you have found a campsite or motorhome location that meets your requirements, you can add it to your favourites. This allows you to quickly find the campsite or motorhome location and recognise it on the map, because favourites receive a distinctive representation.

Contact the campsite 5

Once you have decided on a campsite, you can use the app to call them and check availability.

Another option is to send an e-mail. As from 2018, the app provides the option of booking from home or while underway! Go to page 22 for more information about this option.

For more information about the ACSI Campsites Europe app, go to
▶ *www.EUROCAMPINGS.co.uk/app* ◀

Available for the following devices
The app is suitable for smartphones and tablets (Android 4 and higher, iOS 7 and higher and Windows 10) and for laptops and computers (Windows 10).

Compare ACSI apps

To supplement the ACSI campsite guides, we have three handy apps for smartphones, tablets and laptops: the ACSI Campsites Europe app, the CampingCard ACSI app and the ACSI Great Little Campsites app. See the advantages of these ACSI apps below.

	ACSI Campsites Europe app	CampingCard ACSI app	ACSI Great Little Campsites app
Price	Packages with campsite information from € 0.99	Complete app with campsite information: €3.59	Complete app with campsite information: €2.99
Number of campsites	8,200	3,330	More than 2,000
Type of campsite	All campsites in the ACSI Campinggids Europa	All campsites that accept CampingCard ACSI	Small campsites with max. 50 touring pitches
New! Information about 9,000 motorhome pitches	On sale in combination with campsite information	On sale in combination with campsite information	On sale in combination with campsite information
Suitable for	Smartphone, tablet, laptop and computer	Smartphone, tablet, laptop and computer	Smartphone, tablet, laptop and computer
Can be used on three devices at the same time	✓	✓	✓
Free updates	✓	✓	✓
Can be used offline	✓	✓	✓
Search by country, region, town or campsite name	✓	✓	✓
Search on map/GPS	✓	✓	✓
Search by CC rate and CC acceptance period		✓	
Total search filters	250	150	150
Special filters for motorhome pitches	✓	✓	✓
Book, call or mail campsite via app	✓	✓	✓
Read and submit campsite reviews	✓	✓	✓
Plan route	✓	✓	✓
More information	EUROCAMPINGS.co.uk/app	CAMPINGCARD.com/app	greatlittlecampsites.co.uk/app

Crossings

Travel through Europe

Will you be travelling from the United Kingdom to Ireland, or the other way around? Or do you plan on crossing to the European mainland? It's easy to book your ferry online. Trustworthy websites are:

▶ *www.ferryto.co.uk* ◀
▶ *www.brittany-ferries.co.uk* ◀
▶ *www.aferry.co.uk* ◀
▶ *www.stenaline.co.uk* ◀
▶ *www.directferries.com* ◀
▶ *www.poferries.com* ◀

The map shows you the shipping routes most used to and from the UK, Ireland and the European continent at a glance.

Ireland ←→ United Kingdom

Larne - Troon
Larne - Cairnryan
Belfast - Stranraer
Belfast - Liverpool
Dublin - Liverpool
Dublin - Holyhead
Dun Laoghaire - Holyhead
Rosslare - Fishguard
Rosslare - Pembroke

Ireland ←→ France

Dublin - Cherbourg
Cork - Roscoff
Rosslare - Roscoff
Rosslare - Cherbourg

United Kingdom ←→ France

Rosslare - Roscoff
Plymouth - Roscoff
Plymouth - St. Malo
Poole - Cherbourg
Portsmouth - St. Malo
Portsmouth - Cherbourg
Portsmouth - Caen
Portsmouth - Le Havre
Portsmouth - Dieppe
Newhaven - Le Havre
Newhaven - Dieppe
Dover - Calais
Folkestone - Calais
Dover - Dunkirk

You can also travel under the English Channel with your car on the train through the Eurotunnel. Take note: if your car is fitted with an LPG tank you cannot take it on the train through the Eurotunnel. There are special regulations for integral gas containers in caravans and motorhomes. Portable gas containers are permitted but you must declare them.
See ▶ *www.eurotunnel.com* ◀

United Kingdom ←→ The Netherlands

Harwich - Hook of Holland
Hull - Rotterdam
Newcastle - IJmuiden

United Kingdom ←→ Belgium

Ramsgate - Oostende
Hull - Zeebrugge

United Kingdom ←→ Spain

Plymouth - Santander
Portsmouth - Santander
Portsmouth - Bilbao

Are you planning on driving to the south of France and then taking the ferry to Corsica? Choose from the following ferry connections:

France ←→ Corsica

Marseille - Porto Vecchio
Marseille - Propriano
Marseille - Ajaccio
Marseille - L'Ille Rousse
Marseille - Bastia
Toulon - Ajaccio
Toulon - Bastia
Toulon - L'Ille Rousse
Nice - Bastia
Nice - L'Ille Rousse
Nice - Ajaccio

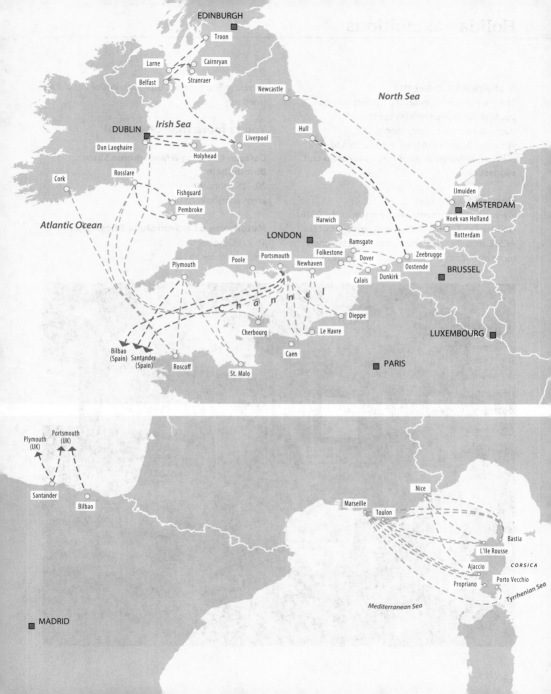

Holiday exhibitions

A chance to meet us!

The start of a new year is the perfect time to begin making your holiday plans, and get yourself into the holiday mood.

We enjoy listening to your experiences of previous holidays, and welcome your ideas and suggestions.

Person to person

We would like to meet you in person at the 2018 Holiday Exhibitions and tell you more about the ACSI Campsite Guide. You can also get to know more about other ACSI products, such as ACSI

Camping Tours (group trips with lots of individual freedom).

You're more than welcome!

Caravan Camping & Motorhome Show, Birmingham
20 - 25 February
www.ccmshow.co.uk

Motorhome & Caravan Show, Birmingham
16 - 21 October
www.mcshow.co.uk

United Kingdom

Approximate exchange rates September 2017: £ 1 = € 1.09. Scotland, the Channel Islands and the Isle of Man have their own notes and coins which cannot always be used outside these areas. ATMs (known locally as cashpoints) can be found in most bank branches and elsewhere: near stations, in larger supermarkets and some convenience stores and pubs.

Credit cards
Credit cards, especially Visa and Mastercard, are widely accepted.

(Mobile) phones
The mobile network works well throughout the United Kingdom except on the west coast of Scotland. There is a 4G network for mobile internet.

Wifi, internet
You can use wifi networks at an increasing number of public locations, often for free.

Opening times/Public holidays
Banks
Open on weekdays until 4:00 pm.

Shops (including pharmacies)
Shops are open from Monday to Saturday until 5:30 pm. Shops stay open later on Wednesday or Thursday evenings. Shops in Scotland are open on Sundays more often than in the rest of the United Kingdom. Pharmacies are open Monday to Friday until 6:00 pm, on Saturday until 1:00 pm.

Post
Post offices are generally open from Monday to Friday until 5:30 pm. On Saturdays in larger towns until 12:30 pm.

General
The United Kingdom is a member of the EU. The capital city is London.

Time
The time in the United Kingdom is the same as in Dublin.

Language
English.

Crossings
There are several ferry services that you can use to make the crossing between Ireland and the United Kingdom. You will find a complete overview of the ferries on page 36.

Currency
The currency in Great Britain is the pound sterling.

Pubs

Most British pubs are open Monday to Sunday from 11:00 am to 11:00 pm. In cities many open at 9:00 am to serve breakfast.

Public holidays

For England and Wales:

New Year's Day, Good Friday, Easter, 7 May (Bank Holiday), 28 May (Bank Holiday), 27 August (Bank Holiday), Christmas Day and 26 December (Boxing Day).

For Scotland:

1 and 2 January, Good Friday, Easter, 7 May (Bank Holiday), 28 May (Bank Holiday), 6 August (Bank Holiday), 30 November (St Andrew's Day), Christmas Day and 26 December (Boxing Day).

Roads and traffic

Traffic regulations

All traffic in the United Kingdom drives on the left and overtakes on the right. Where two main roads meet there is no general rule so you need to look at the signs. Main roads have priority, this is shown by 'Stop' or 'Give way' signs. Traffic on a roundabout has priority over traffic entering it.

Maximum permitted alcohol level is 0.8 promille. Maximum permitted alcohol level in Scotland is 0.5 promille. The use of dipped headlights during the daytime is not compulsory in the United Kingdom unless visibility is less than 100 metres. Phones may only be used hands-free.

Road network

Distances are measured in miles
(1 mile = 1.609 km, 1 km = 0.621 mile).

There is a breakdown service on major roads that you can contact using the Automobile Association (AA) phones. On minor roads call the AA Breakdown number: tel. 0800-887766.

Caravans, motorhomes

You may not drive with a caravan on the outside lane of three-lane roads. Caravans are not permitted on the Isle of Man.

Maximum permitted measurements of combined length

Height 4 metres, width 2.55 metres and maximum length 18.75 metres (of which the trailer is 12 metres maximum). Larger sizes, particularly in width, can lead to problems when entering campsites on narrow roads.

Fuel

Unleaded petrol, LPG and diesel are widely available.

Filling stations

Filling stations on motorways are open 24 hours, other service stations are open until 10:00 pm. You can usually pay by credit card.

Maximum speed

	96	60 mph
	80	50 mph
< 3,5 т	96	60 mph
> 3,5 т	80	50 mph
	112	70 mph
	96	60 mph
< 3,5 т	112	70 mph
> 3,5 т	96	60 mph

Charging stations

The network of public charging stations is quite extended in the United Kingdom, but does not fully cover the less densely populated areas. Make sure to plan your trip carefully. For the exact location of charging stations, check websites like ▶ *chargeyourcar.org.uk* ◀ or ▶ *www.chargemap.com* ◀.

Tolls

A toll must be paid on the M6 north of Birmingham. This also applies to some bridges and tunnels.

Attention! It is not possible to pay at a tollbooth at the Dartford Crossing (ring road London M25). Instead, payment needs to be done beforehand or afterwards (within 24 hours) via internet. If you do not do this, you will receive a hefty fine. More information: ▶ *www.gov.uk/highways/dartford* ◀.

Low emission zone (LEZ):

The 'low emission zone' (LEZ) has been introduced in London to control the air quality. The LEZ does not apply to cars, but it does to motorhomes. If you are planning to visit London with a motorhome, you will need to register your vehicle with Transport for London (TfL) on ▶ *www.tfl.gov.uk* ◀. By not registering you are liable to a fine.

'Congestion charge'

In Central London you also need to pay a 'Congestion Charge'. You can pay online, by SMS, telephone or in shops and post offices. You do not need to pay at weekends, during United Kingdom holidays or between 6:00 pm and 7:00 am. More information about the 'Congestion Charge' ▶ *www.tfl.gov.uk* ◀.

Emergency number

112: the national emergency number for fire, police or ambulance.

Camping

Free camping is allowed in Scotland, in the rest of the United Kingdom you need permission from the landowner. Camping by the side of the road and in car parks is prohibited. On some campsites additional tents will be charged extra.

'Campsite', 'Touringpark' and 'Caravan Park'

The main difference between a 'campsite' and a 'touring park' is that the former is larger and has more permanent places for mobile homes. Touring parks are really for people with their own tent or caravan. Tents are not permitted on caravan parks. It is definitely advisable to reserve in advance if you want to stay on a campsite during a bank holiday or at the weekend.

Clubs

It is possible that you will find a site that is affiliated with a club that only has places for its members. You cannot camp here without being a member. In some cases, the club makes some touring places available for non-members. It is advisable to check this in advance. In this guide, you will only find campsites where you do not need to be a member.

Practical

- Not all gas bottles from other countries can be filled or exchanged because of different valve types. Blue Campingaz 907 bottles are usually available, and sometimes 901 and 904.
- Make sure you have a world adaptor for electrical appliances.
- Tap water is safe to drink.

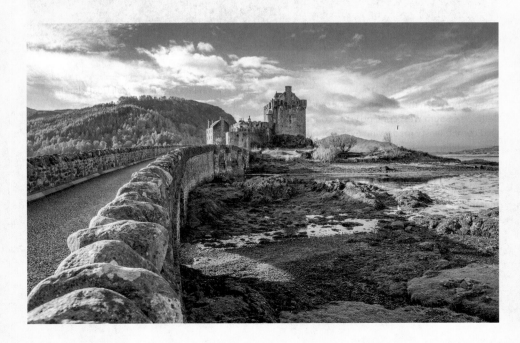

Wild corner of England

Located between the English Channel and the
Celtic Sea, South West England is the country's
wild corner. Twisty roads wind over around and
through hills, forests, river valleys and moors, and
with the rugged, craggy coastline, picturesque
towns and villages, this region is ideal for walkers,
cyclists and outdoor enthusiasts. Did you know
that there's so much more below the surface?
The Jurassic coast in Dorset is a treasure trove of
fossils, and Bath is famous for its hot springs. Tin
was mined in this region, and Salisbury Plain is an
important archaeological hotspot.

Stormy relationship with the sea

If you fancy a boat trip to the Scilly Isles,
Penzance is the place to go. Nearby Marazion

has St Michael's Mount, a small tidal island,
with a fortress that can be reached via a
causeway – be sure to check the tides! The
city of Plymouth might also ring a bell, with
its association with the Pilgrim Fathers, and of
course Sir Francis Drake, who captained the
second circumnavigation of the world in the 16th
century.

Places to go, Things to do

Once a fashionable resort for the upper classes,
Bath is home to the Roman Baths. If you love
literature, there's the Jane Austen Centre, while
fashionistas will adore the Fashion Museum. In
Bristol, the kids will love going 'under' the glass
sea to explore the SS Great Britain ship, and the
Observatory and Caves nearby Clifton has views

robust pastry filled with meat and vegetables and very lightly spiced, and crimped at the edge. Pasties were also taken down into the mines, and left as gifts for 'knockers' – subterranean spirits that guided and protected miners at their work.

that are second to none. Want to see more? Take a hot air balloon flight! Back on earth, adrenaline junkies can surf, canoe, swim along the coast, and active families will love everything on offer at the national parks of Exmoor, Dartmoor, New Forest and Forest of Dean.

Food for knockers

Once you've worked up an appetite, it's time for a cream tea: delicious warm scones with jam served with clotted cream, washed down with tea. The Cornish pasty is another local speciality,

Our tips

1. Take a selfie at the magnificent Durdle Door on the Jurassic coast
2. Like dinosaurs? Check out the Charmouth Heritage Coast Centre
3. Visit the mysterious ancient stone circle at Stonehenge
4. Explore the world's largest indoor rain forest at the Eden Project
5. See amazing artworks at the Weston Sand Sculpture Festival

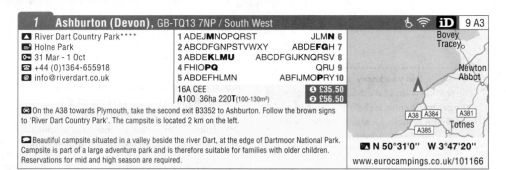

1 Ashburton (Devon), GB-TQ13 7NP / South West

♿ 📶 **iD** 9 A3

- ▲ River Dart Country Park****
- 📧 Holne Park
- 📅 31 Mar - 1 Oct
- ☎ +44 (0)1364-655918
- @ info@riverdart.co.uk

1 ADEJ**M**NOPQRST	JLM**N** 6	
2 ABCDFGNPSTVWXY	ABDE**FGH** 7	
3 ABDE**KLMU**	ABCDFGIJKNQRSV 8	
4 FHIO**PQ**	QRU 9	
5 ABDEFHLMN	ABFIJMOP**R**Y 10	
16A CEE	❶ £35.50	
A100 36ha 220**T**(100-130m²)	❷ £56.50	

🚗 On the A38 towards Plymouth, take the second exit B3352 to Ashburton. Follow the brown signs to 'River Dart Country Park'. The campsite is located 2 km on the left.

🛏 Beautiful campsite situated in a valley beside the river Dart, at the edge of Dartmoor National Park. Campsite is part of a large adventure park and is therefore suitable for families with older children. Reservations for mid and high season are required.

☒ N 50°31'0'' W 3°47'20''

www.eurocampings.co.uk/101166

2 Bath, GB-BA1 3JT / South West

♿ 📶 **iD** 9 B2

- ▲ Bath Marina & Caravan Park
- 📧 Brassmill Lane
- 📅 1 Jan - 31 Dec
- ☎ +44 (0)1225-424301
- @ kevin.soper@bwml.co.uk

1 ACDEGJMOPQRST	**N** 6	
2 COPRSVWXY	ABDE**FGH** 7	
3 A**K**	ABCDEFJNPQRV 8	
4 FH	9	
5 BDM**O**	ABEFHKM**P**R 10	
16A CEE	❶ £26.40	
2ha 88**T**(30-85m²)	❷ £32.80	

🚗 Municipal campsite located on the outskirts of Bath on the A4 direction Bristol.

🛏 A city campsite with simple facilities. Ideal for visiting the historic city of Bath. P&R bus service near the campsite.

☒ N 51°23'17'' W 2°24'12''

www.eurocampings.co.uk/102783

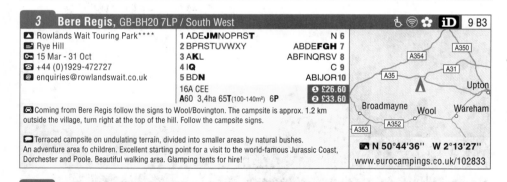

3 Bere Regis, GB-BH20 7LP / South West

♿ 📶 ✿ **iD** 9 B3

- ▲ Rowlands Wait Touring Park****
- 📧 Rye Hill
- 📅 15 Mar - 31 Oct
- ☎ +44 (0)1929-472727
- @ enquiries@rowlandswait.co.uk

1 ADE**JM**NOPRS**T**	**N** 6	
2 BPRSTUVWXY	ABDE**FGH** 7	
3 A**K**L	ABFINQRSV 8	
4 I**Q**	C 9	
5 BD**N**	ABIJOR 10	
16A CEE	❶ £26.60	
A60 3,4ha 65**T**(100-140m²) 6**P**	❷ £33.60	

🚗 Coming from Bere Regis follow the signs to Wool/Bovington. The campsite is approx. 1.2 km outside the village, turn right at the top of the hill. Follow the campsite signs.

🛏 Terraced campsite on undulating terrain, divided into smaller areas by natural bushes. An adventure area fo children. Excellent starting point for a visit to the world-famous Jurassic Coast, Dorchester and Poole. Beautiful walking area. Glamping tents for hire!

☒ N 50°44'36'' W 2°13'27''

www.eurocampings.co.uk/102833

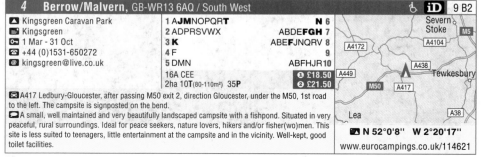

4 Berrow/Malvern, GB-WR13 6AQ / South West

♿ **iD** 9 B2

- ▲ Kingsgreen Caravan Park
- 📧 Kingsgreen
- 📅 1 Mar - 31 Oct
- ☎ +44 (0)1531-650272
- @ kingsgreen@live.co.uk

1 A**JM**NOPQR**T**	**N** 6	
2 ADPRSVWX	ABDE**FGH** 7	
3 **K**	ABE**F**JNQRV 8	
4 F	9	
5 DM**N**	ABFHJR 10	
16A CEE	❶ £18.50	
2ha 10**T**(80-110m²) 35**P**	❷ £21.50	

🚗 A417 Ledbury-Gloucester, after passing M50 exit 2, direction Gloucester, under the M50, 1st road to the left. The campsite is signposted on the bend.
🛏 A small, well maintained and very beautifully landscaped campsite with a fishpond. Situated in very peaceful, rural surroundings. Ideal for peace seekers, nature lovers, hikers and/or fisher(wo)men. This site is less suited to teenagers, little entertainment at the campsite and in the vicinity. Well-kept, good toilet facilities.

☒ N 52°0'8'' W 2°20'17''

www.eurocampings.co.uk/114621

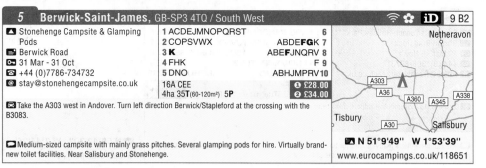

5 Berwick-Saint-James, GB-SP3 4TQ / South West
📶 ✿ **iD** 9 B2

- ▲ Stonehenge Campsite & Glamping Pods
- 🏠 Berwick Road
- 📅 31 Mar - 31 Oct
- ☎ +44 (0)7786-734732
- @ stay@stonehengecampsite.co.uk

1	ACDEJMNOPQRST		6
2	COPSVWX	ABDE**FG**K	7
3	**K**	ABE**F**JNQRV	8
4	FHK	F	9
5	DNO	ABHJMPRV	10

16A CEE	❶ £28.00
4ha 35T(60-120m²) 5**P**	❷ £34.00

🗺 Take the A303 west in Andover. Turn left direction Berwick/Stapleford at the crossing with the B3083.

💬 Medium-sized campsite with mainly grass pitches. Several glamping pods for hire. Virtually brand-new toilet facilities. Near Salisbury and Stonehenge.

📍 **N 51°9'49'' W 1°53'39''**

www.eurocampings.co.uk/118651

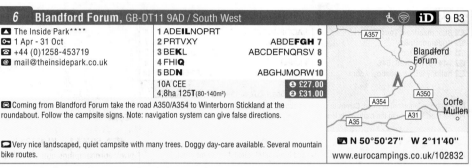

6 Blandford Forum, GB-DT11 9AD / South West
♿ 📶 **iD** 9 B3

- ▲ The Inside Park****
- 📅 1 Apr - 31 Oct
- ☎ +44 (0)1258-453719
- @ mail@theinsidepark.co.uk

1	ADE**IL**NOPRT		6
2	PRTVXY	ABDE**FGH**	7
3	BE**KL**	ABCDEFNQRSV	8
4	FHI**Q**		9
5	BD**N**	ABGHJMORW	10

10A CEE	❶ £27.00
4,8ha 125T(80-140m²)	❷ £31.00

🗺 Coming from Blandford Forum take the road A350/A354 to Winterborn Stickland at the roundabout. Follow the campsite signs. Note: navigation system can give false directions.

💬 Very nice landscaped, quiet campsite with many trees. Doggy day-care available. Several mountain bike routes.

📍 **N 50°50'27'' W 2°11'40''**

www.eurocampings.co.uk/102832

7 Boswinger/Gorran Haven, GB-PL26 6LL / South West
♿ 📶 ✿ **iD** 40a

- ▲ SeaView International*****
- 📅 1 Apr - 30 Sep
- ☎ +44 (0)1726-843425
- @ seaview@swholidayparks.co.uk

1	ADE**JM**NOPRS**T**	ABFQU**X**	6
2	GHNOPRSVWXY	ABDE**FG**HIK	7
3	BELM	ABCDEFGIJLNQRSTUV	8
4		EF	9
5	ABCDEFHMNO	ABFGHIJLMNO**P**RV	10

16A CEE	❶ £30.00
A102 12ha 195T(110-200m²) 82**P**	❷ £40.00

🗺 In St. Austell take the B3273 towards Mevagissey. On the top of the hill (see campsite sign) turn right. Drive towards Gorran Haven, and then in the direction of Boswinger until there are signs to the campsite.

💬 Beautiful, clean, 5-star campsite. Close to the sea. Big, beautiful toilet facilities. Large play area. Heated swimming pool in very nice location. Even grass tennis courts free of charge.

📍 **N 50°14'14'' W 4°49'9''**

www.eurocampings.co.uk/102719

8 Brean Sands, GB-TA8 2RB / South West
♿ 📶 ✿ (CC€17) **iD** 9 A2

- ▲ Holiday Resort Unity***
- 🏠 Coast Road
- 📅 9 Feb - 18 Nov
- ☎ +44 (0)1278-751235
- @ admin@hru.co.uk

1	ACDE**JM**NOPQRS**T** **ABE**HKNQSW**X**		6
2	AEHOPSVW	ABDE**FGH**	7
3	BC**EIJKPS**	ABCDFGIJMNQRSTU	8
4	FHILNO**PQRTV**	AEFUVY	9
5	ACDEFGHLM**O**	ABDGHIKM**P**RYZ	10

16A CEE	❶ £35.00
100ha 446T(100-144m²) 306**P**	❷ £44.90

🗺 Take junction 22 on the M5 and follow the brown 'Brean Leisure Park' signs. Entrance to campsite 200 metres south of entrance to the Leisure Park.

💬 Holiday Resort Unity at Brean Sands is a popular family holiday destination in the South West. Choose either a standard or a fully serviced pitch. Close to the beach and Brean Leisure Park with rides and amusements for children, including swimming pools and play areas. Dogs are welcome.

CC _9/2-28/3   9/4-23/5   4/6-29/6   3/9-25/9   8/10-17/11_

📍 **N 51°16'50'' W 3°0'46''**

www.eurocampings.co.uk/117945

United Kingdom

9 Bridport, GB-DT6 4PT / South West

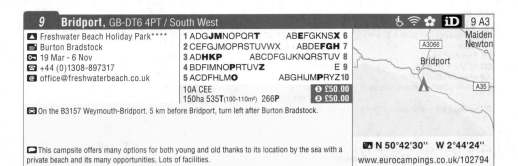

♿ 🛜 ❀ **iD** 9 A3

- 🏕 Freshwater Beach Holiday Park★★★★
- 🏘 Burton Bradstock
- 📅 19 Mar - 6 Nov
- ☎ +44 (0)1308-897317
- @ office@freshwaterbeach.co.uk

1 ADG**JM**NOPQR**T**	ABE**FGKNSX** 6
2 CEFGJMOPRSTUVWX	ABDE**FGH** 7
3 AD**HKP**	ABCDFGIJKNQRSTUV 8
4 BDFIMNO**P**RTUV**Z**	E 9
5 ACDFHLM**O**	ABGHIJM**P**RYZ 10
10A CEE	❶ £50.00
150ha 535**T**(100-110m²) 266**P**	❷ £50.00

📷 On the B3157 Weymouth-Bridport. 5 km before Bridport, turn left after Burton Bradstock.

💬 This campsite offers many options for both young and old thanks to its location by the sea with a private beach and its many opportunities. Lots of facilities.

Maiden Newton
A3066
Bridport
A35

📌 **N 50°42'30'' W 2°44'24''**
www.eurocampings.co.uk/102794

10 Bude, GB-EX23 0NA / South West

♿ 🛜 **iD** 8 B3

- 🏕 Budemeadows Touring Park★★★★
- 🏘 Widemouth Bay
- 📅 1 Jan - 31 Dec
- ☎ +44 (0)1288-361646
- @ holiday@budemeadows.com

1 ACDE**JM**NOPQR**T**	ABFG 6
2 GOPSVWXY	ABDE**FGH** 7
3 AB**KLP**	ABCDEFLNQRSV 8
4 IO**PQ**	9
5 ABDEFHM	ABFGHIJPRV 10
16A CEE	❶ £31.50
A50 3,6ha 145**T**(100-130m²) 6**P**	❷ £41.50

📷 A39 from Camelford to Bude. Campsite is located about 8 km before Bude on the right side in Poundstock. Entrance to the campsite is located near the parking area. It is signposted.

💬 Easily accessible, close to the main road. Quiet and beautifully located. Near to the coast.

Bude
A3072
Holsworthy
A39
Boscastle

📌 **N 50°47'1'' W 4°32'6''**
www.eurocampings.co.uk/102708

11 Bude, GB-EX23 0LP / South West

♿ 🛜 **iD** 8 B3

- 🏕 Upper Lynstone C/PK
- 🏘 Lynstone Road
- 📅 31 Mar - 1 Oct
- ☎ +44 (0)1288-352017
- @ reception@upperlynstone.co.uk

1 ADE**JM**NOPR**T**	N 6
2 FHOPQUVWX	ABDE**FGH** 7
3 A**K**	ABEFMNQRSV 8
4 F	E 9
5 ABDM**N**	ABHJM**P**R 10
10A CEE	❶ £25.00
2,5ha 79**T**(100-120m²) 20**P**	❷ £33.00

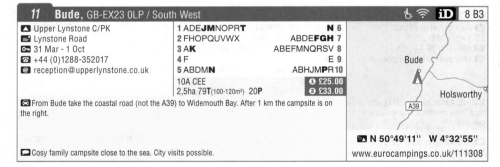

📷 From Bude take the coastal road (not the A39) to Widemouth Bay. After 1 km the campsite is on the right.

💬 Cosy family campsite close to the sea. City visits possible.

Bude
Holsworthy
A39

📌 **N 50°49'11'' W 4°32'55''**
www.eurocampings.co.uk/111308

12 Bude, GB-EX23 9HJ / South West

♿ 🛜 ❀ ⓒⓒ€19 ⚑⚑ **iD** 8 B3

- 🏕 Wooda Farm Holiday Park★★★★★
- 🏘 Poughill
- 📅 1 Apr - 1 Nov
- ☎ +44 (0)1288-352069
- @ enquiries@wooda.co.uk

1 ADE**JM**NOPRS**T**	N 6
2 FPSTVWX	ABDE**FGH**K 7
3 BCJL**MR**	ABEFGIJ**L**NQRSUV 8
4 FIOQ**R**	EJ 9
5 ACDEFHIMN	ABEFGJM**P**RZ 10
16A CEE	❶ £32.00
A75 6ha 210**T**(80-120m²) 57**P**	❷ £42.00

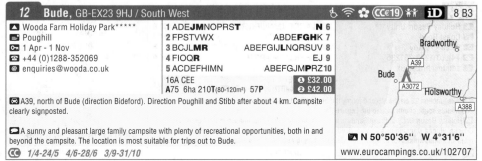

📷 A39, north of Bude (direction Bideford). Direction Poughill and Stibb after about 4 km. Campsite clearly signposted.

💬 A sunny and pleasant large family campsite with plenty of recreational opportunities, both in and beyond the campsite. The location is most suitable for trips out to Bude.

ⓒⓒ 1/4-24/5 4/6-28/6 3/9-31/10

Bradworthy
A39
Bude
A3072
Holsworthy
A388

📌 **N 50°50'36'' W 4°31'6''**
www.eurocampings.co.uk/102707

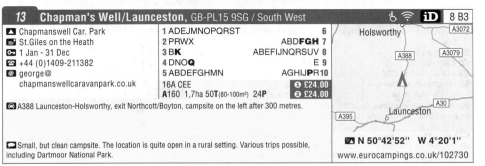

13 Chapman's Well/Launceston, GB-PL15 9SG / South West ♿ 🛜 iD 8 B3

- ⛰ Chapmanswell Car. Park
- 🚉 St.Giles on the Heath
- 📅 1 Jan - 31 Dec
- ☎ +44 (0)1409-211382
- @ george@
  chapmanswellcaravanpark.co.uk

1 ADEJMNOPQRST	6		
2 PRWX	ABD**FGH** 7		
3 B**K**	ABEFIJNQRSUV 8		
4 DNO**Q**	E 9		
5 ABDEFGHMN	AGHIJ**PR**10		
16A CEE	❶ £24.00		
A160 1,7ha 50**T**(80-100m²) 24**P**	❷ £24.00		

🚗 A388 Launceston-Holsworthy, exit Northcott/Boyton, campsite on the left after 300 metres.

💬 Small, but clean campsite. The location is quite open in a rural setting. Various trips possible, including Dartmoor National Park.

📍 N 50°42'52'' W 4°20'1''

www.eurocampings.co.uk/102730

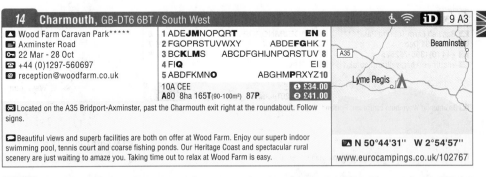

14 Charmouth, GB-DT6 6BT / South West ♿ 🛜 iD 9 A3

- ⛰ Wood Farm Caravan Park*****
- 🚉 Axminster Road
- 📅 22 Mar - 28 Oct
- ☎ +44 (0)1297-560697
- @ reception@woodfarm.co.uk

1 ADE**JM**NOPQR**T**	**EN** 6		
2 FGOPRSTUVWXY	ABDE**FGH**K 7		
3 BC**KLM**S	ABCDFGHIJNPQRSTUV 8		
4 FI**Q**	EI 9		
5 ABDFKMN**O**	ABGHM**PR**XYZ**10**		
10A CEE	❶ £34.00		
A80 8ha 165**T**(90-100m²) 87**P**	❷ £41.00		

🚗 Located on the A35 Bridport-Axminster, past the Charmouth exit right at the roundabout. Follow signs.

💬 Beautiful views and superb facilities are both on offer at Wood Farm. Enjoy our superb indoor swimming pool, tennis court and coarse fishing ponds. Our Heritage Coast and spectacular rural scenery are just waiting to amaze you. Taking time out to relax at Wood Farm is easy.

📍 N 50°44'31'' W 2°54'57''

www.eurocampings.co.uk/102767

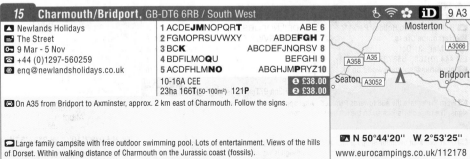

15 Charmouth/Bridport, GB-DT6 6RB / South West ♿ 🛜 ✿ iD 9 A3

- ⛰ Newlands Holidays
- 🚉 The Street
- 📅 9 Mar - 5 Nov
- ☎ +44 (0)1297-560259
- @ enq@newlandsholidays.co.uk

1 ACDE**JM**NOPQR**T**	ABE 6		
2 FGMOPRSUVWXY	ABDE**FGH** 7		
3 BC**K**	ABCDEFJNQRSV 8		
4 BDFILMO**QU**	BEFGHI 9		
5 ACDFHLMN**O**	ABGHJM**PR**YZ**10**		
10-16A CEE	❶ £38.00		
23ha 166**T**(50-100m²) 121**P**	❷ £38.00		

🚗 On A35 from Bridport to Axminster, approx. 2 km east of Charmouth. Follow the signs.

💬 Large family campsite with free outdoor swimming pool. Lots of entertainment. Views of the hills of Dorset. Within walking distance of Charmouth on the Jurassic coast (fossils).

📍 N 50°44'20'' W 2°53'25''

www.eurocampings.co.uk/112178

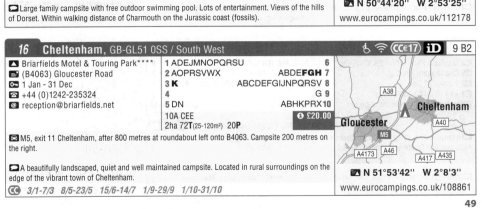

16 Cheltenham, GB-GL51 0SS / South West ♿ 🛜 (CC€17) iD 9 B2

- ⛰ Briarfields Motel & Touring Park****
- 🚉 (B4063) Gloucester Road
- 📅 1 Jan - 31 Dec
- ☎ +44 (0)1242-235324
- @ reception@briarfields.net

1 ADEJMNOPQRSU	6		
2 AOPRSVWX	ABDE**FGH** 7		
3 **K**	ABCDEFGIJNPQRSV 8		
4	G 9		
5 DN	ABHKPRX**10**		
10A CEE	❶ £20.00		
2ha 72**T**(25-120m²) 20**P**			

🚗 M5, exit 11 Cheltenham, after 800 metres at roundabout left onto B4063. Campsite 200 metres on the right.

💬 A beautifully landscaped, quiet and well maintained campsite. Located in rural surroundings on the edge of the vibrant town of Cheltenham.

🎟 3/1-7/3 8/5-23/5 15/6-14/7 1/9-29/9 1/10-31/10

📍 N 51°53'42'' W 2°8'3''

www.eurocampings.co.uk/108861

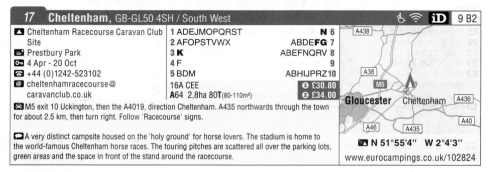

17 Cheltenham, GB-GL50 4SH / South West ♿ 🛜 iD 9 B2

- ▲ Cheltenham Racecourse Caravan Club Site
- ▣ Prestbury Park
- 📅 4 Apr - 20 Oct
- ☎ +44 (0)1242-523102
- @ cheltenhamracecourse@ caravanclub.co.uk

1 ADEJMOPQRST		**N** 6
2 AFOPSTVWX	ABDE**FG** 7
3 **K**	ABEFNQRV 8
4 F	9
5 BDM	ABHIJPRZ 10
16A CEE		❶ £30.80
A64 2,8ha 80**T**(80-110m²)		❷ £34.00

🚗 M5 exit 10 Uckington, then the A4019, direction Cheltenham. A435 northwards through the town for about 2.5 km, then turn right. Follow 'Racecourse' signs.

💬 A very distinct campsite housed on the 'holy ground' for horse lovers. The stadium is home to the world-famous Cheltenham horse races. The touring pitches are scattered all over the parking lots, green areas and the space in front of the stand around the racecourse.

🗺 **N 51°55'4''   W 2°4'3''**
www.eurocampings.co.uk/102824

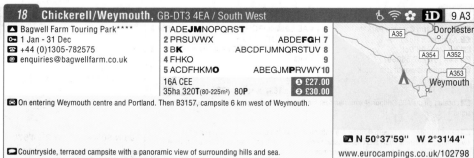

18 Chickerell/Weymouth, GB-DT3 4EA / South West ♿ 🛜 ✿ iD 9 A3

- ▲ Bagwell Farm Touring Park★★★★
- 📅 1 Jan - 31 Dec
- ☎ +44 (0)1305-782575
- @ enquiries@bagwellfarm.co.uk

1 ADE**JM**NOPQRS**T**		6
2 PRSUVWX	ABDE**FG**H 7
3 B**K**	ABCDFIJMNQRSTUV 8
4 FHKO	9
5 ACDFHKM**O**	ABEGJM**P**RVWY 10
16A CEE		❶ £27.00
35ha 320**T**(80-225m²) 80**P**		❷ £30.00

🚗 On entering Weymouth centre and Portland. Then B3157, campsite 6 km west of Weymouth.

💬 Countryside, terraced campsite with a panoramic view of surrounding hills and sea.

🗺 **N 50°37'59''   W 2°31'44''**
www.eurocampings.co.uk/102798

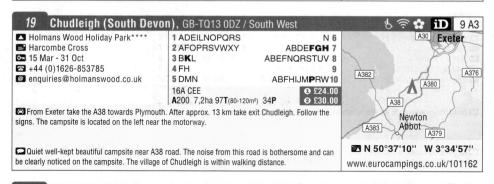

19 Chudleigh (South Devon), GB-TQ13 0DZ / South West ♿ 🛜 ✿ iD 9 A3

- ▲ Holmans Wood Holiday Park★★★★
- ▣ Harcombe Cross
- 📅 15 Mar - 31 Oct
- ☎ +44 (0)1626-853785
- @ enquiries@holmanswood.co.uk

1 ADEILNOPQRS		**N** 6
2 AFOPRSVWXY	ABDE**FGH** 7
3 B**K**L	ABEFNQRSTUV 8
4 FH	9
5 DMN	ABFHIJM**P**RW 10
16A CEE		❶ £24.00
A200 7,2ha 97**T**(80-120m²) 34**P**		❷ £30.00

🚗 From Exeter take the A38 towards Plymouth. After approx. 13 km take exit Chudleigh. Follow the signs. The campsite is located on the left near the motorway.

💬 Quiet well-kept beautiful campsite near A38 road. The noise from this road is bothersome and can be clearly noticed on the campsite. The village of Chudleigh is within walking distance.

🗺 **N 50°37'10''   W 3°34'57''**
www.eurocampings.co.uk/101162

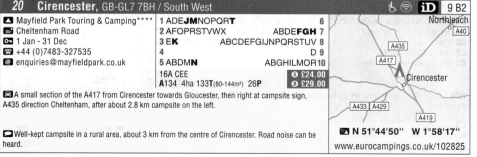

20 Cirencester, GB-GL7 7BH / South West ♿ 🛜 iD 9 B2

- ▲ Mayfield Park Touring & Camping★★★★
- ▣ Cheltenham Road
- 📅 1 Jan - 31 Dec
- ☎ +44 (0)7483-327535
- @ enquiries@mayfieldpark.co.uk

1 ADE**JM**NOPQR**T**		6
2 AFOPRSVWX	ABDE**FGH** 7
3 E**K**	ABCDEFGIJNPQRSTUV 8
4	D 9
5 ABDM**N**	ABGHILMOR 10
16A CEE		❶ £24.00
A134 4ha 133**T**(80-144m²) 26**P**		❷ £29.00

🚗 A small section of the A417 from Cirencester towards Gloucester, then right at campsite sign, A435 direction Cheltenham, after about 2.8 km campsite on the left.

💬 Well-kept campsite in a rural area, about 3 km from the centre of Cirencester. Road noise can be heard.

🗺 **N 51°44'50''   W 1°58'17''**
www.eurocampings.co.uk/102825

United Kingdom

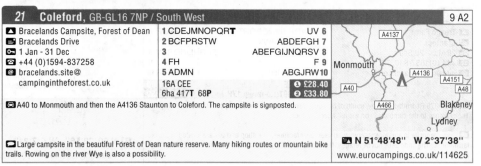

21 Coleford, GB-GL16 7NP / South West — 9 A2

- 🏕 Bracelands Campsite, Forest of Dean
- 🏠 Bracelands Drive
- 📅 1 Jan - 31 Dec
- ☎ +44 (0)1594-837258
- @ bracelands.site@campingintheforest.co.uk

1 CDEJMNOPQRT	UV	6
2 BCFPRSTW	ABDEFGH	7
3	ABEFGIJNQRSV	8
4 FH	F	9
5 ADMN	ABGJRW	10
16A CEE		❶ £28.40
6ha 417T 68P		❷ £33.80

🚗 A40 to Monmouth and then the A4136 Staunton to Coleford. The campsite is signposted.

💬 Large campsite in the beautiful Forest of Dean nature reserve. Many hiking routes or mountain bike trails. Rowing on the river Wye is also a possibility.

📍 N 51°48'48'' W 2°37'38''

www.eurocampings.co.uk/114625

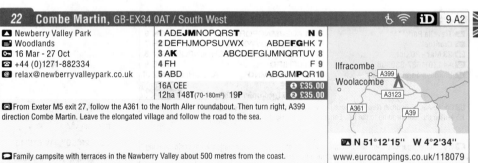

22 Combe Martin, GB-EX34 0AT / South West — 9 A2

- 🏕 Newberry Valley Park
- 🏠 Woodlands
- 📅 16 Mar - 27 Oct
- ☎ +44 (0)1271-882334
- @ relax@newberryvalleypark.co.uk

1 ADEJMNOPQRST	N	6
2 DEFHJMOPSUVWX	ABDEFGHK	7
3 AK	ABCDEFGIJMNQRTUV	8
4 FH	F	9
5 ABD	ABGJMPQR	10
16A CEE		❶ £35.00
12ha 148T (70-180m²) 19P		❷ £35.00

🚗 From Exeter M5 exit 27, follow the A361 to the North Aller roundabout. Then turn right, A399 direction Combe Martin. Leave the elongated village and follow the road to the sea.

💬 Family campsite with terraces in the Nawberry Valley about 500 metres from the coast.

📍 N 51°12'15'' W 4°2'34''

www.eurocampings.co.uk/118079

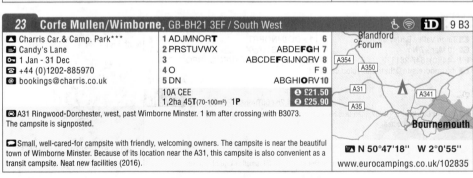

23 Corfe Mullen/Wimborne, GB-BH21 3EF / South West — 9 B3

- 🏕 Charris Car.& Camp. Park***
- 🏠 Candy's Lane
- 📅 1 Jan - 31 Dec
- ☎ +44 (0)1202-885970
- @ bookings@charris.co.uk

1 ADJMNORT		6
2 PRSTUVWX	ABDEFGH	7
3	ABCDEFGIJNQRV	8
4 O	F	9
5 DN	ABGHIORV	10
10A CEE		❶ £21.50
1,2ha 45T (70-100m²) 1P		❷ £25.90

🚗 A31 Ringwood-Dorchester, west, past Wimborne Minster. 1 km after crossing with B3073. The campsite is signposted.

💬 Small, well-cared-for campsite with friendly, welcoming owners. The campsite is near the beautiful town of Wimborne Minster. Because of its location near the A31, this campsite is also convenient as a transit campsite. Neat new facilities (2016).

📍 N 50°47'18'' W 2°0'55''

www.eurocampings.co.uk/102835

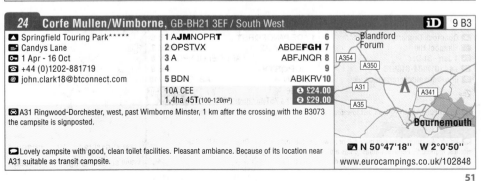

24 Corfe Mullen/Wimborne, GB-BH21 3EF / South West — 9 B3

- 🏕 Springfield Touring Park*****
- 🏠 Candys Lane
- 📅 1 Apr - 16 Oct
- ☎ +44 (0)1202-881719
- @ john.clark18@btconnect.com

1 AJMNOPRT		6
2 OPSTVX	ABDEFGH	7
3 A	ABFJNQR	8
4		9
5 BDN	ABIKRV	10
10A CEE		❶ £24.00
1,4ha 45T (100-120m²)		❷ £29.00

🚗 A31 Ringwood-Dorchester, west, past Wimborne Minster, 1 km after the crossing with the B3073 the campsite is signposted.

💬 Lovely campsite with good, clean toilet facilities. Pleasant ambiance. Because of its location near A31 suitable as transit campsite.

📍 N 50°47'18'' W 2°0'50''

www.eurocampings.co.uk/102848

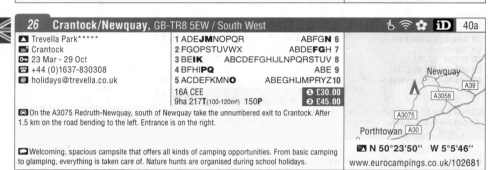

25 Crantock/Newquay, GB-TR8 5QS / South West ♿ iD 40a

- ⛰ Treago Farm***
- 🏕 Crantock
- 📅 28 Mar - 29 Sep
- ☎ +44 (0)1637-830277
- @ info@treagofarm.co.uk

1 ADE**JM**NOPQRT	NQR	6
2 FGPTUVWX	ABDE**FG**HK	7
3 E**KL**	ABEFGHIJNQRSV	8
4 FIOQ	EJ	9
5 ABDFHN	ABGJR	10
10A CEE	❶ £27.00	
2,5ha 89**T**(100-120m²) 17**P**	❷ £35.50	

🚗 On A3075 Redruth-Newquay, south of Newquay take the unnumbered exit direction Crantock. The entrance to the campsite is on the left after Crantock.

💬 Farm campsite in a nature reserve, with neat toilet facilities. The shop and bar are located in the old farm house. The shop sells hot beverages. Next to the shop is a covered seating area. Perfect starting point for beautiful walks.

📍 N 50°23'56'' W 5°7'21''

www.eurocampings.co.uk/102683

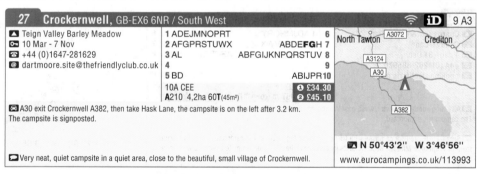

26 Crantock/Newquay, GB-TR8 5EW / South West ♿ 🛜 ❀ iD 40a

- ⛰ Trevella Park*****
- 🏕 Crantock
- 📅 23 Mar - 29 Oct
- ☎ +44 (0)1637-830308
- @ holidays@trevella.co.uk

1 ADE**JM**NOPQR	ABFG**N**	6
2 FGOPSTUVWX	ABDE**FG**H	7
3 BE**IK**	ABCDEFGHIJLNPQRSTUV	8
4 BFHI**PQ**	ABE	9
5 ACDEFKMN**O**	ABEGHIJMPRYZ	10
16A CEE	❶ £30.00	
9ha 217**T**(100-120m²) 150**P**	❷ £45.00	

🚗 On the A3075 Redruth-Newquay, south of Newquay take the unnumbered exit to Crantock. After 1.5 km on the road bending to the left. Entrance is on the right.

💬 Welcoming, spacious campsite that offers all kinds of camping opportunities. From basic camping to glamping, everything is taken care of. Nature hunts are organised during school holidays.

📍 N 50°23'50'' W 5°5'46''

www.eurocampings.co.uk/102681

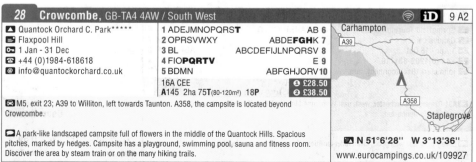

27 Crockernwell, GB-EX6 6NR / South West 🛜 iD 9 A3

- ⛰ Teign Valley Barley Meadow
- 📅 10 Mar - 7 Nov
- ☎ +44 (0)1647-281629
- @ dartmoore.site@thefriendlyclub.co.uk

1 ADE**J**MNOPRT		6
2 AFGPRSTUWX	ABDE**FG**H	7
3 AL	ABFGIJKNPQRSTUV	8
4		9
5 BD	ABIJPR	10
10A CEE	❶ £34.30	
A210 4,2ha 60**T**(45m²)	❷ £45.10	

🚗 A30 exit Crockernwell A382, then take Hask Lane, the campsite is on the left after 3.2 km. The campsite is signposted.

💬 Very neat, quiet campsite in a quiet area, close to the beautiful, small village of Crockernwell.

📍 N 50°43'2'' W 3°46'56''

www.eurocampings.co.uk/113993

28 Crowcombe, GB-TA4 4AW / South West 🛜 iD 9 A2

- ⛰ Quantock Orchard C. Park*****
- 🏕 Flaxpool Hill
- 📅 1 Jan - 31 Dec
- ☎ +44 (0)1984-618618
- @ info@quantockorchard.co.uk

1 ADEJMNOPQRS**T**	AB	6
2 OPRSVWXY	ABDE**FGH**K	7
3 BL	ABCDEFIJLNPQRSV	8
4 FIO**PQRTV**	E	9
5 BDMN	ABFGHJORV	10
16A CEE	❶ £28.50	
A145 2ha 75**T**(80-120m²) 18**P**	❷ £38.50	

🚗 M5, exit 23; A39 to Williton, left towards Taunton. A358, the campsite is located beyond Crowcombe.

💬 A park-like landscaped campsite full of flowers in the middle of the Quantock Hills. Spacious pitches, marked by hedges. Campsite has a playground, swimming pool, sauna and fitness room. Discover the area by steam train or on the many hiking trails.

📍 N 51°6'28'' W 3°13'36''

www.eurocampings.co.uk/109927

United Kingdom

29   Crows-an-Wra/Land's End, GB-TR19 6HX / South West   📶 iD   40a

- ⛺ Cardinney Car. & Camp. Park
- 🏠 Main A30
- 📅 1 Feb - 30 Nov
- ☎ +44 (0)1736-810880
- @ cardinney@btinternet.com

1 ADE**JM**NOPR**T**		6
2 FPSVWXY	ABDE**FGH**	7
3 **K**	ABFJKNQRTUV	8
4 O**Q**		9
5 BDFHJLMN	ABFHJM**P**R**10**	
10A CEE	❶ £21.00	
A130 2ha 90**T**(80-160m²)	❷ £28.00	

🚗 From Penzance take the A30 in the direction of Land's End. The private entrance road to the campsite is located to the right after about 7 km. Follow the campsite signs.

💬 This well-run picture book campsite with 90 pitches is set amid the beauty of Cornwall, 5 miles from Land's End. After a trip out, maybe to Carn Euny which dates from the Iron Age, you can relax in the nostalgic campsite pub. There is also a small restaurant and take away meals can be ordered.

Penzance   A30
⛺ Marazion

📍 N 50°5'36''   W 5°38'12''
www.eurocampings.co.uk/109046

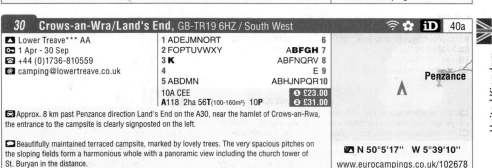

30   Crows-an-Wra/Land's End, GB-TR19 6HZ / South West   📶 ♻ iD   40a

- ⛺ Lower Treave*** AA
- 📅 1 Apr - 30 Sep
- ☎ +44 (0)1736-810559
- @ camping@lowertreave.co.uk

1 ADEJMNOR**T**		6
2 FOPTUVWXY	A**BFGH**	7
3 **K**	ABFNQRV	8
4	E	9
5 ABDMN	ABHJNP**GR10**	
10A CEE	❶ £23.00	
A118 2ha 56**T**(100-160m²) 10**P**	❷ £31.00	

🚗 Approx. 8 km past Penzance direction Land's End on the A30, near the hamlet of Crows-an-Rwa, the entrance to the campsite is clearly signposted on the left.

💬 Beautifully maintained terraced campsite, marked by lovely trees. The very spacious pitches on the sloping fields form a harmonious whole with a panoramic view including the church tower of St. Buryan in the distance.

⛺ Penzance

📍 N 50°5'17''   W 5°39'10''
www.eurocampings.co.uk/102678

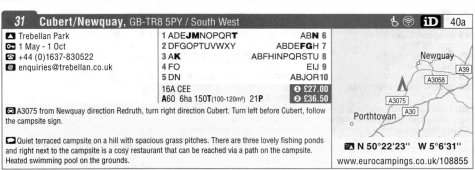

31   Cubert/Newquay, GB-TR8 5PY / South West   ♿ 📶 iD   40a

- ⛺ Trebellan Park
- 📅 1 May - 1 Oct
- ☎ +44 (0)1637-830522
- @ enquiries@trebellan.co.uk

1 ADE**JM**NOPQR**T**	AB**N**	6
2 DFGOPTUVWXY	ABDE**FGH**	7
3 A**K**	ABFHINPQRSTU	8
4 FO	EI**J**	9
5 DN	ABJOR**10**	
16A CEE	❶ £27.00	
A60 6ha 150**T**(100-120m²) 21**P**	❷ £36.50	

🚗 A3075 from Newquay direction Redruth, turn right direction Cubert. Turn left before Cubert, follow the campsite sign.

💬 Quiet terraced campsite on a hill with spacious grass pitches. There are three lovely fishing ponds and right next to the campsite is a cosy restaurant that can be reached via a path on the campsite. Heated swimming pool on the grounds.

Newquay   A39
⛺   A3058
A3075
Porthtowan   A30

📍 N 50°22'23''   W 5°6'31''
www.eurocampings.co.uk/108855

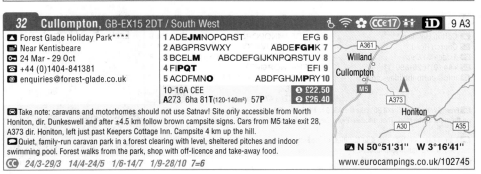

32   Cullompton, GB-EX15 2DT / South West   ♿ 📶 ♻ (CC€17) 🚻 iD   9 A3

- ⛺ Forest Glade Holiday Park****
- 🏠 Near Kentisbeare
- 📅 24 Mar - 29 Oct
- ☎ +44 (0)1404-841381
- @ enquiries@forest-glade.co.uk

1 ADE**JM**NOPQRST	EFG	6
2 ABGPRSVWXY	ABDE**FGH**K	7
3 BCEL**M**	ABCDEFGIJKNPQRSTUV	8
4 F**IPQT**	EFI	9
5 ACDFMN**O**	ABDFGHJM**P**RY**10**	
10-16A CEE	❶ £22.50	
A273 6ha 81**T**(120-140m²) 57**P**	❷ £26.40	

🚗 Take note: caravans and motorhomes should not use Satnav! Site only accessible from North Honiton, dir. Dunkeswell and after ±4.5 km follow brown campsite signs. Cars from M5 take exit 28, A373 dir. Honiton, left just past Keepers Cottage Inn. Campsite 4 km up the hill.

💬 Quiet, family-run caravan park in a forest clearing with level, sheltered pitches and indoor swimming pool. Forest walks from the park, shop with off-licence and take-away food.

Ⓒ 24/3-29/3   14/4-24/5   1/6-14/7   1/9-28/10   7=6

A361
Willand
Cullompton
M5   A373
Honiton
A30   A35

📍 N 50°51'31''   W 3°16'41''
www.eurocampings.co.uk/102745

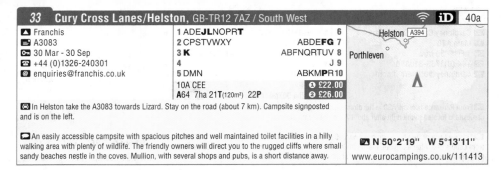

33 Cury Cross Lanes/Helston, GB-TR12 7AZ / South West — iD 40a

- Franchis
- A3083
- 30 Mar - 30 Sep
- +44 (0)1326-240301
- enquiries@franchis.co.uk

1 ADEJLNOPRT		6
2 CPSTVWXY	ABDEFG	7
3 K	ABFNQRTUV	8
4	J	9
5 DMN	ABKMPR	10
10A CEE		❶ £22.00
A64 7ha 21T(120m²) 22P		❷ £26.00

In Helston take the A3083 towards Lizard. Stay on the road (about 7 km). Campsite signposted and is on the left.

An easily accessible campsite with spacious pitches and well maintained toilet facilities in a hilly walking area with plenty of wildlife. The friendly owners will direct you to the rugged cliffs where small sandy beaches nestle in the coves. Mullion, with several shops and pubs, is a short distance away.

N 50°2'19'' W 5°13'11''
www.eurocampings.co.uk/111413

34 Dalwood/Axminster, GB-EX13 7DY / South West — iD 9 A3

- Andrewshayes Holiday Park****
- 24 Mar - 28 Oct
- +44 (0)1404-831225
- info@andrewshayes.co.uk

1 ADEJMNOPQRST	CDFG	6
2 FGPRSTUVWXY	ABDEFGK	7
3 AEKL	ABFGIJNQRSTUV	8
4 FIPQ	E	9
5 ABDFHMN	ABDFHKMPR	10
10A CEE		❶ £27.50
A68 4,4ha 35T(90-100m²) 133P		❷ £33.50

A35 from Axminster to Honiton dir. Dalwood/Stockland at crossroads after 5 km follow campsite sign on right. A35 from Honiton to Dorchester at crossroads after 9 km dir. Dalwood/Stockland, campsite sign.
A terraced campsite with spacious pitches in the middle of the hilly area of East Devon. Indoor heated pool with sliding roof, play rooms for young and old. Close to the Jurassic Coast, the resorts of Charmouth and Lyme Regis and the English Riviera.

CC 24/3-30/3 9/4-3/5 11/5-23/5 2/6-14/7 1/9-27/10 7=6, 14=11

N 50°46'59'' W 3°4'10''
www.eurocampings.co.uk/102766

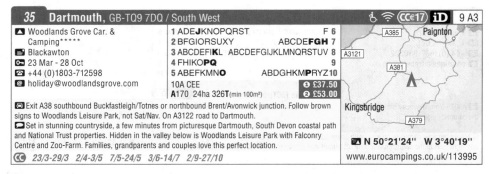

35 Dartmouth, GB-TQ9 7DQ / South West — iD 9 A3

- Woodlands Grove Car. & Camping*****
- Blackawton
- 23 Mar - 28 Oct
- +44 (0)1803-712598
- holiday@woodlandsgrove.com

1 ADEJKNOPQRST	F	6
2 BFGIORSUXY	ABCDEFGH	7
3 ABCDEFIKL ABCDEFGIJKLMNQRSTUV		8
4 FHIKOPQ		9
5 ABEFKMNO	ABDGHKMPRYZ	10
10A CEE		❶ £37.50
A170 24ha 326T(min 100m²)		❷ £53.00

Exit A38 southbound Buckfastleigh/Totnes or northbound Brent/Avonwick junction. Follow brown signs to Woodlands Leisure Park, not Sat/Nav. On A3122 route to Dartmouth.
Set in stunning countryside, a few minutes from picturesque Dartmouth, South Devon coastal path and National Trust properties. Hidden in the valley below is Woodlands Leisure Park with Falconry Centre and Zoo-Farm. Families, grandparents and couples love this perfect location.

CC 23/3-29/3 2/4-3/5 7/5-24/5 3/6-14/7 2/9-27/10

N 50°21'24'' W 3°40'19''
www.eurocampings.co.uk/113995

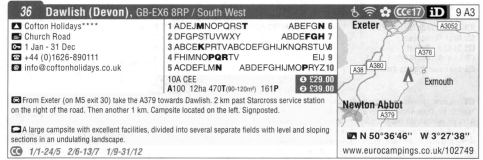

36 Dawlish (Devon), GB-EX6 8RP / South West — iD 9 A3

- Cofton Holidays****
- Church Road
- 1 Jan - 31 Dec
- +44 (0)1626-890111
- info@coftonholidays.co.uk

1 ADEJMNOPQRST	ABEFGN	6
2 DFGPSTUVWXY	ABDEFGH	7
3 ABCEKPRTVABCDEFGHIJKNQRSTUV		8
4 FHIMNOPQRTV	EIJ	9
5 ACDEFLMN	ABDEFGHIJMOPRYZ	10
10A CEE		❶ £29.00
A100 12ha 470T(90-120m²) 161P		❷ £39.00

From Exeter (on M5 exit 30) take the A379 towards Dawlish. 2 km past Starcross service station on the right of the road. Then another 1 km. Campsite located on the left. Signposted.

A large campsite with excellent facilities, divided into several separate fields with level and sloping sections in an undulating landscape.

CC 1/1-24/5 2/6-13/7 1/9-31/12

N 50°36'46'' W 3°27'38''
www.eurocampings.co.uk/102749

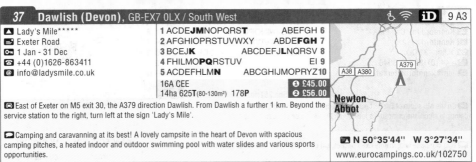

37 Dawlish (Devon), GB-EX7 0LX / South West ♿ 🛜 iD 9 A3

- 🏕 Lady's Mile*****
- ✉ Exeter Road
- 📅 1 Jan - 31 Dec
- ☎ +44 (0)1626-863411
- @ info@ladysmile.co.uk

1 ACDE**JM**NOPQRS**T**	ABEFGH 6
2 AFGHIOPRSTUVWXY	ABDE**FGH** 7
3 BCEJ**K**	ABCDEFJLNQRSV 8
4 FHILMO**PQ**RSTUV	EI 9
5 ACDEFHLM**N**	ABCGHIJMOPRYZ 10

16A CEE ● £45.00
14ha 625T(80-130m²) 178P ● £56.00

🚗 East of Exeter on M5 exit 30, the A379 direction Dawlish. From Dawlish a further 1 km. Beyond the service station to the right, turn left at the sign 'Lady's Mile'.

💬 Camping and caravanning at its best! A lovely campsite in the heart of Devon with spacious camping pitches, a heated indoor and outdoor swimming pool with water slides and various sports opportunities.

🧭 N 50°35'44'' W 3°27'34''
www.eurocampings.co.uk/102750

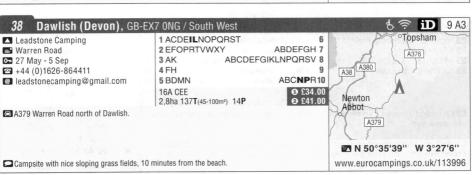

38 Dawlish (Devon), GB-EX7 0NG / South West ♿ 🛜 iD 9 A3

- 🏕 Leadstone Camping
- ✉ Warren Road
- 📅 27 May - 5 Sep
- ☎ +44 (0)1626-864411
- @ leadstonecamping@gmail.com

1 ACDE**IL**NOPQRST	6
2 EFOPRTVWXY	ABDEFGH 7
3 AK	ABCDEFGIKLNPQRSV 8
4 FH	9
5 BDMN	ABC**NPR** 10

16A CEE ● £34.00
2,8ha 137T(45-100m²) 14P ● £41.00

🚗 A379 Warren Road north of Dawlish.

💬 Campsite with nice sloping grass fields, 10 minutes from the beach.

🧭 N 50°35'39'' W 3°27'6''
www.eurocampings.co.uk/113996

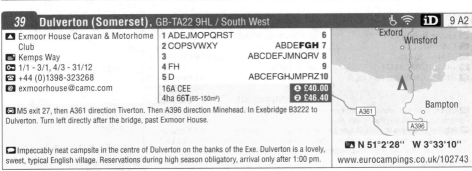

39 Dulverton (Somerset), GB-TA22 9HL / South West ♿ 🛜 iD 9 A2

- 🏕 Exmoor House Caravan & Motorhome Club
- ✉ Kemps Way
- 📅 1/1 - 3/1, 4/3 - 31/12
- ☎ +44 (0)1398-323268
- @ exmoorhouse@camc.com

1 ADEJMOPQRST	6
2 COPSVWXY	ABDE**FGH** 7
3	ABCDEFJMNQRV 8
4 FH	9
5 D	ABCEFGHJMPRZ 10

16A CEE ● £40.00
4ha 66T(65-150m²) ● £46.40

🚗 M5 exit 27, then A361 direction Tiverton. Then A396 direction Minehead. In Exebridge B3222 to Dulverton. Turn left directly after the bridge, past Exmoor House.

💬 Impeccably neat campsite in the centre of Dulverton on the banks of the Exe. Dulverton is a lovely, sweet, typical English village. Reservations during high season obligatory, arrival only after 1:00 pm.

🧭 N 51°2'28'' W 3°33'10''
www.eurocampings.co.uk/102743

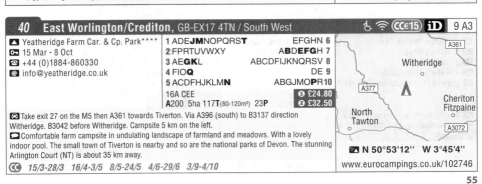

40 East Worlington/Crediton, GB-EX17 4TN / South West ♿ 🛜 (CC€15) iD 9 A3

- 🏕 Yeatheridge Farm Car. & Cp. Park****
- 📅 15 Mar - 8 Oct
- ☎ +44 (0)1884-860330
- @ info@yeatheridge.co.uk

1 ADE**JM**NOPQRS**T**	EFGHN 6
2 FPRTUVWXY	**ABDEFG**H 7
3 AE**GK**L	ABCDFIJKNQRSV 8
4 FIO**Q**	DE 9
5 ACDFHJKLM**N**	ABGJMO**PR** 10

16A CEE ● £24.80
A200 5ha 117T(80-120m²) 23P ● £32.50

🚗 Take exit 27 on the M5 then A361 towards Tiverton. Via A396 (south) to B3137 direction Witheridge. B3042 before Witheridge. Campsite 5 km on the left.

💬 Comfortable farm campsite in undulating landscape of farmland and meadows. With a lovely indoor pool. The small town of Tiverton is nearby and so are the national parks of Devon. The stunning Arlington Court (NT) is about 35 km away.

CC 15/3-28/3 16/4-3/5 8/5-24/5 4/6-29/6 3/9-4/10

🧭 N 50°53'12'' W 3°45'4''
www.eurocampings.co.uk/102746

United Kingdom

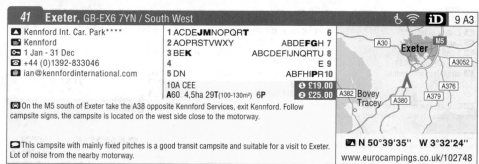

41 Exeter, GB-EX6 7YN / South West iD 9 A3

- ▲ Kennford Int. Car. Park****
- 🛏 Kennford
- 📅 1 Jan - 31 Dec
- ☎ +44 (0)1392-833046
- @ ian@kennfordinternational.com

1 ACDE**JM**NOPQR**T**		6
2 AOPRSTVWXY	ABDE**FG**H	7
3 BE**K**	ABCDEFIJNQRTU	8
4	E	9
5 DN	ABFHI**PR**10	
10A CEE	❶ £19.00	
A60 4,5ha 29**T**(100-130m²) 6**P**	❷ £25.00	

🚗 On the M5 south of Exeter take the A38 opposite Kennford Services, exit Kennford. Follow campsite signs, the campsite is located on the west side close to the motorway.

💬 This campsite with mainly fixed pitches is a good transit campsite and suitable for a visit to Exeter. Lot of noise from the nearby motorway.

📍 N 50°39'35'' W 3°32'24''
www.eurocampings.co.uk/102748

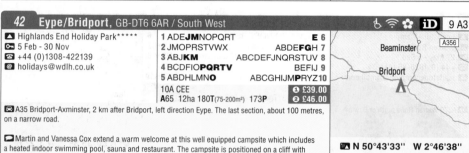

42 Eype/Bridport, GB-DT6 6AR / South West iD 9 A3

- ▲ Highlands End Holiday Park*****
- 📅 5 Feb - 30 Nov
- ☎ +44 (0)1308-422139
- @ holidays@wdlh.co.uk

1 ADE**JM**NOPQRT	**E**	6
2 JMOPRSTVWX	ABDE**FG**H	7
3 ABJ**KM**	ABCDEFJNQRSTUV	8
4 BCDFIO**PQRTV**	BEFIJ	9
5 ABDHLMN**O**	ABCGHIJM**P**RYZ10	
10A CEE	❶ £39.00	
A65 12ha 180**T**(75-200m²) 173**P**	❷ £46.00	

🚗 A35 Bridport-Axminster, 2 km after Bridport, left direction Eype. The last section, about 100 metres, on a narrow road.

💬 Martin and Vanessa Cox extend a warm welcome at this well equipped campsite which includes a heated indoor swimming pool, sauna and restaurant. The campsite is positioned on a cliff with wonderful views over the sea and Lyme Bay.

📍 N 50°43'33'' W 2°46'38''
www.eurocampings.co.uk/102795

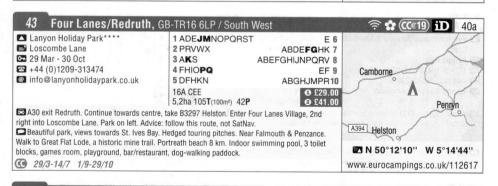

43 Four Lanes/Redruth, GB-TR16 6LP / South West (CC€19) iD 40a

- ▲ Lanyon Holiday Park****
- 🛏 Loscombe Lane
- 📅 29 Mar - 30 Oct
- ☎ +44 (0)1209-313474
- @ info@lanyonholidaypark.co.uk

1 ADE**JM**NOPQRST	**E** 6	
2 PRVWX	ABDE**FG**HK	7
3 A**K**S	ABEFGHIJNPQRV	8
4 FHIO**PQ**	EF	9
5 DFHKN	ABGHJMPR10	
16A CEE	❶ £29.00	
5,2ha 105**T**(100m²) 42**P**	❷ £41.00	

🚗 A30 exit Redruth. Continue towards centre, take B3297 Helston. Enter Four Lanes Village, 2nd right into Loscombe Lane. Park on left. Advice: follow this route, not SatNav.

💬 Beautiful park, views towards St. Ives Bay. Hedged touring pitches. Near Falmouth & Penzance. Walk to Great Flat Lode, a historic mine trail. Portreath beach 8 km. Indoor swimming pool, 3 toilet blocks, games room, playground, bar/restaurant, dog-walking paddock.

CC 29/3-14/7 1/9-29/10

📍 N 50°12'10'' W 5°14'44''
www.eurocampings.co.uk/112617

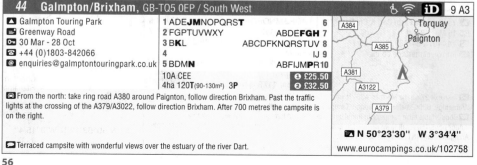

44 Galmpton/Brixham, GB-TQ5 0EP / South West iD 9 A3

- ▲ Galmpton Touring Park
- 🛏 Greenway Road
- 📅 30 Mar - 28 Oct
- ☎ +44 (0)1803-842066
- @ enquiries@galmptontouringpark.co.uk

1 ADE**JM**NOPQRS**T**		6
2 FGPTUVWXY	ABDE**FGH**	7
3 B**K**L	ABCDFKNQRSTUV	8
4	IJ	9
5 BDM**N**	ABFIJM**P**R10	
10A CEE	❶ £25.50	
4ha 120**T**(90-130m²) 3**P**	❷ £32.50	

🚗 From the north: take ring road A380 around Paignton, follow direction Brixham. Past the traffic lights at the crossing of the A379/A3022, follow direction Brixham. After 700 metres the campsite is on the right.

💬 Terraced campsite with wonderful views over the estuary of the river Dart.

📍 N 50°23'30'' W 3°34'4''
www.eurocampings.co.uk/102758

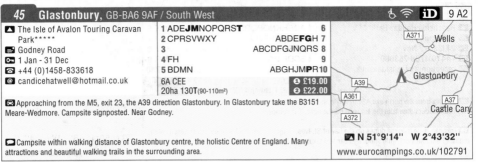

45 Glastonbury, GB-BA6 9AF / South West   ♿ 📶 **iD** 9 A2

🔺 The Isle of Avalon Touring Caravan Park★★★★★
✉ Godney Road
📅 1 Jan - 31 Dec
☎ +44 (0)1458-833618
@ candicehatwell@hotmail.co.uk

1 ADE**JM**NOPQRS**T**		6
2 CPRSVWXY	ABDE**FG**H	7
3	ABCDFGJNQRS	8
4 FH		9
5 BDMN	ABGHJM**P**R	10
6A CEE		➊ £19.00
20ha 130**T**(90-110m²)		➋ £22.00

🔜 Approaching from the M5, exit 23, the A39 direction Glastonbury. In Glastonbury take the B3151 Meare-Wedmore. Campsite signposted. Near Godney.

💬 Campsite within walking distance of Glastonbury centre, the holistic Centre of England. Many attractions and beautiful walking trails in the surrounding area.

📍 N 51°9'14'' W 2°43'32''
www.eurocampings.co.uk/102791

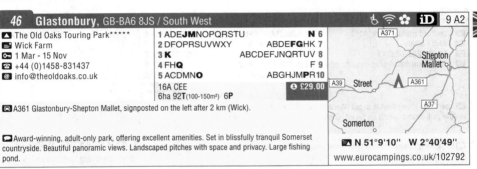

46 Glastonbury, GB-BA6 8JS / South West   ♿ 📶 ✿ **iD** 9 A2

🔺 The Old Oaks Touring Park★★★★★
✉ Wick Farm
📅 1 Mar - 15 Nov
☎ +44 (0)1458-831437
@ info@theoldoaks.co.uk

1 ADE**JM**NOPQRSTU	**N**	6
2 DFOPRSUVWXY	ABDE**FG**HK	7
3 **K**	ABCDEFJNQRTUV	8
4 FH**Q**	F	9
5 ACDMN**O**	ABGHJM**P**R	10
16A CEE		➊ £29.00
6ha 92**T**(100-150m²) 6**P**		

🔜 A361 Glastonbury-Shepton Mallet, signposted on the left after 2 km (Wick).

💬 Award-winning, adult-only park, offering excellent amenities. Set in blissfully tranquil Somerset countryside. Beautiful panoramic views. Landscaped pitches with space and privacy. Large fishing pond.

📍 N 51°9'10'' W 2°40'49''
www.eurocampings.co.uk/102792

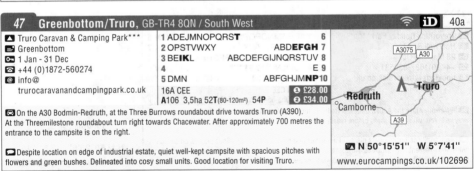

47 Greenbottom/Truro, GB-TR4 8QN / South West   📶 **iD** 40a

🔺 Truro Caravan & Camping Park★★★
✉ Greenbottom
📅 1 Jan - 31 Dec
☎ +44 (0)1872-560274
@ info@
trurocaravanandcampingpark.co.uk

1 ADEJMNOPQRS**T**		6
2 OPSTVWXY	ABD**EFGH**	7
3 BE**IK**L	ABCDEFGIJNQRSTUV	8
4	E	9
5 DMN	ABFGHJM**N**P	10
16A CEE		➊ £28.00
A106 3,5ha 52**T**(80-120m²) 54**P**		➋ £34.00

🔜 On the A30 Bodmin-Redruth, at the Three Burrows roundabout drive towards Truro (A390). At the Threemilestone roundabout turn right towards Chacewater. After approximately 700 metres the entrance to the campsite is on the right.

💬 Despite location on edge of industrial estate, quiet well-kept campsite with spacious pitches with flowers and green bushes. Delineated into cosy small units. Good location for visiting Truro.

📍 N 50°15'51'' W 5°7'41''
www.eurocampings.co.uk/102696

48 Harmans Cross/Swanage, GB-BH19 3EB / South West   ♿ 📶 9 B3

🔺 Haycraft Caravan Clubsite
✉ Haycrafts Lane
📅 15 Mar - 2 Nov
☎ +44 (0)1929-480572
@ haycraft@caravanclub.co.uk

1 DEJMOPQRST		6
2 FIOPRSUVWX	ABDE**FG**	7
3 E	ABCDEFKNQRSV	8
4		9
5 BDMN	ABHIJM**P**R	10
16A CEE		➊ £29.20
2ha 55**T**(60-120m²)		➋ £35.80

🔜 From Corfe Castle follow the A351 direction Swanage. Turn right in Harmans Cross direction Downhay Farm. Cross the railway after the concrete bridge, another 400 metres. Campsite is clearly signposted on the left.

💬 Beautiful terraced campsite with exceptional facilities. Reservations always recommended. On first registration you become a member of the Caravan Club.

📍 N 50°36'58'' W 2°1'25''
www.eurocampings.co.uk/102850

United Kingdom

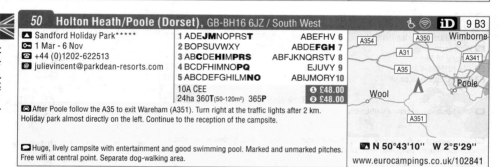

49 Hayle, GB-TR27 5AW / South West

🄐 Beachside Holiday Park★★★★
🏠 Lethlean Lane
🗓 24 Mar - 2 Nov
☎ +44 (0)1736-753080
@ reception@beachside.co.uk

1 ADEHKNOPQRST	ABFGKQX 6
2 EFGHOPTVW	AB**FG**H 7
3 ABE**KLQ**	ABFGHIJNPQRSV 8
4 BCDFI**PQ**	FIJMR 9
5 ACDFH**N**	ABGHIJORZ10
10-16A CEE	❶ £44.00
14,8ha 85T(110m²) 113P	❷ £44.00

🄯 Coming from the north exit A30 in Hayle and head towards the centre. Continue straight on over two roundabouts then take the 1st road on the right. The campsite is signposted there.

💬 This campsite is in the dunes on the bay of St. Ives, 5 minutes from a beautiful sandy beach. With a heated outdoor pool, little shop, and bar and takeaway. No dogs allowed.

Ⓒ 24/3-25/5 2/6-29/6 1/9-1/11

Redruth · Penzance

A30 · A394

📷 N 50°11'46" W 5°24'37"

www.eurocampings.co.uk/108576

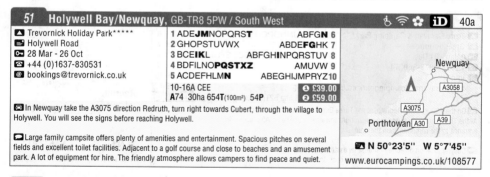

50 Holton Heath/Poole (Dorset), GB-BH16 6JZ / South West

🄐 Sandford Holiday Park★★★★★
🗓 1 Mar - 6 Nov
☎ +44 (0)1202-622513
@ julievincent@parkdean-resorts.com

1 ADE**JM**NOPRS**T**	ABEFHV 6
2 BOPSUVWXY	ABDE**FGH** 7
3 ABC**DE**HI**MPRS**	ABFJKNQRSTV 8
4 BCDFHIMNO**PQ**	EJUVY 9
5 ABCDEFGHILM**NO**	ABIJMORY10
10A CEE	❶ £48.00
24ha 360T(50-120m²) 365P	❷ £48.00

🄯 After Poole follow the A35 to exit Wareham (A351). Turn right at the traffic lights after 2 km. Holiday park almost directly on the left. Continue to the reception of the campsite.

💬 Huge, lively campsite with entertainment and good swimming pool. Marked and unmarked pitches. Free wifi at central point. Separate dog-walking area.

Wimborne · Poole · Wool

A354 · A350 · A31 · A341 · A35 · A351

📷 N 50°43'10" W 2°5'29"

www.eurocampings.co.uk/102841

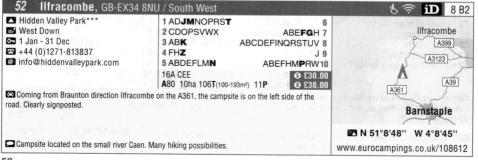

51 Holywell Bay/Newquay, GB-TR8 5PW / South West

🄐 Trevornick Holiday Park★★★★★
🏠 Holywell Road
🗓 28 Mar - 26 Oct
☎ +44 (0)1637-830531
@ bookings@trevornick.co.uk

1 ADE**JM**NOPRS**T**	ABFG**N** 6
2 GHOPSTUVWX	ABDE**FG**HK 7
3 BCE**IKL**	ABFGH**I**NPQRSTUV 8
4 BDFILNO**PQSTXZ**	AMUVW 9
5 ACDEFHLM**N**	ABEGHIJMPRYZ10
10-16A CEE	❶ £39.00
A74 30ha 654T(100m²) 54P	❷ £59.00

🄯 In Newquay take the A3075 direction Redruth, turn right towards Cubert, through the village to Holywell. You will see the signs before reaching Holywell.

💬 Large family campsite offers plenty of amenities and entertainment. Spacious pitches on several fields and excellent toilet facilities. Adjacent to a golf course and close to beaches and an amusement park. A lot of equipment for hire. The friendly atmosphere allows campers to find peace and quiet.

Newquay · Porthtowan

A3058 · A3075 · A30 · A39

📷 N 50°23'5" W 5°7'45"

www.eurocampings.co.uk/108577

---

52 Ilfracombe, GB-EX34 8NU / South West

🄐 Hidden Valley Park★★★
🏠 West Down
🗓 1 Jan - 31 Dec
☎ +44 (0)1271-813837
@ info@hiddenvalleypark.com

1 AD**JM**NOPRS**T**	6
2 CDOPSVWX	ABE**FG**H 7
3 AB**K**	ABCDEFINQRSTUV 8
4 FH**Z**	J 9
5 ABDEFLM**N**	ABEFHMPRW10
16A CEE	❶ £30.00
A80 10ha 106T(100-193m²) 11P	❷ £38.00

🄯 Coming from Braunton direction Ilfracombe on the A361, the campsite is on the left side of the road. Clearly signposted.

💬 Campsite located on the small river Caen. Many hiking possibilities.

Ilfracombe · Barnstaple

A399 · A3123 · A39 · A361

📷 N 51°8'48" W 4°8'45"

www.eurocampings.co.uk/108612

53 Ilfracombe, GB-EX34 9SW / South West — 9 A2

- Napps Camping and Caravan Park***
- Old Coast Road
- 3 Mar - 31 Oct
- +44 (0)1271-882557
- @ bookings@napps.fsnet.co.uk

1 DE**JM**NOPR**T**	ABFGKNX	6
2 EFGHJOPSUVWX	BDE**FGH**	7
3 BLM	ABDFINQRTUV	8
4 FIO**Q**		9
5 CDEFHKM	ABHJMR	10
10A CEE		❶ £26.00
A120 10ha 213T(80-100m²) 150P		❷ £36.00

On the A399 Combe Martin and Ilfracombe, 1 km outside the village. Clearly signposted.

Beautiful campsite with sea views. Beach within walking distance. Large pitches.

N 51°12'41'' W 4°3'41''
www.eurocampings.co.uk/108613

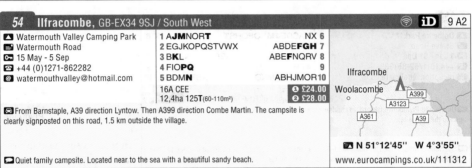

54 Ilfracombe, GB-EX34 9SJ / South West — 9 A2

- Watermouth Valley Camping Park
- Watermouth Road
- 15 May - 5 Sep
- +44 (0)1271-862282
- @ watermouthvalley@hotmail.com

1 A**JM**NOR**T**	NX	6
2 EGJKOPQSTVWX	ABDE**FGH**	7
3 B**KL**	ABEF**N**QRV	8
4 FIO**PQ**		9
5 BDMN	ABHJMOR	10
16A CEE		❶ £24.00
12,4ha 125T(60-110m²)		❷ £28.00

From Barnstaple, A39 direction Lyntow. Then A399 direction Combe Martin. The campsite is clearly signposted on this road, 1.5 km outside the village.

Quiet family campsite. Located near to the sea with a beautiful sandy beach.

N 51°12'45'' W 4°3'55''
www.eurocampings.co.uk/111312

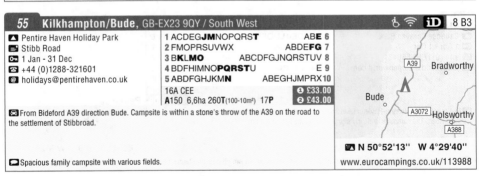

55 Kilkhampton/Bude, GB-EX23 9QY / South West — 8 B3

- Pentire Haven Holiday Park
- Stibb Road
- 1 Jan - 31 Dec
- +44 (0)1288-321601
- @ holidays@pentirehaven.co.uk

1 ACDEG**JM**NOPQRS**T**	ABE**E**	6
2 FMOPRSUVWX	ABDE**FG**	7
3 B**KLMO**	ABCDFGJNQRSTUV	8
4 BDFHIMNO**PQRST**U	E	9
5 ABDFGHJKM**N**	ABEGHJMPRX	10
16A CEE		❶ £33.00
A150 6,6ha 260T(100-10m²) 17P		❷ £43.00

From Bideford A39 direction Bude. Campsite is within a stone's throw of the A39 on the road to the settlement of Stibbroad.

Spacious family campsite with various fields.

N 50°52'13'' W 4°29'40''
www.eurocampings.co.uk/113988

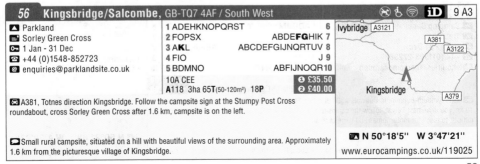

56 Kingsbridge/Salcombe, GB-TQ7 4AF / South West — 9 A3

- Parkland
- Sorley Green Cross
- 1 Jan - 31 Dec
- +44 (0)1548-852723
- @ enquiries@parklandsite.co.uk

1 ADEHKNOPQRST		6
2 FOPSX	ABDE**FG**HIK	7
3 A**KL**	ABCDEFGIJNQRTUV	8
4 FIO	J	9
5 BDMNO	ABFIJNOQR	10
10A CEE		❶ £35.50
A118 3ha 65T(50-120m²) 18P		❷ £40.00

A381, Totnes direction Kingsbridge. Follow the campsite sign at the Stumpy Post Cross roundabout, cross Sorley Green Cross after 1.6 km, campsite is on the left.

Small rural campsite, situated on a hill with beautiful views of the surrounding area. Approximately 1.6 km from the picturesque village of Kingsbridge.

N 50°18'5'' W 3°47'21''
www.eurocampings.co.uk/119025

United Kingdom

United Kingdom

---

57 Lacock (Wiltshire), GB-SN15 2LP / South West · iD 9 B2

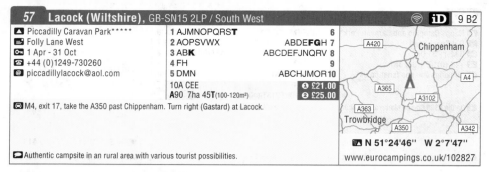

- Piccadilly Caravan Park*****
- Folly Lane West
- 1 Apr - 31 Oct
- +44 (0)1249-730260
- piccadillylacock@aol.com

1 AJMNOPQRS**T**		**6**
2 AOPSVWX	ABDE**FG**H	7
3 AB**K**	ABCDEFJNQRV	8
4 FH		9
5 DMN	ABCHJMOR	10
10A CEE		❶ £21.00
A90 7ha 45**T**(100-120m²)		❷ £25.00

M4, exit 17, take the A350 past Chippenham. Turn right (Gastard) at Lacock.

N 51°24'46'' W 2°7'47''

Authentic campsite in an rural area with various tourist possibilities.

www.eurocampings.co.uk/102827

---

58 Landrake/Saltash, GB-PL12 5AF / South West · iD 8 B3

- Dolbeare Park****
- St. Ive Road
- 1 Jan - 31 Dec
- +44 (0)1752-851332
- reception@dolbeare.co.uk

1 ACDE**JM**NOPQRS**T**		**X 6**
2 PRSTVWX	ABDE**FG**H	7
3 BE**KR**	ABEFGIJLNQRSUV	8
4 FH	AB	9
5 ABDFGMNO	ABFGHJM**PR**	10
16A CEE		❶ £28.00
A100 3,6ha 80**T**(100-130m²) 3**P**		❷ £34.00

On the A38 Plymouth-Liskeard, in Landrake the campsite is signposted St. Ive Road. Follow the signs to the campsite.

N 50°25'50'' W 4°18'19''

Spacious campsite open all year round. Good shelter, spacious pitches. Excellent for trips to Looe and Polperro. North of Plymouth with its many points of interest.

www.eurocampings.co.uk/102735

---

59 Leedstown/Hayle, GB-TR27 5ET / South West · iD 40a

- Calloose Caravan Park
- 1 Apr - 1 Oct
- +44 (0)1736-850431
- johnchadd@btopenworld.com

1 ADE**JL**NOP**R**T	ABFG	**6**
2 CGPRSVWX	ABDE**FG**H	7
3 B**KLM**	ABCDFIJNQRSTV	8
4 BDIN**PQ**	EF	9
5 ABDFHLMN	ABGKMPRVY	10
16A CEE		❶ £38.00
A60 5ha 109**T**(80-100m²) 45**P**		❷ £48.00

Exit the B33202 Helston-Hayle in Leedstown (opposite Leedstown Village Hall) and turn into Trenerth Road. The campsite is clearly signposted on the left after 1 km.

N 50°10'9'' W 5°21'31''

Beautiful, well-kept campsite in the heart of Cornwall with heated swimming pool and tennis court.

www.eurocampings.co.uk/110330

---

60 Looe, GB-PL13 2NA / South West · iD 8 B3

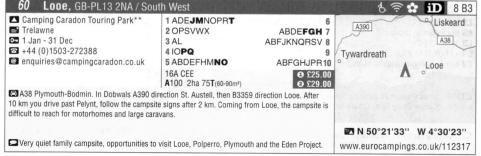

- Camping Caradon Touring Park**
- Trelawne
- 1 Jan - 31 Dec
- +44 (0)1503-272388
- enquiries@campingcaradon.co.uk

1 ADE**JM**NOP**R**T		**6**
2 OPSVWX	ABDE**FG**H	7
3 AL	ABFJKNQRSV	8
4 IO**PQ**		9
5 ABDEFHM**NO**	ABFGHJPR	10
16A CEE		❶ £25.00
A100 2ha 75**T**(60-90m²)		❷ £29.00

A38 Plymouth-Bodmin. In Dobwals A390 direction St. Austell, then B3359 direction Looe. After 10 km you drive past Pelynt, follow the campsite signs after 2 km. Coming from Looe, the campsite is difficult to reach for motorhomes and large caravans.

N 50°21'33'' W 4°30'23''

Very quiet family campsite, opportunities to visit Looe, Polperro, Plymouth and the Eden Project.

www.eurocampings.co.uk/112317

61 Looe, GB-PL13 2JR / South West

   ♿ 🛜 iD 8 B3

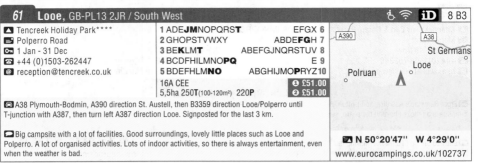

- ⛺ Tencreek Holiday Park★★★★
- 🏠 Polperro Road
- 🔓 1 Jan - 31 Dec
- ☎ +44 (0)1503-262447
- @ reception@tencreek.co.uk

1	ADE**JM**NOPQRS**T**	EFGX	6
2	GHOPSTVWXY	ABDE**FG**H	7
3	BE**KLM**T	ABEFGJNQRSTUV	8
4	BCDFHILMNO**PQ**	E	9
5	BDEFHLM**NO**	ABGHIJMO**P**RYZ	10

16A CEE — ❶ £51.00
5,5ha 250**T**(100-120m²) 220**P** — ❷ £51.00

🚗 A38 Plymouth-Bodmin, A390 direction St. Austell, then B3359 direction Looe/Polperro until T-junction with A387, then turn left A387 direction Looe. Signposted for the last 3 km.

💬 Big campsite with a lot of facilities. Good surroundings, lovely little places such as Looe and Polperro. A lot of organised activities. Lots of indoor activities, so there is always entertainment, even when the weather is bad.

📍 N 50°20'47'' W 4°29'0''
www.eurocampings.co.uk/102737

---

62 Lostwithiel, GB-PL30 5BU / South West

   ♿ 🛜 ❄ (CC€15) iD 40a

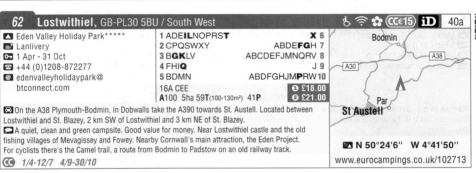

- ⛺ Eden Valley Holiday Park★★★★★
- 🏠 Lanlivery
- 🔓 1 Apr - 31 Oct
- ☎ +44 (0)1208-872277
- @ edenvalleyholidaypark@
  btconnect.com

1	ADE**IL**NOPRS**T**	X	6
2	CPQSWXY	ABDE**FG**H	7
3	B**GK**LV	ABCDEFJMNQRV	8
4	FHI**Q**	J	9
5	BDMN	ABDFGHJM**P**RW	10

16A CEE — ❶ £18.00
A100 5ha 59**T**(100-130m²) 41**P** — ❷ £21.00

🚗 On the A38 Plymouth-Bodmin, in Dobwalls take the A390 towards St. Austell. Located between Lostwithiel and St. Blazey, 2 km SW of Lostwithiel and 3 km NE of St. Blazey.

💬 A quiet, clean and green campsite. Good value for money. Near Lostwithiel castle and the old fishing villages of Mevagissey and Fowey. Nearby Cornwall's main attraction, the Eden Project. For cyclists there's the Camel trail, a route from Bodmin to Padstow on an old railway track.

Ⓒ 1/4-12/7 4/9-30/10

📍 N 50°24'6'' W 4°41'50''
www.eurocampings.co.uk/102713

---

63 Lulworth Cove/Wareham (Dorset), GB-BH20 5PU / South West

   ♿ 🛜 iD 9 B3

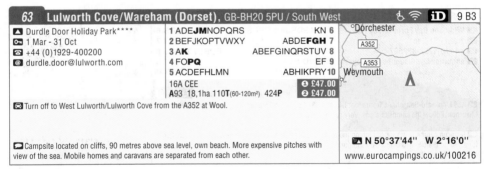

- ⛺ Durdle Door Holiday Park★★★★
- 🔓 1 Mar - 31 Oct
- ☎ +44 (0)1929-400200
- @ durdle.door@lulworth.com

1	ADE**JM**NOPQRS	KN	6
2	BEFJKOPTVWXY	ABDE**FG**H	7
3	A**K**	ABEFGINQRSTUV	8
4	FO**PQ**	EF	9
5	ACDEFHLMN	ABHIKPRY	10

16A CEE — ❶ £47.00
A93 18,1ha 110**T**(60-120m²) 424**P** — ❷ £47.00

🚗 Turn off to West Lulworth/Lulworth Cove from the A352 at Wool.

💬 Campsite located on cliffs, 90 metres above sea level, own beach. More expensive pitches with view of the sea. Mobile homes and caravans are separated from each other.

📍 N 50°37'44'' W 2°16'0''
www.eurocampings.co.uk/100216

---

64 Lyme Regis, GB-DT7 3UU / South West

   ♿ 🛜 iD 9 A3

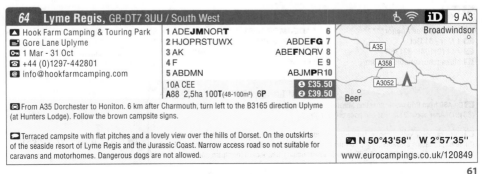

- ⛺ Hook Farm Camping & Touring Park
- 🏠 Gore Lane Uplyme
- 🔓 1 Mar - 31 Oct
- ☎ +44 (0)1297-442801
- @ info@hookfarmcamping.com

1	ADE**JM**NOR**T**		6
2	HJOPRSTUWX	ABDE**FG**	7
3	AK	ABE**F**NQRV	8
4	F	E	9
5	ABDMN	ABJM**P**R	10

10A CEE — ❶ £35.50
A88 2,5ha 100**T**(48-100m²) 6**P** — ❷ £39.50

🚗 From A35 Dorchester to Honiton. 6 km after Charmouth, turn left to the B3165 direction Uplyme (at Hunters Lodge). Follow the brown campsite signs.

💬 Terraced campsite with flat pitches and a lovely view over the hills of Dorset. On the outskirts of the seaside resort of Lyme Regis and the Jurassic Coast. Narrow access road so not suitable for caravans and motorhomes. Dangerous dogs are not allowed.

📍 N 50°43'58'' W 2°57'35''
www.eurocampings.co.uk/120849

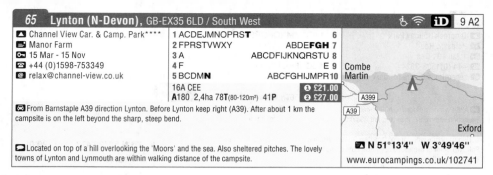

65 Lynton (N-Devon), GB-EX35 6LD / South West   ♿ 🛜 iD   9 A2

- ⛰ Channel View Car. & Camp. Park★★★★
- 🏠 Manor Farm
- 📅 15 Mar - 15 Nov
- ☎ +44 (0)1598-753349
- @ relax@channel-view.co.uk

1 ACDEJMNOPRS**T**		6
2 FPRSTVWXY	ABDE**FGH**	7
3 A	ABCDFIJKNQRSTU	8
4 F	E	9
5 BCDM**N**	ABCFGHIJMPR	10
16A CEE	❶ £21.00	
A180 2,4ha 78**T**(80-120m²) 41**P**	❷ £27.00	

🚗 From Barnstaple A39 direction Lynton. Before Lynton keep right (A39). After about 1 km the campsite is on the left beyond the sharp, steep bend.

💬 Located on top of a hill overlooking the 'Moors' and the sea. Also sheltered pitches. The lovely towns of Lynton and Lynmouth are within walking distance of the campsite.

📍 N 51°13'4'' W 3°49'46''

www.eurocampings.co.uk/102741

66 Merley/Wimb. Minster (Dorset), GB-BH21 3AA / South West   ♿ 🛜 iD   9 B3

- ⛰ Merley Court Touring Park★★★★★
- 📅 1 Feb - 31 Dec
- ☎ +44 (0)1590-648331
- @ holidays@shorefield.co.uk

1 ADG**JM**NOPQRS**T**	ABFG	6
2 PQRSVWX	ABDE**FGH**	7
3 BE**KL**	ABFIJNQRSTUV	8
4 I**Q**	J	9
5 CDEFHN	ABEGHJMORW	10
16A CEE	❶ £47.00	
6ha 100**T**(70-100m²) 6**P**	❷ £47.00	

🚗 From Ringwood take the A31 towards Wimborne Minster. After Wimborne Minster drive towards Dorchester and then the campsite is signposted. It is a separate exit on the roundabout.

💬 Beautiful family campsite with swimming pool. Many facilities for young people.

📍 N 50°47'9'' W 1°59'7''

www.eurocampings.co.uk/110900

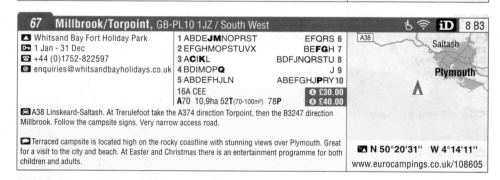

67 Millbrook/Torpoint, GB-PL10 1JZ / South West   ♿ 🛜 iD   8 B3

- ⛰ Whitsand Bay Fort Holiday Park
- 📅 1 Jan - 31 Dec
- ☎ +44 (0)1752-822597
- @ enquiries@whitsandbayholidays.co.uk

1 ABDE**JM**NOPRST	EFQRS	6
2 EFGHMOPSTUVX	BE**FG**H	7
3 A**C**I**KL**	BDFJNQRSTU	8
4 BDIMOP**Q**	J	9
5 ABDEFHJLN	ABEFGHJ**P**RY	10
16A CEE	❶ £30.00	
A70 10,9ha 52**T**(70-100m²) 78**P**	❷ £40.00	

🚗 A38 Linskeard-Saltash. At Trerulefoot take the A374 direction Torpoint, then the B3247 direction Millbrook. Follow the campsite signs. Very narrow access road.

💬 Terraced campsite is located high on the rocky coastline with stunning views over Plymouth. Great for a visit to the city and beach. At Easter and Christmas there is an entertainment programme for both children and adults.

📍 N 50°20'31'' W 4°14'11''

www.eurocampings.co.uk/108605

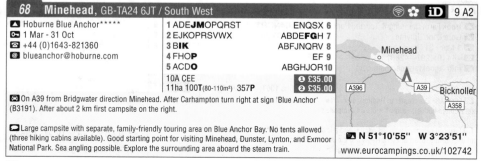

68 Minehead, GB-TA24 6JT / South West   🛜 ❄ iD   9 A2

- ⛰ Hoburne Blue Anchor★★★★★
- 📅 1 Mar - 31 Oct
- ☎ +44 (0)1643-821360
- @ blueanchor@hoburne.com

1 ADE**JM**OPQRST	ENQSX	6
2 EJKOPRSVWX	ABDE**FGH**	7
3 B**I**K	ABFJNQRV	8
4 FHO**P**	EF	9
5 ACD**O**	ABGHJOR	10
10A CEE	❶ £35.00	
11ha 100**T**(80-110m²) 357**P**	❷ £35.00	

🚗 On A39 from Bridgwater direction Minehead. After Carhampton turn right at sign 'Blue Anchor' (B3191). After about 2 km first campsite on the right.

💬 Large campsite with separate, family-friendly touring area on Blue Anchor Bay. No tents allowed (three hiking cabins available). Good starting point for visiting Minehead, Dunster, Lynton, and Exmoor National Park. Sea angling possible. Explore the surrounding area aboard the steam train.

📍 N 51°10'55'' W 3°23'51''

www.eurocampings.co.uk/102742

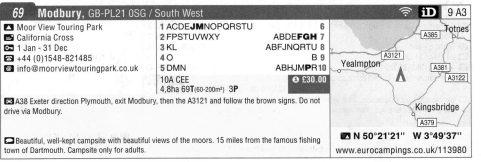

69 Modbury, GB-PL21 0SG / South West · 📶 iD · 9 A3

- ▲ Moor View Touring Park
- 🏕 California Cross
- 🗓 1 Jan - 31 Dec
- ☎ +44 (0)1548-821485
- @ info@moorviewtouringpark.co.uk

1 ACDE**JM**NOPQRSTU		6	
2 FPSTUVWXY	ABDE**FGH** 7		
3 KL	ABFJNQRTU 8		
4 O	B 9		
5 DMN	ABHJMP**R**10		
10A CEE	💶 **£30.00**		
4,8ha 69**T**(60-200m²) 3**P**			

🚗 A38 Exeter direction Plymouth, exit Modbury, then the A3121 and follow the brown signs. Do not drive via Modbury.

💬 Beautiful, well-kept campsite with beautiful views of the moors. 15 miles from the famous fishing town of Dartmouth. Campsite only for adults.

📷 N 50°21'21'' W 3°49'37''

www.eurocampings.co.uk/113980

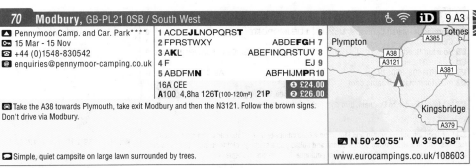

70 Modbury, GB-PL21 0SB / South West · ♿ 📶 iD · 9 A3

- ▲ Pennymoor Camp. and Car. Park****
- 🗓 15 Mar - 15 Nov
- ☎ +44 (0)1548-830542
- @ enquiries@pennymoor-camping.co.uk

1 ACDE**JL**NOPQRS**T**		6	
2 FPRSTWXY	ABDE**FGH** 7		
3 A**K**L	ABEFINQRSTUV 8		
4 F	EJ 9		
5 ABDFM**N**	ABFHIJMP**R**10		
16A CEE	💶 **£24.00**		
A100 4,8ha 126**T**(100-120m²) 21**P**	💶 **£26.00**		

🚗 Take the A38 towards Plymouth, take exit Modbury and then the N3121. Follow the brown signs. Don't drive via Modbury.

💬 Simple, quiet campsite on large lawn surrounded by trees.

📷 N 50°20'55'' W 3°50'58''

www.eurocampings.co.uk/108603

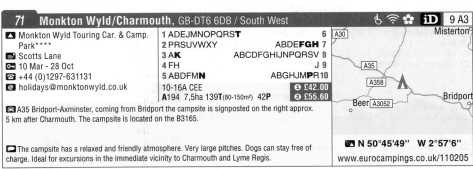

71 Monkton Wyld/Charmouth, GB-DT6 6DB / South West · ♿ 📶 ✿ iD · 9 A3

- ▲ Monkton Wyld Touring Car. & Camp. Park****
- 🏕 Scotts Lane
- 🗓 10 Mar - 28 Oct
- ☎ +44 (0)1297-631131
- @ holidays@monktonwyld.co.uk

1 ADEJMNOPQRS**T**		6	
2 PRSUVWXY	ABDE**FGH** 7		
3 A**K**	ABCDFGHIJNPQRSV 8		
4 FH	J 9		
5 ABDFM**N**	ABGHJMP**R**10		
10-16A CEE	💶 **£42.00**		
A194 7,5ha 139**T**(80-150m²) 42**P**	💶 **£55.60**		

🚗 A35 Bridport-Axminster, coming from Bridport the campsite is signposted on the right approx. 5 km after Charmouth. The campsite is located on the B3165.

💬 The campsite has a relaxed and friendly atmosphere. Very large pitches. Dogs can stay free of charge. Ideal for excursions in the immediate vicinity to Charmouth and Lyme Regis.

📷 N 50°45'49'' W 2°57'6''

www.eurocampings.co.uk/110205

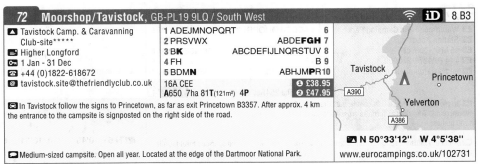

72 Moorshop/Tavistock, GB-PL19 9LQ / South West · 📶 iD · 8 B3

- ▲ Tavistock Camp. & Caravanning Club-site*****
- 🏕 Higher Longford
- 🗓 1 Jan - 31 Dec
- ☎ +44 (0)1822-618672
- @ tavistock.site@thefriendlyclub.co.uk

1 ADEJMNOPQRT		6	
2 PRSVWX	ABDE**FGH** 7		
3 B**K**	ABCDEFIJLNQRSTUV 8		
4 FH	B 9		
5 BDM**N**	ABHJMP**R**10		
16A CEE	💶 **£38.95**		
A650 7ha 81**T**(121m²) 4**P**	💶 **£47.95**		

🚗 In Tavistock follow the signs to Princetown, as far as exit Princetown B3357. After approx. 4 km the entrance to the campsite is signposted on the right side of the road.

💬 Medium-sized campsite. Open all year. Located at the edge of the Dartmoor National Park.

📷 N 50°33'12'' W 4°5'38''

www.eurocampings.co.uk/102731

United Kingdom

United Kingdom

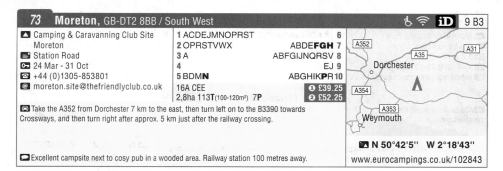

73 Moreton, GB-DT2 8BB / South West ♿ 🛜 iD 9 B3

▲ Camping & Caravanning Club Site
Moreton
🚉 Station Road
📅 24 Mar - 31 Oct
☎ +44 (0)1305-853801
@ moreton.site@thefriendlyclub.co.uk

1 ACDEJMNOPRST	6
2 OPRSTVWX	ABDEFGH 7
3 A	ABFGIJNQRSV 8
4	EJ 9
5 BDMN	ABGHIKPR 10

16A CEE · £39.25
2,8ha 113T(100-120m²) 7P · £52.25

🚗 Take the A352 from Dorchester 7 km to the east, then turn left on to the B3390 towards Crossways, and then turn right after approx. 5 km just after the railway crossing.

💬 Excellent campsite next to cosy pub in a wooded area. Railway station 100 metres away.

N 50°42'5'' W 2°18'43''
www.eurocampings.co.uk/102843

74 Moreton-in-Marsh, GB-GL56 0BT / South West ♿ 🛜 9 B2

▲ Moreton-in-Marsh Caravan & Motorh.
Club*****
🚉 Bourton Road
📅 1 Jan - 31 Dec
☎ +44 (0)1608-650519
@ moretoninmarsh@camc.com

1 DEJMOPQRT	6
2 OPRSWX	ABDEFGH 7
3 AEIKQ	ABCDEFHIJKNPQRSTUV 8
4	9
5 ADMN	ABCEGHJMPRXZ 10

16A CEE · £43.80
A100 8ha 184T(60-100m²) · £49.60

🚗 A44 from Moreton to Evesham, turn right just past the built-up area of Moreton.

💬 Tree-lined attractive Caravan and Motorhome Club campsite in the Cotswolds with modern toilet facilities. Within walking distance of Moreton and suitable as a starting point for trips in the Cotswolds and surroundings. Crazy golf, volleyball and 'petanque' field on site. No tents.

N 51°59'21'' W 1°42'37''
www.eurocampings.co.uk/116501

75 Mortehoe, GB-EX34 7EG / South West 🛜 iD 8 B2

▲ North Morte Farm**
📅 30 Mar - 31 Oct
☎ +44 (0)1271-870381
@ info@northmortefarm.co.uk

1 ADEJMNOQRT	K 6
2 EGHJKMNOPQSTVW	ABDEFGH 7
3 AK	ABFNQRV 8
4 F	E 9
5 ABDMNO	ABEHJMOR 10

16A CEE · £26.00
A60 5ha 155T(80-120m²) 29P · £33.00

🚗 Leave the A361 at the sign for Ilfracombe. After 15 km, turn first left at Mullacott Cross roundabout, direction Mortehoe/Woolacombe. In Mortehoe, at service station, campsite signs on the right.

💬 Spacious campsite on the cliffs, with a magnificent view. The village of Mortehoe is within walking distance.

N 51°11'18'' W 4°12'13''
www.eurocampings.co.uk/111701

76 Mortehoe, GB-EX34 7EJ / South West ♿ 🛜 iD 8 B2

▲ Warcombe Farm Camping Park
🚉 Station Road
📅 15 Mar - 31 Oct
☎ +44 (0)1271-870690
@ info@warcombefarm.co.uk

1 ACDEJMNOPRST	N 6
2 DFOPSVWXY	ABDEFG 7
3 BEK	ABFGIJNQRSTUV 8
4 FH	9
5 ABDFMNO	ABGHIJMPR 10

16A CEE · £40.50
A170 5ha 254T(80-260m²) · £45.50

🚗 On the A361 Barnstaple-Ilfracombe, past Braunton after about 10 km take the B3343 direction Woolacombe. Turn right at Turnpike crossing towards Mortehoe. Campsite on the right after about 1200 metres.

💬 Beautifully situated, spacious campsite with a view of the sea. Modern and spacious toilet facilities. Lovely fishing pond at the campsite.

N 51°10'45'' W 4°10'51''
www.eurocampings.co.uk/102727

77 Mullion/Helston, GB-TR12 7LJ / South West   iD   40a

- ▲ Mullion Holiday Park
- 🚉 Ruan Minor A3083
- 📅 21 Mar - 2 Nov
- ☎ +44 (0)1326-240428
- 📠 +44 (0)1326-241141

1	ADE**JM**NOPRS**T**	ABEFG 6
2	GOPRSVWX	AB**FGH** 7
3	ABCEI**KLP**	ABFHIJNQRSTUV 8
4	BCDFILMNO**PQ**	EJ 9
5	ACDEFHIKLMN	ABFHIJM**N**ORYZ 10

13A CEE   ❶ £47.00
A77 22ha 80**T**(81-120m²) 326**P**   ❷ £47.00

🚗 From Helston follow the A3083 direction Lizard for a while. The park is located near the exit to the B3296. Entrance on the left after 50 metres. Drive to the campsite entrance through the car park (see signs).

💬 The campsite is in a quiet location with spacious pitches in the grounds of a large holiday park with lots of entertainment outside and inside. Heated outdoor and indoor swimming pool. Admission is free. Free wifi point. A bowling centre is also available. Plenty of hiking opportunities.

N 50°1'10'' W 5°12'46''
www.eurocampings.co.uk/102706

78 Newquay, GB-TR8 4NY / South West   (CC€17) iD   40a

- ▲ Hendra Holiday Park*****
- 📅 23 Mar - 3 Nov
- ☎ +44 (0)1637-875778
- @ enquiries@hendra-holidays.com

1	ADE**JM**NOPQRST	AB**EFGHI**OP**X** 6
2	FGOPSTUVWXY	ABDE**FGH**K 7
3	ABCE**KLR**U	ABFHIJNPQRSTUV 8
4	**A**BDHILMNO**P**R	EFMSUVX 9
5	ACDEFGHLM**N**	ABEFGHIKMO**P**Q**P**RWYZ 10

16A CEE   ❶ £36.40
A64 8ha 589**T**(69-120m²) 346**P**   ❷ £53.60

🚗 A30 to exit Highgate Hill. Follow A392 direction Newquay. In Quintrell Downs continue straight ahead at the roundabout. 800 metres further on, Hendra park to the left.

💬 Large family campsite with entertainment for young and old. Swimming pools, restaurant, entertainment and shops are all together, as in a lively little village. Good toilet facilities on the campsite. All energy is sustainably generated. The leisure pool is also open to non-campers.

© 23/3-26/3   9/4-25/5   4/6-29/6   1/9-19/10

N 50°24'5'' W 5°3'0''
www.eurocampings.co.uk/102688

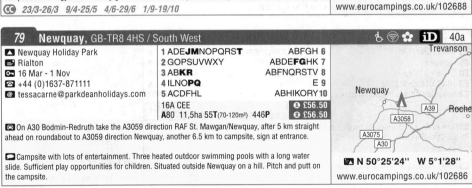

79 Newquay, GB-TR8 4HS / South West   iD   40a

- ▲ Newquay Holiday Park
- 🚉 Rialton
- 📅 16 Mar - 1 Nov
- ☎ +44 (0)1637-871111
- @ tessacarne@parkdeanholidays.com

1	ADE**JM**NOPQRS**T**	ABFGH 6
2	GOPSUVWXY	ABDE**FGH**K 7
3	AB**KR**	ABFNQRSTV 8
4	ILNO**PQ**	E 9
5	ACDFHL	ABHIKORY 10

16A CEE   ❶ £56.50
A80 11,5ha 55**T**(70-120m²) 446**P**   ❷ £56.50

🚗 On A30 Bodmin-Redruth take the A3059 direction RAF St. Mawgan/Newquay, after 5 km straight ahead on roundabout to A3059 direction Newquay, another 6.5 km to campsite, sign at entrance.

💬 Campsite with lots of entertainment. Three heated outdoor swimming pools with a long water slide. Sufficient play opportunities for children. Situated outside Newquay on a hill. Pitch and putt on the campsite.

N 50°25'24'' W 5°1'28''
www.eurocampings.co.uk/102686

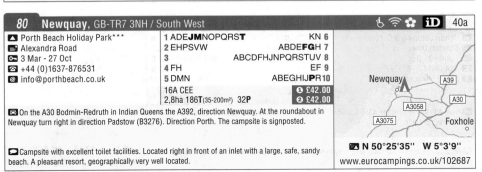

80 Newquay, GB-TR7 3NH / South West   iD   40a

- ▲ Porth Beach Holiday Park***
- 🚉 Alexandra Road
- 📅 3 Mar - 27 Oct
- ☎ +44 (0)1637-876531
- @ info@porthbeach.co.uk

1	ADE**JM**NOPQRS**T**	KN 6
2	EHPSVW	ABDE**FGH** 7
3		ABCDFHJNPQRSTUV 8
4	FH	EF 9
5	DMN	ABEGHIJ**P**R 10

16A CEE   ❶ £42.00
2,8ha 186**T**(35-200m²) 32**P**   ❷ £42.00

🚗 On the A30 Bodmin-Redruth in Indian Queens the A392, direction Newquay. At the roundabout in Newquay turn right in direction Padstow (B3276). Direction Porth. The campsite is signposted.

💬 Campsite with excellent toilet facilities. Located right in front of an inlet with a large, safe, sandy beach. A pleasant resort, geographically very well located.

N 50°25'35'' W 5°3'9''
www.eurocampings.co.uk/102687

United Kingdom

81 Newquay, GB-TR8 4JN / South West

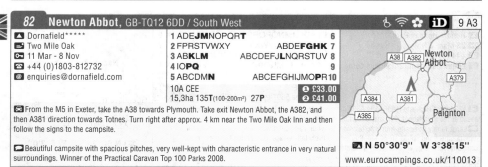

Treloy Tourist Park
20 May - 9 Sep
+44 (0)1637-872063
stay@treloy.co.uk

1 ADE**JM**NOPQRST	ABFG **6**
2 **G**OPSUVWX	ABDE**FG**H **7**
3 BE**KL**	ABCDFHIJNQRSTUV **8**
4 BI**PQ**	**9**
5 ACDEFHM**NO**	ABGHIJM**P**R**10**

16A CEE — ❶ £27.25
A71 8ha 260**T**(95-200m²) 12**P** — ❷ £38.25

On A30 Bodmin-Redruth, take the A39 Newquay/St. Columb Major. At roundabout St. Columb Major/RAF Airport. Roundabout A3059 direction Newquay. After about 5 km the campsite is signposted.

Decorated with greenery and flowering shrubs, well-kept campsite with clean toilet facilities, swimming pool and bar/club house. Not far from the seaside resort of Newquay and 10 minutes from the beautiful sandy beach.

N 50°25'58'' W 5°0'45''

www.eurocampings.co.uk/113963

40a
Wadebridge
Newquay A39
A3058 A30
A3075

82 Newton Abbot, GB-TQ12 6DD / South West

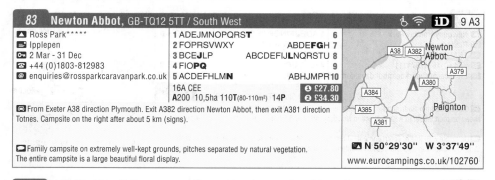

Dornafield*****
Two Mile Oak
11 Mar - 8 Nov
+44 (0)1803-812732
enquiries@dornafield.com

1 ADE**JM**NOPQR**T**	**6**
2 FPRSTVWXY	ABDE**FGHK 7**
3 AB**KLM**	ABCDEFJLNQRSTUV **8**
4 IO**PQ**	**9**
5 ABCDM**N**	ABCEFGHIJMO**P**R**10**

10A CEE — ❶ £33.00
15,3ha 135**T**(100-200m²) 27**P** — ❷ £41.00

From the M5 in Exeter, take the A38 towards Plymouth. Take exit Newton Abbot, the A382, and then A381 direction towards Totnes. Turn right after approx. 4 km near the Two Mile Oak Inn and then follow the signs to the campsite.

Beautiful campsite with spacious pitches, very well-kept with characteristic entrance in very natural surroundings. Winner of the Practical Caravan Top 100 Parks 2008.

N 50°30'9'' W 3°38'15''

www.eurocampings.co.uk/110013

9 A3
A38 A382 Newton Abbot
A379
A384 A381
A385 Paignton

83 Newton Abbot, GB-TQ12 5TT / South West

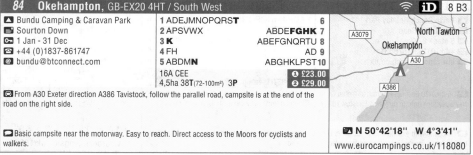

Ross Park*****
Ipplepen
2 Mar - 31 Dec
+44 (0)1803-812983
enquiries@rossparkcaravanpark.co.uk

1 ADEJMNOPQRS**T**	**6**
2 FOPRSVWXY	ABDE**FG**H **7**
3 BCEJLP	ABCDEFIJLNQRSTU **8**
4 FIO**PQ**	**9**
5 ACDEFHLM**N**	ABHJMPR**10**

16A CEE — ❶ £27.80
A200 10,5ha 110**T**(80-110m²) 14**P** — ❷ £34.30

From Exeter A38 direction Plymouth. Exit A382 direction Newton Abbot, then exit A381 direction Totnes. Campsite on the right after about 5 km (signs).

Family campsite on extremely well-kept grounds, pitches separated by natural vegetation. The entire campsite is a large beautiful floral display.

N 50°29'30'' W 3°37'49''

www.eurocampings.co.uk/102760

9 A3
A38 A382 Newton Abbot
A379
A380
A384
A385 Paignton
A381

84 Okehampton, GB-EX20 4HT / South West

Bundu Camping & Caravan Park
Sourton Down
1 Jan - 31 Dec
+44 (0)1837-861747
bundu@btconnect.com

1 ADEJMNOPQRS**T**	**6**
2 APSVWX	ABDE**FGHK 7**
3 **K**	ABEFGNQRTU **8**
4 FH	AD **9**
5 ABDM**N**	ABGHKLPST**10**

16A CEE — ❶ £23.00
4,5ha 38**T**(72-100m²) 3**P** — ❷ £29.00

From A30 Exeter direction A386 Tavistock, follow the parallel road, campsite is at the end of the road on the right side.

Basic campsite near the motorway. Easy to reach. Direct access to the Moors for cyclists and walkers.

N 50°42'18'' W 4°3'41''

www.eurocampings.co.uk/118080

8 B3
A3079 North Tawton
Okehampton
A30
A386

85 Otterton, GB-EX9 7BX / South West
♿ 📶 ❄ (CC€19) ⚐ iD **9 A3**

- ⛺ Ladram Bay Holiday Park
- 📅 16 Mar - 28 Oct
- ☎ +44 (0)1395-568398
- @ info@ladrambay.co.uk

1	ADEJ**M**NOPQRS**T**	**EFG**KNPUX**Y** 6
2	EFGJMPRSTUVW	ABDE**FGH** 7
3	BCDE**IKPU**	ABCDFGHIJNPQRSTU 8
4	BCDFIMNO**PQRTV**	EINPR 9
5	ACDEFHLMN	ABDHIJM**P**RY**Z**10

16A CEE — ❶ £46.00
6ha 90**T**(49-120m²) 223**P** — ❷ £56.00

🚗 From M5 exit 30, then A3052 direction Sidmouth. Right at Newton Poppleford onto B3178 direction Budleigh Salterton. 1.5 km past Colaton Raleigh left towards Otterton. Campsite signposted in Otterton.
💬 Large terraced campsite on a beach with beautiful views of the sea. paved pitches with water and drainage connections. Many amenities and activities including watersports, indoor pool, bowling, disco, adventure playground and supermarket.

CC *16/3-28/3 23/4-2/5 8/5-23/5 5/6-14/7 4/9-27/10 7=6*

🌐 N 50°39'37'' W 3°16'50''
www.eurocampings.co.uk/117318

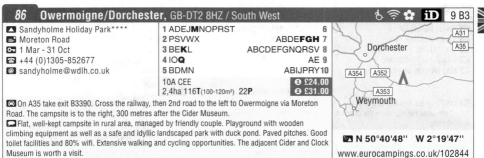

86 Owermoigne/Dorchester, GB-DT2 8HZ / South West
♿ 📶 ❄ iD **9 B3**

- ⛺ Sandyholme Holiday Park****
- 🏠 Moreton Road
- 📅 1 Mar - 31 Oct
- ☎ +44 (0)1305-852677
- @ sandyholme@wdlh.co.uk

1	ADEJ**M**NOPRST	6
2	PSVWX	ABDE**FGH** 7
3	BE**K**L	ABCDEFGNQRSV 8
4	I**O**Q	AE 9
5	BDMN	ABIJPRY 10

10A CEE — ❶ £24.00
2,4ha 116**T**(100-120m²) 22**P** — ❷ £31.00

🚗 On A35 take exit B3390. Cross the railway, then 2nd road to the left to Owermoigne via Moreton Road. The campsite is to the right, 300 metres after the Cider Museum.
💬 Flat, well-kept campsite in rural area, managed by friendly couple. Playground with wooden climbing equipment as well as a safe and idyllic landscaped park with duck pond. Paved pitches. Good toilet facilities and 80% wifi. Extensive walking and cycling opportunities. The adjacent Cider and Clock Museum is worth a visit.

🌐 N 50°40'48'' W 2°19'47''
www.eurocampings.co.uk/102844

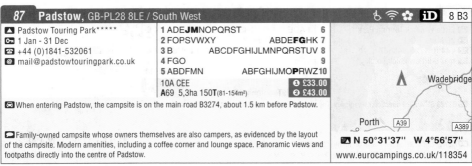

87 Padstow, GB-PL28 8LE / South West
♿ 📶 ❄ iD **8 B3**

- ⛺ Padstow Touring Park*****
- 📅 1 Jan - 31 Dec
- ☎ +44 (0)1841-532061
- @ mail@padstowtouringpark.co.uk

1	ADEJ**M**NOPQRST	6
2	FOPSVWXY	ABDE**FGH**K 7
3	B	ABCDFGHIJLMNPQRSTUV 8
4	FGO	9
5	ABDFMN	ABFGHIJMO**P**RW**Z**10

10A CEE — ❶ £33.00
A69 5,3ha 150**T**(81-154m²) — ❷ £43.00

🚗 When entering Padstow, the campsite is on the main road B3274, about 1.5 km before Padstow.

💬 Family-owned campsite whose owners themselves are also campers, as evidenced by the layout of the campsite. Modern amenities, including a coffee corner and lounge space. Panoramic views and footpaths directly into the centre of Padstow.

🌐 N 50°31'37'' W 4°56'57''
www.eurocampings.co.uk/118354

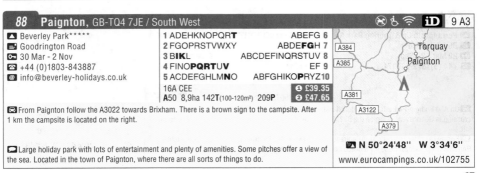

88 Paignton, GB-TQ4 7JE / South West
⊗ ♿ 📶 iD **9 A3**

- ⛺ Beverley Park*****
- 🏠 Goodrington Road
- 📅 30 Mar - 2 Nov
- ☎ +44 (0)1803-843887
- @ info@beverley-holidays.co.uk

1	ADEHKNOPQR**T**	ABEFG 6
2	FGOPRSTVWXY	ABDE**FGH** 7
3	B**I**KL	ABCDEFINQRSTUV 8
4	FINO**PQRTUV**	EF 9
5	ACDEFGHLM**N**O	ABFGHIKO**P**RY**Z**10

16A CEE — ❶ £39.35
A50 8,9ha 142**T**(100-120m²) 209**P** — ❷ £47.65

🚗 From Paignton follow the A3022 towards Brixham. There is a brown sign to the campsite. After 1 km the campsite is located on the left.

💬 Large holiday park with lots of entertainment and plenty of amenities. Some pitches offer a view of the sea. Located in the town of Paignton, where there are all sorts of things to do.

🌐 N 50°24'48'' W 3°34'6''
www.eurocampings.co.uk/102755

United Kingdom

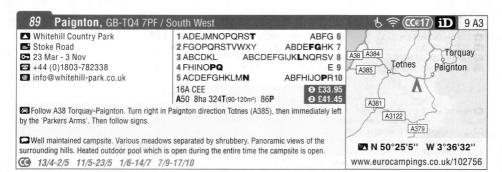

89 Paignton, GB-TQ4 7PF / South West
    ⚷ 🛜 (CC€17) iD   9 A3

- ▲ Whitehill Country Park
- 🖪 Stoke Road
- 🗓 23 Mar - 3 Nov
- ☎ +44 (0)1803-782338
- @ info@whitehill-park.co.uk

1 ADEJMNOPQRS**T**	ABFG	6
2 FGOPQRSTVWXY	ABDE**FG**HK	7
3 ABCDKL	ABCDEFGIJK**L**NQRSV	8
4 FHINO**PQ**	E	9
5 ACDEFGHKLM**N**	ABFHIJO**P**R	10

16A CEE   ❶ £33.95
A50 8ha 324**T**(90-120m²) 86**P**   ❷ £41.45

🖪 Follow A38 Torquay-Paignton. Turn right in Paignton direction Totnes (A385), then immediately left by the 'Parkers Arms'. Then follow signs.

💬 Well maintained campsite. Various meadows separated by shrubbery. Panoramic views of the surrounding hills. Heated outdoor pool which is open during the entire time the campsite is open.

CC 13/4-2/5 11/5-23/5 1/6-14/7 7/9-17/10

🅽 N 50°25'5'' W 3°36'32''
www.eurocampings.co.uk/102756

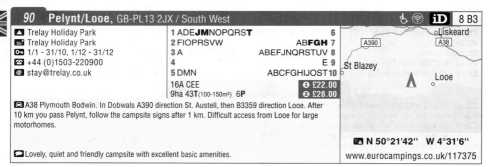

90 Pelynt/Looe, GB-PL13 2JX / South West
    ⚷ 🛜 iD   8 B3

- ▲ Trelay Holiday Park
- 🖪 Trelay Holiday Park
- 🗓 1/1 - 31/10, 1/12 - 31/12
- ☎ +44 (0)1503-220900
- @ stay@trelay.co.uk

1 ADE**JM**NOPQRS**T**		6
2 FIOPRSVW	AB**FGH**	7
3 A	ABEFJNQRSTUV	8
4	E	9
5 DMN	ABCFGHIJOST	10

16A CEE   ❶ £22.00
9ha 43**T**(100-150m²) 6**P**   ❷ £28.00

🖪 A38 Plymouth Bodwin. In Dobwals A390 direction St. Austell, then B3359 direction Looe. After 10 km you pass Pelynt, follow the campsite signs after 1 km. Difficult access from Looe for large motorhomes.

💬 Lovely, quiet and friendly campsite with excellent basic amenities.

🅽 N 50°21'42'' W 4°31'6''
www.eurocampings.co.uk/117375

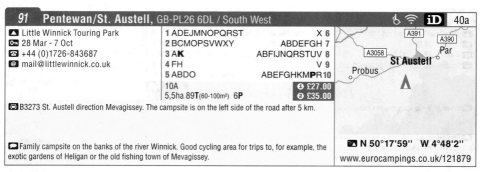

91 Pentewan/St. Austell, GB-PL26 6DL / South West
    ⚷ 🛜 iD   40a

- ▲ Little Winnick Touring Park
- 🗓 28 Mar - 7 Oct
- ☎ +44 (0)1726-843687
- @ mail@littlewinnick.co.uk

1 ADEJMNOPQRST	X	6
2 BCMOPSVWXY	ABDEFGH	7
3 A**K**	ABFIJNQRSTUV	8
4 FH	V	9
5 ABDO	ABEFGHKM**P**R	10

10A   ❶ £27.00
5,5ha 89**T**(60-100m²) 6**P**   ❷ £35.00

🖪 B3273 St. Austell direction Mevagissey. The campsite is on the left side of the road after 5 km.

💬 Family campsite on the banks of the river Winnick. Good cycling area for trips to, for example, the exotic gardens of Heligan or the old fishing town of Mevagissey.

🅽 N 50°17'59'' W 4°48'2''
www.eurocampings.co.uk/121879

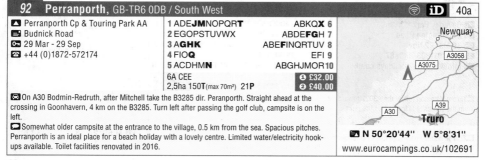

92 Perranporth, GB-TR6 0DB / South West
    🛜 iD   40a

- ▲ Perranporth Cp & Touring Park AA
- 🖪 Budnick Road
- 🗓 29 Mar - 29 Sep
- ☎ +44 (0)1872-572174

1 ADE**JM**NOPQR**T**	ABKQ**X**	6
2 EGOPSTUVWX	ABDE**FG**H	7
3 A**GHK**	ABE**FIN**QRTUV	8
4 FIO**Q**	EFI	9
5 ACDHM**N**	ABGHJMOR	10

6A CEE   ❶ £32.00
2,5ha 150**T**(max 70m²) 21**P**   ❷ £40.00

🖪 On A30 Bodmin-Redruth, after Mitchell take the B3285 dir. Perranporth. Straight ahead at the crossing in Goonhavern, 4 km on the B3285. Turn left after passing the golf club, campsite is on the left.

💬 Somewhat older campsite at the entrance to the village, 0.5 km from the sea. Spacious pitches. Perranporth is an ideal place for a beach holiday with a lovely centre. Limited water/electricity hook-ups available. Toilet facilities renovated in 2016.

🅽 N 50°20'44'' W 5°8'31''
www.eurocampings.co.uk/102691

United Kingdom

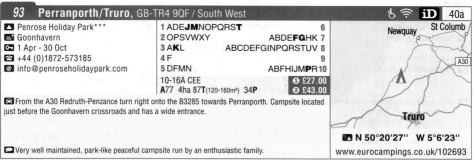

93 Perranporth/Truro, GB-TR4 9QF / South West   iD   40a

- ⛺ Penrose Holiday Park***
- 🏢 Goonhavern
- 📅 1 Apr - 30 Oct
- ☎ +44 (0)1872-573185
- @ info@penroseholidaypark.com

1 ADEJMNOPQRST		6
2 OPSVWXY	ABDEFGHK	7
3 AKL	ABCDEFGINPQRSTUV	8
4 F		9
5 DFMN	ABFHIJMPR	10
10-16A CEE	❶ £27.00	
A77 4ha 87T(120-160m²) 34P	❷ £43.00	

🚗 From the A30 Redruth-Penzance turn right onto the B3285 towards Perranporth. Campsite located just before the Goonhavern crossroads and has a wide entrance.

💬 Very well maintained, park-like peaceful campsite run by an enthusiastic family.

📷 N 50°20'27'' W 5°6'23''

www.eurocampings.co.uk/102693

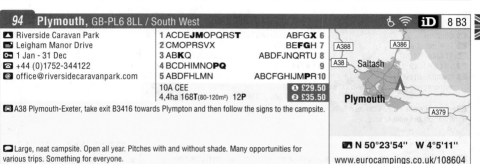

94 Plymouth, GB-PL6 8LL / South West   iD   8 B3

- ⛺ Riverside Caravan Park
- 🏢 Leigham Manor Drive
- 📅 1 Jan - 31 Dec
- ☎ +44 (0)1752-344122
- @ office@riversidecaravanpark.com

1 ACDEJMOPQRST	ABFGX	6
2 CMOPRSVX	BEFGH	7
3 ABKQ	ABDFJNQRTU	8
4 BCDHIMNOPQ		9
5 ABDFHLMN	ABCFGHIJMPR	10
10A CEE	❶ £29.50	
4,4ha 168T(80-120m²) 12P	❷ £35.50	

🚗 A38 Plymouth-Exeter, take exit B3416 towards Plympton and then follow the signs to the campsite.

💬 Large, neat campsite. Open all year. Pitches with and without shade. Many opportunities for various trips. Something for everyone.

📷 N 50°23'54'' W 4°5'11''

www.eurocampings.co.uk/108604

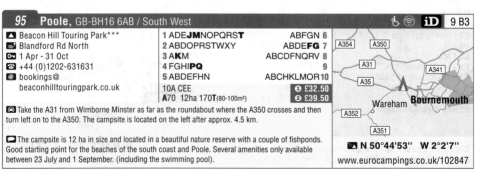

95 Poole, GB-BH16 6AB / South West   iD   9 B3

- ⛺ Beacon Hill Touring Park***
- 🏢 Blandford Rd North
- 📅 1 Apr - 31 Oct
- ☎ +44 (0)1202-631631
- @ bookings@
  beaconhilltouringpark.co.uk

1 ADEJMNOPQRST	ABFGN	6
2 ABDOPRSTWXY	ABDEFG	7
3 AKM	ABCDFNQRV	8
4 FGHIPQ		9
5 ABDEFHN	ABCHKLMOR	10
10A CEE	❶ £32.50	
A70 12ha 170T(80-100m²)	❷ £39.50	

🚗 Take the A31 from Wimborne Minster as far as the roundabout where the A350 crosses and then turn left on to the A350. The campsite is located on the left after approx. 4.5 km.

💬 The campsite is 12 ha in size and located in a beautiful nature reserve with a couple of fishponds. Good starting point for the beaches of the south coast and Poole. Several amenities only available between 23 July and 1 September. (including the swimming pool).

📷 N 50°44'53'' W 2°2'7''

www.eurocampings.co.uk/102847

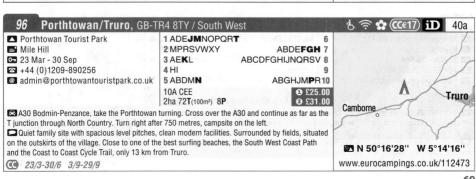

96 Porthtowan/Truro, GB-TR4 8TY / South West   (CC€17) iD   40a

- ⛺ Porthtowan Tourist Park
- 🏢 Mile Hill
- 📅 23 Mar - 30 Sep
- ☎ +44 (0)1209-890256
- @ admin@porthtowantouristpark.co.uk

1 ADEJMNOPQRT		6
2 MPRSVWXY	ABDEFGH	7
3 AEKL	ABCDFGHIJNQRSV	8
4 HI		9
5 ABDMN	ABGHJMPR	10
10A CEE	❶ £25.00	
2ha 72T(100m²) 8P	❷ £31.00	

🚗 A30 Bodmin-Penzance, take the Porthtowan turning. Cross over the A30 and continue as far as the T junction through North Country. Turn right after 750 metres, campsite on the left.

💬 Quiet family site with spacious level pitches, clean modern facilities. Surrounded by fields, situated on the outskirts of the village. Close to one of the best surfing beaches, the South West Coast Path and the Coast to Coast Cycle Trail, only 13 km from Truro.

CC 23/3-30/6 3/9-29/9

📷 N 50°16'28'' W 5°14'16''

www.eurocampings.co.uk/112473

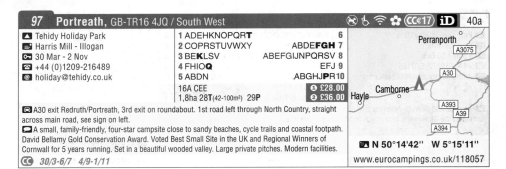

97 Portreath, GB-TR16 4JQ / South West ⊗ & 📶 ✿ (CC€17) iD 40a

▲ Tehidy Holiday Park	1 ADEHKNOPQR**T**	6
🏠 Harris Mill - Illogan	2 COPRSTUVWXY	ABDE**FGH** 7
🕑 30 Mar - 2 Nov	3 BE**K**LSV	ABEFGIJNPQRSV 8
☎ +44 (0)1209-216489	4 FHIO**Q**	EFJ 9
@ holiday@tehidy.co.uk	5 ABDN	ABGHJ**P**R 10
	16A CEE	❶ £28.00
	1,8ha 28**T**(42-100m²) 29**P**	❷ £36.00

🚗 A30 exit Redruth/Portreath, 3rd exit on roundabout. 1st road left through North Country, straight across main road, see sign on left.
💬 A small, family-friendly, four-star campsite close to sandy beaches, cycle trails and coastal footpath. David Bellamy Gold Conservation Award. Voted Best Small Site in the UK and Regional Winners of Cornwall for 5 years running. Set in a beautiful wooded valley. Large private pitches. Modern facilities.
(CC) *30/3-6/7* *4/9-1/11*

📍 N 50°14'42'' W 5°15'11''
www.eurocampings.co.uk/118057

---

98 Priddy/Wells, GB-BA5 3BP / South West 📶 iD 9 A2

▲ Cheddar C. & C. Club****	1 ACDEJMNOPQRST	6
🏠 Townsend	2 FPRSTUVWXY	ABDE**FGH** 7
🕑 11 Mar - 7 Nov	3 A**K**	ABCDFGIJLNPQRSV 8
☎ +44 (0)1749-870241	4 FH	E 9
@ cheddar.site@	5 ABDM**NO**	ABGJ**P**R 10
campingandcaravanningclub.co.uk	16A CEE	❶ £36.10
	A266 7,5ha 90**T**(90-120m²) 2**P**	❷ £47.60

🚗 From Wells take the A39 direction Bath. After 5 km take the B3135 at Green Ore, campsite after 6 km. Narrow and winding road.

💬 Rural campsite in the Mendip Hills with good walking opportunities. Many local attractions.

📍 N 51°15'49'' W 2°41'7''
www.eurocampings.co.uk/102787

---

99 Redhill/Bristol, GB-BS40 5RB / South West 📶 ✿ iD 9 A2

▲ Brook Lodge Farm C. & C. Park***	1 ADE**I**LNOPQRS**T**	6
🏠 A38	2 CGOPRSTWXY	ABDE**FG**HK 7
🕑 1 Mar - 31 Oct	3 A**K**	ABEFNQRSV 8
☎ +44 (0)7954-601447	4 FH	C 9
@ brooklodgefrm@gmail.com	5 BDMN	ABCFKM**P**R 10
	10A CEE	❶ £34.00
	1,5ha 44**T**(100-110m²) 4**P**	❷ £40.00

🚗 From Bristol A38 direction Exeter/Taunton, turn left about 3 km past the airport.

💬 Cosy and ecological family campsite that is ideally located for visiting historic places. Also available for group accommodation. Fishing possibilities in Blagdon Lake.

📍 N 51°21'18'' W 2°44'25''
www.eurocampings.co.uk/108864

---

100 Rejerrah/Newquay, GB-TR8 5QJ / South West & 📶 iD 40a

▲ Newperran Holiday Park*****	1 ACDE**JM**NOPQRST	EFG 6
🏠 Rejerrah	2 FGPSVWX	ABDE**FGH** 7
🕑 30 Mar - 29 Sep	3 AE**K**	ABCDEFIJNQRSTUV 8
☎ +44 (0)1872-572407	4 FHINO**PQ**	E 9
@ holidays@newperran.co.uk	5 ABDEFHLM**N**	ABEFGHIJMORW 10
	16A CEE	❶ £31.65
	A93 11ha 500**T**(100-150m²) 34**P**	❷ £45.95

🚗 On the A3075 Goonhavern-Newquay, immediately past Goonhavern turn left towards Newperran Holiday Park. Continue until sign to the campsite (on right side of the road).

💬 Large, well-cared-for family campsite. Spacious with lots of playing facilities for children, indoor swimming pool and skate park. In early and late season also naturist areas only for people who are members of naturist associations.

📍 N 50°20'42'' W 5°6'18''
www.eurocampings.co.uk/102682

United Kingdom

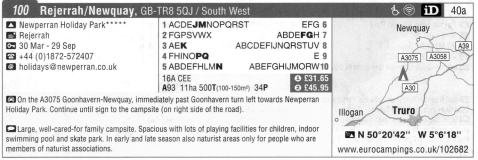

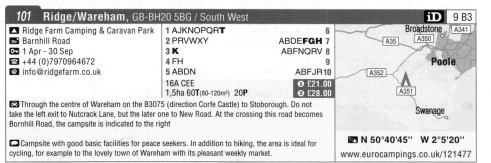

101 Ridge/Wareham, GB-BH20 5BG / South West — iD 9 B3

- ▲ Ridge Farm Camping & Caravan Park
- ✉ Barnhill Road
- 🗓 1 Apr - 30 Sep
- ☎ +44 (0)7970964672
- @ info@ridgefarm.co.uk

1 AJKNOPQR**T**		6
2 PRVWXY	ABDE**FGH**	7
3 **K**	ABF**N**QRV	8
4 FH		9
5 ABDN	ABF**J**R	10
16A CEE	❶ £21.00	
1,5ha 60**T**(80-120m²) 20**P**	❷ £28.00	

🛣 Through the centre of Wareham on the B3075 (direction Corfe Castle) to Stoborough. Do not take the left exit to Nutcrack Lane, but the later one to New Road. At the crossing this road becomes Bornhill Road, the campsite is indicated to the right

💬 Campsite with good basic facilities for peace seekers. In addition to hiking, the area is ideal for cycling, for example to the lovely town of Wareham with its pleasant weekly market.

📍 N 50°40'45'' W 2°5'20''

www.eurocampings.co.uk/121477

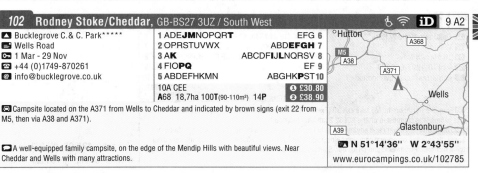

102 Rodney Stoke/Cheddar, GB-BS27 3UZ / South West — ♿ 📶 iD 9 A2

- ▲ Bucklegrove C.& C. Park*****
- ✉ Wells Road
- 🗓 1 Mar - 29 Nov
- ☎ +44 (0)1749-870261
- @ info@bucklegrove.co.uk

1 ADE**JM**NOPQR**T**	EFG	6
2 OPRSTUVWX	ABDE**FGH**	7
3 A**K**	ABCDF**IJL**NQRSV	8
4 FIO**PQ**	EF	9
5 ABDEFHKMN	ABGHK**PST**	10
10A CEE	❶ £30.80	
A68 18,7ha 100**T**(90-110m²) 14**P**	❷ £38.90	

🛣 Campsite located on the A371 from Wells to Cheddar and indicated by brown signs (exit 22 from M5, then via A38 and A371).

💬 A well-equipped family campsite, on the edge of the Mendip Hills with beautiful views. Near Cheddar and Wells with many attractions.

📍 N 51°14'36'' W 2°43'55''

www.eurocampings.co.uk/102785

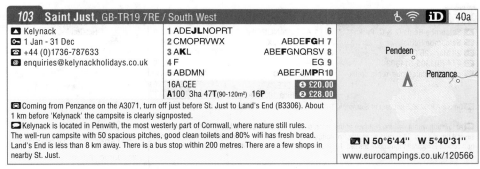

103 Saint Just, GB-TR19 7RE / South West — ♿ 📶 iD 40a

- ▲ Kelynack
- 🗓 1 Jan - 31 Dec
- ☎ +44 (0)1736-787633
- @ enquiries@kelynackholidays.co.uk

1 ADE**JL**NOPRT		6
2 CMOPRVWX	ABDE**FGH**	7
3 A**KL**	ABE**F**GNQRSV	8
4 F	EG	9
5 ABDMN	ABEFJM**P**R	10
16A CEE	❶ £20.00	
A100 3ha 47**T**(90-120m²) 16**P**	❷ £28.00	

🛣 Coming from Penzance on the A3071, turn off just before St. Just to Land's End (B3306). About 1 km before 'Kelynack' the campsite is clearly signposted.

💬 Kelynack is located in Penwith, the most westerly part of Cornwall, where nature still rules. The well-run campsite with 50 spacious pitches, good clean toilets and 80% wifi has fresh bread. Land's End is less than 8 km away. There is a bus stop within 200 metres. There are a few shops in nearby St. Just.

📍 N 50°6'44'' W 5°40'31''

www.eurocampings.co.uk/120566

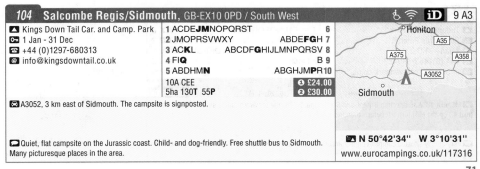

104 Salcombe Regis/Sidmouth, GB-EX10 0PD / South West — ♿ 📶 iD 9 A3

- ▲ Kings Down Tail Car. and Camp. Park
- 🗓 1 Jan - 31 Dec
- ☎ +44 (0)1297-680313
- @ info@kingsdowntail.co.uk

1 ACDE**JM**NOPQRST		6
2 JMOPRSVWXY	ABDE**FGH**	7
3 AC**KL**	ABCDF**G**HIJLMNPQRSV	8
4 FIQ	B	9
5 ABDHM**N**	ABGHJM**P**R	10
10A CEE	❶ £24.00	
5ha 130**T** 55**P**	❷ £30.00	

🛣 A3052, 3 km east of Sidmouth. The campsite is signposted.

💬 Quiet, flat campsite on the Jurassic coast. Child- and dog-friendly. Free shuttle bus to Sidmouth. Many picturesque places in the area.

📍 N 50°42'34'' W 3°10'31''

www.eurocampings.co.uk/117316

United Kingdom

105 Seatown, GB-DT6 6JX / South West · iD · 9 A3

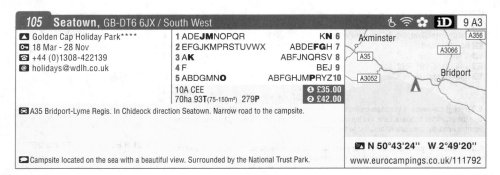

- ▲ Golden Cap Holiday Park****
- 🚐 18 Mar - 28 Nov
- ☎ +44 (0)1308-422139
- @ holidays@wdlh.co.uk

1 ADE**JM**NOPQR	**KN**	6
2 EFGJKMPRSTUVWX	ABDE**FGH**	7
3 A**K**	ABFJNQRSV	8
4 F	BEJ	9
5 ABDGMN**O**	ABFGHJMP**R**YZ	10
10A CEE	❶ £35.00	
70ha 93**T**(75-150m²) 279**P**	❷ £42.00	

🚗 A35 Bridport-Lyme Regis. In Chideock direction Seatown. Narrow road to the campsite.

💬 Campsite located on the sea with a beautiful view. Surrounded by the National Trust Park.

📍 N 50°43'24'' W 2°49'20''

www.eurocampings.co.uk/111792

---

106 Sidmouth, GB-EX10 0PH / South West · iD · 9 A3

- ▲ Oakdown Holiday Park*****
- 🏘 Weston
- 🚐 16 Mar - 4 Nov
- ☎ +44 (0)1297-680387
- @ enquiries@oakdown.co.uk

1 ACDE**JM**NOPQRS**T**		6
2 PRSVWXY	ABDE**FGH**K	7
3 AB**J**	ABCDEFGH**IJ**NQRSTUV	8
4 FIO**Q**	CEJ	9
5 ABDMN	ABFGHJMP**R**Z	10
16A CEE	❶ £25.95	
A171 16ha 159**T**(65-90m²) 64**P**	❷ £29.75	

🚗 From the north: on the M5 take exit 30 (Exeter). Then follow the A3052 towards Sidmouth. The campsite is signposted on the A3052 2 km after Sidmouth.

💬 This spacious, flowery and environmentally friendly campsite is on the main road to Sidmouth. Large, flat pitches on several camping fields, separated by hedges. Modern, spacious and very clean toilet facilities. Playground and snack bar. Starting point for walks along the beach, the Jurassic Coast and lovely towns.

📍 N 50°42'20'' W 3°10'50''

www.eurocampings.co.uk/112121

---

107 Sidmouth, GB-EX10 0JH / South West · iD · 9 A3

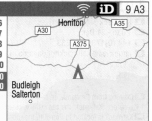

- ▲ Salcombe Regis C. & C. Park*****
- 🏘 Salcombe Regis
- 🚐 23 Mar - 28 Oct
- ☎ +44 (0)1395-514303
- @ contact@salcombe-regis.co.uk

1 ADE**JM**NOPQRS**T**		6
2 MPRSVWX	ABDE**FGH**	7
3 A**KLP**	ABCDFGHIJNQRSTU	8
4 F	E	9
5 ABDM**NO**	ABFGJMP**R**	10
10-16A CEE	❶ £30.50	
A180 16ha 100**T**(80-120m²) 36**P**	❷ £37.10	

🚗 On the A3052, 2.5 km east of Sidmouth. There are signs to the campsite.

💬 At low tide within walking distance of the resort of Sidmouth. The shuttle bus runs to Sidmouth several times a day. This quiet and attractive campsite with plenty of open natural spaces and a 9-hole golf course is located high above the sea. Footpaths lead from the campsite to the beaches and the Jurassic Coast. Attractive villages in the area.

📍 N 50°41'45'' W 3°12'19''

www.eurocampings.co.uk/108575

---

108 Slimbridge (Glos), GB-GL2 7BP / South West · iD · 9 B2

- ▲ Tudor Caravan Park***
- 🏘 Shepherds Patch
- 🚐 1 Jan - 31 Dec
- ☎ +44 (0)1453-890483
- @ info@tudorcaravanpark.co.uk

1 ADE**IL**NOPQRS**T**	**NX**	6
2 ACPRSVWX	ABDE**FG**	7
3 **K**	ABCDEFGIJNQRSV	8
4 FH**Q**	QV	9
5 DMN	ABIJP**R**Z	10
16A CEE	❶ £22.00	
3ha 94**T**(80-120m²)	❷ £26.00	

🚗 M5, exit 13. A38 direction Bristol, exit Slimbridge. Follow the brown campsite signs. After 8 km (exit 13 on the M5) turn left before aqueduct.

💬 Very quietly situated campsite on a channel with only tourist boat traffic. Pub/restaurant next to the campsite.

📍 N 51°44'7'' W 2°23'45''

www.eurocampings.co.uk/102790

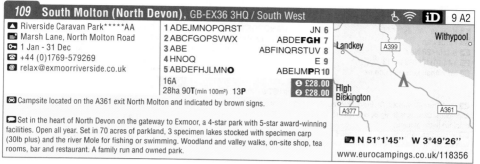

109 South Molton (North Devon), GB-EX36 3HQ / South West

🏕 Riverside Caravan Park*****AA
📧 Marsh Lane, North Molton Road
📅 1 Jan - 31 Dec
☎ +44 (0)1769-579269
@ relax@exmoorriverside.co.uk

1 ADEJMNOPQRST	JN 6
2 ABCFGOPSVWX	ABDE**FGH** 7
3 ABE	ABFINQRSTUV 8
4 HNOQ	E 9
5 ABDEFHJLMN**O**	ABEIJM**P**R 10
16A	❶ £28.00
28ha 90**T**(min 100m²) 13**P**	❷ £28.00

🚗 Campsite located on the A361 exit North Molton and indicated by brown signs.

💬 Set in the heart of North Devon on the gateway to Exmoor, a 4-star park with 5-star award-winning facilities. Open all year. Set in 70 acres of parkland, 3 specimen lakes stocked with specimen carp (30lb plus) and the river Mole for fishing or swimming. Woodland and valley walks, on-site shop, tea rooms, bar and restaurant. A family run and owned park.

🧭 N 51°1'45'' W 3°49'26''

www.eurocampings.co.uk/118356

♿ 📶 **iD** 9 A2

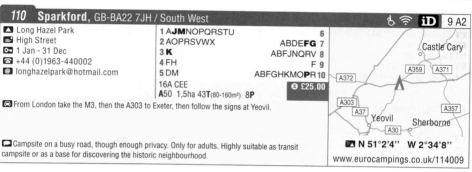

110 Sparkford, GB-BA22 7JH / South West

🏕 Long Hazel Park
📧 High Street
📅 1 Jan - 31 Dec
☎ +44 (0)1963-440002
@ longhazelpark@hotmail.com

1 A**JM**NOPQRSTU	6
2 AOPRSVWX	ABDE**FG** 7
3 **K**	ABFJNQRV 8
4 FH	F 9
5 DM	ABFGHKMO**P**R 10
16A CEE	❶ £25.00
A50 1,5ha 43**T**(80-160m²) 8**P**	

🚗 From London take the M3, then the A303 to Exeter, then follow the signs at Yeovil.

💬 Campsite on a busy road, though enough privacy. Only for adults. Highly suitable as transit campsite or as a base for discovering the historic neighbourhood.

🧭 N 51°2'4'' W 2°34'8''

www.eurocampings.co.uk/114009

♿ 📶 **iD** 9 A2

111 St. Agnes, GB-TR5 0NU / South West

🏕 Beacon Cottage Farm*****
📧 Beacon Drive
📅 28 Mar - 30 Sep
☎ +44 (0)1872-552347
@ jane@
   beaconcottagefarmholidays.co.uk

1 ADEG**JM**NOPQR**T**	QS**X** 6
2 FMPRSTUVWX	ABDE**FGH** 7
3 B**K**	ABCDEFGIJNQRSV 8
4 F	J 9
5 BDM**N**	ABGHJMO**R** 10
10-16A CEE	❶ £30.50
A120 1,6ha 70**T**(100-200m²) 2**P**	❷ £37.50

🚗 A30 Bodmin-Redruth, turn right at Three Burrows roundabout B3277 to St. Agnes. In St. Agnes towards Beacon. Follow the campsite signs to a narrow entrance. Coming from Porthtowan through the village, uphill and follow the campsite signs.
💬 Active family farm in a nature reserve. The South West Coast footpath is next to the site with the best views of Cornwall. The site is divided into 6 fields, some overlook the sea, others are sheltered by trees.

CC 28/3-25/5 3/6-29/6 2/9-29/9

🧭 N 50°18'23'' W 5°13'35''

www.eurocampings.co.uk/102692

📶 (CC€19) **iD** 40a

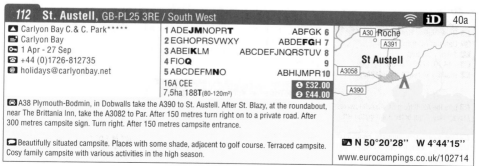

112 St. Austell, GB-PL25 3RE / South West

🏕 Carlyon Bay C.& C. Park*****
📧 Carlyon Bay
📅 1 Apr - 27 Sep
☎ +44 (0)1726-812735
@ holidays@carlyonbay.net

1 ADE**JM**NOP R**T**	ABFGK 6
2 EGHOPRSVWXY	ABDE**FGH** 7
3 ABEI**KLM**	ABCDEFJNQRSTUV 8
4 FIO**Q**	9
5 ABCDEFM**N**O	ABHIJMPR 10
16A CEE	❶ £32.00
7,5ha 188**T**(80-120m²)	❷ £44.00

🚗 A38 Plymouth-Bodmin, in Dobwalls take the A390 to St. Austell. After St. Blazy, at the roundabout, near The Brittania Inn, take the A3082 to Par. After 150 metres turn right on to a private road. After 300 metres campsite sign. Turn right. After 150 metres campsite entrance.

💬 Beautifully situated campsite. Places with some shade, adjacent to golf course. Terraced campsite. Cosy family campsite with various activities in the high season.

🧭 N 50°20'28'' W 4°44'15''

www.eurocampings.co.uk/102714

📶 **iD** 40a

United Kingdom

113 St. Austell, GB-PL26 6EL / South West   40a

- ▲ Heligan Woods***
- 🛏 Pentewan
- 📅 8 Jan - 26 Nov
- ☎ +44 (0)1726-844142
- @ info@heliganwoods.co.uk

1 ADE**JM**NOPRS**T**		6
2 BFHPRSTUVWXY	ABDE**FGH**	7
3 A	ABCDEFJNQRSTUV	8
4	E	9
5 ABDMN**O**	ABFGHJMR	10
16A CEE	**❶ £31.60**	
A71 8ha 89**T**(80-120m²) 24**P**	**❷ £39.10**	

St Austell   Par
A3058   A390

Portscatho

🚗 A390 Truro-St. Austell. On the double roundabout B3273 direction Mevagissey. After London App. follow the campsite signs, also the brown signs of Heligan Gardens. Campsite is just before the entrance to the gardens.
🏕 Terraced campsite possibly for families. Thanks to its location there are views over farmland with the sea in the distance from almost everywhere. 'The Lost Gardens of Heligan' are close to the campsite.

📍 N 50°17'19'' W 4°48'45''
www.eurocampings.co.uk/111309

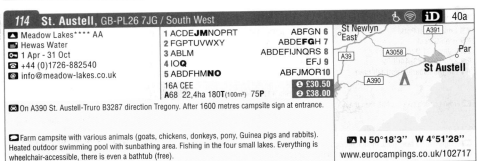

114 St. Austell, GB-PL26 7JG / South West   40a

- ▲ Meadow Lakes**** AA
- 🛏 Hewas Water
- 📅 1 Apr - 31 Oct
- ☎ +44 (0)1726-882540
- @ info@meadow-lakes.co.uk

1 ACDE**JM**NOPRT	ABFGN	6
2 FGPTUVWXY	ABDE**FGH**	7
3 ABLM	ABDEFIJNQRS	8
4 IO**Q**	EFJ	9
5 ABDFHMN**O**	ABFJMOR	10
16A CEE	**❶ £30.50**	
A68 22,4ha 180**T**(100m²) 75**P**	**❷ £38.00**	

St Newlyn East   A391
A39   A3058   Par
St Austell
A390

🚗 On A390 St. Austell-Truro B3287 direction Tregony. After 1600 metres campsite sign at entrance.

🏕 Farm campsite with various animals (goats, chickens, donkeys, pony, Guinea pigs and rabbits). Heated outdoor swimming pool with sunbathing area. Fishing in the four small lakes. Everything is wheelchair-accessible, there is even a bathtub (free).

📍 N 50°18'3'' W 4°51'28''
www.eurocampings.co.uk/102717

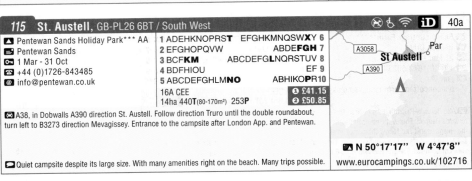

115 St. Austell, GB-PL26 6BT / South West   40a

- ▲ Pentewan Sands Holiday Park*** AA
- 🛏 Pentewan Sands
- 📅 1 Mar - 31 Oct
- ☎ +44 (0)1726-843485
- @ info@pentewan.co.uk

1 ADEHKNOPRS**T**	EFGHKMNQSWX**Y**	6
2 EFGHOPQVW	ABDE**FGH**	7
3 BCF**KM**	ABCDEFG**L**NQRSTUV	8
4 BDFHIOU	EF	9
5 ABCDEFGHLM**NO**	ABHIKO**P**R	10
16A CEE	**❶ £41.15**	
14ha 440**T**(80-170m²) 253**P**	**❷ £50.85**	

A3058   Par
St Austell
A390

🚗 A38, in Dobwalls A390 direction St. Austell. Follow direction Truro until the double roundabout, turn left to B3273 direction Mevagissey. Entrance to the campsite after London App. and Pentewan.

🏕 Quiet campsite despite its large size. With many amenities right on the beach. Many trips possible.

📍 N 50°17'17'' W 4°47'8''
www.eurocampings.co.uk/102716

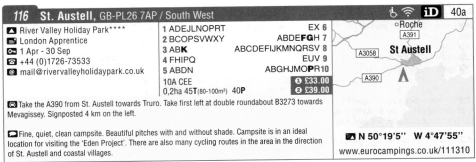

116 St. Austell, GB-PL26 7AP / South West   40a

- ▲ River Valley Holiday Park****
- 🛏 London Apprentice
- 📅 1 Apr - 30 Sep
- ☎ +44 (0)1726-73533
- @ mail@rivervalleyholidaypark.co.uk

1 ADEJLNOPRT	EX	6
2 BCOPSVWXY	ABDE**FGH**	7
3 AB**K**	ABCDEFIJKMNQRSV	8
4 FHIPQ	EUV	9
5 ABDN	ABGHJMO**P**R	10
10A CEE	**❶ £33.00**	
0,2ha 45**T**(80-100m²) 40**P**	**❷ £39.00**	

Roche
A391
A3058   St Austell
A390

🚗 Take the A390 from St. Austell towards Truro. Take first left at double roundabout B3273 towards Mevagissey. Signposted 4 km on the left.

🏕 Fine, quiet, clean campsite. Beautiful pitches with and without shade. Campsite is in an ideal location for visiting the 'Eden Project'. There are also many cycling routes in the area in the direction of St. Austell and coastal villages.

📍 N 50°19'5'' W 4°47'55''
www.eurocampings.co.uk/111310

United Kingdom

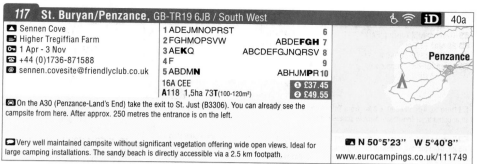

117 St. Buryan/Penzance, GB-TR19 6JB / South West

40a

- ▲ Sennen Cove
- 🏠 Higher Tregiffian Farm
- 📅 1 Apr - 3 Nov
- ☎ +44 (0)1736-871588
- @ sennen.covesite@friendlyclub.co.uk

1 ADEJMNOPRST			6
2 FGHMOPSVW	ABDE**FGH**		7
3 AE**KQ**	ABCDEFGJNQRSV		8
4 F			9
5 ABDM**N**	ABHJM**P**R		10
16A CEE			
A118 1,5ha 73T(100-120m²)		❶ £37.45	
		❷ £49.55	

Penzance

🚗 On the A30 (Penzance-Land's End) take the exit to St. Just (B3306). You can already see the campsite from here. After approx. 250 metres the entrance is on the left.

💬 Very well maintained campsite without significant vegetation offering wide open views. Ideal for large camping installations. The sandy beach is directly accessible via a 2.5 km footpath.

📍 N 50°5'23'' W 5°40'8''
www.eurocampings.co.uk/111749

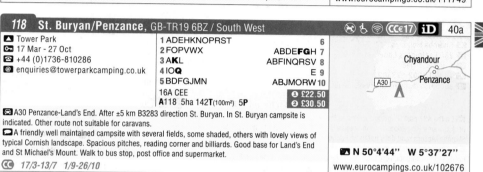

118 St. Buryan/Penzance, GB-TR19 6BZ / South West

40a

- ▲ Tower Park
- 📅 17 Mar - 27 Oct
- ☎ +44 (0)1736-810286
- @ enquiries@towerparkcamping.co.uk

1 ADEHKNOPRST			6
2 FOPVWX	ABDE**FGH**		7
3 A**KL**	ABFINQRSV		8
4 I**OQ**	E		9
5 BDFGJMN	ABJMORW		10
16A CEE			
A118 5ha 142T(100m²) 5P		❶ £22.50	
		❷ £30.50	

Chyandour
Penzance

🚗 A30 Penzance-Land's End. After ±5 km B3283 direction St. Buryan. In St. Buryan campsite is indicated. Other route not suitable for caravans.

💬 A friendly well maintained campsite with several fields, some shaded, others with lovely views of typical Cornish landscape. Spacious pitches, reading corner and billiards. Good base for Land's End and St Michael's Mount. Walk to bus stop, post office and supermarket.

📍 N 50°4'44'' W 5°37'27''
www.eurocampings.co.uk/102676

CC 17/3-13/7 1/9-26/10

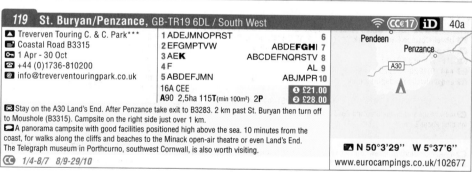

119 St. Buryan/Penzance, GB-TR19 6DL / South West

40a

- ▲ Treverven Touring C. & C. Park***
- 🏠 Coastal Road B3315
- 📅 1 Apr - 30 Oct
- ☎ +44 (0)1736-810200
- @ info@treverventouringpark.co.uk

1 ADEJMNOPRST			6
2 EFGMPTVW	ABDE**FGHI**		7
3 AE**K**	ABCDEFNQRSTV		8
4 F	AL		9
5 ABDEFJMN	ABJMPR		10
16A CEE			
A90 2,5ha 115T(min 100m²) 2P		❶ £21.00	
		❷ £28.00	

Pendeen
Penzance

🚗 Stay on the A30 Land's End. After Penzance take exit to B3283. 2 km past St. Buryan then turn off to Moushole (B3315). Campsite on the right side just over 1 km.

💬 A panorama campsite with good facilities positioned high above the sea. 10 minutes from the coast, for walks along the cliffs and beaches to the Minack open-air theatre or even Land's End. The Telegraph museum in Porthcurno, southwest Cornwall, is also worth visiting.

📍 N 50°3'29'' W 5°37'6''
www.eurocampings.co.uk/102677

CC 1/4-8/7 8/9-29/10

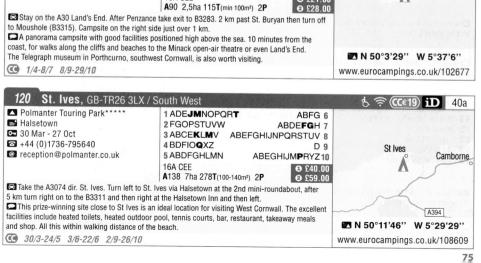

120 St. Ives, GB-TR26 3LX / South West

40a

- ▲ Polmanter Touring Park*****
- 🏠 Halsetown
- 📅 30 Mar - 27 Oct
- ☎ +44 (0)1736-795640
- @ reception@polmanter.co.uk

1 ADE**JM**NOPQR**T**	ABFG		6
2 FGOPSTUVW	ABDE**FGH**		7
3 ABCE**KLM**V	ABEFGHIJNPQRSTUV		8
4 BDFIO**Q**XZ	D		9
5 ABDFGHLMN	ABEGHIJM**P**RYZ		10
16A CEE			
A138 7ha 278T(100-140m²) 2P		❶ £40.00	
		❷ £59.00	

St Ives
Camborne

🚗 Take the A3074 dir. St. Ives. Turn left to St. Ives via Halsetown at the 2nd mini-roundabout, after 5 km turn right on to the B3311 and then right at the Halsetown Inn and then left.

💬 This prize-winning site close to St Ives is an ideal location for visiting West Cornwall. The excellent facilities include heated toilets, heated outdoor pool, tennis courts, bar, restaurant, takeaway meals and shop. All this within walking distance of the beach.

📍 N 50°11'46'' W 5°29'29''
www.eurocampings.co.uk/108609

CC 30/3-24/5 3/6-22/6 2/9-26/10

United Kingdom

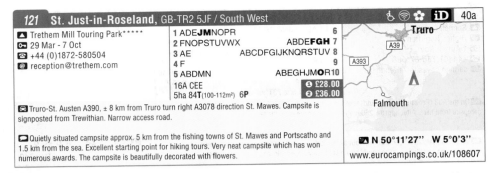

121 St. Just-in-Roseland, GB-TR2 5JF / South West
♿ 📶 ❄ **iD** 40a

- ⛺ Trethem Mill Touring Park*****
- 📅 29 Mar - 7 Oct
- ☎ +44 (0)1872-580504
- @ reception@trethem.com

1 ADE**JM**NOPR		6
2 FNOPSTUVWX	ABDE**FGH**	7
3 AE	ABCDFGIJKNQRSTUV	8
4 F		9
5 ABDMN	ABEGHJM**O**R	10
16A CEE		❶ £28.00
5ha 84**T**(100-112m²) 6**P**		❷ £36.00

🚗 Truro-St. Austen A390, ± 8 km from Truro turn right A3078 direction St. Mawes. Campsite is signposted from Trewithian. Narrow access road.

💬 Quietly situated campsite approx. 5 km from the fishing towns of St. Mawes and Portscatho and 1.5 km from the sea. Excellent starting point for hiking tours. Very neat campsite which has won numerous awards. The campsite is beautifully decorated with flowers.

📍 N 50°11'27'' W 5°0'3''
www.eurocampings.co.uk/108607

122 St. Leonards/Ringwood, GB-BH24 2SB / South West
♿ 📶 ❄ (CC€19) **iD** 9 B3

- ⛺ Shamba Holidays****
- 🏠 230 Eastmoors Lane
- 📅 1 Jan - 31 Dec
- ☎ +44 (0)1202-873302
- @ enquiries@shambaholidays.co.uk

1 ADE**JM**NOPQRS	EFG	6
2 OPQRSVWX	ABDE**FGH**	7
3 BE	ABCDFGIKNQRSV	8
4 IO**PQ**		9
5 ACDFHL**N**	ABGHIKM**O**R	10
16A CEE		❶ £40.00
7,6ha 147**T**(100m²) 37**P**		❷ £48.00

🚗 On the A31 past Ringwood ± 5 km to the west, past the 'Little Chef', at the next roundabout turn back towards Ringwood. Then immediately left into Eastmoors Lane, signs on the north side showing Shamba. Access road does not have a good surface.

💬 Private campsite surrounded by bushes and trees. Lovely level grounds. Excellent toilet facilities, lovely swimming pool, very friendly and helpful staff. Close to the New Forest, a beautiful natural area.

(CC) 4/1-29/3 16/4-4/5 8/5-25/5 4/6-14/7 3/9-21/12

📍 N 50°49'28'' W 1°51'13''
www.eurocampings.co.uk/102837

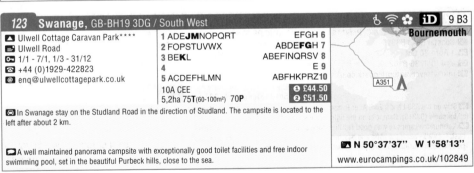

123 Swanage, GB-BH19 3DG / South West
♿ 📶 ❄ **iD** 9 B3

- ⛺ Ulwell Cottage Caravan Park****
- 🏠 Ulwell Road
- 📅 1/1 - 7/1, 1/3 - 31/12
- ☎ +44 (0)1929-422823
- @ enq@ulwellcottagepark.co.uk

1 ADE**JM**NOPQRT	EFGH	6
2 FOPSTUVWX	ABDE**FG**H	7
3 BE**KL**	ABEFINQRSV	8
4	E	9
5 ACDEFHLMN	ABFHKPRZ	10
10A CEE		❶ £44.50
5,2ha 75**T**(60-100m²) 70**P**		❷ £51.50

🚗 In Swanage stay on the Studland Road in the direction of Studland. The campsite is located to the left after about 2 km.

💬 A well maintained panorama campsite with exceptionally good toilet facilities and free indoor swimming pool, set in the beautiful Purbeck hills, close to the sea.

📍 N 50°37'37'' W 1°58'13''
www.eurocampings.co.uk/102849

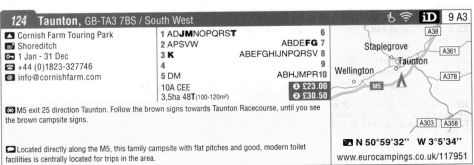

124 Taunton, GB-TA3 7BS / South West
♿ 📶 **iD** 9 A3

- ⛺ Cornish Farm Touring Park
- 🏠 Shoreditch
- 📅 1 Jan - 31 Dec
- ☎ +44 (0)1823-327746
- @ info@cornishfarm.com

1 AD**JM**NOPQRS**T**		6
2 APSVW	ABDE**FG**	7
3 **K**	ABEFGHIJNPQRSV	8
4		9
5 DM	ABHJMPR	10
10A CEE		❶ £23.00
3,5ha 48**T**(100-120m²)		❷ £30.50

🚗 M5 exit 25 direction Taunton. Follow the brown signs towards Taunton Racecourse, until you see the brown campsite signs.

💬 Located directly along the M5, this family campsite with flat pitches and good, modern toilet facilities is centrally located for trips in the area.

📍 N 50°59'32'' W 3°5'34''
www.eurocampings.co.uk/117951

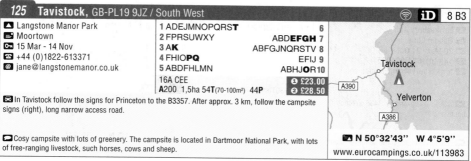

125 Tavistock, GB-PL19 9JZ / South West
🛜 iD 8 B3

- 🏕 Langstone Manor Park
- 🏤 Moortown
- 📅 15 Mar - 14 Nov
- ☎ +44 (0)1822-613371
- @ jane@langstonemanor.co.uk

1	ADEJMNOPQRST		6
2	FPRSUWXY	ABD**EFGH**	7
3	A**K**	ABFGJNQRSTV	8
4	FHIO**PQ**	EFIJ	9
5	ABDFHLMN	ABHJ**OR**	10
16A CEE			💶 £23.00
A200	1,5ha 54**T**(70-100m²)	44**P**	💶 £28.50

🚗 In Tavistock follow the signs for Princeton to the B3357. After approx. 3 km, follow the campsite signs (right), long narrow access road.

💬 Cosy campsite with lots of greenery. The campsite is located in Dartmoor National Park, with lots of free-ranging livestock, such horses, cows and sheep.

Tavistock
Yelverton
A390
A386

🧭 N 50°32'43'' W 4°5'9''

www.eurocampings.co.uk/113983

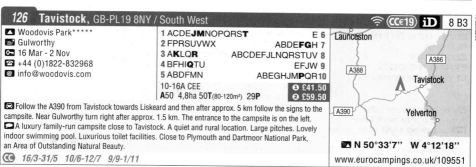

126 Tavistock, GB-PL19 8NY / South West
📶 (CC€19) iD 8 B3

- 🏕 Woodovis Park*****
- 🏤 Gulworthy
- 📅 16 Mar - 2 Nov
- ☎ +44 (0)1822-832968
- @ info@woodovis.com

1	ACDE**JM**NOPQRST	E	6
2	FPRSUVWX	ABD**EFGH**	7
3	A**KLQR**	ABCDEFJLNQRSTUV	8
4	BFHI**QTU**	EFJW	9
5	ABDFMN	ABEGHJM**PQR**	10
10-16A CEE			💶 £41.50
A50	4,8ha 50**T**(80-120m²)	29**P**	💶 £59.50

🚗 Follow the A390 from Tavistock towards Liskeard and then after approx. 5 km follow the signs to the campsite. Near Gulworthy turn right after approx. 1.5 km. The entrance to the campsite is on the left.
💬 A luxury family-run campsite close to Tavistock. A quiet and rural location. Large pitches. Lovely indoor swimming pool. Luxurious toilet facilities. Close to Plymouth and Dartmoor National Park, an Area of Outstanding Natural Beauty.

(CC) 16/3-31/5 10/6-12/7 9/9-1/11

Launceston
A388
A390
A386
Tavistock
Yelverton

🧭 N 50°33'7'' W 4°12'18''

www.eurocampings.co.uk/109551

United Kingdom

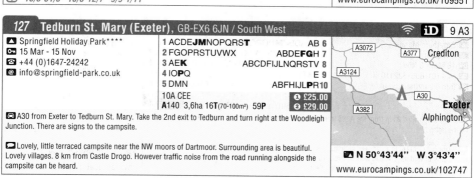

127 Tedburn St. Mary (Exeter), GB-EX6 6JN / South West
📶 iD 9 A3

- 🏕 Springfield Holiday Park****
- 📅 15 Mar - 15 Nov
- ☎ +44 (0)1647-24242
- @ info@springfield-park.co.uk

1	ACDE**JM**NOPQRST	AB	6
2	FGOPRSTUVWX	ABD**EFGH**	7
3	AE**K**	ABCDFIJLNQRSTV	8
4	IO**PQ**	E	9
5	DMN	ABFHIJL**PR**	10
10A CEE			💶 £25.00
A140	3,6ha 16**T**(70-100m²)	59**P**	💶 £29.00

🚗 A30 from Exeter to Tedburn St. Mary. Take the 2nd exit to Tedburn and turn right at the Woodleigh Junction. There are signs to the campsite.

💬 Lovely, little terraced campsite near the NW moors of Dartmoor. Surrounding area is beautiful. Lovely villages. 8 km from Castle Drogo. However traffic noise from the road running alongside the campsite can be heard.

A3072
A377 Crediton
A3124
A30
A382
Exeter
Alphington

🧭 N 50°43'44'' W 3°43'4''

www.eurocampings.co.uk/102747

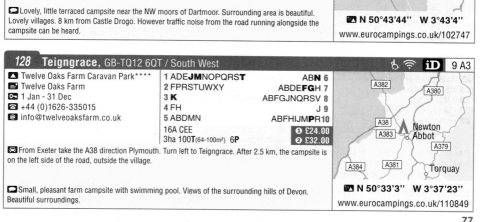

128 Teigngrace, GB-TQ12 6QT / South West
♿ 📶 iD 9 A3

- 🏕 Twelve Oaks Farm Caravan Park****
- 🏤 Twelve Oaks Farm
- 📅 1 Jan - 31 Dec
- ☎ +44 (0)1626-335015
- @ info@twelveoaksfarm.co.uk

1	ADE**JM**NOPQRST	AB**N**	6
2	FPRSTUWXY	ABD**EFGH**	7
3	**K**	ABFGJNQRSV	8
4	FH	J	9
5	ABDMN	ABFHIJM**PR**	10
16A CEE			💶 £24.00
3ha 100**T**(64-100m²)	6**P**		💶 £32.00

🚗 From Exeter take the A38 direction Plymouth. Turn left to Teigngrace. After 2.5 km, the campsite is on the left side of the road, outside the village.

💬 Small, pleasant farm campsite with swimming pool. Views of the surrounding hills of Devon. Beautiful surroundings.

A382
A380
A38
A383 Newton Abbot
A379
A384
A381
Torquay

🧭 N 50°33'3'' W 3°37'23''

www.eurocampings.co.uk/110849

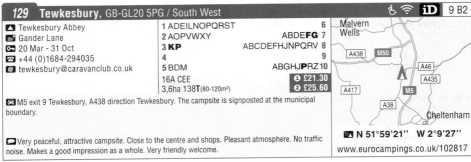

129 Tewkesbury, GB-GL20 5PG / South West ♿ 📶 iD 9 B2

- 🏕 Tewkesbury Abbey
- ✉ Gander Lane
- 📅 20 Mar - 31 Oct
- ☎ +44 (0)1684-294035
- @ tewkesbury@caravanclub.co.uk

1 ADEILNOPQRST		6
2 AOPVWXY	ABDE**FG**	7
3 **KP**	ABCDEFHJNPQRV	8
4		9
5 BDM	ABGHJ**P**R**Z**	10
16A CEE	❶ £21.30	
3,6ha 138**T**(80-120m²)	❷ £25.60	

🚗 M5 exit 9 Tewkesbury, A438 direction Tewkesbury. The campsite is signposted at the municipal boundary.

💬 Very peaceful, attractive campsite. Close to the centre and shops. Pleasant atmosphere. No traffic noise. Makes a good impression as a whole. Very friendly welcome.

📍 N 51°59'21'' W 2°9'27''

www.eurocampings.co.uk/102817

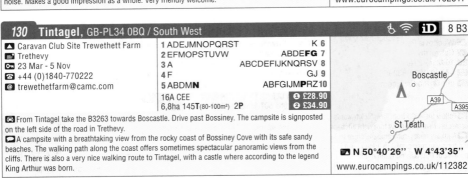

130 Tintagel, GB-PL34 0BQ / South West ♿ 📶 iD 8 B3

- 🏕 Caravan Club Site Trewethett Farm
- ✉ Trethevy
- 📅 23 Mar - 5 Nov
- ☎ +44 (0)1840-770222
- @ trewethetfarm@camc.com

1 ADEJMNOPQRST	K	6
2 EFMOPSTUVW	ABDE**FG**	7
3 A	ABCDEFIJKNQRSV	8
4 F	GJ	9
5 ABDM**N**	ABFGIJM**P**R**Z**	10
16A CEE	❶ £28.90	
6,8ha 145**T**(80-100m²) 2**P**	❷ £34.90	

🚗 From Tintagel take the B3263 towards Boscastle. Drive past Bossiney. The campsite is signposted on the left side of the road in Trethevy.

💬 A campsite with a breathtaking view from the rocky coast of Bossiney Cove with its safe sandy beaches. The walking path along the coast offers sometimes spectacular panoramic views from the cliffs. There is also a very nice walking route to Tintagel, with a castle where according to the legend King Arthur was born.

📍 N 50°40'26'' W 4°43'35''

www.eurocampings.co.uk/112382

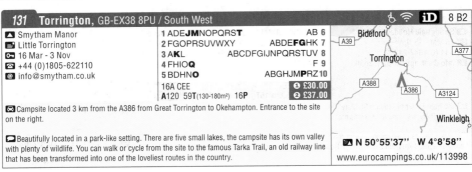

131 Torrington, GB-EX38 8PU / South West ♿ 📶 iD 8 B2

- 🏕 Smytham Manor
- ✉ Little Torrington
- 📅 16 Mar - 3 Nov
- ☎ +44 (0)1805-622110
- @ info@smytham.co.uk

1 ADE**JM**NOPQRS**T**	AB	6
2 FGOPRSUVWXY	ABDE**FG**HK	7
3 A**KL**	ABCDFGIJNPQRSTUV	8
4 FHIO**Q**	F	9
5 BDHN**O**	ABGHJM**P**R**Z**	10
16A CEE	❶ £30.00	
A120 59**T**(130-180m²) 16**P**	❷ £37.00	

🚗 Campsite located 3 km from the A386 from Great Torrington to Okehampton. Entrance to the site on the right.

💬 Beautifully located in a park-like setting. There are five small lakes, the campsite has its own valley with plenty of wildlife. You can walk or cycle from the site to the famous Tarka Trail, an old railway line that has been transformed into one of the loveliest routes in the country.

📍 N 50°55'37'' W 4°8'58''

www.eurocampings.co.uk/113998

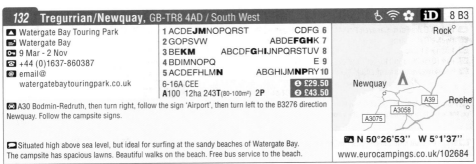

132 Tregurrian/Newquay, GB-TR8 4AD / South West ♿ 📶 ✿ iD 8 B3

- 🏕 Watergate Bay Touring Park
- ✉ Watergate Bay
- 📅 9 Mar - 2 Nov
- ☎ +44 (0)1637-860387
- @ email@
  watergatebaytouringpark.co.uk

1 ACDE**JM**NOPQRST	CDFG	6
2 GOPSVW	ABDE**FGH**K	7
3 BE**KM**	ABCDF**GHI**JNPQRSTUV	8
4 BDIMNOPQ	E	9
5 ACDEFHLM**N**	ABGHIJM**N**P**RY**	10
6-16A CEE	❶ £29.50	
A100 12ha 243**T**(80-100m²) 2**P**	❷ £43.50	

🚗 A30 Bodmin-Redruth, then turn right, follow the sign 'Airport', then turn left to the B3276 direction Newquay. Follow the campsite signs.

💬 Situated high above sea level, but ideal for surfing at the sandy beaches of Watergate Bay. The campsite has spacious lawns. Beautiful walks on the beach. Free bus service to the beach.

📍 N 50°26'53'' W 5°1'37''

www.eurocampings.co.uk/102684

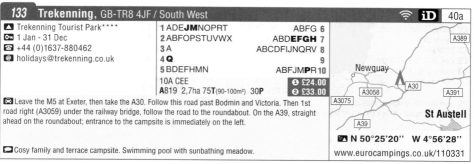

133 Trekenning, GB-TR8 4JF / South West ⏚ iD 40a

- 🏕 Trekenning Tourist Park****
- 📅 1 Jan - 31 Dec
- ☎ +44 (0)1637-880462
- @ holidays@trekenning.co.uk

1 ADEJMNOPRT	ABFG 6
2 ABFOPSTUVWX	ABDEFGH 7
3 A	ABCDFIJNQRV 8
4 Q	9
5 BDEFHMN	ABFJMPR 10
10A CEE	❶ £24.00
A819 2,7ha 75T(90-100m²) 30P	❷ £33.00

🚗 Leave the M5 at Exeter, then take the A30. Follow this road past Bodmin and Victoria. Then 1st road right (A3059) under the railway bridge, follow the road to the roundabout. On the A39, straight ahead on the roundabout; entrance to the campsite is immediately on the left.

💬 Cosy family and terrace campsite. Swimming pool with sunbathing meadow.

N 50°25'20'' W 4°56'28''

www.eurocampings.co.uk/110331

134 Truro, GB-TR3 6JJ / South West ♿ ⏚ ✿ iD 40a

- 🏕 Carnon Downs C. & C. Park*****
- 🚩 Carnon Downs
- 📅 1 Jan - 31 Dec
- ☎ +44 (0)1872-862283
- @ info@
  carnon-downs-caravanpark.co.uk

1 ADEJMNOPQRST	6
2 OPSVWXY	ABDEFGH 7
3 BEKLV	ABCDEFHIJMNPQRSTUV 8
4 FHIO	EF 9
5 DMN	ABGHIJMOR 10
10-16A CEE	❶ £33.00
A94 10ha 180T(100-180m²) 2P	❷ £40.00

🚗 Campsite is located along the A39 Truro-Falmouth, at the 3rd roundabout south-southwest of Truro. Campsite sign on the soundproofing wall by the roadside.

💬 Very easy access for caravans, spacious separate fields. Opportunity for many interesting trips in the area. Older campers in particular will appreciate the high quality of the toilet facilities. Campsite focuses on peace and order. No organised events or activities, therefore less suitable for families with children. There is a good playground.

N 50°13'31'' W 5°4'48''

www.eurocampings.co.uk/102701

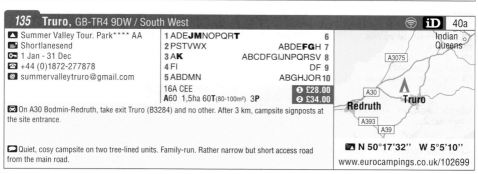

135 Truro, GB-TR4 9DW / South West ⏚ iD 40a

- 🏕 Summer Valley Tour. Park**** AA
- 🚩 Shortlanesend
- 📅 1 Jan - 31 Dec
- ☎ +44 (0)1872-277878
- @ summervalleytruro@gmail.com

1 ADEJMNOPQRT	6
2 PSTVWX	ABDEFGH 7
3 AK	ABCDFGIJNPQRSV 8
4 FI	DF 9
5 ABDMN	ABGHJOR 10
16A CEE	❶ £28.00
A60 1,5ha 60T(80-100m²) 3P	❷ £34.00

🚗 On A30 Bodmin-Redruth, take exit Truro (B3284) and no other. After 3 km, campsite signposts at the site entrance.

💬 Quiet, cosy campsite on two tree-lined units. Family-run. Rather narrow but short access road from the main road.

N 50°17'32'' W 5°5'10''

www.eurocampings.co.uk/102699

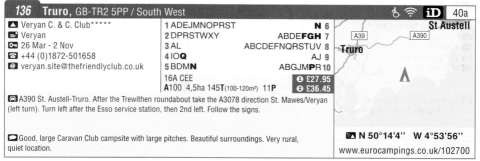

136 Truro, GB-TR2 5PP / South West ♿ ⏚ iD 40a

- 🏕 Veryan C. & C. Club*****
- 🚩 Veryan
- 📅 26 Mar - 2 Nov
- ☎ +44 (0)1872-501658
- @ veryan.site@thefriendlyclub.co.uk

1 ADEJMNOPRST	N 6
2 DPRSTWXY	ABDEFGH 7
3 AL	ABCDEFNQRSTUV 8
4 IOQ	AJ 9
5 BDMN	ABGJMPR 10
16A CEE	❶ £27.95
A100 4,5ha 145T(100-120m²) 11P	❷ £36.45

🚗 A390 St. Austell-Truro. After the Trewithen roundabout take the A3078 direction St. Mawes/Veryan (left turn). Turn left after the Esso service station, then 2nd left. Follow the signs.

💬 Good, large Caravan Club campsite with large pitches. Beautiful surroundings. Very rural, quiet location.

N 50°14'4'' W 4°53'56''

www.eurocampings.co.uk/102700

United Kingdom

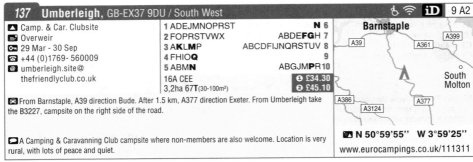

137 Umberleigh, GB-EX37 9DU / South West   9 A2

- Camp. & Car. Clubsite
- Overweir
- 29 Mar - 30 Sep
- +44 (0)1769- 560009
- umberleigh.site@
  thefriendlyclub.co.uk

1 ADEJMNOPRST	**N** 6	
2 FOPRSTVWX	ABDE**FGH** 7	
3 A**KLMP**	ABCDFIJNQRSTUV 8	
4 FHIO**Q**	9	
5 ABM**N**	ABGJM**P**R 10	
16A CEE	❶ £34.30	
3,2ha 67**T**(30-100m²)	❷ £45.10	

Barnstaple

From Barnstaple, A39 direction Bude. After 1.5 km, A377 direction Exeter. From Umberleigh take the B3227, campsite on the right side of the road.

A Camping & Caravanning Club campsite where non-members are also welcome. Location is very rural, with lots of peace and quiet.

N 50°59'55'' W 3°59'25''

www.eurocampings.co.uk/111311

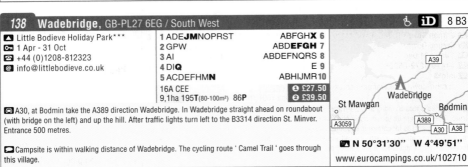

138 Wadebridge, GB-PL27 6EG / South West   8 B3

- Little Bodieve Holiday Park***
- 1 Apr - 31 Oct
- +44 (0)1208-812323
- info@littlebodieve.co.uk

1 ADE**JM**NOPRST	ABFGH**X** 6	
2 GPW	ABDE**FGH** 7	
3 AI	ABDEFNQRS 8	
4 DI**Q**	E 9	
5 ACDEFHM**N**	ABHIJMR 10	
16A CEE	❶ £27.50	
9,1ha 195**T**(80-100m²) 86**P**	❷ £39.50	

A30, at Bodmin take the A389 direction Wadebridge. In Wadebridge straight ahead on roundabout (with bridge on the left) and up the hill. After traffic lights turn left to the B3314 direction St. Minver. Entrance 500 metres.

Campsite is within walking distance of Wadebridge. The cycling route ' Camel Trail ' goes through this village.

N 50°31'30'' W 4°49'51''

www.eurocampings.co.uk/102710

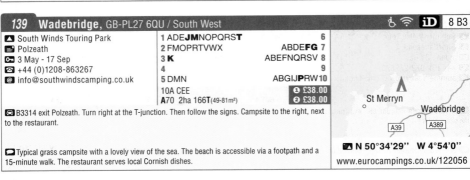

139 Wadebridge, GB-PL27 6QU / South West   8 B3

- South Winds Touring Park
- Polzeath
- 3 May - 17 Sep
- +44 (0)1208-863267
- info@southwindscamping.co.uk

1 ADE**JM**NOPQRS**T**	6	
2 FMOPRTVWX	ABDE**FG** 7	
3 **K**	ABEFNQRSV 8	
4	9	
5 DMN	ABGIJ**P**RW 10	
10A CEE	❶ £38.00	
A70 2ha 166**T**(49-81m²)	❷ £38.00	

B3314 exit Polzeath. Turn right at the T-junction. Then follow the signs. Campsite to the right, next to the restaurant.

Typical grass campsite with a lovely view of the sea. The beach is accessible via a footpath and a 15-minute walk. The restaurant serves local Cornish dishes.

N 50°34'29'' W 4°54'0''

www.eurocampings.co.uk/122056

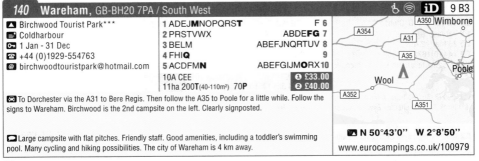

140 Wareham, GB-BH20 7PA / South West   9 B3

- Birchwood Tourist Park***
- Coldharbour
- 1 Jan - 31 Dec
- +44 (0)1929-554763
- birchwoodtouristpark@hotmail.com

1 ADE**JM**NOPQRS**T**	F 6	
2 PRSTVWX	ABDE**FG** 7	
3 BELM	ABEFJNQRTUV 8	
4 FHI**Q**	9	
5 ACDFM**N**	ABEFGIJM**O**RX 10	
10A CEE	❶ £33.00	
11ha 200**T**(40-110m²) 70**P**	❷ £40.00	

To Dorchester via the A31 to Bere Regis. Then follow the A35 to Poole for a little while. Follow the signs to Wareham. Birchwood is the 2nd campsite on the left. Clearly signposted.

Large campsite with flat pitches. Friendly staff. Good amenities, including a toddler's swimming pool. Many cycling and hiking possibilities. The city of Wareham is 4 km away.

N 50°43'0'' W 2°8'50''

www.eurocampings.co.uk/100979

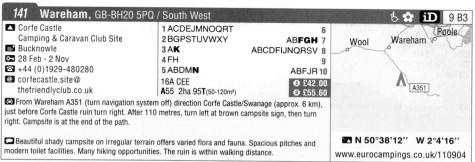

141 Wareham, GB-BH20 5PQ / South West
9 B3

- Corfe Castle
  Camping & Caravan Club Site
- Bucknowle
- 28 Feb - 2 Nov
- +44 (0)1929-480280
- corfecastle.site@
  thefriendlyclub.co.uk

1	ACDEJMNOQRT		6
2	BGPSTUVWXY	AB**FGH**	7
3	A**K**	ABCDFIJNQRSV	8
4	FH		9
5	ABDM**N**	AB**F**JR	10
16A	CEE		**€42.00**
A55	2ha 95T(50-120m²)		**€55.60**

From Wareham A351 (turn navigation system off) direction Corfe Castle/Swanage (approx. 6 km), just before Corfe Castle ruin turn right. After 110 metres, turn left at brown campsite sign, then turn right. Campsite is at the end of the path.

Beautiful shady campsite on irregular terrain offers varied flora and fauna. Spacious pitches and modern toilet facilities. Many hiking opportunities. The ruin is within walking distance.

N 50°38'12''   W 2°4'16''

www.eurocampings.co.uk/110904

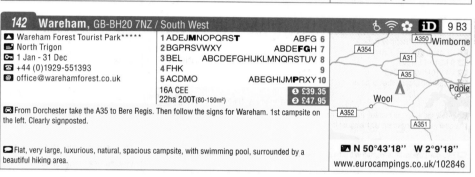

142 Wareham, GB-BH20 7NZ / South West
9 B3

- Wareham Forest Tourist Park*****
- North Trigon
- 1 Jan - 31 Dec
- +44 (0)1929-551393
- office@warehamforest.co.uk

1	ADEJ**M**NOPQRS**T**	ABFG	6
2	BGPRSVWXY	ABDE**FG**H	7
3	BEL	ABCDEFGHIJKLMNQRSTUV	8
4	FHK		9
5	ACDMO	ABEGHIJM**P**RXY	10
16A	CEE		**€39.35**
22ha	200T(80-150m²)		**€47.95**

From Dorchester take the A35 to Bere Regis. Then follow the signs for Wareham. 1st campsite on the left. Clearly signposted.

Flat, very large, luxurious, natural, spacious campsite, with swimming pool, surrounded by a beautiful hiking area.

N 50°43'18''   W 2°9'18''

www.eurocampings.co.uk/102846

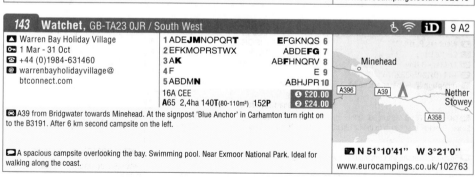

143 Watchet, GB-TA23 0JR / South West
9 A2

- Warren Bay Holiday Village
- 1 Mar - 31 Oct
- +44 (0)1984-631460
- warrenbayholidayvillage@
  btconnect.com

1	ADEJ**M**NOPQR**T**	**E**FGKNQS	6
2	EFKMOPRSTWX	ABDE**FG**	7
3	A**K**	AB**F**HNQRV	8
4	F		E 9
5	ABDM**N**	ABHJPR	10
16A	CEE		**€20.00**
A65	2,4ha 140T(80-110m²) 152P		**€24.00**

A39 from Bridgwater towards Minehead. At the signpost 'Blue Anchor' in Carhamton turn right on to the B3191. After 6 km second campsite on the left.

A spacious campsite overlooking the bay. Swimming pool. Near Exmoor National Park. Ideal for walking along the coast.

N 51°10'41''   W 3°21'0''

www.eurocampings.co.uk/102763

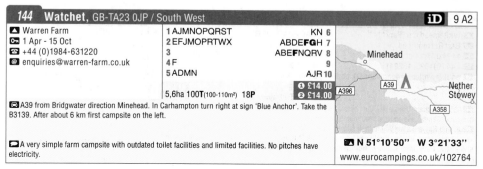

144 Watchet, GB-TA23 0JP / South West
9 A2

- Warren Farm
- 1 Apr - 15 Oct
- +44 (0)1984-631220
- enquiries@warren-farm.co.uk

1	AJMNOPQRST	KN	6
2	EFJMOPRTWX	ABDE**FG**H	7
3		ABE**F**NQRV	8
4	F		9
5	ADMN	AJR	10
			€14.00
5,6ha	100T(100-110m²) 18P		**€14.00**

A39 from Bridgwater direction Minehead. In Carhamton turn right at sign 'Blue Anchor'. Take the B3139. After about 6 km first campsite on the left.

A very simple farm campsite with outdated toilet facilities and limited facilities. No pitches have electricity.

N 51°10'50''   W 3°21'33''

www.eurocampings.co.uk/102764

United Kingdom

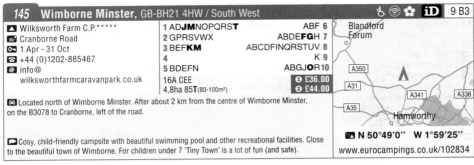

145 Wimborne Minster, GB-BH21 4HW / South West
9 B3

- ▲ Wilksworth Farm C.P.*****
- ✉ Cranborne Road
- ☷ 1 Apr - 31 Oct
- ☎ +44 (0)1202-885467
- @ info@
  wilksworthfarmcaravanpark.co.uk

1 ADJMNOPQRST	ABF	6
2 GPRSVWX	ABDEFGH	7
3 BEFKM	ABCDFINQRSTUV	8
4	K	9
5 BDEFN	ABGJOR	10
16A CEE	❶ £36.00	
4,8ha 85T(80-100m²)	❷ £44.00	

🚗 Located north of Wimborne Minster. After about 2 km from the centre of Wimborne Minster, on the B3078 to Cranborne, left of the road.

💬 Cosy, child-friendly campsite with beautiful swimming pool and other recreational facilities. Close to the beautiful town of Wimborne. For children under 7 'Tiny Town' is a lot of fun (and safe).

📍 N 50°49'0'' W 1°59'25''
www.eurocampings.co.uk/102834

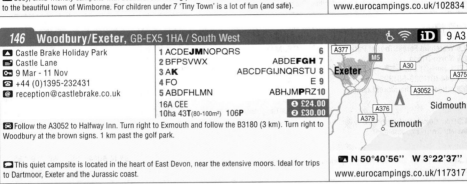

146 Woodbury/Exeter, GB-EX5 1HA / South West
9 A3

- ▲ Castle Brake Holiday Park
- ✉ Castle Lane
- ☷ 9 Mar - 11 Nov
- ☎ +44 (0)1395-232431
- @ reception@castlebrake.co.uk

1 ACDEJMNOPQRS		6
2 BFPSVWX	ABDEFGH	7
3 AK	ABCDFGIJNQRSTU	8
4 FO	E	9
5 ABDFHLMN	ABHJMPRZ	10
16A CEE	❶ £24.00	
10ha 43T(80-100m²) 106P	❷ £30.00	

🚗 Follow the A3052 to Halfway Inn. Turn right to Exmouth and follow the B3180 (3 km). Turn right to Woodbury at the brown signs. 1 km past the golf park.

💬 This quiet campsite is located in the heart of East Devon, near the extensive moors. Ideal for trips to Dartmoor, Exeter and the Jurassic coast.

📍 N 50°40'56'' W 3°22'37''
www.eurocampings.co.uk/117317

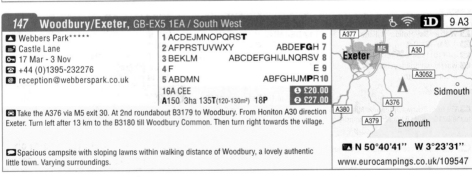

147 Woodbury/Exeter, GB-EX5 1EA / South West
9 A3

- ▲ Webbers Park*****
- ✉ Castle Lane
- ☷ 17 Mar - 3 Nov
- ☎ +44 (0)1395-232276
- @ reception@webberspark.co.uk

1 ACDEJMNOPQRST		6
2 AFPRSTUVWXY	ABDEFGH	7
3 BEKLM	ABCDEFGHIJLNQRSV	8
4 F	E	9
5 ABDMN	ABFGHIJMPR	10
16A CEE	❶ £20.00	
A150 3ha 135T(120-130m²) 18P	❷ £27.00	

🚗 Take the A376 via M5 exit 30. At 2nd roundabout B3179 to Woodbury. From Honiton A30 direction Exeter. Turn left after 13 km to the B3180 till Woodbury Common. Then turn right towards the village.

💬 Spacious campsite with sloping lawns within walking distance of Woodbury, a lovely authentic little town. Varying surroundings.

📍 N 50°40'41'' W 3°23'31''
www.eurocampings.co.uk/109547

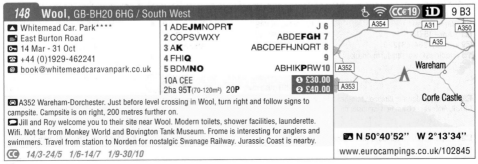

148 Wool, GB-BH20 6HG / South West
9 B3

- ▲ Whitemead Car. Park****
- ✉ East Burton Road
- ☷ 14 Mar - 31 Oct
- ☎ +44 (0)1929-462241
- @ book@whitemeadcaravanpark.co.uk

1 ADEJMNOPRT	J	6
2 COPSVWXY	ABDEFGH	7
3 AK	ABCDEFHJNQRT	8
4 FHIQ		9
5 BDMNO	ABHIKPRW	10
10A CEE	❶ £30.00	
2ha 95T(70-120m²) 20P	❷ £40.00	

🚗 A352 Wareham-Dorchester. Just before level crossing in Wool, turn right and follow signs to campsite. Campsite is on right, 200 metres further on.

💬 Jill and Roy welcome you to their site near Wool. Modern toilets, shower facilities, launderette. Wifi. Not far from Monkey World and Bovington Tank Museum. Frome is interesting for anglers and swimmers. Travel from station to Norden for nostalgic Swanage Railway. Jurassic Coast is nearby.

© 14/3-24/5 1/6-14/7 1/9-30/10

📍 N 50°40'52'' W 2°13'34''
www.eurocampings.co.uk/102845

149 Woolacombe, GB-EX34 7EH / South West ♿ 📶 **iD** 8 B2

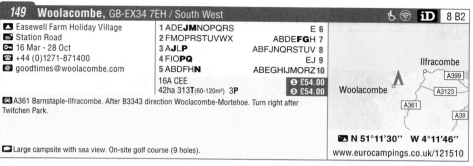

△ Easewell Farm Holiday Village
🏠 Station Road
📅 16 Mar - 28 Oct
☎ +44 (0)1271-871400
@ goodtimes@woolacombe.com

1 ADE**JM**NOPQRS	E 6
2 FMOPRSTUVWX	ABDE**FGH** 7
3 A**JLP**	ABFJNQRSTUV 8
4 FIO**PQ**	EJ 9
5 ABDF**HN**	ABEGHIJMORZ 10
16A CEE	❶ £54.00
42ha 313**T**(60-120m²) 3**P**	❷ £54.00

🚗 A361 Barnstaple-Ilfracombe. After B3343 direction Woolacombe-Mortehoe. Turn right after Twitchen Park.

💬 Large campsite with sea view. On-site golf course (9 holes).

Woolacombe ● Ilfracombe — A399 / A3123 / A361 / A39

📷 **N 51°11'30" W 4°11'46"**
www.eurocampings.co.uk/121510

150 Woolacombe, GB-EX34 7HW / South West 🚫 📶 **iD** 8 B2

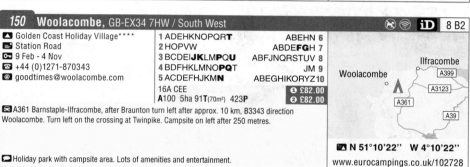

△ Golden Coast Holiday Village****
🏠 Station Road
📅 9 Feb - 4 Nov
☎ +44 (0)1271-870343
@ goodtimes@woolacombe.com

1 ADEHKNOPQR**T**	ABEHN 6
2 HOPVW	ABDE**FGH** 7
3 BCDEI**JKLMPQU**	ABFJNQRSTUV 8
4 BDFHKLMNO**PQT**	JM 9
5 ACDEFHJKM**N**	ABEGHIKORYZ 10
16A CEE	❶ £82.00
A100 5ha 91**T**(70m²) 423**P**	❷ £82.00

🚗 A361 Barnstaple-Ilfracombe, after Braunton turn left after approx. 10 km, B3343 direction Woolacombe. Turn left on the crossing at Twinpike. Campsite on left after 250 metres.

💬 Holiday park with campsite area. Lots of amenities and entertainment.

Woolacombe ● Ilfracombe — A399 / A3123 / A361 / A39

📷 **N 51°10'22" W 4°10'22"**
www.eurocampings.co.uk/102728

151 Woolacombe, GB-EX34 7ES / South West 📶 **iD** 8 B2

△ Twitchen House Holiday Village****
🏠 Mortehoe Station Road
📅 16 Mar - 29 Oct
☎ +44 (0)1271-870848
@ th.gm@woolacombe.com

1 ADE**JM**NOR	ABEFGHN 6
2 GHKOPSTUVWX	ABDE**FGH** 7
3 BCEI**K**LSUV	ABEFGIJNQRSTUV 8
4 BDFIMNO**PQRS**T	EIJ 9
5 ABDEFHL	ABEGHIJMO**P**RYZ 10
16A CEE	❶ £72.00
A50 6,5ha 355**T**(100m²) 611**P**	❷ £72.00

🚗 A361 Bramstaple-Ilfracombe. After Braunton, drive approx. 10 km on the B3343 towards Woolacombe/Mortehoe. At the Turnpike junction turn left towards Mortehoe. Campsite is on the left after 2.5 km.

💬 Large, luxury, terraced campsite with lots of activity. Many organised activities for guests during the high season. Mobile homes and cabins can also be rented.

Woolacombe ● Ilfracombe — A399 / A3123 / A361 / A39

📷 **N 51°11'5" W 4°11'52"**
www.eurocampings.co.uk/102729

152 Woolacombe, GB-EX34 7AH / South West 📶 **iD** 8 B2

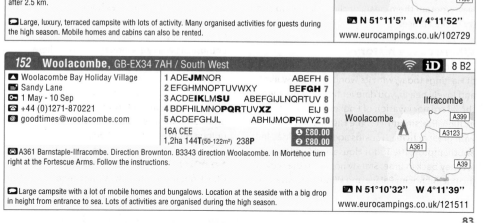

△ Woolacombe Bay Holiday Village
🏠 Sandy Lane
📅 1 May - 10 Sep
☎ +44 (0)1271-870221
@ goodtimes@woolacombe.com

1 ADE**JM**NOR	ABEFH 6
2 EFGHMNOPTUVWXY	BE**FGH** 7
3 ACDEI**K**LM**SU**	ABEFGIJLNQRTUV 8
4 BDFHILMNO**PQR**TUV**XZ**	EIJ 9
5 ACDEFGHJL	ABHIJMO**P**RWYZ 10
16A CEE	❶ £80.00
1,2ha 144**T**(50-122m²) 238**P**	❷ £80.00

🚗 A361 Barnstaple-Ilfracombe. Direction Brownton. B3343 direction Woolacombe. In Mortehoe turn right at the Fortescue Arms. Follow the instructions.

💬 Large campsite with a lot of mobile homes and bungalows. Location at the seaside with a big drop in height from entrance to sea. Lots of activities are organised during the high season.

Woolacombe ● Ilfracombe — A399 / A3123 / A361 / A39

📷 **N 51°10'32" W 4°11'39"**
www.eurocampings.co.uk/121511

Shining cliffs

Surrounded by the English Channel, North Sea, East Anglia and South West England, the rolling hills, gardens and rivers add to the gentle beauty of this region. The iconic white cliffs are impressive from both angles: admire the gleaming chalk face from the sea below as the waves pound them clean, or climb to the top and try to see France.

Where to see history

Strolling through the beautiful mediaeval town of Hastings today, with its wonderful cliff walks and lovely beach, you'd never think it was where the last major invasion of England took place in 1066. Portsmouth has the Historic Dockyard, with great activities for kids aged 6 and older. In Southampton, the Tudor House and Garden is a journey back in time. Stately homes in the region include Blenheim Palace and Windsor Castle, and

Downton Abbey fans will recognise Highclere Castle in Berkshire. And of course everyone knows London, the capital, with Buckingham Palace, Big Ben, the Tower Bridge and so many other sights.

Dreaming spires, fantastic forests

Steventon, Hampshire, was home to celebrated novelist Jane Austen, who was educated in Oxford: "the city of dreaming spires". Outdoor enthusiasts will like Ashdown Forest, where writer AA Milne set his stories of Winnie-the-Pooh - get the kids to find the actual Hundred Acre Wood! Enjoy a superb recreation of Chaucer's time in Canterbury, or spend a day in Brighton, with its great pier, beach, and the truly unique Hindu-Gothic Pavilion.

So much to do, see - and eat

Check out the White Cliffs Visitor centre, with the

Lamb's Tail Pie, followed by a Gypsy tart, Lenten Pudding Pie, or Eton Mess. Undecided? Try a Bedfordshire Clanger. Wash down with beer, or try some of the locally-produced English wines. While you're here, visit an English vineyard!

mysterious Fan Bay Deep Shelter. Near Eastbourne, Beachy Head and the nearby Seven Sisters are very scenic. Inland, the Bedgebury Pinetum and Forest is ideal for walkers, cyclists, horse riders and nature-lovers, with family activities as well. Chessington World of Adventures is a guaranteed hit with the whole family.

Hungry yet? Try a Dredgerman's breakfast – with oysters – and a huffkin, with local cheese, or

Our tips

1. Enjoy history and beautiful grounds at Hever Castle and Gardens, Kent
2. Accio visitor! See the Harry Potter movie sets at Warner Bros studios, Leavesden
3. Into art? Visit the Henry Moore Foundation, Perry Green, Much Hadham
4. Take a boat trip to Red Sand forts on the Thames Estuary
5. Walk the magical woods of Ashridge in the Chiltern Hills

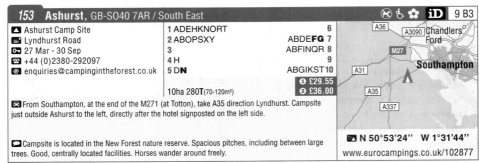

153 Ashurst, GB-SO40 7AR / South East

⊗ ♿ ❀ **iD** 9 B3

- ▲ Ashurst Camp Site
- ▤ Lyndhurst Road
- ☰ 27 Mar - 30 Sep
- ☎ +44 (0)2380-292097
- @ enquiries@campingintheforest.co.uk

1 ADEHKNORT		6
2 ABOPSXY	ABDE**FG**	7
3	ABFINQR	8
4 H		9
5 D**N**	ABGIKST	10

❶ £29.55
❷ £36.00

10ha 280**T**(70-120m²)

🚗 From Southampton, at the end of the M271 (at Totton), take A35 direction Lyndhurst. Campsite just outside Ashurst to the left, directly after the hotel signposted on the left side.

💬 Campsite is located in the New Forest nature reserve. Spacious pitches, including between large trees. Good, centrally located facilities. Horses wander around freely.

📷 N 50°53'24'' W 1°31'44''
www.eurocampings.co.uk/102877

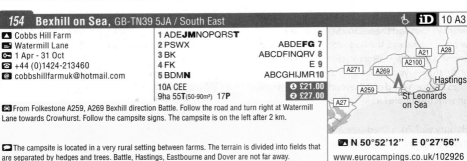

154 Bexhill on Sea, GB-TN39 5JA / South East

♿ **iD** 10 A3

- ▲ Cobbs Hill Farm
- ▤ Watermill Lane
- ☰ 1 Apr - 31 Oct
- ☎ +44 (0)1424-213460
- @ cobbshillfarmuk@hotmail.com

1 ADE**JMN**OPQRS**T**		6
2 PSWX	ABDE**FG**	7
3 BK	ABCDFINQRV	8
4 FK	E	9
5 BDM**N**	ABCGHIJMR	10

10A CEE
❶ £21.00
❷ £27.00
9ha 55**T**(50-90m²) 17**P**

🚗 From Folkestone A259, A269 Bexhill direction Battle. Follow the road and turn right at Watermill Lane towards Crowhurst. Follow the campsite signs. The campsite is on the left after 2 km.

💬 The campsite is located in a very rural setting between farms. The terrain is divided into fields that are separated by hedges and trees. Battle, Hastings, Eastbourne and Dover are not far away.

📷 N 50°52'12'' E 0°27'56''
www.eurocampings.co.uk/102926

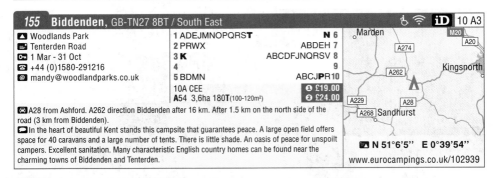

155 Biddenden, GB-TN27 8BT / South East

♿ 🛜 **iD** 10 A3

- ▲ Woodlands Park
- ▤ Tenterden Road
- ☰ 1 Mar - 31 Oct
- ☎ +44 (0)1580-291216
- @ mandy@woodlandparks.co.uk

1 ADEJMNOPQRS**T**	**N**	6
2 PRWX	ABDEH	7
3 **K**	ABCDFJNQRSV	8
4		9
5 BDM**N**	ABCJ**P**R	10

10A CEE
❶ £19.00
❷ £24.00
A54 3,6ha 180**T**(100-120m²)

🚗 A28 from Ashford. A262 direction Biddenden after 16 km. After 1.5 km on the north side of the road (3 km from Biddenden).

💬 In the heart of beautiful Kent stands this campsite that guarantees peace. A large open field offers space for 40 caravans and a large number of tents. There is little shade. An oasis of peace for unspoilt campers. Excellent sanitation. Many characteristic English country homes can be found near the charming towns of Biddenden and Tenterden.

📷 N 51°6'5'' E 0°39'54''
www.eurocampings.co.uk/102939

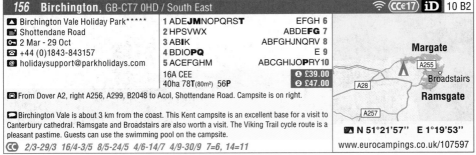

156 Birchington, GB-CT7 0HD / South East

🛜 (CC€17) **iD** 10 B2

- ▲ Birchington Vale Holiday Park*****
- ▤ Shottendane Road
- ☰ 2 Mar - 29 Oct
- ☎ +44 (0)1843-843157
- @ holidaysupport@parkholidays.com

1 ADE**JMN**OPQRS**T**	EFGH	6
2 HPSVWX	ABDE**FG**	7
3 AB**I**K	ABFGHJNQRV	8
4 BDIO**PQ**	E	9
5 ACEFGHM	ABCGHIJO**P**RY	10

16A CEE
❶ £39.00
❷ £47.00
40ha 78**T**(80m²) 56**P**

🚗 From Dover A2, right A256, A299, B2048 to Acol, Shottendane Road. Campsite is on right.

💬 Birchington Vale is about 3 km from the coast. This Kent campsite is an excellent base for a visit to Canterbury cathedral. Ramsgate and Broadstairs are also worth a visit. The Viking Trail cycle route is a pleasant pastime. Guests can use the swimming pool on the campsite.

(CC) 2/3-29/3 16/4-3/5 8/5-24/5 4/6-14/7 4/9-30/9 7=6, 14=11

📷 N 51°21'57'' E 1°19'53''
www.eurocampings.co.uk/107597

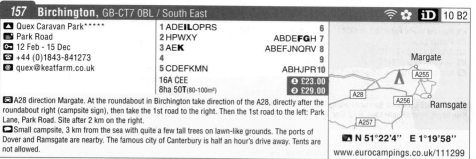

157 Birchington, GB-CT7 0BL / South East

🏕 Quex Caravan Park*****
🏠 Park Road
📅 12 Feb - 15 Dec
☎ +44 (0)1843-841273
@ quex@keatfarm.co.uk

1	ADEILOPRS		6
2	HPWXY		7
3	AEK	ABDEFGH	7
4		ABEFJNQRV	8
5	CDEFKMN		9
		ABHJPR	10
16A	CEE	❶ £23.00	
	8ha 50T(80-100m²)	❷ £29.00	

🗺 10 B2

A28 direction Margate. At the roundabout in Birchington take direction of the A28, directly after the roundabout right (campsite sign), then take the 1st road to the right. Then the 1st road to the left: Park Lane, Park Road. Site after 2 km on the right.

💬 Small campsite, 3 km from the sea with quite a few tall trees on lawn-like grounds. The ports of Dover and Ramsgate are nearby. The famous city of Canterbury is half an hour's drive away. Tents are not allowed.

🧭 N 51°22'4'' E 1°19'58''

www.eurocampings.co.uk/111299

158 Bletchingdon/Oxford, GB-OX5 3DR / South East

🏕 Diamond Farm C.& C. Park****
🏠 Islip Road
📅 1 Jan - 31 Dec
☎ +44 (0)1869-350909
@ warden@diamondpark.co.uk

1	AJMNOQRT	ABN	6
2	AFGOPRSVWXY	ABDEFGH	7
3	AEK	ABCDFJNQR	8
4	IOPQ		9
5	BDFHKMN	ABFGHKMPST	10
16A	CEE	❶ £22.00	
	A71 1,4ha 55T(80-100m²)	❷ £28.00	

🗺 9 B2

North of Oxford on the A34 take the B4027 and then follow the signs.

💬 This small rural family campsite has a heated outdoor swimming pool. Some pitches are marked out. During the high season the pub is open and serves snacks. Neat toilet facilities. Excellent location for a visit to Oxford, Blenheim Palace and the Cotswolds.

🧭 N 51°50'56'' W 1°15'19''

www.eurocampings.co.uk/102869

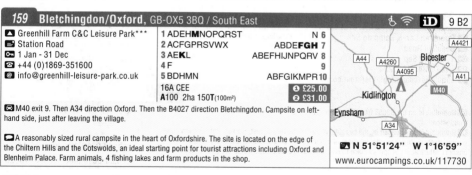

159 Bletchingdon/Oxford, GB-OX5 3BQ / South East

🏕 Greenhill Farm C&C Leisure Park***
🏠 Station Road
📅 1 Jan - 31 Dec
☎ +44 (0)1869-351600
@ info@greenhill-leisure-park.co.uk

1	ADEHMNOPQRST	N	6
2	ACFGPRSVWX	ABDEFGH	7
3	AEKL	ABEFHIJNPQRV	8
4	F		9
5	BDHMN	ABFGIKMPR	10
16A	CEE	❶ £25.00	
	A100 2ha 150T(100m²)	❷ £31.00	

🗺 9 B2

M40 exit 9. Then A34 direction Oxford. Then the B4027 direction Bletchingdon. Campsite on left-hand side, just after leaving the village.

💬 A reasonably sized rural campsite in the heart of Oxfordshire. The site is located on the edge of the Chiltern Hills and the Cotswolds, an ideal starting point for tourist attractions including Oxford and Blenheim Palace. Farm animals, 4 fishing lakes and farm products in the shop.

🧭 N 51°51'24'' W 1°16'59''

www.eurocampings.co.uk/117730

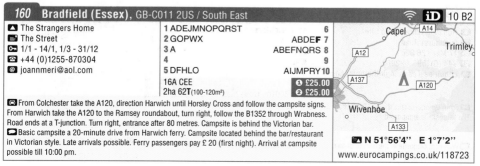

160 Bradfield (Essex), GB-C011 2US / South East

🏕 The Strangers Home
🏠 The Street
📅 1/1 - 14/1, 1/3 - 31/12
☎ +44 (0)1255-870304
@ joannmeri@aol.com

1	ADEJMNOPQRST		6
2	GOPWX	ABDEF	7
3	A	ABEFNQRS	8
4			9
5	DFHLO	AIJMPRY	10
16A	CEE	❶ £25.00	
	2ha 62T(100-120m²)	❷ £25.00	

🗺 10 B2

From Colchester take the A120, direction Harwich until Horsley Cross and follow the campsite signs. From Harwich take the A120 to the Ramsey roundabout, turn right, follow the B1352 through Wrabness. Road ends at a T-junction. Turn right, entrance after 80 metres. Campsite is behind the Victorian bar.

💬 Basic campsite a 20-minute drive from Harwich ferry. Campsite located behind the bar/restaurant in Victorian style. Late arrivals possible. Ferry passengers pay £ 20 (first night). Arrival at campsite possible till 10:00 pm.

🧭 N 51°56'4'' E 1°7'2''

www.eurocampings.co.uk/118723

United Kingdom

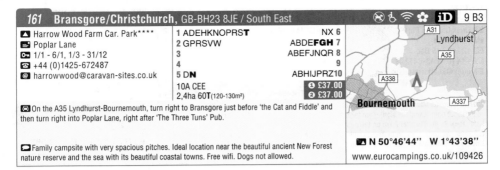

161 Bransgore/Christchurch, GB-BH23 8JE / South East 🌐 ♿ 📶 ⚙ **iD** 9 B3

▲ Harrow Wood Farm Car. Park****	1 ADEHKNOPRS**T**	NX 6
🏠 Poplar Lane	2 GPRSVW	ABDE**FGH** 7
📅 1/1 - 6/1, 1/3 - 31/12	3	ABEFJNQR 8
☎ +44 (0)1425-672487	4	9
@ harrowwood@caravan-sites.co.uk	5 D**N**	ABHIJPRZ10
	10A CEE	❶ £37.00
	2,4ha 60**T**(120-130m²)	❷ £37.00

🔲 On the A35 Lyndhurst-Bournemouth, turn right to Bransgore just before 'the Cat and Fiddle' and then turn right into Poplar Lane, right after 'The Three Tuns' Pub.

💬 Family campsite with very spacious pitches. Ideal location near the beautiful ancient New Forest nature reserve and the sea with its beautiful coastal towns. Free wifi. Dogs not allowed.

📍 N 50°46'44'' W 1°43'38''
www.eurocampings.co.uk/109426

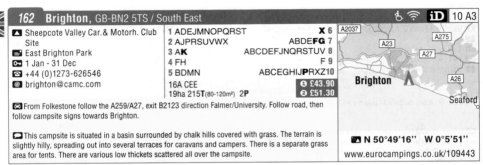

162 Brighton, GB-BN2 5TS / South East ♿ 📶 **iD** 10 A3

▲ Sheepcote Valley Car.& Motorh. Club Site	1 ADEJMNOPQRST	X 6
🏠 East Brighton Park	2 AJPRSUVWX	ABDE**FG** 7
	3 A**K**	ABCDEFJNQRSTUV 8
📅 1 Jan - 31 Dec	4 FH	F 9
☎ +44 (0)1273-626546	5 BDMN	ABCEGHIJ**P**RXZ10
@ brighton@camc.com	16A CEE	❶ £43.90
	19ha 215**T**(80-120m²) 2**P**	❷ £51.30

🔲 From Folkestone follow the A259/A27, exit B2123 direction Falmer/University. Follow road, then follow campsite signs towards Brighton.

💬 This campsite is situated in a basin surrounded by chalk hills covered with grass. The terrain is slightly hilly, spreading out into several terraces for caravans and campers. There is a separate grass area for tents. There are various low thickets scattered all over the campsite.

📍 N 50°49'16'' W 0°5'51''
www.eurocampings.co.uk/109443

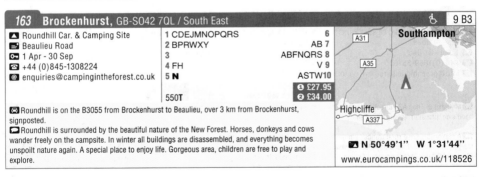

163 Brockenhurst, GB-SO42 7QL / South East ♿ 9 B3

▲ Roundhill Car. & Camping Site	1 CDEJMNOPQRS	6
🏠 Beaulieu Road	2 BPRWXY	AB 7
📅 1 Apr - 30 Sep	3	ABFNQRS 8
☎ +44 (0)845-1308224	4 FH	V 9
@ enquiries@campingintheforest.co.uk	5 **N**	ASTW10
	550**T**	❶ £27.95
		❷ £34.00

🔲 Roundhill is on the B3055 from Brockenhurst to Beaulieu, over 3 km from Brockenhurst, signposted.

💬 Roundhill is surrounded by the beautiful nature of the New Forest. Horses, donkeys and cows wander freely on the campsite. In winter all buildings are disassembled, and everything becomes unspoilt nature again. A special place to enjoy life. Gorgeous area, children are free to play and explore.

📍 N 50°49'1'' W 1°31'44''
www.eurocampings.co.uk/118526

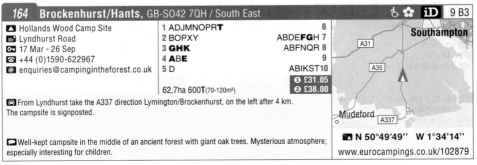

164 Brockenhurst/Hants, GB-SO42 7QH / South East ♿ ⚙ **iD** 9 B3

▲ Hollands Wood Camp Site	1 ADJMNOPR**T**	6
🏠 Lyndhurst Road	2 BOPXY	ABDE**FGH** 7
📅 17 Mar - 26 Sep	3 **GHK**	ABFNQR 8
☎ +44 (0)1590-622967	4 A**B**E	9
@ enquiries@campingintheforest.co.uk	5 D	ABIKST10
	62,7ha 600**T**(70-120m²)	❶ £31.05
		❷ £38.00

🔲 From Lyndhurst take the A337 direction Lymington/Brockenhurst, on the left after 4 km. The campsite is signposted.

💬 Well-kept campsite in the middle of an ancient forest with giant oak trees. Mysterious atmosphere; especially interesting for children.

📍 N 50°49'49'' W 1°34'14''
www.eurocampings.co.uk/102879

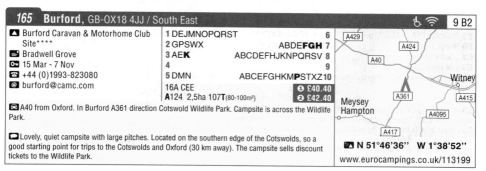

165 Burford, GB-OX18 4JJ / South East

♿ 📶 9 B2

- ▲ Burford Caravan & Motorhome Club Site★★★★
- ▤ Bradwell Grove
- ☛ 15 Mar - 7 Nov
- ☎ +44 (0)1993-823080
- @ burford@camc.com

1 DEJMNOPQRST			6
2 GPSWX		ABDE**FGH**	7
3 AE**K**	ABCDEFHJKNPQRSV		8
4			9
5 DMN	ABCEFGHKM**P**STXZ		10

16A CEE   **➊ £40.40**
A124   2,5ha   107**T**(80-100m²)   **➋ £42.40**

🚗 A40 from Oxford. In Burford A361 direction Cotswold Wildlife Park. Campsite is across the Wildlife Park.

💬 Lovely, quiet campsite with large pitches. Located on the southern edge of the Cotswolds, so a good starting point for trips to the Cotswolds and Oxford (30 km away). The campsite sells discount tickets to the Wildlife Park.

📷 **N 51°46'36'' W 1°38'52''**

www.eurocampings.co.uk/113199

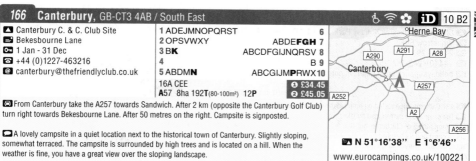

166 Canterbury, GB-CT3 4AB / South East

♿ 📶 ✿ **iD** 10 B2

- ▲ Canterbury C. & C. Club Site
- ▤ Bekesbourne Lane
- ☛ 1 Jan - 31 Dec
- ☎ +44 (0)1227-463216
- @ canterbury@thefriendlyclub.co.uk

1 ADEJMNOPQRST			6
2 OPSVWXY		ABDE**FGH**	7
3 B**K**	ABCDFGIJNQRSV		8
4		B	9
5 ABDM**N**	ABCGIJM**P**RWX		10

16A CEE   **➊ £34.45**
A57   8ha   192**T**(80-100m²)   12**P**   **➋ £45.05**

🚗 From Canterbury take the A257 towards Sandwich. After 2 km (opposite the Canterbury Golf Club) turn right towards Bekesbourne Lane. After 50 metres on the right. Campsite is signposted.

💬 A lovely campsite in a quiet location next to the historical town of Canterbury. Slightly sloping, somewhat terraced. The campsite is surrounded by high trees and is located on a hill. When the weather is fine, you have a great view over the sloping landscape.

📷 **N 51°16'38'' E 1°6'46''**

www.eurocampings.co.uk/100221

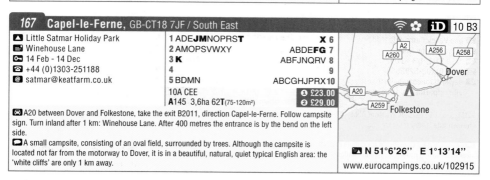

167 Capel-le-Ferne, GB-CT18 7JF / South East

📶 ✿ **iD** 10 B3

- ▲ Little Satmar Holiday Park
- ▤ Winehouse Lane
- ☛ 14 Feb - 14 Dec
- ☎ +44 (0)1303-251188
- @ satmar@keatfarm.co.uk

1 ADE**JM**NOPRS**T**		X	6
2 AMOPSVWXY		ABDE**FG**	7
3 **K**	ABFJNQRV		8
4			9
5 BDMN	ABCGHJPRX		10

10A CEE   **➊ £23.00**
A145   3,6ha   62**T**(75-120m²)   **➋ £29.00**

🚗 A20 between Dover and Folkestone, take the exit B2011, direction Capel-le-Ferne. Follow campsite sign. Turn inland after 1 km: Winehouse Lane. After 400 metres the entrance is by the bend on the left side.

💬 A small campsite, consisting of an oval field, surrounded by trees. Although the campsite is located not far from the motorway to Dover, it is in a beautiful, natural, quiet typical English area: the 'white cliffs' are only 1 km away.

📷 **N 51°6'26'' E 1°13'14''**

www.eurocampings.co.uk/102915

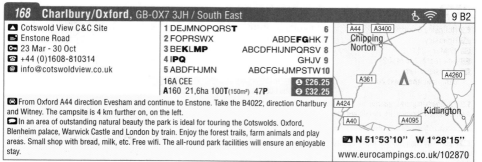

168 Charlbury/Oxford, GB-OX7 3JH / South East

♿ 📶 9 B2

- ▲ Cotswold View C&C Site
- ▤ Enstone Road
- ☛ 23 Mar - 30 Oct
- ☎ +44 (0)1608-810314
- @ info@cotswoldview.co.uk

1 DEJMNOPQRS**T**			6
2 FOPRSWX		ABDE**FG**HK	7
3 BE**KLMP**	ABCDFHIJNPQRSV		8
4 I**PQ**		GHJV	9
5 ABDFHJMN	ABCFGHJM**P**STW		10

16A CEE   **➊ £26.25**
A160   21,6ha   100**T**(150m²)   47**P**   **➋ £32.25**

🚗 From Oxford A44 direction Evesham and continue to Enstone. Take the B4022, direction Charlbury and Witney. The campsite is 4 km further on, on the left.

💬 In an area of outstanding natural beauty the park is ideal for touring the Cotswolds. Oxford, Blenheim palace, Warwick Castle and London by train. Enjoy the forest trails, farm animals and play areas. Small shop with bread, milk, etc. Free wifi. The all-round park facilities will ensure an enjoyable stay.

📷 **N 51°53'10'' W 1°28'15''**

www.eurocampings.co.uk/102870

United Kingdom

United Kingdom

169 Chertsey/London, GB-KT16 8JX / South East

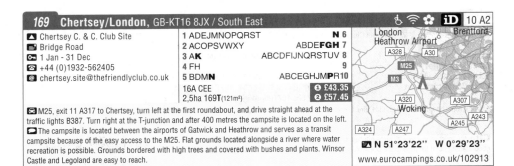

▲ Chertsey C. & C. Club Site	1 ADEJMNOPQRST	**N** 6	
🏠 Bridge Road	2 ACOPSVWXY	ABDE**FGH** 7	
📅 1 Jan - 31 Dec	3 A**K**	ABCDFIJNQRSTUV 8	
☎ +44 (0)1932-562405	4 FH	9	
@ chertsey.site@thefriendlyclub.co.uk	5 BDM**N**	ABCEGHJM**P**R10	
	16A CEE	❶ £43.35	
	2,5ha 169**T**(121m²)	❷ £57.45	

🚗 M25, exit 11 A317 to Chertsey, turn left at the first roundabout, and drive straight ahead at the traffic lights B387. Turn right at the T-junction and after 400 metres the campsite is located on the left.
💬 The campsite is located between the airports of Gatwick and Heathrow and serves as a transit campsite because of the easy access to the M25. Flat grounds located alongside a river where water recreation is possible. Grounds bordered with high trees and covered with bushes and plants. Winsor Castle and Legoland are easy to reach.

🗺 N 51°23'22'' W 0°29'23''
www.eurocampings.co.uk/102913

10 A2

---

170 Chichester, GB-PO20 1QH / South East

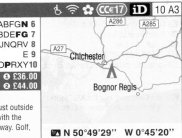

▲ Chichester Lakeside Holiday Park	1 ADE**JM**NOPQRS**T**	ABFG**N** 6	
🏠 Vinnetrow Road	2 APWXY	ABDE**FG** 7	
📅 2 Mar - 29 Oct	3 AE**K**	ABFJNQRV 8	
☎ +44 (0)1243-787715	4 BDFHIO**PQ**	E 9	
@ holidaysupport@parkholidays.com	5 ABDFGHLM	ABCHIO**PR**XY10	
	16A CEE	❶ £36.00	
	1,2ha 340**T**(100m²) 113**P**	❷ £44.00	

🚗 A27 Campsite signposted on both sides near Chichester.
💬 The campsite is surrounded by lakes where you can fish if you buy a permit. It is also just outside the historic town of Chichester but also in beautiful Sussex countryside. A lovely location with the south coast and its beaches or the traditional town of Bognor Regis just a few kilometres away. Golf, zoos, castles: everything is close by.

©© 2/3-29/3 16/4-3/5 8/5-24/5 4/6-27/6 2/7-15/7 4/9-30/9 7=6, 14=11

🗺 N 50°49'29'' W 0°45'20''
www.eurocampings.co.uk/118655

10 A3

---

171 Chingford/London, GB-E4 7RA / South East

▲ Lee Valley Camp Site*****	1 ADE**JM**NOPQRST	6	
🏠 Sewardstone Road	2 AOPSVWXY	ABDE**FGH** 7	
📅 1/1 - 31/1, 1/3 - 31/12	3 A	ABEFJNQRSTU 8	
☎ +44 (0)208-5295689	4 FH	F 9	
@ sewardstonecampsite@	5 ACDM**N**	ABFGHJMPRXZ10	
vibrantpartnerships.co.uk	10A CEE	❶ £31.00	
	5ha 92**T**(80-130m²) 63**P**	❷ £43.00	

🚗 M25, exit 26 towards Waltham Abbey. Then take the A112 in the direction of Chelmsford. The campsite is clearly signposted.

💬 Good, pleasant campsite in the middle of a natural area, with spacious pitches and all amenities. Ideal as a starting point for a visit to London. Day tickets for London and a bus stop on the campsite (1-hour drive). Also log cabins for rent.

🗺 N 51°39'17'' W 0°0'22''
www.eurocampings.co.uk/102922

10 A2

---

172 Christchurch, GB-BH23 7EQ / South East

▲ Holmsley Campsite	1 ADEJMNORST	6	
🏠 Holmsley	2 BPRSWXY	ABDE**FG** 7	
📅 17 Mar - 31 Oct	3 A	ABFGIJNQRS 8	
☎ +44 (0)1425-674502	4 FH	9	
@ holmsley.site@	5 ACDF**N**	ABGIJR10	
campingintheforest.co.uk	10A CEE	❶ £35.75	
	A60 36ha 600**T**(70-80m²)	❷ £41.80	

🚗 A35 Southampton-Christchurch, about 14 km after Lyndhurst turn right direction Bransgore. After 1 km direction Thorney Hill, then follow campsite signs.

💬 Real family campsite with plenty of space on the edge of the New Forest. Campsite is on a former airfield from World War II.

🗺 N 50°47'28'' W 1°41'43''
www.eurocampings.co.uk/102838

9 B3

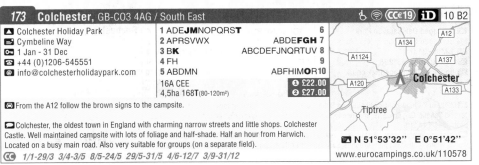

173 Colchester, GB-CO3 4AG / South East
🔥 ᐁ (CC19) **iD** 10 B2

- 🏔 Colchester Holiday Park
- 🏠 Cymbeline Way
- ⊙ 1 Jan - 31 Dec
- ☎ +44 (0)1206-545551
- @ info@colchesterholidaypark.com

1 ADE**JM**NOPQRST		6
2 APRSVWX	ABDE**FGH**	7
3 B**K**	ABCDEFJNQRTUV	8
4 FH		9
5 ABDMN	ABFHIM**OR**	10
16A CEE		❶ £22.00
4,5ha 168**T**(80-120m²)		❷ £27.00

🚗 From the A12 follow the brown signs to the campsite.

💬 Colchester, the oldest town in England with charming narrow streets and little shops. Colchester Castle. Well maintained campsite with lots of foliage and half-shade. Half an hour from Harwich. Located on a busy main road. Also very suitable for groups (on a separate field).

(CC) 1/1-29/3 3/4-3/5 8/5-24/5 29/5-31/5 4/6-12/7 3/9-31/12

▰ N 51°53'32'' E 0°51'42''
www.eurocampings.co.uk/110578

174 Crowborough, GB-TN6 2TN / South East
🔥 ᐁ **iD** 10 A3

- 🏔 C. & C. Club Site Crowborough
- 🏠 Eridge Road
- ⊙ 29 Mar - 5 Nov
- ☎ +44 (0)1892-664021
- @ crowborough.site@
  thefriendlyclub.co.uk

1 ACDE**JM**NOPQRST	**E**	6
2 OPRSTUVWX	ABDE**FGH**	7
3 KL	ABCDEFIJNQRSV	8
4 FHI	**B**	9
5 BDM**N**	ABHIJM**ORW**	10
16A CEE		❶ £37.75
A184 3ha 71**T**(50-120m²) 12**P**		❷ £49.90

🚗 On the A26, on the north side of Crowborough. Follow the sign 'Leisure Centre'.

💬 A beautiful campsite adjacent to Ashdown Forest in Sussex. London is easily accessible from this campsite. Membership of the Camping and Caravanning Club gives a substantial discount. Next to the campsite are free indoor play areas and an indoor pool with a discount for campsite guests.

▰ N 51°3'46'' E 0°10'6''
www.eurocampings.co.uk/108854

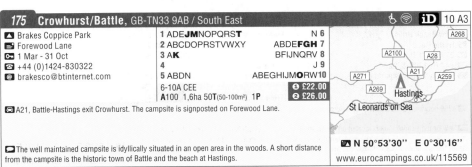

175 Crowhurst/Battle, GB-TN33 9AB / South East
🔥 ᐁ **iD** 10 A3

- 🏔 Brakes Coppice Park
- 🏠 Forewood Lane
- ⊙ 1 Mar - 31 Oct
- ☎ +44 (0)1424-830322
- @ brakesco@btinternet.com

1 ADE**JM**NOPQRST	**N**	6
2 ABCDOPRSTVWXY	ABDE**FGH**	7
3 A**K**	BFIJNQRV	8
4	**J**	9
5 ABDN	ABEGHIJM**ORW**	10
6-10A CEE		❶ £22.00
A100 1,6ha 50**T**(50-100m²) 1**P**		❷ £26.00

🚗 A21, Battle-Hastings exit Crowhurst. The campsite is signposted on Forewood Lane.

💬 The well maintained campsite is idyllically situated in an open area in the woods. A short distance from the campsite is the historic town of Battle and the beach at Hastings.

▰ N 50°53'30'' E 0°30'16''
www.eurocampings.co.uk/115569

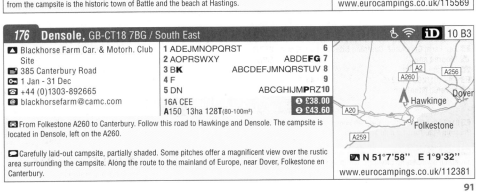

176 Densole, GB-CT18 7BG / South East
🔥 ᐁ **iD** 10 B3

- 🏔 Blackhorse Farm Car. & Motorh. Club Site
- 🏠 385 Canterbury Road
- ⊙ 1 Jan - 31 Dec
- ☎ +44 (0)1303-892665
- @ blackhorsefarm@camc.com

1 ADE**JM**NOPQRST		6
2 AOPRSWXY	ABDE**FG**	7
3 B**K**	ABCDEFJMNQRSTUV	8
4 F		9
5 DN	ABCGHIJM**PRZ** 10
16A CEE		❶ £38.00
A150 13ha 128**T**(80-100m²)		❷ £43.60

🚗 From Folkestone A260 to Canterbury. Follow this road to Hawkinge and Densole. The campsite is located in Densole, left on the A260.

💬 Carefully laid-out campsite, partially shaded. Some pitches offer a magnificent view over the rustic area surrounding the campsite. Along the route to the mainland of Europe, near Dover, Folkestone en Canterbury.

▰ N 51°7'58'' E 1°9'32''
www.eurocampings.co.uk/112381

United Kingdom

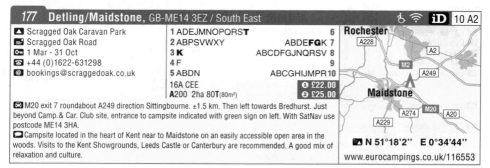

177 Detling/Maidstone, GB-ME14 3EZ / South East
  🚲 📶 **iD** 10 A2

- 🏕 Scragged Oak Caravan Park
- 🏠 Scragged Oak Road
- 📅 1 Mar - 31 Oct
- ☎ +44 (0)1622-631298
- @ bookings@scraggedoak.co.uk

1 ADEJMNOPQRS**T**	6
2 ABPSVWXY	ABDE**FG**K 7
3 **K**	ABCDFGJNQRSV 8
4 F	9
5 ABDN	ABCGHIJMPR 10
16A CEE	❶ £22.00
A200 2ha 80T(80m²)	❷ £25.00

🚗 M20 exit 7 roundabout A249 direction Sittingbourne. ±1.5 km. Then left towards Bredhurst. Just beyond Camp.& Car. Club site, entrance to campsite indicated with green sign on left. With SatNav use postcode ME14 3HA.

💬 Campsite located in the heart of Kent near to Maidstone on an easily accessible open area in the woods. Visits to the Kent Showgrounds, Leeds Castle or Canterbury are recommended. A good mix of relaxation and culture.

📍 N 51°18'2'' E 0°34'44''

www.eurocampings.co.uk/116553

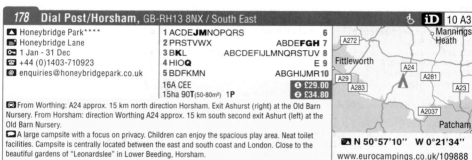

178 Dial Post/Horsham, GB-RH13 8NX / South East
  🚲 **iD** 10 A3

- 🏕 Honeybridge Park****
- 🏠 Honeybridge Lane
- 📅 1 Jan - 31 Dec
- ☎ +44 (0)1403-710923
- @ enquiries@honeybridgepark.co.uk

1 ACDE**JM**NOPQRS	6
2 PRSTVWX	ABDE**FGH** 7
3 B**KL**	ABCDEFIJLMNQRSTUV 8
4 HIO**Q**	E 9
5 BDFKMN	ABGHIJMR 10
16A CEE	❶ £29.00
15ha 90T(50-80m²) 1P	❷ £34.80

🚗 From Worthing: A24 approx. 15 km north direction Horsham. Exit Ashurst (right) at the Old Barn Nursery. From Horsham: direction Worthing A24 approx. 15 km south second exit Ashurt (left) at the Old Barn Nursery.

💬 A large campsite with a focus on privacy. Children can enjoy the spacious play area. Neat toilet facilities. Campsite is centrally located between the east and south coast and London. Close to the beautiful gardens of "Leonardslee" in Lower Beeding, Horsham.

📍 N 50°57'10'' W 0°21'34''

www.eurocampings.co.uk/109888

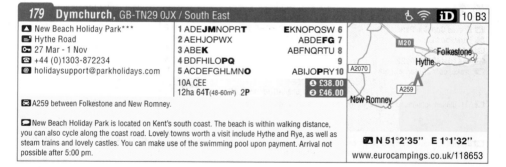

179 Dymchurch, GB-TN29 0JX / South East
  🚲 📶 **iD** 10 B3

- 🏕 New Beach Holiday Park***
- 🏠 Hythe Road
- 📅 27 Mar - 1 Nov
- ☎ +44 (0)1303-872234
- @ holidaysupport@parkholidays.com

1 ADE**JM**NOPRT	EKNOPQSW 6
2 AEHJOPWX	ABDE**FG** 7
3 ABE**K**	ABFNQRTU 8
4 BDFHILO**PQ**	9
5 ACDEFGHLMNO	ABIJOP**R**Y 10
10A CEE	❶ £38.00
12ha 64T(48-60m²) 2P	❷ £46.00

🚗 A259 between Folkestone and New Romney.

💬 New Beach Holiday Park is located on Kent's south coast. The beach is within walking distance, you can also cycle along the coast road. Lovely towns worth a visit include Hythe and Rye, as well as steam trains and lovely castles. You can make use of the swimming pool upon payment. Arrival not possible after 5:00 pm.

📍 N 51°2'35'' E 1°1'32''

www.eurocampings.co.uk/118653

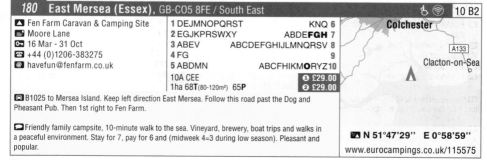

180 East Mersea (Essex), GB-CO5 8FE / South East
  🚲 📶 10 B2

- 🏕 Fen Farm Caravan & Camping Site
- 🏠 Moore Lane
- 📅 16 Mar - 31 Oct
- ☎ +44 (0)1206-383275
- @ havefun@fenfarm.co.uk

1 DEJMNOPQRST	KNQ 6
2 EGJKPRSWXY	ABDE**FGH** 7
3 ABEV	ABCDEFGHIJLMNQRSV 8
4 FG	9
5 ABDMN	ABCFHIKM**O**RYZ 10
10A CEE	❶ £29.00
1ha 68T(80-120m²) 65P	❷ £29.00

🚗 B1025 to Mersea Island. Keep left direction East Mersea. Follow this road past the Dog and Pheasant Pub. Then 1st right to Fen Farm.

💬 Friendly family campsite, 10-minute walk to the sea. Vineyard, brewery, boat trips and walks in a peaceful environment. Stay for 7, pay for 6 (midweek 4=3 during low season). Pleasant and popular.

📍 N 51°47'29'' E 0°58'59''

www.eurocampings.co.uk/115575

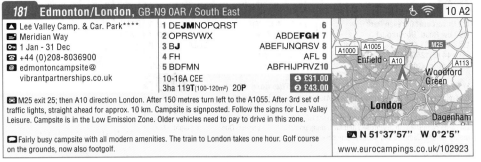

181 Edmonton/London, GB-N9 0AR / South East ♿ 🛜 | 10 A2

- ▲ Lee Valley Camp. & Car. Park****
- 🏕 Meridian Way
- 📅 1 Jan - 31 Dec
- ☎ +44 (0)208-8036900
- @ edmontoncampsite@ vibrantpartnerships.co.uk

1 DEJMNOPQRST	6
2 OPRSVWX	ABDEFGH 7
3 BJ	ABEFIJNQRSV 8
4 FH	AFL 9
5 BDFMN	ABFHIJPRVZ10
10-16A CEE	❶ £31.00
3ha 119T(100-120m²) 20P	❷ £43.00

🚗 M25 exit 25; then A10 direction London. After 150 metres turn left to the A1055. After 3rd set of traffic lights, straight ahead for approx. 10 km. Campsite is signposted. Follow the signs for Lee Valley Leisure. Campsite is in the Low Emission Zone. Older vehicles need to pay to drive in this zone.

💬 Fairly busy campsite with all modern amenities. The train to London takes one hour. Golf course on the grounds, now also footgolf.

📐 N 51°37'57'' W 0°2'5''

www.eurocampings.co.uk/102923

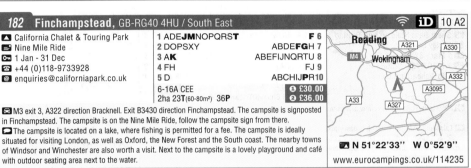

182 Finchampstead, GB-RG40 4HU / South East 🛜 iD | 10 A2

- ▲ California Chalet & Touring Park
- 🏕 Nine Mile Ride
- 📅 1 Jan - 31 Dec
- ☎ +44 (0)118-9733928
- @ enquiries@californiapark.co.uk

1 ADEJMNOPQRST	F 6
2 DOPSXY	ABDEFGH 7
3 AK	ABEFIJNQRTU 8
4 FH	FJ 9
5 D	ABCHIJPR10
6-16A CEE	❶ £30.00
2ha 23T(60-80m²) 36P	❷ £36.00

🚗 M3 exit 3, A322 direction Bracknell. Exit B3430 direction Finchampstead. The campsite is signposted in Finchampstead. The campsite is on the Nine Mile Ride, follow the campsite sign from there.

💬 The campsite is located on a lake, where fishing is permitted for a fee. The campsite is ideally situated for visiting London, as well as Oxford, the New Forest and the South coast. The nearby towns of Windsor and Winchester are also worth a visit. Next to the campsite is a lovely playground and café with outdoor seating area next to the water.

📐 N 51°22'33'' W 0°52'9''

www.eurocampings.co.uk/114235

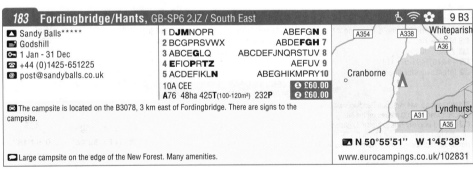

183 Fordingbridge/Hants, GB-SP6 2JZ / South East ♿ 🛜 ✿ | 9 B3

- ▲ Sandy Balls*****
- 🏕 Godshill
- 📅 1 Jan - 31 Dec
- ☎ +44 (0)1425-651225
- @ post@sandyballs.co.uk

1 DJMNOPR	ABEFGN 6
2 BCGPRSVWX	ABDEFGH 7
3 ABCEGLQ	ABCDEFJNQRSTUV 8
4 EFIOPRTZ	AEFUV 9
5 ACDEFIKLN	ABEGHIKMPRY10
10A CEE	❶ £60.00
A76 48ha 425T(100-120m²) 232P	❷ £60.00

🚗 The campsite is located on the B3078, 3 km east of Fordingbridge. There are signs to the campsite.

💬 Large campsite on the edge of the New Forest. Many amenities.

📐 N 50°55'51'' W 1°45'38''

www.eurocampings.co.uk/102831

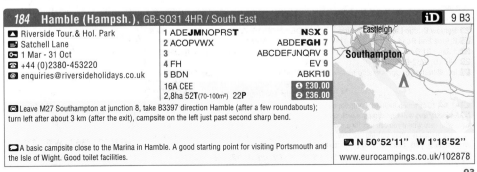

184 Hamble (Hampsh.), GB-SO31 4HR / South East iD | 9 B3

- ▲ Riverside Tour.& Hol. Park
- 🏕 Satchell Lane
- 📅 1 Mar - 31 Oct
- ☎ +44 (0)2380-453220
- @ enquiries@riversideholidays.co.uk

1 ADEJMNOPRST	NSX 6
2 ACOPVWX	ABDEFGH 7
3	ABCDEFJNQRV 8
4 FH	EV 9
5 BDN	ABKR10
16A CEE	❶ £30.00
2,8ha 52T(70-100m²) 22P	❷ £36.00

🚗 Leave M27 Southampton at junction 8, take B3397 direction Hamble (after a few roundabouts); turn left after about 3 km (after the exit), campsite on the left just past second sharp bend.

💬 A basic campsite close to the Marina in Hamble. A good starting point for visiting Portsmouth and the Isle of Wight. Good toilet facilities.

📐 N 50°52'11'' W 1°18'52''

www.eurocampings.co.uk/102878

United Kingdom

United Kingdom

185 Harwich/Essex, GB-CO12 3TZ / South East

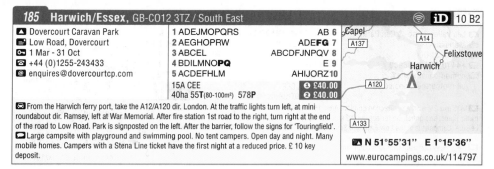

🏕 Dovercourt Caravan Park
📧 Low Road, Dovercourt
📅 1 Mar - 31 Oct
☎ +44 (0)1255-243433
@ enquires@dovercourtcp.com

1 ADEJMOPQRS	AB 6
2 AEGHOPRW	ADE**FG** 7
3 ABCEL	ABCDFJNPQV 8
4 BDILMNO**PQ**	E 9
5 ACDEFHLM	AHIJORZ 10
15A CEE	❶ £40.00
40ha 55**T**(80-100m²) 578**P**	❷ £40.00

🚗 From the Harwich ferry port, take the A12/A120 dir. London. At the traffic lights turn left, at mini roundabout dir. Ramsey, left at War Memorial. After fire station 1st road to the right, turn right at the end of the road to Low Road. Park is signposted on the left. After the barrier, follow the signs for 'Touringfield'.
💬 Large campsite with playground and swimming pool. No tent campers. Open day and night. Many mobile homes. Campers with a Stena Line ticket have the first night at a reduced price. £ 10 key deposit.

📷 N 51°55'31'' E 1°15'36''
www.eurocampings.co.uk/114797

186 Hastings, GB-TN35 5DX / South East

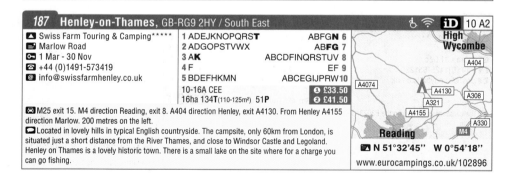

🏕 Shear Barn Holidays and Touring
📧 Barley Lane
📅 1 Mar - 31 Oct
☎ +44 (0)1424-423583
@ info@shearbarn.co.uk

1 ADE**JM**NOPQRS**T**	E**FG** 6
2 JMOPSVWX	ABDE**FG** 7
3 BC**K**	ABCDEFJNQRTV 8
4 FO**PQ**	J 9
5 DFHLN	ABHIJM**P**RW 10
16A CEE	❶ £33.00
A95 13,6ha 440**T**(160m²) 20**P**	❷ £33.00

🚗 A259 from Folkestone. Follow campsite signs in Hastings.

💬 This family campsite, which is easily accessible from Dover, is located on the eastern cliff in Hastings Country Park, with fantastic views and the town and the beach within walking distance. Excellent base for discovering Sussex, Kent or London. Discount on train journey to London via Tourist Information Centre.

📷 N 50°51'55'' E 0°36'42''
www.eurocampings.co.uk/100220

187 Henley-on-Thames, GB-RG9 2HY / South East

🏕 Swiss Farm Touring & Camping*****
📧 Marlow Road
📅 1 Mar - 30 Nov
☎ +44 (0)1491-573419
@ info@swissfarmhenley.co.uk

1 ADEJKNOPQRS**T**	ABF**GN** 6
2 ADGOPSTVWX	AB**FG** 7
3 A**K**	ABCDFINQRSTUV 8
4 F	EF 9
5 BDEFHKMN	ABCEGIJPRW 10
10-16A CEE	❶ £33.50
16ha 134**T**(110-125m²) 51**P**	❷ £41.50

🚗 M25 exit 15. M4 direction Reading, exit 8. A404 direction Henley, exit A4130. From Henley A4155 direction Marlow. 200 metres on the left.
💬 Located in lovely hills in typical English countryside. The campsite, only 60km from London, is situated just a short distance from the River Thames, and close to Windsor Castle and Legoland. Henley on Thames is a lovely historic town. There is a small lake on the site where for a charge you can go fishing.

📷 N 51°32'45'' W 0°54'18''
www.eurocampings.co.uk/102896

188 Henlow (Bedfordshire), GB-SG16 6LN / South East

🏕 Henlow Bridge Lakes & Riverside
📧 Bridge End Road
📅 1 Jan - 31 Dec
☎ +44 (0)1462-812645
@ info@henlowbridgelakes.co.uk

1 ADEILNOPQRS**T**	**N** 6
2 ACDOPRSVWX	ABDE**FG**HK 7
3 AB**KQ**	ABCDFHIJKNPQRST 8
4 O	BFJ 9
5 ABDMN**O**	ABFKMOSTVY 10
10A CEE	❶ £32.00
A75 16ha 163**T**(121m²) 15**P**	❷ £40.00

🚗 A1 exit 10 direction Bedford. Campsite on the left on the 507 at the roundabout in Henlow.
💬 A friendly and well kept campsite with several fields. Heated toilet block with wifi. There are several lakes with carp where you can fish for a charge. London King's Cross station is just 30 minutes by train, the station is within walking distance. Good starting point for trips out to Bedford, Cambridge or Woburn Safari Park. Suitable for larger motorhomes.

ⓒⓒ 3/4-3/5 7/5-9/5 14/5-17/5 22/5-24/5 29/5-14/7 4/9-31/12 7=6, 14=11

📷 N 52°1'36'' W 0°16'9''
www.eurocampings.co.uk/122240

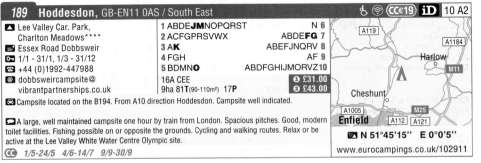

189 Hoddesdon, GB-EN11 0AS / South East
     (CC€19) iD 10 A2

- ▲ Lee Valley Car. Park, Charlton Meadows****
- ▤ Essex Road Dobbsweir
- ☀ 1/1 - 31/1, 1/3 - 31/12
- ☎ +44 (0)1992-447988
- @ dobbsweircampsite@ vibrantpartnerships.co.uk

1 ABDEJMNOPQRST		N	6
2 ACFGPRSVWX	ABDEFG		7
3 AK	ABEFJNQRV		8
4 FGH	AF		9
5 BDMNO	ABDFGHIJMORVZ		10
16A CEE		❶ £31.00	
9ha 81T(90-110m²)	17P	❷ £43.00	

🚉 Campsite located on the B194. From A10 direction Hoddesdon. Campsite well indicated.

💬 A large, well maintained campsite one hour by train from London. Spacious pitches. Good, modern toilet facilities. Fishing possible on or opposite the grounds. Cycling and walking routes. Relax or be active at the Lee Valley White Water Centre Olympic site.

CC 1/5-24/5 4/6-14/7 9/9-30/9

⯅ N 51°45'15'' E 0°0'5''

www.eurocampings.co.uk/102911

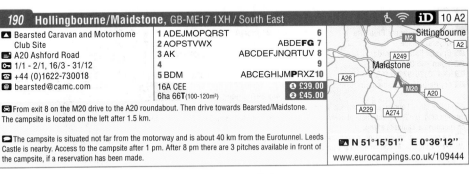

190 Hollingbourne/Maidstone, GB-ME17 1XH / South East
     iD 10 A2

- ▲ Bearsted Caravan and Motorhome Club Site
- ▤ A20 Ashford Road
- ☀ 1/1 - 2/1, 16/3 - 31/12
- ☎ +44 (0)1622-730018
- @ bearsted@camc.com

1 ADEJMOPQRST			6
2 AOPSTVWX	ABDEFG		7
3 AK	ABCDEFJNQRTUV		8
4			9
5 BDM	ABCEGHIJMPRXZ		10
16A CEE		❶ £39.00	
6ha 66T(100-120m²)		❷ £45.00	

🚉 From exit 8 on the M20 drive to the A20 roundabout. Then drive towards Bearsted/Maidstone. The campsite is located on the left after 1.5 km.

💬 The campsite is situated not far from the motorway and is about 40 km from the Eurotunnel. Leeds Castle is nearby. Access to the campsite after 1 pm. After 8 pm there are 3 pitches available in front of the campsite, if a reservation has been made.

⯅ N 51°15'51'' E 0°36'12''

www.eurocampings.co.uk/109444

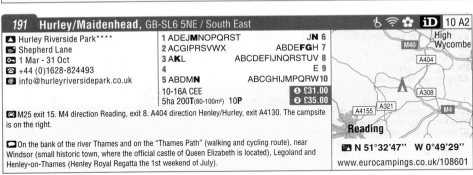

191 Hurley/Maidenhead, GB-SL6 5NE / South East
     iD 10 A2

- ▲ Hurley Riverside Park****
- ▤ Shepherd Lane
- ☀ 1 Mar - 31 Oct
- ☎ +44 (0)1628-824493
- @ info@hurleyriversidepark.co.uk

1 ADEJMNOPQRST		JN	6
2 ACGIPRSVWX	ABDEFGH		7
3 AKL	ABCDEFIJNQRSTUV		8
4	E		9
5 ABDMN	ABCGHIJMPQRW		10
10-16A CEE		❶ £31.00	
5ha 200T(80-100m²)	10P	❷ £35.00	

🚉 M25 exit 15. M4 direction Reading, exit 8. A404 direction Henley/Hurley, exit A4130. The campsite is on the right.

💬 On the bank of the river Thames and on the "Thames Path" (walking and cycling route), near Windsor (small historic town, where the official castle of Queen Elizabeth is located), Legoland and Henley-on-Thames (Henley Royal Regatta the 1st weekend of July).

⯅ N 51°32'47'' W 0°49'29''

www.eurocampings.co.uk/108601

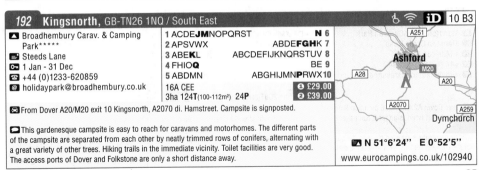

192 Kingsnorth, GB-TN26 1NQ / South East
     iD 10 B3

- ▲ Broadhembury Carav. & Camping Park*****
- ▤ Steeds Lane
- ☀ 1 Jan - 31 Dec
- ☎ +44 (0)1233-620859
- @ holidaypark@broadhembury.co.uk

1 ACDEJMNOPQRST		N	6
2 APSVWX	ABDEFGHK		7
3 ABEKL	ABCDEFIJKNQRSTUV		8
4 FHIOQ	BE		9
5 ABDMN	ABGHIJMNPRWX		10
16A CEE		❶ £29.00	
3ha 124T(100-112m²)	24P	❷ £39.00	

🚉 From Dover A20/M20 exit 10 Kingsnorth, A2070 di. Hamstreet. Campsite is signposted.

💬 This gardenesque campsite is easy to reach for caravans and motorhomes. The different parts of the campsite are separated from each other by neatly trimmed rows of conifers, alternating with a great variety of other trees. Hiking trails in the immediate vicinity. Toilet facilities are very good. The access ports of Dover and Folkstone are only a short distance away.

⯅ N 51°6'24'' E 0°52'5''

www.eurocampings.co.uk/102940

United Kingdom

193 Lingfield, GB-RH7 6LE / South East

🚳 📶 iD 10 A2

- ⛺ Long Acres Caravan & Camping****
- 🏠 New Chapel Road
- 📅 1 Jan - 31 Dec
- ☎ +44 (0)1342-833205
- @ info@longacrescamping.co.uk

1 ADE**JM**NOPQRS**T**		6	
2 APRSWX	ABDE**FG** 7		
3 **K**	ABCDE**FIJ**NQRV 8		
4	F 9		
5 DMN	ABCGIKM**P**RVW 10		
10-16A CEE			
A55 8ha 65**T**(70-100m²) 13**P**			

❶ £20.50
❷ £26.50

🚗 From M25 exit 6 by Godstone, A22 direction East Grinstead. After 9 km turn right, B2028 direction Lingfield. Not the B2029. The campsite is 500 metres further on.

💬 The campsite has an authentic rural atmosphere. Not far from Gatwick Airport. Good base for discovering the beautiful surroundings. It is also possible to visit London by train.

📍 N 51°10'1'' W 0°2'34''

www.eurocampings.co.uk/102914

194 London, GB-SE19 1UF / South East

🚳 📶 iD 10 A2

- ⛺ Car.& Motorhome Club Site Crystal Palace
- 🏠 Crystal Palace Parade
- 📅 1 Jan - 16 Dec
- ☎ +44 (0)20-87787155
- @ crystalpalace@camc.com

1 ADEJMNOPQRST		6	
2 OPRSTVWX	ABDE**FG** 7		
3	ABCDEFNQRSV 8		
4	9		
5 BDMN	ABCGHIJ**P**RXZ 10		
16A CEE			
A113 2,4ha 89**T**(35-100m²)			

❶ £43.70
❷ £51.50

🚗 M25 south of London, exit 7, Croydon. In Croydon A23 till exit A205 (Sth Circular Rd East; 10 km through city). Dir. Dover. Turn right at 'Harvester Pub'. At traffic lights turn right Sydenham Hill. Right on roundabout, campsite at end.

💬 In a gardenlike environment: sloping lawns for tents, paved pitches for caravans and motorhomes. Well-kept campsite. Motorhomes must be registered with Transport For London (free) due to Low Emission Zone.

📍 N 51°25'33'' W 0°4'24''

www.eurocampings.co.uk/102912

195 London/Abbey Wood, GB-SE2 0LS / South East

🚳 📶 iD 10 A2

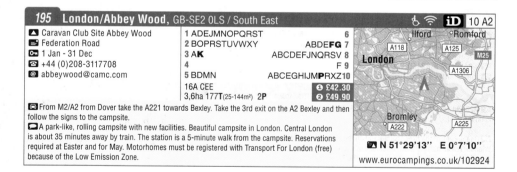

- ⛺ Caravan Club Site Abbey Wood
- 🏠 Federation Road
- 📅 1 Jan - 31 Dec
- ☎ +44 (0)208-3117708
- @ abbeywood@camc.com

1 ADEJMNOPQRST		6	
2 BOPRSTUVWXY	ABDE**FG** 7		
3 A**K**	ABCDEFJNQRSV 8		
4	F 9		
5 BDMN	ABCEGHIJM**P**RXZ 10		
16A CEE			
3,6ha 177**T**(25-144m²) 2**P**			

❶ £42.30
❷ £49.90

🚗 From M2/A2 from Dover take the A221 towards Bexley. Take the 3rd exit on the A2 Bexley and then follow the signs to the campsite.

💬 A park-like, rolling campsite with new facilities. Beautiful campsite in London. Central London is about 35 minutes away by train. The station is a 5-minute walk from the campsite. Reservations required at Easter and for May. Motorhomes must be registered with Transport For London (free) because of the Low Emission Zone.

📍 N 51°29'13'' E 0°7'10''

www.eurocampings.co.uk/102924

196 Manston/Ramsgate, GB-CT12 5AU / South East

📶 iD 10 B2

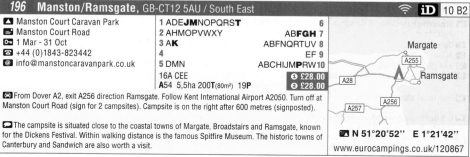

- ⛺ Manston Court Caravan Park
- 🏠 Manston Court Road
- 📅 1 Mar - 31 Oct
- ☎ +44 (0)1843-823442
- @ info@manstoncaravanpark.co.uk

1 ADE**JM**NOPQRS**T**		6	
2 AHMOPVWXY	AB**FGH** 7		
3 A**K**	ABFNQRTUV 8		
4	EF 9		
5 DMN	ABCHIJM**P**RW 10		
16A CEE			
A54 5,5ha 200**T**(80m²) 19**P**			

❶ £28.00
❷ £28.00

🚗 From Dover A2, exit A256 direction Ramsgate. Follow Kent International Airport A2050. Turn off at Manston Court Road (sign for 2 campsites). Campsite is on the right after 600 metres (signposted).

💬 The campsite is situated close to the coastal towns of Margate, Broadstairs and Ramsgate, known for the Dickens Festival. Within walking distance is the famous Spitfire Museum. The historic towns of Canterbury and Sandwich are also worth a visit.

📍 N 51°20'52'' E 1°21'42''

www.eurocampings.co.uk/120867

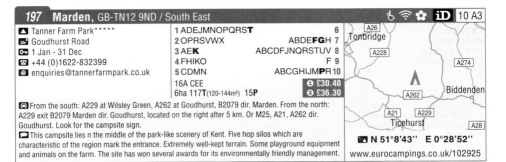

197 Marden, GB-TN12 9ND / South East

♿ 🌐 ⚙ **iD** 10 A3

- 🏕 Tanner Farm Park*****
- 🛣 Goudhurst Road
- 📅 1 Jan - 31 Dec
- ☎ +44 (0)1622-832399
- @ enquiries@tannerfarmpark.co.uk

1 ADEJMNOPQRS**T**			6
2 OPRSVWX		ABDE**FGH**	7
3 AE**K**	ABCDFJNQRSTUV		8
4 FHIKO		F	9
5 CDMN	ABCGHIJMP**R**		10

16A CEE — ❶ £30.40
6ha 117**T**(120-144m²) **15P** — ❷ £36.30

🚗 From the south: A229 at Wilsley Green, A262 at Goudhurst, B2079 dir. Marden. From the north: A229 exit B2079 Marden dir. Goudhurst, located on the right after 5 km. Or M25, A21, A262 dir. Goudhurst. Look for the campsite sign.

💬 This campsite lies n the middle of the park-like scenery of Kent. Five hop silos which are characteristic of the region mark the entrance. Extremely well-kept terrain. Some playground equipment and animals on the farm. The site has won several awards for its environmentally friendly management.

🧭 **N 51°8'43" E 0°28'52"**

www.eurocampings.co.uk/102925

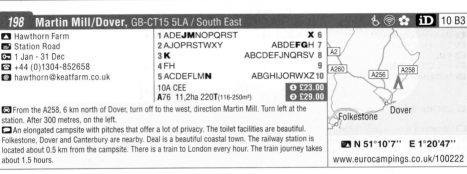

198 Martin Mill/Dover, GB-CT15 5LA / South East

♿ 🌐 ⚙ **iD** 10 B3

- 🏕 Hawthorn Farm
- 🛣 Station Road
- 📅 1 Jan - 31 Dec
- ☎ +44 (0)1304-852658
- @ hawthorn@keatfarm.co.uk

1 ADE**JM**NOPQRST		**X**	6
2 AJOPRSTWXY		ABDE**FGH**	7
3 **K**	ABCDEFJNQRSV		8
4 FH			9
5 ACDEFLM**N**	ABGHIJORWXZ		10

10A CEE — ❶ £23.00
A76 11,2ha 220**T**(116-250m²) — ❷ £29.00

🚗 From the A258, 6 km north of Dover, turn off to the west, direction Martin Mill. Turn left at the station. After 300 metres, on the left.

💬 An elongated campsite with pitches that offer a lot of privacy. The toilet facilities are beautiful. Folkestone, Dover and Canterbury are nearby. Deal is a beautiful coastal town. The railway station is located about 0.5 km from the campsite. There is a train to London every hour. The train journey takes about 1.5 hours.

🧭 **N 51°10'7" E 1°20'47"**

www.eurocampings.co.uk/100222

United Kingdom

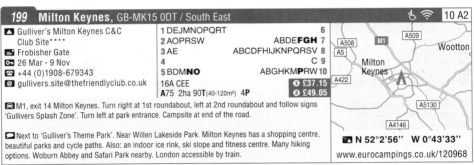

199 Milton Keynes, GB-MK15 0DT / South East

♿ 🌐 10 A2

- 🏕 Gulliver's Milton Keynes C&C Club Site****
- 🛣 Frobisher Gate
- 📅 26 Mar - 9 Nov
- ☎ +44 (0)1908-679343
- @ gullivers.site@thefriendlyclub.co.uk

1 DEJMNOPQRT			6
2 AOPRSW		ABDE**FGH**	7
3 AE	ABCDFHIJKNPQRSV		8
4		C	9
5 BDM**NO**	ABGHKMP**RW**		10

16A CEE — ❶ £37.15
A75 2ha 90**T**(40-120m²) **4P** — ❷ £49.05

🚗 M1, exit 14 Milton Keynes. Turn right at 1st roundabout, left at 2nd roundabout and follow signs 'Gullivers Splash Zone'. Turn left at park entrance. Campsite at end of the road.

💬 Next to 'Gulliver's Theme Park'. Near Willen Lakeside Park. Milton Keynes has a shopping centre, beautiful parks and cycle paths. Also: an indoor ice rink, ski slope and fitness centre. Many hiking options. Woburn Abbey and Safari Park nearby. London accessible by train.

🧭 **N 52°2'56" W 0°43'33"**

www.eurocampings.co.uk/120968

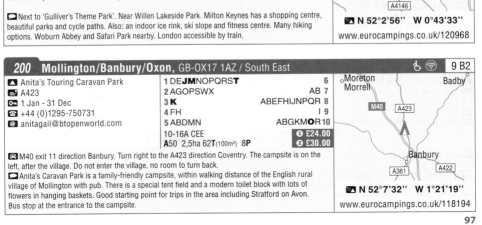

200 Mollington/Banbury/Oxon, GB-OX17 1AZ / South East

♿ 🌐 9 B2

- 🏕 Anita's Touring Caravan Park
- 🛣 A423
- 📅 1 Jan - 31 Dec
- ☎ +44 (0)1295-750731
- @ anitagail@btopenworld.com

1 DE**JM**NOPQRS**T**			6
2 AGOPSWX		AB	7
3 **K**	ABEFHIJNPQR		8
4 FH		I	9
5 ABDMN	ABGKM**O**R		10

10-16A CEE — ❶ £24.00
A50 2,5ha 62**T**(100m²) **8P** — ❷ £30.00

🚗 M40 exit 11 direction Banbury. Turn right to the A423 direction Coventry. The campsite is on the left, after the village. Do not enter the village, no room to turn back.

💬 Anita's Caravan Park is a family-friendly campsite, within walking distance of the English rural village of Mollington with pub. There is a special tent field and a modern toilet block with lots of flowers in hanging baskets. Good starting point for trips in the area including Stratford on Avon. Bus stop at the entrance to the campsite.

🧭 **N 52°7'32" W 1°21'19"**

www.eurocampings.co.uk/118194

201 Netley Abbey/Southampton, GB-SO31 8GD / South East   (CC€19) **iD** 9 B3

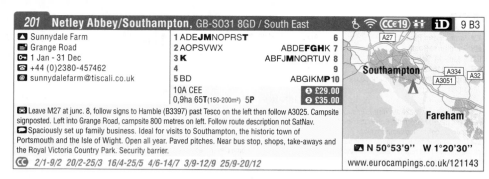

▲ Sunnydale Farm
🏠 Grange Road
📅 1 Jan - 31 Dec
☎ +44 (0)2380-457462
@ sunnydalefarm@tiscali.co.uk

1 ADE**JM**NOPRS**T**			6
2 AOPSVWX		ABDE**FGH**K	7
3 **K**		ABF**JM**NQRTUV	8
4			9
5 BD		ABGIKM**P**	10
10A CEE		❶ £29.00	
0,9ha 65T(150-200m²) 5**P**		❷ £35.00	

🗺 Leave M27 at junc. 8, follow signs to Hamble (B3397) past Tesco on the left then follow A3025. Campsite signposted. Left into Grange Road, campsite 800 metres on left. Follow route description not SatNav.
💬 Spaciously set up family business. Ideal for visits to Southampton, the historic town of Portsmouth and the Isle of Wight. Open all year. Paved pitches. Near bus stop, shops, take-aways and the Royal Victoria Country Park. Security barrier.
(CC) 2/1-9/2 20/2-25/3 16/4-25/5 4/6-14/7 3/9-12/9 25/9-20/12

Southampton   Fareham

📍 N 50°53'9'' W 1°20'30''
www.eurocampings.co.uk/121143

202 New Romney, GB-TN28 8UE / South East   (CC€17) **iD** 10 B3

▲ Marlie Holiday Park***
🏠 Dymchurch Road
📅 9 Mar - 29 Oct
☎ +44 (0)1797-363060
@ holidaysupport@parkholidays.com

1 ADE**JM**NOPQRT		EFG**X**	6
2 AHJOPW		ABDE**FG**	7
3 **K**		ABFIJNQRV	8
4 BDILO**PQ**		EY	9
5 ACDEFGHLM**O**		ABCHIJMO**P**RY	10
10A CEE		❶ £33.00	
40ha 71T(90m²) 49**P**		❷ £41.00	

🗺 A259 between Folkestone and Hastings.

💬 The campsite is conveniently located on the south Kent coast with a beach about 1 km away and between the towns of New Romney and Dymchurch. A site where guests have free use of the indoor swimming pool. You can visit zoos, castles and special trains in the area.
(CC) 9/3-29/3 16/4-3/5 8/5-24/5 4/6-14/7 4/9-30/9 7=6, 14=11

Hythe   New Romney

📍 N 50°59'37'' E 0°57'12''
www.eurocampings.co.uk/108627

203 Oxford, GB-OX1 4XG / South East   9 B2

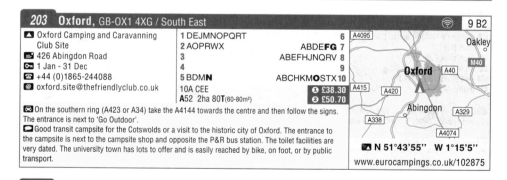

▲ Oxford Camping and Caravanning Club Site
🏠 426 Abingdon Road
📅 1 Jan - 31 Dec
☎ +44 (0)1865-244088
@ oxford.site@thefriendlyclub.co.uk

1 DE**J**MNOPQRT			6
2 AOPRWX		ABDE**FG**	7
3		ABEFHJNQRV	8
4			9
5 BDM**N**		ABCHKM**O**STX	10
10A CEE		❶ £38.30	
A52 2ha 80T(60-80m²)		❷ £50.70	

🗺 On the southern ring (A423 or A34) take the A4144 towards the centre and then follow the signs. The entrance is next to 'Go Outdoor'.
💬 Good transit campsite for the Cotswolds or a visit to the historic city of Oxford. The entrance to the campsite is next to the campsite shop and opposite the P&R bus station. The toilet facilities are very dated. The university town has lots to offer and is easily reached by bike, on foot, or by public transport.

Oakley   Oxford   Abingdon

📍 N 51°43'55'' W 1°15'5''
www.eurocampings.co.uk/102875

204 Ramsgate, GB-CT11 0RX / South East   **iD** 10 B2

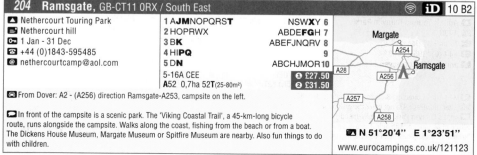

▲ Nethercourt Touring Park
🏠 Nethercourt hill
📅 1 Jan - 31 Dec
☎ +44 (0)1843-595485
@ nethercourtcamp@aol.com

1 A**J**MNOPQRS**T**		NSW**XY**	6
2 HOPRWX		ABDE**FGH**	7
3 B**K**		ABEFJNQRV	8
4 HI**PQ**			9
5 D**N**		ABCHJMOR	10
5-16A CEE		❶ £27.50	
A52 0,7ha 52T(25-80m²)		❷ £31.50	

🗺 From Dover: A2 - (A256) direction Ramsgate-A253, campsite on the left.

💬 In front of the campsite is a scenic park. The 'Viking Coastal Trail', a 45-km-long bicycle route, runs alongside the campsite. Walks along the coast, fishing from the beach or from a boat. The Dickens House Museum, Margate Museum or Spitfire Museum are nearby. Also fun things to do with children.

Margate   Ramsgate

📍 N 51°20'4'' E 1°23'51''
www.eurocampings.co.uk/121123

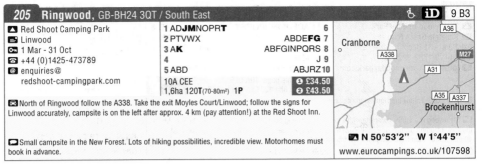

205 Ringwood, GB-BH24 3QT / South East · ♿ iD · 9 B3

- ▲ Red Shoot Camping Park
- 🚏 Linwood
- 📅 1 Mar - 31 Oct
- ☎ +44 (0)1425-473789
- @ enquiries@redshoot-campingpark.com

1 AD**JM**NOP**R**T		6
2 PTVWX	ABDE**FG**	7
3 A**K**	ABFGINPQRS	8
4	J	9
5 ABD	ABJRZ	10
10A CEE		❶ £34.50
1,6ha 120T(70-80m²) 1P		❷ £43.50

🚗 North of Ringwood follow the A338. Take the exit Moyles Court/Linwood; follow the signs for Linwood accurately, campsite is on the left after approx. 4 km (pay attention!) at the Red Shoot Inn.

💬 Small campsite in the New Forest. Lots of hiking possibilities, incredible view. Motorhomes must book in advance.

📍 N 50°53'2'' W 1°44'5''
www.eurocampings.co.uk/107598

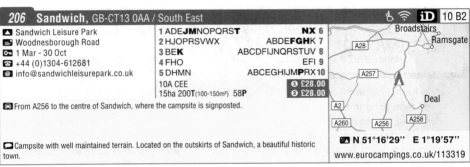

206 Sandwich, GB-CT13 0AA / South East · ♿ 🛜 iD · 10 B2

- ▲ Sandwich Leisure Park
- 🚏 Woodnesborough Road
- 📅 1 Mar - 30 Oct
- ☎ +44 (0)1304-612681
- @ info@sandwichleisurepark.co.uk

1 ADE**JM**NOPQRS**T**	**NX**	6
2 HJOPRSVWX	ABDE**FGH**K	7
3 BE**K**	ABCDFIJNQRSTUV	8
4 FHO	EFI	9
5 DHMN	ABCEGHIJM**P**R**X**	10
10A CEE		❶ £28.00
15ha 200T(100-150m²) 58P		❷ £28.00

🚗 From A256 to the centre of Sandwich, where the campsite is signposted.

💬 Campsite with well maintained terrain. Located on the outskirts of Sandwich, a beautiful historic town.

📍 N 51°16'29'' E 1°19'57''
www.eurocampings.co.uk/113319

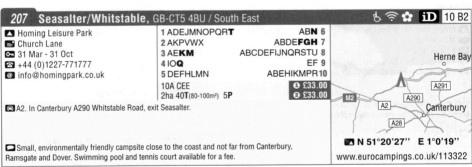

207 Seasalter/Whitstable, GB-CT5 4BU / South East · ♿ 🛜 ✿ iD · 10 B2

- ▲ Homing Leisure Park
- 🚏 Church Lane
- 📅 31 Mar - 31 Oct
- ☎ +44 (0)1227-771777
- @ info@homingpark.co.uk

1 ADEJMNOPQR**T**	AB**N**	6
2 AKPVWX	ABDE**FGH**	7
3 AE**KM**	ABCDEFIJNQRSTU	8
4 IO**Q**	EF	9
5 DEFHLMN	ABEHIKMPR	10
10A CEE		❶ £33.00
2ha 40T(80-100m²) 5P		❷ £33.00

🚗 A2. In Canterbury A290 Whitstable Road, exit Seasalter.

💬 Small, environmentally friendly campsite close to the coast and not far from Canterbury, Ramsgate and Dover. Swimming pool and tennis court available for a fee.

📍 N 51°20'27'' E 1°0'19''
www.eurocampings.co.uk/113322

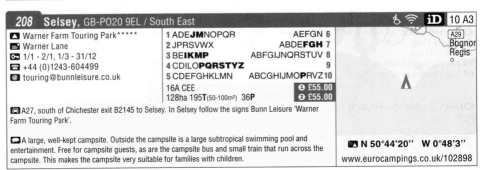

208 Selsey, GB-PO20 9EL / South East · ♿ 🛜 iD · 10 A3

- ▲ Warner Farm Touring Park*****
- 🚏 Warner Lane
- 📅 1/1 - 2/1, 1/3 - 31/12
- ☎ +44 (0)1243-604499
- @ touring@bunnleisure.co.uk

1 ADE**JM**NOPQR	AEFGN	6
2 JPRSVWX	ABDE**FGH**	7
3 BE**IKMP**	ABFGIJNQRSTUV	8
4 CDILO**PQRSTYZ**		9
5 CDEFGHKLMN	ABCGHIJMO**P**RVZ	10
16A CEE		❶ £55.00
128ha 195T(50-100m²) 36P		❷ £55.00

🚗 A27, south of Chichester exit B2145 to Selsey. In Selsey follow the signs Bunn Leisure 'Warner Farm Touring Park'.

💬 A large, well-kept campsite. Outside the campsite is a large subtropical swimming pool and entertainment. Free for campsite guests, as are the campsite bus and small train that run across the campsite. This makes the campsite very suitable for families with children.

📍 N 50°44'20'' W 0°48'3''
www.eurocampings.co.uk/102898

United Kingdom

209 Sevenoaks/London, GB-TN15 7PB / South East   ♿ 📶 ✿ (CC€19) iD   10 A2

🏕 Thriftwood Holiday Park
📧 Plaxdale Green road
🗓 1 Jan - 31 Dec
☎ +44 (0)1732-822261
@ info@thriftwoodholidaypark.com

1 ADE**JM**NOPQRS**T**	AB	6
2 ABPRSTWXY	ABDE**FGH**	7
3 A**K**	ABFIJNQRSTV	8
4 I**O**P	E	9
5 BDEFHKMN	ABCDEGHIJMOR	10

Ad on this page 10A CEE
A190 6,8ha 125T(80-180m²) 22P

❶ £35.00
❷ £41.00

🚗 M20 exit 3. Follow the signs to the campsite.

💬 Thriftwood is a family campsite with a heated swimming pool included in the price. Many sights in the area including picturesque Sevenoaks and Maidstone. Leeds Castle is also worth a visit. Just 40 minutes by train from London. 4 km from the railway station.

(CC) 1/1-29/3 3/4-3/5 7/5-24/5 4/6-23/6 9/9-31/12

📷 N 51°19'27'' E 0°17'34''

www.eurocampings.co.uk/100219

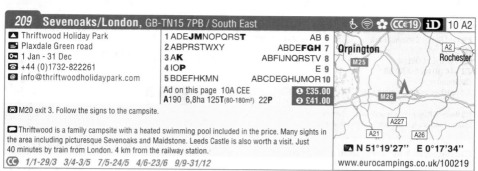

210 Southbourne, GB-PO10 8JH / South East   ♿ 📶 iD   9 B3

🏕 Chichester, Cp. & Car. Club Site
📧 Main Road
🗓 6 Feb - 16 Nov
☎ +44 (0)1243-373202
@ chichester.site@thefriendlyclub.co.uk

1 ADEJMNOQRT		6
2 AOPSVWX	ABDE**FG**	7
3	ABCDFNQRV	8
4 FH		9
5 BDM**N**	ABCK**P**R	10

16A CEE
1ha 58T(55-121m²)

❶ £43.35
❷ £57.45

🚗 A27, exit Fishbourne direction Southbourne. The campsite is located on the A259, exactly on the border between Nutbourne and Southbourne.

💬 A small, well-kept campsite, reservations required in the high season and at weekends. Many cycling and hiking opportunities. The lovely town of Southbourne is located near Portsmouth and Chicester with its beautiful cathedral.

📷 N 50°50'41'' W 0°54'10''

www.eurocampings.co.uk/109445

211 Southsea/Portsmouth, GB-PO4 9TB / South East   📶 iD   9 B3

🏕 Southsea Holiday & Leisure Park
📧 Melville Road
🗓 1 Jan - 31 Dec
☎ +44 (0)23-92735070
@ info@southsealeisurepark.com

1 ADE**JM**NOPQRS**T**	ABFKNQS	6
2 AEGJOPRSVWX	ABDE**FG**	7
3 B**KLQ**	ABFJNQRV	8
4 **O**Q	EJ	9
5 DEFGHL	ABCIJOR	10

16A CEE
5ha 22T(50-100m²) 12P

❶ £39.00
❷ £39.00

🚗 From M27/A27/A3M take exit A2030. Follow the signs to Southsea. Then follow the campsite signs.

💬 Good family campsite, especially if you like the (pebble) beach and the sea. The beach is separated by a dike and can be reached from the campsite. The pitches are on grass or on gravel. The campsite offers many opportunities for (water) recreation.

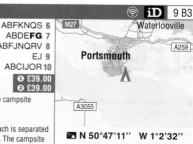

📷 N 50°47'11'' W 1°2'32''

www.eurocampings.co.uk/100218

212 Standlake/Oxford, GB-OX29 7RH / South East ♿ 🛜 iD 9 B2

🏕 Lincoln Farm Park Oxfordshire*****
🏠 High Street
📅 15 Feb - 5 Nov
☎ +44 (0)1865-300239
@ info@lincolnfarmpark.co.uk

1 ACDE**JM**NOPQRS**T**	**EFG** 6
2 GOPRSVWXY	ABDE**FG**HK 7
3 BEI**K**	ABCDFIJNQRSV 8
4 FI**RSTVX**	9
5 BDMN	ABEFHJM**PQ**STX 10
10-16A CEE	❶ £28.80
A64 3,2ha 90T(150m²)	❷ £36.00

🚗 From Oxford A40 direction Cheltenham to Witney or A420 direction Swindon to Kingston Bagpuize. Then A415 to Standlake, follow the road to the garage. Signposted from garage.
💬 The typical English rural life is here on this excellent campsite. Many trees provide shade and shelter. Fitness Centre and indoor swimming pool round off this campsite. The toilet facilities are perfect. There is a separate tent field with covered cooking area. A good starting point for trips to Oxford and the Cotswolds. Swimming pool (not free).

📍 N 51°43'23'' W 1°25'43''
www.eurocampings.co.uk/102874

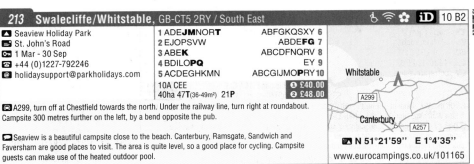

213 Swalecliffe/Whitstable, GB-CT5 2RY / South East ♿ 🛜 ✿ iD 10 B2

🏕 Seaview Holiday Park
🏠 St. John's Road
📅 1 Mar - 30 Sep
☎ +44 (0)1227-792246
@ holidaysupport@parkholidays.com

1 ADE**JM**NOR**T**	ABFGKQSXY 6
2 EJOPSVW	ABDE**FG** 7
3 ABE**K**	ABCDFNQRV 8
4 BDILO**PQ**	EY 9
5 ACDEGHKMN	ABCGIJMO**P**RY 10
10A CEE	❶ £40.00
40ha 47T(36-49m²) 21P	❷ £48.00

🚗 A299, turn off at Chestfield towards the north. Under the railway line, turn right at roundabout. Campsite 300 metres further on the left, by a bend opposite the pub.

💬 Seaview is a beautiful campsite close to the beach. Canterbury, Ramsgate, Sandwich and Faversham are good places to visit. The area is quite level, so a good place for cycling. Campsite guests can make use of the heated outdoor pool.

📍 N 51°21'59'' E 1°4'35''
www.eurocampings.co.uk/101165

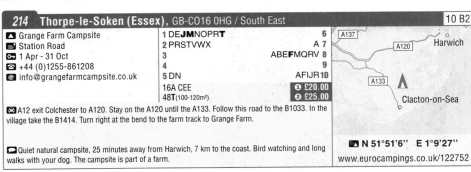

214 Thorpe-le-Soken (Essex), GB-CO16 0HG / South East 10 B2

🏕 Grange Farm Campsite
🏠 Station Road
📅 1 Apr - 31 Oct
☎ +44 (0)1255-861208
@ info@grangefarmcampsite.co.uk

1 DE**JM**NOPR**T**	6
2 PRSTVWX	A 7
3	ABE**F**MQRV 8
4	9
5 DN	AFIJR 10
16A CEE	❶ £20.00
48T(100-120m²)	❷ £25.00

🚗 A12 exit Colchester to A120. Stay on the A120 until the A133. Follow this road to the B1033. In the village take the B1414. Turn right at the bend to the farm track to Grange Farm.

💬 Quiet natural campsite, 25 minutes away from Harwich, 7 km to the coast. Bird watching and long walks with your dog. The campsite is part of a farm.

📍 N 51°51'6'' E 1°9'27''
www.eurocampings.co.uk/122752

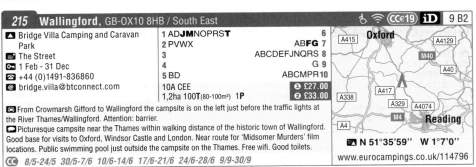

215 Wallingford, GB-OX10 8HB / South East ♿ 🛜 (CC€19) iD 9 B2

🏕 Bridge Villa Camping and Caravan Park
🏠 The Street
📅 1 Feb - 31 Dec
☎ +44 (0)1491-836860
@ bridge.villa@btconnect.com

1 AD**JM**NOPRS**T**	6
2 PVWX	AB**FG** 7
3	ABCDEFJNQRS 8
4	G 9
5 BD	ABCMPR 10
10A CEE	❶ £27.00
1,2ha 100T(80-100m²) 1P	❷ £33.00

🚗 From Crowmarsh Gifford to Wallingford the campsite is on the left just before the traffic lights at the River Thames/Wallingford. Attention: barrier.
💬 Picturesque campsite near the Thames within walking distance of the historic town of Wallingford. Good base for visits to Oxford, Windsor Castle and London. Near route for 'Midsomer Murders' film locations. Public swimming pool just outside the campsite on the Thames. Free wifi. Good toilets.
CC 8/5-24/5 30/5-7/6 10/6-14/6 17/6-21/6 24/6-28/6 9/9-30/9

📍 N 51°35'59'' W 1°7'0''
www.eurocampings.co.uk/114796

United Kingdom

216 West Horsley, GB-KT24 6PE / South East   ♿ 🛜 iD   10 A2

- ▲ Horsley C. & C. Club Site
- 🏢 Ockham Road North
- 📅 29 Mar - 5 Nov
- ☎ +44 (0)1483-283273
- @ horsley.site@thefriendlyclub.co.uk

1 ADEJMNOPQRST	N	6
2 ADPRSVWX	ABDE**FGH**	7
3 A**KL**	ABCDEFIJNQRSV	8
4 FHI**Q**	B	9
5 BDM**N**	ABCIJM**PR**	10
10A CEE	❶ £35.60	
A52 4,8ha 108T(121m²) 24P	❷ £47.20	

🚗 From the M25 exit 10, A3 Guildford-Portsmouth. After 3 km take the B2039 Ockham-East Horsley. First signpost after 3 km. The campsite is on the right.

📷 Located on a pond with ducks, coots and geese. Surrounded by high tree-lined fields which both sunny and shaded areas. Fishing is allowed in the pond. This all less than 15 minutes away from the railway station, with trains to the centre of London.

📍 N 51°17'13''   W 0°26'44''
www.eurocampings.co.uk/108853

217 West Wittering, GB-PO20 8ED / South East   ♿ 🛜 (CC€17) ♟ iD   9 B3

- ▲ Scotts Farm
- 🏢 Cakeham road
- 📅 1 Mar - 31 Oct
- ☎ +44 (0)1243-671720
- @ scottsfarm@live.com

1 ADEJMNOPQRS	NOQRS**X**Y	6
2 AEGHJOPRVW	ABDE**FG**	7
3 BE**K**	ABFGNQRV	8
4 F	F	9
5 DM**NO**	AIJMPR	10
Ad on this page 10A CEE	❶ £33.00	
10ha 650T(49-120m²) 102P	❷ £33.00	

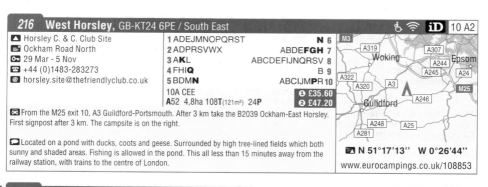

🚗 On the A27, south of Chichester, exit A286. After about 6 km turn left and follow the B2198 in dir. of East Wittering. Turn right after Lively Lady Pub. Campsite is located after the village, on the right.

📷 Family site with playground, plenty of sun and sea. Sandy/pebble beach in walking distance. Cycling opportunities. Good toilet facilities. 10 minutes from East Wittering with a large choice of (takeaway) restaurants, authentic pubs and shops.

CC   1/3-28/3   17/4-2/5   8/5-23/5   4/6-30/6   14/9-30/10

📍 N 50°46'14''   W 0°52'40''
www.eurocampings.co.uk/102897

218 Wick/Littlehampton, GB-BN17 7PH / South East   ♿ 🛜 iD   10 A3

- ▲ Littlehampton Car. & Motorhome Club Site*****
- 🏢 Mill Lane
- 📅 1/1 - 3/1, 18/3 - 31/12
- ☎ +44 (0)1903-716176
- @ littlehampton@camc.com

1 ADEJMOPQRST		6
2 AOPSVWX	ABDE**FG**	7
3 B**K**	ABCDEFJKNQRSTUV	8
4 FH		9
5 DM	ABCEFGHIJMP**RZ**	10
16A CEE	❶ £38.00	
2,8ha 108T(81m²)	❷ £43.40	

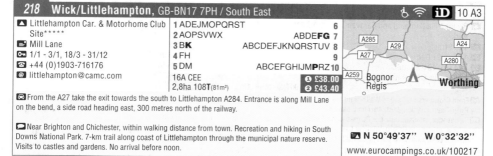

🚗 From the A27 take the exit towards the south to Littlehampton A284. Entrance is along Mill Lane on the bend, a side road heading east, 300 metres north of the railway.

📷 Near Brighton and Chichester, within walking distance from town. Recreation and hiking in South Downs National Park. 7-km trail along coast of Littlehampton through the municipal nature reserve. Visits to castles and gardens. No arrival before noon.

📍 N 50°49'37''   W 0°32'32''
www.eurocampings.co.uk/100217

219 Winchester, GB-SO21 1HL / South East   ♿ iD   9 B3

🔺 Morn Hill Caravan Club Site
📧 Morn Hill
📅 28 Mar - 4 Nov
☎ +44 (0)1962-869877
@ mornhill@camc.co.uk

1 ADJMNOPRS**T**		6	
2 AOPVX	ABDE**FGH**	7	
3 **K**	ABCDEFNQRV	8	
4		9	
5 BD	ABHKMRZ	10	

16A CEE
A103 3,6ha 90**T**(120m²)

❶ £34.70
❷ £39.70

🚗 From London M3 to Southhampton, exit 9. Take A31 to Alton. On the second roundabout follow the signs to the campsite. 15 metres past this roundabout turn right before the pub. Then 150 metres to the site.

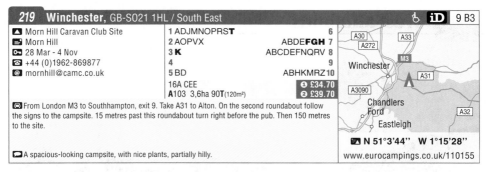

🛏 N 51°3'44" W 1°15'28"
www.eurocampings.co.uk/110155

💬 A spacious-looking campsite, with nice plants, partially hilly.

The original Middle Earth

The West Midlands are quintessential England, located between Wales and the East Midlands, where monuments to Britain's Industrial Revolution are surrounded by stunning countryside. It's no surprise that places like the Shropshire Hills, the Malvern Hills, Cannock Chase, the Wye Valley and the Cotwolds inspired writer JRR Tolkien. Who hasn't seen The Lord of the Rings?

Formerly the Anglo-Saxon kingdom of Mercia, and later in 1642 the location of the Battle of Edgehill and the start of the English Civil War, the West Midlands are where the Industrial Revolution started out in Britain, specifically in the Black Country, west of Birmingham. The Iron Bridge Gorge is the first of its kind in the world, and thus the birthplace of modern industry.

'To be or not to be'

Famous cities and towns are Birmingham, with the Bullring, Jewellery Quarter, Botanical Gardens, and for chocoholics, Cadbury World is the Mother Ship; Coventry has hidden gems like the Litchfield Cottages and St Mary's Guildhall, and is home to the legend of Lady Godiva; Wolverhampton has Mosely Old Hall with its ornate Elizabethan gardens, as well as the Wolverhampton Art Gallery; and you can't miss Stratford-upon-Avon, William Shakespeare's home town: highlights include Anne Hathaway's Cottage – Shakespeare's wife, not the actress – and Mary Arden's Farm.

Places to go, things to do

The kids will love Warwick Castle, where history is made fun and exciting. If you like water sports, Kingsbury Waterpark is a great day out, with

their own: Brummie Bacon cakes, pikelets, pig's trotters (hooves), bread and dripping, pease pudding, faggots (meatballs) and peas, and pork scratchings. Did you know that Indian Balti dishes were actually invented in Birmingham? For something sweet, try Simnel cake or frumenty, washed down with cider, wassail or a type of beer known as 'mild'.

plenty for hikers and cyclists as well. Mosely Bog and Joy's Wood Nature Reserve is where Tolkien played as a boy, and at Dudley Zoo & Castle, keep an eye out for the ghost of the Grey Lady! Finally, the Commandery at Worcester, the Royalist Headquarters during the English Civil, brings history to vivid life.

What to eat and drink

Worcester sauce might be world-famous, but West Midland specialities are in a league of

Our tips

1. *Birmingham Comedy Festival, an annual 10 day arts festival*
2. *Explore historic locations along the Wye River Valley*
3. *The Rockhouses at Kinver Edge provide a fascinating glimpse into the past*
4. *Enjoy Lichfield Cathedral and see the city's beautiful Georgian buildings*
5. *Acton Scott Historic Working Farm and Museum*

220 Aston Cantlow, GB-B95 6JP / West Midlands   9 B1

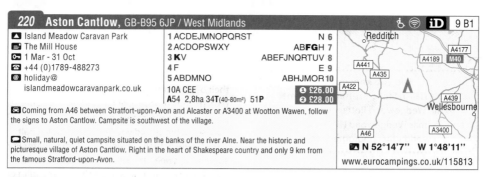

- ▲ Island Meadow Caravan Park
- 🏠 The Mill House
- 📅 1 Mar - 31 Oct
- ☎ +44 (0)1789-488273
- @ holiday@
  islandmeadowcaravanpark.co.uk

1 ACDEJMNOPQRST	N 6
2 ACDOPSWXY	ABFGH 7
3 KV	ABEFJNQRTUV 8
4 F	E 9
5 ABDMNO	ABHJMOR 10
10A CEE	❶ £26.00
A54 2,8ha 34T(40-80m²) 51P	❷ £28.00

🚗 Coming from A46 between Stratfort-upon-Avon and Alcaster or A3400 at Wootton Wawen, follow the signs to Aston Cantlow. Campsite is southwest of the village.

💬 Small, natural, quiet campsite situated on the banks of the river Alne. Near the historic and picturesque village of Aston Cantlow. Right in the heart of Shakespeare country and only 9 km from the famous Stratford-upon-Avon.

⬛ N 52°14'7'' W 1°48'11''

www.eurocampings.co.uk/115813

221 Bridgnorth Shrops, GB-WV15 6DT / West Midlands   9 B1

- ▲ Stanmore Hall Touring Park
- 🏠 Stourbridge Road
- 📅 1 Jan - 31 Dec
- ☎ +44 (0)1746-761761
- @ stanmore@morris-leisure.co.uk

1 ADEJMNOPQRST	6
2 FOPRSVWXY	ABDEFGH 7
3 AK	ABCDEFHJNPQRSTUV 8
4	9
5 BDMN	ABEFGHIKLMPRX 10
16A CEE	❶ £29.30
A91 3ha 134T(80-120m²)	❷ £34.30

🚗 From Bridgnorth follow the A458 to the east in the direction of Stourbridge. Campsite is located on the right after approx. 2.5 km, clearly signposted at the roundabouts. Do not follow navigation system.

💬 A very nice campsite, located in a beautiful park with large old trees around a beautifully landscaped pond. This rural campsite, with high-quality facilities, is a short distance from the lovely shopping town of Bridgnorth on the river Severn.

⬛ N 52°31'38'' W 2°22'41''

www.eurocampings.co.uk/111414

222 Cotton/Alton Towers (Staf.sh.), GB-ST10 3DW / West Midlands   9 B1

- ▲ C & C Club Site Alton, The Star****
- 🚩 B5417
- 📅 1 Mar - 8 Nov
- ☎ +44 (0)1538-702219

1 ACDEJMNOPQRST	6
2 BFOPRSTVWXY	ABDEFGH 7
3 BEKL	ABEFGHIJLNQRSTUV 8
4 F	BE 9
5 BDMN	ABGHIJMNPR 10
16A CEE	❶ £34.50
A251 20ha 183T(120m²) 63P	❷ £45.10

🚗 The A52 from Stoke to Ashbourne. Take the exit B5417. The campsite is located before the village of Cotton.

💬 Wonderful family campsite near Alton Towers theme park. Many facilities for people with disabilities. National winner of the Loo of the Year Award 2005 and the Rose Award 2005/2006. Discount for Camping & Caravanning Club members.

⬛ N 53°0'32'' W 1°54'6''

www.eurocampings.co.uk/108856

223 Hadnall/Shrewsbury (Shropsh.), GB-SY4 4AA / West Midlands   9 B1

- ▲ Beaconsfield Farm*****
- 🏠 Upper Battlefield
- 📅 2 Feb - 31 Dec
- ☎ +44 (0)1939-210370
- @ mail@beaconsfieldholidaypark.co.uk

1 ADEJMOPQRSU	EN 6
2 ADOPRSVW	BEFGH 7
3 K	BCDFLNQRT 8
4 FHV	EF 9
5 DKM	ABGHJMOR 10
10A CEE	❶ £31.00
A91 5ha 60T(50-80m²) 60P	

🚗 In Shrewsbury A49 direction Whitchurch. In Hadnall the campsite is signposted, the entrance to the campsite is on Astley Lane

💬 Clean campsite for campers looking for tranquillity. No children, vans or tents allowed. The restaurant is cash only and open from Friday evening till Sunday afternoon 2:00 pm.

⬛ N 52°45'54'' W 2°42'44''

www.eurocampings.co.uk/109710

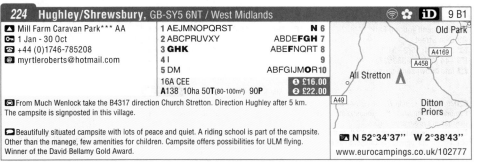

224 Hughley/Shrewsbury, GB-SY5 6NT / West Midlands 9 B1

- Mill Farm Caravan Park*** AA
- 1 Jan - 30 Oct
- +44 (0)1746-785208
- myrtleroberts@hotmail.com

1 AEJMNOPQRST	N 6
2 ABCPRUVXY	ABDEFGH 7
3 GHK	ABEFNQRT 8
4 I	9
5 DM	ABFGIJMOR 10
16A CEE	❶ £16.00
A138 10ha 50T(80-100m²) 90P	❷ £22.00

From Much Wenlock take the B4317 direction Church Stretton. Direction Hughley after 5 km. The campsite is signposted in this village.

Beautifully situated campsite with lots of peace and quiet. A riding school is part of the campsite. Other than the manege, few amenities for children. Campsite offers possibilities for ULM flying. Winner of the David Bellamy Gold Award.

N 52°34'37'' W 2°38'43''

www.eurocampings.co.uk/102777

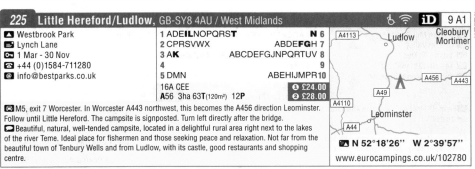

225 Little Hereford/Ludlow, GB-SY8 4AU / West Midlands 9 A1

- Westbrook Park
- Lynch Lane
- 1 Mar - 30 Nov
- +44 (0)1584-711280
- info@bestparks.co.uk

1 ADEILNOPQRST	N 6
2 CPRSVWX	ABDEFGH 7
3 AK	ABCDEFGJNPQRTUV 8
4	9
5 DMN	ABEHIJMPR 10
16A CEE	❶ £24.00
A56 3ha 63T(120m²) 12P	❷ £28.00

M5, exit 7 Worcester. In Worcester A443 northwest, this becomes the A456 direction Leominster. Follow until Little Hereford. The campsite is signposted. Turn left directly after the bridge.

Beautiful, natural, well-tended campsite, located in a delightful rural area right next to the lakes of the river Teme. Ideal place for fishermen and those seeking peace and relaxation. Not far from the beautiful town of Tenbury Wells and from Ludlow, with its castle, good restaurants and shopping centre.

N 52°18'26'' W 2°39'57''

www.eurocampings.co.uk/102780

226 Ludlow, GB-SY8 4AD / West Midlands 9 A1

- Ludlow Touring Park
- Overton Road
- 1 Jan - 31 Dec
- +44 (0)1584-878788
- ludlow@morris-leisure.co.uk

1 ADEJMNOPQRST	N 6
2 CFGOPRSVWXY	ABDEFGH 7
3 BJ	ABCDEFGHIJKNPQRSTUV 8
4	9
5 ABDMN	ABEFGHIJLMNPRX 10
16A CEE	❶ £30.80
4ha 115T(90-140m²) 20P	❷ £35.80

On the A49 between Hereford-Shrewsbury the campsite is signposted with brown signs on both sides of the road. Take the B4361 direction Ludlow at the T-junction. Campsite is on the right after ± 750 metres.

Campsite situated in a rural area on the banks of the river Teme within walking distance (2.5 km) of the lovely town of Ludlow, famous for its ancient castle and special restaurants.

N 52°20'41'' W 2°43'8''

www.eurocampings.co.uk/121494

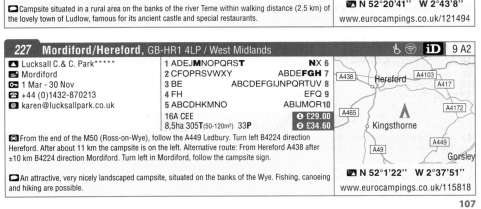

227 Mordiford/Hereford, GB-HR1 4LP / West Midlands 9 A2

- Lucksall C.& C. Park*****
- Mordiford
- 1 Mar - 30 Nov
- +44 (0)1432-870213
- karen@lucksallpark.co.uk

1 ADEJMNOPQRST	NX 6
2 CFOPRSVWXY	ABDEFGH 7
3 BE	ABCDEFGIJNPQRTUV 8
4 FH	EFQ 9
5 ABCDHKMNO	ABIJMOR 10
16A CEE	❶ £29.00
8,5ha 305T(50-120m²) 33P	❷ £34.60

From the end of the M50 (Ross-on-Wye), follow the A449 Ledbury. Turn left B4224 direction Hereford. After about 11 km the campsite is on the left. Alternative route: From Hereford A438 after ±10 km B4224 direction Mordiford. Turn left in Mordiford, follow the campsite sign.

An attractive, very nicely landscaped campsite, situated on the banks of the Wye. Fishing, canoeing and hiking are possible.

N 52°1'22'' W 2°37'51''

www.eurocampings.co.uk/115818

United Kingdom

United Kingdom

228 Pembridge, GB-HR6 9HB / West Midlands

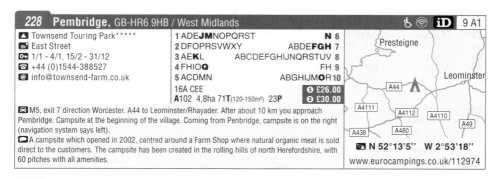

 ♿ ᯤ iD 9 A1

- ▲ Townsend Touring Park*****
- ✉ East Street
- 🗓 1/1 - 4/1, 15/2 - 31/12
- ☎ +44 (0)1544-388527
- @ info@townsend-farm.co.uk

1 ADE**JM**NOPQRST	**N**	6
2 DFOPRSVWXY	ABDE**FGH**	7
3 AE**KL**	ABCDEFGHIJNQRSTUV	8
4 FHIO**Q**	FH	9
5 ACDMN	ABGHIJM**O**R	10

16A CEE
A102 4,8ha 71**T**(120-150m²) 23**P**

❶ £26.00
❷ £30.00

🅿 M5, exit 7 direction Worcester. A44 to Leominster/Rhayader. After about 10 km you approach Pembridge. Campsite at the beginning of the village. Coming from Penbridge, campsite is on the right (navigation system says left).
💬 A campsite which opened in 2002, centred around a Farm Shop where natural organic meat is sold direct to the customers. The campsite has been created in the rolling hills of north Herefordshire, with 60 pitches with all amenities.

📷 **N 52°13'5'' W 2°53'18''**

www.eurocampings.co.uk/112974

229 Peterchurch, GB-HR2 0SF / West Midlands

 ♿ ᯤ ❀ iD 9 A2

- ▲ Poston Mill Park*****
- ✉ Golden Valley
- 🗓 1 Jan - 31 Dec
- ☎ +44 (0)1981-550225
- @ info@poston-mill.co.uk

1 ADE**JM**NOPQRS**T**	N	6
2 CFOPRSVWX	ABDE**FG**HK	7
3 BEJKLMQ	ABCDEFGHIJNQRSTUV	8
4 FIQ	EJ	9
5 ABCDEFHLMN	ABEHIJLM**P**R	10

16A CEE
A110 13ha 38**T**(100-125m²) 19**P**

❶ £24.00
❷ £28.00

🅿 From Hereford A465 direction Abergavanny, then B4348 direction Peterchurch. Campsite is signposted.

💬 A lovely landscaped natural campsite, situated on the banks of the river Dore. In a beautiful rural setting. With many opportunities for young and old. Fishing, golf, hiking and sports field. Enjoy the beautiful nature.

📷 **N 52°1'41'' W 2°56'22''**

www.eurocampings.co.uk/102778

230 Ross-on-Wye, GB-HR9 7BW / West Midlands

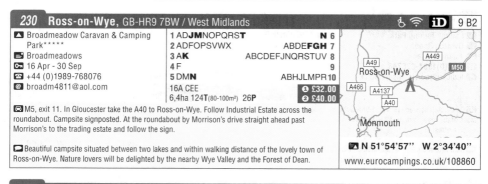

 ♿ ᯤ iD 9 B2

- ▲ Broadmeadow Caravan & Camping Park*****
- ✉ Broadmeadows
- 🗓 16 Apr - 30 Sep
- ☎ +44 (0)1989-768076
- @ broadm4811@aol.com

1 AD**JM**NOPQRS**T**	**N**	6
2 ADFOPSVWX	ABDE**FGH**	7
3 A**K**	ABCDEFJNQRSTUV	8
4 F		9
5 DM**N**	ABHJLMPR	10

16A CEE
6,4ha 124**T**(80-100m²) 26**P**

❶ £32.00
❷ £40.00

🅿 M5, exit 11. In Gloucester take the A40 to Ross-on-Wye. Follow Industrial Estate across the roundabout. Campsite signposted. At the roundabout by Morrison's drive straight ahead past Morrison's to the trading estate and follow the sign.

💬 Beautiful campsite situated between two lakes and within walking distance of the lovely town of Ross-on-Wye. Nature lovers will be delighted by the nearby Wye Valley and the Forest of Dean.

📷 **N 51°54'57'' W 2°34'40''**

www.eurocampings.co.uk/108860

231 Shobdon/Leominster (Heref.), GB-HR6 9NQ / West Midlands

 ♿ ᯤ ❀ iD 9 A1

- ▲ Pearl Lake Leisure Park*****
- 🗓 1 Mar - 30 Nov
- ☎ +44 (0)1568-708326
- @ info@pearllake.co.uk

1 ADE**JM**NOPQRS**T**	N**X**	6
2 DOPRSVWXY	ABDE**FGH**	7
3 BE**J**P	ABEFGHJNPQRSTUV	8
4 FNO**Q**	EJ	9
5 DHLMN	ABEHIM**O**RZ	10

16A CEE
A152 32ha 15**T**(50-100m²) 193**P**

❶ £24.00
❷ £28.00

🅿 A49 Hereford direction Shrewsbury. Turn left at Woofferton to the B4362. After about 10 km (Shobdon) the campsite is on the right. Clearly signposted with brown signs.

💬 A small, quiet and well-kept campsite, which is part of a large park with 200 holiday cottages. Also a golf course, bowling area, play area, fishing pond, soccer and recreation field available. A campsite for active people. On the main road.

📷 **N 52°15'9'' W 2°53'28''**

www.eurocampings.co.uk/112334

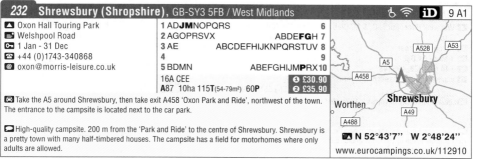

232 Shrewsbury (Shropshire), GB-SY3 5FB / West Midlands   iD   9 A1

- ⬆ Oxon Hall Touring Park
- ✉ Welshpool Road
- ⊙ 1 Jan - 31 Dec
- ☎ +44 (0)1743-340868
- @ oxon@morris-leisure.co.uk

1 ADJMNOPQRS		6
2 AGOPRSVX	ABDEFGH	7
3 AE	ABCDEFHIJKNPQRSTUV	8
4		9
5 BDMN	ABEFGHIJMPRX	10

16A CEE
A87 10ha 115T(54-79m²) 60P

- ❶ £30.90
- ❷ £35.90

Take the A5 around Shrewsbury, then take exit A458 'Oxon Park and Ride', northwest of the town. The entrance to the campsite is located next to the car park.

High-quality campsite. 200 m from the 'Park and Ride' to the centre of Shrewsbury. Shrewsbury is a pretty town with many half-timbered houses. The campsite has a field for motorhomes where only adults are allowed.

www.eurocampings.co.uk/112910

233 Stratford-upon-Avon, GB-CV37 9SR / West Midlands   9 B2

- ⬆ Dodwell Park***
- ✉ Evesham Road
- ⊙ 1 Jan - 31 Dec
- ☎ +44 (0)1789-204957
- @ enquiries@dodwellpark.co.uk

1 DEJMNOPQRT		6
2 AOPRSTWX	AB	7
3 EK	ABEFJNQRV	8
4		9
5 CDMNO	ABHJMR	10

16A CEE
A50 2,5ha 50T(100m²)

- ❶ £22.50
- ❷ £26.50

About 3 km from Stratford, on B439 direction Bidford/Evesham. Turn left after the second hill. The campsite is signposted.

Tidy campsite just outside the historic town of Stratford-upon-Avon. Well situated for excursions to Stratford, Warwick and the picturesque Cotswolds. Tents are welcome.

N 52°10'56'' W 1°45'26''

www.eurocampings.co.uk/102872

234 Stratford-upon-Avon, GB-CV37 7AB / West Midlands   9 B2

- ⬆ Riverside Caravan Park
- ✉ Tiddington Road
- ⊙ 1 Apr - 31 Oct
- ☎ +44 (0)1789-292312
- @ riverside@stratfordcaravans.co.uk

1 DEJMOPRS	NXYZ	6
2 COPRWX	ABDEFGH	7
3 AIK	ABCDFJNQRV	8
4	EJ	9
5 DHJLM	ABGHJMPR	10

10A CEE
2,5ha 110T(min 100m²) 31P

- ❶ £31.50
- ❷ £35.50

From Stratford, take the B4086 Tiddington Road. Park is on the left side of the road when entering Tiddington.

Large, quietly located campsite with modern toilet facilities. Located on the bank of the river Avon. Own transport by water taxi to Stratford and many opportunities for trips in the area, including Oxford, Warwick and the Cotswolds. No tents; motorhomes and caravans only!

N 52°12'1'' W 1°40'56''

www.eurocampings.co.uk/115040

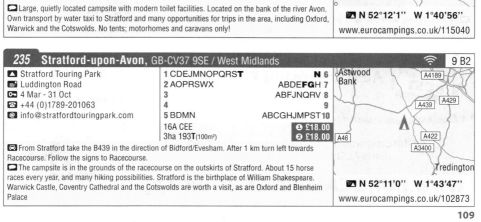

235 Stratford-upon-Avon, GB-CV37 9SE / West Midlands   9 B2

- ⬆ Stratford Touring Park
- ✉ Luddington Road
- ⊙ 4 Mar - 31 Oct
- ☎ +44 (0)1789-201063
- @ info@stratfordtouringpark.com

1 CDEJMNOPQRST	N	6
2 AOPRSWX	ABDEFGH	7
3	ABFJNQRV	8
4		9
5 BDMN	ABCGHJMPST	10

16A CEE
3ha 193T(100m²)

- ❶ £18.00
- ❷ £18.00

From Stratford take the B439 in the direction of Bidford/Evesham. After 1 km turn left towards Racecourse. Follow the signs to Racecourse.

The campsite is in the grounds of the racecourse on the outskirts of Stratford. About 15 horse races every year, and many hiking possibilities. Stratford is the birthplace of William Shakespeare. Warwick Castle, Coventry Cathedral and the Cotswolds are worth a visit, as are Oxford and Blenheim Palace.

N 52°11'0'' W 1°43'47''

www.eurocampings.co.uk/102873

United Kingdom

236 Warwick, GB-CV34 6HN / West Midlands   ♿ 9 B1

- ⛺ Warwick Racecourse C. & M. Club Site***
- ✉ Hampton Street
- 📅 1 Mar - 31 Dec
- ☎ +44 (0)1926-495448
- @ warwickracecourse@camc.com

1 BDEJMOPQRST		6
2 AOPSWXY	ABDE**FG**	7
3 **K**	ABEFJNPQR	8
4		9
5 DM	ABGHJMSTZ	10
16A CEE	❶ £37.60	
A65 1,5ha 55T(85-100m²)	❷ £43.00	

🗺 Located in the city of Warwick. Follow the signs 'Racecourse'.

💬 This is the campsite for people who like horse racing. Within walking distance of Warwick Castle. The campsite is run by the Caravan Club and is situated within the racecourse. During a race only accessible by foot. Very suitable for trips in the area.

📌 N 52°16'47'' W 1°35'48''
www.eurocampings.co.uk/102868

237 Wem (Shropshire), GB-SY4 5RP / West Midlands   ♿ 🛜 iD 9 B1

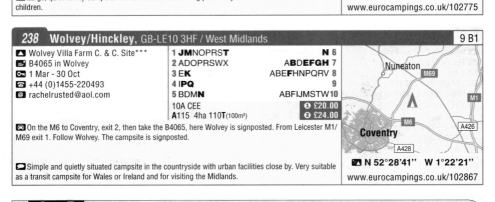

- ⛺ Lower Lacon Caravan Park***
- ✉ B5065
- 📅 1 Jan - 31 Dec
- ☎ +44 (0)1939-232376
- @ info@llcp.co.uk

1 ADE**JM**NOPQRST	ABFG	6
2 BGOPRSVWXY	**ABDEFGH**	7
3 BEI**K**	ABDFNQRS	8
4 INO**PQ**	BE	9
5 BDEFGHKM**N**	ABHIKM**O**RWYZ	10
16A CEE	❶ £26.50	
A81 19ha 460T(80-120m²) 82P	❷ £32.50	

🗺 From Shrewsbury follow the A49 direction Whitchurch. Take the B5065 direction Wem at Prees Green. 1 km before Wem the campsite is located on the right.

💬 Large, quiet family campsite with a beautiful swimming pool. Very suitable for families with children.

📌 N 52°51'51'' W 2°42'7''
www.eurocampings.co.uk/102775

238 Wolvey/Hinckley, GB-LE10 3HF / West Midlands   9 B1

- ⛺ Wolvey Villa Farm C. & C. Site***
- ✉ B4065 in Wolvey
- 📅 1 Mar - 30 Oct
- ☎ +44 (0)1455-220493
- @ rachelrusted@aol.com

1 **JM**NOPRS**T**	**N**	6
2 ADOPRSWX	**ABDEFGH**	7
3 E**K**	ABE**F**HNPQRV	8
4 I**PQ**		9
5 BDM**N**	ABFIJMSTW	10
10A CEE	❶ £20.00	
A115 4ha 110T(100m²)	❷ £24.00	

🗺 On the M6 to Coventry, exit 2, then take the B4065, here Wolvey is signposted. From Leicester M1/M69 exit 1. Follow Wolvey. The campsite is signposted.

💬 Simple and quietly situated campsite in the countryside with urban facilities close by. Very suitable as a transit campsite for Wales or Ireland and for visiting the Midlands.

📌 N 52°28'41'' W 1°22'21''
www.eurocampings.co.uk/102867

This is Old England

Extending from the mountainous Peak District to the hilly North Sea Coast, from Grimsby to Skegness, with rocky crags, moors, stone walls and forests, this is the England of Robin Hood and William the Conqueror, and of fictional heroes such as Mr Darcy and Mr Rochester. You might even have already seen Stanage Edge or Chatsworth House on the silver screen.

Walking through the town of Lincoln is like walking back in time. The kids will love the Castle and Cathedral buildings, and the walk up Steep Hill is lined with cafés and shops. Lincoln also holds an annual German-style Christmas market. Chesterfield to the west is home to Hardwick Hall, built during Tudor times by the formidable Bess of Hardwick, and nearby is Bolsover Castle, perched on a hilltop with spectacular views. And

of course you can't visit Nottingham without hearing about Robin Hood, the heroic outlaw who, legend has it, robbed the rich to feed the poor.

On your feet, tick tock!

Here's a fun fact about the English shoe industry: Northamptonshire, specifically Wollaston, is forever associated with 'Docs, or Dr. Martens' shoes, they were made here until 2003. The Northampton Museum & Art Gallery features a large collection of shoes, as does Pickford's House in Derby. If you're more into clocks and watches, you'll love the British Horological Museum at Upton House near Newark-on-Trent.

Activities above and below the ground

The Peak District National Park is the oldest

in the UK, and is a favourite place for hikers, climbers, cyclists, and equestrians, while cavers will flock to the town of Castleton to explore the underground caverns. Other activities include the Alton Towers Resort, and Butlins at Skegness,

> **Did you know ...?**
> Sir Isaac Newton, the scientist who discovered gravity, was born in Woolsthorpe Manor, Lincolnshire, which is open to visitors.

Our tips

1. Enjoy a great day for family among the treetops in Weasenham Woods
2. Love opera, natural spas, and fabulous architecture? Spend a few days in Buxton
3. Tour the world's first complete factory in beautiful surroundings at Derwent Valley Mills
4. Watch for ghosts at the infamous Galleries of Justice in Nottingham
5. Visit Althorp House and estate, home and resting place of the Queen of Hearts, Lady Diana

and animal lovers will enjoy the Donna Nook seal nursery and Gibraltar Point Nature Reserve all year round.

What to eat and drink

Stilton cheese and Red Leicester originate here, as do Melton-Mowbray pork pasties, meat pies, Lincolnshire sausages, and what's more English than roast beef? The aptly-named town Bakewell is known for Bakewell tarts, as well as an annual baking festival.

239 Alsop-en-le-Dale, GB-DE6 1QU / East Midlands   iD   5 B3

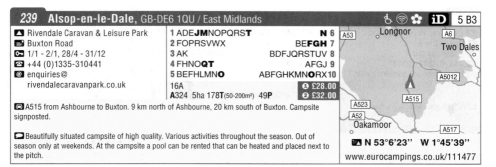

- ▲ Rivendale Caravan & Leisure Park
- ▤ Buxton Road
- ◔ 1/1 - 2/1, 28/4 - 31/12
- ☎ +44 (0)1335-310441
- @ enquiries@
  rivendalecaravanpark.co.uk

1 ADE**JM**NOPQRS**T**	**N** 6
2 FOPRSVWX	BE**FGH** 7
3 AK	BDFJQRSTUV 8
4 FHNO**QT**	AFGJ 9
5 BEFHLMN**O**	ABFGHKMN**O**RX 10
16A	❶ £28.00
A324 5ha 178**T**(50-200m²) 49**P**	❷ £32.00

🚗 A515 from Ashbourne to Buxton. 9 km north of Ashbourne, 20 km south of Buxton. Campsite signposted.

💬 Beautifully situated campsite of high quality. Various activities throughout the season. Out of season only at weekends. At the campsite a pool can be rented that can be heated and placed next to the pitch.

📷 N 53°6'23" W 1°45'39"
www.eurocampings.co.uk/111477

---

240 Baslow/Bakewell, GB-DE45 1PN / East Midlands   iD   5 B3

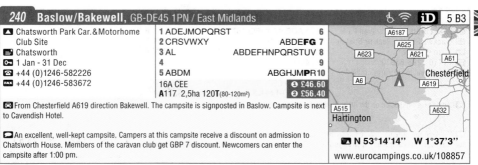

- ▲ Chatsworth Park Car.&Motorhome Club Site
- ▤ Chatsworth
- ◔ 1 Jan - 31 Dec
- ☎ +44 (0)1246-582226
- 📠 +44 (0)1246-583672

1 ADEJMOPQRST	6
2 CRSVWXY	ABDE**FG** 7
3 AL	ABDEFHNPQRSTUV 8
4	9
5 ABDM	ABGHJM**P**R 10
16A CEE	❶ £46.60
A117 2,5ha 120**T**(80-120m²)	❷ £56.40

🚗 From Chesterfield A619 direction Bakewell. The campsite is signposted in Baslow. Campsite is next to Cavendish Hotel.

💬 An excellent, well-kept campsite. Campers at this campsite receive a discount on admission to Chatsworth House. Members of the caravan club get GBP 7 discount. Newcomers can enter the campsite after 1:00 pm.

📷 N 53°14'14" W 1°37'3"
www.eurocampings.co.uk/108857

---

241 Burgh Le Marsh, GB-PE24 5HN / East Midlands   iD   6 A3

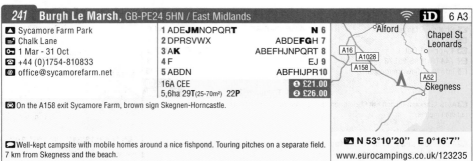

- ▲ Sycamore Farm Park
- ▤ Chalk Lane
- ◔ 1 Mar - 31 Oct
- ☎ +44 (0)1754-810833
- @ office@sycamorefarm.net

1 ADE**JM**NOPQR**T**	**N** 6
2 DPRSVWX	ABDE**FGH** 7
3 A**K**	ABEFHJNPQRT 8
4 F	EJ 9
5 ABDN	ABFHIJPR 10
16A CEE	❶ £21.00
5,6ha 29**T**(25-70m²) 22**P**	❷ £26.00

🚗 On the A158 exit Sycamore Farm, brown sign Skegnen-Horncastle.

💬 Well-kept campsite with mobile homes around a nice fishpond. Touring pitches on a separate field. 7 km from Skegness and the beach.

📷 N 53°10'20" E 0°16'7"
www.eurocampings.co.uk/123235

---

242 Buxton, GB-SK17 6UJ / East Midlands   iD   5 B3

- ▲ Buxton Caravan and Motorhome Club
- ▤ Grin Low Road, Ladmanlow
- ◔ 1 Jun - 31 Oct
- ☎ +44 (0)1298-77735
- @ buxton@camc.com

1 ADJMNOPQRST	6
2 SVWX	ABDE**FG** 7
3 A	ABEFJKNPQRS 8
4 F	9
5 BDM	ABEGHJRZ 10
16A CEE	❶ £32.90
A400 117**T**(100m²)	❷ £37.70

🚗 10 km past Bakewell Tunnel turn left to A5270. After about 3.5 km at the T-junction turn right to A515 Ashbourne-Buxton. After 200 metres turn left to B5053 Langrier-Harpur Hill. Turn right direction Grinlow. After ± 3 km direction A53. After 2 km turn right to campsite.

💬 On your way to the campsite you start wondering if this is the end of the world. Located in an unexpected spot in a remote valley. Yet it is a perfect starting point for trips to the places of interest in the National Park Peak District.

📷 N 53°14'42" W 1°55'59"
www.eurocampings.co.uk/112378

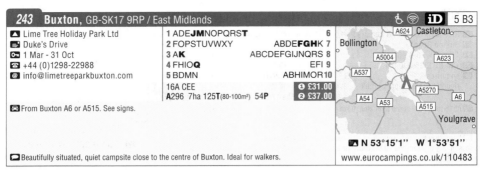

243 Buxton, GB-SK17 9RP / East Midlands   iD   5 B3

- Lime Tree Holiday Park Ltd
- Duke's Drive
- 1 Mar - 31 Oct
- +44 (0)1298-22988
- info@limetreeparkbuxton.com

1 ADEJMNOPQRST		6
2 FOPSTUVWXY	ABDEFGHK	7
3 AK	ABCDEFGIJNQRS	8
4 FHIOQ	EFI	9
5 BDMN	ABHIMOR	10
16A CEE		❶ £31.00
A296 7ha 125T(80-100m²) 54P		❷ £37.00

From Buxton A6 or A515. See signs.

Beautifully situated, quiet campsite close to the centre of Buxton. Ideal for walkers.

N 53°15'1'' W 1°53'51''
www.eurocampings.co.uk/110483

244 Buxton (Derbyshire), GB-SK17 9TQ / East Midlands   iD   5 B3

- Beech Croft Farm Caravan Park
- Blackwell-in-the-Peak nr Buxton
- 1 Jan - 31 Dec
- +44 (0)1298-85330
- mail@beechcroftfarm.co.uk

1 ADEJMNOPQRST		6
2 FPSTVWX	ABDEFGHK	7
3 A	ABCDEFJNQRTV	8
4 FK		9
5 BMN	ABEGHJMPRZ	10
10-16A CEE		❶ £25.00
1,5ha 70T(64-150m²)		❷ £31.00

Campsite is signposted on the A6 at Blackwell between Buxton and Bakewell.

Well-kept campsite on sloping terrain. Most pitches offer a lovely view of the beautiful surroundings. The campsite is open all year round for caravans and motorhomes. Also open for tents from March to October.

N 53°14'42'' W 1°48'55''
www.eurocampings.co.uk/121564

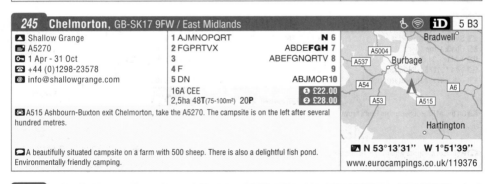

245 Chelmorton, GB-SK17 9FW / East Midlands   iD   5 B3

- Shallow Grange
- A5270
- 1 Apr - 31 Oct
- +44 (0)1298-23578
- info@shallowgrange.com

1 AJMNOPQRT		N 6
2 FGPRTVX	ABDEFGH	7
3	ABEFGNQRTV	8
4 F		9
5 DN	ABJMOR	10
16A CEE		❶ £22.00
2,5ha 48T(75-100m²) 20P		❷ £28.00

A515 Ashbourn-Buxton exit Chelmorton, take the A5270. The campsite is on the left after several hundred metres.

A beautifully situated campsite on a farm with 500 sheep. There is also a delightful fish pond. Environmentally friendly camping.

N 53°13'31'' W 1°51'39''
www.eurocampings.co.uk/119376

246 Cromwell/Newark, GB-NG23 6JE / East Midlands   iD   6 A3

- Caravan Site Club Site Milestone*****
- Great North Road
- 1 Jan - 31 Dec
- +44 (0)1636-821244
- enquiries@milestonepark.co.uk

1 ADEJMOPQRST		N 6
2 ADOPRSVWX	ABDEFGH	7
3 K	ABEFGJNQRV	8
4 FH		9
5 M	ABGHIKMPRX	10
16A CEE		❶ £28.85
7ha 87T(100m²) 120P		❷ £34.55

A1, exit Cromwell, 8 km north of Newark-on-Trent. Follow the signs (the campsite is located after 1 km).

Very neat, medium-sized campsite with a choice of grass or gravel pitches. Very orderly and beautiful park with large fish pond. The local brewery is worth a visit.

N 53°8'59'' W 0°48'25''
www.eurocampings.co.uk/110486

247 Greetham/Oakham, GB-LE15 7NX / East Midlands   iD   10 A1

- ▲ Rutland Caravan & Camping AA5*
- ✉ Park Lane
- ☰ 1 Jan - 31 Dec
- ☎ +44 (0)1572-813520
- @ info@
  rutlandcaravanandcamping.co.uk

1 ADEJMNOPQRST	E 6
2 AGOPRSVW	ABDEFG 7
3 AKV	ABEFJNQRSV 8
4 FHI	F 9
5 ABDM	ABHIJMOPR 10
16A CEE	❶ £28.90
A121 2ha 132T(100m²) 7P	❷ £35.30

🚗 On A1 take the B668 direction Greetham. Turn right before the village to Thistleon Lane, then 2nd road to the left.

💬 A spacious campsite in a rural area, with heated indoor swimming pool. 300 m from the village of Greetham, connected to the campsite by a footpath. Many opportunities for excursions close by, including Burghley House & Gardens.

📷 N 52°43'52'' W 0°37'53''
www.eurocampings.co.uk/112976

248 Hope (Derbyshire), GB-S33 6RR / East Midlands   iD   5 B3

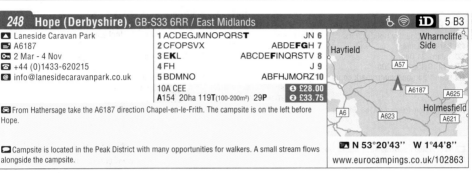

- ▲ Laneside Caravan Park
- ✉ A6187
- ☰ 2 Mar - 4 Nov
- ☎ +44 (0)1433-620215
- @ info@lanesidecaravanpark.co.uk

1 ACDEGJMNOPQRST	JN 6
2 CFOPSVX	ABDEFGH 7
3 EKL	ABCDEFINQRSTV 8
4 FH	J 9
5 BDMNO	ABFHJMORZ 10
10A CEE	❶ £28.00
A154 20ha 119T(100-200m²) 29P	❷ £33.75

🚗 From Hathersage take the A6187 direction Chapel-en-le-Frith. The campsite is on the left before Hope.

💬 Campsite is located in the Peak District with many opportunities for walkers. A small stream flows alongside the campsite.

📷 N 53°20'43'' W 1°44'8''
www.eurocampings.co.uk/102863

249 Hubberts Bridge/Boston, GB-PE20 3QU / East Midlands   iD   10 A1

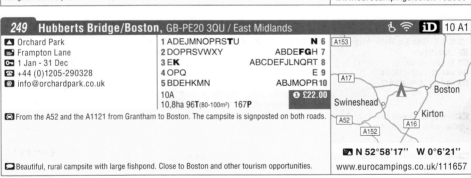

- ▲ Orchard Park
- ✉ Frampton Lane
- ☰ 1 Jan - 31 Dec
- ☎ +44 (0)1205-290328
- @ info@orchardpark.co.uk

1 ADEJMNOPRSTU	N 6
2 DOPRSVWXY	ABDEFGH 7
3 EK	ABCDEFJLNQRT 8
4 OPQ	E 9
5 BDEHKMN	ABJMOPR 10
10A	❶ £22.00
10,8ha 96T(80-100m²) 167P	

🚗 From the A52 and the A1121 from Grantham to Boston. The campsite is signposted on both roads.

💬 Beautiful, rural campsite with large fishpond. Close to Boston and other tourism opportunities.

📷 N 52°58'17'' W 0°6'21''
www.eurocampings.co.uk/111657

250 Ingoldmells, GB-PE25 1JJ / East Midlands   iD   6 A3

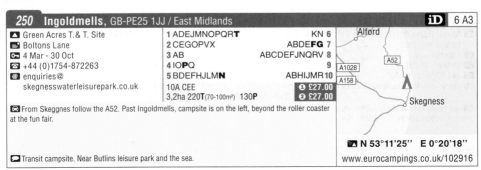

- ▲ Green Acres T.& T. Site
- ✉ Boltons Lane
- ☰ 4 Mar - 30 Oct
- ☎ +44 (0)1754-872263
- @ enquiries@
  skegnesswaterleisurepark.co.uk

1 ADEJMNOPQRT	KN 6
2 CEGOPVX	ABDEFG 7
3 AB	ABCDEFJNQRV 8
4 IOPQ	9
5 BDEFHJLMN	ABHIJMR 10
10A CEE	❶ £27.00
3,2ha 220T(70-100m²) 130P	❷ £27.00

🚗 From Skegness follow the A52. Past Ingoldmells, campsite is on the left, beyond the roller coaster at the fun fair.

💬 Transit campsite. Near Butlins leisure park and the sea.

📷 N 53°11'25'' E 0°20'18''
www.eurocampings.co.uk/102916

United Kingdom

United Kingdom

251 Kings Clipstone, GB-NG21 9HW / East Midlands   ♿ 🛜 iD   6 A3

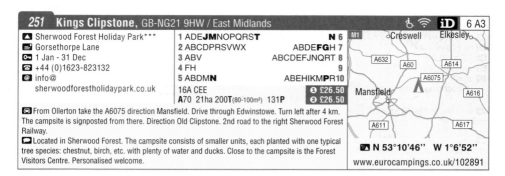

🏕 Sherwood Forest Holiday Park***
📧 Gorsethorpe Lane
📅 1 Jan - 31 Dec
📞 +44 (0)1623-823132
@ info@
  sherwoodforestholidaypark.co.uk

1 ADE**JM**NOPQRS**T**	**N 6**
2 ABCDPRSVWX	ABDE**FGH** 7
3 ABV	ABCDEFJNQR**T** 8
4 FH	9
5 ABDM**N**	ABEHIKM**P**R10
16A CEE	❸ £26.50
A70 21ha 200**T**(80-100m²) 131**P**	❷ £26.50

🚗 From Ollerton take the A6075 direction Mansfield. Drive through Edwinstowe. Turn left after 4 km. The campsite is signposted from there. Direction Old Clipstone. 2nd road to the right Sherwood Forest Railway.
💬 Located in Sherwood Forest. The campsite consists of smaller units, each planted with one typical tree species: chestnut, birch, etc. with plenty of water and ducks. Close to the campsite is the Forest Visitors Centre. Personalised welcome.

🧭 **N 53°10'46" W 1°6'52"**
www.eurocampings.co.uk/102891

252 Lincoln, GB-LN3 5DF / East Midlands   iD   6 A3

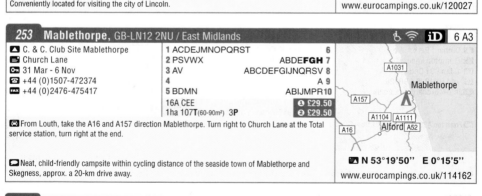

🏕 Barlings Country Holiday Park
📧 Barlings Lane
📅 1 Jan - 31 Dec
📞 +44 (0)1522-753200
@ sean@barlingscountrypark.co.uk

1 ADEJMNOPQRS**T**	**N 6**
2 BCDFGOPRSVWXY	ABDE**FG** 7
3 EV	ABEFGHIJNPQRSV 8
4 F	E**F** 9
5 DM	ABFHIJMR10
10A CEE	❸ £21.50
12ha 79**T**(54-100m²) 52**P**	❷ £25.50

🚗 From Lincoln follow the A158. Turn right in the village of Langworth. Follow the sign 'Lakeside Park'.

💬 Quiet location, surrounded by nature, next to a fish pond. Many cycling and hiking possibilities. Conveniently located for visiting the city of Lincoln.

🧭 **N 53°16'13" W 0°24'2"**
www.eurocampings.co.uk/120027

253 Mablethorpe, GB-LN12 2NU / East Midlands   ♿ 🛜 iD   6 A3

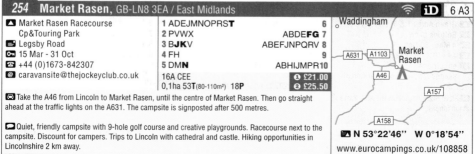

🏕 C. & C. Club Site Mablethorpe
📧 Church Lane
📅 31 Mar - 6 Nov
📞 +44 (0)1507-472374
📠 +44 (0)2476-475417

1 ACDEJMNOPQRST	6
2 PSVWX	ABDE**FGH** 7
3 AV	ABCDEFGIJNQRSV 8
4	A 9
5 BDMN	AB**I**JMPR10
16A CEE	❸ £29.50
1ha 107**T**(60-90m²) 3**P**	❷ £29.50

🚗 From Louth, take the A16 and A157 direction Mablethorpe. Turn right to Church Lane at the Total service station, turn right at the end.

💬 Neat, child-friendly campsite within cycling distance of the seaside town of Mablethorpe and Skegness, approx. a 20-km drive away.

🧭 **N 53°19'50" E 0°15'5"**
www.eurocampings.co.uk/114162

254 Market Rasen, GB-LN8 3EA / East Midlands   🛜 iD   6 A3

🏕 Market Rasen Racecourse
  Cp&Touring Park
📧 Legsby Road
📅 15 Mar - 31 Oct
📞 +44 (0)1673-842307
@ caravansite@thejockeyclub.co.uk

1 ADEJMNOPRS**T**	6
2 PVWX	ABDE**FG** 7
3 **B**JK**V**	ABEFJNPQRV 8
4 FH	9
5 DM**N**	ABHIJMPR10
16A CEE	❸ £21.00
0,1ha 53**T**(80-110m²) 18**P**	❷ £25.50

🚗 Take the A46 from Lincoln to Market Rasen, until the centre of Market Rasen. Then go straight ahead at the traffic lights on the A631. The campsite is signposted after 500 metres.

💬 Quiet, friendly campsite with 9-hole golf course and creative playgrounds. Racecourse next to the campsite. Discount for campers. Trips to Lincoln with cathedral and castle. Hiking opportunities in Lincolnshire 2 km away.

🧭 **N 53°22'46" W 0°18'54"**
www.eurocampings.co.uk/108858

255 Market Rasen, GB-LN8 3UN / East Midlands 🛜 iD 6 A3

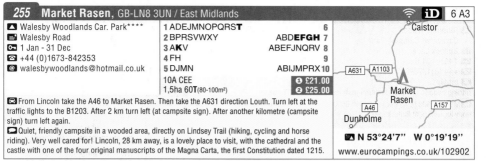

- ⛰ Walesby Woodlands Car. Park****
- 🏕 Walesby Road
- 📅 1 Jan - 31 Dec
- ☎ +44 (0)1673-842353
- @ walesbywoodlands@hotmail.co.uk

1 ADEJMNOPQRS**T**		6
2 BPRSVWXY	ABD**EFGH**	7
3 A**K**V	ABEFJNQRV	8
4 FH		9
5 DJMN	ABIJMPRX	10
10A CEE	❶ £21.00	
1,5ha 60**T**(80-100m²)	❷ £25.00	

🚗 From Lincoln take the A46 to Market Rasen. Then take the A631 direction Louth. Turn left at the traffic lights to the B1203. After 2 km turn left (at campsite sign). After another kilometre (campsite sign) turn left again.

💬 Quiet, friendly campsite in a wooded area, directly on Lindsey Trail (hiking, cycling and horse riding). Very well cared for! Lincoln, 28 km away, is a lovely place to visit, with the cathedral and the castle with one of the four original manuscripts of the Magna Carta, the first Constitution dated 1215.

🏴 N 53°24'7'' W 0°19'19''
www.eurocampings.co.uk/102902

256 Melton Mowbray, GB-LE14 2TD / East Midlands ♿ 🛜 iD 10 A1

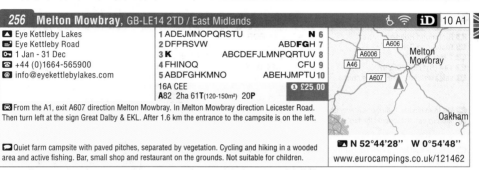

- ⛰ Eye Kettleby Lakes
- 🏕 Eye Kettleby Road
- 📅 1 Jan - 31 Dec
- ☎ +44 (0)1664-565900
- @ info@eyekettlebylakes.com

1 ADEJMNOPQRSTU	**N**	6
2 DFPRSVW	ABD**FG**H	7
3 **K**	ABCDEFJLMNPQRTUV	8
4 FHINOQ	CFU	9
5 ABDFGHKMNO	ABEHJMPTU	10
16A CEE	❶ £25.00	
A82 2ha 61**T**(120-150m²) 20**P**		

🚗 From the A1, exit A607 direction Melton Mowbray. In Melton Mowbray direction Leicester Road. Then turn left at the sign Great Dalby & EKL. After 1.6 km the entrance to the campsite is on the left.

💬 Quiet farm campsite with paved pitches, separated by vegetation. Cycling and hiking in a wooded area and active fishing. Bar, small shop and restaurant on the grounds. Not suitable for children.

🏴 N 52°44'28'' W 0°54'48''
www.eurocampings.co.uk/121462

257 Newhaven/Buxton (Derbyshire), GB-SK17 0DT / East Midlands ♿ iD 5 B3

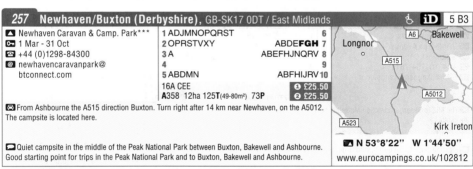

- ⛰ Newhaven Caravan & Camp. Park***
- 📅 1 Mar - 31 Oct
- ☎ +44 (0)1298-84300
- @ newhavencaravanpark@btconnect.com

1 ADJMNOPQRST		6
2 OPRSTVXY	ABDE**FGH**	7
3 A	ABEFHJNQRV	8
4		9
5 ABDMN	ABFHIJRV	10
16A CEE	❶ £25.50	
A358 12ha 125**T**(49-80m²) 73**P**	❷ £25.50	

🚗 From Ashbourne the A515 direction Buxton. Turn right after 14 km near Newhaven, on the A5012. The campsite is located here.

💬 Quiet campsite in the middle of the Peak National Park between Buxton, Bakewell and Ashbourne. Good starting point for trips in the Peak National Park and to Buxton, Bakewell and Ashbourne.

🏴 N 53°8'22'' W 1°44'50''
www.eurocampings.co.uk/102812

258 Northampton, GB-NN3 9DA / East Midlands ♿ 🛜 ❀ 10 A2

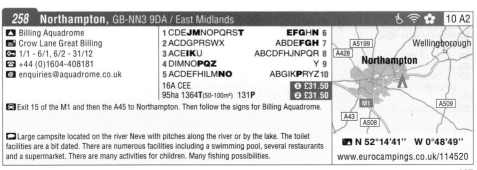

- ⛰ Billing Aquadrome
- 🏕 Crow Lane Great Billing
- 📅 1/1 - 6/1, 6/2 - 31/12
- ☎ +44 (0)1604-408181
- @ enquiries@aquadrome.co.uk

1 CDE**JM**NOPQRS**T**	**EFGH**N	6
2 ACDGPRSWX	ABDE**FGH**	7
3 ACE**IK**U	ABCDFHJNPQR	8
4 DIMNO**PQZ**	Y	9
5 ACDEFHILM**NO**	ABGIK**P**RYZ	10
16A CEE	❶ £31.50	
95ha 1364**T**(50-100m²) 131**P**	❷ £31.50	

🚗 Exit 15 of the M1 and then the A45 to Northampton. Then follow the signs for Billing Aquadrome.

💬 Large campsite located on the river Neve with pitches along the river or by the lake. The toilet facilities are a bit dated. There are numerous facilities including a swimming pool, several restaurants and a supermarket. There are many activities for children. Many fishing possibilities.

🏴 N 52°14'41'' W 0°48'49''
www.eurocampings.co.uk/114520

259 Riddings, GB-DE55 4BP / East Midlands ♿ 🛜 iD 9 B1

- ⛰ Riddings Wood
  Caravan & Camping Park
- 🏕 Bullock Lane
- 📅 1 Mar - 31 Dec
- ☎ +44 (0)1773-605160
- @ info@
  riddingswoodcaravanandcampingpark.co.uk

1 ADE**JM**NOPQRS**T**		6
2 AFOPRSTVWXY	A**BDEFG**	7
3 A**K**	ABE**FG**NQRTUV	8
4 FH	F	9
5 MN	ABCFGHJMPR	10
10A CEE	❶ £29.00	
2ha 150**T**(40-65m²) 7**P**	❷ £33.00	

🚗 M1 exit A608 turn right to Alfreton B600 Selton, turn left B6016 Jacksdale. Then turn right B6016 Ironville, turn right Bullock Lane.

💬 Lovely campsite with a beautiful panoramic view. Friendly staff at reception, very cosy.

📌 N 53°3'56'' W 1°21'22''
www.eurocampings.co.uk/122973

260 Skegness, GB-PE25 3TQ / East Midlands ♿ 🛜 iD 10 A1

- ⛰ Richmond Holiday Centre
- 🏕 Richmond Drive
- 📅 1 Mar - 31 Oct
- ☎ +44 (0)1754-762097
- @ sales@richmondholidays.com

1 ADE**JM**OPQR	E	6
2 GOPVX	A**BDEFGH**	7
3 ABE**K**	ABCDFJNQRSV	8
4 BCDIMO**PQRSTU**	E	9
5 ACDEFHJLMN	ABGHIKORYZ	10
16A CEE	❶ £28.00	
20ha 58**T**(80-100m²) 825**P**	❷ £28.00	

🚗 A52 from Boston. Follow one way system through Skegness on A52 direction Boston, then immediately turn left towards the bus station about 1 km further on. Follow campsite signs.

💬 Campsite with large indoor pool, spacious shop, including solarium and evening entertainment. 1 km from the beach. 6 km from the 'English Disneyland'.

📌 N 53°8'11'' E 0°19'48''
www.eurocampings.co.uk/100208

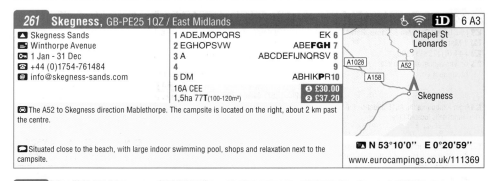

261 Skegness, GB-PE25 1QZ / East Midlands ♿ 🛜 iD 6 A3

- ⛰ Skegness Sands
- 🏕 Winthorpe Avenue
- 📅 1 Jan - 31 Dec
- ☎ +44 (0)1754-761484
- @ info@skegness-sands.com

1 ADEJMOPQRS	EK	6
2 EGHOPSVW	ABE**FGH**	7
3 A	ABCDEFIJNQRSV	8
4		9
5 DM	ABHIK**PR**	10
16A CEE	❶ £30.00	
1,5ha 77**T**(100-120m²)	❷ £37.20	

🚗 The A52 to Skegness direction Mablethorpe. The campsite is located on the right, about 2 km past the centre.

💬 Situated close to the beach, with large indoor swimming pool, shops and relaxation next to the campsite.

📌 N 53°10'0'' E 0°20'59''
www.eurocampings.co.uk/111369

262 Skegness, GB-PE25 1JF / East Midlands ♿ 🛜 iD 6 A3

- ⛰ Skegness Water Leisure Park
- 🏕 Walls Lane
- 📅 1 Mar - 20 Nov
- ☎ +44 (0)1754-899400
- @ enquiries@
  skegnesswaterleisurepark.co.uk

1 ADE**JM**NOPQRST	K**N**	6
2 DEGHOPSVX	ABDE**FGH**	7
3 B**K**	ABCDFIJNQRSV	8
4 INO**PQZ**	BJV	9
5 ABCDEFHJKLMN	ABFGHIJLMOR	10
16A CEE	❶ £27.00	
71ha 653**T**(100m²) 314**P**	❷ £27.00	

🚗 A52 from Skegness direction Ingoldmells. Follow the brown sign 'Water Leisure Park'.

💬 Very large campsite with a cosy part for touring pitches. With water skiing, cable car (1 km), beach, good playground, cosy bar/restaurant and coffee shop. Friendly and helpful staff. 1 km from the 'English Disneyland'.

📌 N 53°10'46'' E 0°20'14''
www.eurocampings.co.uk/110942

263 Skegness, GB-PE25 2LA / East Midlands 📶 iD 6 A3

- ⛰ Southview Leisure Park
- 🏠 Burgh Road
- 📅 1 Jan - 31 Dec
- ☎ +44 (0)1754-896000
- @ holidays@parkdean-resorts.com

1 ADEJMOPQR	**EFGHN**	6
2 GOSVWX	ABDE**FG**	7
3 BE**IJ**	ABCDFIJNQRSTU	8
4 BCDIJMO**PQRST**UVZ	E	9
5 ACDEFHJKL	ABFGHIKMO**PQR**YZ	10

16A CEE
48ha 98T(42-48m²) 1186P

🕐 £42.00
🕐 £42.00

🚗 A158 Lincoln direction Skegness, through Burgh le Marsh. The campsite is on the left after 5 km (waterfalls).

💬 A small village with everything in good style: swimming pool, golf, fitness area, restaurant, shop, show, sauna, snooker and a separate area for tourists, away from the annual pitches.

📍 N 53°9'20'' E 0°18'25''

www.eurocampings.co.uk/111368

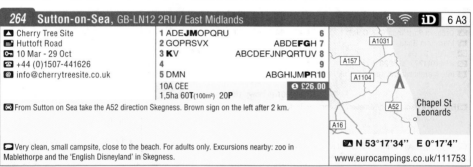

264 Sutton-on-Sea, GB-LN12 2RU / East Midlands ♿ 📶 iD 6 A3

- ⛰ Cherry Tree Site
- 🏠 Huttoft Road
- 📅 10 Mar - 29 Oct
- ☎ +44 (0)1507-441626
- @ info@cherrytreesite.co.uk

1 ADE**JM**OPQRU		6
2 GOPRSVX	ABDE**FG**H	7
3 **K**V	ABCDEFJNPQRTUV	8
4		9
5 DMN	ABGHIJM**PR**	10

10A CEE
1,5ha 60T(100m²) 20P

🕐 £26.00

🚗 From Sutton on Sea take the A52 direction Skegness. Brown sign on the left after 2 km.

💬 Very clean, small campsite, close to the beach. For adults only. Excursions nearby: zoo in Mablethorpe and the 'English Disneyland' in Skegness.

📍 N 53°17'34'' E 0°17'4''

www.eurocampings.co.uk/111753

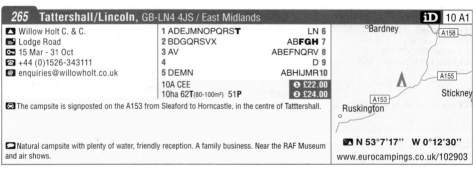

265 Tattershall/Lincoln, GB-LN4 4JS / East Midlands iD 10 A1

- ⛰ Willow Holt C. & C.
- 🏠 Lodge Road
- 📅 15 Mar - 31 Oct
- ☎ +44 (0)1526-343111
- @ enquiries@willowholt.co.uk

1 ADEJMNOPQRS**T**	LN	6
2 BDGQRSVX	AB**FGH**	7
3 AV	ABEFNQRV	8
4	D	9
5 DEMN	ABHIJMR	10

10A CEE
10ha 62T(80-100m²) 51P

🕐 £22.00
🕐 £24.00

🚗 The campsite is signposted on the A153 from Sleaford to Horncastle, in the centre of Tatttershall.

💬 Natural campsite with plenty of water, friendly reception. A family business. Near the RAF Museum and air shows.

📍 N 53°7'17'' W 0°12'30''

www.eurocampings.co.uk/102903

266 Teversal, GB-NG17 3JJ / East Midlands ♿ 📶 iD 5 B3

- ⛰ Teversal Cp. and Car. Clubsite*****
- 🏠 Silverhill Lane
- 📅 1 Jan - 31 Dec
- ☎ +44 (0)1623-551838
- @ teversal@
  campingandcaravanningclub.co.uk

1 ACDGJMNOPQRS**T**		6
2 AOPRSVWX	ABDE**FGH**	7
3 BE**GHK**L	ABCDEFIJKNQRSTUV	8
4 FH	BEFUV	9
5 ABDMN	ABFGHIJLM**N**P**R**	10

16A CEE
A177 3ha 101T(45-90m²) 5P

🕐 £40.40
🕐 £53.40

🚗 M1 exit 29, left at roundabout direction A6175 (Clay Cross), left at 2nd roundabout direction B6039 (Tibshelf), left at roundabout after ± 5 km direction B6014 (Mansfield). Left at Carnavon Arms pub direction Silverlane. Site 300 metres on the left.
💬 Excellent campsite at Mansfield. Sherwood Forest (Robin Hood) is nearby. Good walking and cycling opportunities. Winner of the Gold Award National Finals Enjoy England Excellence Awards 2005.

📍 N 53°8'55'' W 1°17'48''

www.eurocampings.co.uk/111470

United Kingdom

267 Trusthorpe, GB-LN12 2QQ / East Midlands   6 A3

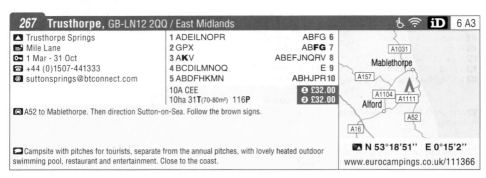

- ▲ Trusthorpe Springs
- 🏠 Mile Lane
- 📅 1 Mar - 31 Oct
- ☎ +44 (0)1507-441333
- @ suttonsprings@btconnect.com

1 ADEILNOPR	ABFG	6
2 GPX	ABFG	7
3 AKV	ABEFJNQRV	8
4 BCDILMNOQ	E	9
5 ABDFHKMN	ABHJPR	10
10A CEE	❶ £32.00	
10ha 31T(70-80m²) 116P	❷ £32.00	

🚗 A52 to Mablethorpe. Then direction Sutton-on-Sea. Follow the brown signs.

💬 Campsite with pitches for tourists, separate from the annual pitches, with lovely heated outdoor swimming pool, restaurant and entertainment. Close to the coast.

📍 N 53°18'51'' E 0°15'2''

www.eurocampings.co.uk/111366

268 Tuxford, GB-NG22 0PY / East Midlands   6 A3

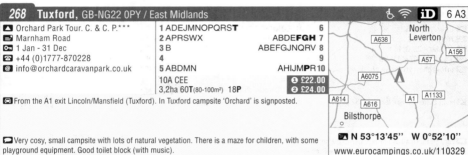

- ▲ Orchard Park Tour. C. & C. P.***
- 🏠 Marnham Road
- 📅 1 Jan - 31 Dec
- ☎ +44 (0)1777-870228
- @ info@orchardcaravanpark.co.uk

1 ADEJMNOPQRST		6
2 APRSWX	ABDEFGH	7
3 B	ABEFGJNQRV	8
4		9
5 ABDMN	AHIJMPR	10
10A CEE	❶ £22.00	
3,2ha 60T(80-100m²) 18P	❷ £24.00	

🚗 From the A1 exit Lincoln/Mansfield (Tuxford). In Tuxford campsite 'Orchard' is signposted.

💬 Very cosy, small campsite with lots of natural vegetation. There is a maze for children, with some playground equipment. Good toilet block (with music).

📍 N 53°13'45'' W 0°52'10''

www.eurocampings.co.uk/110329

269 West Ashby, GB-LN9 5PP / East Midlands   6 A3

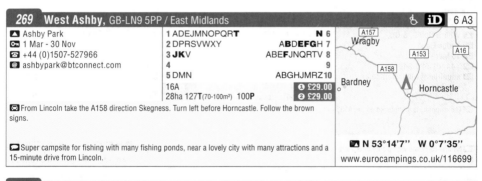

- ▲ Ashby Park
- 📅 1 Mar - 30 Nov
- ☎ +44 (0)1507-527966
- @ ashbypark@btconnect.com

1 ADEJMNOPQRT	N	6
2 DPRSVWXY	ABDEFGH	7
3 JKV	ABEFJNQRTV	8
4		9
5 DMN	ABGHJMRZ	10
16A	❶ £29.00	
28ha 127T(70-100m²) 100P	❷ £29.00	

🚗 From Lincoln take the A158 direction Skegness. Turn left before Horncastle. Follow the brown signs.

💬 Super campsite for fishing with many fishing ponds, near a lovely city with many attractions and a 15-minute drive from Lincoln.

📍 N 53°14'7'' W 0°7'35''

www.eurocampings.co.uk/116699

270 Woodhall Spa, GB-LN10 6QH / East Midlands   6 A3

- ▲ Petwood Caravan Park
- 🏠 Off Stixwould Road
- 📅 17 Mar - 15 Oct
- ☎ +44 (0)1526-354799
- @ info@petwoodcaravanpark.co.uk

1 ADEJMNOPQRST		6
2 OPRSVWX	ABFG	7
3 AKV	ABEFGNPQRSTUV	8
4 FH		9
5 BDN	ABHIKMPR	10
16A CEE	❶ £25.00	
2,6ha 98T(56-90m²)	❷ £29.00	

🚗 On the B1191 from Lincoln, left via roundabout 2nd exit centre after 200 metres left Wood Hall Spa. Or from Tettershall in Woodhall Spa continue for 200 metres, turn left.

💬 Quiet family campsite next to a beautiful swimming pool. Recreation park with many walking and cycling opportunities, around an old town 'Woodhall Spa'. Located in a wooded area.

📍 N 53°9'17'' W 0°13'19''

www.eurocampings.co.uk/121889

271 Woodhall Spa, GB-LN10 6UJ / East Midlands   ♿ 🛜 iD   6 A3

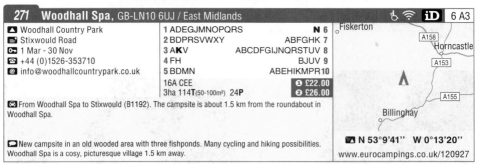

- ⛰ Woodhall Country Park
- ✉ Stixwould Road
- 🅿 1 Mar - 30 Nov
- ☎ +44 (0)1526-353710
- @ info@woodhallcountrypark.co.uk

1 ADEGJMNOPQRS	N 6
2 BDPRSVWXY	ABFGHK 7
3 A**K**V	ABCDFGIJNQRSTUV 8
4 FH	BJUV 9
5 BDMN	ABEHIKMPR 10

| 16A CEE | ❶ £22.00 |
| 3ha 114**T**(50-100m²) 24**P** | ❷ £26.00 |

🚗 From Woodhall Spa to Stixwould (B1192). The campsite is about 1.5 km from the roundabout in Woodhall Spa.

💬 New campsite in an old wooded area with three fishponds. Many cycling and hiking possibilities. Woodhall Spa is a cosy, picturesque village 1.5 km away.

📷 N 53°9'41''   W 0°13'20''

www.eurocampings.co.uk/120927

272 Worksop, GB-S80 3AE / East Midlands   ♿ 🛜 iD   6 A3

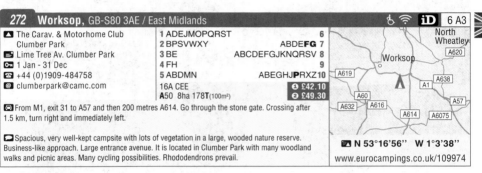

- ⛰ The Carav. & Motorhome Club Clumber Park
- ✉ Lime Tree Av. Clumber Park
- 🅿 1 Jan - 31 Dec
- ☎ +44 (0)1909-484758
- @ clumberpark@camc.com

1 ADEJMOPQRST	6
2 BPSVWXY	ABDE**FG** 7
3 BE	ABCDEFGJKNQRSV 8
4 FH	9
5 ABDMN	ABEGHJ**P**RXZ 10

| 16A CEE | ❶ £42.10 |
| **A**50 8ha 178**T**(100m²) | ❷ £49.30 |

🚗 From M1, exit 31 to A57 and then 200 metres A614. Go through the stone gate. Crossing after 1.5 km, turn right and immediately left.

💬 Spacious, very well-kept campsite with lots of vegetation in a large, wooded nature reserve. Business-like approach. Large entrance avenue. It is located in Clumber Park with many woodland walks and picnic areas. Many cycling possibilities. Rhododendrons prevail.

📷 N 53°16'56''   W 1°3'38''

www.eurocampings.co.uk/109974

United Kingdom

Dual personality

When the sun shines on East Anglia, this largely flat region is vivid with colour and life. The North Sea mists transform it into a mysterious and ephemeral land, the coastline subtly reshaped by the sea every winter. It's easy to believe in ghosts in this misty, marshy land! East Anglia was also conquered by Anglo-Saxons, Romans and Vikings, so you never know ...

Historic towns and cities

Historically extremely important for maritime activity, Harwich, now the port for the ferry that sails to the Hook of Holland, includes the circular fort Harwich Redoubt built in 1808. Inland is Norwich, the best preserved mediaeval city in England, with its famous cathedral, an imposing building and the centre of a mini-city in its own

right. In Colchester, the kids will love the Roman Circus Centre, while the town of Long Melford is a mecca for antiques hunters.

Out in the great wide open

No visit to East Anglia is complete without seeing Sutton Hoo - England's own Valley of the Kings, with a museum. Blakeney is a great place for seal-watching, and in West Stow Anglo-Saxon village you can even dress up and live as an Anglo-Saxon!

Several stately homes are also located in East Anglia: Helmingham Hall has a courtyard and moat, and the drawbridges are raised every night; Holkam Hall is classic English Palladian, while Ickworth House is Italianate Georgian, and Blickling Hall is said to be haunted by the ghost of Ann Boleyn, second wife of Henry VII. Spooky!

More things to do and try

Cambridge is a terrific location for water-based activities such as boating and punting, and hikers and horse-riders will love the routes through the Fens. Coastal town Aldeburgh has a fine beach and a forest park, with canoeing and kayaking on the Alde Estuary. Cromer and Great Yarmouth are famous bathing resorts, and if you like life on the water, you'll love the Blue Marshes Nature Reserve and The Broads between Norwich and Great Yarmouth.

All this exploring works up an appetite, so to take the edge off, try a God's Kitchel, a local speciality consisting of pastry filled with dried fruit. And naturally, given the location, seafood is quite popular. Cromer crab is a local speciality.

Our tips

1. *Fancy riding a steam train? Check out the North Norfolk Railway*
2. *Sheringham is home to the Fisherman's Heritage Centre and a beautiful estate*
3. *Walk the spectacular grounds of Framlingham Castle*
4. *Like a good scare? Enjoy a ghost walk in Peterborough*
5. *The Gruffalo Trail in Thetford Forest Park is a guaranteed hit with children*

United Kingdom

273 Belton/Great Yarmouth, GB-NR31 9NE / East Anglia

🦽 📶 ❄ **iD** 10 B1

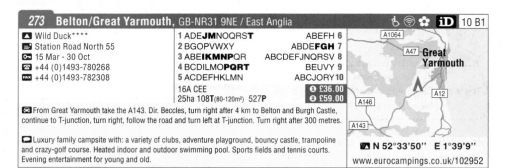

- 🔼 Wild Duck****
- 🏠 Station Road North 55
- 🗓 15 Mar - 30 Oct
- ☎ +44 (0)1493-780268
- 📠 +44 (0)1493-782308

1 ADE**JM**NOQRS**T**	ABEFH	6
2 BGOPVWXY	ABDE**FGH**	7
3 ABEI**KMNP**QR	ABCDEFJNQRSV	8
4 BCDILMO**PQRT**	BEUVY	9
5 ACDEFHKLMN	ABCJORY	10

16A CEE **❶ £36.00**
25ha 108T(80-120m²) 527P **❷ £59.00**

🚗 From Great Yarmouth take the A143. Dir. Beccles, turn right after 4 km to Belton and Burgh Castle, continue to T-junction, turn right, follow the road and turn left at T-junction. Turn right after 300 metres.

💬 Luxury family campsite with: a variety of clubs, adventure playground, bouncy castle, trampoline and crazy-golf course. Heated indoor and outdoor swimming pool. Sports fields and tennis courts. Evening entertainment for young and old.

📍 N 52°33'50'' E 1°39'9''

www.eurocampings.co.uk/102952

274 Bungay, GB-NR35 1HG / East Anglia

📶 **iD** 10 B1

- 🔼 Outney Meadow Park***
- 🏠 Outney Meadow
- 🗓 1 Mar - 30 Oct
- ☎ +44 (0)1986-892338
- @ info@outneymeadow.co.uk

1 ADEJMNOPQRS**T**	JNVX	6
2 CDGOPSWXY	A**BDEFG**H	7
3 **J**	ABFNQRV	8
4 FH	PQ	9
5 DFM**N**	ABFIMOR	10

10A CEE **❶ £28.00**
2,5ha 60T(80-100m²) 18P **❷ £35.00**

🚗 The campsite is on the A143, next to the roundabout towards the village of Bungay.

💬 Cosy family campsite within walking distance of the historic Bungay, located on a river with canoe and bike rental. Well-marked pitches on grass. Separate area for young people.

📍 N 52°27'37'' E 1°25'59''

www.eurocampings.co.uk/100213

275 Cambridge, GB-CB1 8NQ / East Anglia

🦽 📶 10 A2

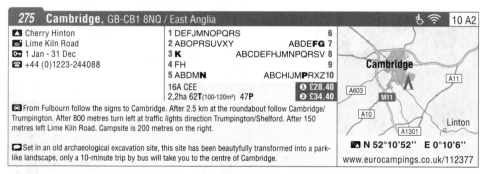

- 🔼 Cherry Hinton
- 🏠 Lime Kiln Road
- 🗓 1 Jan - 31 Dec
- ☎ +44 (0)1223-244088

1 DEFJMNOPQRS		6
2 ABOPRSUVXY	ABDE**FG**	7
3 **K**	ABCDEFHJMNPQRSV	8
4 FH		9
5 ABDM**N**	ABCHIJM**P**RXZ	10

16A CEE **❶ £28.40**
2,2ha 62T(100-120m²) 47P **❷ £34.40**

🚗 From Fulbourn follow the signs to Cambridge. After 2.5 km at the roundabout follow Cambridge/Trumpington. After 800 metres turn left at traffic lights direction Trumpington/Shelford. After 150 metres left Lime Kiln Road. Campsite is 200 metres on the right.

💬 Set in an old archaeological excavation site, this site has been beautyfully transformed into a park-like landscape, only a 10-minute trip by bus will take you to the centre of Cambridge.

📍 N 52°10'52'' E 0°0'6''

www.eurocampings.co.uk/112377

276 Clippesby, GB-NR29 3BL / East Anglia

🦽 📶 ❄ **iD** 10 B1

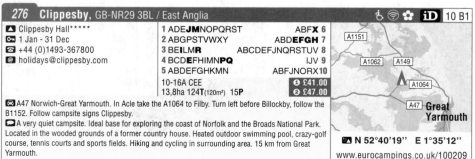

- 🔼 Clippesby Hall*****
- 🗓 1 Jan - 31 Dec
- ☎ +44 (0)1493-367800
- @ holidays@clippesby.com

1 ADE**JM**NOPQRST	ABF**X**	6
2 ABGPSTVWXY	ABD**EFGH**	7
3 BEILM**R**	ABCDEFJNQRSTUV	8
4 BCD**EF**HIMN**PQ**	IJV	9
5 ABDEFGHKMN	ABFJNORX	10

10-16A CEE **❶ £41.00**
13,8ha 124T(120m²) 15P **❷ £47.00**

🚗 A47 Norwich-Great Yarmouth. In Acle take the A1064 to Filby. Turn left before Billockby, follow the B1152. Follow campsite signs Clippesby.
💬 A very quiet campsite. Ideal base for exploring the coast of Norfolk and the Broads National Park. Located in the wooded grounds of a former country house. Heated outdoor swimming pool, crazy-golf course, tennis courts and sports fields. Hiking and cycling in surrounding area. 15 km from Great Yarmouth.

📍 N 52°40'19'' E 1°35'12''

www.eurocampings.co.uk/100209

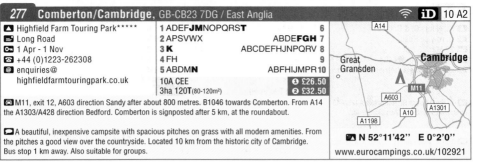

277 Comberton/Cambridge, GB-CB23 7DG / East Anglia 📶 iD 10 A2

- ▲ Highfield Farm Touring Park★★★★★
- ✉ Long Road
- ⊙ 1 Apr - 1 Nov
- ☎ +44 (0)1223-262308
- @ enquiries@
  highfieldfarmtouringpark.co.uk

1	ADEF**JMN**OPQRS**T**	6
2	APSVWX	ABDE**FGH** 7
3	**K**	ABCDEFHJNPQRV 8
4	FH	9
5	ABDM**N**	ABFHIJMPR 10
10A CEE		❶ £26.50
3ha 120**T**(80-120m²)		❷ £32.50

🚗 M11, exit 12, A603 direction Sandy after about 800 metres. B1046 towards Comberton. From A14 the A1303/A428 direction Bedford. Comberton is signposted after 5 km, at the roundabout.

💬 A beautiful, inexpensive campsite with spacious pitches on grass with all modern amenities. From the pitches a good view over the countryside. Located 10 km from the historic city of Cambridge. Bus stop 1 km away. Also suitable for groups.

N 52°11'42'' E 0°2'0''
www.eurocampings.co.uk/102921

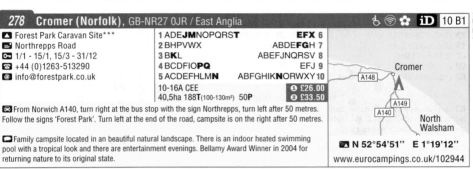

278 Cromer (Norfolk), GB-NR27 0JR / East Anglia ♿ 📶 ✿ iD 10 B1

- ▲ Forest Park Caravan Site★★★
- ✉ Northrepps Road
- ⊙ 1/1 - 15/1, 15/3 - 31/12
- ☎ +44 (0)1263-513290
- @ info@forestpark.co.uk

1	ADE**JMN**OPQRS**T**	**EFX** 6
2	BHPVWX	ABDE**FGH** 7
3	B**KL**	ABEFJNQRSV 8
4	BCDFIO**PQ**	EFJ 9
5	ACDEFHLM**N**	ABFGHIK**N**ORWXY 10
10-16A CEE		❶ £26.00
40,5ha 188**T**(100-130m²) 50**P**		❷ £33.50

🚗 From Norwich A140, turn right at the bus stop with the sign Northrepps, turn left after 50 metres. Follow the signs 'Forest Park'. Turn left at the end of the road, campsite is on the right after 50 metres.

💬 Family campsite located in an beautiful natural landscape. There is an indoor heated swimming pool with a tropical look and there are entertainment evenings. Bellamy Award Winner in 2004 for returning nature to its original state.

N 52°54'51'' E 1°19'12''
www.eurocampings.co.uk/102944

279 Cromer (Norfolk), GB-NR27 9PX / East Anglia ♿ 📶 ✿ iD 10 B1

- ▲ Woodhill Park★★★★★
- ✉ East Runton
- ⊙ 1 Mar - 30 Nov
- ☎ +44 (0)1263-512242
- @ info@woodhill-park.com

1	ADE**JMN**OPQRS**T**	**KNX** 6
2	EFGHOPSTVW	ABDE**FGH** 7
3	BE**GHIJKLMQ**	ABCDEFGIJNQRSTUV 8
4	F	E 9
5	ABDM**N**	ABFGHIJMPRVZ 10
16A CEE		❶ £22.00
15,4ha 250**T**(80-100m²) 36**P**		❷ £25.00

🚗 From Cromer follow the A149 to Sheringham. The campsite is located on the right side of the road after East Runton, 2.5 km distance from Cromer.

💬 A campsite located by the sea. Spacious with marked pitches and little shade. The campsite has spacious games and sports fields. You can also use the crazy-golf course, table-tennis table and giant chess game. Sea fishing is also possible.

N 52°56'12'' E 1°15'44''
www.eurocampings.co.uk/102942

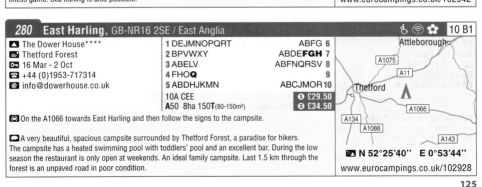

280 East Harling, GB-NR16 2SE / East Anglia ♿ 📶 ✿ 10 B1

- ▲ The Dower House★★★★
- ✉ Thetford Forest
- ⊙ 16 Mar - 2 Oct
- ☎ +44 (0)1953-717314
- @ info@dowerhouse.co.uk

1	DEJMNOPQRT	ABFG 6
2	BPVWXY	ABDE**FGH** 7
3	ABELV	ABFNQRSV 8
4	FHO**Q**	9
5	ABDHJKMN	ABCJMOR 10
10A CEE		❶ £29.50
A50 8ha 150**T**(80-150m²)		❷ £34.50

🚗 On the A1066 towards East Harling and then follow the signs to the campsite.

💬 A very beautiful, spacious campsite surrounded by Thetford Forest, a paradise for hikers. The campsite has a heated swimming pool with toddlers' pool and an excellent bar. During the low season the restaurant is only open at weekends. An ideal family campsite. Last 1.5 km through the forest is an unpaved road in poor condition.

N 52°25'40'' E 0°53'44''
www.eurocampings.co.uk/102928

United Kingdom

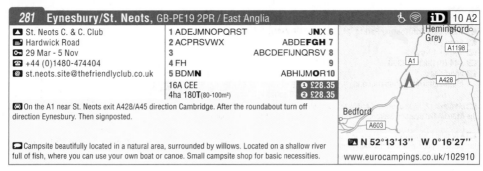

281 Eynesbury/St. Neots, GB-PE19 2PR / East Anglia   10 A2

- St. Neots C. & C. Club
- Hardwick Road
- 29 Mar - 5 Nov
- +44 (0)1480-474404
- st.neots.site@thefriendlyclub.co.uk

1 ADEJMNOPQRST	JNX 6
2 ACPRSVWX	ABDEFGH 7
3	ABCDEFIJNQRSV 8
4 FH	9
5 BDMN	ABHIJMOR 10
16A CEE	❶ £28.35
4ha 180T(80-100m²)	❷ £28.35

On the A1 near St. Neots exit A428/A45 direction Cambridge. After the roundabout turn off direction Eynesbury. Then signposted.

Campsite beautifully located in a natural area, surrounded by willows. Located on a shallow river full of fish, where you can use your own boat or canoe. Small campsite shop for basic necessities.

N 52°13'13'' W 0°16'27''
www.eurocampings.co.uk/102910

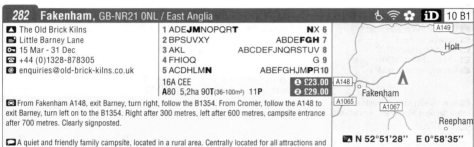

282 Fakenham, GB-NR21 0NL / East Anglia   10 B1

- The Old Brick Kilns
- Little Barney Lane
- 15 Mar - 31 Dec
- +44 (0)1328-878305
- enquiries@old-brick-kilns.co.uk

1 ADEJMNOPQRT	NX 6
2 BPSUVXY	ABDEFGH 7
3 AKL	ABCDEFJNQRSTUV 8
4 FHIOQ	G 9
5 ACDHLMN	ABEFGHJMPR 10
16A CEE	❶ £23.00
A80 5,2ha 90T(36-100m²) 11P	❷ £29.00

From Fakenham A148, exit Barney, turn right, follow the B1354. From Cromer, follow the A148 to exit Barney, turn left on to the B1354. Right after 300 metres, left after 600 metres, campsite entrance after 700 metres. Clearly signposted.

A quiet and friendly family campsite, located in a rural area. Centrally located for all attractions and things to do in North Norfolk.

N 52°51'28'' E 0°58'35''
www.eurocampings.co.uk/114400

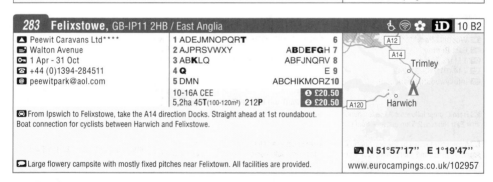

283 Felixstowe, GB-IP11 2HB / East Anglia   10 B2

- Peewit Caravans Ltd****
- Walton Avenue
- 1 Apr - 31 Oct
- +44 (0)1394-284511
- peewitpark@aol.com

1 ADEJMNOPQRT	6
2 AJPRSVWXY	ABDEFGH 7
3 ABKLQ	ABFJNQRV 8
4 Q	E 9
5 DMN	ABCHIKMORZ 10
10-16A CEE	❶ £20.50
5,2ha 45T(100-120m²) 212P	❷ £20.50

From Ipswich to Felixstowe, take the A14 direction Docks. Straight ahead at 1st roundabout. Boat connection for cyclists between Harwich and Felixstowe.

Large flowery campsite with mostly fixed pitches near Felixtown. All facilities are provided.

N 51°57'17'' E 1°19'47''
www.eurocampings.co.uk/102957

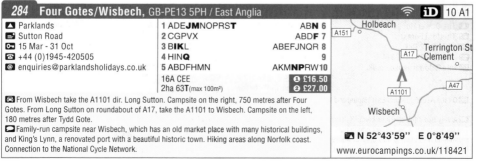

284 Four Gotes/Wisbech, GB-PE13 5PH / East Anglia   10 A1

- Parklands
- Sutton Road
- 15 Mar - 31 Oct
- +44 (0)1945-420505
- enquiries@parklandsholidays.co.uk

1 ADEJMNOPRST	ABN 6
2 CGPVX	ABDF 7
3 BIKL	ABEFJNQR 8
4 HINQ	9
5 ABDFHMN	AKMNPRW 10
16A CEE	❶ £16.50
2ha 63T(max 100m²)	❷ £27.00

From Wisbech take the A1101 dir. Long Sutton. Campsite on the right, 750 metres after Four Gotes. From Long Sutton on roundabout of A17, take the A1101 to Wisbech. Campsite on the left, 180 metres after Tydd Gote.

Family-run campsite near Wisbech, which has an old market place with many historical buildings, and King's Lynn, a renovated port with a beautiful historic town. Hiking areas along Norfolk coast. Connection to the National Cycle Network.

N 52°43'59'' E 0°8'49''
www.eurocampings.co.uk/118421

United Kingdom

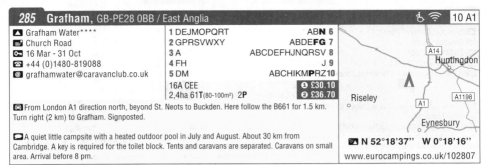

285 Grafham, GB-PE28 0BB / East Anglia

♿ 🛜 **10 A1**

- ▲ Grafham Water****
- ✉ Church Road
- 📅 16 Mar - 31 Oct
- ☎ +44 (0)1480-819088
- @ grafhamwater@caravanclub.co.uk

1	DEJMOPQRT	AB**N**	6
2	GPRSVWXY	ABDE**FG**	7
3	A	ABCDEFHJNQRSV	8
4	FH	J	9
5	DM	ABCHIKM**P**RZ	10

16A CEE
2,4ha 61T(80-100m²) 2P

💶 ❶ £30.10
💶 ❷ £36.70

From London A1 direction north, beyond St. Neots to Buckden. Here follow the B661 for 1.5 km. Turn right (2 km) to Grafham. Signposted.

A quiet little campsite with a heated outdoor pool in July and August. About 30 km from Cambridge. A key is required for the toilet block. Tents and caravans are separated. Caravans on small area. Arrival before 8 pm.

🧭 N 52°18'37'' W 0°18'16''

www.eurocampings.co.uk/102807

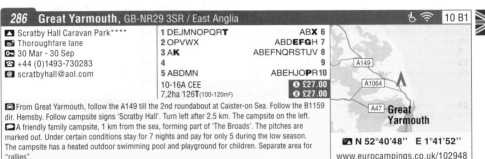

286 Great Yarmouth, GB-NR29 3SR / East Anglia

♿ 🛜 **10 B1**

- ▲ Scratby Hall Caravan Park****
- ✉ Thoroughfare lane
- 📅 30 Mar - 30 Sep
- ☎ +44 (0)1493-730283
- @ scratbyhall@aol.com

1	DEJMNOPQR**T**	AB**X**	6
2	OPVWX	ABD**EFG**H	7
3	A**K**	ABEFNQRSTUV	8
4			9
5	ABDMN	ABEHJO**PR**	10

10-16A CEE
7,2ha 126T(100-120m²)

💶 ❶ £27.00
💶 ❷ £27.00

From Great Yarmouth, follow the A149 till the 2nd roundabout at Caister-on Sea. Follow the B1159 dir. Hemsby. Follow campsite signs 'Scratby Hall'. Turn left after 2.5 km. The campsite on the left.

A friendly family campsite, 1 km from the sea, forming part of 'The Broads'. The pitches are marked out. Under certain conditions stay for 7 nights and pay for only 5 during the low season. The campsite has a heated outdoor swimming pool and playground for children. Separate area for "rallies".

🧭 N 52°40'48'' E 1°41'52''

www.eurocampings.co.uk/102948

287 Great Yarmouth, GB-NR30 1TB / East Anglia

⊗ ♿ 🛜 ✿ **iD** **10 B1**

- ▲ Vauxhall Holiday Park****
- ✉ Acle New Road
- 📅 24/3-1/4,19/5-23/9,21/10-30/10
- ☎ +44 (0)1493-857231
- @ info@vauxhallholidays.co.uk

1	ADEHKNOPQRS	EFHI	6
2	EGOPRSVW	ABE**FG**H	7
3	ABCE**IKL**MPUV	ABEFNQRSTUV	8
4	**A**BCDIJLMNO**PQRSTXZ**	BEFILUVY	9
5	ACDEFGHIKLM**N**	ABEFGHIPRVXYZ	10

16A CEE
47ha 180T(90-140m²) 926P

💶 ❶ £44.00
💶 ❷ £44.00

Take the A47 from Norwich towards Great Yarmouth. On the left of the road before Great Yarmouth. Campsite signposted.

A luxury family campsite with extensive, high-quality facilities. For children and adults, a tropical indoor pool, heated outdoor pool and sun terrace. There is also a large playground, child-care services, bicycle hire and fitness centre with solarium. Amusement arcade and entertainment evenings.

🧭 N 52°37'7'' E 1°42'59''

www.eurocampings.co.uk/102950

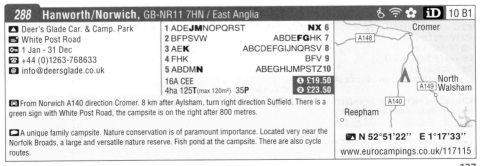

288 Hanworth/Norwich, GB-NR11 7HN / East Anglia

♿ 🛜 ✿ **iD** **10 B1**

- ▲ Deer's Glade Car. & Camp. Park
- ✉ White Post Road
- 📅 1 Jan - 31 Dec
- ☎ +44 (0)1263-768633
- @ info@deersglade.co.uk

1	ADE**JM**NOPQRST	**NX**	6
2	BFPSVW	ABDE**FG**HK	7
3	AE**K**	ABCDEFGIJNQRSV	8
4	FHK	BFV	9
5	ABDM**N**	ABEGHIJMPSTZ	10

16A CEE
4ha 125T(max 120m²) 35P

💶 ❶ £19.50
💶 ❷ £23.50

From Norwich A140 direction Cromer. 8 km after Aylsham, turn right direction Suffield. There is a green sign with White Post Road, the campsite is on the right after 800 metres.

A unique family campsite. Nature conservation is of paramount importance. Located very near the Norfolk Broads, a large and versatile nature reserve. Fish pond at the campsite. There are also cycle routes.

🧭 N 52°51'22'' E 1°17'33''

www.eurocampings.co.uk/117115

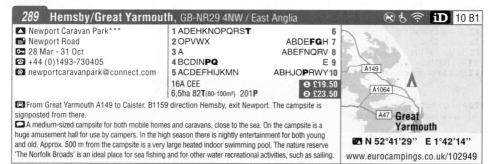

289 Hemsby/Great Yarmouth, GB-NR29 4NW / East Anglia · 10 B1

- Newport Caravan Park***
- Newport Road
- 28 Mar - 31 Oct
- +44 (0)1493-730405
- @ newportcaravanpark@connect.com

1 ADEHKNOPQRS**T**	6
2 OPVWX	ABDE**FGH** 7
3 A	ABEFNQRV 8
4 BCDINP**Q**	E 9
5 ACDEFHIJKMN	ABHJO**PR**WY 10

16A CEE
6,5ha 82**T**(80-100m²) 201**P**

- £19.50
- £23.50

From Great Yarmouth A149 to Caister. B1159 direction Hemsby, exit Newport. The campsite is signposted from there.

A medium-sized campsite for both mobile homes and caravans, close to the sea. On the campsite is a huge amusement hall for use by campers. In the high season there is nightly entertainment for both young and old. Approx. 500 m from the campsite is a very large heated indoor swimming pool. The nature reserve 'The Norfolk Broads' is an ideal place for sea fishing and for other water recreational activities, such as sailing.

A149 · A1064 · A47 · **Great Yarmouth**

N 52°41'29'' E 1°42'14''

www.eurocampings.co.uk/102949

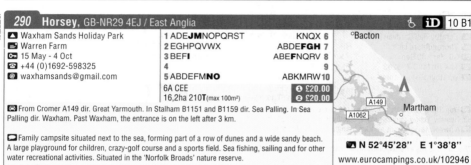

290 Horsey, GB-NR29 4EJ / East Anglia · 10 B1

- Waxham Sands Holiday Park
- Warren Farm
- 15 May - 4 Oct
- +44 (0)1692-598325
- @ waxhamsands@gmail.com

1 ADE**JM**NOPQRST	KNQX 6
2 EGHPQVWX	ABDE**FGH** 7
3 BEF**I**	ABEFNQRV 8
4	9
5 ABDEFM**NO**	ABKMRW 10

6A CEE
16,2ha 210**T**(max 100m²)

- £20.00
- £20.00

From Cromer A149 dir. Great Yarmouth. In Stalham B1151 and B1159 dir. Sea Palling. In Sea Palling dir. Waxham. Past Waxham, the entrance is on the left after 3 km.

Family campsite situated next to the sea, forming part of a row of dunes and a wide sandy beach. A large playground for children, crazy-golf course and a sports field. Sea fishing, sailing and for other water recreational activities. Situated in the 'Norfolk Broads' nature reserve.

°Bacton · A149 · A1062 · Martham

N 52°45'28'' E 1°38'8''

www.eurocampings.co.uk/102946

291 Hunstanton, GB-PE36 5BB / East Anglia · 10 A1

- Searles of Hunstanton*****
- South Beach
- 1/1 - 24/12, 26/12 - 31/12
- +44 (0)1485-534211
- @ bookings@searles.co.uk

1 ADE**JM**NOPQRST	ABEFHK**N**QSW**X**Y 6
2 EGHOPQRSVWX	ABDE**FGH** 7
3 BCE**IJKLM**NPQ	ABCDEFJNQRSTUV 8
4 **A**BCDEILO**PQR**TU**XZ**	EFVY 9
5 ACDEFHKM**N**	ABEFGHIKMNPRVYZ 10

10-16A CEE
20,2ha 316**T**(80-130m²) 162**P**

- £54.50
- £54.50

From King's Lynn the A149 as far as Hunstanton. Turn left towards South Beach at 1st roundabout, drive on to the 2nd roundabout, then straight ahead and turn left after 15 metres.

Large campsite by the North Sea. Tennis, bowling, golf course, 2 large fish ponds, large heated indoor pool, internet. Evening entertainment. Good starting point for water sports and boat trips. Fairground attractions along the boulevard towards the town centre.

A149 · Dersingham

N 52°55'50'' E 0°28'59''

www.eurocampings.co.uk/102917

292 Kessingland, GB-NR33 7SL / East Anglia · 10 B1

- C. & C. Club Site Kessingland
- Whites Lane
- 29 Mar - 1 Oct
- +44 (0)1502-742040
- @ kessingland-site@ campingandcaravanningclub.co.uk

1 ADE**J**MNOPQRT	6
2 OPRWX	ABDE**FGH** 7
3 A**K**	ABCDFIJNQRSV 8
4 FH	B 9
5 BDM**N**	ABMP**R** 10

16A CEE
2,5ha 90**T**(max 90m²) 5**P**

- £36.10
- £47.90

From the south, follow Kessingland at the 2nd roundabout, then follow the signs for Africa Wildlife. Note: the campsite is not signposted here.

Beautiful campsite for transit and residence. Close to Suffolk Wildlife park. Discounted price if campers have a CCI carnet. Two windmills next to the campsite.

A143 · Beccles · Lowestoft · A145 · A12

N 52°25'9'' E 1°42'20''

www.eurocampings.co.uk/114402

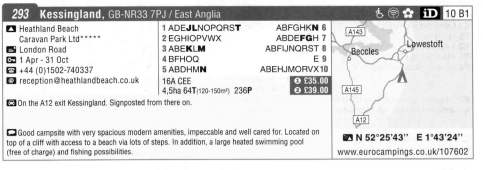

293 Kessingland, GB-NR33 7PJ / East Anglia ♿ 🛜 ✿ iD 10 B1

- ⛰ Heathland Beach
  Caravan Park Ltd*****
- 🏠 London Road
- 📅 1 Apr - 31 Oct
- ☎ +44 (0)1502-740337
- @ reception@heathlandbeach.co.uk

1 ADE**JL**NOPQRS**T**	ABFGHK**N** 6
2 EGHIOPVWX	ABDE**FGH** 7
3 ABE**KLM**	ABFIJNQRST 8
4 BFHOQ	E 9
5 ABDHM**N**	ABEHJMORVX 10
16A CEE	❶ £35.00
4,5ha 64**T**(120-150m²) 236**P**	❷ £39.00

🚗 On the A12 exit Kessingland. Signposted from there on.

💬 Good campsite with very spacious modern amenities, impeccable and well cared for. Located on top of a cliff with access to a beach via lots of steps. In addition, a large heated swimming pool (free of charge) and fishing possibilities.

📌 N 52°25'43'' E 1°43'24''
www.eurocampings.co.uk/107602

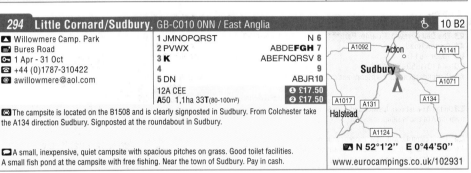

294 Little Cornard/Sudbury, GB-CO10 0NN / East Anglia ♿ 10 B2

- ⛰ Willowmere Camp. Park
- 🏠 Bures Road
- 📅 1 Apr - 31 Oct
- ☎ +44 (0)1787-310422
- @ awillowmere@aol.com

1 JMNOPQRST	N 6
2 PVWX	ABDE**FGH** 7
3 **K**	ABEFNQRSV 8
4	9
5 DN	ABJR 10
12A CEE	❶ £17.50
A50 1,1ha 33**T**(80-100m²)	❷ £17.50

🚗 The campsite is located on the B1508 and is clearly signposted in Sudbury. From Colchester take the A134 direction Sudbury. Signposted at the roundabout in Sudbury.

💬 A small, inexpensive, quiet campsite with spacious pitches on grass. Good toilet facilities. A small fish pond at the campsite with free fishing. Near the town of Sudbury. Pay in cash.

📌 N 52°1'2'' E 0°44'50''
www.eurocampings.co.uk/102931

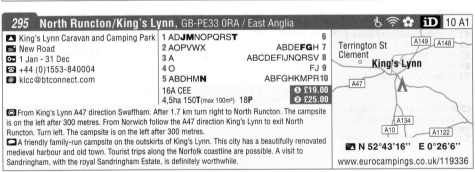

295 North Runcton/King's Lynn, GB-PE33 0RA / East Anglia ♿ 🛜 ✿ iD 10 A1

- ⛰ King's Lynn Caravan and Camping Park
- 🏠 New Road
- 📅 1 Jan - 31 Dec
- ☎ +44 (0)1553-840004
- @ klcc@btconnect.com

1 AD**JM**NOPQRS**T**	6
2 AOPVWX	ABDE**FGH** 7
3 A	ABCDEFIJNQRSV 8
4 O	FJ 9
5 ABDHM**N**	ABFGHKMPR 10
16A CEE	❶ £19.00
4,5ha 150**T**(max 100m²) 18**P**	❷ £25.00

🚗 From King's Lynn A47 direction Swaffham. After 1.7 km turn right to North Runcton. The campsite is on the left after 300 metres. From Norwich follow the A47 direction King's Lynn to exit North Runcton. Turn left. The campsite is on the left after 300 metres.
💬 A friendly family-run campsite on the outskirts of King's Lynn. This city has a beautifully renovated medieval harbour and old town. Tourist trips along the Norfolk coastline are possible. A visit to Sandringham, with the royal Sandringham Estate, is definitely worthwhile.

📌 N 52°43'16'' E 0°26'6''
www.eurocampings.co.uk/119336

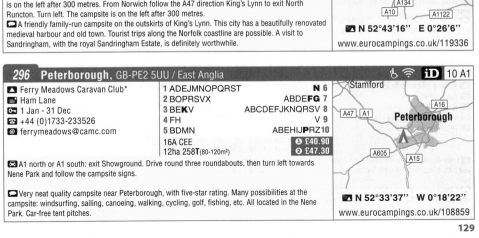

296 Peterborough, GB-PE2 5UU / East Anglia ♿ 🛜 iD 10 A1

- ⛰ Ferry Meadows Caravan Club*
- 🏠 Ham Lane
- 📅 1 Jan - 31 Dec
- ☎ +44 (0)1733-233526
- @ ferrymeadows@camc.com

1 ADEJMNOPQRST	**N** 6
2 BOPRSVX	ABDE**FG** 7
3 BE**KV**	ABCDEFJKNQRSV 8
4 FH	V 9
5 BDMN	ABEHIJ**PRZ** 10
16A CEE	❶ £40.90
12ha 258**T**(80-120m²)	❷ £47.30

🚗 A1 north or A1 south: exit Showground. Drive round three roundabouts, then turn left towards Nene Park and follow the campsite signs.

💬 Very neat quality campsite near Peterborough, with five-star rating. Many possibilities at the campsite: windsurfing, sailing, canoeing, walking, cycling, golf, fishing, etc. All located in the Nene Park. Car-free tent pitches.

📌 N 52°33'37'' W 0°18'22''
www.eurocampings.co.uk/108859

United Kingdom

United Kingdom

297 Theberton, GB-IP16 4TE / East Anglia ♿ 🛜 iD 10 B2

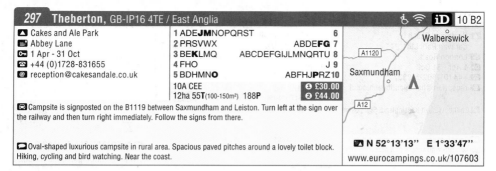

- 🔺 Cakes and Ale Park
- 📧 Abbey Lane
- 🔓 1 Apr - 31 Oct
- ☎ +44 (0)1728-831655
- @ reception@cakesandale.co.uk

1 ADEJMNOPQRST		6
2 PRSVWX	ABDEFG	7
3 BEKLMQ	ABCDEFGIJLMNQRTU	8
4 FHO		J 9
5 BDHMNO	ABFHJPRZ	10
10A CEE		❶ £30.00
12ha 55T(100-150m²) 188P		❷ £44.00

🗺 Campsite is signposted on the B1119 between Saxmundham and Leiston. Turn left at the sign over the railway and then turn right immediately. Follow the signs from there.

💬 Oval-shaped luxurious campsite in rural area. Spacious paved pitches around a lovely toilet block. Hiking, cycling and bird watching. Near the coast.

📍 N 52°13'13'' E 1°33'47''

www.eurocampings.co.uk/107603

298 Thurston/Bury St. Edmunds, GB-IP31 3RB / East Anglia ♿ 🛜 10 B2

- 🔺 The Dell Caravan & Camp. Park***
- 📧 Beyton Road
- 🔓 1 Mar - 31 Oct
- ☎ +44 (0)1359-270121
- @ thedellcaravanpark@btconnect.com

1 DEJMNOPQRT		6
2 APRSVWX	ABDEFGH	7
3	ABCDEFIJKLNPQRSV	8
4 FH		9
5 DMN	ABCHLMPRX	10
10A CEE		❶ £21.00
A50 3ha 50T(90-130m²)		❷ £27.00

🗺 On the A14 between Ipswich and Bury St. Edmunds, take the exit Thurston. The campsite is 1 km from the A14 and is signposted.

💬 Natural campsite with neat, modern and heated toilet facilities. 3/4-hour drive from Cambridge and 1 hour from Harwich. One section of the campsite is reserved for families, another part is for adults only. Noise from the motorway day and night.

📍 N 52°14'27'' E 0°49'25''

www.eurocampings.co.uk/110234

299 Upper Stoke, GB-NR14 8NG / East Anglia 🧗 ♿ 🛜 10 B1

- 🔺 Broadlands Naturistencamping***
- 📧 Brickle Road 31
- 🔓 1 Mar - 31 Oct
- ☎ +44 (0)1508-492907
- @ holidays@broadlandsun.co.uk

1 DEJMNOQRT	EN	6
2 ABGPY	ABDEFGH	7
3 BELMQ	ABEFGJNQRV	8
4 IOQRT	DK	9
5 DEN	ABJPRV	10
16A CEE		❶ £26.50
9,7ha 44T(80-100m²) 111P		❷ £26.50

🗺 On B1332 in Poringland roundabout at Railway Tavern direction Upper Stoke (Stoke Load). Turn left at the phone booth, direction Shotesham All Saints. Turn left after 275 metres, continue till the barrier.

💬 A campsite hidden in a forest landscape, with a private lake for swimming. Also an indoor heated swimming pool, sports courts, 'petanque' field and a children's playground. Users of this site must be members of a naturist association.

📍 N 52°34'9'' E 1°19'31''

www.eurocampings.co.uk/102953

300 Weybourne, GB-NR25 7HW / East Anglia ♿ 🛜 ✿ iD 10 B1

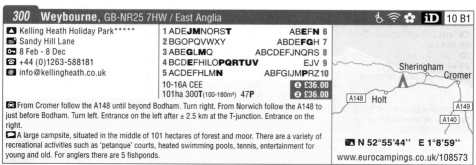

- 🔺 Kelling Heath Holiday Park*****
- 📧 Sandy Hill Lane
- 🔓 8 Feb - 8 Dec
- ☎ +44 (0)1263-588181
- @ info@kellingheath.co.uk

1 ADEJMNORST	ABEFN	6
2 BGOPQVWXY	ABDEFGH	7
3 ABEGLMQ	ABCDEFJNQRS	8
4 BCDEFHILOPQRTUV	EJV	9
5 ACDEFHLMN	ABFGIJMPRZ	10
10-16A CEE		❶ £36.00
101ha 300T(100-180m²) 47P		❷ £36.00

🗺 From Cromer follow the A148 until beyond Bodham. Turn right. From Norwich follow the A148 to just before Bodham. Turn left. Entrance on the left after ± 2.5 km at the T-junction. Entrance on the right.

💬 A large campsite, situated in the middle of 101 hectares of forest and moor. There are a variety of recreational activities such as 'petanque' courts, heated swimming pools, tennis, entertainment for young and old. For anglers there are 5 fishponds.

📍 N 52°55'44'' E 1°8'59''

www.eurocampings.co.uk/108573

301 Willingham/Cambridge, GB-CB24 5LT / East Anglia ⏶ 10 A1

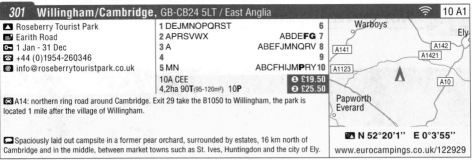

- ⏶ Roseberry Tourist Park
- ✉ Earith Road
- 🗓 1 Jan - 31 Dec
- ☎ +44 (0)1954-260346
- @ info@roseberrytouristpark.co.uk

1 DEJMNOPQRST		6
2 APRSVWX	ABDEFG	7
3 A	ABEFJMNQRV	8
4		9
5 MN	ABCFHIJMPRY	10
10A CEE		❶ £19.50
4,2ha 90T(95-120m²) 10P		❷ £25.50

🚗 A14: northern ring road around Cambridge. Exit 29 take the B1050 to Willingham, the park is located 1 mile after the village of Willingham.

💬 Spaciously laid out campsite in a former pear orchard, surrounded by estates, 16 km north of Cambridge and in the middle, between market towns such as St. Ives, Huntingdon and the city of Ely.

📷 N 52°20'1'' E 0°3'55''
www.eurocampings.co.uk/122929

302 Woodbridge, GB-IP12 3NF / East Anglia ♿ 10 B2

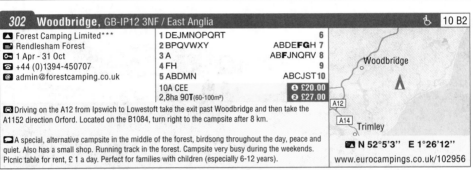

- ⏶ Forest Camping Limited***
- ✉ Rendlesham Forest
- 🗓 1 Apr - 31 Oct
- ☎ +44 (0)1394-450707
- @ admin@forestcamping.co.uk

1 DEJMNOPQRT		6
2 BPQVWXY	ABDEFGH	7
3 A	ABFJNQRV	8
4 FH		9
5 ABDMN	ABCJST	10
10A CEE		❶ £20.00
2,8ha 90T(60-100m²)		❷ £27.00

🚗 Driving on the A12 from Ipswich to Lowestoft take the exit past Woodbridge and then take the A1152 direction Orford. Located on the B1084, turn right to the campsite after 8 km.

💬 A special, alternative campsite in the middle of the forest, birdsong throughout the day, peace and quiet. Also has a small shop. Running track in the forest. Campsite very busy during the weekends. Picnic table for rent, £ 1 a day. Perfect for families with children (especially 6-12 years).

📷 N 52°5'3'' E 1°26'12''
www.eurocampings.co.uk/102956

303 Woodbridge, GB-IP12 4NS / East Anglia ♿ ⏶ iD 10 B2

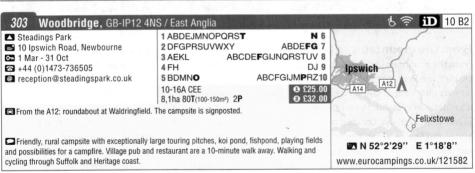

- ⏶ Steadings Park
- ✉ 10 Ipswich Road, Newbourne
- 🗓 1 Mar - 31 Oct
- ☎ +44 (0)1473-736505
- @ reception@steadingspark.co.uk

1 ABDEJMNOPQRST	N	6
2 DFGPRSUVWXY	ABDEFG	7
3 AEKL	ABCDEFGIJNQRSTUV	8
4 FH	DJ	9
5 BDMNO	ABCFGIJMPRZ	10
10-16A CEE		❶ £25.00
8,1ha 80T(100-150m²) 2P		❷ £32.00

🚗 From the A12: roundabout at Waldringfield. The campsite is signposted.

💬 Friendly, rural campsite with exceptionally large touring pitches, koi pond, fishpond, playing fields and possibilities for a campfire. Village pub and restaurant are a 10-minute walk away. Walking and cycling through Suffolk and Heritage coast.

📷 N 52°2'29'' E 1°18'8''
www.eurocampings.co.uk/121582

From the mountains to the sea

From the mountains and lakes of the Lake District, the Pennines, to the Yorkshire Dales with its picturesque farmlands, the landscape dominates in every film or television series set in Northern England. Located between the Irish and North Seas, and just south of Scotland, this region also has numerous historic cities such as Newcastle, York, and Liverpool, and many great literary associations: who hasn't read Lewis Carroll's Alice in Wonderland, or loved the illustrated works of Beatrix Potter?

She loves you, yeah, yeah, yeah

What's your favourite Beatles song? Liverpool, now synonymous with the legendary band, was also a major port during the Industrial revolution, and was bombed during World War II. Sheffield is home to the National Centre for Popular Music,

and is also one of the greenest cities in the UK. Lancaster hosts an annual Music Festival that features music from all over the world. Want to explore other eras? Go further back in time and contemplate the majesty of the spectacular York Minster in York, a city founded by Viking settlers. York is also a good base for visiting Chatsworth House and Castle Howard. The city of Newcastle, capital of the north, is famous for its ship-building activities, and sights include the BALTIC Centre of the Arts and the Gateshead Millennium Bridge.

Calories? What calories?

All this exploring will make you peckish, so try some local specialities: how about a sweet snack like Eccles cake, or a stottie cake with butter or clotted cream and jam, with quintessential English tea. Want something meatier? Try scouse

Did you know ...?
The Victorian-era house Cragside, near Rothbury, Northumberland, is the oldest house in the world powered by hydroelectricity?

District National Park and the Yorkshire Dales National Park.

And it needn't stop when the sun goes down: the towns and cities of Northern England are famous for their night life.

with Yorkshire pudding, or some steak and kidney pie, or even tripe and onions, washed down with a local beer. Then walk some more.

Activities 24-7

All fed and ready for the great outdoors? Durham is a great location for quad-biking, off-road driving, paintball and archery, as well as lovely coastal walks, river cruises and boat hire. Want a challenge? There's hiking, climbing, kayaking, canoeing, and other extreme sports in the Lake

Our tips

1. Relax on the Sunderland coast by the river Wear
2. Take in a football match at any of Northern England's great stadiums
3. Check out the 'camera obscura' at the Ryledale Folk Museum, York Moors National Park
4. Cycle along Hadrian's Wall, erected by the Romans
5. Take the kids ghost-hunting in the Treasurer's House in Beverly, Yorkshire

United Kingdom

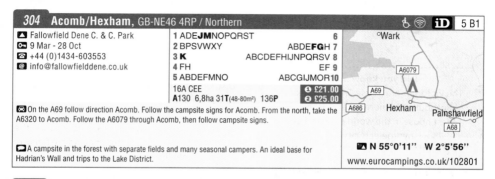

304 Acomb/Hexham, GB-NE46 4RP / Northern   5 B1

- ▲ Fallowfield Dene C. & C. Park
- ☛ 9 Mar - 28 Oct
- ☎ +44 (0)1434-603553
- @ info@fallowfielddene.co.uk

1 ADE**JM**NOPQRST	6
2 BPSVWXY	ABDE**FGH** 7
3 **K**	ABCDEFHIJNPQRSV 8
4 FH	EF 9
5 ABDEFMNO	ABCGIJMOR 10

16A CEE   ❶ £21.00
A130 **6,8**ha **31T**(48-80m²) 136**P**   ❷ £25.00

On the A69 follow direction Acomb. Follow the campsite signs for Acomb. From the north, take the A6320 to Acomb. Follow the A6079 through Acomb, then follow campsite signs.

A campsite in the forest with separate fields and many seasonal campers. An ideal base for Hadrian's Wall and trips to the Lake District.

◤N 55°0'11" W 2°5'56"
www.eurocampings.co.uk/102801

305 Allerston, GB-YO18 7PQ / Yorkshire & Humberside   6 A2

- ▲ Vale of Pickering C.Park*****
- 🏠 Carr House Farm
- ☛ 1/1 - 2/1, 7/3 - 31/12
- ☎ +44 (0)1723-859280
- @ info@valeofpickering.co.uk

1 ACDE**JM**NOPQR**T**	6
2 PRSVWX	ABDE**FGH**K 7
3 BE**K**	ABCDE**F**GIJNQRST 8
4	9
5 CDM**N**O	ABFGHJMPST 10

10A CEE   ❶ £27.00
A50 **8**ha **80T**(70-90m²) 80**P**   ❷ £31.00

On the A170 between Pickering and Scarborough. Then in Allerston take the B1415 direction Malton and follow the campsite signs. Campsite after about 3 km.

Lovely campsite (grassland) located in an open field with beautiful new (2015) toilet facilities (even bathtubs). Gravel pitches.

◤N 54°13'7" W 0°39'0"
www.eurocampings.co.uk/102901

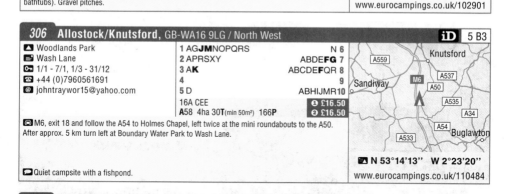

306 Allostock/Knutsford, GB-WA16 9LG / North West   5 B3

- ▲ Woodlands Park
- 🏠 Wash Lane
- ☛ 1/1 - 7/1, 1/3 - 31/12
- ☎ +44 (0)7960561691
- @ johntraywor15@yahoo.com

1 AG**JM**NOPQRS	N 6
2 APRSXY	ABDE**FG** 7
3 A**K**	ABCDE**F**QR 8
4	9
5 D	ABHIJMR 10

16A CEE   ❶ £16.50
A58 **4**ha **30T**(min 50m²) 166**P**   ❷ £16.50

M6, exit 18 and follow the A54 to Holmes Chapel, left twice at the mini roundabouts to the A50. After approx. 5 km turn left at Boundary Water Park to Wash Lane.

Quiet campsite with a fishpond.

◤N 53°14'13" W 2°23'20"
www.eurocampings.co.uk/110484

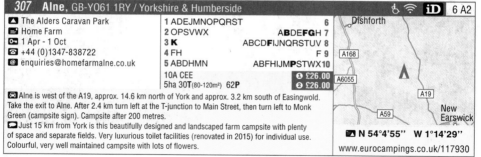

307 Alne, GB-YO61 1RY / Yorkshire & Humberside   6 A2

- ▲ The Alders Caravan Park
- 🏠 Home Farm
- ☛ 1 Apr - 1 Oct
- ☎ +44 (0)1347-838722
- @ enquiries@homefarmalne.co.uk

1 ADE**JM**NOPQRST	6
2 OPSVWX	A**B**DE**FGH** 7
3 **K**	ABCD**F**IJNQRSTUV 8
4 FH	F 9
5 ABDHMN	ABFHIJM**P**STWX 10

10A CEE   ❶ £26.00
5ha **30T**(80-120m²) 62**P**   ❷ £26.00

Alne is west of the A19, approx. 14.6 km north of York and approx. 3.2 km south of Easingwold. Take the exit to Alne. After 2.4 km turn left at the T-junction to Main Street, then turn left to Monk Green (campsite sign). Campsite after 200 metres.

Just 15 km from York is this beautifully designed and landscaped farm campsite with plenty of space and separate fields. Very luxurious toilet facilities (renovated in 2015) for individual use. Colourful, very well maintained campsite with lots of flowers.

◤N 54°4'55" W 1°14'29"
www.eurocampings.co.uk/117930

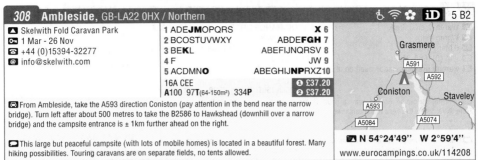

308 Ambleside, GB-LA22 0HX / Northern

♿ 📶 ✿ **iD** 5 B2

- 🏕 Skelwith Fold Caravan Park
- 📅 1 Mar - 26 Nov
- ☎ +44 (0)15394-32277
- @ info@skelwith.com

1	ADE**JM**OPQRS	**X**	6
2	BCOSTUVWXY	ABDE**FGH**	7
3	BE**KL**	ABEFIJNQRSV	8
4	F	JW	9
5	ACDMN**O**	ABEGHIJ**NP**RXZ	10

16A CEE — 💶 £37.20
A100 97T(64-150m²) 334P — 💶 £37.20

🚗 From Ambleside, take the A593 direction Coniston (pay attention in the bend near the narrow bridge). Turn left after about 500 metres to take the B2586 to Hawkshead (downhill over a narrow bridge) and the campsite entrance is ± 1km further ahead on the right.

💬 This large but peaceful campsite (with lots of mobile homes) is located in a beautiful forest. Many hiking possibilities. Touring caravans are on separate fields, no tents allowed.

📍 N 54°24'49'' W 2°59'4''

www.eurocampings.co.uk/114208

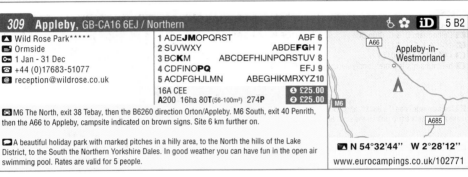

309 Appleby, GB-CA16 6EJ / Northern

♿ ✿ **iD** 5 B2

- 🏕 Wild Rose Park*****
- 🏘 Ormside
- 📅 1 Jan - 31 Dec
- ☎ +44 (0)17683-51077
- @ reception@wildrose.co.uk

1	ADE**JM**OPQRST	ABF	6
2	SUVWXY	ABDE**FGH**	7
3	BC**KM**	ABCDEFHIJNPQRSTUV	8
4	CDFINO**PQ**	EFJ	9
5	ACDFGHJLMN	ABEGHIKMRXYZ	10

16A CEE — 💶 £25.00
A200 16ha 80T(56-100m²) 274P — 💶 £25.00

🚗 M6 The North, exit 38 Tebay, then the B6260 direction Orton/Appleby. M6 South, exit 40 Penrith, then the A66 to Appleby, campsite indicated on brown signs. Site 6 km further on.

💬 A beautiful holiday park with marked pitches in a hilly area, to the North the hills of the Lake District, to the South the Northern Yorkshire Dales. In good weather you can have fun in the open air swimming pool. Rates are valid for 5 people.

📍 N 54°32'44'' W 2°28'12''

www.eurocampings.co.uk/102771

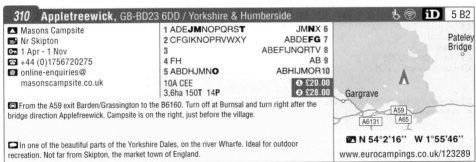

310 Appletreewick, GB-BD23 6DD / Yorkshire & Humberside

♿ 📶 **iD** 5 B2

- 🏕 Masons Campsite
- 🏘 Nr Skipton
- 📅 1 Apr - 1 Nov
- ☎ +44 (0)1756720275
- @ online-enquiries@ masonscampsite.co.uk

1	ADE**JM**NOPQRS**T**	JMN**X**	6
2	CFGIKNOPRVWXY	ABDE**FG**	7
3		ABEFIJNQRTV	8
4	FH	AB	9
5	ABDHJMN**O**	ABHIJMOR	10

10A CEE — 💶 £20.00
3,6ha 150T 14P — 💶 £28.00

🚗 From the A59 exit Barden/Grassington to the B6160. Turn off at Burnsal and turn right after the bridge direction Applefreewick. Campsite is on the right, just before the village.

💬 In one of the beautiful parts of the Yorkshire Dales, on the river Wharfe. Ideal for outdoor recreation. Not far from Skipton, the market town of England.

📍 N 54°2'16'' W 1°55'46''

www.eurocampings.co.uk/123289

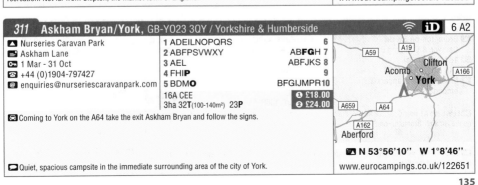

311 Askham Bryan/York, GB-YO23 3QY / Yorkshire & Humberside

📶 **iD** 6 A2

- 🏕 Nurseries Caravan Park
- 🏘 Askham Lane
- 📅 1 Mar - 31 Oct
- ☎ +44 (0)1904-797427
- @ enquiries@nurseriescaravanpark.com

1	ADEILNOPQRS		6
2	ABFPSVWXY	AB**FGH**	7
3	AEL	ABFJKS	8
4	FHI**P**		9
5	BDM**O**	BFGIJMPR	10

16A CEE — 💶 £18.00
3ha 32T(100-140m²) 23P — 💶 £24.00

🚗 Coming to York on the A64 take the exit Askham Bryan and follow the signs.

💬 Quiet, spacious campsite in the immediate surrounding area of the city of York.

📍 N 53°56'10'' W 1°8'46''

www.eurocampings.co.uk/122651

United Kingdom

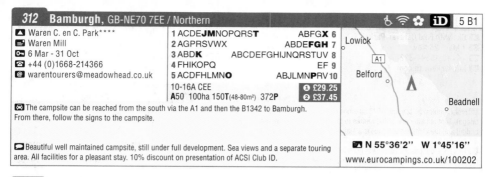

312 Bamburgh, GB-NE70 7EE / Northern   ♿ 📶 ⚙ iD 5 B1

- 🏕 Waren C. en C. Park★★★★
- 📧 Waren Mill
- 📅 6 Mar - 31 Oct
- ☎ +44 (0)1668-214366
- @ warentourers@meadowhead.co.uk

1 ACDEJMNOPQRST	ABFGX	6
2 AGPRSVWX	ABDEFGH	7
3 ABDK	ABCDEFGHIJNQRSTUV	8
4 FHIKOPQ	EF	9
5 ACDFHLMNO	ABJLMNPRV	10

10-16A CEE ❶ £29.25
A50 100ha 150T(48-80m²) 372P ❷ £37.45

🗺 The campsite can be reached from the south via the A1 and then the B1342 to Bamburgh. From there, follow the signs to the campsite.

💬 Beautiful well maintained campsite, still under full development. Sea views and a separate touring area. All facilities for a pleasant stay. 10% discount on presentation of ACSI Club ID.

📍 N 55°36'2'' W 1°45'16''
www.eurocampings.co.uk/100202

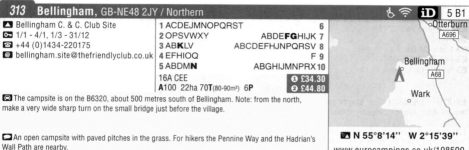

313 Bellingham, GB-NE48 2JY / Northern   ♿ 📶 iD 5 B1

- 🏕 Bellingham C. & C. Club Site
- 📅 1/1 - 4/1, 1/3 - 31/12
- ☎ +44 (0)1434-220175
- @ bellingham.site@thefriendlyclub.co.uk

1 ACDEJMNOPQRST		6
2 OPSVWXY	ABDEFGHIJK	7
3 ABKLV	ABCDEFHJNPQRSV	8
4 EFHIOQ	F	9
5 ABDMN	ABGHIJMNPRX	10

16A CEE ❶ £34.30
A100 22ha 70T(80-90m²) 6P ❷ £44.80

🗺 The campsite is on the B6320, about 500 metres south of Bellingham. Note: from the north, make a very wide sharp turn on the small bridge just before the village.

💬 An open campsite with paved pitches in the grass. For hikers the Pennine Way and the Hadrian's Wall Path are nearby.

📍 N 55°8'14'' W 2°15'39''
www.eurocampings.co.uk/108590

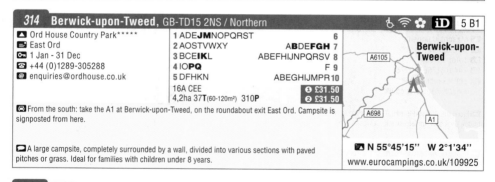

314 Berwick-upon-Tweed, GB-TD15 2NS / Northern   ♿ 📶 ⚙ iD 5 B1

- 🏕 Ord House Country Park★★★★★
- 📧 East Ord
- 📅 1 Jan - 31 Dec
- ☎ +44 (0)1289-305288
- @ enquiries@ordhouse.co.uk

1 ADEJMNOPQRST		6
2 AOSTVWXY	ABDEFGH	7
3 BCEIKL	ABEFHIJNPQRSV	8
4 IOPQ	F	9
5 DFHKN	ABEGHIJMPR	10

16A CEE ❶ £31.50
4,2ha 37T(60-120m²) 310P ❷ £31.50

🗺 From the south: take the A1 at Berwick-upon-Tweed, on the roundabout exit East Ord. Campsite is signposted from here.

💬 A large campsite, completely surrounded by a wall, divided into various sections with paved pitches or grass. Ideal for families with children under 8 years.

📍 N 55°45'15'' W 2°1'34''
www.eurocampings.co.uk/109925

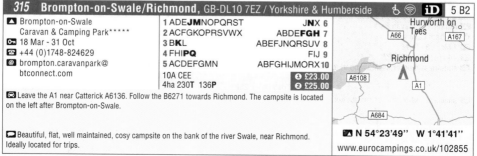

315 Brompton-on-Swale/Richmond, GB-DL10 7EZ / Yorkshire & Humberside   ♿ 📶 iD 5 B2

- 🏕 Brompton-on-Swale Caravan & Camping Park★★★★★
- 📅 18 Mar - 31 Oct
- ☎ +44 (0)1748-824629
- @ brompton.caravanpark@ btconnect.com

1 ADEJMNOPQRST	JNX	6
2 ACFGKOPRSVWX	ABDEFGH	7
3 BKL	ABEFJNQRSUV	8
4 FHIPQ	FIJ	9
5 ACDEFGMN	ABFGHIJMORX	10

10A CEE ❶ £23.00
4ha 230T 136P ❷ £25.00

🗺 Leave the A1 near Catterick A6136. Follow the B6271 towards Richmond. The campsite is located on the left after Brompton-on-Swale.

💬 Beautiful, flat, well maintained, cosy campsite on the bank of the river Swale, near Richmond. Ideally located for trips.

📍 N 54°23'49'' W 1°41'41''
www.eurocampings.co.uk/102855

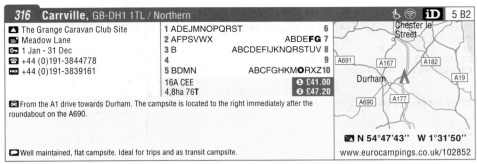

316 Carrville, GB-DH1 1TL / Northern — 5 B2

- ▲ The Grange Caravan Club Site
- ✉ Meadow Lane
- 📅 1 Jan - 31 Dec
- ☎ +44 (0)191-3844778
- 📠 +44 (0)191-3839161

1 ADEJMNOPQRST		6
2 AFPSVWX	ABDE**FG**	7
3 B	ABCDEFIJKNQRSTUV	8
4		9
5 BDMN	ABCFGHKM**O**RXZ	10

16A CEE
4,8ha 76**T**

❶ £41.00
❷ £47.20

🚗 From the A1 drive towards Durham. The campsite is located on the right immediately after the roundabout on the A690.

💬 Well maintained, flat campsite. Ideal for trips and as transit campsite.

🧭 N 54°47'43'' W 1°31'50''

www.eurocampings.co.uk/102852

317 Cayton Bay/Scarborough, GB-YO11 3NN / Yorkshire & Humberside — 6 A2

- ▲ Cayton Village Caravan Park
- ✉ Mill Lane
- 📅 1 Mar - 31 Oct
- ☎ +44 (0)1723-583171
- @ info@caytontouring.co.uk

1 ACDEJMNOPQRST		6
2 AOPRSVWXY	ABDE**FGH**	7
3 BE**K**	ABCDEFGIJNQRSTUV	8
4 F		9
5 ABDMN	ABFHIJMORX	10

10-16A CEE
11ha 310**T**(81-100m²)

❶ £31.00
❷ £35.00

🚗 From the A64 take the B1261 to Filey. In Cayton Village take the 2nd exit after the Blacksmiths Arms to Mill Lane. After ± 140 metres the campsite is on the left.

💬 A campsite within walking distance of the sea, on the edge of the village. Many comfort pitches on hard surface. Environmentally friendly and excellent toilet facilities. Bus connections from the campsite.

🧭 N 54°14'8'' W 0°22'35''

www.eurocampings.co.uk/118380

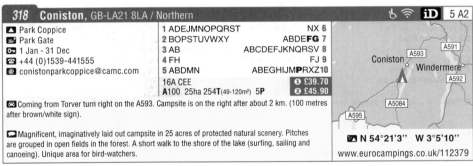

318 Coniston, GB-LA21 8LA / Northern — 5 A2

- ▲ Park Coppice
- ✉ Park Gate
- 📅 1 Jan - 31 Dec
- ☎ +44 (0)1539-441555
- @ conistonparkcoppice@camc.com

1 ADEJMNOPQRST	NX	6
2 BOPSTUVWXY	ABDE**FG**	7
3 AB	ABCDEFJKNQRSV	8
4 FH	FJ	9
5 ABDMN	ABEGHIJM**P**RXZ	10

16A CEE
A100 25ha 254**T**(49-120m²) 5**P**

❶ £39.70
❷ £45.90

🚗 Coming from Torver turn right on the A593. Campsite is on the right after about 2 km. (100 metres after brown/white sign).

💬 Magnificent, imaginatively laid out campsite in 25 acres of protected natural scenery. Pitches are grouped in open fields in the forest. A short walk to the shore of the lake (surfing, sailing and canoeing). Unique area for bird-watchers.

🧭 N 54°21'3'' W 3°5'10''

www.eurocampings.co.uk/112379

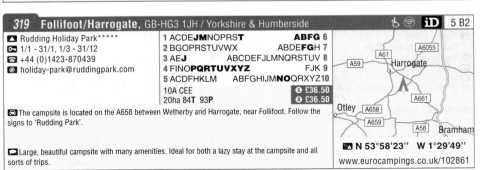

319 Follifoot/Harrogate, GB-HG3 1JH / Yorkshire & Humberside — 5 B2

- ▲ Rudding Holiday Park*****
- 📅 1/1 - 31/1, 1/3 - 31/12
- ☎ +44 (0)1423-870439
- @ holiday-park@ruddingpark.com

1 ACDE**JM**NOPRS**T**	**ABFG**	6
2 BGOPRSTUVWX	ABDE**FGH**	7
3 AE**J**	ABCDEFJLMNQRSTUV	8
4 FINO**PQRTUVXYZ**	FJK	9
5 ACDFHKLM	ABFGHIJMM**NO**QRXYZ	10

10A CEE
20ha 84**T** 93**P**

❶ £36.50
❷ £36.50

🚗 The campsite is located on the A658 between Wetherby and Harrogate, near Follifoot. Follow the signs to 'Rudding Park'.

💬 Large, beautiful campsite with many amenities. Ideal for both a lazy stay at the campsite and all sorts of trips.

🧭 N 53°58'23'' W 1°29'49''

www.eurocampings.co.uk/102861

United Kingdom

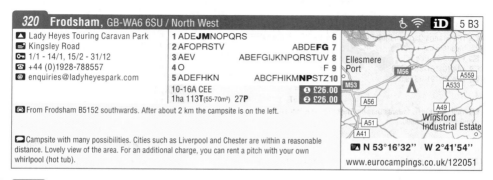

320 Frodsham, GB-WA6 6SU / North West 5 B3

▲ Lady Heyes Touring Caravan Park
✉ Kingsley Road
🕐 1/1 - 14/1, 15/2 - 31/12
☎ +44 (0)1928-788557
@ enquiries@ladyheyespark.com

1 ADE**JM**NOPQRS		6
2 AFOPRSTV	ABDE**FG**	7
3 AEV	ABEFGIJKNPQRSTUV	8
4 O		F 9
5 ADEFHKN	ABCFHIKM**NPS**TZ	10
10-16A CEE	❶ £26.00	
1ha 113**T**(55-70m²) 27**P**	❷ £26.00	

🚗 From Frodsham B5152 southwards. After about 2 km the campsite is on the left.

💬 Campsite with many possibilities. Cities such as Liverpool and Chester are within a reasonable distance. Lovely view of the area. For an additional charge, you can rent a pitch with your own whirlpool (hot tub).

📷 N 53°16'32'' W 2°41'54''
www.eurocampings.co.uk/122051

321 Fylingdales (Whitby), GB-YO22 4QH / Yorkshire & Humberside 6 A2

▲ Grouse Hill Caravan & Camping Park***
✉ A171 Whitby to Scarborough Rd.
🕐 8 Mar - 4 Oct
☎ +44 (0)1947-880543
@ info@grousehill.co.uk

1 ADE**IL**NOPQRS**T**		6
2 CDFGPSTUVWX	ABDE**FG**H	7
3 AB	ABCDFGINQRSTUV	8
4 F	BCEFJ	9
5 BDHKLM**N**	ABJMN**O**R	10
10A CEE	❶ £30.00	
15ha 97**T**(120-240m²) 140**P**	❷ £33.00	

🚗 On the A171, halfway between Scarborough and Whitby.

💬 Large, open terrain with a great view of the North York Moors. For fans of tranquillity and nature.

📷 N 54°23'35'' W 0°34'8''
www.eurocampings.co.uk/108582

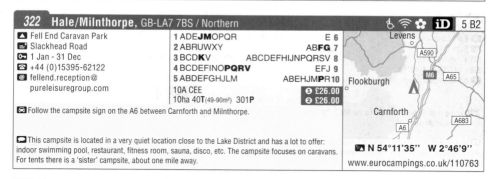

322 Hale/Milnthorpe, GB-LA7 7BS / Northern 5 B2

▲ Fell End Caravan Park
✉ Slackhead Road
🕐 1 Jan - 31 Dec
☎ +44 (0)15395-62122
@ fellend.reception@
  pureleisuregroup.com

1 ADE**JM**OPQR	E 6	
2 ABRUWXY	AB**FG**	7
3 BCD**K**V	ABCDEFHIJNPQRSV	8
4 BCDEFINO**PQRV**	EFJ	9
5 ABDEFGHJLM	ABEHJM**P**R	10
10A CEE	❶ £26.00	
10ha 40**T**(49-90m²) 301**P**	❷ £26.00	

🚗 Follow the campsite sign on the A6 between Carnforth and Milnthorpe.

💬 This campsite is located in a very quiet location close to the Lake District and has a lot to offer: indoor swimming pool, restaurant, fitness room, sauna, disco, etc. The campsite focuses on caravans. For tents there is a 'sister' campsite, about one mile away.

📷 N 54°11'35'' W 2°46'9''
www.eurocampings.co.uk/110763

323 Haltwhistle, GB-NE49 9PG / Northern 5 B1

▲ Hadrian's Wall
  Camping and Caravan Site
✉ Melkridge Tilery
🕐 1 Jan - 31 Dec
☎ +44 (0)1434-320495
@ info@hadrianswallcampsite.co.uk

1 ACDEJ**M**NOPQRS**T**		6
2 FGOPSTUVWX	ABDE**FG**HIK	7
3 **K**	ABEFHJLMNPQRSV	8
4 FH		9
5 ABDGJN	ABGJMPR	10
16A CEE	❶ £27.00	
1ha 50**T**(45-120m²) 16**P**	❷ £33.00	

🚗 A69 north, exit Melkridge. Follow this road to the campsite.

💬 Within walking distance of Hadrian's Wall and with all facilities. Hiking trails from the campsite in all directions, with views, archaeological places and history. Packaged breakfast and lunch for trips. Ideal for campers who love peace and beauty. All-inclusive excursions for groups of six or more.

📷 N 54°59'9'' W 2°25'22''
www.eurocampings.co.uk/119016

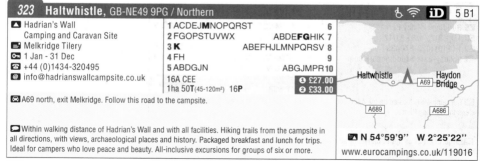

United Kingdom

United Kingdom

324 Harome/Helmsley, GB-Y062 7SD / Yorkshire & Humberside 6 A2

- Foxholme Touring Caravan Park
- Gale Lane
- 31 Mar - 30 Oct
- +44 (0)1439-772336
- foxholme@outlook.com

1 JMNOPQRTU	N 6
2 FGOPSWX	ABDEFGH 7
3	ABCDEFJNQRV 8
4 FHK	9
5	ABEHIJMRW 10
6A	£20.00
4,5ha 90T(100m²) 67P	£20.00

From the A170 through Helmsley 5 km east. Through Beadlam turn right Gale Lane. Campsite is on the left after 2 km.

Basic, very quiet campsite for adults only. Perfect for nature lovers.

Helmsley A170 Pickering
Hovingham

N 54°14'17'' W 0°59'16''
www.eurocampings.co.uk/123025

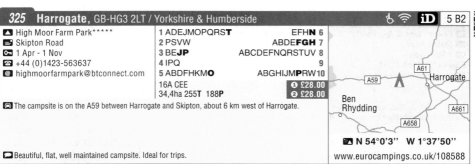

325 Harrogate, GB-HG3 2LT / Yorkshire & Humberside 5 B2

- High Moor Farm Park*****
- Skipton Road
- 1 Apr - 1 Nov
- +44 (0)1423-563637
- highmoorfarmpark@btconnect.com

1 ADEJMOPQRST	EFHN 6
2 PSVW	ABDEFGH 7
3 BEJP	ABCDEFNQRSTUV 8
4 IPQ	9
5 ABDFHKMO	ABGHIJMPRW 10
16A CEE	£28.00
34,4ha 255T 188P	£28.00

The campsite is on the A59 between Harrogate and Skipton, about 6 km west of Harrogate.

Beautiful, flat, well maintained campsite. Ideal for trips.

A61 A59 Harrogate Ben Rhydding A661 A658

N 54°0'3'' W 1°37'50''
www.eurocampings.co.uk/108588

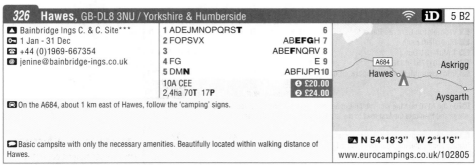

326 Hawes, GB-DL8 3NU / Yorkshire & Humberside 5 B2

- Bainbridge Ings C. & C. Site***
- 1 Jan - 31 Dec
- +44 (0)1969-667354
- jenine@bainbridge-ings.co.uk

1 ADEJMNOPQRST	6
2 FOPSVX	ABEFGH 7
3	ABEFNQRV 8
4 FG	E 9
5 DMN	ABFIJPR 10
10A CEE	£20.00
2,4ha 70T 17P	£24.00

On the A684, about 1 km east of Hawes, follow the 'camping' signs.

Basic campsite with only the necessary amenities. Beautifully located within walking distance of Hawes.

A684 Askrigg Hawes Aysgarth

N 54°18'3'' W 2°11'6''
www.eurocampings.co.uk/102805

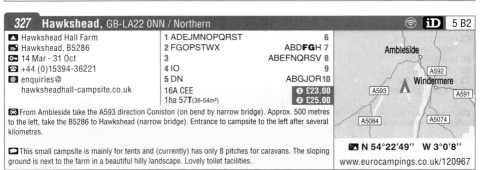

327 Hawkshead, GB-LA22 0NN / Northern 5 B2

- Hawkshead Hall Farm
- Hawkshead, B5286
- 14 Mar - 31 Oct
- +44 (0)15394-36221
- enquiries@ hawksheadhall-campsite.co.uk

1 ADEJMNOPQRST	6
2 FGOPSTWX	ABDFGH 7
3	ABEFNQRSV 8
4 IO	9
5 DN	ABGJOR 10
16A CEE	£23.00
1ha 57T(36-64m²)	£25.00

From Ambleside take the A593 direction Coniston (on bend by narrow bridge). Approx. 500 metres to the left, take the B5286 to Hawkshead (narrow bridge). Entrance to campsite to the left after several kilometres.

This small campsite is mainly for tents and (currently) has only 8 pitches for caravans. The sloping ground is next to the farm in a beautiful hilly landscape. Lovely toilet facilities.

Ambleside A592 Windermere A593 A591 A5084 A5074

N 54°22'49'' W 3°0'8''
www.eurocampings.co.uk/120967

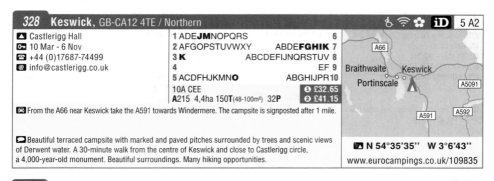

328 Keswick, GB-CA12 4TE / Northern

  ♿ 🛜 ⚙ **iD** 5 A2

🏕 Castlerigg Hall
📅 10 Mar - 6 Nov
☎ +44 (0)17687-74499
@ info@castlerigg.co.uk

1 ADE**JM**NOPQRS		6
2 AFGOPSTUVWXY	ABDE**FGHIK**	7
3 **K**	ABCDEFIJNQRSTUV	8
4		EF 9
5 ACDFHJKMN**O**	ABGHIJPR	10
10A CEE		€ £32.65
A215 4,4ha 150**T**(48-100m²) 32**P**		€ £41.15

🗺 From the A66 near Keswick take the A591 towards Windermere. The campsite is signposted after 1 mile.

💬 Beautiful terraced campsite with marked and paved pitches surrounded by trees and scenic views of Derwent water. A 30-minute walk from the centre of Keswick and close to Castlerigg circle, a 4,000-year-old monument. Beautiful surroundings. Many hiking opportunities.

📍 N 54°35'35" W 3°6'43"
www.eurocampings.co.uk/109835

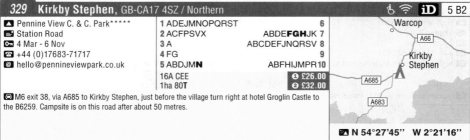

329 Kirkby Stephen, GB-CA17 4SZ / Northern

  ♿ 🛜 **iD** 5 B2

🏕 Pennine View C. & C. Park*****
📧 Station Road
📅 4 Mar - 6 Nov
☎ +44 (0)17683-71717
@ hello@pennineviewpark.co.uk

1 ADEJMNOPQRST		6
2 ACFPSVX	ABDE**FGH**JK	7
3 A	ABCDEFJNQRSV	8
4 FG		9
5 ABDJM**N**	ABFHIJMPR	10
16A CEE		€ £26.00
1ha 80**T**		€ £32.00

🗺 M6 exit 38, via A685 to Kirkby Stephen, just before the village turn right at hotel Groglin Castle to the B6259. Campsite is on this road after about 50 metres.

💬 Lovely, flat, well-maintained, neat campsite. Ideal for trips.

📍 N 54°27'45" W 2°21'16"
www.eurocampings.co.uk/102804

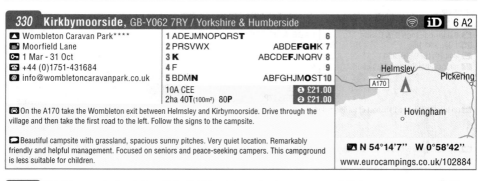

330 Kirkbymoorside, GB-Y062 7RY / Yorkshire & Humberside

  🛜 **iD** 6 A2

🏕 Wombleton Caravan Park****
📧 Moorfield Lane
📅 1 Mar - 31 Oct
☎ +44 (0)1751-431684
@ info@wombletoncaravanpark.co.uk

1 ADEJMNOPQRS**T**		6
2 PRSVWX	ABDE**FGH**K	7
3 **K**	ABCDEFJNQRV	8
4 F		9
5 BDM**N**	ABFGHJM**O**S**T**	10
10A CEE		€ £21.00
2ha 40**T**(100m²) 80**P**		€ £21.00

🗺 On the A170 take the Wombleton exit between Helmsley and Kirbymoorside. Drive through the village and then take the first road to the left. Follow the signs to the campsite.

💬 Beautiful campsite with grassland, spacious sunny pitches. Very quiet location. Remarkably friendly and helpful management. Focused on seniors and peace-seeking campers. This campground is less suitable for children.

📍 N 54°14'7" W 0°58'42"
www.eurocampings.co.uk/102884

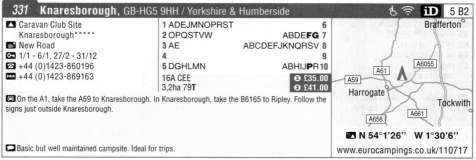

331 Knaresborough, GB-HG5 9HH / Yorkshire & Humberside

  ♿ 🛜 **iD** 5 B2

🏕 Caravan Club Site
   Knaresborough*****
📧 New Road
📅 1/1 - 6/1, 27/2 - 31/12
☎ +44 (0)1423-860196
📠 +44 (0)1423-869163

1 ADEJMNOPRST		6
2 OPQSTVW	ABDE**FG**	7
3 AE	ABCDEFJKNQRSV	8
4		9
5 DGHLMN	ABHIJP**R**	10
16A CEE		€ £35.00
3,2ha 79**T**		€ £41.00

🗺 On the A1, take the A59 to Knaresborough. In Knaresborough, take the B6165 to Ripley. Follow the signs just outside Knaresborough.

💬 Basic but well maintained campsite. Ideal for trips.

📍 N 54°1'26" W 1°30'6"
www.eurocampings.co.uk/110717

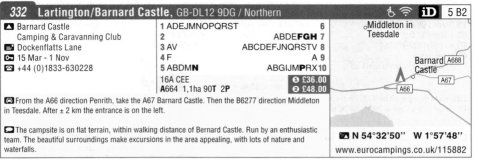

332 Lartington/Barnard Castle, GB-DL12 9DG / Northern   iD   5 B2

- ▲ Barnard Castle
  Camping & Caravanning Club
- ▣ Dockenflatts Lane
- ☷ 15 Mar - 1 Nov
- ☎ +44 (0)1833-630228

1 ADEJMNOPQRST		6
2	ABDE**FGH**	7
3 AV	ABCDEFJNQRSTV	8
4 F	A	9
5 ABDM**N**	ABGIJM**P**RX	10
16A CEE		❶ £36.00
A664 1,1ha 90**T** 2**P**		❷ £48.00

Middleton in Teesdale

Barnard Castle   A688   A67

A66

From the A66 direction Penrith, take the A67 Barnard Castle. Then the B6277 direction Middleton in Teesdale. After ± 2 km the entrance is on the left.

The campsite is on flat terrain, within walking distance of Bernard Castle. Run by an enthusiastic team. The beautiful surroundings make excursions in the area appealing, with lots of nature and waterfalls.

N 54°32'50''   W 1°57'48''

www.eurocampings.co.uk/115882

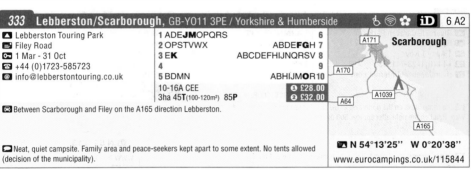

333 Lebberston/Scarborough, GB-YO11 3PE / Yorkshire & Humberside   iD   6 A2

- ▲ Lebberston Touring Park
- ▣ Filey Road
- ☷ 1 Mar - 31 Oct
- ☎ +44 (0)1723-585723
- @ info@lebberstontouring.co.uk

1 ADE**JM**OPQRS		6
2 OPSTVWX	ABDE**FGH**	7
3 E**K**	ABCDEFHIJNQRSV	8
4		9
5 BDMN	ABHIJM**OR**	10
10-16A CEE		❶ £28.00
3ha 45**T**(100-120m²) 85**P**		❷ £32.00

A171   **Scarborough**

A170

A64   A1039

A165

Between Scarborough and Filey on the A165 direction Lebberston.

Neat, quiet campsite. Family area and peace-seekers kept apart to some extent. No tents allowed (decision of the municipality).

N 54°13'25''   W 0°20'38''

www.eurocampings.co.uk/115844

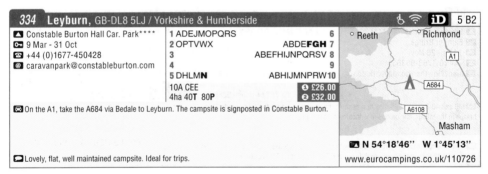

334 Leyburn, GB-DL8 5LJ / Yorkshire & Humberside   iD   5 B2

- ▲ Constable Burton Hall Car. Park★★★★
- ☷ 9 Mar - 31 Oct
- ☎ +44 (0)1677-450428
- @ caravanpark@constableburton.com

1 ADEJMOPQRS		6
2 OPTVWX	ABDE**FGH**	7
3	ABEFHIJNPQRSV	8
4		9
5 DHLM**N**	ABHIJMNPRW	10
10A CEE		❶ £26.00
4ha 40**T** 80**P**		❷ £32.00

Reeth   Richmond

A1

A684

A6108

Masham

On the A1, take the A684 via Bedale to Leyburn. The campsite is signposted in Constable Burton.

Lovely, flat, well maintained campsite. Ideal for trips.

N 54°18'46''   W 1°45'13''

www.eurocampings.co.uk/110726

335 Osmotherley/Northallerton, GB-DL6 3AH / Yorkshire & Humberside   iD   6 A2

- ▲ Cote Ghyll Car. & Camp. Park★★★★★
- ☷ 1 Mar - 31 Oct
- ☎ +44 (0)1609-883425
- @ hills@coteghyll.com

1 ADEJMNOPQRS**T**		6
2 ACOPSTUX	ABDE**FGH**	7
3 A	ABCDEFGNQRSTUV	8
4 FH	EGJ	9
5 ABDFIJKM**N**	ABEGHIJ**P**RW	10
10A CEE		❶ £27.50
3,2ha 69**T**(100-165m²) 36**P**		❷ £38.50

Great Broughton

A19   A172

Northallerton

A168

A167

Go north on the A19, take exit A684 Northallerton/Osmotherley. In Osmotherley turn left at the T-junction, turn right after about 1 km.

On the border of the moors is this customer-friendly campsite in the forest with great focus on greenery and flowers. This is an excellent campsite for discovering the beauty of the North Yorkshire Moors with good roads and great hiking trails.

N 54°22'35''   W 1°17'35''

www.eurocampings.co.uk/114107

United Kingdom

336 Oswaldkirk/Helmsley, GB-YO62 5YQ / Yorkshire & Humberside — 6 A2

- 🏕 Golden Square*****
- 🕐 1 Mar - 31 Oct
- ☎ +44 (0)1439-788269
- @ reception@
  goldensquarecaravanpark.com

1 AE**JM**NOPQRS**T**		6
2 FGOPRSUVWX	ABDE**FGHK**	7
3 ABCE**IKL**	ABCDEFGIJNQRSTUV	8
4 FHI**Q**		DV 9
5 ABCDM**NO**	ABEFGHIJM**O**RWX	10

10-16A CEE — ❶ £27.00
A500 4,9ha 126**T**(80m²) 71**P** — ❷ £31.00

🚗 Drive to Helmsley via the B1257 in the direction of Malton. Turn right towards Ampleforth. The campsite is located on the right after approx. 1 km.

💬 High, terraced campsite. Panoramic views from the highest terraces towards the east. Good play facilities for children including an old tractor, a small cable track and a football pitch.

📍 N 54°12'34'' W 1°4'23''
www.eurocampings.co.uk/102882

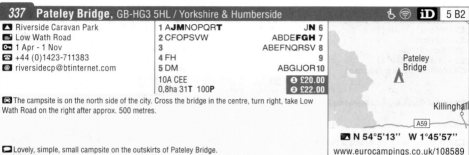

337 Pateley Bridge, GB-HG3 5HL / Yorkshire & Humberside — 5 B2

- 🏕 Riverside Caravan Park
- 🛣 Low Wath Road
- 🕐 1 Apr - 1 Nov
- ☎ +44 (0)1423-711383
- @ riversidecp@btinternet.com

1 A**JM**NOPQR**T**		JN 6
2 CFOPSVW	ABDE**FGH**	7
3	ABEFNQRSV	8
4 FH		9
5 DM	ABGIJOR	10

10A CEE — ❶ £20.00
0,8ha 31**T** 100**P** — ❷ £22.00

🚗 The campsite is on the north side of the city. Cross the bridge in the centre, turn right, take Low Wath Road on the right after approx. 500 metres.

💬 Lovely, simple, small campsite on the outskirts of Pateley Bridge.

📍 N 54°5'13'' W 1°45'57''
www.eurocampings.co.uk/108589

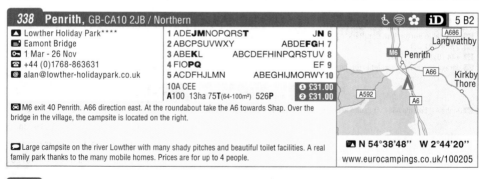

338 Penrith, GB-CA10 2JB / Northern — 5 B2

- 🏕 Lowther Holiday Park****
- 🛣 Eamont Bridge
- 🕐 1 Mar - 26 Nov
- ☎ +44 (0)1768-863631
- @ alan@lowther-holidaypark.co.uk

1 ADE**JM**NOPQRS**T**		JN 6
2 ABCPSUVWXY	ABDE**FGH**	7
3 ABE**KL**	ABCDEFHINPQRSTUV	8
4 FIO**PQ**		EF 9
5 ACDFHJLMN	ABEGHIJMORWY	10

10A CEE — ❶ £31.00
A100 13ha 75**T**(64-100m²) 526**P** — ❷ £31.00

🚗 M6 exit 40 Penrith. A66 direction east. At the roundabout take the A6 towards Shap. Over the bridge in the village, the campsite is located on the right.

💬 Large campsite on the river Lowther with many shady pitches and beautiful toilet facilities. A real family park thanks to the many mobile homes. Prices are for up to 4 people.

📍 N 54°38'48'' W 2°44'20''
www.eurocampings.co.uk/100205

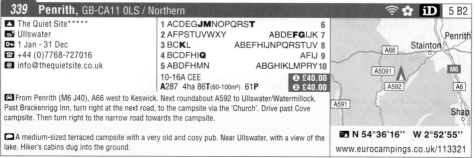

339 Penrith, GB-CA11 0LS / Northern — 5 B2

- 🏕 The Quiet Site*****
- 🛣 Ullswater
- 🕐 1 Jan - 31 Dec
- ☎ +44 (0)7768-727016
- @ info@thequietsite.co.uk

1 ACDEG**JM**NOPQRS**T**		6
2 AFPSTUVWXY	ABDE**FG**IJK	7
3 BC**KL**	ABEFHIJNPQRSTUV	8
4 BCDFHI**Q**		AFIJ 9
5 ABDFHMN	ABGHIKLMPRY	10

10-16A CEE — ❶ £40.00
A287 4ha 86**T**(60-100m²) 61**P** — ❷ £40.00

🚗 From Penrith (M6 J40), A66 west to Keswick. Next roundabout A592 to Ullswater/Watermillock. Past Brackenrigg Inn, turn right at the next road, to the campsite via the 'Church'. Drive past Cove campsite. Then turn right to the narrow road towards the campsite.

💬 A medium-sized terraced campsite with a very old and cosy pub. Near Ullswater, with a view of the lake. Hiker's cabins dug into the ground.

📍 N 54°36'16'' W 2°52'55''
www.eurocampings.co.uk/113321

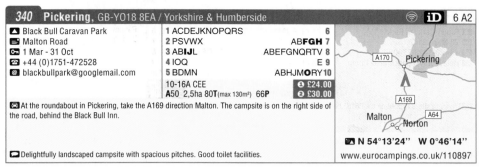

340 Pickering, GB-YO18 8EA / Yorkshire & Humberside   6 A2

- ⛰ Black Bull Caravan Park
- 🏠 Malton Road
- 🗓 1 Mar - 31 Oct
- ☎ +44 (0)1751-472528
- @ blackbullpark@googlemail.com

1 ACDEJKNOPQRS	6
2 PSVWX	ABFGH 7
3 ABIJL	ABEFGNQRTV 8
4 IOQ	E 9
5 BDMN	ABHJMORY 10
10-16A CEE	❶ £24.00
A50 2,5ha 80T(max 130m²) 66P	❷ £30.00

🚗 At the roundabout in Pickering, take the A169 direction Malton. The campsite is on the right side of the road, behind the Black Bull Inn.

💬 Delightfully landscaped campsite with spacious pitches. Good toilet facilities.

🧭 N 54°13'24'' W 0°46'14''

www.eurocampings.co.uk/110897

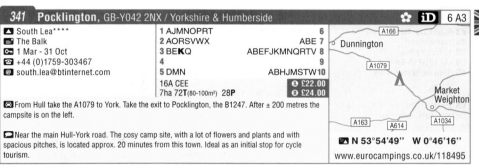

341 Pocklington, GB-YO42 2NX / Yorkshire & Humberside   6 A3

- ⛰ South Lea****
- 🏠 The Balk
- 🗓 1 Mar - 31 Oct
- ☎ +44 (0)1759-303467
- @ south.lea@btinternet.com

1 AJMNOPRT	6
2 AORSVWX	ABE 7
3 BEKQ	ABEFJKMNQRTV 8
4	9
5 DMN	ABHJMSTW 10
16A CEE	❶ £22.00
7ha 72T(80-100m²) 28P	❷ £24.00

🚗 From Hull take the A1079 to York. Take the exit to Pocklington, the B1247. After ± 200 metres the campsite is on the left.

💬 Near the main Hull-York road. The cosy camp site, with a lot of flowers and plants and with spacious pitches, is located approx. 20 minutes from this town. Ideal as an initial stop for cycle tourism.

🧭 N 53°54'49'' W 0°46'16''

www.eurocampings.co.uk/118495

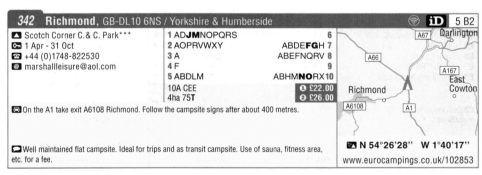

342 Richmond, GB-DL10 6NS / Yorkshire & Humberside   5 B2

- ⛰ Scotch Corner C.& C. Park***
- 🗓 1 Apr - 31 Oct
- ☎ +44 (0)1748-822530
- @ marshallleisure@aol.com

1 ADJMNOPQRS	6
2 AOPRVWXY	ABDEFGH 7
3 A	ABEFNQRV 8
4 F	9
5 ABDLM	ABHMNORX 10
10A CEE	❶ £22.00
4ha 75T	❷ £26.00

🚗 On the A1 take exit A6108 Richmond. Follow the campsite signs after about 400 metres.

💬 Well maintained flat campsite. Ideal for trips and as transit campsite. Use of sauna, fitness area, etc. for a fee.

🧭 N 54°26'28'' W 1°40'17''

www.eurocampings.co.uk/102853

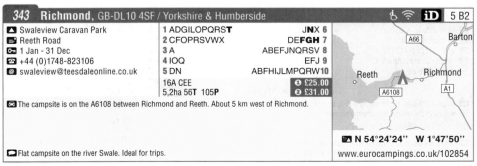

343 Richmond, GB-DL10 4SF / Yorkshire & Humberside   5 B2

- ⛰ Swaleview Caravan Park
- 🏠 Reeth Road
- 🗓 1 Jan - 31 Dec
- ☎ +44 (0)1748-823106
- @ swaleview@teesdaleonline.co.uk

1 ADGILOPQRST	JNX 6
2 CFOPRSVWX	DEFGH 7
3 A	ABEFJNQRSV 8
4 IOQ	EFJ 9
5 DN	ABFHIJLMPQRW 10
16A CEE	❶ £25.00
5,2ha 56T 105P	❷ £31.00

🚗 The campsite is on the A6108 between Richmond and Reeth. About 5 km west of Richmond.

💬 Flat campsite on the river Swale. Ideal for trips.

🧭 N 54°24'24'' W 1°47'50''

www.eurocampings.co.uk/102854

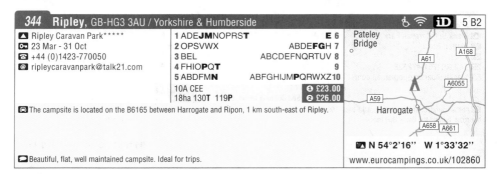

344 Ripley, GB-HG3 3AU / Yorkshire & Humberside — 5 B2

▲ Ripley Caravan Park*****
🕙 23 Mar - 31 Oct
☎ +44 (0)1423-770050
@ ripleycaravanpark@talk21.com

1	ADE**JM**NOPRS**T**	**E** 6
2	OPSVWX	ABDE**FGH** 7
3	BEL	ABCDEFNQRTUV 8
4	FHIO**PQT**	9
5	ABDFM**N**	ABFGHIJM**P**QRWXZ 10
10A CEE		❶ £23.00
18ha 130**T** 119**P**		❷ £26.00

📷 The campsite is located on the B6165 between Harrogate and Ripon, 1 km south-east of Ripley.

💬 Beautiful, flat, well maintained campsite. Ideal for trips.

N 54°2'16'' W 1°33'32''
www.eurocampings.co.uk/102860

345 Ripon, GB-HG4 2QR / Yorkshire & Humberside — 5 B2

▲ River Laver Holiday Park Ltd.
🏠 Studley Road
🕙 1 Mar - 30 Nov
☎ +44 (0)1765-690508
@ riverlaver@lineone.net

1	AJMNOR**T**	**N** 6
2	CPRSVW	ABDE**FGH** 7
3		ABCDEFJNPQRSTUV 8
4	F	9
5	BDMN	ABEFHIJ**PR** 10
10A CEE		❶ £23.50
5,5ha 8**T**(max 15m²) 106**P**		❷ £29.00

📷 From the A1 take the B6265 via Ripon to Pately Bridge. Drive through Ripon. Just outside the city, the campsite is signposted.

💬 Simple, small, well-kept campsite on the outskirts of Ripon. Well located for excursions.

N 54°7'59'' W 1°32'45''
www.eurocampings.co.uk/110719

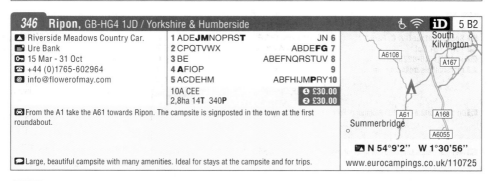

346 Ripon, GB-HG4 1JD / Yorkshire & Humberside — 5 B2

▲ Riverside Meadows Country Car.
🏠 Ure Bank
🕙 15 Mar - 31 Oct
☎ +44 (0)1765-602964
@ info@flowerofmay.com

1	ADE**JM**NOPRS**T**	JN 6
2	CPQTVWX	ABDE**FG** 7
3	BE	ABEFNQRSTUV 8
4	**A**FIOP	9
5	ACDEHM	ABFHIJM**P**RY 10
10A CEE		❶ £30.00
2,8ha 14**T** 340**P**		❷ £30.00

📷 From the A1 take the A61 towards Ripon. The campsite is signposted in the town at the first roundabout.

💬 Large, beautiful campsite with many amenities. Ideal for stays at the campsite and for trips.

N 54°9'2'' W 1°30'56''
www.eurocampings.co.uk/110725

347 Rosedale Abbey/Pickering, GB-YO18 8SA / Yorkshire & Humberside — 6 A2

▲ Rosedale C. & C. Park
🕙 15 Mar - 31 Oct
☎ +44 (0)1751-417272
@ rosedalecaravanpark@
   moorsweb.co.uk

1	ADE**J**KNOPQRS	**N** 6
2	COPSTVXY	ABDE**FGH** 7
3	B**KL**	ABCDEFGINQRSV 8
4	F	FI 9
5	ACDM**NO**	ABFHJM**O**STY 10
10A CEE		❶ £31.00
A140 5ha 19**T**(40-140m²) 51**P**		❷ £37.00

📷 On the A170 between Pickering and Kirbymoorside, turn off direction Cropton/Rosedale. Campsite at entrance to the village, left after the caravan park.

💬 This lovely campsite (grassland) is located in a hilly area in the middle of a beautiful nature reserve. Signposted walks starting from the campsite. Left after caravan park.

N 54°21'9'' W 0°53'12''
www.eurocampings.co.uk/102880

United Kingdom

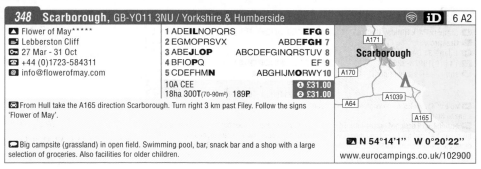

348 Scarborough, GB-YO11 3NU / Yorkshire & Humberside ⊚ iD 6 A2

- ▲ Flower of May*****
- 🏢 Lebberston Cliff
- 🗓 27 Mar - 31 Oct
- ☎ +44 (0)1723-584311
- @ info@flowerofmay.com

1 ADE**IL**NOPQRS	**EFG** 6
2 EGMOPRSVX	ABDE**FGH** 7
3 ABE**JLOP**	ABCDEFGINQRSTUV 8
4 BFIO**PQ**	EF 9
5 CDEFHM**N**	ABGHIJM**O**RWY 10
10A CEE	❶ £31.00
18ha 300**T**(70-90m²) 189**P**	❷ £31.00

🚗 From Hull take the A165 direction Scarborough. Turn right 3 km past Filey. Follow the signs 'Flower of May'.

💬 Big campsite (grassland) in open field. Swimming pool, bar, snack bar and a shop with a large selection of groceries. Also facilities for older children.

📍 N 54°14'1'' W 0°20'22''

www.eurocampings.co.uk/102900

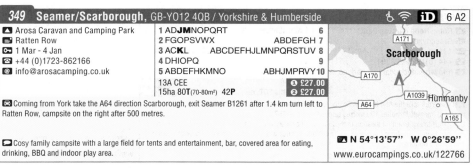

349 Seamer/Scarborough, GB-YO12 4QB / Yorkshire & Humberside ♿ ⊚ iD 6 A2

- ▲ Arosa Caravan and Camping Park
- 🏢 Ratten Row
- 🗓 1 Mar - 4 Jan
- ☎ +44 (0)1723-862166
- @ info@arosacamping.co.uk

1 AD**JM**NOPQRT	6
2 FGOPSVWX	ABDEFGH 7
3 AC**KL**	ABCDEFHJLMNPQRSTUV 8
4 DHIOPQ	9
5 ABDEFHKMNO	ABHJMPRVY 10
13A CEE	❶ £27.00
15ha 80**T**(70-80m²) 42**P**	❷ £27.00

🚗 Coming from York take the A64 direction Scarborough, exit Seamer B1261 after 1.4 km turn left to Ratten Row, campsite on the right after 500 metres.

💬 Cosy family campsite with a large field for tents and entertainment, bar, covered area for eating, drinking, BBQ and indoor play area.

📍 N 54°13'57'' W 0°26'59''

www.eurocampings.co.uk/122766

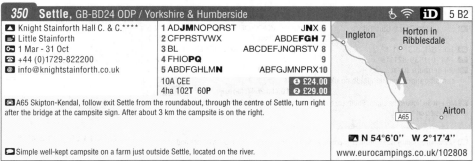

350 Settle, GB-BD24 0DP / Yorkshire & Humberside ♿ ⊚ iD 5 B2

- ▲ Knight Stainforth Hall C. & C.****
- 🏢 Little Stainforth
- 🗓 1 Mar - 31 Oct
- ☎ +44 (0)1729-822200
- @ info@knightstainforth.co.uk

1 AD**JM**NOPQRST	**JN**X 6
2 CFPRSTVWX	ABDE**FGH** 7
3 BL	ABCDEFJNQRSTV 8
4 FHIO**PQ**	9
5 ABDFGHLM**N**	ABFGJMNPRX 10
10A CEE	❶ £24.00
4ha 102**T** 60**P**	❷ £29.00

🚗 A65 Skipton-Kendal, follow exit Settle from the roundabout, through the centre of Settle, turn right after the bridge at the campsite sign. After about 3 km the campsite is on the right.

💬 Simple well-kept campsite on a farm just outside Settle, located on the river.

📍 N 54°6'0'' W 2°17'4''

www.eurocampings.co.uk/102808

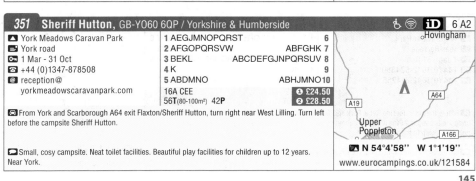

351 Sheriff Hutton, GB-YO60 6QP / Yorkshire & Humberside ♿ ⊚ iD 6 A2

- ▲ York Meadows Caravan Park
- 🏢 York road
- 🗓 1 Mar - 31 Oct
- ☎ +44 (0)1347-878508
- @ reception@ yorkmeadowscaravanpark.com

1 AEGJMNOPQRST	6
2 AFGOPQRSVW	ABFGHK 7
3 BEKL	ABCDEFGJNPQRSUV 8
4 K	9
5 ABDMNO	ABHJMNO 10
16A CEE	❶ £24.50
56**T**(80-100m²) 42**P**	❷ £28.50

🚗 From York and Scarborough A64 exit Flaxton/Sheriff Hutton, turn right near West Lilling. Turn left before the campsite Sheriff Hutton.

💬 Small, cosy campsite. Neat toilet facilities. Beautiful play facilities for children up to 12 years. Near York.

📍 N 54°4'58'' W 1°1'19''

www.eurocampings.co.uk/121584

United Kingdom

352 Silloth, GB-CA7 4HH / Northern
♿ 🛜 (CC€19) iD 5 A2

- 🔺 Stanwix Park Holiday Centre*****
- 🚩 Greenrow
- 🗓 1 Jan - 31 Dec
- ☎ +44 (0)16973-32666
- @ enquiries@stanwix.com

1	ADE**JM**NOPQRS		ABEFGHX	6
2	GOSVWX		ABDE**FGH**IK	7
3	BCD**IKLMP**	ABCDEFHIJLPQRSTUV		8
4	BCDILMNOP**QRS**TUV		EFIUV	9
5	ACDEFHIJM**N**		ABGHKO**P**RYZ	10
10A CEE				
10ha 121**T**(64m²) 486**P**			❶ £27.20 ❷ £37.20	

Anthorn

Wigton

A596 A595

🔢 M6 exit 41, via B5305 to Wigton, then via B5302 to Silloth. In Silloth turn left, and then follow the signs to Stanwix.

💬 Beautiful, well designed and maintained campsite with indoor and outdoor pools. Relax in the sauna, the steam bath and the jacuzzi and then have a bite to eat in the self-service restaurant or a drink in one of the bars. There is entertainment for children and adults. There are well-equipped toilet facilities.

CC 7/5-25/5 4/6-13/7 3/9-5/10

🔢 N 54°51'41" W 3°23'13"

www.eurocampings.co.uk/101153

---

353 Slingsby, GB-Y062 4AP / Yorkshire & Humberside
🛜 (CC€19) ♟♟ iD 6 A2

- 🔺 Robin Hood Caravan Park*****
- 🚩 Greendyke Lane
- 🗓 1 Mar - 4 Nov
- ☎ +44 (0)1653-628391
- @ info@robinhoodcaravanpark.co.uk

1	ADEILNOPQR**T**			6
2	OPSVX		ABDE**FGH**	7
3	AB**K**	ABCDEFNQRSTUV		8
4			E	9
5	BDMN**O**		ABDHJM**P**R	10
16A CEE				
A100 4ha 30**T**(90m²) 32**P**			❶ £29.00 ❷ £29.00	

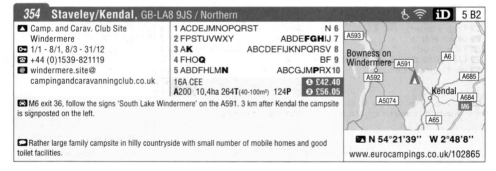

Pickering

A170

A169

Malton Norton

A64

🔢 From York take the A64 towards Scarborough. Take exit Castle Howard/Slingsby. In Slingsby turn right and immediately after 100 metres turn left to the B1257.

💬 Campsite in a beautiful location in the hills in the countryside. Less than 5 km from Castle Howard and less than 30 km from the beautiful city of York. Pitches with pebbles or grass. Plenty of walking and cycling options.

CC 1/3-27/3 7/4-23/5 3/6-30/6 2/9-3/11

🔢 N 54°9'44" W 0°55'46"

www.eurocampings.co.uk/111331

---

354 Staveley/Kendal, GB-LA8 9JS / Northern
♿ 🛜 iD 5 B2

- 🔺 Camp. and Carav. Club Site Windermere
- 🗓 1/1 - 8/1, 8/3 - 31/12
- ☎ +44 (0)1539-821119
- @ windermere.site@ campingandcaravanningclub.co.uk

1	ACDEJMNOPQRST		N	6
2	FPSTUVWXY		ABDE**FGH**IJ	7
3	A**K**	ABCDEFIJKNPQRSV		8
4	FHO**Q**		BF	9
5	ABDFHLM**N**		ABCGJM**P**RX	10
16A CEE				
A200 10,4ha 264**T**(40-100m²) 124**P**			❶ £42.40 ❷ £56.05	

A593

Bowness on Windermere A591 A6

A592 A685

Kendal A684

A5074 M6

A65

🔢 M6 exit 36, follow the signs 'South Lake Windermere' on the A591. 3 km after Kendal the campsite is signposted on the left.

💬 Rather large family campsite in hilly countryside with small number of mobile homes and good toilet facilities.

🔢 N 54°21'39" W 2°48'8"

www.eurocampings.co.uk/102865

---

355 Stockton-on-Tees, GB-TS18 2QW / Northern
♿ 🛜 iD 6 A2

- 🔺 White Water Park
- 🚩 Tees Barrage
- 🗓 1 Jan - 31 Dec
- ☎ +44 (0)1642-634880
- 📠 +44 (0)1642-614255

1	ADEJMNOPQRST		NUVW	6
2	ACOSVX		ABDE**FG**	7
3	A**K**MN**OP**	ABCDEFJNQRSTUV		8
4	FHIO**P**QR		QR	9
5	BDFHIKLMN		ABFGHJM**P**RXZ	10
16A CEE				
8ha 100**T**			❶ £40.00 ❷ £46.00	

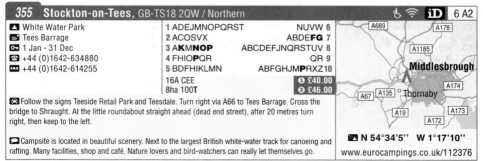

A689 A178

A1185

Middlesbrough

A174

A67 A135 Thornaby

A19 A173

A172

🔢 Follow the signs Teeside Retail Park and Teesdale. Turn right via A66 to Tees Barrage. Cross the bridge to Shraught. At the little roundabout straight ahead (dead end street), after 20 metres turn right, then keep to the left.

💬 Campsite is located in beautiful scenery. Next to the largest British white-water track for canoeing and rafting. Many facilities, shop and café. Nature lovers and bird-watchers can really let themselves go.

🔢 N 54°34'5" W 1°17'10"

www.eurocampings.co.uk/112376

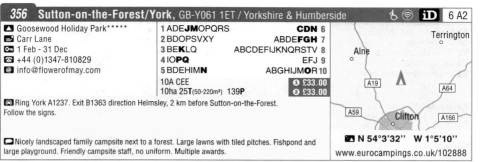

356 Sutton-on-the-Forest/York, GB-Y061 1ET / Yorkshire & Humberside ♿ 📶 **iD** 6 A2

🔺 Gooseowood Holiday Park*****
📧 Carr Lane
📅 1 Feb - 31 Dec
☎ +44 (0)1347-810829
@ info@flowerofmay.com

1	ADEJMOPQRS	**CDN** 6
2	BDOPSVXY	ABDE**FGH** 7
3	BE**K**LQ	ABCDEFIJKNQRSTV 8
4	IO**PQ**	EFJ 9
5	BDEHIM**N**	ABGHIJM**OR** 10
10A CEE		➊ £33.00
10ha 25T(50-220m²) 139P		➋ £33.00

🔄 Ring York A1237. Exit B1363 direction Helmsley, 2 km before Sutton-on-the-Forest. Follow the signs.

💬 Nicely landscaped family campsite next to a forest. Large lawns with tiled pitches. Fishpond and large playground. Friendly campsite staff, no uniform. Multiple awards.

📍 N 54°3'32'' W 1°5'10''
www.eurocampings.co.uk/102888

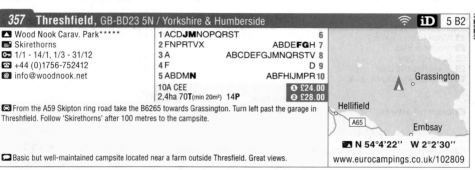

357 Threshfield, GB-BD23 5N / Yorkshire & Humberside 📶 **iD** 5 B2

🔺 Wood Nook Carav. Park*****
📧 Skirethorns
📅 1/1 - 14/1, 1/3 - 31/12
☎ +44 (0)1756-752412
@ info@woodnook.net

1	ACDJMNOPQRST	6
2	FNPRTVX	ABDE**FGH** 7
3	A	ABCDEFGJMNQRSTV 8
4	F	D 9
5	ABDM**N**	ABFHIJMPR 10
10A CEE		➊ £24.00
2,4ha 70T(min 20m²) 14P		➋ £28.00

🔄 From the A59 Skipton ring road take the B6265 towards Grassington. Turn left past the garage in Threshfield. Follow 'Skirethorns' after 100 metres to the campsite.

💬 Basic but well-maintained campsite located near a farm outside Thresfield. Great views.

📍 N 54°4'22'' W 2°2'30''
www.eurocampings.co.uk/102809

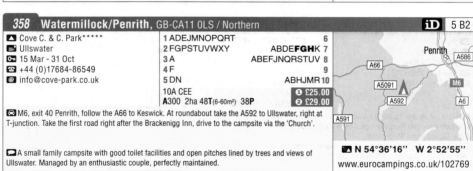

358 Watermillock/Penrith, GB-CA11 0LS / Northern **iD** 5 B2

🔺 Cove C. & C. Park*****
📧 Ullswater
📅 15 Mar - 31 Oct
☎ +44 (0)17684-86549
@ info@cove-park.co.uk

1	ADEJMNOPQRT	6
2	FGPSTUVWXY	ABDE**FGH** 7
3	A	ABEFJNQRSTUV 8
4	F	9
5	DN	ABHJMR 10
10A CEE		➊ £25.00
A300 2ha 48T(6-60m²) 38P		➋ £29.00

🔄 M6, exit 40 Penrith, follow the A66 to Keswick. At roundabout take the A592 to Ullswater, right at T-junction. Take the first road right after the Brackenigg Inn, drive to the campsite via the 'Church'.

💬 A small family campsite with good toilet facilities and open pitches lined by trees and views of Ullswater. Managed by an enthusiastic couple, perfectly maintained.

📍 N 54°36'16'' W 2°52'55''
www.eurocampings.co.uk/102769

359 Watermillock/Penrith, GB-CA11 0LR / Northern ♿ 📶 **iD** 5 B2

🔺 Ullswater Holiday Park***
📅 1 Mar - 14 Nov
☎ +44 (0)17684-86666
@ info@ullswaterholidaypark.co.uk

1	ADE**JM**NOPQRS**T**	**NQSXYZ** 6
2	AFGOPSTUVWXY	ABDE**FGH**K 7
3	A**K**V	ABEFINQRSTUV 8
4	FHIMO**PQ**	EFJ 9
5	ABDFHM**NO**	ABEGJMOR 10
10A CEE		➊ £26.50
A200 8ha 178T(100m²) 68P		➋ £31.50

🔄 M6, exit 40 Penrith. A66 direction Keswick, at roundabout on A592 direction Ullswater and follow the A592 by the lake. Second turning right after 'Brackenrigg' Hotel by the phone box.

💬 An open campsite surrounded by trees with beautiful pitches and well maintained and modern toilet facilities. Campers can use the Marine Park (marina), which is 1.5 km from the campsite.

📍 N 54°35'50'' W 2°52'30''
www.eurocampings.co.uk/102770

360 Weeton, GB-PR4 3NB / North West
  ♿ 🛜 iD 5 A3

- ▲ Ream Hills Holiday Park
- 🏠 Mythop Road
- 🕐 1/1 - 10/1, 1/3 - 31/12
- ☎ +44 (0)1253836587
- @ enquiries@reamhills.co.uk

1 ADE**JM**NOPQRS**T**		6
2 ADFSV	A**BFG**	7
3 A**K**	ABFJNQRSTUV	8
4	FJQR	9
5 DEFHM	ABCFGHIKPRW	10
16A CEE		❶ £35.00
2ha 92**T**(54-80m²) 18**P**		❷ £39.00

🚗 Leave the M55 at the 4th exit (j4) Blackpool. At roundabout 3rd exit, third crossroads turn right at traffic lights (Mythop Road). After 2.5 km the campsite is on the right.

💬 Quietly located campsite. Blackpool is 6 km away. At the campsite you can spend the night in a real Lynx helicopter. Canoe rental and possibility to go waveboarding.

📍 N 53°48'0'' W 2°57'25''
www.eurocampings.co.uk/122545

361 Wigginton/York, GB-YO32 2RH / Yorkshire & Humberside
  ♿ 6 A2

- ▲ Willow House Caravan Park***
- 🏠 Wigginton Road
- 🕐 1 Jan - 31 Dec
- ☎ +44 (0)1904-750060
- @ info@willowhouseyork.co.uk

1 **JM**NOPQRS**TU**	**N**	6
2 PSW		7
3	**NR**	8
4		9
5 ABCEFKMN		10
10A		❶ £25.00
2ha 39**T**(90-100m²)		❷ £31.00

🚗 North of York on the B1363, on the road to Wigginton. After 600 metres the campsite is on the right.

💬 Neat campsite, only for people aged 18 and above. Large separate tent field. Extensive farm shop and café.

📍 N 54°0'10'' W 1°5'21''
www.eurocampings.co.uk/115494

362 Windermere, GB-LA23 3PG / Northern
  ♿ 🛜 ✿ iD 5 B2

- ▲ Park Cliffe*****
- 🏠 Birks Road
- 🕐 1 Mar - 12 Nov
- ☎ +44 (0)15395-31344
- @ info@parkcliffe.co.uk

1 ADE**JM**NOPQRS**T**		6
2 FGPSTUVWXY	ABDE**FGH**	7
3 B**KL**	ABEFIJNQRSTUV	8
4 FIO**Q**	EF	9
5 ABDFHJLMN**O**	ABCGHIJMPQRY	10
10A CEE		❶ £35.00
10ha 132**T**(56-100m²) 38**P**		❷ £41.00

🚗 From the M6 exit 36, A590 towards The Lakes/Barrow. Turn right on to the A592 in the direction of Windermere near Newby Bridge. After 6.5 km the campsite is located on the right on a rather steep slope. Do not go via Windermere.

💬 Big, open, well-kept campsite with various amenities, beautiful views from the campsite. Just a short walk from a magnificent view of Lake Windermere. Various tent fields with different options. Outdoor centre nearby.

📍 N 54°18'38'' W 2°56'22''
www.eurocampings.co.uk/108594

363 Winksley, GB-HG4 3PG / Yorkshire & Humberside
  ♿ 🛜 iD 5 B2

- ▲ Woodhouse Farm
- 🕐 15 Mar - 31 Oct
- ☎ +44 (0)1765-658309
- @ woodhouse.farm@talk21.com

1 ADE**JM**NOPQRS**T**	**N**	6
2 FOPTWX	ABDE**FGH**	7
3 BEL	ABCDEFIJK**L**NQRSV	8
4 FIO**PQ**	F	9
5 ABDEFHLMN	ABIJM**N**ORWX	10
10A CEE		❶ £25.00
56ha 160**T** 48**P**		❷ £27.00

🚗 From the B6265 between Ripon and Pately Bridge, the campsite is signposted approx. 5 km before Ripon. The suggested navigation route is not suitable for caravans and large motorhomes.

💬 Large campsite on a farm in a rural setting. Strategically located for trips.

📍 N 54°8'19'' W 1°38'4''
www.eurocampings.co.uk/108587

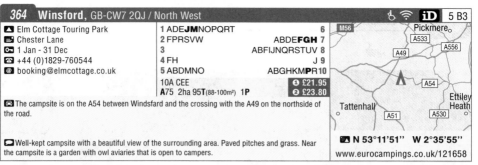

364 Winsford, GB-CW7 2QJ / North West   5 B3

- ▲ Elm Cottage Touring Park
- 🚉 Chester Lane
- 📅 1 Jan - 31 Dec
- ☎ +44 (0)1829-760544
- @ booking@elmcottage.co.uk

1 ADE**JM**NOPQRT	6
2 FPRSVW	ABDE**FGH** 7
3	ABFIJNQRSTUV 8
4 FH	J 9
5 ABDMNO	ABGHKM**P**R 10

10A CEE   ❶ £21.95
A75   2ha   95**T**(88-100m²)   1**P**   ❷ £23.80

🚏 The campsite is on the A54 between Windsford and the crossing with the A49 on the northside of the road.

💬 Well-kept campsite with a beautiful view of the surrounding area. Paved pitches and grass. Near the campsite is a garden with owl aviaries that is open to campers.

📷 N 53°11'51''   W 2°35'55''
www.eurocampings.co.uk/121658

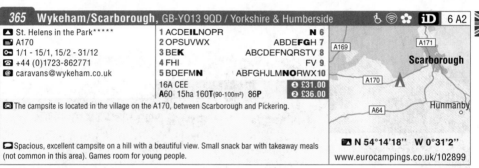

365 Wykeham/Scarborough, GB-YO13 9QD / Yorkshire & Humberside   6 A2

- ▲ St. Helens in the Park*****
- 🚉 A170
- 📅 1/1 - 15/1, 15/2 - 31/12
- ☎ +44 (0)1723-862771
- @ caravans@wykeham.co.uk

1 ACDE**IL**NOPR	**N** 6
2 OPSUVWX	ABDE**FG**H 7
3 BE**K**	ABCDEFNQRSTV 8
4 FHI	FV 9
5 BDEFM**N**	ABFGHJLM**NO**RWX 10

16A CEE   ❶ £31.00
A60   15ha   160**T**(90-100m²)   86**P**   ❷ £36.00

🚏 The campsite is located in the village on the A170, between Scarborough and Pickering.

💬 Spacious, excellent campsite on a hill with a beautiful view. Small snack bar with takeaway meals (not common in this area). Games room for young people.

📷 N 54°14'18''   W 0°31'2''
www.eurocampings.co.uk/102899

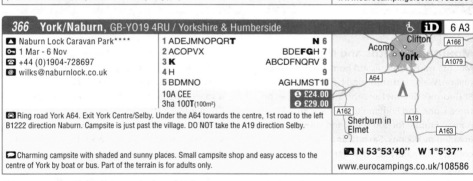

366 York/Naburn, GB-YO19 4RU / Yorkshire & Humberside   6 A3

- ▲ Naburn Lock Caravan Park****
- 📅 1 Mar - 6 Nov
- ☎ +44 (0)1904-728697
- @ wilks@naburnlock.co.uk

1 ADEJMNOPQR**T**	**N** 6
2 ACOPVX	BDE**FG**H 7
3 **K**	ABCDFNQRV 8
4 H	9
5 BDMNO	AGHJMST 10

10A CEE   ❶ £24.00
3ha   100**T**(100m²)   ❷ £29.00

🚏 Ring road York A64. Exit York Centre/Selby. Under the A64 towards the centre, 1st road to the left B1222 direction Naburn. Campsite is just past the village. DO NOT take the A19 direction Selby.

💬 Charming campsite with shaded and sunny places. Small campsite shop and easy access to the centre of York by boat or bus. Part of the terrain is for adults only.

📷 N 53°53'40''   W 1°5'37''
www.eurocampings.co.uk/108586

United Kingdom

Mountains, myths and music

Mountainous, remote, and home to just three million, Wales is surrounded by the Irish Sea, St George's Channel and the Bristol Channel on three sides, and England to the east. Ruled by the Roman Empire for 300 years, and subsequently invaded by Vikings, Saxons, and Normans, the country ultimately came under English rule in 1282. Wales provided much of the coal and metal that powered Britain's Industrial Revolution, and today is most densely populated in the north and south of the country, with the middle being comparatively empty.

Folk memories of King Arthur live on, with many associated places: Arthur's Stone is at Gower, while Caerleon is said to have been Camelot, and legend has it that Arthur sleeps with his warriors in Craig y Dolinas cave at Pontneddfeckan. There are also tales of a ghostly White Lady at Ewenny and nearby Ogmore Castle, so tell the kids to watch out! Besides looking for ghosts, you can also visit the Ewenny Pottery workshops and Coed-y-Bwl Nature Reserve. If you're interested in architecture, the castles and town walls in Gwynned, built by King Edward I, are well worth checking out.

Wales has so many fantastic singers that it's been called the Land of Song. Llangollen hosts the annual National Eisteddfod, or festival of singing. Wales has also produced many artists such as poets Dylan Thomas and Vernon Watkins, and painter Alfred Janes.

Daytrips and outdoor activities

For the more active, there's mountain-climbing and even skiing in Snowdonia National Park.

Brecon Beacons National Park is great for cycling and mountain-biking and in Black Mountains there's kayaking, paragliding, horse-riding and exploring caves. For more sedentary tourists, Tenby in South Wales is a lovely seaside town with a great beach, as well as narrow cobbled streets lined with cafés and shops. In North Wales, the town and castle of Conwy are so beautifully preserved, you will feel like you've travelled through time.

What to eat in Wales

Most locally produced meat is from sheep, so cawl or lamb stew is very popular. Other typical Welsh foods are laverbread, which is made from seaweed, cawl cennin or soup, and bara brith, a type of fruit loaf. Locally distilled whisky and cider made from local apples are highly recommended.

Our tips

1. Cardiff Castle, built by Victorian architect William Burgess
2. Visit Italian-inspired Portmeirion in north Wales
3. Marvel at the views from the Great Orme Cable Car at Llandudno
4. Check out the Big Pit National Coal Museum at Blaenavon
5. Go bog snorkelling at Llanwrtyd Wells in middle Wales

367 Aberaeron, GB-SA46 0JF / Wales
♿ 🛰 iD 9 A1

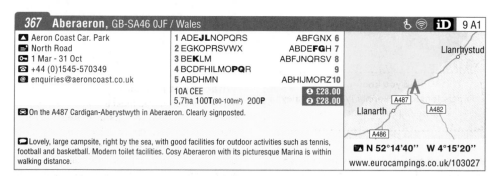

- 🏕 Aeron Coast Car. Park
- 📧 North Road
- 📅 1 Mar - 31 Oct
- ☎ +44 (0)1545-570349
- @ enquiries@aeroncoast.co.uk

1 ADE**JL**NOPQRS	ABFGNX 6
2 EGKOPRSVWX	ABDE**FG**H 7
3 BE**KLM**	ABFJNQRSV 8
4 BCDFHILMO**PQR**	9
5 ABDHMN	ABHIJMORZ 10

| 10A CEE | ❶ £28.00 |
| 5,7ha 100**T**(80-100m²) 200**P** | ❷ £28.00 |

🔲 On the A487 Cardigan-Aberystwyth in Aberaeron. Clearly signposted.

🔲 Lovely, large campsite, right by the sea, with good facilities for outdoor activities such as tennis, football and basketball. Modern toilet facilities. Cosy Aberaeron with its picturesque Marina is within walking distance.

🔳 **N 52°14'40'' W 4°15'20''**

www.eurocampings.co.uk/103027

---

368 Abergavenny, GB-NP7 8BG / Wales
♿ 🛰 iD 9 A2

- 🏕 Blossom Touring & Camping Park
- 📧 Tredilion Llantilio Pertholey
- 📅 1 Mar - 31 Oct
- ☎ +44 (0)7802-605050
- @ james.harris27@btinternet.com

1 ADE**JM**NOPQRST	6
2 FPRSTVWX	ABDE**FG** 7
3 **K**	AB**FG**JNQRTUV 8
4 FH	9
5 DN	ABCIJM**P**R 10

| 16A CEE | ❶ £20.00 |
| A160 7,5ha 84**T**(100-120m²) 40**P** | ❷ £30.00 |

🔲 Campsite is about 2.5 km north of Abergavenny. On the A465 take the exit to the B4521. The campsite is signposted with brown signs.

🔲 Campsite in a former orchard with beautiful views of the hills. The spacious pitches offer a lot of privacy. From the campsite you can walk to one of the most beautiful places in Wales. Picturesque Abergavenny is well worth a visit.

🔳 **N 51°49'49'' W 2°58'53''**

www.eurocampings.co.uk/121373

---

369 Abergavenny, GB-NP7 9DS / Wales
♿ 🛰 iD 9 A2

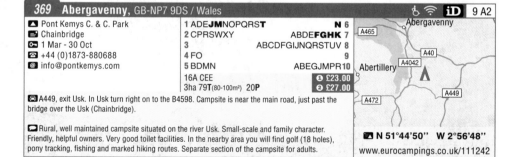

- 🏕 Pont Kemys C. & C. Park
- 📧 Chainbridge
- 📅 1 Mar - 30 Oct
- ☎ +44 (0)1873-880688
- @ info@pontkemys.com

1 ADE**JM**NOPQRS**T**	**N** 6
2 CPRSWXY	ABDE**FGHK** 7
3	ABCDFGIJNQRSTUV 8
4 FO	9
5 BDMN	ABEGJM**P**R 10

| 16A CEE | ❶ £23.00 |
| 3ha 79**T**(80-100m²) 20**P** | ❷ £27.00 |

🔲 A449, exit Usk. In Usk turn right on to the B4598. Campsite is near the main road, just past the bridge over the Usk (Chainbridge).

🔲 Rural, well maintained campsite situated on the river Usk. Small-scale and family character. Friendly, helpful owners. Very good toilet facilities. In the nearby area you will find golf (18 holes), pony tracking, fishing and marked hiking routes. Separate section of the campsite for adults.

🔳 **N 51°44'50'' W 2°56'48''**

www.eurocampings.co.uk/111242

---

370 Abersoch/Gwynedd, GB-LL53 7UL / Wales
♿ 🛰 ❀ iD 8 B1

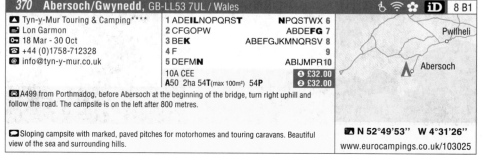

- 🏕 Tyn-y-Mur Touring & Camping****
- 📧 Lon Garmon
- 📅 18 Mar - 30 Oct
- ☎ +44 (0)1758-712328
- @ info@tyn-y-mur.co.uk

1 ADE**IL**NOPQRS**T**	**N**PQSTWX 6
2 CFGOPW	ABDE**FG** 7
3 BE**K**	ABEFGJKMNQRSV 8
4 F	9
5 DEFM**N**	ABIJMPR 10

| 10A CEE | ❶ £32.00 |
| A50 2ha 54**T**(max 100m²) 54**P** | ❷ £32.00 |

🔲 A499 from Porthmadog, before Abersoch at the beginning of the bridge, turn right uphill and follow the road. The campsite is on the left after 800 metres.

🔲 Sloping campsite with marked, paved pitches for motorhomes and touring caravans. Beautiful view of the sea and surrounding hills.

🔳 **N 52°49'53'' W 4°31'26''**

www.eurocampings.co.uk/103025

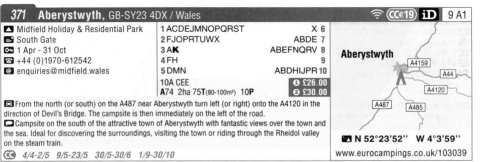

371 Aberystwyth, GB-SY23 4DX / Wales

🛜 (CC€19) 📱 iD 9 A1

▲ Midfield Holiday & Residential Park	1 ACDEJMNOPQRST	X 6
🏠 South Gate	2 FJOPRTUWX	ABDE 7
📅 1 Apr - 31 Oct	3 AK	ABEFNQRV 8
☎ +44 (0)1970-612542	4 FH	9
@ enquiries@midfield.wales	5 DMN	ABDHIJPR 10
	10A CEE	❶ £26.00
	A74 2ha 75T(80-100m²) 10P	❷ £30.00

🗺 From the north (or south) on the A487 near Aberystwyth turn left (or right) onto the A4120 in the direction of Devil's Bridge. The campsite is then immediately on the left of the road.

💬 Campsite on the south of the attractive town of Aberystwyth with fantastic views over the town and the sea. Ideal for discovering the surroundings, visiting the town or riding through the Rheidol valley on the steam train.

Aberystwyth

📍 N 52°23'52'' W 4°3'59''

www.eurocampings.co.uk/103039

CC 4/4-2/5 9/5-23/5 30/5-30/6 1/9-30/10

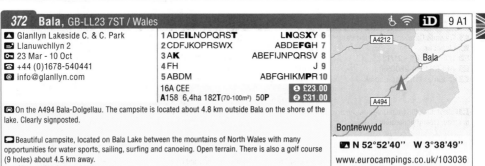

372 Bala, GB-LL23 7ST / Wales

♿ 🛜 iD 9 A1

▲ Glanllyn Lakeside C. & C. Park	1 ADEILNOPQRST	LNQSXY 6
🏠 Llanuwchllyn 2	2 CDFJKOPRSWX	ABDEFGH 7
📅 23 Mar - 10 Oct	3 AK	ABEFIJNPQRSV 8
☎ +44 (0)1678-540441	4 FH	J 9
@ info@glanllyn.com	5 ABDM	ABFGHIKMPR 10
	16A CEE	❶ £23.00
	A158 6,4ha 182T(70-100m²) 50P	❷ £31.00

🗺 On the A494 Bala-Dolgellau. The campsite is located about 4.8 km outside Bala on the shore of the lake. Clearly signposted.

💬 Beautiful campsite, located on Bala Lake between the mountains of North Wales with many opportunities for water sports, sailing, surfing and canoeing. Open terrain. There is also a golf course (9 holes) about 4.5 km away.

Bala

Bontnewydd

📍 N 52°52'40'' W 3°38'49''

www.eurocampings.co.uk/103036

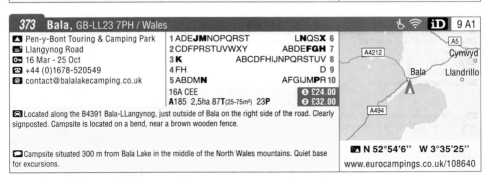

373 Bala, GB-LL23 7PH / Wales

♿ 🛜 iD 9 A1

▲ Pen-y-Bont Touring & Camping Park	1 ADEJMNOPQRST	LNQSX 6
🏠 Llangynog Road	2 CDFPRSTUVWXY	ABDEFGH 7
📅 16 Mar - 25 Oct	3 K	ABCDFHIJNPQRSTUV 8
☎ +44 (0)1678-520549	4 FH	D 9
@ contact@balalakecamping.co.uk	5 ABDMN	AFGIJMPR 10
	16A CEE	❶ £24.00
	A185 2,5ha 87T(25-75m²) 23P	❷ £32.00

🗺 Located along the B4391 Bala-LLangynog, just outside of Bala on the right side of the road. Clearly signposted. Campsite is located on a bend, near a brown wooden fence.

💬 Campsite situated 300 m from Bala Lake in the middle of the North Wales mountains. Quiet base for excursions.

Cynwyd

Bala Llandrillo

📍 N 52°54'6'' W 3°35'25''

www.eurocampings.co.uk/108640

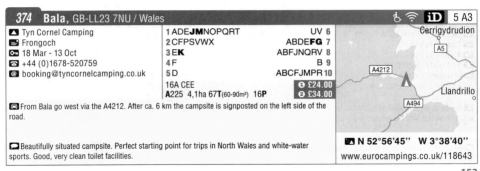

374 Bala, GB-LL23 7NU / Wales

♿ 🛜 iD 5 A3

▲ Tyn Cornel Camping	1 ADEJMNOPQRT	UV 6
🏠 Frongoch	2 CFPSVWX	ABDEFG 7
📅 18 Mar - 13 Oct	3 EK	ABFJNQRV 8
☎ +44 (0)1678-520759	4 F	B 9
@ booking@tyncornelcamping.co.uk	5 D	ABCFJMPR 10
	16A CEE	❶ £24.00
	A225 4,1ha 67T(60-90m²) 16P	❷ £34.00

🗺 From Bala go west via the A4212. After ca. 6 km the campsite is signposted on the left side of the road.

💬 Beautifully situated campsite. Perfect starting point for trips in North Wales and white-water sports. Good, very clean toilet facilities.

Cerrigydrudion

Llandrillo

📍 N 52°56'45'' W 3°38'40''

www.eurocampings.co.uk/118643

United Kingdom

375 Bala/Gwynedd, GB-LL23 7EP / Wales 🛜 iD 9 A1

▲ Tytandderwenn Caravan Park
🏠 Llangynog Road
🗓 1 Mar - 31 Oct
☎ +44 (0)1678-520273
@ robert@tytandderwen.plus.com

1 AJMNOPQRS	N 6
2 FGPTW	ABDEFG 7
3 A	ABFJNPQRSV 8
4	9
5 MN	ABHIJMPR 10
10A CEE	⏱ £21.00
A270 2,2ha 55T(80-100m²) 60P	⏱ £21.00

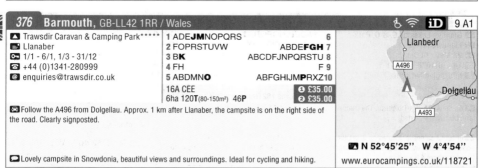

🛣 From the A494 turn immediately left in Bala to the B4401. After about 3 km turn left. Campsite is clearly signposted. Narrow access road (small bridge, cattle grid). Straight ahead after the entrance gate and turn right after 150 metres.

💬 Campsite with lovely view. Very spacious pitches. Ideal to relax.

📷 N 52°54'46" W 3°33'40"

www.eurocampings.co.uk/123059

376 Barmouth, GB-LL42 1RR / Wales ♿ 🛜 iD 9 A1

▲ Trawsdir Caravan & Camping Park*****
🏠 Llanaber
🗓 1/1 - 6/1, 1/3 - 31/12
☎ +44 (0)1341-280999
@ enquiries@trawsdir.co.uk

1 ADEJMNOPQRS	6
2 FOPRSTUVW	ABDEFGH 7
3 BK	ABCDFJNPQRSTU 8
4 FH	F 9
5 ABDMNO	ABFGHIJMPRXZ 10
16A CEE	⏱ £35.00
6ha 120T(80-150m²) 46P	⏱ £35.00

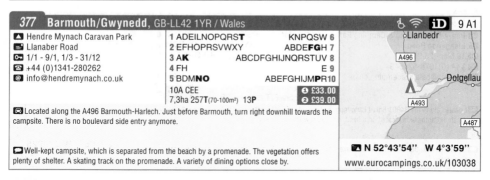

🛣 Follow the A496 from Dolgellau. Approx. 1 km after Llanaber, the campsite is on the right side of the road. Clearly signposted.

💬 Lovely campsite in Snowdonia, beautiful views and surroundings. Ideal for cycling and hiking.

📷 N 52°45'25" W 4°4'54"

www.eurocampings.co.uk/118721

377 Barmouth/Gwynedd, GB-LL42 1YR / Wales ♿ 🛜 iD 9 A1

▲ Hendre Mynach Caravan Park
🏠 Llanaber Road
🗓 1/1 - 9/1, 1/3 - 31/12
☎ +44 (0)1341-280262
@ info@hendremynach.co.uk

1 ADEILNOPQRST	KNPQSW 6
2 EFHOPRSVWXY	ABDEFGH 7
3 AK	ABCDFGHIJNQRSTUV 8
4 FH	E 9
5 BDMNO	ABEFGHIJMPR 10
10A CEE	⏱ £33.00
7,3ha 257T(70-100m²) 13P	⏱ £39.00

🛣 Located along the A496 Barmouth-Harlech. Just before Barmouth, turn right downhill towards the campsite. There is no boulevard side entry anymore.

💬 Well-kept campsite, which is separated from the beach by a promenade. The vegetation offers plenty of shelter. A skating track on the promenade. A variety of dining options close by.

📷 N 52°43'54" W 4°3'59"

www.eurocampings.co.uk/103038

378 Beddgelert, GB-LL55 4UU / Wales ♿ iD 5 A3

▲ Beddgelert Forest C. & C. Site
🏠 Caernarfon Road
🗓 1 Jan - 31 Dec
☎ +44 (0)1766-890288
@ beddgelert.site@
    campinginthforest.co.uk

1 ACDEJMNOPQRST	J 6
2 BCOPRSTVWXY	ABDEFG 7
3 AK	ABCDEFJNQRV 8
4 FI	9
5 ABDGMN	ABFGHIJMR 10
16A CEE	⏱ £28.50
A111 25ha 195T(80-120m²)	⏱ £33.80

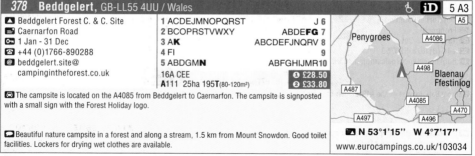

🛣 The campsite is located on the A4085 from Beddgelert to Caernarfon. The campsite is signposted with a small sign with the Forest Holiday logo.

💬 Beautiful nature campsite in a forest and along a stream, 1.5 km from Mount Snowdon. Good toilet facilities. Lockers for drying wet clothes are available.

📷 N 53°1'15" W 4°7'17"

www.eurocampings.co.uk/103034

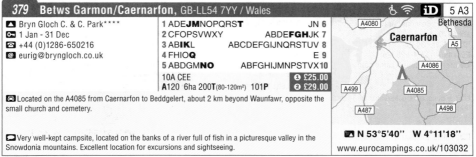

379 Betws Garmon/Caernarfon, GB-LL54 7YY / Wales ♿ 🛜 iD 5 A3

- ▲ Bryn Gloch C. & C. Park★★★★
- 🗓 1 Jan - 31 Dec
- ☎ +44 (0)1286-650216
- @ eurig@bryngloch.co.uk

1 ADE**JM**NOPQRS**T**		JN 6
2 CFOPSVWXY	ABDE**FGH**JK 7
3 AB**IKL**	ABCDEFGIJNQRSTUV 8
4 FHIO**Q**	E 9
5 ABDGM**NO**	ABFGHIJMNPSTVX 10

10A CEE	❶ £25.00
A120 6ha 200**T**(80-120m²) 101**P**	❷ £29.00

🚐 Located on the A4085 from Caernarfon to Beddgelert, about 2 km beyond Waunfawr, opposite the small church and cemetery.

💬 Very well-kept campsite, located on the banks of a river full of fish in a picturesque valley in the Snowdonia mountains. Excellent location for excursions and sightseeing.

🧭 N 53°5'40'' W 4°11'18''
www.eurocampings.co.uk/103032

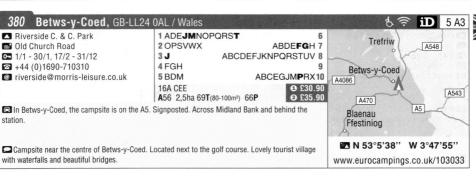

380 Betws-y-Coed, GB-LL24 0AL / Wales ♿ 🛜 iD 5 A3

- ▲ Riverside C. & C. Park
- 🏠 Old Church Road
- 🗓 1/1 - 30/1, 17/2 - 31/12
- ☎ +44 (0)1690-710310
- @ riverside@morris-leisure.co.uk

1 ADE**JM**NOPQRS**T**		6
2 OPSVWX	ABDE**FGH** 7
3 **J**	ABCDEFJKNPQRSTUV 8
4 FGH	9
5 BDM	ABCEGJM**P**RX 10

16A CEE	❶ £30.90
A56 2,5ha 69**T**(80-100m²) 66**P**	❷ £35.90

🚐 In Betws-y-Coed, the campsite is on the A5. Signposted. Across Midland Bank and behind the station.

💬 Campsite near the centre of Betws-y-Coed. Located next to the golf course. Lovely tourist village with waterfalls and beautiful bridges.

🧭 N 53°5'38'' W 3°47'55''
www.eurocampings.co.uk/103033

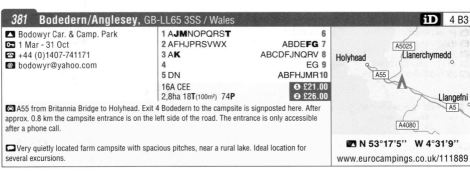

381 Bodedern/Anglesey, GB-LL65 3SS / Wales iD 4 B3

- ▲ Bodowyr Car. & Camp. Park
- 🗓 1 Mar - 31 Oct
- ☎ +44 (0)1407-741171
- @ bodowyr@yahoo.com

1 A**JM**NOPQRS**T**		6
2 AFHJPRSVWX	ABDE**FG** 7
3 A**K**	ABCDFJNQRV 8
4	EG 9
5 DN	ABFHJMR 10

16A CEE	❶ £21.00
2,8ha 18**T**(100m²) 74**P**	❷ £26.00

🚐 A55 from Britannia Bridge to Holyhead. Exit 4 Bodedern to the campsite is signposted here. After approx. 0.8 km the campsite entrance is on the left side of the road. The entrance is only accessible after a phone call.

💬 Very quietly located farm campsite with spacious pitches, near a rural lake. Ideal location for several excursions.

🧭 N 53°17'5'' W 4°31'9''
www.eurocampings.co.uk/111889

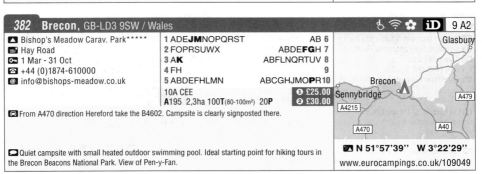

382 Brecon, GB-LD3 9SW / Wales ♿ 🛜 ⚙ iD 9 A2

- ▲ Bishop's Meadow Carav. Park★★★★★
- 🏠 Hay Road
- 🗓 1 Mar - 31 Oct
- ☎ +44 (0)1874-610000
- @ info@bishops-meadow.co.uk

1 ADE**JM**NOPQRST		AB 6
2 FOPRSUWX	ABDE**FG**H 7
3 A**K**	ABFLNQRTUV 8
4 FH	9
5 ABDEFHLMN	ABCGHJMO**P**R 10

10A CEE	❶ £25.00
A195 2,3ha 100**T**(80-100m²) 20**P**	❷ £30.00

🚐 From A470 direction Hereford take the B4602. Campsite is clearly signposted there.

💬 Quiet campsite with small heated outdoor swimming pool. Ideal starting point for hiking tours in the Brecon Beacons National Park. View of Pen-y-Fan.

🧭 N 51°57'39'' W 3°22'29''
www.eurocampings.co.uk/109049

United Kingdom

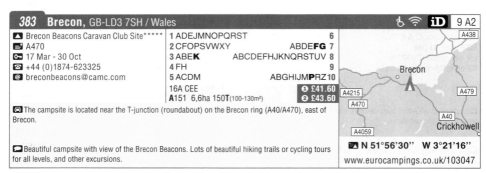

383 Brecon, GB-LD3 7SH / Wales
♿ 📶 **iD** 9 A2

- 🔺 Brecon Beacons Caravan Club Site*****
- 🚌 A470
- 📅 17 Mar - 30 Oct
- ☎ +44 (0)1874-623325
- @ breconbeacons@camc.com

1 ADEJMNOPQRST		6
2 CFOPSVWXY	ABDE**FG**	7
3 ABE**K**	ABCDEFHJKNQRSTUV	8
4 FH		9
5 ACDM	ABGHIJM**PRZ**	10

16A CEE   ❶ £41.60   ❷ £43.60
A151   6,6ha 150T(100-130m²)

🅿 The campsite is located near the T-junction (roundabout) on the Brecon ring (A40/A470), east of Brecon.

💬 Beautiful campsite with view of the Brecon Beacons. Lots of beautiful hiking trails or cycling tours for all levels, and other excursions.

🧭 **N 51°56'30" W 3°21'16"**
www.eurocampings.co.uk/103047

United Kingdom

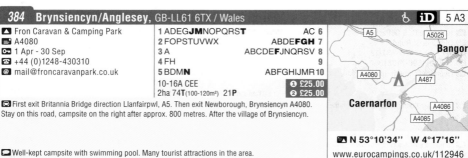

384 Brynsiencyn/Anglesey, GB-LL61 6TX / Wales
♿ **iD** 5 A3

- 🔺 Fron Caravan & Camping Park
- 🚌 A4080
- 📅 1 Apr - 30 Sep
- ☎ +44 (0)1248-430310
- @ mail@froncaravanpark.co.uk

1 ADEG**JM**NOPQRS**T**		AC 6
2 FOPSTUVWX	ABDE**FGH**	7
3 A	ABCDE**F**JNQRSV	8
4 FH		9
5 BDM**N**	ABFGHIJMR	10

10-16A CEE   ❶ £25.00   ❷ £25.00
2ha 74**T**(100-120m²)   21**P**

🅿 First exit Britannia Bridge direction Llanfairpwl, A5. Then exit Newborough, Brynsiencyn A4080. Stay on this road, campsite on the right after approx. 800 metres. After the village of Brynsiencyn.

💬 Well-kept campsite with swimming pool. Many tourist attractions in the area.

🧭 **N 53°10'34" W 4°17'16"**
www.eurocampings.co.uk/112946

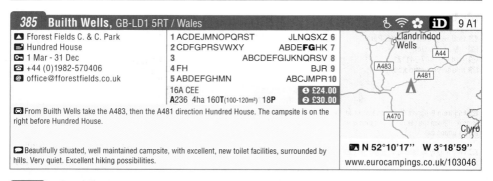

385 Builth Wells, GB-LD1 5RT / Wales
♿ 📶 ⚙ **iD** 9 A1

- 🔺 Fforest Fields C. & C. Park
- 🚌 Hundred House
- 📅 1 Mar - 31 Dec
- ☎ +44 (0)1982-570406
- @ office@fforestfields.co.uk

1 ACDEJMNOPQRST	JLNQSXZ	6
2 CDFGPRSVWXY	ABDE**FG**HK	7
3	ABCDEFGIJKNQRSV	8
4 FH	BJR	9
5 ABDEFGHMN	ABCJMPR	10

16A CEE   ❶ £24.00   ❷ £30.00
A236   4ha 160T(100-120m²)   18**P**

🅿 From Builth Wells take the A483, then the A481 direction Hundred House. The campsite is on the right before Hundred House.

💬 Beautifully situated, well maintained campsite, with excellent, new toilet facilities, surrounded by hills. Very quiet. Excellent hiking possibilities.

🧭 **N 52°10'17" W 3°18'59"**
www.eurocampings.co.uk/103046

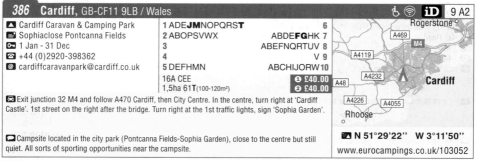

386 Cardiff, GB-CF11 9LB / Wales
♿ 📶 **iD** 9 A2

- 🔺 Cardiff Caravan & Camping Park
- 🚌 Sophiaclose Pontcanna Fields
- 📅 1 Jan - 31 Dec
- ☎ +44 (0)2920-398362
- @ cardiffcaravanpark@cardiff.co.uk

1 ADE**JM**NOPQRS**T**		6
2 ABOPSVWX	ABDE**FG**HK	7
3	ABEFNQRTUV	8
4	V	9
5 DEFHMN	ABCHIJORW	10

16A CEE   ❶ £40.00   ❷ £40.00
1,5ha 61**T**(100-120m²)

🅿 Exit junction 32 M4 and follow A470 Cardiff, then City Centre. In the centre, turn right at 'Cardiff Castle'. 1st street on the right after the bridge. Turn right at the 1st traffic lights, sign 'Sophia Garden'.

💬 Campsite located in the city park (Pontcanna Fields-Sophia Garden), close to the centre but still quiet. All sorts of sporting opportunities near the campsite.

🧭 **N 51°29'22" W 3°11'50"**
www.eurocampings.co.uk/103052

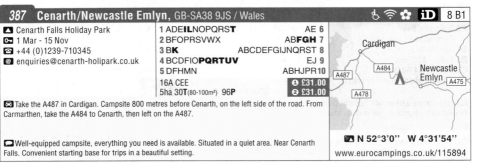

387 Cenarth/Newcastle Emlyn, GB-SA38 9JS / Wales

🚿 📶 ♿ **iD** | 8 B1

- ▲ Cenarth Falls Holiday Park
- 📅 1 Mar - 15 Nov
- ☎ +44 (0)1239-710345
- @ enquiries@cenarth-holipark.co.uk

1 ADE**IL**NOPQRS**T**	AE 6
2 BFOPRSVWX	AB**FGH** 7
3 B**K**	ABCDEFGIJNQRST 8
4 BCDFIO**PQRTUV**	EJ 9
5 DFHMN	ABHJPR 10
16A CEE	❶ £31.00
5ha 30**T**(80-100m²) 96**P**	❷ £31.00

🗺 Take the A487 in Cardigan. Campsite 800 metres before Cenarth, on the left side of the road. From Carmarthen, take the A484 to Cenarth, then left on the A487.

💬 Well-equipped campsite, everything you need is available. Situated in a quiet area. Near Cenarth Falls. Convenient starting base for trips in a beautiful setting.

📍 N 52°3'0'' W 4°31'54''
www.eurocampings.co.uk/115894

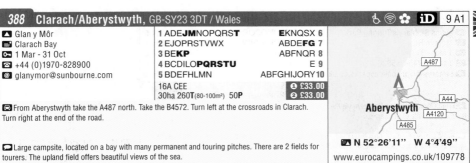

388 Clarach/Aberystwyth, GB-SY23 3DT / Wales

🚿 📶 ♿ **iD** | 9 A1

- ▲ Glan y Môr
- 🏖 Clarach Bay
- 📅 1 Mar - 31 Oct
- ☎ +44 (0)1970-828900
- @ glanymor@sunbourne.com

1 ADE**JM**NOPQRS**T**	E**K**NQSX 6
2 EJOPRSTVWX	ABDE**FG** 7
3 BE**KP**	ABFNQR 8
4 BCDILO**PQRSTU**	E 9
5 BDEFHLMN	ABFGHIJORY 10
16A CEE	❶ £33.00
30ha 260**T**(80-100m²) 50**P**	❷ £33.00

🗺 From Aberystwyth take the A487 north. Take the B4572. Turn left at the crossroads in Clarach. Turn right at the end of the road.

💬 Large campsite, located on a bay with many permanent and touring pitches. There are 2 fields for tourers. The upland field offers beautiful views of the sea.

📍 N 52°26'11'' W 4°4'49''
www.eurocampings.co.uk/109778

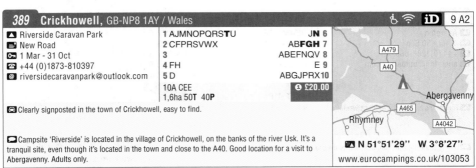

389 Crickhowell, GB-NP8 1AY / Wales

🚿 📶 **iD** | 9 A2

- ▲ Riverside Caravan Park
- 🏖 New Road
- 📅 1 Mar - 31 Oct
- ☎ +44 (0)1873-810397
- @ riversidecaravanpark@outlook.com

1 AJMNOPQRS**T**U	J**N** 6
2 CFPRSVWX	AB**FGH** 7
3	ABEFNQV 8
4 FH	E 9
5 D	ABGJPRX 10
10A CEE	❶ £20.00
1,6ha 50**T** 40**P**	

🗺 Clearly signposted in the town of Crickhowell, easy to find.

💬 Campsite 'Riverside' is located in the village of Crickhowell, on the banks of the river Usk. It's a tranquil site, even though it's located in the town and close to the A40. Good location for a visit to Abergavenny. Adults only.

📍 N 51°51'29'' W 3°8'27''
www.eurocampings.co.uk/103053

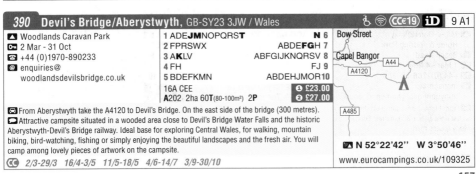

390 Devil's Bridge/Aberystwyth, GB-SY23 3JW / Wales

🚿 📶 **CC€19** **iD** | 9 A1

- ▲ Woodlands Caravan Park
- 📅 2 Mar - 31 Oct
- ☎ +44 (0)1970-890233
- @ enquiries@
  woodlandsdevilsbridge.co.uk

1 ADE**JM**NOPQRS**T**	N 6
2 FPRSWX	ABDE**FGH** 7
3 A**KL**V	ABFGIJKNQRSV 8
4 FH	FJ 9
5 BDEFKMN	ABDEHJMOR 10
16A CEE	❶ £23.00
A202 2ha 60**T**(80-100m²) 2**P**	❷ £27.00

🗺 From Aberystwyth take the A4120 to Devil's Bridge. On the east side of the bridge (300 metres).
💬 Attractive campsite situated in a wooded area close to Devil's Bridge Water Falls and the historic Aberystwyth-Devil's Bridge railway. Ideal base for exploring Central Wales, for walking, mountain biking, bird-watching, fishing or simply enjoying the beautiful landscapes and the fresh air. You will camp among lovely pieces of artwork on the campsite.

CC 2/3-29/3 16/4-3/5 11/5-18/5 4/6-14/7 3/9-30/10

📍 N 52°22'42'' W 3°50'46''
www.eurocampings.co.uk/109325

United Kingdom

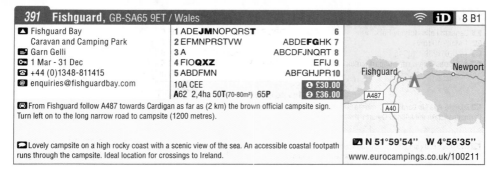

391 Fishguard, GB-SA65 9ET / Wales   📶 iD   8 B1

🏕 Fishguard Bay
Caravan and Camping Park
🏠 Garn Gelli
📅 1 Mar - 31 Dec
☎ +44 (0)1348-811415
@ enquiries@fishguardbay.com

1 ADEJMNOPQRST	6
2 EFMNPRSTVW	ABDEFGHK 7
3 A	ABCDFJNQRT 8
4 FIOQXZ	EFIJ 9
5 ABDFMN	ABFGHJPR 10
10A CEE	❶ £30.00
A62 2,4ha 50T(70-80m²) 65P	❷ £36.00

🚗 From Fishguard follow A487 towards Cardigan as far as (2 km) the brown official campsite sign. Turn left on to the long narrow road to campsite (1200 metres).

💬 Lovely campsite on a high rocky coast with a scenic view of the sea. An accessible coastal footpath runs through the campsite. Ideal location for crossings to Ireland.

📍 N 51°59'54" W 4°56'35"

www.eurocampings.co.uk/100211

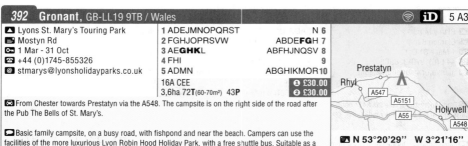

392 Gronant, GB-LL19 9TB / Wales   📶 iD   5 A3

🏕 Lyons St. Mary's Touring Park
🏠 Mostyn Rd
📅 1 Mar - 31 Oct
☎ +44 (0)1745-855326
@ stmarys@lyonsholidayparks.co.uk

1 ADEJMNOPQRST	N 6
2 FGHJOPRSVW	ABDEFGH 7
3 AEGHKL	ABFHJNQSV 8
4 FHI	9
5 ADMN	ABGHIKMOR 10
16A CEE	❶ £30.00
3,6ha 72T(60-70m²) 43P	❷ £30.00

🚗 From Chester towards Prestatyn via the A548. The campsite is on the right side of the road after the Pub The Bells of St. Mary's.

💬 Basic family campsite, on a busy road, with fishpond and near the beach. Campers can use the facilities of the more luxurious Lyon Robin Hood Holiday Park, with a free shuttle bus. Suitable as a transit campsite.

📍 N 53°20'29" W 3°21'16"

www.eurocampings.co.uk/109556

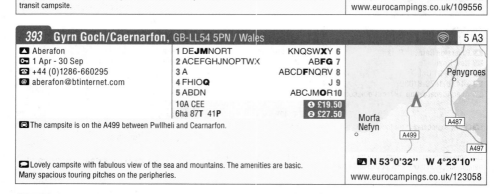

393 Gyrn Goch/Caernarfon, GB-LL54 5PN / Wales   📶   5 A3

🏕 Aberafon
📅 1 Apr - 30 Sep
☎ +44 (0)1286-660295
@ aberafon@btinternet.com

1 DEJMNORT	KNQSWXY 6
2 ACEFGHJNOPTWX	ABFG 7
3 A	ABCDFNQRV 8
4 FHIOQ	J 9
5 ABDN	ABCJMOR 10
10A CEE	❶ £19.50
6ha 87T 41P	❷ £27.50

🚗 The campsite is on the A499 between Pwllheli and Cearnarfon.

💬 Lovely campsite with fabulous view of the sea and mountains. The amenities are basic. Many spacious touring pitches on the peripheries.

📍 N 53°0'32" W 4°23'10"

www.eurocampings.co.uk/123058

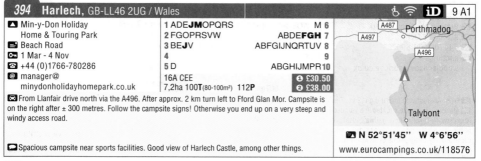

394 Harlech, GB-LL46 2UG / Wales   ♿ 📶 iD   9 A1

🏕 Min-y-Don Holiday
Home & Touring Park
🏠 Beach Road
📅 1 Mar - 4 Nov
☎ +44 (0)1766-780286
@ manager@
minydonholidayhomepark.co.uk

1 ADEJMOPQRS	M 6
2 FGOPRSVW	ABDEFGH 7
3 BEJV	ABFGIJNQRTUV 8
4	9
5 D	ABGHIJMPR 10
16A CEE	❶ £30.50
7,2ha 100T(80-100m²) 112P	❷ £38.00

🚗 From Llanfair drive north via the A496. After approx. 2 km turn left to Fford Glan Mor. Campsite is on the right after ± 300 metres. Follow the campsite signs! Otherwise you end up on a very steep and windy access road.

💬 Spacious campsite near sports facilities. Good view of Harlech Castle, among other things.

📍 N 52°51'45" W 4°6'56"

www.eurocampings.co.uk/118576

395 Horton (Gower), GB-SA3 1LL / Wales   ♿ 🛜 (CC€17) iD   8 B2

- 🏕 Bank Farm Leisure, Camp. & Car. Park
- 🗓 1 Mar - 31 Dec
- ☎ +44 (0)1792-390228
- @ enquiries@bankfarmleisure.co.uk

1 ADE**JM**NOPQRS**T**	CDFGKNQSX	6
2 EFGHKMOPTW	AB**FGH**	7
3 BE**KM**	ABFNQRSV	8
4 I O**PQ**	J	9
5 ACDEFHKM**N**	ABJNORZ	10
10A CEE	❶ £29.60	
A62 30ha 230**T**(80-120m²) 85**P**	❷ £29.60	

🚗 On the A4118 Killay-Port Eynon, turn left towards Horton just before Port Eynon and follow the campsite signs. This way is better than using SatNav which selects roads that are too narrow.
🛏 Large campsite on open meadows with lovely views of the sea. If the sea is too cold, the heated swimming pool offers plenty of fun in the water. The beautiful countryside around Gower is an invitation to go out for walks.

(CC) 1/3-28/3 2/4-3/5 7/5-23/5 4/6-30/6 2/9-31/12

🏴 N 51°33'22"   W 4°12'51"
www.eurocampings.co.uk/103030

Gowerton
Waunarlwydd

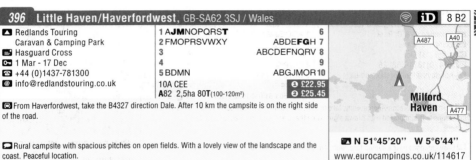

396 Little Haven/Haverfordwest, GB-SA62 3SJ / Wales   🛜 iD   8 B2

- 🏕 Redlands Touring
  Caravan & Camping Park
- ▦ Hasguard Cross
- 🗓 1 Mar - 17 Dec
- ☎ +44 (0)1437-781300
- @ info@redlandstouring.co.uk

1 **A**J**MN**OPQRS**T**		6
2 FMOPRSVWXY	ABDE**FGH**	7
3	ABCDEFNQRV	8
4		9
5 BDMN	ABGJMOR	10
10A CEE	❶ £22.95	
A82 2,5ha 80**T**(100-120m²)	❷ £25.45	

🚗 From Haverfordwest, take the B4327 direction Dale. After 10 km the campsite is on the right side of the road.

🛏 Rural campsite with spacious pitches on open fields. With a lovely view of the landscape and the coast. Peaceful location.

🏴 N 51°45'20"   W 5°6'44"
www.eurocampings.co.uk/114617

A487   A40
Milford
Haven   A477

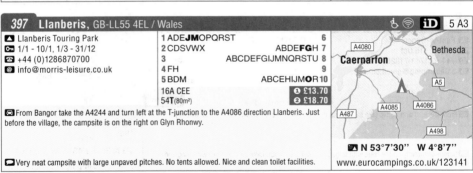

397 Llanberis, GB-LL55 4EL / Wales   ♿ 🛜 iD   5 A3

- 🏕 Llanberis Touring Park
- 🗓 1/1 - 10/1, 1/3 - 31/12
- ☎ +44 (0)1286870700
- @ info@morris-leisure.co.uk

1 ADE**JM**OPQRST		6
2 CDSVWX	ABDE**FGH**	7
3	ABCDEFGIJMNQRSTU	8
4 FH		9
5 BDM	ABCEHIJM**OR**	10
16A CEE	❶ £13.70	
54**T**(80m²)	❷ £18.70	

🚗 From Bangor take the A4244 and turn left at the T-junction to the A4086 direction Llanberis. Just before the village, the campsite is on the right on Glyn Rhonwy.

🛏 Very neat campsite with large unpaved pitches. No tents allowed. Nice and clean toilet facilities.

🏴 N 53°7'30"   W 4°8'7"
www.eurocampings.co.uk/123141

A4080   Bethesda
Caernarfon
A5
A487   A4085   A4086
A498

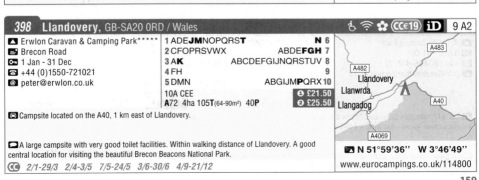

398 Llandovery, GB-SA20 0RD / Wales   ♿ 🛜 ✿ (CC€19) iD   9 A2

- 🏕 Erwlon Caravan & Camping Park*****
- ▦ Brecon Road
- 🗓 1 Jan - 31 Dec
- ☎ +44 (0)1550-721021
- @ peter@erwlon.co.uk

1 ADE**JM**NOPQRS**T**	**N**	6
2 CFOPRSVWX	ABDE**FGH**	7
3 A**K**	ABCDEFGIJNQRSTUV	8
4 FH		9
5 DMN	ABGIJM**PQRX**	10
10A CEE	❶ £21.50	
A72 4ha 105**T**(64-90m²) 40**P**	❷ £25.50	

🚗 Campsite located on the A40, 1 km east of Llandovery.

🛏 A large campsite with very good toilet facilities. Within walking distance of Llandovery. A good central location for visiting the beautiful Brecon Beacons National Park.

(CC) 2/1-29/3 2/4-3/5 7/5-24/5 3/6-30/6 4/9-21/12

🏴 N 51°59'36"   W 3°46'49"
www.eurocampings.co.uk/114800

A483
A482
Llandovery
Llanwrda
Llangadog
A40
A4069

United Kingdom

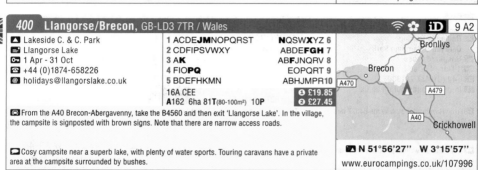

399 Llanfwrog (Anglesey), GB-LL65 4YG / Wales
4 B3

- ▲ Penrhyn Bay Caravan Park
- 📅 12 Mar - 31 Oct
- ☎ +44 (0)1407-730496
- @ mail@penrhynbay.com

1 ADEJMNOPQRT	EFGKNOPQSWXY	6
2 AEFGHMPV	ABDEFGH	7
3 BELM	ABCDFJNQRSTUV	8
4 FIPQ		9
5 ABDMNO	ABFHIJMPR	10

10A CEE ❶ £38.00
12,8ha 49T(100-150m²) 147P ❷ £38.00

Holyhead

🚗 A5025, exit to Llanfwrog. After centre, follow the signs 'Sandybeach/Penryn'. The campsite is on the coast. Another 3 km after the sign.

💬 Spacious campsite with limited shelter and water supply at all pitches. Situated directly on the coast with spectacular views of the shipping traffic.

📍 N 53°19'29" W 4°34'16"
www.eurocampings.co.uk/112944

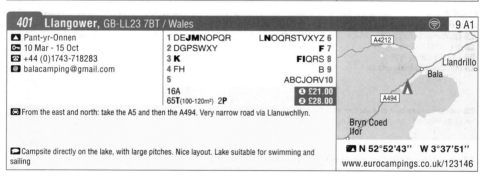

400 Llangorse/Brecon, GB-LD3 7TR / Wales
9 A2

- ▲ Lakeside C. & C. Park
- 🛥 Llangorse Lake
- 📅 1 Apr - 31 Oct
- ☎ +44 (0)1874-658226
- @ holidays@llangorselake.co.uk

1 ACDEJMNOPQRST	NQSWXYZ	6
2 CDFIPSVWXY	ABDEFGH	7
3 AK	ABFJNQRV	8
4 FIOPQ	EOPQRT	9
5 BDEFHKMN	ABHJMPR	10

16A CEE ❶ £19.85
A162 6ha 81T(80-100m²) 10P ❷ £27.45

Bronllys
Brecon
Crickhowell

🚗 From the A40 Brecon-Abergavenny, take the B4560 and then exit 'Llangorse Lake'. In the village, the campsite is signposted with brown signs. Note that there are narrow access roads.

💬 Cosy campsite near a superb lake, with plenty of water sports. Touring caravans have a private area at the campsite surrounded by bushes.

📍 N 51°56'27" W 3°15'57"
www.eurocampings.co.uk/107996

401 Llangower, GB-LL23 7BT / Wales
9 A1

- ▲ Pant-yr-Onnen
- 📅 10 Mar - 15 Oct
- ☎ +44 (0)1743-718283
- @ balacamping@gmail.com

1 DEJMNOPQR	LNOQRSTVXYZ	6
2 DGPSWXY	F	7
3 K	FIQRS	8
4 FH	B	9
5	ABCJORV	10

16A ❶ £21.00
65T(100-120m²) 2P ❷ £28.00

Llandrillo
Bala
Bryn Coed Ifor

🚗 From the east and north: take the A5 and then the A494. Very narrow road via Llanuwchllyn.

💬 Campsite directly on the lake, with large pitches. Nice layout. Lake suitable for swimming and sailing

📍 N 52°52'43" W 3°37'51"
www.eurocampings.co.uk/123146

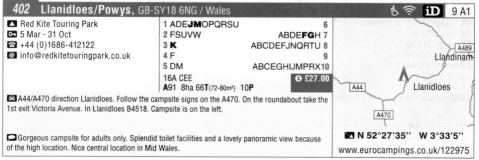

402 Llanidloes/Powys, GB-SY18 6NG / Wales
9 A1

- ▲ Red Kite Touring Park
- 📅 5 Mar - 31 Oct
- ☎ +44 (0)1686-412122
- @ info@redkitetouringpark.co.uk

1 ADEJMOPQRSU		6
2 FSUVW	ABDEFGH	7
3 K	ABCDEFJNQRTU	8
4 F		9
5 DM	ABCEGHIJMPRX	10

16A CEE ❶ £27.00
A91 8ha 66T(72-80m²) 10P

Llandinam
Llanidloes

🚗 A44/A470 direction Llanidloes. Follow the campsite signs on the A470. On the roundabout take the 1st exit Victoria Avenue. In Llanidloes B4518. Campsite is on the left.

💬 Gorgeous campsite for adults only. Splendid toilet facilities and a lovely panoramic view because of the high location. Nice central location in Mid Wales.

📍 N 52°27'35" W 3°33'5"
www.eurocampings.co.uk/122975

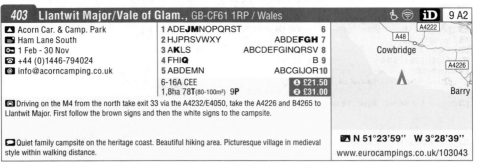

403 Llantwit Major/Vale of Glam., GB-CF61 1RP / Wales 9 A2

- Acorn Car. & Camp. Park
- Ham Lane South
- 1 Feb - 30 Nov
- +44 (0)1446-794024
- info@acorncamping.co.uk

1 ADE**JM**NOPQRST		6
2 HJPRSVWXY	ABDE**FGH**	7
3 A**K**LS	ABCDEFGINQRSV	8
4 FHI**Q**	B	9
5 ABDEMN	ABCGIJOR	10
6-16A CEE		❶ £21.50
1,8ha 78T(80-100m²) 9P		❷ £31.00

Driving on the M4 from the north take exit 33 via the A4232/E4050, take the A4226 and B4265 to Llantwit Major. First follow the brown signs and then the white signs to the campsite.

Quiet family campsite on the heritage coast. Beautiful hiking area. Picturesque village in medieval style within walking distance.

N 51°23'59'' W 3°28'39''
www.eurocampings.co.uk/103043

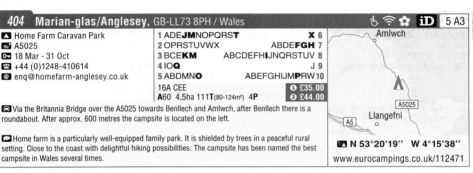

404 Marian-glas/Anglesey, GB-LL73 8PH / Wales 5 A3

- Home Farm Caravan Park
- A5025
- 18 Mar - 31 Oct
- +44 (0)1248-410614
- enq@homefarm-anglesey.co.uk

1 ADE**JM**NOPQRS**T**		X 6
2 OPRSTUVWX	ABDE**FGH**	7
3 BCE**KM**	ABCDEFHIJNQRSTUV	8
4 IO**Q**	J	9
5 ABDMN**O**	ABEFGHIJMP**R**W	10
16A CEE		❶ £35.00
A60 4,5ha 111T(80-124m²) 4P		❷ £44.00

Via the Britannia Bridge over the A5025 towards Benllech and Amlwch, after Benllech there is a roundabout. After approx. 600 metres the campsite is located on the left.

Home farm is a particularly well-equipped family park. It is shielded by trees in a peaceful rural setting. Close to the coast with delightful hiking possibilities. The campsite has been named the best campsite in Wales several times.

N 53°20'19'' W 4°15'38''
www.eurocampings.co.uk/112471

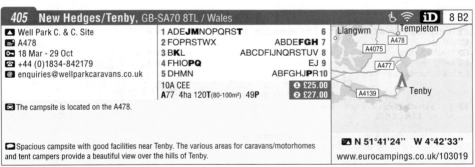

405 New Hedges/Tenby, GB-SA70 8TL / Wales 8 B2

- Well Park C. & C. Site
- A478
- 18 Mar - 29 Oct
- +44 (0)1834-842179
- enquiries@wellparkcaravans.co.uk

1 ADE**JM**NOPQRS**T**		6
2 FOPRSTWX	ABDE**FGH**	7
3 B**KL**	ABCDFIJNQRSTUV	8
4 FHIO**PQ**	EJ	9
5 DHMN	ABFGHJ**P**R	10
10A CEE		❶ £25.00
A77 4ha 120T(80-100m²) 49P		❷ £27.00

The campsite is located on the A478.

Spacious campsite with good facilities near Tenby. The various areas for caravans/motorhomes and tent campers provide a beautiful view over the hills of Tenby.

N 51°41'24'' W 4°42'33''
www.eurocampings.co.uk/103019

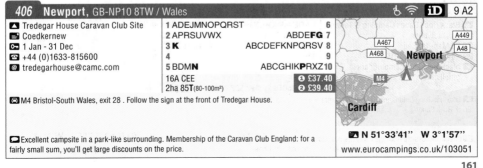

406 Newport, GB-NP10 8TW / Wales 9 A2

- Tredegar House Caravan Club Site
- Coedkernew
- 1 Jan - 31 Dec
- +44 (0)1633-815600
- tredegarhouse@camc.com

1 ADEJMNOPQRST		6
2 APRSUVWX	ABDE**FG**	7
3 **K**	ABCDEFKNPQRSV	8
4		9
5 BDM**N**	ABCGHIK**P**RXZ	10
16A CEE		❶ £37.40
2ha 85T(80-100m²)		❷ £39.40

M4 Bristol-South Wales, exit 28 . Follow the sign at the front of Tredegar House.

Excellent campsite in a park-like surrounding. Membership of the Caravan Club England: for a fairly small sum, you'll get large discounts on the price.

N 51°33'41'' W 3°1'57''
www.eurocampings.co.uk/103051

407 Newport (Pembrokeshire), GB-SA42 OLX / Wales ♿ 🛜 iD 8 B1

- 🏔 Llwyngwair Manor Holiday Park
- 📧 Llwyngwair Manor
- 📅 24 Mar - 31 Oct
- ☎ +44 (0)1239-820498
- @ enquiries@
  pembrokeshireholidaypark.co.uk

1 ADE**JM**NOPQRS**T**	**N** 6
2 CGMOPRSVWXY	ABD**FG**H 7
3 AKLM	ABCDFNQRV 8
4 FIO**PQ**	ABD 9
5 DEFMN	ABFHJMOR 10
10A CEE	❶ £27.00
80T(max 100m²) 39P	❷ £31.00

🚗 Campsite is on the A487, approx. 1.5 km east of Newport and signposted (Llwyngwair Manor).

💬 Campsite in the 'backyard' of Llwyngwair Manor. The picturesque town of Newport houses many artists, galleries and places to eat and is about 2 km away.

📌 N 52°0'59'' W 4°48'39''
www.eurocampings.co.uk/122328

---

408 Pandy/Abergavenny, GB-NP7 8DR / Wales ♿ 🛜 iD 9 A2

- 🏔 Pandy Caravan Club Site****
- 📅 1 Apr - 5 Nov
- ☎ +44 (0)1873-890370
- @ pandy@caravanclub.co.uk

1 ADE**J**MOPQRT	**N** 6
2 CFOPSVWXY	ABDE**FG** 7
3 **K**	ABCDEFJNQRV 8
4	9
5 DMN	ABCGHIKM**P**RZ 10
16A CEE	❶ £26.40
A106 5ha 50T(80-100m²)	❷ £32.40

🚗 On the A465, approx. 10 km from Abergavenny, direction Hereford. Turn left at Old Pandy Inn. The campsite is located directly after the railway viaduct.

💬 Campsite is on the river Honddu, where fishing is permitted. Abergavenny has a beautiful castle. A good starting point for hikers.

📌 N 51°53'54'' W 2°58'8''
www.eurocampings.co.uk/110883

---

409 Pencelli/Brecon, GB-LD3 7LX / Wales ⊗ ♿ 🛜 ✿ iD 9 A2

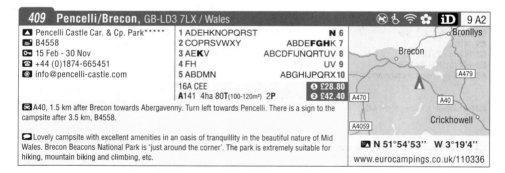

- 🏔 Pencelli Castle Car. & Cp. Park*****
- 📧 B4558
- 📅 15 Feb - 30 Nov
- ☎ +44 (0)1874-665451
- @ info@pencelli-castle.com

1 ADE**H**KNOPQRST	**N** 6
2 COPRSVWXY	ABDE**FGH**K 7
3 AE**KV**	ABCDFIJNQRTUV 8
4 FH	UV 9
5 ABDMN	ABGHIJPQRX 10
16A CEE	❶ £28.80
A141 4ha 80T(100-120m²) 2P	❷ £42.40

🚗 A40, 1.5 km after Brecon towards Abergavenny. Turn left towards Pencelli. There is a sign to the campsite after 3.5 km, B4558.

💬 Lovely campsite with excellent amenities in an oasis of tranquillity in the beautiful nature of Mid Wales. Brecon Beacons National Park is 'just around the corner'. The park is extremely suitable for hiking, mountain biking and climbing, etc.

📌 N 51°54'53'' W 3°19'4''
www.eurocampings.co.uk/110336

---

410 Porthmadog, GB-LL49 9YH / Wales ♿ 🛜 ✿ iD 5 A3

- 🏔 Black Rock Sands Camping & Touring
- 📧 Morfa Bychan
- 📅 23 Mar - 30 Sep
- ☎ +44 (0)1766-513919
- @ blackrocksandscampingpark@
  gmail.com

1 ADE**J**MNOPQRST	K**N**PQSWX 6
2 EFHMPQVWX	ABDE**FG** 7
3 A**K**	ABEFHNQRV 8
4 F	9
5 DFGMN	ABCIJOR 10
10A CEE	❶ £40.00
4,8ha 150T(90-110m²) 30P	❷ £40.00

🚗 Take exit Graig Dolu/Black Rock in the centre of Portmadog. Follow this road. Last campsite is 'Black Rock Sands'.

💬 Directly accessible from the campsite is a passageway to the wide sandy beach. The campsite has simple décor with well-tended natural vegetation. Good toilet facilities.

📌 N 52°54'55'' W 4°11'27''
www.eurocampings.co.uk/103035

United Kingdom

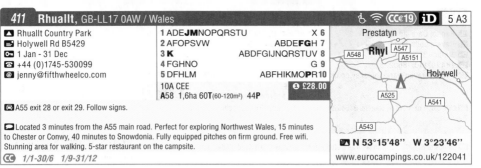

411 Rhuallt, GB-LL17 0AW / Wales

 ♿ 🛜 (CC€19) iD   5 A3

- 🏕 Rhuallt Country Park
- 🛣 Holywell Rd B5429
- 📅 1 Jan - 31 Dec
- ☎ +44 (0)1745-530099
- @ jenny@fifthwheelco.com

1	ADE**JM**NOPQRSTU	X 6
2	AFOPSVW	ABDE**FG**H 7
3	**K**	ABDFGIJNQRSTUV 8
4	FGHNO	G 9
5	DFHLM	ABFHIKMO**P**R 10
10A	CEE	❶ £28.00

A58 1,6ha 60T(60-120m²) 44P

🛰 A55 exit 28 or exit 29. Follow signs.

💬 Located 3 minutes from the A55 main road. Perfect for exploring Northwest Wales, 15 minutes to Chester or Conwy, 40 minutes to Snowdonia. Fully equipped pitches on firm ground. Free wifi. Stunning area for walking. 5-star restaurant on the campsite.

(CC) 1/1-30/6 1/9-31/12

Prestatyn
Rhyl A548 A547 A5151
Holywell
A525 A541
A543

📍 N 53°15'48'' W 3°23'46''

www.eurocampings.co.uk/122041

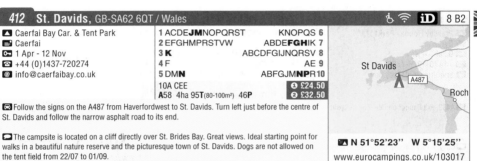

412 St. Davids, GB-SA62 6QT / Wales

 ♿ 🛜 iD   8 B2

- 🏕 Caerfai Bay Car. & Tent Park
- 🛣 Caerfai
- 📅 1 Apr - 12 Nov
- ☎ +44 (0)1437-720274
- @ info@caerfaibay.co.uk

1	ACDE**JM**NOPQRST	KNOPQS 6
2	EFGHMPRSTVW	ABDE**FGH**IK 7
3	**K**	ABCDFGIJNQRSV 8
4	F	AE 9
5	DM**N**	ABFGJMN**P**R 10
10A	CEE	❶ £24.50
		❷ £32.50

A58 4ha 95T(80-100m²) 46P

🛰 Follow the signs on the A487 from Haverfordwest to St. Davids. Turn left just before the centre of St. Davids and follow the narrow asphalt road to its end.

💬 The campsite is located on a cliff directly over St. Brides Bay. Great views. Ideal starting point for walks in a beautiful nature reserve and the picturesque town of St. Davids. Dogs are not allowed on the tent field from 22/07 to 01/09.

St Davids
A487
Roch

📍 N 51°52'23'' W 5°15'25''

www.eurocampings.co.uk/103017

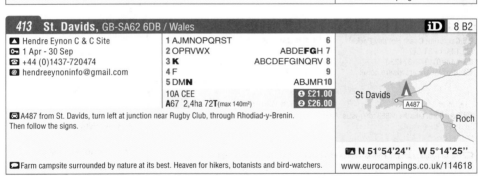

413 St. Davids, GB-SA62 6DB / Wales

 iD   8 B2

- 🏕 Hendre Eynon C & C Site
- 📅 1 Apr - 30 Sep
- ☎ +44 (0)1437-720474
- @ hendreeynoninfo@gmail.com

1	AJMNOPQRST	6
2	OPRVWX	ABDE**FG**H 7
3	**K**	ABCDEFGINQRV 8
4	F	9
5	DM**N**	ABJMR 10
10A	CEE	❶ £21.00
		❷ £26.00

A67 2,4ha 72T(max 140m²)

🛰 A487 from St. Davids, turn left at junction near Rugby Club, through Rhodiad-y-Brenin. Then follow the signs.

💬 Farm campsite surrounded by nature at its best. Heaven for hikers, botanists and bird-watchers.

St Davids
A487
Roch

📍 N 51°54'24'' W 5°14'25''

www.eurocampings.co.uk/114618

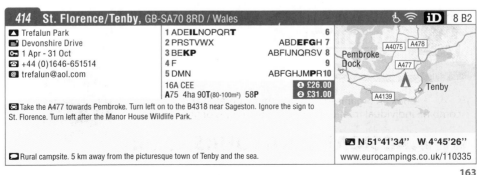

414 St. Florence/Tenby, GB-SA70 8RD / Wales

 ♿ 🛜 iD   8 B2

- 🏕 Trefalun Park
- 🛣 Devonshire Drive
- 📅 1 Apr - 31 Oct
- ☎ +44 (0)1646-651514
- @ trefalun@aol.com

1	ADE**IL**NOPQR**T**	6
2	PRSTVWX	ABDE**FG**H 7
3	BE**KP**	ABFIJNQRSV 8
4	F	9
5	DMN	ABFGHJM**P**R 10
16A	CEE	❶ £26.00
		❷ £31.00

A75 4ha 90T(80-100m²) 58P

🛰 Take the A477 towards Pembroke. Turn left on to the B4318 near Sageston. Ignore the sign to St. Florence. Turn left after the Manor House Wildlife Park.

💬 Rural campsite. 5 km away from the picturesque town of Tenby and the sea.

Pembroke Dock
A4075 A478
A477
A4139
Tenby

📍 N 51°41'34'' W 4°45'26''

www.eurocampings.co.uk/110335

United Kingdom

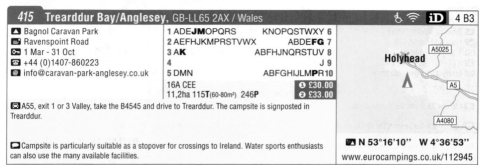

415 Trearddur Bay/Anglesey, GB-LL65 2AX / Wales — 4 B3

- Bagnol Caravan Park
- Ravenspoint Road
- 1 Mar - 31 Oct
- +44 (0)1407-860223
- info@caravan-park-anglesey.co.uk

1 ADE**JM**OPQRS	KNOPQSTWXY 6
2 AEFHJKMPRSTVWX	ABDE**FG** 7
3 A**K**	ABFHJNQRSTUV 8
4	J 9
5 DMN	ABFGHIJLM**P**R 10

16A CEE
11,2ha 115T(60-80m²) 246P

❶ £30.00
❷ £33.00

A55, exit 1 or 3 Valley, take the B4545 and drive to Trearddur. The campsite is signposted in Trearddur.

Campsite is particularly suitable as a stopover for crossings to Ireland. Water sports enthusiasts can also use the many available facilities.

N 53°16'10" W 4°36'53"
www.eurocampings.co.uk/112945

416 Wrexham, GB-LL13 0SP / Wales — 5 A3

- Plassey Holiday Park*****
- Eyton
- 9 Feb - 4 Nov
- +44 (0)1978-780277
- enquiries@plassey.com

1 ADE**JM**NOPQRS**T**	EN 6
2 PRSVWX	ABDE**FGH** 7
3 BC**JKL**T	ABCDEFGHIJKNQRTV 8
4 FHI**PQRTXZ**	9
5 ACDEFGHKLM**N**	ABCEFGHIJM**P**RZ 10

16A CEE
A59 4ha 130T(80-120m²) 60P

❶ £33.50
❷ £48.10

A483, exit Bangor on Dee. The campsite is signposted from this exit.

Cosy, luxury campsite with a lot of on-site activities. With wifi, a tea garden, 9-hole golf course and restaurant.

N 53°0'1" W 2°58'13"
www.eurocampings.co.uk/114650

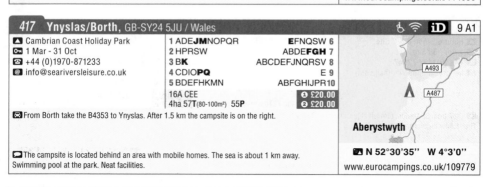

417 Ynyslas/Borth, GB-SY24 5JU / Wales — 9 A1

- Cambrian Coast Holiday Park
- 1 Mar - 31 Oct
- +44 (0)1970-871233
- info@seariversleisure.co.uk

1 ADE**JM**NOPQR	E**F**NQSW 6
2 HPRSW	ABDE**FGH** 7
3 B**K**	ABCDEFJNQRSV 8
4 CDIO**PQ**	E 9
5 BDEFHKMN	ABFGHIJPR 10

16A CEE
4ha 57T(80-100m²) 55P

❶ £20.00
❷ £20.00

From Borth take the B4353 to Ynyslas. After 1.5 km the campsite is on the right.

The campsite is located behind an area with mobile homes. The sea is about 1 km away. Swimming pool at the park. Neat facilities.

N 52°30'35" W 4°3'0"
www.eurocampings.co.uk/109779

Scotland

'You take the high road, I'll take the low road ...'

Home of bagpipes, haggis, whisky, and the Loch Ness Monster, Scotland is the northernmost country of the United Kingdom, with a wild coastline and remote highlands. The capital Edinburgh is a World Heritage site, while Glasgow and Aberdeen are known for significant developments in industry and engineering.

The mountains, valleys, lakes and islands of Scotland were created during the Ice Age, and later, tribes from many other lands settled here. Scotland was briefly occupied by ancient Rome, but the greatest influence was Ireland – so many Irish settled in the Highlands that their language and culture became dominant. English became the main language of eastern Scotland during the

Middle Ages, and the countries were united in the early 16th century, with the union formalised in 1701.

Edinburgh and Glasgow

Castle Rock looms over Edinburgh, the capital on the River Tay. Tell the kids that this is where the Scottish Crown Jewels are, and they'll start hunting for treasure! Castle Rock is linked to Holyrood Palace by the Royal Mile, with plenty of shops, cafés and sights along the way.

Glasgow, located on the River Clyde, is home to Mackintosh House, the former residence of architect and artist Charles Mackintosh. Buchanan Street, a major shopping street, fuses Victorian with modern architecture, while Argyle Street is home to the innovative Kelvingrove Art Gallery.

Scotland

Neeps and tatties with a wee dram

The fertile countryside ensures rich game and meat, while the sea means an endless supply of fish. Traditional Scottish dishes are turnip with potatoes, oatcakes and haggis, sheep's stomach filled with minced other innards, onion, oatmeal and suet remains the national dish, with a delicious nutty flavour. Be sure to try Scotch whisky and the Scottish liqueur Drambuie.

Did you know ...?
Edinburgh hosts the largest Fringe festival in the world.

Wild Highlands

Feeling stuffed? Fort William, located in the Scottish Highlands close to Ben Nevis and the Munro mountains, is a great base for hikers and mountain climbers, and for day excursions to Loch Ness. Nature lovers enjoy Creag Meagaidh Nature Reserve, and water sports activities vary from lake cruises to white-water rafting. Magnificent Cairngorms National Park, the largest in the British Isles, is located between Edinburgh and Inverness.

Our tips

1. See the Highlands from a Scottish gondola, or cable car
2. Look for the Loch Ness Monster on an excursion from Inverness or Fort William
3. Enjoy the rugged coastline and ancient ruins of the Isle of Skye
4. Browse the incredibly diverse collection of the National Museum of Scotland in Edinburgh
5. Check out the Scottish Kiltmaker Visitor Centre in Inverness

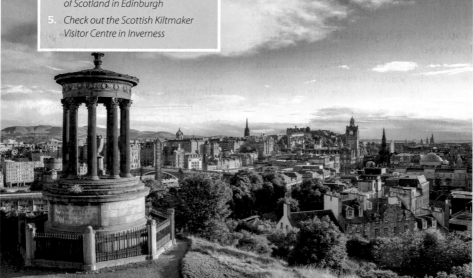

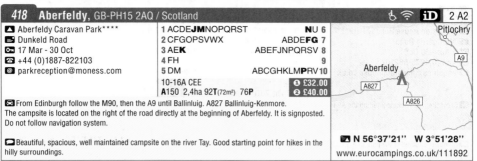

418 Aberfeldy, GB-PH15 2AQ / Scotland

♿ 🛜 iD · 2 A2

- ⛺ Aberfeldy Caravan Park****
- ✉ Dunkeld Road
- 📅 17 Mar - 30 Oct
- ☎ +44 (0)1887-822103
- @ parkreception@moness.com

1 ACDE**JM**NOPQRST	**N**U 6	
2 CFGOPSVWX	ABDE**FG** 7	
3 AE**K**	ABEFJNPQRSV 8	
4 FH	9	
5 DM	ABCGHKLM**P**RV 10	
10-16A CEE	❶ £32.00	
A150 2,4ha 92**T**(72m²) 76**P**	❷ £40.00	

🚗 From Edinburgh follow the M90, then the A9 until Ballinluig. A827 Ballinluig-Kenmore. The campsite is located on the right of the road directly at the beginning of Aberfeldy. It is signposted. Do not follow navigation system.

💬 Beautiful, spacious, well maintained campsite on the river Tay. Good starting point for hikes in the hilly surroundings.

📍 N 56°37'21'' W 3°51'28''

www.eurocampings.co.uk/111892

419 Aberfoyle/Stirling, GB-FK8 3SA / Scotland

🛜 ✿ iD · 2 A3

- ⛺ Trossachs Holiday Park*****
- ✉ A81
- 📅 1 Mar - 31 Oct
- ☎ +44 (0)1877-382614
- @ info@trossachsholidays.co.uk

1 ADEJMNOPQRS**T**	6	
2 OPRSTUVWXY	ABDE**FGH** 7	
3 A**K**	ABEFIJNQRTUV 8	
4 FHIO**Q**	EF 9	
5 ABDMN	ABEFHJMO**P**R 10	
16A CEE	❶ £26.00	
4ha 66**T**(70-80m²) 87**P**	❷ £30.00	

🚗 Campsite is 5 km south of Aberfoyle on the A81 and is clearly signposted.

💬 Beautifully laid out terraced campsite with clearly marked-out paved pitches and separate grounds for tents. The site borders a lovely nature park that offers good walking and cycling opportunities. Friendly coffee room with free wifi if you buy a drink.

📍 N 56°8'19'' W 4°21'37''

www.eurocampings.co.uk/108635

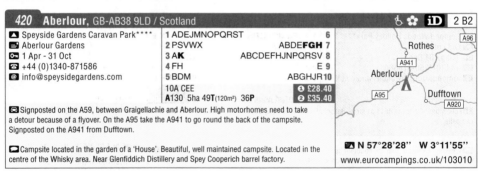

420 Aberlour, GB-AB38 9LD / Scotland

♿ ✿ iD · 2 B2

- ⛺ Speyside Gardens Caravan Park****
- ✉ Aberlour Gardens
- 📅 1 Apr - 31 Oct
- ☎ +44 (0)1340-871586
- @ info@speysidegardens.com

1 ADEJMNOPQRST	6	
2 PSVWX	ABDE**FGH** 7	
3 A**K**	ABCDEFHJNPQRSV 8	
4 FH	E 9	
5 BDM	ABGHJR 10	
10A CEE	❶ £28.40	
A130 5ha 49**T**(120m²) 36**P**	❷ £35.40	

🚗 Signposted on the A59, between Graigellachie and Aberlour. High motorhomes need to take a detour because of a flyover. On the A95 take the A941 to go round the back of the campsite. Signposted on the A941 from Dufftown.

💬 Campsite located in the garden of a 'House'. Beautiful, well maintained campsite. Located in the centre of the Whisky area. Near Glenfiddich Distillery and Spey Cooperich barrel factory.

📍 N 57°28'28'' W 3°11'55''

www.eurocampings.co.uk/103010

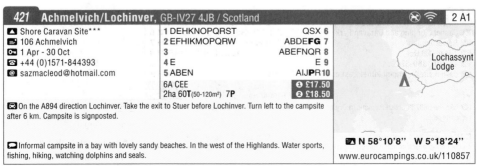

421 Achmelvich/Lochinver, GB-IV27 4JB / Scotland

⊗ 🛜 · 2 A1

- ⛺ Shore Caravan Site***
- ✉ 106 Achmelvich
- 📅 1 Apr - 30 Oct
- ☎ +44 (0)1571-844393
- @ sazmacleod@hotmail.com

1 DEHKNOPQRST	QSX 6	
2 EFHIKMOPQRW	ABDE**FG** 7	
3	ABEFNQR 8	
4 E	E 9	
5 ABEN	AIJ**P**R 10	
6A CEE	❶ £17.50	
2ha 60**T**(50-120m²) 7**P**	❷ £18.50	

🚗 On the A894 direction Lochinver. Take the exit to Stuer before Lochinver. Turn left to the campsite after 6 km. Campsite is signposted.

💬 Informal campsite in a bay with lovely sandy beaches. In the west of the Highlands. Water sports, fishing, hiking, watching dolphins and seals.

📍 N 58°10'8'' W 5°18'24''

www.eurocampings.co.uk/110857

United Kingdom

422 Alford (Aberdeensh.), GB-AB33 8NA / Scotland 🔌 📶 ⚙ iD 2 B2

- 🏔 Haughton House Holiday Park***
- 🏠 Montgarrie Road
- 📅 1 Apr - 30 Oct
- ☎ +44 (0)1975-562107
- @ enquiries@haughtonhouse.co.uk

1 ADEJMNOPQRST	N 6
2 COPRSTVWXY	ABDEFGH 7
3 BEIKV	ABEFJNQRV 8
4 FH	E 9
5 DMN	AGHJMPR 10
16A CEE	❶ £23.40
A139 7,7ha 70T(100-120m²) 83P	❷ £29.20

🗺 Campsite clearly signposted on the A944 in Alford.

💬 Campsite situated in the park of a 'House'. Beautiful surroundings for walks. Everything is very well maintained. Near various museums.

📍 N 57°14'15'' W 2°42'8''
www.eurocampings.co.uk/103011

423 Ballater, GB-AB35 5QW / Scotland 🔌 📶 iD 2 B2

- 🏔 Ballater Caravanpark***
- 🏠 Anderson Road
- 📅 1 Apr - 31 Oct
- ☎ +44 (0)1339-755727
- @ bookings@ballaterpark.co.uk

1 ACDEJMNOPQRST	JNV 6
2 CFOPSVWXY	ABDEFGH 7
3 BKV	ABEFHJNPQRSV 8
4 EFH	9
5 DMN	ABGHJMPRV 10
16A CEE	❶ £29.00
A190 3,2ha 82T(100-120m²) 17P	❷ £29.00

🗺 Follow the A93. Signposted in Ballater. Turn off to Victoria Road and then turn left to Brachlie Road. Follow the sign 'Fire Station'. (Do not follow your navigation system; this will guide you to a narrow street)

💬 Beautiful, tidy campsite on the river Dee. Good base for visiting Balmoral Castle and the Highlands. The old station of Ballater is also worth visiting. Many amenities nearby.

📍 N 57°2'45'' W 3°2'23''
www.eurocampings.co.uk/117790

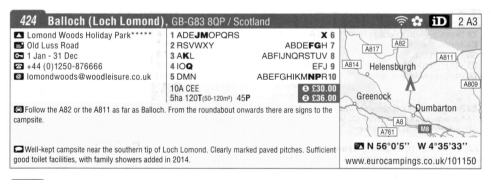

424 Balloch (Loch Lomond), GB-G83 8QP / Scotland 📶 ⚙ iD 2 A3

- 🏔 Lomond Woods Holiday Park*****
- 🏠 Old Luss Road
- 📅 1 Jan - 31 Dec
- ☎ +44 (0)1250-876666
- @ lomondwoods@woodleisure.co.uk

1 ADEJMOPQRS	X 6
2 RSVWXY	ABDEFGH 7
3 AKL	ABFIJNQRSTUV 8
4 IOQ	EFJ 9
5 DMN	ABEFGHIKMNPR 10
10A CEE	❶ £30.00
5ha 120T(50-120m²) 45P	❷ £36.00

🗺 Follow the A82 or the A811 as far as Balloch. From the roundabout onwards there are signs to the campsite.

💬 Well-kept campsite near the southern tip of Loch Lomond. Clearly marked paved pitches. Sufficient good toilet facilities, with family showers added in 2014.

📍 N 56°0'5'' W 4°35'33''
www.eurocampings.co.uk/101150

425 Balmaha, GB-G63 0AW / Scotland iD 2 A3

- 🏔 Cashel Camping and Caravan Park
- 🏠 Rowardennan
- 📅 1 Mar - 23 Oct
- ☎ +44 (0)1360-870234
- @ cashel.site@campingintheforest.co.uk

1 ADEGJMNOPQRST	LNQSUVXYZ 6
2 BDFJPRSVWXY	ABCDEFGH 7
3 A	ABCDFHIJNPQRSTU 8
4 FH	9
5 ABDJMNO	ABHJR 10
16A CEE	❶ £29.95
4ha 168T(168-100m²)	❷ £36.65

🗺 Take the B837 direction Balmaha in Drymen. In Balmaha direction Rowardennan and follow the campsite sign.

💬 This campsite is on the West Highland Way, on the shore of Loch Lomond. Some pitches directly on the pebble beach or in the forest. The lake accommodates many water sports, while the area makes lovely walks or mountain bike trails appealing.

📍 N 56°6'45'' W 4°34'52''
www.eurocampings.co.uk/114488

United Kingdom

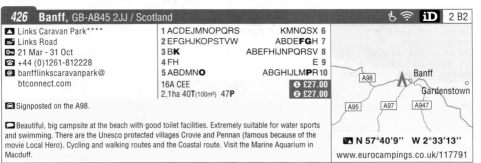

426 Banff, GB-AB45 2JJ / Scotland

🔵 2 B2

- ⛰ Links Caravan Park★★★★
- 🏕 Links Road
- 📅 21 Mar - 31 Oct
- ☎ +44 (0)1261-812228
- @ banfflinkscaravanpark@
  btconnect.com

🚗 Signposted on the A98.

1 ACDEJMNOPQRS	KMNQSX 6
2 EFGHJKOPSTVW	ABDEFGH 7
3 BK	ABEFHIJNPQRSV 8
4 FH	E 9
5 ABDMNO	ABGHIJLMPR 10
16A CEE	❶ £27.00
2,1ha 40T(100m²) 47P	❷ £27.00

💬 Beautiful, big campsite at the beach with good toilet facilities. Extremely suitable for water sports and swimming. There are the Unesco protected villages Crovie and Pennan (famous because of the movie Local Hero). Cycling and walking routes and the Coastal route. Visit the Marine Aquarium in Macduff.

📷 N 57°40'9'' W 2°33'13''

www.eurocampings.co.uk/117791

427 Blair Atholl, GB-PH18 5SR / Scotland

🔵 2 A2

- ⛰ Blair Castle Caravan Park★★★★★
- 📅 1 Mar - 20 Nov
- ☎ +44 (0)1796-481263
- @ mail@blaircastlecaravanpark.co.uk

1 ADEJMNOPQRST	LN 6
2 ACFGKOPRSVWXY	ABDEFGH 7
3 BEHIKLQ ABCDEFHJLMNPQRSTUV 8	
4 AFHIOQXZ	EFJUV 9
5 ABDMN	ABFGHIJLMPR 10
16A CEE	❶ £31.00
A100 14ha 159T(16-100m²) 167P	❷ £37.00

🚗 A9, exit Blair Atholl, direction Blair Atholl. Campsite signposted along the B8079.

💬 Thanks to its location on the A9, this is a suitable transit campsite. But it's also great for a longer stay. Near the castle.

📷 N 56°46'2'' W 3°50'36''

www.eurocampings.co.uk/101148

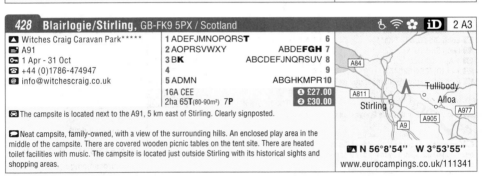

428 Blairlogie/Stirling, GB-FK9 5PX / Scotland

🔵 2 A3

- ⛰ Witches Craig Caravan Park★★★★★
- 🏕 A91
- 📅 1 Apr - 31 Oct
- ☎ +44 (0)1786-474947
- @ info@witchescraig.co.uk

1 ADEFJMNOPQRST	6
2 AOPRSVWXY	ABDEFGH 7
3 BK	ABCDEFJNQRSUV 8
4	9
5 ADMN	ABGHKMPR 10
16A CEE	❶ £27.00
2ha 65T(80-90m²) 7P	❷ £30.00

🚗 The campsite is located next to the A91, 5 km east of Stirling. Clearly signposted.

💬 Neat campsite, family-owned, with a view of the surrounding hills. An enclosed play area in the middle of the campsite. There are covered wooden picnic tables on the tent site. There are heated toilet facilities with music. The campsite is located just outside Stirling with its historical sights and shopping areas.

📷 N 56°8'54'' W 3°53'55''

www.eurocampings.co.uk/111341

429 Borgue/Kirkcudbright, GB-DG6 4TS / Scotland

🔵 5 A2

- ⛰ Brighouse Bay Hol. Park AA★★★★★
- 📅 1 Jan - 31 Dec
- ☎ +44 (0)1557-870267
- @ info@gillespie-leisure.co.uk

1 ADEJMNOPRST	EFGKNQSXY 6
2 EHJKMPRSTUVWXY	ABDEFGH 7
3 BEGHIJP	ABCDEFJLNQRSTUV 8
4 FIOPQRUV	EFJQ 9
5 ACDFHJLMN	ABEFGJMNOPRXY 10
16A CEE	❶ £26.00
10ha 150T(80-100m²) 240P	❷ £30.00

🚗 From the A75, at exit Gatehouse or Fleet take the A755 towards Kirkcudbright. Then A727 direction Borgue. Campsite signposted.

💬 Fully equipped campsite on a headland with a sandy beach and the freedom to explore 1200 acres. The campsite is an ideal base for all kinds of activities such as cycling, walking, angling, canoeing and golf. The little town of Kirkcudbright (approx. 10 km) is known for its many galleries and artists.

📷 N 54°47'15'' W 4°7'45''

www.eurocampings.co.uk/102993

United Kingdom

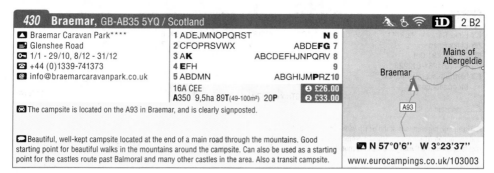

430 Braemar, GB-AB35 5YQ / Scotland — 2 B2

- ⛺ Braemar Caravan Park****
- Glenshee Road
- 1/1 - 29/10, 8/12 - 31/12
- +44 (0)1339-741373
- info@braemarcaravanpark.co.uk

1 ADEJMNOPQRST	**N** 6
2 CFOPRSVWX	ABDE**FG** 7
3 A**K**	ABCDEFHJNPQRV 8
4 **E**FH	9
5 ABDMN	ABGHIJM**P**R**Z**10

16A CEE — ❶ £26.00
A350 9,5ha 89T(49-100m²) 20P — ❷ £33.00

🅿 The campsite is located on the A93 in Braemar, and is clearly signposted.

💬 Beautiful, well-kept campsite located at the end of a main road through the mountains. Good starting point for beautiful walks in the mountains around the campsite. Can also be used as a starting point for the castles route past Balmoral and many other castles in the area. Also a transit campsite.

Mains of Abergeldie · Braemar · A93

◼ N 57°0'6'' W 3°23'37''
www.eurocampings.co.uk/103003

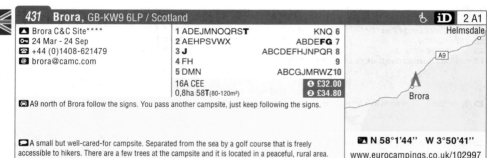

431 Brora, GB-KW9 6LP / Scotland — 2 A1

- ⛺ Brora C&C Site****
- 24 Mar - 24 Sep
- +44 (0)1408-621479
- brora@camc.com

1 ADEJMNOQRS**T**	KNQ 6
2 AEHPSVWX	ABDE**FG** 7
3 **J**	ABCDEFHJNPQR 8
4 FH	9
5 DMN	ABCGJMRWZ10

16A CEE — ❶ £32.00
0,8ha 58T(80-120m²) — ❷ £34.80

🅿 A9 north of Brora follow the signs. You pass another campsite, just keep following the signs.

💬 A small but well-cared-for campsite. Separated from the sea by a golf course that is freely accessible to hikers. There are a few trees at the campsite and it is located in a peaceful, rural area.

Helmsdale · A9 · Brora

◼ N 58°1'44'' W 3°50'41''
www.eurocampings.co.uk/102997

432 Castle Douglas, GB-DG7 1EZ / Scotland — 5 A1

- ⛺ Loch Side C.& C. Site***
- Loch Side Park
- 1 Apr - 31 Oct
- +44 (0)7824-528467
- lochside.caravan@dumgal.gov.uk

1 AJMNOPRS**T**	**N** 6
2 DGPRSVWXY	ABDE**FGH** 7
3 A**K**	ABCDEFNQRV 8
4	PQT 9
5 AD	ABKRX10

16A CEE — ❶ £24.00
5ha 150T(60-80m²) 46P — ❷ £24.00

🅿 Follow the A75 until Castle Douglas, and then follow the signs to the campsite.

💬 Campsite is situated on the edge of Castle Douglas, a pleasant town. Near the campsite is a recreational lake, visited by many day trippers and anglers. Swimming in the lake is not possible, but there is rowing-boat and canoe rental.

A713 · A762 · Castle Douglas · A75 · A745 · A711 · A755 · Kirkcudbright · A710

◼ N 54°56'11'' W 3°55'48''
www.eurocampings.co.uk/102990

433 Corpach/Fort William, GB-PH33 7NL / Scotland — 2 A2

- ⛺ Linnhe Lochside Holidays****
- 1/1 - 31/10, 15/12 - 31/12
- +44 (0)1397-772376
- relax@linnhe-lochside-holidays.co.uk

1 ADE**JM**NOPQRS**T**	KLNPQSU**X**YZ 6
2 DEFJKMOPSUVWXY	ABDE**FG**HK 7
3 BC**K**	ABCDEFHIJNPQRSTV 8
4 H	EJR 9
5 ACDMN**O**	ABDGHIJMPQR10

Ad on page 171 10-16A CEE — ❶ £23.50
5ha 105T(45-90m²) 95P — ❷ £27.50

🅿 Follow the A82 northwards. Take the A830 direction Corpach in Fort William. Campsite on the left after about 8 km. Well signposted.

💬 Beautiful terraced campsite in a lush garden with a beautiful view over the lochs and the surrounding mountains. Modern facilities. Here you can relax or have an active holiday.

CC 8/1-29/1 19/2-28/2 1/5-18/5 1/6-30/6 1/9-27/9 1/10-14/10

A830 · Banavie · Fort William · A82

◼ N 56°50'51'' W 5°9'39''
www.eurocampings.co.uk/110577

Linnhe Lochside Holidays ★ ★ ★ ★

Linnhe Lochside Holidays is open from 15-12 until 31-10. Just 8 km from Fort William, this is the perfect operating base for exploring the Scottish Highlands. Enjoy the magnificent views of the bays of Loch Eil and Loch Linnhe, with a stunning view of the Ben Nevis from the private beach. The large number of paved pitches, modern facilities, a familial atmosphere and beautiful gardens ensure that this is the perfect place to enjoy your holiday. Perfect for relaxing and active holidays.

PH33 7NL Corpach/Fort William • Tel. 01397-772376
E-mail: relax@linnhe-lochside-holidays.co.uk
Internet: www.linnhe-lochside-holidays.co.uk

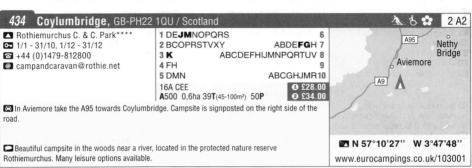

434 Coylumbridge, GB-PH22 1QU / Scotland — 2 A2

- Rothiemurchus C. & C. Park★★★★
- 1/1 - 31/10, 1/12 - 31/12
- +44 (0)1479-812800
- campandcaravan@rothie.net

1 DE**JM**NOPQRS		6
2 BCOPRSTVXY	ABDE**FGH**	7
3 **K**	ABCDEFHIJMNPQRTUV	8
4 FH		9
5 DMN	ABCGHJMR	10
16A CEE	❶ £28.00	
A500 0,6ha 39**T**(45-100m²) 50**P**	❷ £34.00	

In Aviemore take the A95 towards Coylumbridge. Campsite is signposted on the right side of the road.

Beautiful campsite in the woods near a river, located in the protected nature reserve Rothiemurchus. Many leisure options available.

A95 — Nethy Bridge — Aviemore — A9

N 57°10'27'' W 3°47'48''
www.eurocampings.co.uk/103001

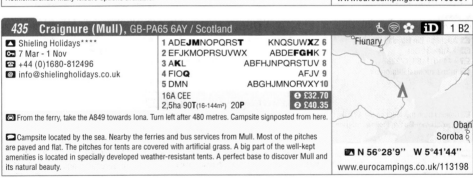

435 Craignure (Mull), GB-PA65 6AY / Scotland — 1 B2

- Shieling Holidays★★★★
- 7 Mar - 1 Nov
- +44 (0)1680-812496
- info@shielingholidays.co.uk

1 ADE**JM**NOPQRS**T**	KNQSUW**XZ**	6
2 EFJKMOPRSUVWX	ABDE**FGH**K	7
3 A**K**L	ABFHJNPQRSTUV	8
4 FIO**Q**	AFJV	9
5 DMN	ABGHJMNORVXY	10
16A CEE	❶ £32.70	
2,5ha 90**T**(16-144m²) 20**P**	❷ £40.35	

From the ferry, take the A849 towards Iona. Turn left after 480 metres. Campsite signposted from here.

Campsite located by the sea. Nearby the ferries and bus services from Mull. Most of the pitches are paved and flat. The pitches for tents are covered with artificial grass. A big part of the well-kept amenities is located in specially developed weather-resistant tents. A perfect base to discover Mull and its natural beauty.

Fiunary — Oban — Soroba

N 56°28'9'' W 5°41'44''
www.eurocampings.co.uk/113198

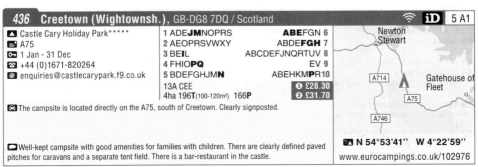

436 Creetown (Wightownsh.), GB-DG8 7DQ / Scotland — 5 A1

- Castle Cary Holiday Park★★★★★
- A75
- 1 Jan - 31 Dec
- +44 (0)1671-820264
- enquiries@castlecarypark.f9.co.uk

1 ADE**JM**NOPRS	**ABE**FGN	6
2 AEOPRSVWXY	ABDE**FGH**	7
3 BEIL	ABCDEFJNQRTUV	8
4 FHIO**PQ**	EV	9
5 BDEFGHJM**N**	ABEHKM**P**R	10
13A CEE	❶ £28.30	
4ha 196**T**(100-120m²) 166**P**	❷ £31.70	

The campsite is located directly on the A75, south of Creetown. Clearly signposted.

Well-kept campsite with good amenities for families with children. There are clearly defined paved pitches for caravans and a separate tent field. There is a bar-restaurant in the castle.

Newton Stewart — A714 — Gatehouse of Fleet — A75 — A746

N 54°53'41'' W 4°22'59''
www.eurocampings.co.uk/102976

United Kingdom

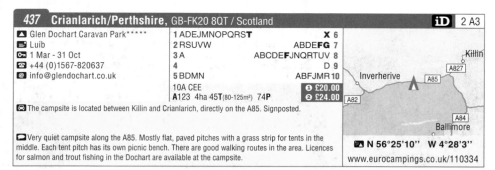

437 Crianlarich/Perthshire, GB-FK20 8QT / Scotland — iD 2 A3

▲ Glen Dochart Caravan Park*****
🏠 Luib
🕐 1 Mar - 31 Oct
☎ +44 (0)1567-820637
@ info@glendochart.co.uk

1	ADEJMNOPQRS**T**		**X** 6
2	RSUVW	ABDE**FG**	7
3	A	ABCDE**F**JNQRTUV	8
4		D	9
5	BDMN	ABFJMR	10
10A CEE		❶ £20.00
A123 4ha 45**T**(80-125m²) 74**P**		❷ £24.00

🚗 The campsite is located between Killin and Crianlarich, directly on the A85. Signposted.

💬 Very quiet campsite along the A85. Mostly flat, paved pitches with a grass strip for tents in the middle. Each tent pitch has its own picnic bench. There are good walking routes in the area. Licences for salmon and trout fishing in the Dochart are available at the campsite.

📷 N 56°25'10'' W 4°28'3''
www.eurocampings.co.uk/110334

438 Dalbeattie/Sandyhills, GB-DG5 4NY / Scotland — 🛜 iD 5 A2

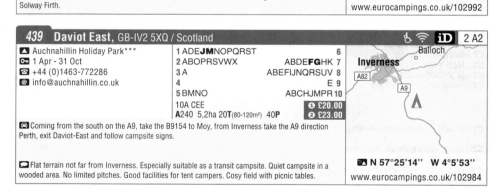

▲ Sandyhills Bay Leisure Park****
🏠 Sandy Hills
🕐 12 Apr - 31 Oct
☎ +44 (0)1387-780257
@ info@gillespie-leisure.co.uk

1	ADE**JM**NOPRST		**KN** 6
2	EFGHMOPQWXY	ABDE**FGH**	7
3	A**K**	ABCDEFNQRV	8
4	F	EF	9
5	ABDEM**N**	ABJ**P**R	10
16A CEE		❶ £26.50
3ha 70**T**(80-120m²) 37**P**		❷ £30.50

🚗 The campsite is located on the A710, 10 km south of Dalbeattie. Drive on until past the sign for 'Sandyhills' and then follow the signs to the campsite. Reception is tucked away behind a building on the hill, approx. 100 metres before the entrance.

💬 Rolling terrain, separated from the beach by just a strip of vegetation. The sandy beach is accessible from the campsite and is also visited by locals. From the beach magnificent views over the Solway Firth.

📷 N 54°52'48'' W 3°43'51''
www.eurocampings.co.uk/102992

439 Daviot East, GB-IV2 5XQ / Scotland — 🧑‍🦽 🛜 iD 2 A2

▲ Auchnahillin Holiday Park***
🕐 1 Apr - 31 Oct
☎ +44 (0)1463-772286
@ info@auchnahillin.co.uk

1	ADE**JM**NOPQRST		6
2	ABOPRSVWX	ABDE**FG**HK	7
3	A	ABEFIJNQRSUV	8
4		E	9
5	BMNO	ABCHJMPR	10
10A CEE		❶ £20.00
A240 5,2ha 20**T**(80-120m²) 40**P**		❷ £23.00

🚗 Coming from the south on the A9, take the B9154 to Moy, from Inverness take the A9 direction Perth, exit Daviot-East and follow campsite signs.

💬 Flat terrain not far from Inverness. Especially suitable as a transit campsite. Quiet campsite in a wooded area. No limited pitches. Good facilities for tent campers. Cosy field with picnic tables.

📷 N 57°25'14'' W 4°5'53''
www.eurocampings.co.uk/102984

440 Dingwall (Ross-shire), GB-IV15 9QZ / Scotland — 🧑‍🦽 🛜 iD 2 A2

▲ C. & C. Jubilee Park Site****
🏠 Jubilee Park Road
🕐 29 Mar - 29 Oct
☎ +44 (0)1349-862236
@ dingwall.site@
campingandcaravanningclub.co.uk

1	ADEJMNOPQRT		6
2	APRSVWX	ABDE**FGH**	7
3	E	ABEFNQRV	8
4			9
5	BDM**N**	ABGHJ**P**R	10
16A CEE		❶ £31.45
1,5ha 77**T**		❷ £41.15

🚗 In the centre of Dingwall on the A862, follow the (white) sign to the Railway Station and caravan site etc. After that follow the signs to the campsite and then turn left directly after crossing the railway bridge.

💬 Flat campsite close to a town with trees and flowerbeds. A neat, secluded campsite with a park-like feel. The site is located by a tidal river right next to a sports ground and stadium. The centre of Dingwall is accessible via a path.

📷 N 57°35'51'' W 4°25'8''
www.eurocampings.co.uk/102982

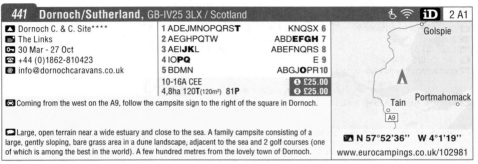

441 Dornoch/Sutherland, GB-IV25 3LX / Scotland

2 A1

- Dornoch C. & C. Site****
- The Links
- 30 Mar - 27 Oct
- +44 (0)1862-810423
- info@dornochcaravans.co.uk

1 ADEJMNOPQRS**T**		KNQSX	6
2 AEGHPQTW		ABD**EFGH**	7
3 AEI**JKL**		ABEFNQRS	8
4 IO**PQ**		E	9
5 BDMN		ABGJ**O**PR	10
10-16A CEE		❶ £25.00	
4,8ha 120**T**(120m²) 81**P**		❷ £25.00	

Coming from the west on the A9, follow the campsite sign to the right of the square in Dornoch.

Large, open terrain near a wide estuary and close to the sea. A family campsite consisting of a large, gently sloping, bare grass area in a dune landscape, adjacent to the sea and 2 golf courses (one of which is among the best in the world). A few hundred metres from the lovely town of Dornoch.

N 57°52'36'' W 4°1'19''

www.eurocampings.co.uk/102981

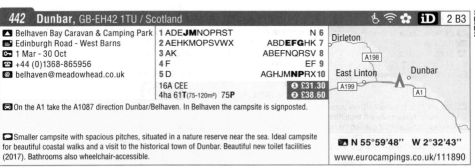

442 Dunbar, GB-EH42 1TU / Scotland

2 B3

- Belhaven Bay Caravan & Camping Park
- Edinburgh Road - West Barns
- 1 Mar - 30 Oct
- +44 (0)1368-865956
- belhaven@meadowhead.co.uk

1 ADE**JM**NOPRST		N	6
2 AEHKMOPSVWX		ABD**EFGH**K	7
3 AK		ABEFNQRSV	8
4 F		EF	9
5 D		AGHJM**NP**RX	10
16A CEE		❶ £31.30	
4ha 61**T**(75-120m²) 75**P**		❷ £38.60	

On the A1 take the A1087 direction Dunbar/Belhaven. In Belhaven the campsite is signposted.

Smaller campsite with spacious pitches, situated in a nature reserve near the sea. Ideal campsite for beautiful coastal walks and a visit to the historical town of Dunbar. Beautiful new toilet facilities (2017). Bathrooms also wheelchair-accessible.

N 55°59'48'' W 2°32'43''

www.eurocampings.co.uk/111890

443 Durness, GB-IV27 4PZ / Scotland

2 A1

- Sango Sands Caravan Site AA***
- 28 Durine
- 20 Mar - 31 Oct
- +44 (0)1971-511726
- keith.durness@btinternet.com

1 DEJMNOPQRST		KNQSWX	6
2 EHPQRSTUVW		ABDE**FGH**I	7
3 K		ABEFNQR	8
4 EFNQ		E	9
5 CDEFHLN		ABGJPR	10
16A CEE		❶ £20.00	
3,5ha 160**T**(55-120m²) 2**P**		❷ £29.00	

The campsite is on the A838 in the village.

A campsite on the cliffs where you can hear the waves crashing on the (rocky) beach. It is located on the edge of the village of Durness and consists of a rolling, bare grass area with magnificent views.

N 58°34'7'' W 4°44'36''

www.eurocampings.co.uk/102978

444 East Calder/Edinburgh, GB-EH53 0HT / Scotland

2 A3

- Linwater Caravan Park****
- West Clifton by East Calder
- 1 Jan - 31 Dec
- +44 (0)131-3333326
- queries@linwater.co.uk

1 ADEJMNOPQRST			6
2 APRSVWX		ABDE**FG**	7
3 A**K**		ABCDEFJNQRSV	8
4		FJ	9
5 BDM**N**		ABGHJMNPR	10
16A CEE		❶ £26.00	
A95 2ha 60**T**(40-120m²) 5**P**		❷ £31.50	

At Edinburgh City Bypass (A720) exit for the M8. Take the exit 'airport'. The campsite is signposted from the roundabout. The campsite is on a side road off the B7030.

Countryside farm campsite with an enthusiastic and welcoming family. Mostly flat pitches and clean toilet facilities. Campers can use the garden furniture and herb garden. Flower beds adorn the whole site. There is a Park and Ride connection with Edinburgh from the A8 and A71.

N 55°54'39'' W 3°26'9''

www.eurocampings.co.uk/111736

United Kingdom

445 Ecclefechan/Lockerbie, GB-DG11 3DR / Scotland — 5 A1

- ▲ Cressfield Caravan Park*****
- ▣ Townfoot
- 1 Jan - 31 Dec
- ☎ +44 (0)1576-300702
- @ cressfieldcaravanpark@gmx.com

1 ADEJMNOPRS		6
2 ACGOPRSVW	ABDEFGH	7
3 AEK	ABCDEFJNQRUV	8
4		9
5 DN	AHMPRW	10

16A CEE
6ha 78T(70-90m²) 79P

❶ £20.00
❷ £20.00

🚗 Follow A74(M) to exit 19 Ecclefechan B7076. Then follow campsite signs. Site located right in the town.

💬 Campsite with spacious, mostly paved touring pitches for caravans and a large field for tents. The toilet block is located a little further from the touring section, but offers plenty of good, clean facilities. A bathtub is available. Given its location, a good transit campsite.

📍 N 55°3'27'' W 3°15'28''

www.eurocampings.co.uk/103007

United Kingdom

446 Ecclefechan/Lockerbie, GB-DG11 1AS / Scotland — 5 A1

- ▲ Hoddom Castle Caravan Park*****
- ▣ Hoddom
- 24 Mar - 30 Oct
- ☎ +44 (0)1576-300251
- @ hoddomcastle@gmail.com

1 ADEJMNOPR	N	6
2 ACPRSTVWX	ABDEFGH	7
3 BIJKL	ABCDEFIJNQRTUV	8
4 EFHIPQ	F	9
5 ABDEFHKMN	ABGHJMR	10

10A CEE
A52 11ha 76T(60-75m²) 157P

❶ £26.00
❷ £35.00

🚗 M74, exit 19 to Ecclefechan. Drive through the village. Take B725 towards Dalton at the church. The entrance to the campsite is 3 km further and is signposted.

💬 Park-like landscaped campsite on the estate of an old castle. Many facilities are located in the annexed buildings. The campsite offers spacious pitches and good, clean toilet facilities. There is a separate tent field. There are plenty of sports and games for young and old, but peace-seekers also feel comfortable here.

📍 N 55°2'38'' W 3°19'26''

www.eurocampings.co.uk/109235

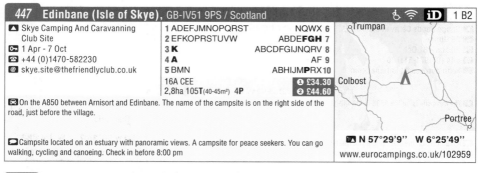

447 Edinbane (Isle of Skye), GB-IV51 9PS / Scotland — 1 B2

- ▲ Skye Camping And Caravanning Club Site
- 1 Apr - 7 Oct
- ☎ +44 (0)1470-582230
- @ skye.site@thefriendlyclub.co.uk

1 ADEFJMNOPQRST	NQWX	6
2 EFKOPRSTUVW	ABDEFGH	7
3 K	ABCDFGIJNQRV	8
4 A	AF	9
5 BMN	ABHIJMPRX	10

16A CEE
2,8ha 105T(40-45m²) 4P

❶ £34.30
❷ £44.60

🚗 On the A850 between Arnisort and Edinbane. The name of the campsite is on the right side of the road, just before the village.

💬 Campsite located on an estuary with panoramic views. A campsite for peace seekers. You can go walking, cycling and canoeing. Check in before 8:00 pm

📍 N 57°29'9'' W 6°25'49''

www.eurocampings.co.uk/102959

448 Edinburgh, GB-EH16 6TJ / Scotland — 2 B3

- ▲ Mortonhall Caravan & Camping Park****
- ▣ 38 Mortonhall Gate
- 1 Jan - 31 Dec
- ☎ +44 (0)131-6641533
- @ mortonhall@meadowhead.co.uk

1 ADEJMNOPQRS		6
2 AOPRSTVWXY	ABDEFGHIJK	7
3 BEK	ABCDEFHIJNPQRSTUV	8
4 FIOPQ	DEFL	9
5 ACDEHJLMN	ABFGHIJLMNNPRX	10

16A CEE
A130 9ha 320T(60-120m²) 50P

❶ £34.50
❷ £41.50

🚗 A720 (Edinburgh City Bypass). On the A720 take the exit Lothianburn junction (A702) or Straiton junction (A701), and follow the signs for Mortonhall. At Mortonhall gate (garden centre) continue for 500 metres to the entrance of the campsite.

💬 Busy campsite on the outskirts of Edinburgh. Spacious pitches on large fields. The campsite is part of a historic estate. The restaurant is located in the old stables. The bus to the centre of Edinburgh stops 500 m from the campsite.

📍 N 55°54'0'' W 3°10'33''

www.eurocampings.co.uk/100200

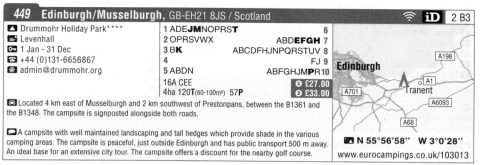

449 Edinburgh/Musselburgh, GB-EH21 8JS / Scotland
🛜 iD 2 B3

- 🏕 Drummohr Holiday Park****
- 📧 Levenhall
- 🗓 1 Jan - 31 Dec
- ☎ +44 (0)131-6656867
- @ admin@drummohr.org

1 ADE**JM**NOPRS**T**		6
2 OPRSVWX	ABD**EFGH**	7
3 B**K**	ABCDFHJNPQRSTUV	8
4		FJ 9
5 ABDN	ABFGHJM**P**R	10
16A CEE		❶ £27.00
4ha 120T(60-100m²) 57**P**		❷ £33.00

🚗 Located 4 km east of Musselburgh and 2 km southwest of Prestonpans, between the B1361 and the B1348. The campsite is signposted alongside both roads.

💬 A campsite with well maintained landscaping and tall hedges which provide shade in the various camping areas. The campsite is peaceful, just outside Edinburgh and has public transport 500 m away. An ideal base for an extensive city tour. The campsite offers a discount for the nearby golf course.

🧭 N 55°56'58'' W 3°0'28''

www.eurocampings.co.uk/103013

---

450 Edzell, GB-DD9 7YP / Scotland
♿ 🛜 iD 2 B2

- 🏕 Glenesk Caravan Park****
- 🗓 1 Apr - 31 Oct
- ☎ +44 (0)1356-648565
- @ gleneskcaravans@btconnect.com

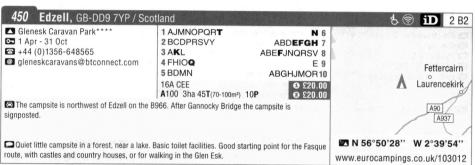

1 AJMNOPQR**T**		**N** 6
2 BCDPRSVY	ABD**EFGH**	7
3 A**K**L	ABE**F**JNQRSV	8
4 FHIO**Q**		E 9
5 BDMN	ABGHJMOR	10
16A CEE		❶ £20.00
A100 3ha 45T(70-100m²) 10**P**		❷ £20.00

🚗 The campsite is northwest of Edzell on the B966. After Gannocky Bridge the campsite is signposted.

💬 Quiet little campsite in a forest, near a lake. Basic toilet facilities. Good starting point for the Fasque route, with castles and country houses, or for walking in the Glen Esk.

🧭 N 56°50'28'' W 2°39'54''

www.eurocampings.co.uk/103012

---

451 Embo/Dornoch, GB-IV25 3QD / Scotland
🛜 iD 2 A1

- 🏕 Grannie's Heilan' Hame AA****
- 🗓 22 May - 29 Oct
- ☎ +44 (0)1862-810383
- @ stevenmure@parkdeanholidays.com

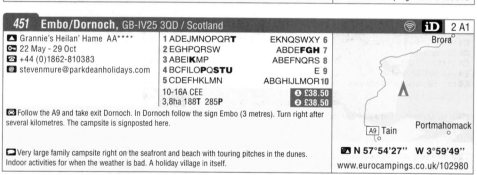

1 ADEJMNOPQR**T**	EKNQSWXY	6
2 EGHPQRSW	ABDE**FGH**	7
3 ABEI**K**MP	ABEFNQRS	8
4 BCFILO**PQSTU**		E 9
5 CDEFHKLMN	ABGHIJLMOR	10
10-16A CEE		❶ £38.50
3,8ha 188T 285**P**		❷ £38.50

🚗 Follow the A9 and take exit Dornoch. In Dornoch follow the sign Embo (3 metres). Turn right after several kilometres. The campsite is signposted here.

💬 Very large family campsite right on the seafront and beach with touring pitches in the dunes. Indoor activities for when the weather is bad. A holiday village in itself.

🧭 N 57°54'27'' W 3°59'49''

www.eurocampings.co.uk/102980

---

452 Forfar, GB-DD8 2RY / Scotland
♿ 🛜 iD 2 B3

- 🏕 Foresterseat Caravan Park****
- 📧 Arbroath Road
- 🗓 1 Apr - 30 Nov
- ☎ +44 (0)1307-818880
- @ emma@foresterseat.co.uk

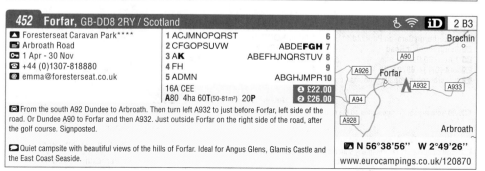

1 ACJMNOPQRST		6
2 CFGOPSUVW	ABD**EFGH**	7
3 A**K**	ABEFHJNQRSTUV	8
4 FH		9
5 ADMN	ABGHJMPR	10
16A CEE		❶ £22.00
A80 4ha 60T(50-81m²) 20**P**		❷ £26.00

🚗 From the south A92 Dundee to Arbroath. Then turn left A932 to just before Forfar, left side of the road. Or Dundee A90 to Forfar and then A932. Just outside Forfar on the right side of the road, after the golf course. Signposted.

💬 Quiet campsite with beautiful views of the hills of Forfar. Ideal for Angus Glens, Glamis Castle and the East Coast Seaside.

🧭 N 56°38'56'' W 2°49'26''

www.eurocampings.co.uk/120870

United Kingdom

453 Fort Augustus, GB-PH32 4BG / Scotland ♿ 📶 | 2 A2

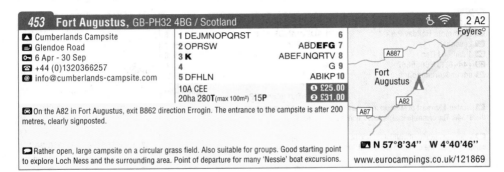

▲ Cumberlands Campsite
🏠 Glendoe Road
📅 6 Apr - 30 Sep
☎ +44 (0)1320366257
@ info@cumberlands-campsite.com

1	DEJMNOPQRST		6
2	OPRSW	ABDEFG	7
3	K	ABEFJNQRTV	8
4		G	9
5	DFHLN	ABIKP	10
10A CEE		❶ £25.00	
20ha 280T(max 100m²) 15P		❷ £31.00	

🚗 On the A82 in Fort Augustus, exit B862 direction Errogin. The entrance to the campsite is after 200 metres, clearly signposted.

💬 Rather open, large campsite on a circular grass field. Also suitable for groups. Good starting point to explore Loch Ness and the surrounding area. Point of departure for many 'Nessie' boat excursions.

Foyers°

📷 N 57°8'34'' W 4°40'46''
www.eurocampings.co.uk/121869

454 Fort William, GB-PH33 6SX / Scotland ♿ 📶 iD | 2 A2

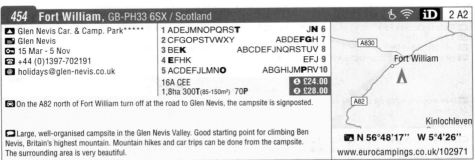

▲ Glen Nevis Car. & Camp. Park*****
🏠 Glen Nevis
📅 15 Mar - 5 Nov
☎ +44 (0)1397-702191
@ holidays@glen-nevis.co.uk

1	ADEJMNOPQRST	JN	6
2	CFGOPSTVWXY	ABDEFGH	7
3	BEK	ABCDEFJNQRSTUV	8
4	EFHK	EFJ	9
5	ACDEFJLMNO	ABGHIJMPRV	10
16A CEE		❶ £24.00	
1,8ha 300T(85-150m²) 70P		❷ £28.00	

🚗 On the A82 north of Fort William turn off at the road to Glen Nevis, the campsite is signposted.

💬 Large, well-organised campsite in the Glen Nevis Valley. Good starting point for climbing Ben Nevis, Britain's highest mountain. Mountain hikes and car trips can be done from the campsite. The surrounding area is very beautiful.

Kinlochleven

📷 N 56°48'17'' W 5°4'26''
www.eurocampings.co.uk/102971

455 Fort William, GB-PH33 7NF / Scotland 📶 iD | 2 A2

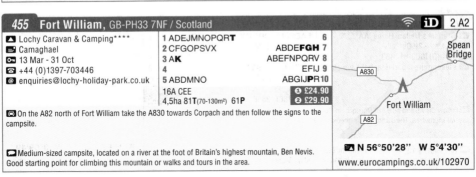

▲ Lochy Caravan & Camping****
🏠 Camaghael
📅 13 Mar - 31 Oct
☎ +44 (0)1397-703446
@ enquiries@lochy-holiday-park.co.uk

1	ADEJMNOPQRT		6
2	CFGOPSVX	ABDEFGH	7
3	AK	ABEFNPQRV	8
4		EFIJ	9
5	ABDMNO	ABGIJPR	10
16A CEE		❶ £24.90	
4,5ha 81T(70-130m²) 61P		❷ £29.90	

🚗 On the A82 north of Fort William take the A830 towards Corpach and then follow the signs to the campsite.

💬 Medium-sized campsite, located on a river at the foot of Britain's highest mountain, Ben Nevis. Good starting point for climbing this mountain or walks and tours in the area.

Spean Bridge

📷 N 56°50'28'' W 5°4'30''
www.eurocampings.co.uk/102970

456 Fraserburgh, GB-AB43 9BT / Scotland 📶 iD | 2 B2

▲ Fraserburgh Caravan Park Ltd.***
🏠 South Harbour Road
📅 1 Apr - 30 Oct
☎ +44 (0)134-6379162
@ fraserburgh-campsite@hotmail.com

1	ACJMNOPQRST	KNQSWXY	6
2	EFGHJPSVW	ABDEFGH	7
3	K	ABEFNQRV	8
4	FH	E	9
5	DM	AHKMPR	10
16A CEE		❶ £23.00	
0,7ha 38T(80m²) 12P		❷ £27.00	

🚗 A90 from the south, signposted on the roundabout R past Fraserburg Bay.

💬 Small campsite at Fraserburg Bay with beautiful view over the bay. Near the lighthouse museum. The campsite is located on the coastal route.

Fraserburgh
Strichen

📷 N 57°41'12'' W 2°0'4''
www.eurocampings.co.uk/117793

457 Gairloch/Ross-shire, GB-IV21 2DL / Scotland

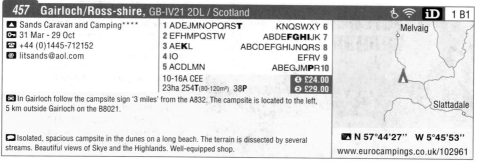

1 B1

- △ Sands Caravan and Camping****
- 31 Mar - 29 Oct
- +44 (0)1445-712152
- litsands@aol.com

1 ADEJMNOPQRS**T**	KNQSWXY	6
2 EFHMPQSTW	ABDE**FGHI**JK	7
3 AE**K**L	ABCDEFGHIJNQRS	8
4 IO	EFRV	9
5 ACDLMN	ABEGJM**P**R	10
10-16A CEE		❶ £24.00
23ha 254**T**(80-120m²) 38**P**		❷ £29.00

In Gairloch follow the campsite sign '3 miles' from the A832. The campsite is located to the left, 5 km outside Gairloch on the B8021.

Isolated, spacious campsite in the dunes on a long beach. The terrain is dissected by several streams. Beautiful views of Skye and the Highlands. Well-equipped shop.

N 57°44'27'' W 5°45'53''
www.eurocampings.co.uk/102961

458 Gartmore (Stirlingshire), GB-FK8 3RR / Scotland

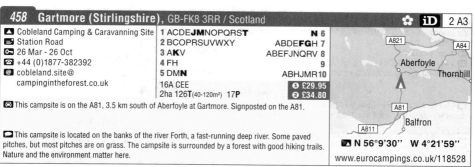

2 A3

- △ Cobleland Camping & Caravanning Site
- Station Road
- 26 Mar - 26 Oct
- +44 (0)1877-382392
- cobleland.site@campingintheforest.co.uk

1 ACDE**JM**NOPQRS**T**	**N**	6
2 BCOPRSUVWXY	ABDE**FGH**	7
3 A**K**V	ABEFJNQRV	8
4 FH		9
5 DM**N**	ABHJMR	10
16A CEE		❶ £29.95
2ha 126**T**(40-120m²) 17**P**		❷ £34.80

This campsite is on the A81, 3.5 km south of Aberfoyle at Gartmore. Signposted on the A81.

This campsite is located on the banks of the river Forth, a fast-running deep river. Some paved pitches, but most pitches are on grass. The campsite is surrounded by a forest with good hiking trails. Nature and the environment matter here.

N 56°9'30'' W 4°21'59''
www.eurocampings.co.uk/118528

459 Gatehouse-of-Fleet, GB-DG7 2EX / Scotland

5 A2

- △ Auchenlarie Holiday Park****
- A75
- 1 Mar - 31 Oct
- +44 (0)1556-506200
- enquiries@auchenlarie.co.uk

1 ADEJMNOPRS	**EFG**KNQSW**X**Y	6
2 EFGHJKMOPQRSTUVW	ABDE**FGH**	7
3 ACE**IK**L	ABEFIJNQRSTV	8
4 MO**PQRST**	EUV	9
5 ACDEFHJKM**N**	ABGHKM**NP**RY	10
16A CEE		❶ £27.00
A50 8,2ha 90**T**(40-80m²) 330**P**		❷ £27.00

Campsite is 8 km west of Gatehouse-of-Fleet, directly on the A75. Signposted.

Large holiday park with lots of sporting facilities. Among the many mobile homes is a small tourist area with access to a sheltered sandy beach. The campsite overlooks a large bay.

N 54°50'37'' W 4°16'48''
www.eurocampings.co.uk/108637

460 Glencoe/Argyll, GB-PH49 4HP / Scotland

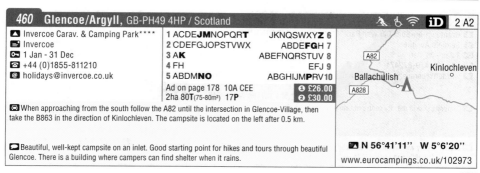

2 A2

- △ Invercoe Carav. & Camping Park****
- Invercoe
- 1 Jan - 31 Dec
- +44 (0)1855-811210
- holidays@invercoe.co.uk

1 ACDE**JM**NOPQR**T**	JKNQSWXY**Z**	6
2 CDEFGJOPSTVWX	ABDE**FGH**	7
3 A**K**	ABEFNQRSTUV	8
4 FH	EFJ	9
5 ABDM**NO**	ABGHIJMP**R**V	10
Ad on page 178 10A CEE		❶ £26.00
2ha 80**T**(75-80m²) 17**P**		❷ £30.00

When approaching from the south follow the A82 until the intersection in Glencoe-Village, then take the B863 in the direction of Kinlochleven. The campsite is located on the left after 0.5 km.

Beautiful, well-kept campsite on an inlet. Good starting point for hikes and tours through beautiful Glencoe. There is a building where campers can find shelter when it rains.

N 56°41'11'' W 5°6'20''
www.eurocampings.co.uk/102973

United Kingdom

INVERCOE is located on the shores of Loch Leven and surrounded by powerful panoramic views of the Loch, mountains and forest. This is a small-scale and quiet family campsite where you will receive a warm welcome. The campsite is qualified as 'excellent'. It is the perfect operating base for exploring the West Highlands.

Invercoe
PH49 4HP Glencoe/Argyll
Tel. and fax 01855-811210
E-mail: holidays@invercoe.co.uk
Internet: www.invercoe.co.uk

---

461 Glendaruel/Argyll, GB-PA22 3AB / Scotland   1 B3

- ⌂ Glendaruel Car. & Camping Park*****
- A886
- 1 Apr - 31 Oct
- +44 (0)1369-820267
- @ mail@glendaruelcaravanpark.com

1 ADEJMNOPQR**T**	**NX**	6
2 BCPRSVWXY	ABDE**FGH**	7
3 A**R**V	ABEFJNQRTUV	8
4 FH	EF	9
5 BMN	ABHJLMORWX	10
16A CEE	❶ **£22.50**	
4ha 32**T**(70-80m²) 38**P**	❷ **£27.50**	

From the A83 at Cairndow, take the A815 direction Glendaruel. Take the A886 at Strachur. Campsite is signposted (A836 from Dunoon less suited for caravans).

Friendly family-run campsite on a historical forest estate. It is surrounded by hills on the pristine Cowal peninsula. The area offers many hiking opportunities (on different levels). Waterfall behind the campsite. The toilet facilities were renovated in 2017. Outdoor seating area.

⚓ N 56°1'54'' W 5°12'19''

www.eurocampings.co.uk/111735

---

462 Glenmore, GB-PH22 1QU / Scotland   2 A2

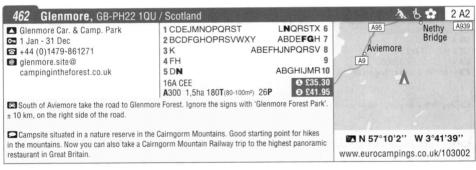

- ⌂ Glenmore Car. & Camp. Park
- 1 Jan - 31 Dec
- +44 (0)1479-861271
- @ glenmore.site@ campingintheforest.co.uk

1 CDEJMNOPQRST	**L**N**QRSTX**	6
2 BCDFGHOPRSVWXY	ABDE**FG**H	7
3 K	ABEFHJNPQRSV	8
4 FH		9
5 D**N**	ABGHIJMR	10
16A CEE	❶ **£35.30**	
A300 1,5ha 180**T**(80-100m²) 26**P**	❷ **£41.95**	

South of Aviemore take the road to Glenmore Forest. Ignore the signs with 'Glenmore Forest Park'. ± 10 km, on the right side of the road.

Campsite situated in a nature reserve in the Cairngorm Mountains. Good starting point for hikes in the mountains. Now you can also take a Cairngorm Mountain Railway trip to the highest panoramic restaurant in Great Britain.

⚓ N 57°10'2'' W 3°41'39''

www.eurocampings.co.uk/103002

---

463 Grantown-on-Spey, GB-PH26 3JQ / Scotland   2 A2

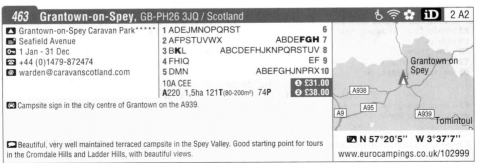

- ⌂ Grantown-on-Spey Caravan Park*****
- Seafield Avenue
- 1 Jan - 31 Dec
- +44 (0)1479-872474
- @ warden@caravanscotland.com

1 ADEJMNOPQRST		6
2 AFPSTUVWX	ABDE**FGH**	7
3 B**KL**	ABCDEFHJKNPQRSTUV	8
4 FHIQ	EF	9
5 DMN	ABEFGHJNPRX	10
10A CEE	❶ **£31.00**	
A220 1,5ha 121**T**(80-200m²) 74**P**	❷ **£38.00**	

Campsite sign in the city centre of Grantown on the A939.

Beautiful, very well maintained terraced campsite in the Spey Valley. Good starting point for tours in the Cromdale Hills and Ladder Hills, with beautiful views.

⚓ N 57°20'5'' W 3°37'7''

www.eurocampings.co.uk/102999

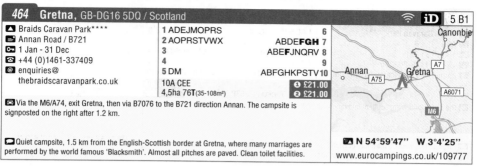

464 Gretna, GB-DG16 5DQ / Scotland

5 B1

- Braids Caravan Park★★★★
- Annan Road / B721
- 1 Jan - 31 Dec
- +44 (0)1461-337409
- enquiries@
  thebraidscaravanpark.co.uk

1 ADEJMOPRS		6
2 AOPRSTVWX	ABDEFGH	7
3	ABEFJNQRV	8
4		9
5 DM	ABFGHKPSTV	10
10A CEE	❶ £21.00	
4,5ha 76T(35-108m²)	❷ £21.00	

Via the M6/A74, exit Gretna, then via B7076 to the B721 direction Annan. The campsite is signposted on the right after 1.2 km.

Quiet campsite, 1.5 km from the English-Scottish border at Gretna, where many marriages are performed by the world famous 'Blacksmith'. Almost all pitches are paved. Clean toilet facilities.

N 54°59'47" W 3°4'25"

www.eurocampings.co.uk/109777

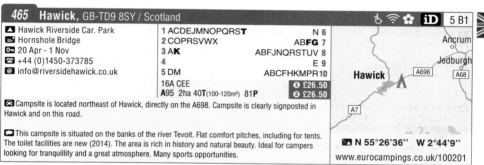

465 Hawick, GB-TD9 8SY / Scotland

5 B1

- Hawick Riverside Car. Park
- Hornshole Bridge
- 20 Apr - 1 Nov
- +44 (0)1450-373785
- info@riversidehawick.co.uk

1 ACDEJMNOPQRST	N	6
2 COPRSVWX	ABFG	7
3 AK	ABFJNQRSTUV	8
4	E	9
5 DM	ABCFHKMPR	10
16A CEE	❶ £26.50	
A95 2ha 40T(100-120m²) 81P	❷ £26.50	

Campsite is located northeast of Hawick, directly on the A698. Campsite is clearly signposted in Hawick and on this road.

This campsite is situated on the banks of the river Tevoit. Flat comfort pitches, including for tents. The toilet facilities are new (2014). The area is rich in history and natural beauty. Ideal for campers looking for tranquillity and a great atmosphere. Many sports opportunities.

N 55°26'36" W 2°44'9"

www.eurocampings.co.uk/100201

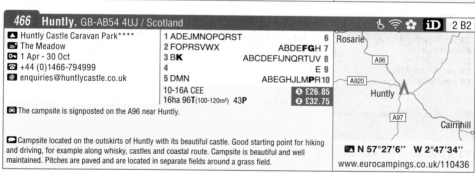

466 Huntly, GB-AB54 4UJ / Scotland

2 B2

- Huntly Castle Caravan Park★★★★
- The Meadow
- 1 Apr - 30 Oct
- +44 (0)1466-794999
- enquiries@huntlycastle.co.uk

1 ADEJMNOPQRST		6
2 FOPRSVWX	ABDEFGH	7
3 BK	ABCDEFIJNQRTUV	8
4	E	9
5 DMN	ABEGHJLMPR	10
10-16A CEE	❶ £26.85	
16ha 96T(100-120m²) 43P	❷ £32.75	

The campsite is signposted on the A96 near Huntly.

Campsite located on the outskirts of Huntly with its beautiful castle. Good starting point for hiking and driving, for example along whisky, castles and coastal route. Campsite is beautiful and well maintained. Pitches are paved and are located in separate fields around a grass field.

N 57°27'6" W 2°47'34"

www.eurocampings.co.uk/110436

467 Innerwick/Dunbar, GB-EH42 1SA / Scotland

2 B3

- Thurston Manor Leisure Park
- 1/1 - 7/1, 14/2 - 31/12
- +44 (0)1368-840643
- info@thurstonmanor.co.uk

1 ADEILOPQRS	EN	6
2 AOPRSTUVWX	ABDEFGH	7
3 BK	ABCDEFGINQRSTUV	8
4 BDFILOPQRST	EF	9
5 ACDEFHJLMNO	ABHIKMORYZ	10
10A CEE	❶ £31.00	
40ha 50T(40-120m²) 105P	❷ £36.00	

This campsite is in Innerwick southwest of Dunbar and is clearly signposted on the A1.

This campground offers large pitches on the terraces. The spaciousness and variety of facilities make this campsite very suitable for families with children, but hikers and fly fisherman will also enjoy their time here.

N 55°57'35" W 2°27'40"

www.eurocampings.co.uk/121662

United Kingdom

468 Inveraray/Argyll, GB-PA32 8XT / Scotland ♿ 📶 ⚙ iD 2 A3

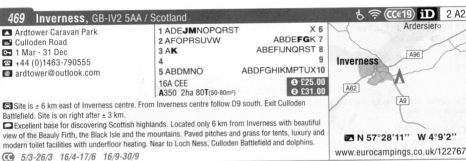

- 🏕 Argyll Caravan Park*****
- 🚍 A83
- 📅 1 Apr - 31 Oct
- ☎ +44 (0)1499-302285
- @ enquiries@argyllcaravanpark.com

1 ADEJMOPQRS	NOPQSWXYZ	6
2 DEFGKOPRSVWX	ABDE**FGH**	7
3 AE**GHKLM**	ABCDEFJNQRSTV	8
4 I**PQ**	EFP	9
5 ABDFHJKMN	ABGHKMORW	10

16A CEE
20ha 57**T**(80-90m²) 263**P**

❶ £25.00
❷ £25.00

🚗 The campsite is 4 km south of Inverary on the A83, campsite is signposted.

💬 Large holiday park on the shore of Loch Fyne. Small campsite behind the many mobile homes. Good facilities. The area offers many tourist attractions and sports options.

A819
Inveraray
A83
Furnace
Minard

📍 N 56°12'8" W 5°6'27"

www.eurocampings.co.uk/100197

469 Inverness, GB-IV2 5AA / Scotland ♿ 📶 (CC€19) iD 2 A2

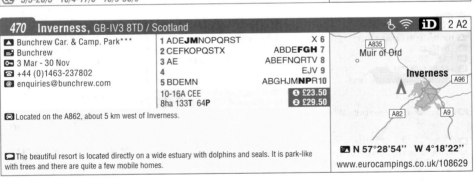

- 🏕 Ardtower Caravan Park
- 🚍 Culloden Road
- 📅 1 Mar - 31 Dec
- ☎ +44 (0)1463-790555
- @ ardtower@outlook.com

1 ADE**JM**NOPQRST	X	6
2 AFOPRSUVW	ABDE**FG**K	7
3 A**K**	ABEFIJNQRST	8
4		9
5 ABDMNO	ABDFGHIKMPTUX	10

16A CEE
A350 2ha 80**T**(50-80m²)

❶ £25.00
❷ £31.00

🚗 Site is ± 6 km east of Inverness centre. From Inverness centre follow D9 south. Exit Culloden Battlefield. Site is on right after ± 3 km.

💬 Excellent base for discovering Scottish highlands. Located only 6 km from Inverness with beautiful view of the Beauly Firth, the Black Isle and the mountains. Paved pitches and grass for tents, luxury and modern toilet facilities with underfloor heating. Near to Loch Ness, Culloden Battlefield and dolphins.

Ⓒ 5/3-26/3 16/4-17/6 16/9-30/9

Ardersier
A96
Inverness
A82
A9

📍 N 57°28'11" W 4°9'2"

www.eurocampings.co.uk/122767

470 Inverness, GB-IV3 8TD / Scotland ♿ 📶 iD 2 A2

- 🏕 Bunchrew Car. & Camp. Park***
- 🚍 Bunchrew
- 📅 3 Mar - 30 Nov
- ☎ +44 (0)1463-237802
- @ enquiries@bunchrew.com

1 ADE**JM**NOPQRST	X	6
2 CEFKOPQSTX	ABDE**FGH**	7
3 AE	ABEFNQRTV	8
4	EJV	9
5 BDEMN	ABGHJM**NPR**	10

10-16A CEE
8ha 133**T** 64**P**

❶ £23.50
❷ £29.50

🚗 Located on the A862, about 5 km west of Inverness.

💬 The beautiful resort is located directly on a wide estuary with dolphins and seals. It is park-like with trees and there are quite a few mobile homes.

A835
Muir of Ord
Inverness
A96
A82
A9

📍 N 57°28'54" W 4°18'22"

www.eurocampings.co.uk/108629

471 Inverness, GB-IV3 8JL / Scotland ♿ 📶 iD 2 A2

- 🏕 Torvean Car. Park*****
- 🚍 Glenurquhart Road
- 📅 23 Mar - 22 Oct
- ☎ +44 (0)1463-220582
- @ info@torvean.com

1 ADE**JM**OPQR		6
2 AOPRSVWX	**ABDEFG**H	7
3 **J**	ABEFJNQRT	8
4	E	9
5 D	ABGHJPR	10

10A CEE
1,2ha 53**T**(70-80m²) 6**P**

❶ £28.50
❷ £28.50

🚗 Next to the A82, approx. 3 km southwest of Inverness centre. The campsite is behind the sales area for caravans.

💬 A small, neatly enclosed campsite on the outskirts of Inverness. Located on the Caledonian Canal and a golf resort. Good base for city and nature visits. As of 2017 two motorhomes for hire.

Muir of Ord
Inverness
A96
A82
A9

📍 N 57°27'54" W 4°14'43"

www.eurocampings.co.uk/108628

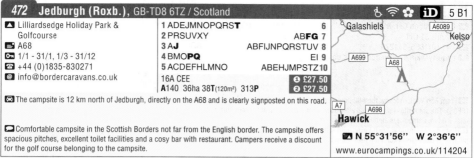

472 Jedburgh (Roxb.), GB-TD8 6TZ / Scotland
5 B1

- Lilliardsedge Holiday Park & Golfcourse
- A68
- 1/1 - 31/1, 1/3 - 31/12
- +44 (0)1835-830271
- info@bordercaravans.co.uk

1 ADEJMNOPQRST		6
2 PRSUVXY	ABFG	7
3 AJ	ABFIJNPQRSTUV	8
4 BMOPQ	EI	9
5 ACDEFHLMNO	ABEHJMPSTZ	10
16A CEE		❶ £27.50
A140 36ha 38T(120m²) 313P		❷ £27.50

The campsite is 12 km north of Jedburgh, directly on the A68 and is clearly signposted on this road.

Comfortable campsite in the Scottish Borders not far from the English border. The campsite offers spacious pitches, excellent toilet facilities and a cosy bar with restaurant. Campers receive a discount for the golf course belonging to the campsite.

N 55°31'56'' W 2°36'6''
www.eurocampings.co.uk/114204

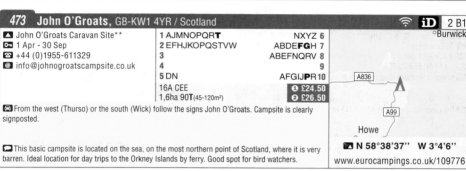

473 John O'Groats, GB-KW1 4YR / Scotland
2 B1

- John O'Groats Caravan Site**
- 1 Apr - 30 Sep
- +44 (0)1955-611329
- info@johnogroatscampsite.co.uk

1 AJMNOPQRT	NXYZ	6
2 EFHJKOPQSTVW	ABDEFGH	7
3	ABEFNQRV	8
4		9
5 DN	AFGIJPR	10
16A CEE		❶ £24.50
1,6ha 90T(45-120m²)		❷ £26.50

From the west (Thurso) or the south (Wick) follow the signs John O'Groats. Campsite is clearly signposted.

This basic campsite is located on the sea, on the most northern point of Scotland, where it is very barren. Ideal location for day trips to the Orkney Islands by ferry. Good spot for bird watchers.

N 58°38'37'' W 3°4'6''
www.eurocampings.co.uk/109776

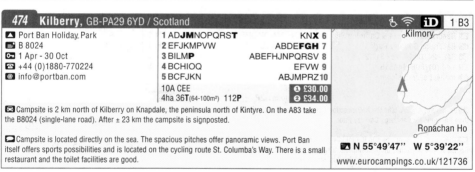

474 Kilberry, GB-PA29 6YD / Scotland
1 B3

- Port Ban Holiday Park
- B 8024
- 1 Apr - 30 Oct
- +44 (0)1880-770224
- info@portban.com

1 ADJMNOPQRST	KNX	6
2 EFJKMPVW	ABDEFGH	7
3 BILMP	ABEFHJNPQRSV	8
4 BCHIOQ	EFVW	9
5 BCFJKN	ABJMPRZ	10
10A CEE		❶ £30.00
4ha 36T(64-100m²) 112P		❷ £34.00

Campsite is 2 km north of Kilberry on Knapdale, the peninsula north of Kintyre. On the A83 take the B8024 (single-lane road). After ± 23 km the campsite is signposted.

Campsite is located directly on the sea. The spacious pitches offer panoramic views. Port Ban itself offers sports possibilities and is located on the cycling route St. Columba's Way. There is a small restaurant and the toilet facilities are good.

N 55°49'47'' W 5°39'22''
www.eurocampings.co.uk/121736

475 Killin, GB-FK21 8TN / Scotland
2 A3

- Maragowan Caravan Club Site
- Aberfeldy Road
- 1 Apr - 31 Oct
- +44 (0)1567-820245
- maragowan@caravanclub.co.uk

1 ADEJMOPQRST	NX	6
2 CRSVWXY	ABDEFG	7
3 AJK	ABCDEFHJKNPQRS	8
4		9
5 DMN	ABGHJPRXZ	10
16A CEE		❶ £39.60
A108 3,4ha 99T(100-120m²)		❷ £45.80

The campsite is on the A827 (Abeifeldy Road), just north of Killin.

Located next to a river on the edge of Killin, a tourist attraction because of its waterfalls. In principle no tents are allowed, but a small tent next to a caravan is permitted The facilities are well maintained. Flat, paved, spacious pitches.

N 56°28'26'' W 4°19'19''
www.eurocampings.co.uk/102987

United Kingdom

476 Kinlochleven/Argyll, GB-PH50 4RJ / Scotland — 2 A2

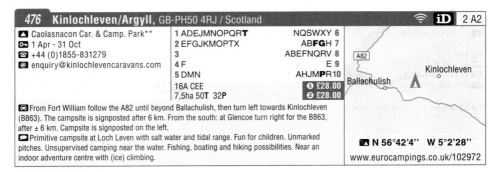

- ▲ Caolasnacon Car. & Camp. Park**
- 🗓 1 Apr - 31 Oct
- ☎ +44 (0)1855-831279
- @ enquiry@kinlochlevencaravans.com

1 ADEJMNOPQR**T**	NQSWXY 6
2 EFGJKMOPTX	AB**FGH** 7
3	ABEFNQRV 8
4 F	E 9
5 DMN	AHJMP**R** 10
16A CEE	❶ £28.00
7,5ha 50**T** 32**P**	❷ £28.00

🚗 From Fort William follow the A82 until beyond Ballachulish, then turn left towards Kinlochleven (B863). The campsite is signposted after 6 km. From the south: at Glencoe turn right for the B863, after ± 6 km. Campsite is signposted on the left.

💬 Primitive campsite at Loch Leven with salt water and tidal range. Fun for children. Unmarked pitches. Unsupervised camping near the water. Fishing, boating and hiking possibilities. Near an indoor adventure centre with (ice) climbing.

📍 N 56°42'4'' W 5°2'28''
www.eurocampings.co.uk/102972

477 Kirkcudbright, GB-DG6 4BT / Scotland — 5 A2

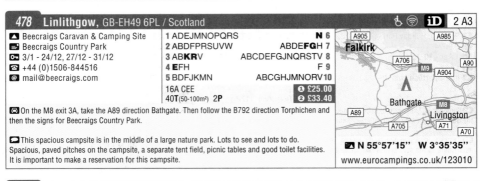

- ▲ Silvercraigs C. & C. Site****
- 🏕 Silvercraigs
- 🗓 1 Apr - 31 Oct
- ☎ +44 (0)1557-332050
- @ silvercraigscaravanpark@gmail.com

1 AJMNOPRS	6
2 FOPSTVWX	ABDE**FGH** 7
3 AE**K**	ABCDEFNPQRSV 8
4	9
5 D**N**	ABHJ**P**R 10
16A CEE	❶ £24.00
3ha 52**T**(90-100m²) 15**P**	❷ £24.00

🚗 The campsite is located on the A711 and is signposted from the centre of Kirkcudbright.

💬 Nice, smaller campsite at the top edge of Kirkcudbright, traditionally an artists' town. Views over the town and the hills to the coast.

📍 N 54°50'6'' W 4°2'51''
www.eurocampings.co.uk/102994

478 Linlithgow, GB-EH49 6PL / Scotland — 2 A3

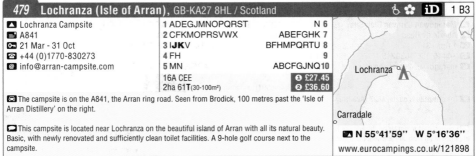

- ▲ Beecraigs Caravan & Camping Site
- 🏕 Beecraigs Country Park
- 🗓 3/1 - 24/12, 27/12 - 31/12
- ☎ +44 (0)1506-844516
- @ mail@beecraigs.com

1 ADEJMNOPQRS	**N** 6
2 ABDFPRSUVW	ABDE**FGH** 7
3 AB**KRV**	ABCDEFGJNQRSTV 8
4 E**FH**	F 9
5 BDFJKMN	ABCGHJMNORV 10
16A CEE	❶ £25.00
40**T**(50-100m²) 2**P**	❷ £33.40

🚗 On the M8 exit 3A, take the A89 direction Bathgate. Then follow the B792 direction Torphichen and then the signs for Beecraigs Country Park.

💬 This spacious campsite is in the middle of a large nature park. Lots to see and lots to do. Spacious, paved pitches on the campsite, a separate tent field, picnic tables and good toilet facilities. It is important to make a reservation for this campsite.

📍 N 55°57'15'' W 3°35'35''
www.eurocampings.co.uk/123010

479 Lochranza (Isle of Arran), GB-KA27 8HL / Scotland — 1 B3

- ▲ Lochranza Campsite
- 🏕 A841
- 🗓 21 Mar - 31 Oct
- ☎ +44 (0)1770-830273
- @ info@arran-campsite.com

1 ADEGJMNOPQRST	N 6
2 CFKMOPRSVWX	ABEFGHK 7
3 I**J**K**V**	BFHMPQRTU 8
4 FH	9
5 MN	ABCFGJNQ 10
16A CEE	❶ £27.45
2ha 61**T**(30-100m²)	❷ £36.60

🚗 The campsite is on the A841, the Arran ring road. Seen from Brodick, 100 metres past the 'Isle of Arran Distillery' on the right.

💬 This campsite is located near Lochranza on the beautiful island of Arran with all its natural beauty. Basic, with newly renovated and sufficiently clean toilet facilities. A 9-hole golf course next to the campsite.

📍 N 55°41'59'' W 5°16'36''
www.eurocampings.co.uk/121898

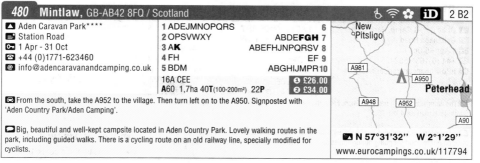

480 Mintlaw, GB-AB42 8FQ / Scotland — iD 2 B2

- ▲ Aden Caravan Park****
- ▤ Station Road
- ⊙ 1 Apr - 31 Oct
- ☎ +44 (0)1771-623460
- @ info@adencaravanandcamping.co.uk

1 ADEJMNOPQRS	6
2 OPSVWXY	ABDEFGH 7
3 AK	ABEFHJNPQRSV 8
4 FH	EF 9
5 BDM	ABGHIJMPR 10
16A CEE	❶ £26.00
A60 1,7ha 40T(100-200m²) 22P	❷ £34.00

🚐 From the south, take the A952 to the village. Then turn left on to the A950. Signposted with 'Aden Country Park/Aden Camping'.

💬 Big, beautiful and well-kept campsite located in Aden Country Park. Lovely walking routes in the park, including guided walks. There is a cycling route on an old railway line, specially modified for cyclists.

📍 N 57°31'32'' W 2°1'29''

www.eurocampings.co.uk/117794

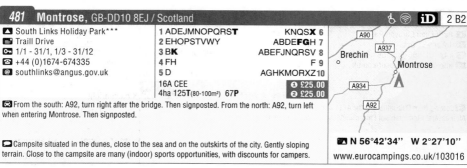

481 Montrose, GB-DD10 8EJ / Scotland — iD 2 B2

- ▲ South Links Holiday Park***
- ▤ Traill Drive
- ⊙ 1/1 - 31/1, 1/3 - 31/12
- ☎ +44 (0)1674-674335
- @ southlinks@angus.gov.uk

1 ADEJMNOPQRST	KNQSX 6
2 EHOPSTVWY	ABDEFGH 7
3 BK	ABEFJNQRSV 8
4 FH	F 9
5 D	AGHKMORXZ 10
16A CEE	❶ £25.00
4ha 125T(80-100m²) 67P	❷ £25.00

🚐 From the south: A92, turn right after the bridge. Then signposted. From the north: A92, turn left when entering Montrose. Then signposted.

💬 Campsite situated in the dunes, close to the sea and on the outskirts of the city. Gently sloping terrain. Close to the campsite are many (indoor) sports opportunities, with discounts for campers.

📍 N 56°42'34'' W 2°27'10''

www.eurocampings.co.uk/103016

482 Newtonmore, GB-PH20 1BE / Scotland — 2 A2

- ▲ Invernahavon Caravan Site***
- ▤ Glentruim
- ⊙ 1 Apr - 16 Oct
- ☎ +44 (0)1540-673534
- @ enquiries@invernahavon.com

1 JMNOPQRST	N 6
2 CFPRSVWX	ABDEFGH 7
3 AK	ABEFHJNPQRSV 8
4	9
5 DM	AEGHJMPR 10
16A CEE	❶ £22.00
A240 5ha 89T(80-120m²)	❷ £26.60

🚐 On the A9 take exit Lagan. The campsite is signposted.

💬 Large, open, slightly sloping terrain in the middle of the rugged Highlands. The campsite is adjacent to a small river with fishing opportunities Many hiking possibilities nearby.

📍 N 57°1'35'' W 4°9'48''

www.eurocampings.co.uk/101434

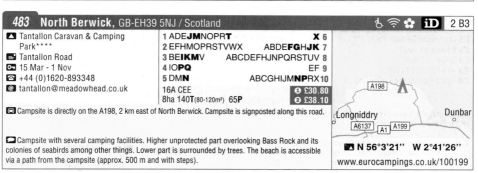

483 North Berwick, GB-EH39 5NJ / Scotland — iD 2 B3

- ▲ Tantallon Caravan & Camping Park****
- ▤ Tantallon Road
- ⊙ 15 Mar - 1 Nov
- ☎ +44 (0)1620-893348
- @ tantallon@meadowhead.co.uk

1 ADEJMNOPRT	X 6
2 EFHMOPRSTVWX	ABDEFGHJK 7
3 BEIKMV	ABCDEFHJNPQRSTUV 8
4 IOPQ	EF 9
5 DMN	ABCGHIJMNPRX 10
16A CEE	❶ £30.80
8ha 140T(80-120m²) 65P	❷ £38.10

🚐 Campsite is directly on the A198, 2 km east of North Berwick. Campsite is signposted along this road.

💬 Campsite with several camping facilities. Higher unprotected part overlooking Bass Rock and its colonies of seabirds among other things. Lower part is surrounded by trees. The beach is accessible via a path from the campsite (approx. 500 m and with steps).

📍 N 56°3'21'' W 2°41'26''

www.eurocampings.co.uk/100199

United Kingdom

484 Oban/Gallanach, GB-PA34 4QH / Scotland 🛜 iD 1 B3

- 🏕 Oban Car. & Camp. Park****
- 🚐 Gallanach Road
- 📅 1 Apr - 5 Oct
- ☎ +44 (0)1631-562425
- @ info@obancaravanpark.com

1 ADEJMNOPRST	KNOPQSWXY	6
2 EFJMOPRSTUWX	ABDEFGHIK	7
3 AK	ABEFNQR	8
4 IOPQ	EFJ	9
5 ABDMNO	AFHJLMOQRVWY	10

10-16A CEE   ❶ £24.00
130ha 150T(90-120m²) 20P   ❷ £30.00

🚗 The campsite is 4 km south of Oban. From the centre of Oban follow camping signs for Gallanach. Single-lane road for 4 km.

💬 A large terraced campsite by the sea with plenty of watersports activities. The attractive town of Oban offers good shopping opportunities and ferries to the islands. Toilet facilities completely renovated in 2014.

🚩 N 56°23'24" W 5°31'1"

www.eurocampings.co.uk/108631

485 Palnackie/Castle Douglas, GB-DG7 1PF / Scotland 🛜 iD 5 A2

- 🏕 Barlochan Caravan Park****
- 📅 1 Apr - 31 Oct
- ☎ +44 (0)1556-600256
- @ info@gillespie-leisure.co.uk

1 ADEJMNOPQRST	AB	6
2 FPRSTUVWXY	ABDEFGH	7
3 AK	ABCDEFNPQRV	8
4 IOQ	EF	9
5 B	AFGHIJMOR	10

10A CEE   ❶ £21.00
4ha 21T(65-100m²) 56P   ❷ £25.00

🚗 Coming from Dalbeattie take the A711 direction Kirkcudbright. This is the coastal road. After several kilometres exit Palnackie/Auchencairn. Campsite is signposted.

💬 The campsite 'Barlochan' is on a hill and offers great views. Nice terraced campsite.

🚩 N 54°53'45" W 3°50'30"

www.eurocampings.co.uk/102991

486 Parton, GB-DG7 3NE / Scotland ♿ 🛜 ✿ iD 5 A1

- 🏕 Loch Ken Holiday Park****
- 🚐 A713
- 📅 1 Mar - 10 Nov
- ☎ +44 (0)1644-470282
- @ office@lochkenholidaypark.co.uk

1 ADEJMNOPRST	JLNQSWXYZ	6
2 CDFGOPQRSUVWXY	ABDEFGH	7
3 AEKL	ABCDEFGIJKNQRSTV	8
4 BH	BEJPQRU	9
5 ABDFMNO	ABHJMPR	10

10A CEE   ❶ £26.50
A60 4ha 97T(85-95m²) 61P   ❷ £30.50

🚗 Located 500 metres north of Parton, directly on the A713. Signposted.

💬 Quiet campsite in a beautiful location right by Loch Ken. Both the lake and Galloway Forest Park have a lot to offer for sports people and nature lovers. There is a separate field for tents. Caravans and motorhomes have gravel pitches on the terraces.

🚩 N 55°0'34" W 4°3'17"

www.eurocampings.co.uk/102989

487 Peebles, GB-EH45 8ED / Scotland ♿ 🛜 iD 5 B1

- 🏕 Crossburn Caravan Park****
- 🚐 Edinburgh Road
- 📅 1 Apr - 31 Oct
- ☎ +44 (0)1721-720501
- @ info@crossburncaravans.co.uk

1 ADEJMNOPQRST	N	6
2 COPRSVWXY	ABDEFGH	7
3 BK	ABCDEFJNQRSV	8
4	F	9
5 BDMN	ABFGHJMPR	10

10A CEE   ❶ £27.00
A181 2,5ha 70T(80-100m²) 87P   ❷ £27.00

🚗 The campsite is located on the north side of Peebles, on the A703, in the direction of Edinburgh, next to the Shell service station.

💬 Campsite with different features. Paved areas with young plants, but also a tent field along the small river with lots of mature trees. Located just outside Peebles in the Tweed Valley. The campsite shop also sells camping equipment. Modern, clean toilet facilities.

🚩 N 55°39'44" W 3°11'36"

www.eurocampings.co.uk/103006

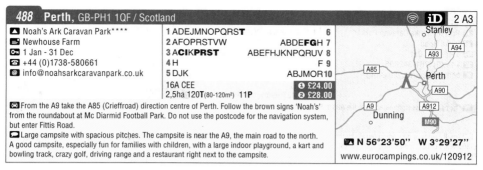

488 Perth, GB-PH1 1QF / Scotland 2 A3

- ▲ Noah's Ark Caravan Park****
- 🏠 Newhouse Farm
- 🗓 1 Jan - 31 Dec
- ☎ +44 (0)1738-580661
- @ info@noahsarkcaravanpark.co.uk

1 ADEJMNOPQRST	6
2 AFOPRSTVW	ABDE**FGH** 7
3 A**CIKPRST**	ABEFHJKNPQRUV 8
4 H	F 9
5 DJK	ABJMOR 10

16A CEE   ❶ £24.00
2,5ha 120T(80-120m²) 11P   ❷ £28.00

🚗 From the A9 take the A85 (Crieffroad) direction centre of Perth. Follow the brown signs 'Noah's' from the roundabout at Mc Diarmid Football Park. Do not use the postcode for the navigation system, but enter Fittis Road.

💬 Large campsite with spacious pitches. The campsite is near the A9, the main road to the north. A good campsite, especially fun for families with children, with a large indoor playground, a kart and bowling track, crazy golf, driving range and a restaurant right next to the campsite.

🧭 N 56°23'50'' W 3°29'27''
www.eurocampings.co.uk/120912

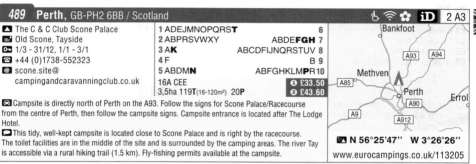

489 Perth, GB-PH2 6BB / Scotland 2 A3

- ▲ The C & C Club Scone Palace
- 🏠 Old Scone, Tayside
- 🗓 1/3 - 31/12, 1/1 - 3/1
- ☎ +44 (0)1738-552323
- @ scone.site@
  campingandcaravanningclub.co.uk

1 ADEJMNOPQRST	6
2 ABPRSVWXY	ABDE**FGH** 7
3 A**K**	ABCDFIJNQRSTUV 8
4 F	B 9
5 ABDM**N**	ABFGHKLM**PR** 10

16A CEE   ❶ £33.50
3,5ha 119T(16-120m²) 20P   ❷ £43.60

🚗 Campsite is directly north of Perth on the A93. Follow the signs for Scone Palace/Racecourse from the centre of Perth, then follow the campsite signs. Campsite entrance is located after The Lodge Hotel.

💬 This tidy, well-kept campsite is located close to Scone Palace and is right by the racecourse. The toilet facilities are in the middle of the site and is surrounded by the camping areas. The river Tay is accessible via a rural hiking trail (1.5 km). Fly-fishing permits available at the campsite.

🧭 N 56°25'47'' W 3°26'26''
www.eurocampings.co.uk/113205

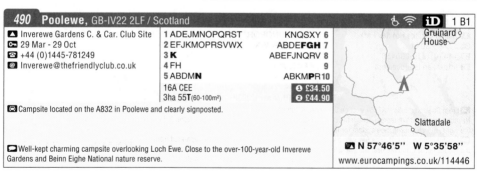

490 Poolewe, GB-IV22 2LF / Scotland 1 B1

- ▲ Inverewe Gardens C. & Car. Club Site
- 🗓 29 Mar - 29 Oct
- ☎ +44 (0)1445-781249
- @ Inverewe@thefriendlyclub.co.uk

1 ADEJMNOPQRST	KNQSXY 6
2 EFJKMOPRSVWX	ABDE**FGH** 7
3 K	ABEFJNQRV 8
4 FH	9
5 ABDM**N**	ABKM**PR** 10

16A CEE   ❶ £34.50
3ha 55T(60-100m²)   ❷ £44.90

🚗 Campsite located on the A832 in Poolewe and clearly signposted.

💬 Well-kept charming campsite overlooking Loch Ewe. Close to the over-100-year-old Inverewe Gardens and Beinn Eighe National nature reserve.

🧭 N 57°46'5'' W 5°35'58''
www.eurocampings.co.uk/114446

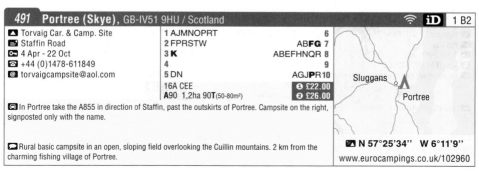

491 Portree (Skye), GB-IV51 9HU / Scotland 1 B2

- ▲ Torvaig Car. & Camp. Site
- 🏠 Staffin Road
- 🗓 4 Apr - 22 Oct
- ☎ +44 (0)1478-611849
- @ torvaigcampsite@aol.com

1 AJMNOPRT	6
2 FPRSTW	AB**FG** 7
3 K	ABEFHNQR 8
4	9
5 DN	AGJ**PR** 10

16A CEE   ❶ £22.00
A90 1,2ha 90T(50-80m²)   ❷ £26.00

🚗 In Portree take the A855 in direction of Staffin, past the outskirts of Portree. Campsite on the right, signposted only with the name.

💬 Rural basic campsite in an open, sloping field overlooking the Cuillin mountains. 2 km from the charming fishing village of Portree.

🧭 N 57°25'34'' W 6°11'9''
www.eurocampings.co.uk/102960

United Kingdom

492 Portsoy, GB-AB45 2RQ / Scotland   2 B2

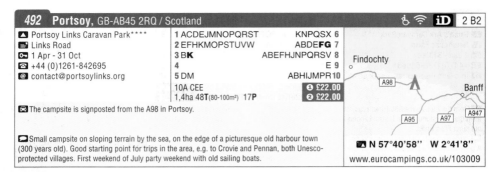

- ▲ Portsoy Links Caravan Park★★★★
- ▤ Links Road
- ▣ 1 Apr - 31 Oct
- ☎ +44 (0)1261-842695
- @ contact@portsoylinks.org

1 ACDEJMNOPQRST	KNPQSX 6
2 EFHKMOPSTUVW	ABDE**FG** 7
3 B**K**	ABEFHJNPQRSV 8
4	E 9
5 DM	ABHIJMPR 10
10A CEE	❶ £22.00
1,4ha 48T(80-100m²) 17**P**	❷ £22.00

🗺 The campsite is signposted from the A98 in Portsoy.

💬 Small campsite on sloping terrain by the sea, on the edge of a picturesque old harbour town (300 years old). Good starting point for trips in the area, e.g. to Crovie and Pennan, both Unesco-protected villages. First weekend of July party weekend with old sailing boats.

🧭 N 57°40'58'' W 2°41'8''

www.eurocampings.co.uk/103009

493 Powfoot/Annan, GB-DG12 5PN / Scotland   5 A1

- ▲ Queensberry Bay Holiday Park
- ▣ 10 Jan - 30 Nov
- ☎ +44 (0)1461-700205
- @ info@queensberrybay.co.uk

1 ADE**JM**OPQRS	KN 6
2 EFIOPRVW	**FGH**K 7
3 **K**	ABCD**F**JNQRV 8
4 **K**T**XZ**	EF 9
5 ABDM	ABCPR 10
10-16A CEE	❶ £27.00
7,5ha 26T(190-340m²) 36**P**	❷ £33.00

🗺 From A75 follow B721 direction Annan and then B724 direction Powfoot. In Powfoot follow the coastal road to the campsite. The campsite is signposted.

💬 Campsite located directly on the Solway Firth, very spacious pitches. Good toilet facilities and lovely views. Enthusiasts can use the luxurious spa with many extras.

🧭 N 54°58'29'' W 3°20'48''

www.eurocampings.co.uk/121663

494 Sandhead, GB-DG9 9JR / Scotland   4 B2

- ▲ Sands of Luce Holiday Park
- ▣ 1 Mar - 30 Nov
- ☎ +44 (0)1776-830456
- @ info@sandsofluce.com

1 ADEJMNOPQRT	KNQSWXY 6
2 EGHIOPSWX	ABDE**FG** 7
3 B	ABEFJNPQRTV 8
4 FIMO**PQ**	E 9
5 DEFHJK	ABGHJ**P**R 10
16A CEE	❶ £25.00
12ha 30T(50-80m²) 290**P**	❷ £25.00

🗺 From Stranraer: follow A716 direction Sandhead/Drummore. Campsite is signposted. From Newton Stewart: at Whitecrook follow the B7077/B7084 direction Sandhead/Drummore. Note: follow the signs, not your navigation system for the last part of the route!

💬 Luxury holiday park at Luce Bay with a wide sandy beach. The touring pitches are separated from the mobile homes, and are near the sea, a long way behind the mobile homes. The campsite has a large playground for younger family members and dance and disco evenings for older children.

🧭 N 54°48'53'' W 4°57'24''

www.eurocampings.co.uk/114195

495 Scourie, GB-IV27 4TF / Scotland   2 A1

- ▲ Scourie C. & C. Park★★★
- ▤ Harbour Road
- ▣ 1 Apr - 30 Sep
- ☎ +44 (0)1971-502060
- @ info@scouriecampsitesutherland.com

1 ADEJMNOPQRS**T**	KNOQSX 6
2 EFHKPRSTUW	ABDE**FG** 7
3	ABEFNQR 8
4	9
5 DEFHLN	AJPR 10
16A CEE	❶ £20.00
1,5ha 95T(30-60m²)	❷ £28.00

🗺 Located on the A838 in Scourie.

💬 The campsite is located on an open grass area, partly on terraces, in a sheltered bay with a beautiful view and on the edge of a farming village. Plenty to do for fishermen, hikers and also for bird lovers on the neighbouring island of Handa.

🧭 N 58°21'6'' W 5°9'21''

www.eurocampings.co.uk/102965

496 Shawhead/Dumfries, GB-DG2 9SQ / Scotland — iD 5 A1

- Barnsoul Caravan Park
- 1 Mar - 31 Oct
- +44 (0)1557-814351
- elspeth@murray-usher.co.uk

1	ADJMNOPQR	N 6
2	ABGPRSVWX	AB**FGHIJK** 7
3	A	ABEFHJNQRSV 8
4		F 9
5	D	ABJMRV 10

16A CEE — ❶ £17.00
19ha 40T(80-100m²) 19P — ❷ £27.00

A75, exit Shawhead (approx. 10 km west of Dumfries). Then follow the campsite signs. Do not use the postal code for navigation systems!

In a wooded area with fishpond and marked footpaths. Flat pitches surrounding the grass fields. In high season, the local fishmonger sells his produce on the campsite.

N 55°4'41'' W 3°45'49''
www.eurocampings.co.uk/122832

497 St. Andrews, GB-KY16 8PQ / Scotland — iD 2 B3

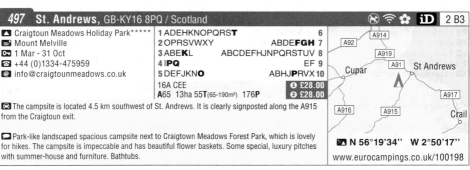

- Craigtoun Meadows Holiday Park*****
- Mount Melville
- 1 Mar - 31 Oct
- +44 (0)1334-475959
- info@craigtounmeadows.co.uk

1	ADEHKNOPQRS**T**	6
2	OPRSVWXY	ABDE**FGH** 7
3	ABE**KL**	ABCDEFHJNPQRSTUV 8
4	I**PQ**	EF 9
5	DEFJKN**O**	ABHJ**PR**VX 10

16A CEE — ❶ £28.00
A65 13ha 55T(65-190m²) 176P — ❷ £28.00

The campsite is located 4.5 km southwest of St. Andrews. It is clearly signposted along the A915 from the Craigtoun exit.

Park-like landscaped spacious campsite next to Craigtown Meadows Forest Park, which is lovely for hikes. The campsite is impeccable and has beautiful flower baskets. Some special, luxury pitches with summer-house and furniture. Bathtubs.

N 56°19'34'' W 2°50'17''
www.eurocampings.co.uk/100198

498 St. Andrews (Fife), GB-KY16 8NN / Scotland — iD 2 B3

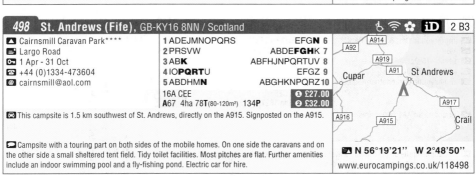

- Cairnsmill Caravan Park****
- Largo Road
- 1 Apr - 31 Oct
- +44 (0)1334-473604
- cairnsmill@aol.com

1	ADEJMNOPQRS	EF**GN** 6
2	PRSVW	ABDE**FGH**K 7
3	AB**K**	ABFHJNPQRTUV 8
4	IO**PQRT**U	EFGZ 9
5	ABDHM**N**	ABGHKNPQRZ 10

16A CEE — ❶ £27.00
A67 4ha 78T(80-120m²) 134P — ❷ £32.00

This campsite is 1.5 km southwest of St. Andrews, directly on the A915. Signposted on the A915.

Campsite with a touring part on both sides of the mobile homes. On one side the caravans and on the other side a small sheltered tent field. Tidy toilet facilities. Most pitches are flat. Further amenities include an indoor swimming pool and a fly-fishing pond. Electric car for hire.

N 56°19'21'' W 2°48'50''
www.eurocampings.co.uk/118498

499 Staffin (Skye), GB-IV51 9JX / Scotland — iD 1 B1

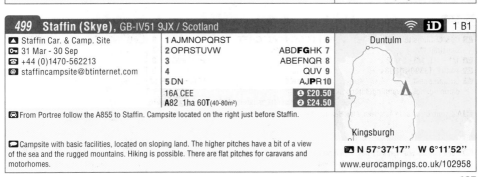

- Staffin Car. & Camp. Site
- 31 Mar - 30 Sep
- +44 (0)1470-562213
- staffincampsite@btinternet.com

1	AJMNOPQRST	6
2	OPRSTUVW	ABD**FG**HK 7
3		ABEFNQR 8
4		QUV 9
5	DN	AJ**PR** 10

16A CEE — ❶ £20.50
A82 1ha 60T(40-80m²) — ❷ £24.50

From Portree follow the A855 to Staffin. Campsite located on the right just before Staffin.

Campsite with basic facilities, located on sloping land. The higher pitches have a bit of a view of the sea and the rugged mountains. Hiking is possible. There are flat pitches for caravans and motorhomes.

N 57°37'17'' W 6°11'52''
www.eurocampings.co.uk/102958

500 Stonehaven, GB-AB39 2RD / Scotland
   iD 2 B2

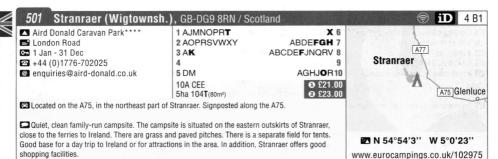

- ▲ Queen Elizabeth Caravan & Motorhome Club***
- ▤ Beach Road, Cowie
- ◔ 1/1 - 4/1, 3/3 - 31/12
- ☎ +44 (0)1569-760088
- @ stonehaven@camc.com

1 ABDEJMNOPQRST	KNSW	6
2 EJOSVW	ABDEFG	7
3 AK	ABCDEFHJMNPQRSTUV	8
4 FH		9
5 BDMN	ABCEGHKPRZ	10

16A CEE   ❶ £39.60
2ha 77T(100m²)   ❷ £45.40

🗺 Located in the centre of Stonehaven, from Aberdeen A90 direction Dundee. Signposted from the Stonehaven exit.

💬 Beautiful campsite by the sea. Brand-new and very well maintained toilet block. Right next to the campsite is a beautiful heated swimming pool and a large playground. A lot of history nearby. Please call to make a reservation, the campsite is very popular.

N 56°58'13'' W 2°12'13''
www.eurocampings.co.uk/110437

501 Stranraer (Wigtownsh.), GB-DG9 8RN / Scotland
iD 4 B1

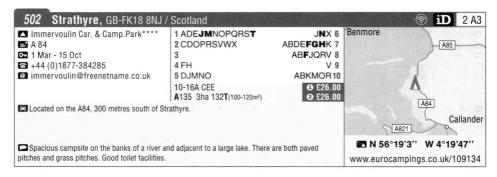

- ▲ Aird Donald Caravan Park****
- ▤ London Road
- ◔ 1 Jan - 31 Dec
- ☎ +44 (0)1776-702025
- @ enquiries@aird-donald.co.uk

1 AJMNOPRT	X	6
2 AOPRSVWXY	ABDEFGH	7
3 AK	ABCDEFJNQRV	8
4		9
5 DM	AGHJOR	10

10A CEE   ❶ £21.00
5ha 104T(80m²)   ❷ £23.00

🗺 Located on the A75, in the northeast part of Stranraer. Signposted along the A75.

💬 Quiet, clean family-run campsite. The campsite is situated on the eastern outskirts of Stranraer, close to the ferries to Ireland. There are grass and paved pitches. There is a separate field for tents. Good base for a day trip to Ireland or for attractions in the area. In addition, Stranraer offers good shopping facilities.

N 54°54'3'' W 5°0'23''
www.eurocampings.co.uk/102975

502 Strathyre, GB-FK18 8NJ / Scotland
iD 2 A3

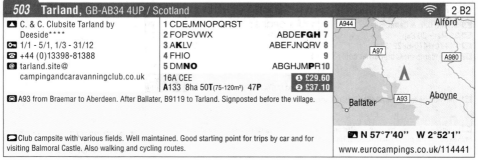

- ▲ Immervoulin Car. & Camp.Park****
- ▤ A 84
- ◔ 1 Mar - 15 Oct
- ☎ +44 (0)1877-384285
- @ immervoulin@freenetname.co.uk

1 ADEJMNOPQRST	JNX	6
2 CDOPRSVWX	ABDEFGHK	7
3	ABFJQRV	8
4 FH	V	9
5 DJMNO	ABKMOR	10

10-16A CEE   ❶ £26.00
A135 3ha 132T(100-120m²)   ❷ £26.00

🗺 Located on the A84, 300 metres south of Strathyre.

💬 Spacious campsite on the banks of a river and adjacent to a large lake. There are both paved pitches and grass pitches. Good toilet facilities.

N 56°19'3'' W 4°19'47''
www.eurocampings.co.uk/109134

503 Tarland, GB-AB34 4UP / Scotland
  2 B2

- ▲ C. & C. Clubsite Tarland by Deeside****
- ◔ 1/1 - 5/1, 1/3 - 31/12
- ☎ +44 (0)13398-81388
- @ tarland.site@ campingandcaravanningclub.co.uk

1 CDEJMNOPQRST		6
2 FOPSVWX	ABDEFGH	7
3 AKLV	ABEFJNQRV	8
4 FHIO		9
5 DMNO	ABGHJMPR	10

16A CEE   ❶ £29.60
A133 8ha 50T(75-120m²) 47P   ❷ £37.10

🗺 A93 from Braemar to Aberdeen. After Ballater, B9119 to Tarland. Signposted before the village.

💬 Club campsite with various fields. Well maintained. Good starting point for trips by car and for visiting Balmoral Castle. Also walking and cycling routes.

N 57°7'40'' W 2°52'1''
www.eurocampings.co.uk/114441

504 Thurso, GB-KW14 8XO / Scotland   ♿ iD   2 B1

- ⛰ Dunnet Bay Caravan Club Site
- 🏘 Dunnet
- 📅 24 Mar - 1 Oct
- ☎ +44 (0)1847-821319
- @ dunnetbay@caravanclub.co.uk

1	ADEJMNOPQRST	NPQS	6
2	EFGHOPQVW	ABDE**FG**	7
3	**K**	ABCDEFHJNPQRV	8
4	**E**FH		9
5	BDMN	ABGJMRZ	10
16A CEE		❶ £19.60	
2ha 56**T**(70-80m²)		❷ £22.40	

🚗 A836 east (John O'Groats) to west (Thurso), the campsite is ± 0.8 km after the village of Dunnet. A836 west (Thurso) to east (John O'Groats), 3.8 km past Castletown on the left side of the road.

💬 Lovely campsite on a bay with a magnificent view.

🅿 N 58°36'56'' W 3°20'42''

www.eurocampings.co.uk/117290

505 Thurso, GB-KW14 7JY / Scotland   📶 iD   2 B1

- ⛰ Thurso C. & C. Site***
- 🏘 Smith Terrace
- 📅 1 Apr - 30 Sep
- ☎ +44 (0)1847-892244
- @ alan@thursobaycamping.co.uk

1	ADEILNOPQR**T**	KNQSW**XZ**	6
2	EFGHJKMOPRSTW	ABDE**FG**H	7
3	AE**K**	ABEFNQRV	8
4		E	9
5	DL	AGJPR	10
16A CEE		❶ £22.00	
1,1ha 84**T**(min 80m²) 10**P**		❷ £26.00	

🚗 Follow the A836 to the city until you see the sign with 'Thurso Caravan Site'.

💬 A bare grass field campsite on the cliffs in the town of Thurso, above the beach near a large bay from which a car ferry leaves for the Orkney Islands. Lovely bay with views of the cliffs.

🅿 N 58°35'52'' W 3°31'46''

www.eurocampings.co.uk/102996

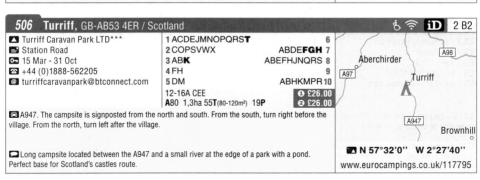

506 Turriff, GB-AB53 4ER / Scotland   ♿ 📶 iD   2 B2

- ⛰ Turriff Caravan Park LTD***
- 🏘 Station Road
- 📅 15 Mar - 31 Oct
- ☎ +44 (0)1888-562205
- @ turriffcaravanpark@btconnect.com

1	ACDEJMNOPQRS**T**		6
2	COPSVWX	ABDE**FGH**	7
3	AB**K**	ABEFHJNQRS	8
4	FH		9
5	DM	ABHKMPR	10
12-16A CEE		❶ £26.00	
A80 1,3ha 55**T**(80-120m²) 19**P**		❷ £26.00	

🚗 A947. The campsite is signposted from the north and south. From the south, turn right before the village. From the north, turn left after the village.

💬 Long campsite located between the A947 and a small river at the edge of a park with a pond. Perfect base for Scotland's castles route.

🅿 N 57°32'0'' W 2°27'40''

www.eurocampings.co.uk/117795

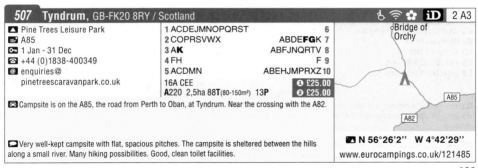

507 Tyndrum, GB-FK20 8RY / Scotland   ♿ 📶 ✿ iD   2 A3

- ⛰ Pine Trees Leisure Park
- 🏘 A85
- 📅 1 Jan - 31 Dec
- ☎ +44 (0)1838-400349
- @ enquiries@ pinetreescaravanpark.co.uk

1	ACDEJMNOPQRST		6
2	COPRSVWX	ABDE**FG**K	7
3	A**K**	ABFJNQRTV	8
4	FH	F	9
5	ACDMN	ABEHJMPRXZ	10
16A CEE		❶ £25.00	
A220 2,5ha 88**T**(80-150m²) 13**P**		❷ £25.00	

🚗 Campsite is on the A85, the road from Perth to Oban, at Tyndrum. Near the crossing with the A82.

💬 Very well-kept campsite with flat, spacious pitches. The campsite is sheltered between the hills along a small river. Many hiking possibilities. Good, clean toilet facilities.

🅿 N 56°26'2'' W 4°42'29''

www.eurocampings.co.uk/121485

United Kingdom

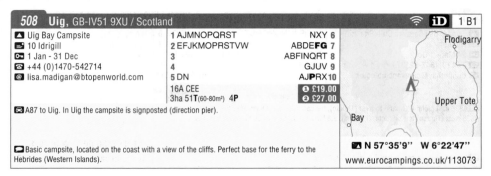

508 Uig, GB-IV51 9XU / Scotland
📶 iD 1 B1

- 🏕 Uig Bay Campsite
- 📧 10 Idrigill
- 📅 1 Jan - 31 Dec
- ☎ +44 (0)1470-542714
- @ lisa.madigan@btopenworld.com

1	AJMNOPQRST	NXY 6
2	EFJKMOPRSTVW	ABDEFG 7
3		ABFINQRT 8
4		GJUV 9
5	DN	AJPRX 10

16A CEE
3ha 51T(60-80m²) 4P

❶ £19.00
❷ £27.00

🚗 A87 to Uig. In Uig the campsite is signposted (direction pier).

💬 Basic campsite, located on the coast with a view of the cliffs. Perfect base for the ferry to the Hebrides (Western Islands).

📍 N 57°35'9'' W 6°22'47''

www.eurocampings.co.uk/113073

509 Ullapool/Ross-shire, GB-IV26 2TN / Scotland
♿ 📶 iD 2 A1

- 🏕 Ardmair Point Holiday Park****
- 📅 30 Mar - 31 Oct
- ☎ +44 (0)1854-612054
- @ park@ardmair.com

1	ADEJMNOPQRST	KNOQSWXZ 6
2	EFGJKMOPRSVWX	ABDEFG 7
3	K	ABEFNQRV 8
4		9
5	ABDKMN	ABJPR 10

10A CEE
2ha 140T(60-120m²) 8P

❶ £23.00
❷ £27.00

🚗 The campsite is located on the A835, 5 km north of Ullapool.

💬 This good campsite is situated on a narrow spit of land in an inlet with a pebble beach. It is a grassland with low bushes in a beautiful environment with panoramic views, a few kilometres from Ullapool.

📍 N 57°56'2'' W 5°11'48''

www.eurocampings.co.uk/102966

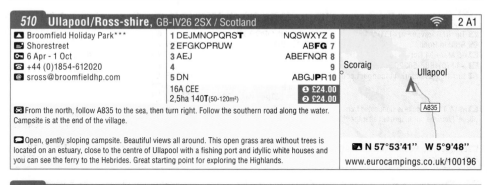

510 Ullapool/Ross-shire, GB-IV26 2SX / Scotland
📶 2 A1

- 🏕 Broomfield Holiday Park***
- 📧 Shorestreet
- 📅 6 Apr - 1 Oct
- ☎ +44 (0)1854-612020
- @ sross@broomfieldhp.com

1	DEJMNOPQRST	NQSWXYZ 6
2	EFGKOPRUW	ABFG 7
3	AEJ	ABEFNQR 8
4		9
5	DN	ABGJPR 10

16A CEE
2,5ha 140T(50-120m²)

❶ £24.00
❷ £24.00

🚗 From the north, follow A835 to the sea, then turn right. Follow the southern road along the water. Campsite is at the end of the village.

💬 Open, gently sloping campsite. Beautiful views all around. This open grass area without trees is located on an estuary, close to the centre of Ullapool with a fishing port and idyllic white houses and you can see the ferry to the Hebrides. Great starting point for exploring the Highlands.

📍 N 57°53'41'' W 5°9'48''

www.eurocampings.co.uk/100196

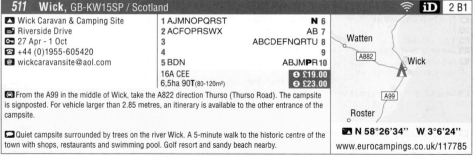

511 Wick, GB-KW15SP / Scotland
📶 iD 2 B1

- 🏕 Wick Caravan & Camping Site
- 📧 Riverside Drive
- 📅 27 Apr - 1 Oct
- ☎ +44 (0)1955-605420
- @ wickcaravansite@aol.com

1	AJMNOPQRST	N 6
2	ACFOPRSWX	AB 7
3		ABCDEFNQRTU 8
4		9
5	BDN	ABJMPR 10

16A CEE
6,5ha 90T(80-120m²)

❶ £19.00
❷ £23.00

🚗 From the A99 in the middle of Wick, take the A822 direction Thurso (Thurso Road). The campsite is signposted. For vehicle larger than 2.85 metres, an itinerary is available to the other entrance of the campsite.

💬 Quiet campsite surrounded by trees on the river Wick. A 5-minute walk to the historic centre of the town with shops, restaurants and swimming pool. Golf resort and sandy beach nearby.

📍 N 58°26'34'' W 3°6'24''

www.eurocampings.co.uk/117785

Northern Ireland

A terrible beauty

This small, mountainous north-east corner of the island of Ireland has a turbulent history. Part of the old province of Ulster, it borders the Republic of Ireland. Partitioned in 1921, Northern Ireland remains officially part of the United Kingdom.

Rocky coastline

You're never far from the sea in Northern Ireland. Follow the Causeway Coastal Route between (London)Derry and Belfast, which takes in the Gobbins Cliff path, Carrick-a-Rede rope bridge, Dunluce Castle, the Rathlin Island ferry, and the Giant's Causeway. The Mourne Coastal Route south-east of Belfast includes Castle Ward, which Game of Thrones fans will recognise as 'Winterfell'.

All kinds of culture

While we're on the subject of Game of Thrones: the Dark Hedges, Ballymoney; Tollymore Forest Park, and Ballintoy Harbour are just a few of the locations. Did you know that before Westeros came to Northern Ireland, the region already inspired creators as diverse as C.S. Lewis (Chronicles of Narnia) and the rock legends of Led Zeppelin?

Belfast, the capital, is full of places to see: City Hall, the Cathedral Quarter, and you can't miss Titanic Belfast. (London)Derry is famous for its city walls and St Columb's Cathedral, while newer structures include the Peace Bridge. You'll see striking large murals in both Belfast and Derry, tours of these are available. Did you know that

Halloween originated in Ireland, and (London) Derry hosts a huge Halloween Festival every year?

Our tips

1. Take in a traditional Irish music session at Cushendall, the Glens of Antrim

2. Experience the recent history of Northern Ireland at Crumlin Road Gaol, Belfast

3. Want an adrenaline rush? Go surfing at Portrush or cliff-jumping at Ballintoy

4. Visit Florence Court House and the Marble Arch Caves

5. See puffins and seals on Rathlin Island

Outdoor activities

Go sailing on the Fermanagh Lakelands, or, more challenging, try Portballintrae near Dunluce Castle for water sports. The kids will be all over the wooden sculpture of red deer and squirrels in Gortin Forest Park near Omagh.

Worked up an appetite? Tuck into an Ulster fry, complete with soda farls and potato cake. Locals enjoy black bacon, cheese, Dulce seaweed, beer, and of course the famous Bushmills Whiskey. Got a sweet tooth? You'll enjoy Yellow Man toffee, a staple at the Antrim Auld Lammas Fair.

512 Ballycastle, GB-BT54 6DB / Northern Ireland   ♿ 🛜 iD   4 B1

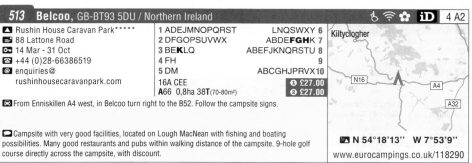

- ⛺ Causeway Coast Holiday Park
- 🏠 21 Clare Road
- 📅 1 Mar - 31 Oct
- ☎ +44 (0)28-20762550
- @ lisa@hagansleisure.co.uk

1 ADEJMOPQRST	**EFG**H 6
2 FGMOPSTVW	AB**FGH** 7
3 B**K**	ABEFNQRSV 8
4 FHI**QU**	EFIJ 9
5 DM	ABHIM**P**R 10
16A CEE	❶ £32.60
28ha 53**T**(70m²) 311**P**	❷ £32.60

🚗 In Ballycastle at the end of the A44, turn left to North Street which becomes Clare Road. Then the campsite is on the right.

💬 The only campsite in the region with an (indoor) swimming pool. Near the lovely centre of Ballycastle and the sea. The park restaurant often holds musical evenings at the weekends.

📍 N 55°12'34'' W 6°14'55''

www.eurocampings.co.uk/122327

513 Belcoo, GB-BT93 5DU / Northern Ireland   ♿ 🛜 ⚙ iD   4 A2

- ⛺ Rushin House Caravan Park*****
- 🏠 88 Lattone Road
- 📅 14 Mar - 31 Oct
- ☎ +44 (0)28-66386519
- @ enquiries@
  rushinhousecaravanpark.com

1 ADEJMNOPQRST	LNQSWXY 6
2 DFGOPSUVWX	ABDE**FGH**K 7
3 BE**K**LQ	ABEFJKNQRSTU 8
4 FH	9
5 DM	ABCGHJPRVX 10
16A CEE	❶ £27.00
A66 0,8ha 38**T**(70-80m²)	❷ £27.00

🚗 From Enniskillen A4 west, in Belcoo turn right to the B52. Follow the campsite signs.

💬 Campsite with very good facilities, located on Lough MacNean with fishing and boating possibilities. Many good restaurants and pubs within walking distance of the campsite. 9-hole golf course directly across the campsite, with discount.

📍 N 54°18'13'' W 7°53'9''

www.eurocampings.co.uk/118290

514 Blaney/Enniskillen, GB-BT93 7ER / Northern Ireland   ♿ 🛜 iD   4 A2

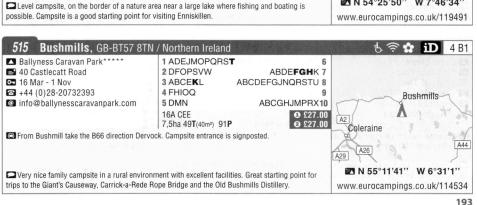

- ⛺ Blaney Caravan Park and Camping Site
- 🏠 323 Loughshore Road
- 📅 11 Mar - 1 Nov
- ☎ +44 (0)28-68641634
- @ info@blaneycaravanpark.com

1 AJMNOPQRST	6
2 GPSUVWX	ABD**EFGH** 7
3 A**K**	ABE**F**JNQRUV 8
4 FH	9
5 D	ABGHIJMOST 10
10A CEE	❶ £23.00
A58 1ha 27**T**(80m²) 32**P**	❷ £23.00

🚗 Campsite located on A46 Enniskillen-Belleek. Campsite is on right of road about 14 km from Enniskillen centre. Signposted.

💬 Level campsite, on the border of a nature area near a large lake where fishing and boating is possible. Campsite is a good starting point for visiting Enniskillen.

📍 N 54°25'50'' W 7°46'34''

www.eurocampings.co.uk/119491

515 Bushmills, GB-BT57 8TN / Northern Ireland   ♿ 🛜 ⚙ iD   4 B1

- ⛺ Ballyness Caravan Park*****
- 🏠 40 Castlecatt Road
- 📅 16 Mar - 1 Nov
- ☎ +44 (0)28-20732393
- @ info@ballynesscaravanpark.com

1 ADEJMOPQRS**T**	6
2 DFOPSVW	ABDE**FGH**K 7
3 ABCE**K**L	ABCDEFGJNQRSTU 8
4 FHIOQ	9
5 DMN	ABCGHJMPRX 10
16A CEE	❶ £27.00
7,5ha 49**T**(40m²) 91**P**	❷ £27.00

🚗 From Bushmill take the B66 direction Dervock. Campsite entrance is signposted.

💬 Very nice family campsite in a rural environment with excellent facilities. Great starting point for trips to the Giant's Causeway, Carrick-a-Rede Rope Bridge and the Old Bushmills Distillery.

📍 N 55°11'41'' W 6°31'1''

www.eurocampings.co.uk/114534

United Kingdom

516 Bushmills, GB-BT57 8UJ / Northern Ireland   iD   4 B1

- 🔺 Bush Caravan Park
- 📧 Priestland Road 97
- 📅 25 Mar - 30 Sep
- ☎ +44 (0)20-731678
- @ rebahenderson@icloud.com

1 ADEILNOPQRS**T**	6
2 FOPSVW	ABDE**FG**H 7
3 AB**K**	ABEFJNQRV 8
4 O	9
5 DMN	ABGHJMRVX **10**
16A CEE	❶ £22.00
A90 4ha 54**T**(60m²)	❷ £26.00

🔲 Take the B17 in Bushmills towards Coleraine. The campsite is located about 3 km outside the village.

💬 Excellent campsite near a beautiful coastal area with various walking routes. On request, trips to Belfast. Great starting point for trips to the Giant's Causeway, Carrick-a-Rede Rope Bridge and the Old Bushmills Distillery.

📍 N 55°10'30''   W 6°34'17''

www.eurocampings.co.uk/112625

---

517 Coleraine, GB-BT52 2JB / Northern Ireland   iD   4 B1

- 🔺 Tullans Country Holiday Park
- 📧 46 Newmills Road
- 📅 17 Mar - 31 Oct
- ☎ +44 (0)28-70342309
- @ info@tullans.com

1 ADEJMNOPQR**T**	6
2 OPSVW	AB**FG**H 7
3 ABCE**K**	ABEFIJNQRSTU 8
4 IO**Q**	J 9
5 DMN	ABCHKMPR **10**
16A CEE	❶ £24.00
A60 2ha 36**T**(40-60m²) 81**P**	❷ £24.00

🔲 1.5 km south of Coleraine, on the A29 between Lodge Road and Ballycastle Road, at the roundabout direction Newmills Road; campsite signposted.

💬 Quietly situated campsite in a rural setting. Near the beautiful coastline of North Antrim with, among other things the Giant's Causeway and Carrick-a-Rede Rope Bridge. 10% discount with ACSI CLUB ID.

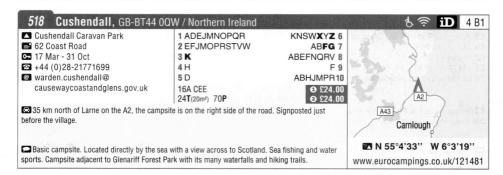

📍 N 55°7'30''   W 6°37'47''

www.eurocampings.co.uk/116181

---

518 Cushendall, GB-BT44 0QW / Northern Ireland   iD   4 B1

- 🔺 Cushendall Caravan Park
- 📧 62 Coast Road
- 📅 17 Mar - 31 Oct
- ☎ +44 (0)28-21771699
- @ warden.cushendall@causewaycoastandglens.gov.uk

1 ADEJMNOPQR	KNSW**XYZ** 6
2 EFJMOPRSTVW	AB**FG** 7
3 **K**	ABEFNQRV 8
4 H	F 9
5 D	ABHJMPR **10**
16A CEE	❶ £24.00
24**T**(20m²) 70**P**	❷ £24.00

🔲 35 km north of Larne on the A2, the campsite is on the right side of the road. Signposted just before the village.

💬 Basic campsite. Located directly by the sea with a view across to Scotland. Sea fishing and water sports. Campsite adjacent to Glenariff Forest Park with its many waterfalls and hiking trails.

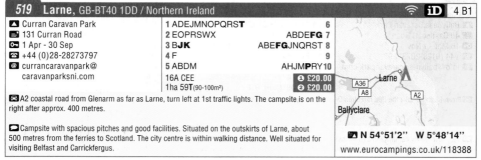

📍 N 55°4'33''   W 6°3'19''

www.eurocampings.co.uk/121481

---

519 Larne, GB-BT40 1DD / Northern Ireland   iD   4 B1

- 🔺 Curran Caravan Park
- 📧 131 Curran Road
- 📅 1 Apr - 30 Sep
- ☎ +44 (0)28-28273797
- @ currancaravanpark@caravanparksni.com

1 ADEJMNOPQRS**T**	6
2 EOPRSWX	ABDE**FG** 7
3 B**JK**	ABE**FG**JNQRST 8
4 F	9
5 ABDM	AHJM**P**RY **10**
16A CEE	❶ £20.00
1ha 59**T**(90-100m²)	❷ £20.00

🔲 A2 coastal road from Glenarm as far as Larne, turn left at 1st traffic lights. The campsite is on the right after approx. 400 metres.

💬 Campsite with spacious pitches and good facilities. Situated on the outskirts of Larne, about 500 metres from the ferries to Scotland. The city centre is within walking distance. Well situated for visiting Belfast and Carrickfergus.

📍 N 54°51'2''   W 5°48'14''

www.eurocampings.co.uk/118388

520 Lisnarick, GB-BT94 1PP / Northern Ireland ⚡ 📶 **iD** 4 A2

- 🏕 Castle Archdale****
- ✉ Irvinestown
- 📅 19 Mar - 31 Oct
- ☎ +44 (0)28-68621333
- @ info@castlearchdale.com

1 ADEJMNOPQRST	L**N**QSWXYZ	**6**	
2 BDFJPRSVWXY	ABDE**FGH**	**7**	
3 B**GHK**T	ABCDEFIJNQRSTUV	**8**	
4 BFHIO**Q**	EMNOPQRUVY	**9**	
5 ABDEFHKM**O**	ABCEGHIJMP**R**Z	**10**	
10A CEE		❶ £25.00	
A50 11ha 123**T**(40-80m²) 173**P**		❷ £25.00	

🚗 The campsite is on the B82 Enniskillen to Kesh and is signposted.

💬 The campsite, with very good facilities, is located in the park of Castle Archdale. There is a large lake: Loch Erne, on which you can make a boat trip. In the park's forests you can enjoy the deer and the birds.

📍 N 54°28'43'' W 7°43'51''
www.eurocampings.co.uk/110769

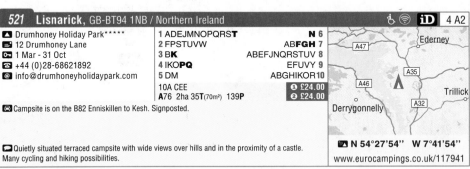

521 Lisnarick, GB-BT94 1NB / Northern Ireland ⚡ 📶 **iD** 4 A2

- 🏕 Drumhoney Holiday Park*****
- ✉ 12 Drumhoney Lane
- 📅 1 Mar - 31 Oct
- ☎ +44 (0)28-68621892
- @ info@drumhoneyholidaypark.com

1 ADEJMNOPQRS**T**	**N**	**6**	
2 FPSTUVW	AB**FGH**	**7**	
3 B**K**	ABEFJNQRSTUV	**8**	
4 IKO**PQ**	EFUVY	**9**	
5 DM	ABGHIKOR	**10**	
10A CEE		❶ £24.00	
A76 2ha 35**T**(70m²) 139**P**		❷ £24.00	

🚗 Campsite is on the B82 Enniskillen to Kesh. Signposted.

💬 Quietly situated terraced campsite with wide views over hills and in the proximity of a castle. Many cycling and hiking possibilities.

📍 N 54°27'54'' W 7°41'54''
www.eurocampings.co.uk/117941

522 Lisnaskea, GB-BT92 0EQ / Northern Ireland ⚡ 📶 **iD** 4 A2

- 🏕 Share Discovery Village
- ✉ Smith's Strand
- 📅 1 Apr - 30 Sep
- ☎ +44 (0)28-67722122
- @ info@sharevillage.org

1 ABDEJMNOPQRST	**FG**LSTUWXY**Z**	**6**	
2 DPSVWX	ABDE**FG**	**7**	
3 ABE**KRTU**V	ABCDEFNQRSV	**8**	
4 **A**BCDE**FHIRT**	JPQRUV	**9**	
5 ADH	ABCGHKMOSTZ	**10**	
16A CEE		❶ £22.00	
A58 24ha 47**T**(70-95m²) 65**P**		❷ £22.00	

🚗 A4 Dungannon. Enniskillen, then to the A34 direction Lisnaskea. Then B127 ±4 km south of Lisnaskea, Share Holliday Village signposted.

💬 Camping situated directly on the Upper Lough Erne (lake). Adventure programme at the campsite for all ages, at an additional cost.

📍 N 54°12'42'' W 7°28'39''
www.eurocampings.co.uk/114532

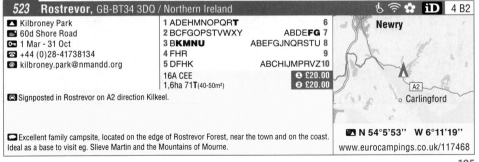

523 Rostrevor, GB-BT34 3DQ / Northern Ireland ⚡ 📶 ⚙ **iD** 4 B2

- 🏕 Kilbroney Park
- ✉ 60d Shore Road
- 📅 1 Mar - 31 Oct
- ☎ +44 (0)28-41738134
- @ kilbroney.park@nmandd.org

1 ADEHMNOPQR**T**		**6**	
2 BCFGOPSTVWXY	ABDE**FG**	**7**	
3 B**KMNU**	ABEFGJNQRSTU	**8**	
4 FHR		**9**	
5 DFHK	ABCHIJMPRVZ	**10**	
16A CEE		❶ £20.00	
1,6ha 71**T**(40-50m²)		❷ £20.00	

🚗 Signposted in Rostrevor on A2 direction Kilkeel.

💬 Excellent family campsite, located on the edge of Rostrevor Forest, near the town and on the coast. Ideal as a base to visit eg. Slieve Martin and the Mountains of Mourne.

📍 N 54°5'53'' W 6°11'19''
www.eurocampings.co.uk/117468

United Kingdom

Ireland

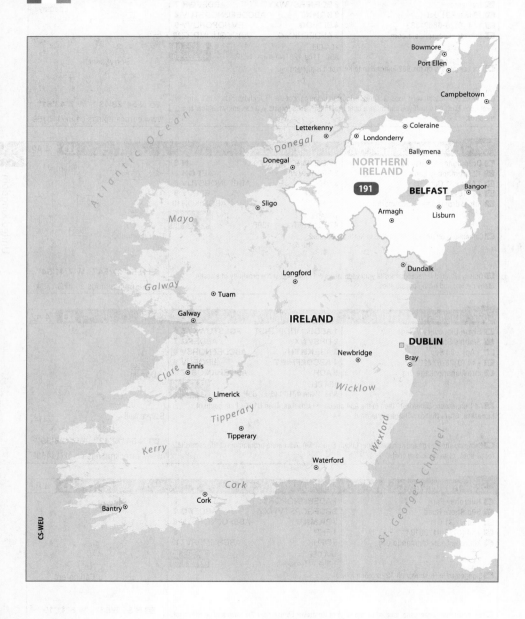

Atlantic Ocean

Bowmore
Port Ellen
Campbeltown

Letterkenny
Coleraine
Londonderry
Ballymena

Donegal
Donegal

NORTHERN
IRELAND

191

BELFAST
Bangor

Sligo
Armagh
Lisburn

Mayo

Longford
Dundalk

Galway
Tuam

Galway

IRELAND

DUBLIN

Newbridge
Bray

Clare
Ennis

Wicklow

Limerick

Tipperary

Tipperary
Wexford

Kerry
Waterford

St. George's Channel

Cork

Bantry
Cork

CS-WEU

General
Ireland is a member of the EU. The capital city is Dublin.

Time
The time in Ireland is the same as in London.

Languages
Irish and English.

Crossing
There are several ferry services that you can use to make the crossing between Ireland and the United Kingdom. You will find a complete overview of the ferries on page 36.

Currency
The currency in Ireland is the euro. Approximate exchange rates September 2017: € 1 = £ 0.92. You can exchange money in post offices. Debit cards not carrying the Maestro, Visa Debit or Mastercard logos are not accepted. ATMs are usually located outside bank branches, but increasingly can be found in convenience stores, supermarkets, petrol stations and even bars. Before you travel to Ireland, check with your bank that your card is activated for use in both the Republic of Ireland and Northern Ireland (United Kingdom). Otherwise, you may have problems withdrawing cash.

Credit cards
Credit cards like Visa, Mastercard/Eurocard are very widely accepted in Ireland.

(Mobile) phones
The mobile network works well throughout Ireland. There is a 4G network for mobile internet.

Wifi, internet
You can use wifi networks at more and more public locations, often for free.

Opening times/Public holidays
Banks
Banks are open Monday to Friday until 4:30 pm. On Thursdays banks are open until 5:00 pm.

Shops (including pharmacies)
In general open until 6:00 pm. In many towns the shops are open on Thursday or Friday until 8:00 pm. Ireland also has Sunday opening. Pharmacies are open Monday to Friday until 6:00 pm. A number of pharmacies in Dublin open 7 days a week until 11:00 pm.

Post
Open Monday to Friday until 5:30 pm. Post offices are open on Saturdays until 1:00 pm and in larger towns also from 2:15 pm to 5:00 pm.

Public holidays
New Year's Day, 17 March (St. Patrick's Day), Good Friday, Easter, first Monday in May (Bank Holiday), Whit Sunday, first Monday in June (Bank Holiday), first Monday in August (Bank Holiday), last Monday in October (Bank Holiday/Halloween), Christmas.

Roads and traffic
Traffic regulations
All traffic drives on the left and overtakes on the right. If you are from Britain you will need to attach a GB sticker to the rear, unless your number plate incorporates a GB identifier. Traffic on main roads always has priority at intersections. Vehicles on main roads have priority over vehicles on minor roads. On a roundabout you have priority over vehicles entering the roundabout.

Use of dipped headlights during the day is not mandatory. Use of phones is only permitted hands-free. The maximum permitted alcohol level is 0.5 promille.

Road network
The Republic of Ireland officially uses the metric

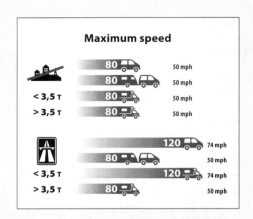

system, road signs denoting speed limits are in kilometres not miles. (Since 2011.) Older directional signs are in miles and kilometres, newer signs in kilometres only.

Main roads (shown by the letter 'N') and secondary roads ('R') generally have a good surface but are much narrower than the roads you will be used to. Minor roads are so narrow that passing places are provided so that you can pass traffic coming in the opposite direction. All traffic signs are in English and Irish. The Irish AA patrols major roads night and day: tel. 1800-667788.

Maximum permitted measurements of combined length
Height 4.65 metres, width 2.55 metres and maximum length 18.75 metres (of which the trailer is 12 metres maximum).

Fuel
Unleaded petrol and diesel are readily available. There is limited availability of LPG.

Filling stations

Filling stations are generally open from 7:30 am to 10:00 pm. Make sure you have enough fuel in your tank on major roads as filling stations can be a long way from each other.

Charging stations

The network of public charging stations does not fully cover the country yet. Therefore, travelling through Ireland with an electric car requires careful planning and preparation. You will find enough charging stations in the Dublin area. For the precise location of charging stations, we advise you to check websites like ▶ *www.chargemap.com* ◀, ▶ *www.plugsurfing.com* ◀ or ▶ *openchargemap.org* ◀.

Tolls

Tolls are charged on various bridges and roads. You cannot pay in cash on the M50 motorway around Dublin. Cameras register your number plate. You must pay no later than 8:00 pm the following day. For more information ▶ *www.eflow.ie* ◀.

Emergency number

112: the national emergency number for fire, police and ambulance.

Camping

Most campsites are located in the countryside and along the coast. The majority of sites are small and modest. The narrow twisting coast roads to the campsites will demand quite a bit of your time! Irish campsites often have well maintained grassy areas and there are often hardened pitches for caravans and motorhomes.

Practical

- Make sure you have a world adaptor for electrical appliances. UK 13A plugs fit electrical sockets in Ireland.
- Tap water is safe to drink.

Ireland

To the waters and the wild

Located on the edge of the North Atlantic, with the Irish Sea to the East, the Republic of Ireland borders Northern Ireland. The forty shades of green are not exaggerated, and the dramatic rocky coastline includes the Cliffs of Moher and Slieve League, alternating with glorious beaches.

Where history is folklore

Visit the Céide Fields in Mayo, Ireland's most famous pre-Celtic Neolithic village. Old stories tell of earlier tribes migrating underground to become fairies when the Celts arrived. Later invasions were the Vikings, but not the ancient Roman Empire – was it the weather? St Patrick is credited with bringing Christianity to Ireland, later Norman invaders came in 1169, heralding the start of English rule in Ireland.

Everywhere you go, you'll see Norman castles and old monasteries. The largest is Trim Castle in Meath, but others are the Rock of Cashel and Cahir Castle in Tipperary. The monastery at Glendalough, with its soaring round tower, is picture-perfect. Kilkenny city has beautiful mediaeval streets, while Dublin and Limerick have gorgeous Georgian houses. A great place to see the variety of structures is Bunratty Folk Park in Clare – and the kids will explore the nooks and crannies in Bunratty Castle. If you're here in May, make sure you visit Victorian-era Muckross House and Park near Killarney.

Things to do, places to see

Lovers of traditional music and dance head west to Clare, Kerry, Galway and Mayo. If you like sport, ask about the nearest GAA pitch where you can

Did you know …?

The last port the Titanic ever docked at before sailing into legend was Queenstown, now Cobh, near Cork city.

could subsist on rashers with black and white pudding, and delicious spiced beef. And you shouldn't pass up fresh Atlantic salmon or cod!

watch hurling or Gaelic football. Like nature? Walkers adore Connemara National Park, and there's world-class surfing at Sligo and Bundoran. Fota Wildlife Park near Cork is fun for all the family, and the Karst landscape of the Burren makes you feel like you're walking on the moon.

Food and drink

Who doesn't know Guinness? Other famous drinks are Smithwicks and Bulmers cider. Tuck into Irish stew served with soda bread, or bacon and cabbage, or Dublin coddle, or boxty. Irish

Our tips

1. Cross the sea by cable car to Dursey Island, Béara Peninsula

2. Experience midwinter light at Newgrange Passage Tomb

3. Learn traditional Irish tunes and dances at the Willie Clancy Summer School

4. Sample the produce at the Cork English Market and the Limerick Milk Market

5. Visit Kilmainham Gaol in Dublin, where rebels of the 1916 Rising were executed

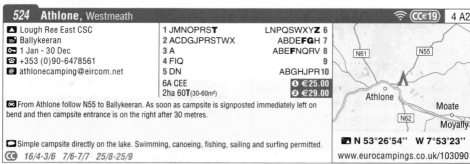

524 Athlone, Westmeath ⏏ CC€19 4 A2

- ⛰ Lough Ree East CSC
- 📧 Ballykeeran
- 📅 1 Jan - 30 Dec
- ☎ +353 (0)90-6478561
- @ athlonecamping@eircom.net

1 JMNOPRS**T**	LNPQSWXYZ**Z**	6
2 ACDGJPRSTWX	ABDE**FG**H	7
3 A	ABE**F**NQRV	8
4 FIQ		9
5 DN	ABGHJPR	10
6A CEE	❶ €25.00	
2ha 60**T**(30-60m²)	❷ €29.00	

🚗 From Athlone follow N55 to Ballykeeran. As soon as campsite is signposted immediately left on bend and then campsite entrance is on the right after 30 metres.

💬 Simple campsite directly on the lake. Swimming, canoeing, fishing, sailing and surfing permitted.
CC 16/4-3/6 7/6-7/7 25/8-25/9

📍 N 53°26'54'' W 7°53'23''
www.eurocampings.co.uk/103090

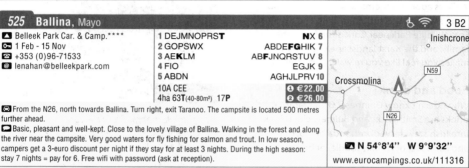

525 Ballina, Mayo ♿ 🛜 3 B2

- ⛰ Belleek Park Car. & Camp.****
- 📅 1 Feb - 15 Nov
- ☎ +353 (0)96-71533
- @ lenahan@belleekpark.com

1 DEJMNOPRS**T**	N**X**	6
2 GOPSWX	ABDE**FG**HIK	7
3 AE**K**LM	AB**F**JNQRSTUV	8
4 FIO	EGJK	9
5 ABDN	AGHJLPRV	10
10A CEE	❶ €22.00	
4ha 63**T**(40-80m²) 17**P**	❷ €26.00	

🚗 From the N26, north towards Ballina. Turn right, exit Taranoo. The campsite is located 500 metres further ahead.
💬 Basic, pleasant and well-kept. Close to the lovely village of Ballina. Walking in the forest and along the river near the campsite. Very good waters for fly fishing for salmon and trout. In low season, campers get a 3-euro discount per night if they stay for at least 3 nights. During the high season: stay 7 nights = pay for 6. Free wifi with password (ask at reception).

📍 N 54°8'4'' W 9°9'32''
www.eurocampings.co.uk/111316

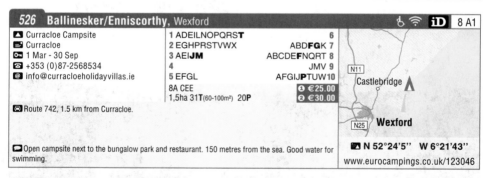

526 Ballinesker/Enniscorthy, Wexford ♿ 🛜 iD 8 A1

- ⛰ Curracloe Campsite
- 📧 Curracloe
- 📅 1 Mar - 30 Sep
- ☎ +353 (0)87-2568534
- @ info@curracloeholidayvillas.ie

1 ADEILNOPQRS**T**		6
2 EGHPRSTVWX	ABD**FG**K	7
3 AEI**JM**	ABCDE**F**NQRT	8
4	JMV	9
5 EFGL	AFGIJ**P**TUW	10
8A CEE	❶ €25.00	
1,5ha 31**T**(60-100m²) 20**P**	❷ €30.00	

🚗 Route 742, 1.5 km from Curracloe.

💬 Open campsite next to the bungalow park and restaurant. 150 metres from the sea. Good water for swimming.

📍 N 52°24'5'' W 6°21'43''
www.eurocampings.co.uk/123046

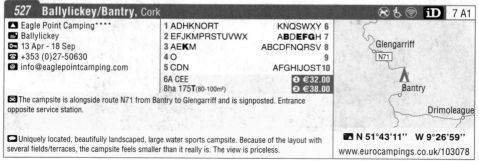

527 Ballylickey/Bantry, Cork ✖ ♿ 🛜 iD 7 A1

- ⛰ Eagle Point Camping****
- 📧 Ballylickey
- 📅 13 Apr - 18 Sep
- ☎ +353 (0)27-50630
- @ info@eaglepointcamping.com

1 ADHKNORT	KNQSWXY	6
2 EFJKMPRSTUVWX	AB**DEFG**H	7
3 AE**K**M	ABCD**F**NQRSV	8
4 O		9
5 CDN	AFGHIJOST	10
6A CEE	❶ €32.00	
8ha 175**T**(80-100m²)	❷ €38.00	

🚗 The campsite is alongside route N71 from Bantry to Glengarriff and is signposted. Entrance opposite service station.

💬 Uniquely located, beautifully landscaped, large water sports campsite. Because of the layout with several fields/terraces, the campsite feels smaller than it really is. The view is priceless.

📍 N 51°43'11'' W 9°26'59''
www.eurocampings.co.uk/103078

Ireland

528 Ballyshannon, Donegal

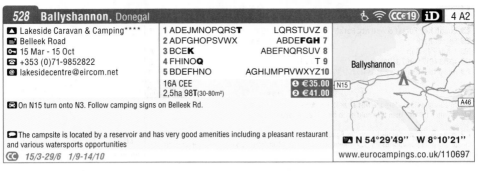

CCE19 iD 4 A2

- ▲ Lakeside Caravan & Camping****
- 🏠 Belleek Road
- 📅 15 Mar - 15 Oct
- ☎ +353 (0)71-9852822
- @ lakesidecentre@eircom.net

1 ADEJMNOPQRS**T**	LQRSTUVZ 6
2 ADFGHOPSVWX	ABDE**FGH** 7
3 BCE**K**	ABEFNQRSUV 8
4 FHINO**Q**	T 9
5 BDEFHNO	AGHIJMPRVWXYZ 10
16A CEE	❶ €35.00
2,5ha 98**T**(30-80m²)	❷ €41.00

🚗 On N15 turn onto N3. Follow camping signs on Belleek Rd.

💬 The campsite is located by a reservoir and has very good amenities including a pleasant restaurant and various watersports opportunities

CC 15/3-29/6 1/9-14/10

Ballyshannon N15 A46

📍 N 54°29'49'' W 8°10'21''
www.eurocampings.co.uk/110697

529 Ballyvary/Castlebar, Mayo

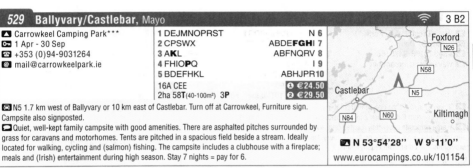

3 B2

- ▲ Carrowkeel Camping Park***
- 📅 1 Apr - 30 Sep
- ☎ +353 (0)94-9031264
- @ mail@carrowkeelpark.ie

1 DEJMNOPRST	N 6
2 CPSWX	ABDE**FGH**I 7
3 A**K**L	ABFNQRV 8
4 FHIO**PQ**	I 9
5 BDEFHKL	ABHJPR 10
16A CEE	❶ €24.50
2ha 58**T**(40-100m²) 3**P**	❷ €29.50

🚗 N5 1.7 km west of Ballyvary or 10 km east of Castlebar. Turn off at Carrowkeel, Furniture sign. Campsite also signposted.

💬 Quiet, well-kept family campsite with good amenities. There are asphalted pitches surrounded by grass for caravans and motorhomes. Tents are pitched in a spacious field beside a stream. Ideally located for walking, cycling and (salmon) fishing. The campsite includes a clubhouse with a fireplace; meals and (Irish) entertainment during high season. Stay 7 nights = pay for 6.

Foxford N26 N58 N5 Castlebar N84 N60 Kiltimagh

📍 N 53°54'28'' W 9°11'0''
www.eurocampings.co.uk/101154

530 Bennettsbridge, Kilkenny

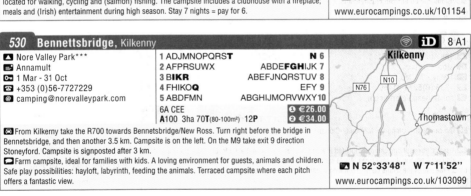

iD 8 A1

- ▲ Nore Valley Park***
- 🏠 Annamult
- 📅 1 Mar - 31 Oct
- ☎ +353 (0)56-7727229
- @ camping@norevalleypark.com

1 ADJMNOPQRS**T**	N 6
2 AFPRSUWX	ABDE**FGH**IJK 7
3 B**IKR**	ABEFJNQRSTUV 8
4 FHIKO**Q**	EFY 9
5 ABDFMN	ABGHIJMORVWXY 10
6A CEE	❶ €26.00
A100 3ha 70**T**(80-100m²) 12**P**	❷ €34.00

🚗 From Kilkerny take the R700 towards Bennetsbridge/New Ross. Turn right before the bridge in Bennetsbridge, and then another 3.5 km. Campsite is on the left. On the M9 take exit 9 direction Stoneyford. Campsite is signposted after 3 km.

💬 Farm campsite, ideal for families with kids. A loving environment for guests, animals and children. Safe play possibilities: hayloft, labyrinth, feeding the animals. Terraced campsite where each pitch offers a fantastic view.

Kilkenny N76 N10 Thomastown

📍 N 52°33'48'' W 7°11'52''
www.eurocampings.co.uk/103099

531 Blarney, Cork

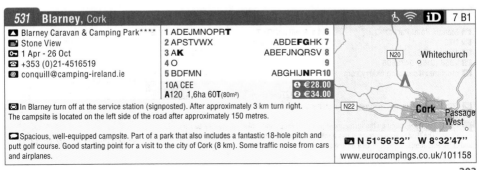

iD 7 B1

- ▲ Blarney Caravan & Camping Park****
- 🏠 Stone View
- 📅 1 Apr - 26 Oct
- ☎ +353 (0)21-4516519
- @ conquill@camping-ireland.ie

1 ADEJMNOPR**T**	6
2 APSTVWX	ABDE**FG**HK 7
3 A**K**	ABEFJNQRSV 8
4 O	9
5 BDFMN	ABGHIJ**N**PR 10
10A CEE	❶ €28.00
A120 1,6ha 60**T**(80m²)	❷ €34.00

🚗 In Blarney turn off at the service station (signposted). After approximately 3 km turn right. The campsite is located on the left side of the road after approximately 150 metres.

💬 Spacious, well-equipped campsite. Part of a park that also includes a fantastic 18-hole pitch and putt golf course. Good starting point for a visit to the city of Cork (8 km). Some traffic noise from cars and airplanes.

N20 Whitechurch N22 Cork Passage West

📍 N 51°56'52'' W 8°32'47''
www.eurocampings.co.uk/101158

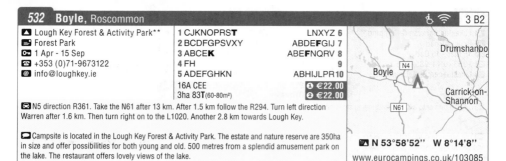

532 Boyle, Roscommon

♿ 📶 3 B2

🔺 Lough Key Forest & Activity Park**
🏕 Forest Park
🅿 1 Apr - 15 Sep
☎ +353 (0)71-9673122
@ info@loughkey.ie

1 CJKNOPRS**T**	LNXYZ 6
2 BCDFGPSVXY	ABDE**F**GIJ 7
3 ABCE**K**	ABE**F**NQRV 8
4 FH	9
5 ADEFGHKN	ABHIJLPR 10
16A CEE	❶ €22.00
3ha 83**T**(60-80m²)	❷ €22.00

🛣 N5 direction R361. Take the N61 after 13 km. After 1.5 km follow the R294. Turn left direction Warren after 1.6 km. Then turn right on to the L1020. Another 2.8 km towards Lough Key.

💬 Campsite is located in the Lough Key Forest & Activity Park. The estate and nature reserve are 350ha in size and offer possibilities for both young and old. 500 metres from a splendid amusement park on the lake. The restaurant offers lovely views of the lake.

📍 **N 53°58'52'' W 8°14'8''**

www.eurocampings.co.uk/103085

533 Caherdaniel, Kerry

📶 (CC€19) iD 7 A1

🔺 Wave Crest C. & C. Park****
🅿 1 Jan - 31 Dec
☎ +353 (0)66-9475188
@ wavecrest@eircom.net

1 ADJMNOPRS**T**	KNOPQSTUVWXY 6
2 EFJKMOPRSTUVWX	ABDE**FG**HK 7
3 A**GH**	ABE**F**NQRV 8
4 IO**Q**	9
5 ACDFGHKMN	AHIJ**N**PRZ 10
13A CEE	❶ €28.00
2,2ha 110**T**(40-80m²) 50**P**	❷ €32.00

🛣 Clearly signed on the ring road from Kerry. Coming from Kenmare, 2nd campsite on the left before Caherdaniel. From Cahirciveen 2nd campsite on the left after Caherdaniel.

💬 A large campsite beautifully located on the Atlantic. Extensive reception with plenty of information about the area. Fishing tackle on sale. Cafe/restaurant serving light meals and an extensive shop with provisions and other main requirements.

ⓒⓒ 1/3-29/6 1/9-31/10

📍 **N 51°45'32'' W 10°5'28''**

www.eurocampings.co.uk/103062

534 Cahir, Tipperary

❌ ♿ ♿ (CC€15) iD 7 B1

🔺 The Apple Farm KI.A***
🏕 Moorstown
🅿 1 May - 30 Sep
☎ +353 (0)5274-41459
@ con@theapplefarm.com

1 ADEHKNOPQRST	6
2 APRSWXY	ABDE**FG** 7
3 A**K**M	ABE**F**NQRV 8
4 IQ	9
5 DMN	ABGHJOR 10
16A CEE	❶ €16.50
A95 1,5ha 32**T**(100-110m²)	❷ €25.50

🛣 The campsite is along the N24 Cahir-Clonmel, 6 km from Cahir.

💬 A small, atmospheric campsite located in a fruit orchard. Sample the apple juice and enjoy a relaxing walk among the fruit trees. Apple juice, jam and cider are on sale in the shop. Ideal for day trips. Free use of the tennis courts. Drinking water from own source.

ⓒⓒ 1/5-31/5 4/6-17/6 3/9-29/9

📍 **N 52°22'35'' W 7°50'33''**

www.eurocampings.co.uk/103091

535 Cahirciveen, Kerry

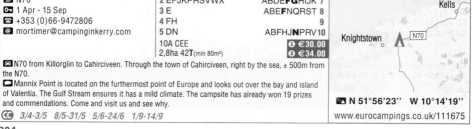

📶 (CC€19) iD 7 A1

🔺 Mannix Point Park***
🏕 N70
🅿 1 Apr - 15 Sep
☎ +353 (0)66-9472806
@ mortimer@campinginkerry.com

1 AJMNOPRST	KNPQSWX 6
2 EFJKPRSVWX	ABDE**FG**HIJK 7
3 E	ABE**F**NQRST 8
4 FH	9
5 DN	ABFHJ**N**PRV 10
10A CEE	❶ €30.00
2,8ha 42**T**(min 80m²)	❷ €34.00

🛣 N70 from Killorglin to Cahirciveen. Through the town of Cahirciveen, right by the sea, ± 500m from the N70.

💬 Mannix Point is located on the furthermost point of Europe and looks out over the bay and island of Valentia. The Gulf Stream ensures it has a mild climate. The campsite has already won 19 prizes and commendations. Come and visit us and see why.

ⓒⓒ 3/4-3/5 8/5-31/5 5/6-24/6 1/9-14/9

📍 **N 51°56'23'' W 10°14'19''**

www.eurocampings.co.uk/111675

Ireland

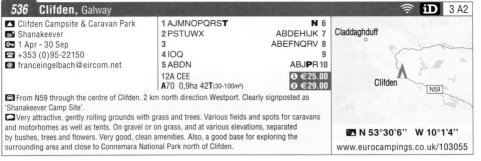

536 Clifden, Galway 📶 iD 3 A2

- 🏕 Clifden Campsite & Caravan Park
- ✉ Shanakeever
- 🕐 1 Apr - 30 Sep
- ☎ +353 (0)95-22150
- @ franceingelbach@eircom.net

1 AJMNOPQRS**T**	**N** 6
2 PSTUWX	ABDEHIJK 7
3	ABEFNQRV 8
4 IOQ	9
5 ABDN	ABJ**PR**10
12A CEE	❶ €25.00
A70 0,9ha 42**T**(30-100m²)	❷ €29.00

🚗 From N59 through the centre of Clifden. 2 km north direction Westport. Clearly signposted as 'Shanakeever Camp Site'.

💬 Very attractive, gently rolling grounds with grass and trees. Various fields and spots for caravans and motorhomes as well as tents. On gravel or on grass, and at various elevations, separated by bushes, trees and flowers. Very good, clean amenities. Also, a good base for exploring the surrounding area and close to Connemara National Park north of Clifden.

Claddaghduff

Clifden N59

🗺 N 53°30'6'' W 10°1'4''

www.eurocampings.co.uk/103055

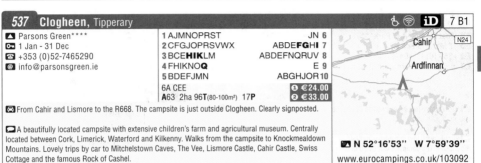

537 Clogheen, Tipperary ♿ 📶 iD 7 B1

- 🏕 Parsons Green****
- 🕐 1 Jan - 31 Dec
- ☎ +353 (0)52-7465290
- @ info@parsonsgreen.ie

1 AJMNOPRST	JN 6
2 CFGJOPRSVWX	ABDE**FGH**I 7
3 BCE**HIK**LM	ABDEFNQRUV 8
4 FHIKNO**Q**	E 9
5 BDEFJMN	ABGHJOR10
6A CEE	❶ €24.00
A63 2ha 96**T**(80-100m²) 17**P**	❷ €33.00

🚗 From Cahir and Lismore to the R668. The campsite is just outside Clogheen. Clearly signposted.

💬 A beautifully located campsite with extensive children's farm and agricultural museum. Centrally located between Cork, Limerick, Waterford and Kilkenny. Walks from the campsite to Knockmealdown Mountains. Lovely trips by car to Mitchelstown Caves, The Vee, Lismore Castle, Cahir Castle, Swiss Cottage and the famous Rock of Cashel.

Cahir N24

Ardfinnan

🗺 N 52°16'53'' W 7°59'39''

www.eurocampings.co.uk/103092

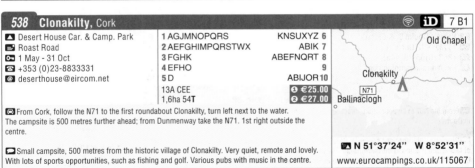

538 Clonakilty, Cork 📶 iD 7 B1

- 🏕 Desert House Car. & Camp. Park
- ✉ Roast Road
- 🕐 1 May - 31 Oct
- ☎ +353 (0)23-8833331
- @ deserthouse@eircom.net

1 AGJMNOPQRS	KNSUXYZ 6
2 AEFGHIMPQRSTWX	ABIK 7
3 FGHK	ABEFNQRT 8
4 EFHO	9
5 D	ABIJOR10
13A CEE	❶ €25.00
1,6ha 54**T**	❷ €27.00

🚗 From Cork, follow the N71 to the first roundabout Clonakilty, turn left next to the water. The campsite is 500 metres further ahead; from Dunmenway take the N71. 1st right outside the centre.

💬 Small campsite, 500 metres from the historic village of Clonakilty. Very quiet, remote and lovely. With lots of sports opportunities, such as fishing and golf. Various pubs with music in the centre.

Old Chapel

Clonakilty N71

Ballinaclogh

🗺 N 51°37'24'' W 8°52'31''

www.eurocampings.co.uk/115067

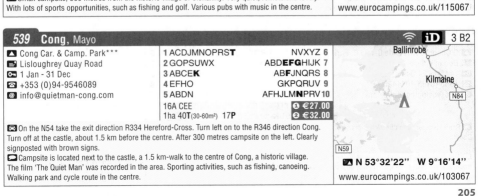

539 Cong, Mayo 📶 iD 3 B2

- 🏕 Cong Car. & Camp. Park***
- ✉ Lisloughrey Quay Road
- 🕐 1 Jan - 31 Dec
- ☎ +353 (0)94-9546089
- @ info@quietman-cong.com

1 ACDJMNOPRS**T**	NVXYZ 6
2 GOPSUWX	ABD**EFG**HIJK 7
3 ABCE**K**	AB**F**JNQRS 8
4 EFHO	GKPQRUV 9
5 ABDN	AFHJLM**N**PRV10
16A CEE	❶ €27.00
1ha 40**T**(30-60m²) 17**P**	❷ €32.00

🚗 On the N54 take the exit direction R334 Hereford-Cross. Turn left on to the R346 direction Cong. Turn off at the castle, about 1.5 km before the centre. After 300 metres campsite on the left. Clearly signposted with brown signs.

💬 Campsite is located next to the castle, a 1.5 km-walk to the centre of Cong, a historic village. The film 'The Quiet Man' was recorded in the area. Sporting activities, such as fishing, canoeing. Walking park and cycle route in the centre.

Ballinrobe

Kilmaine N84

N59

🗺 N 53°32'22'' W 9°16'14''

www.eurocampings.co.uk/103067

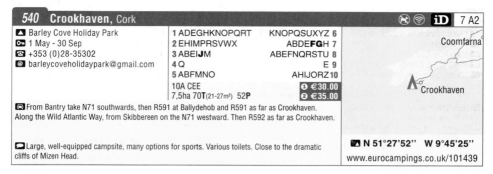

540 Crookhaven, Cork · 7 A2

- ▲ Barley Cove Holiday Park
- 1 May - 30 Sep
- ☎ +353 (0)28-35302
- @ barleycoveholidaypark@gmail.com

1 ADEGHKNOPQRT	KNOPQSUXYZ 6
2 EHIMPRSVWX	ABDE**FG**H 7
3 ABEI**JM**	ABEFNQRSTU 8
4 Q	E 9
5 ABFMNO	AHIJORZ 10
10A CEE	❶ €30.00
7,5ha 70T(21-27m²) 52P	❷ €35.00

From Bantry take N71 southwards, then R591 at Ballydehob and R591 as far as Crookhaven. Along the Wild Atlantic Way, from Skibbereen on the N71 westward. Then R592 as far as Crookhaven.

Large, well-equipped campsite, many options for sports. Various toilets. Close to the dramatic cliffs of Mizen Head.

N 51°27'52'' W 9°45'25''

www.eurocampings.co.uk/101439

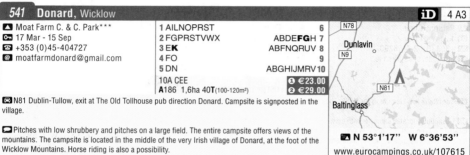

541 Donard, Wicklow · 4 A3

- ▲ Moat Farm C. & C. Park***
- 17 Mar - 15 Sep
- ☎ +353 (0)45-404727
- @ moatfarmdonard@gmail.com

1 AILNOPRST	6
2 FGPRSTVWX	ABDE**FG**H 7
3 E**K**	ABFNQRUV 8
4 FO	9
5 DN	ABGHIJMRV 10
10A CEE	❶ €23.00
A186 1,6ha 40T(100-120m²)	❷ €29.00

N81 Dublin-Tullow, exit at The Old Tollhouse pub direction Donard. Campsite is signposted in the village.

Pitches with low shrubbery and pitches on a large field. The entire campsite offers views of the mountains. The campsite is located in the middle of the very Irish village of Donard, at the foot of the Wicklow Mountains. Horse riding is also a possibility.

N 53°1'17'' W 6°36'53''

www.eurocampings.co.uk/107615

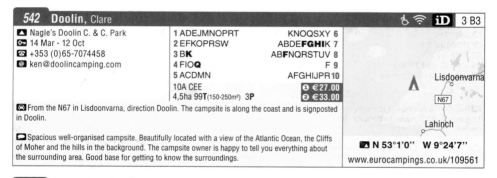

542 Doolin, Clare · 3 B3

- ▲ Nagle's Doolin C. & C. Park
- 14 Mar - 12 Oct
- ☎ +353 (0)65-7074458
- @ ken@doolincamping.com

1 ADEJMNOPRT	KNOQSXY 6
2 EFKOPRSW	ABDE**FGHI**K 7
3 B**K**	AB**F**NQRSTUV 8
4 FIO**Q**	F 9
5 ACDMN	AFGHIJPR 10
10A CEE	❶ €27.00
4,5ha 99T(150-250m²) 3P	❷ €33.00

From the N67 in Lisdoonvarna, direction Doolin. The campsite is along the coast and is signposted in Doolin.

Spacious well-organised campsite. Beautifully located with a view of the Atlantic Ocean, the Cliffs of Moher and the hills in the background. The campsite owner is happy to tell you everything about the surrounding area. Good base for getting to know the surroundings.

N 53°1'0'' W 9°24'7''

www.eurocampings.co.uk/109561

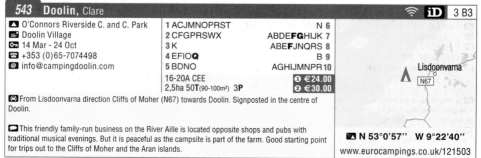

543 Doolin, Clare · 3 B3

- ▲ O'Connors Riverside C. and C. Park
- ▤ Doolin Village
- 14 Mar - 24 Oct
- ☎ +353 (0)65-7074498
- @ info@campingdoolin.com

1 ACJMNOPRST	N 6
2 CFGPRSWX	ABDE**FG**HIJK 7
3 K	ABE**F**JNQRS 8
4 EFIO**Q**	B 9
5 BDNO	AGHIJMNPR 10
16-20A CEE	❶ €24.00
2,5ha 50T(90-100m²) 3P	❷ €30.00

From Lisdoonvarna direction Cliffs of Moher (N67) towards Doolin. Signposted in the centre of Doolin.

This friendly family-run business on the River Aille is located opposite shops and pubs with traditional musical evenings. But it is peaceful as the campsite is part of the farm. Good starting point for trips out to the Cliffs of Moher and the Aran islands.

N 53°0'57'' W 9°22'40''

www.eurocampings.co.uk/121503

Ireland

🔺 Camac Valley
　 Caravan & Camping Park****
📧 Corkargh Park, Green Isle Link Road
📅 1 Jan - 31 Dec
📞 +353 (0)1-4640644
@ reservations@camacvalley.com

1	ADEJMNOPRST		6
2	AOPSVWXY	ABDE**FGH**K	7
3	B**K**	AB**F**JNQRSTUV	8
4	FHO		9
5	DMN	ABGHILPRZ	10

Ad on this page　10A CEE
A100　6ha 163**T**(120-140m²)

❶ €28.00
❷ €31.00

🚗 From Dublin follow the N7. Campsite located on the right about 2 km beyond the M50 roundabout. Turn left immediately. Follow campsite signs.

💬 Large and busy campsite during the high season, part of Corkagh Park. The park also includes a multifunctional sports field, possibilities for fishing and a children's farm. Large pitches surrounded by bushes. Bus to Dublin stops just outside the campsite. Traffic on the motorway is noticeable.

🧭 N 53°18'16'' W 6°24'53''
www.eurocampings.co.uk/109135

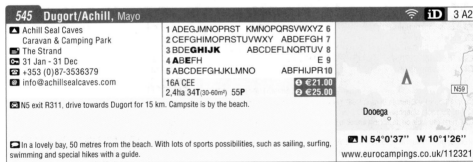

Ireland

🔺 Achill Seal Caves
　 Caravan & Camping Park
📧 The Strand
📅 31 Jan - 31 Dec
📞 +353 (0)87-3536379
@ info@achillsealcaves.com

1	ADEGJMNOPRST	KMNOPQRSVWXYZ	6
2	CEFGHIMOPRSTUVWXY	ABDEFGH	7
3	BDE**GHIJK**	ABCDEFLNQRTUV	8
4	**AB**EFH	E	9
5	ABCDEFGHJKLMNO	ABFHIJPR	10

16A CEE
2,4ha 34**T**(30-60m²) 55**P**

❶ €21.00
❷ €25.00

🚗 N5 exit R311, drive towards Dugort for 15 km. Campsite is by the beach.

💬 In a lovely bay, 50 metres from the beach. With lots of sports possibilities, such as sailing, surfing, swimming and special hikes with a guide.

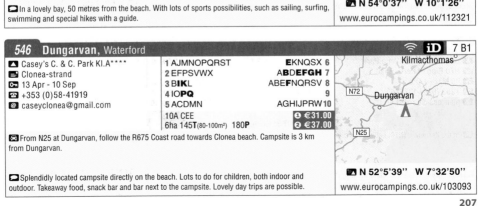

🧭 N 54°0'37'' W 10°1'26''
www.eurocampings.co.uk/112321

🔺 Casey's C. & C. Park Kl.A****
📧 Clonea-strand
📅 13 Apr - 10 Sep
📞 +353 (0)58-41919
@ caseyclonea@gmail.com

1	AJMNOPQRST	E**K**NQSX	6
2	EFPSVWX	A**BDEFGH**	7
3	B**I**KL	ABE**F**NQRSV	8
4	IO**PQ**		9
5	ACDMN	AGHIJPRW	10

10A CEE
6ha 145**T**(80-100m²) 180**P**

❶ €31.00
❷ €37.00

🚗 From N25 at Dungarvan, follow the R675 Coast road towards Clonea beach. Campsite is 3 km from Dungarvan.

💬 Splendidly located campsite directly on the beach. Lots to do for children, both indoor and outdoor. Takeaway food, snack bar and bar next to the campsite. Lovely day trips are possible.

🧭 N 52°5'39'' W 7°32'50''
www.eurocampings.co.uk/103093

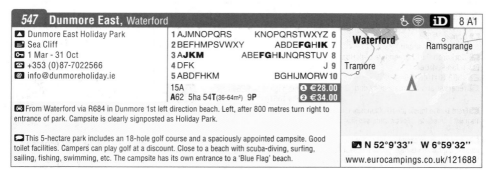

547 Dunmore East, Waterford ⚓ 📶 iD 8 A1

- ▲ Dunmore East Holiday Park
- 🏠 Sea Cliff
- 📅 1 Mar - 31 Oct
- ☎ +353 (0)87-7022566
- @ info@dunmoreholiday.ie

1 AJMNOPQRS	KNOPQRSTWXYZ 6
2 BEFHMPSVWXY	ABDE**FGHIK** 7
3 A**JKM**	ABE**FGH**IJNQRSTUV 8
4 DFK	J 9
5 ABDFHKM	BGHIJMORW 10
15A	❶ €28.00
A62 5ha 54T(36-64m²) 9P	❷ €34.00

🚗 From Waterford via R684 in Dunmore 1st left direction beach. Left, after 800 metres turn right to entrance of park. Campsite is clearly signposted as Holiday Park.

💬 This 5-hectare park includes an 18-hole golf course and a spaciously appointed campsite. Good toilet facilities. Campers can play golf at a discount. Close to a beach with scuba-diving, surfing, sailing, fishing, swimming, etc. The campsite has its own entrance to a 'Blue Flag' beach.

📷 N 52°9'33'' W 6°59'32''
www.eurocampings.co.uk/121688

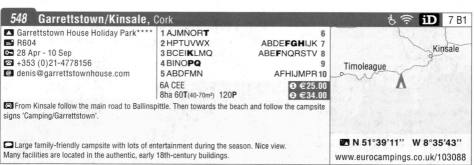

548 Garrettstown/Kinsale, Cork ⚓ 📶 iD 7 B1

- ▲ Garrettstown House Holiday Park****
- 🏠 R604
- 📅 28 Apr - 10 Sep
- ☎ +353 (0)21-4778156
- @ denis@garrettstownhouse.com

1 AJMNOR**T**	6
2 HPTUVWX	ABDE**FGH**IJK 7
3 BCEI**KLMQ**	ABE**F**NQRSTV 8
4 BINO**PQ**	9
5 ABDFMN	AFHIJMPR 10
6A CEE	❶ €25.00
8ha 60T(40-70m²) 120P	❷ €34.00

🚗 From Kinsale follow the main road to Ballinspittle. Then towards the beach and follow the campsite signs 'Camping/Garrettstown'.

💬 Large family-friendly campsite with lots of entertainment during the season. Nice view. Many facilities are located in the authentic, early 18th-century buildings.

📷 N 51°39'11'' W 8°35'43''
www.eurocampings.co.uk/103088

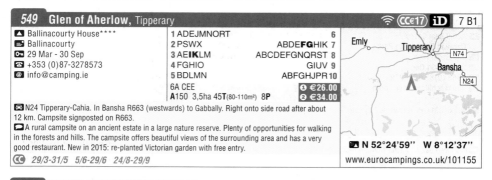

549 Glen of Aherlow, Tipperary 📶 CC€17 iD 7 B1

- ▲ Ballinacourty House****
- 🏠 Ballinacourty
- 📅 29 Mar - 30 Sep
- ☎ +353 (0)87-3278573
- @ info@camping.ie

1 ADEJMNORT	6
2 PSWX	ABDE**FGH**IK 7
3 AEI**KLM**	ABCDEFGNQRST 8
4 FGHIO	GIUV 9
5 BDLMN	ABFGHJPR 10
6A CEE	❶ €26.00
A150 3,5ha 45T(80-110m²) 8P	❷ €34.00

🚗 N24 Tipperary-Cahia. In Bansha R663 (westwards) to Gabbally. Right onto side road after about 12 km. Campsite signposted on R663.

💬 A rural campsite on an ancient estate in a large nature reserve. Plenty of opportunities for walking in the forests and hills. The campsite offers beautiful views of the surrounding area and has a very good restaurant. New in 2015: re-planted Victorian garden with free entry.

CC 29/3-31/5 5/6-29/6 24/8-29/9

📷 N 52°24'59'' W 8°12'37''
www.eurocampings.co.uk/101155

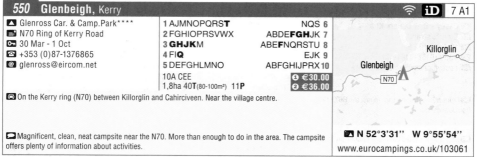

550 Glenbeigh, Kerry 📶 iD 7 A1

- ▲ Glenross Car. & Camp.Park****
- 🏠 N70 Ring of Kerry Road
- 📅 30 Mar - 1 Oct
- ☎ +353 (0)87-1376865
- @ glenross@eircom.net

1 AJMNOPQRS**T**	NQS 6
2 FGHIOPRSVWX	ABDE**FGH**JK 7
3 **GHJK**M	ABE**F**NQRSTU 8
4 FI**Q**	EJK 9
5 DEFGHLMNO	ABFGHIJPRX 10
10A CEE	❶ €30.00
1,8ha 40T(80-100m²) 11P	❷ €36.00

🚗 On the Kerry ring (N70) between Killorglin and Cahirciveen. Near the village centre.

💬 Magnificent, clean, neat campsite near the N70. More than enough to do in the area. The campsite offers plenty of information about activities.

📷 N 52°3'31'' W 9°55'54''
www.eurocampings.co.uk/103061

Ireland

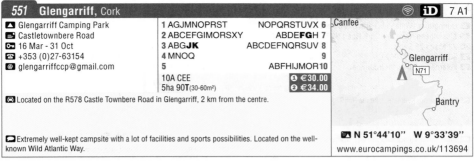

551 Glengarriff, Cork · 🛜 iD · 7 A1

- 🏕 Glengarriff Camping Park
- 📮 Castletownbere Road
- 📅 16 Mar - 31 Oct
- ☎ +353 (0)27-63154
- @ glengarriffccp@gmail.com

1 AGJMNOPRST	NOPQRSTUVX	6
2 ABCEFGIMORSXY	ABDE**FG**H	7
3 ABG**JK**	ABCDEFNQRSUV	8
4 MNOQ		9
5	ABFHIJMOR	10

10A CEE
5ha 90T(30-60m²)
- ❶ €30.00
- ❷ €34.00

🚗 Located on the R578 Castle Townbere Road in Glengarriff, 2 km from the centre.

💬 Extremely well-kept campsite with a lot of facilities and sports possibilities. Located on the well-known Wild Atlantic Way.

📷 N 51°44'10'' W 9°33'39''
www.eurocampings.co.uk/113694

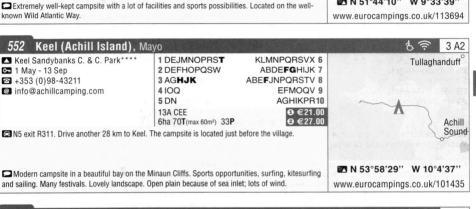

552 Keel (Achill Island), Mayo · ♿ 🛜 · 3 A2

- 🏕 Keel Sandybanks C. & C. Park****
- 📅 1 May - 13 Sep
- ☎ +353 (0)98-43211
- @ info@achillcamping.com

1 DEJMNOPRS**T**	KLMNPQRSVX	6
2 DEFHOPQSW	ABDE**FG**HIJK	7
3 AG**HJK**	ABE**F**JNPQRSTV	8
4 IOQ	EFMOQV	9
5 DN	AGHIKPR	10

13A CEE
6ha 70T(max 60m²) 33P
- ❶ €21.00
- ❷ €27.00

🚗 N5 exit R311. Drive another 28 km to Keel. The campsite is located just before the village.

💬 Modern campsite in a beautiful bay on the Minaun Cliffs. Sports opportunities, surfing, kitesurfing and sailing. Many festivals. Lovely landscape. Open plain because of sea inlet; lots of wind.

📷 N 53°58'29'' W 10°4'37''
www.eurocampings.co.uk/101435

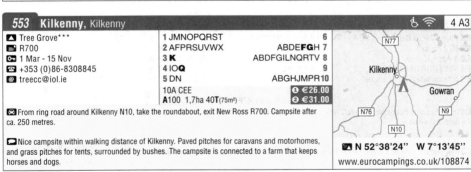

553 Kilkenny, Kilkenny · ♿ 🛜 · 4 A3

- 🏕 Tree Grove***
- 📮 R700
- 📅 1 Mar - 15 Nov
- ☎ +353 (0)86-8308845
- @ treecc@iol.ie

1 JMNOPQRST		6
2 AFPRSUVWX	ABDE**FG**H	7
3 **K**	ABDFGILNQRTV	8
4 IO**Q**		9
5 DN	ABGHJMPR	10

10A CEE
A100 1,7ha 40T(75m²)
- ❶ €26.00
- ❷ €31.00

🚗 From ring road around Kilkenny N10, take the roundabout, exit New Ross R700. Campsite after ca. 250 metres.

💬 Nice campsite within walking distance of Kilkenny. Paved pitches for caravans and motorhomes, and grass pitches for tents, surrounded by bushes. The campsite is connected to a farm that keeps horses and dogs.

📷 N 52°38'24'' W 7°13'45''
www.eurocampings.co.uk/108874

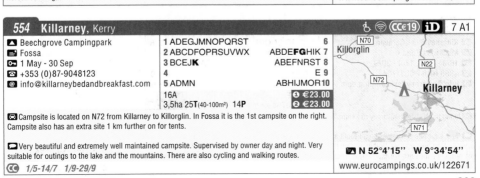

554 Killarney, Kerry · ♿ 🛜 CCe19 iD · 7 A1

- 🏕 Beechgrove Campingpark
- 📮 Fossa
- 📅 1 May - 30 Sep
- ☎ +353 (0)87-9048123
- @ info@killarneybedandbreakfast.com

1 ADEGJMNOPQRST		6
2 ABCDFOPRSUVWX	ABDE**FG**HIK	7
3 BCEJ**K**	ABEFNRST	8
4	E	9
5 ADMN	ABHIJMOR	10

16A
3,5ha 25T(40-100m²) 14P
- ❶ €23.00
- ❷ €23.00

🚗 Campsite is located on N72 from Killarney to Killorglin. In Fossa it is the 1st campsite on the right. Campsite also has an extra site 1 km further on for tents.

💬 Very beautiful and extremely well maintained campsite. Supervised by owner day and night. Very suitable for outings to the lake and the mountains. There are also cycling and walking routes.

CC 1/5-14/7 1/9-29/9

📷 N 52°4'15'' W 9°34'54''
www.eurocampings.co.uk/122671

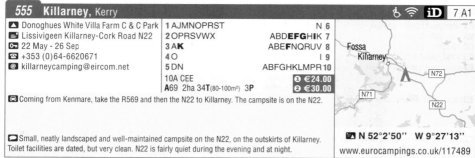

555 Killarney, Kerry · 7 A1

- Donoghues White Villa Farm C & C Park
- Lissivigeen Killarney-Cork Road N22
- 22 May - 26 Sep
- +353 (0)64-6620671
- @ killarneycamping@eircom.net

1 AJMNOPRST	N	6
2 OPRSVWX	ABD**EFG**HIK	7
3 A**K**	ABE**F**NQRUV	8
4 O	I	9
5 DN	ABFGHKLMPR	10

10A CEE
A69 2ha 34T(80-100m²) 3P
❶ €24.00
❷ €30.00

Coming from Kenmare, take the R569 and then the N22 to Killarney. The campsite is on the N22.

Small, neatly landscaped and well-maintained campsite on the N22, on the outskirts of Killarney. Toilet facilities are dated, but very clean. N22 is fairly quiet during the evening and at night.

N 52°2'50'' W 9°27'13''
www.eurocampings.co.uk/117489

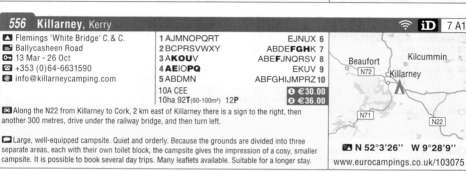

556 Killarney, Kerry · 7 A1

- Flemings 'White Bridge' C.& C.
- Ballycasheen Road
- 13 Mar - 26 Oct
- +353 (0)64-6631590
- @ info@killarneycamping.com

1 AJMNOPQRT	EJNUX	6
2 BCPRSVWXY	ABDE**FGH**K	7
3 A**KOU**V	ABE**F**JNQRSV	8
4 **AEI**OPQ	EKUV	9
5 ABDMN	ABFGHIJMPRZ	10

10A CEE
10ha 92T(60-100m²) 12P
❶ €30.00
❷ €36.00

Along the N22 from Killarney to Cork, 2 km east of Killarney there is a sign to the right, then another 300 metres, drive under the railway bridge, and then turn left.

Large, well-equipped campsite. Quiet and orderly. Because the grounds are divided into three separate areas, each with their own toilet block, the campsite gives the impression of a cosy, smaller campsite. It is possible to book several day trips. Many leaflets available. Suitable for a longer stay.

N 52°3'26'' W 9°28'9''
www.eurocampings.co.uk/103075

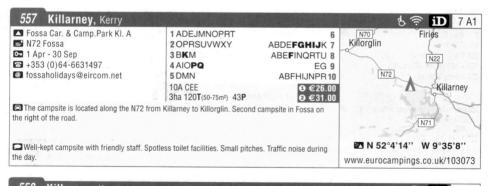

557 Killarney, Kerry · 7 A1

- Fossa Car. & Camp.Park Kl. A
- N72 Fossa
- 1 Apr - 30 Sep
- +353 (0)64-6631497
- @ fossaholidays@eircom.net

1 ADEJMNOPRT		6
2 OPRSUVWXY	ABDE**FGHIJ**K	7
3 B**K**M	ABE**F**INQRTU	8
4 AIO**PQ**	EG	9
5 DMN	ABFHIJNPR	10

10A CEE
3ha 120T(50-75m²) 43P
❶ €26.00
❷ €31.00

The campsite is located along the N72 from Killarney to Killorglin. Second campsite in Fossa on the right of the road.

Well-kept campsite with friendly staff. Spotless toilet facilities. Small pitches. Traffic noise during the day.

N 52°4'14'' W 9°35'8''
www.eurocampings.co.uk/103073

558 Killarney, Kerry · 7 A1

- Killarney Flesk Caravan Park****
- Muckross Road
- 16/3 - 20/3, 13/4 - 30/9
- +353 (0)64-6631704
- @ info@killarneyfleskcamping.com

1 ADEGILNOPR	E	6
2 PQRSTVWX	**AB**D**EFG**HK	7
3 **K**MO	ABE**F**NQRS	8
4 AFH	UV	9
5 DFHLN	ABGHIJPR	10

10A CEE
2,8ha 80T(40-60m²)
❶ €31.00
❷ €37.00

Along the N71 from Killarney to Kenmare. 2 km outside Killarney centre on the left.

Neat, spacious campsite with a beautiful, centrally located toilet block. Typical city campsite with a view of the built-up area. Within walking distance of many pubs and restaurants. Clear rules for the campers and the rules are expressly enforced. Has its own restaurant and bar - swimming pool, next to the campsite, 50 metres (admission fee).

N 52°2'35'' W 9°29'58''
www.eurocampings.co.uk/109563

Ireland

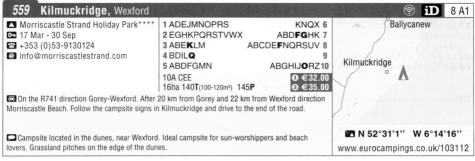

559 Kilmuckridge, Wexford ⬢ iD 8 A1

- ⛰ Morriscastle Strand Holiday Park****
- 📅 17 Mar - 30 Sep
- ☎ +353 (0)53-9130124
- @ info@morriscastlestrand.com

1 ADEJMNOPRS	KNQX	6
2 EGHKPQRSTVWX	ABD**FG**HK	7
3 ABE**K**LM	ABCDE**F**NQRSUV	8
4 BDIL**Q**		9
5 ABDFGMN	ABGHIJ**O**RZ	10
10A CEE	❶ €32.00	
16ha 140T(100-120m²) 145P	❷ €35.00	

🚗 On the R741 direction Gorey-Wexford. After 20 km from Gorey and 22 km from Wexford direction Morriscastle Beach. Follow the campsite signs in Kilmuckridge and drive to the end of the road.

💬 Campsite located in the dunes, near Wexford. Ideal campsite for sun-worshippers and beach lovers. Grassland pitches on the edge of the dunes.

📷 N 52°31'1'' W 6°14'16''

www.eurocampings.co.uk/103112

560 Knightstown, Kerry ⬢ CC€19 iD 7 A1

- ⛰ Valentia Island Caravan & Camping Park
- 📅 1 Apr - 1 Oct
- ☎ +353 (0)879673673
- @ info@valentiaislandcamping.com

1 AJMNOPQRST	KNOPQRSTUVWXYZ	6
2 AEFGHJKMORSTUVW	ABDE**FG**I**K**	7
3 ACMNST	ABCDE**F**GNQRSTUV	8
4 BCDEFHIJKLMNQ		9
5 DEFGHKLNO	ABF**H**IJPR	10
10A CEE	❶ €28.00	
43T(min 50m²)	❷ €32.00	

🚗 Take ferry to Valentia Island from the mainland on the N70 past Caherciveen. Campsite located 2 km beyond Knightstown. Back to mainland on R565 to Portmagee.

💬 Completely new campsite. Exceptionally well maintained. Run by very friendly, young managers. Just outside the centre. Various options for sports, such as canoeing, walking, cycling and swimming.

CC 1/4-3/5 8/5-31/5 5/6-6/7 1/9-30/9

📷 N 51°55'21'' W 10°17'47''

www.eurocampings.co.uk/122764

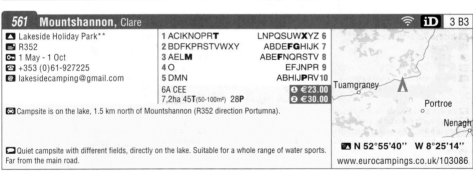

561 Mountshannon, Clare ⬢ iD 3 B3

- ⛰ Lakeside Holiday Park**
- 🛣 R352
- 📅 1 May - 1 Oct
- ☎ +353 (0)61-927225
- @ lakesidecamping@gmail.com

1 ACIKNOPR**T**	LNPQSUW**X**YZ	6
2 BDFKPRSTVWXY	ABDE**FG**HIJK	7
3 AEL**M**	ABE**F**NQRSTV	8
4 O	EFJNPR	9
5 DMN	ABHIJ**P**RV	10
6A CEE	❶ €23.00	
7,2ha 45T(50-100m²) 28P	❷ €30.00	

🚗 Campsite is on the lake, 1.5 km north of Mountshannon (R352 direction Portumna).

💬 Quiet campsite with different fields, directly on the lake. Suitable for a whole range of water sports. Far from the main road.

📷 N 52°55'40'' W 8°25'14''

www.eurocampings.co.uk/103086

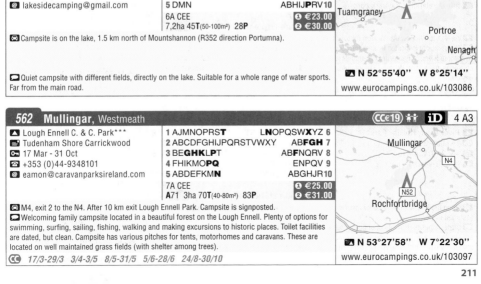

562 Mullingar, Westmeath CC€19 ⛹ iD 4 A3

- ⛰ Lough Ennell C. & C. Park***
- 🛣 Tudenham Shore Carrickwood
- 📅 17 Mar - 31 Oct
- ☎ +353 (0)44-9348101
- @ eamon@caravanparksireland.com

1 AJMNOPRS**T**	L**N**OPQSW**X**YZ	6
2 ABCDFGHIJPQRSTVWXY	AB**FGH**	7
3 BE**GHKL**P**T**	AB**F**NQRV	8
4 FHIKMO**PQ**	ENPQV	9
5 ABDEFKM**N**	ABGHJR	10
7A CEE	❶ €25.00	
A71 3ha 70T(40-80m²) 83P	❷ €31.00	

🚗 M4, exit 2 to the N4. After 10 km exit Lough Ennell Park. Campsite is signposted.
💬 Welcoming family campsite located in a beautiful forest on the Lough Ennell. Plenty of options for swimming, surfing, sailing, fishing, walking and making excursions to historic places. Toilet facilities are dated, but clean. Campsite has various pitches for tents, motorhomes and caravans. These are located on well maintained grass fields (with shelter among trees).

CC 17/3-29/3 3/4-3/5 8/5-31/5 5/6-28/6 24/8-30/10

📷 N 53°27'58'' W 7°22'30''

www.eurocampings.co.uk/103097

Ireland

563 Portsalon, Donegal · 📶 iD · 4 A1

- 🏔 Knockalla Car. & Camp. Park★★★★
- 🏕 Magherawarden
- 📅 14 Mar - 31 Oct
- ☎ +353 (0)74-9159108
- @ enquiries@knockallacaravanpark.com

1 ADEJMNOPQRST	NQSXY 6
2 FGHPSTUVW	ABDEFG 7
3 BEKM	ABEFJNQRSTUV 8
4 FIOQ	9
5 ABDMNO	ABGHIJOR 10

10-16A CEE
10ha 29T(20m²) 130P

➊ €25.00
➋ €30.00

🚗 From Kerrykeel to Portsalon via R246. Turn right after 5 km, and again after 3.2 km.

💬 This friendly family-managed campsite is located by the second most beautiful beach in Ireland. They serve homemade products in the café and the shop sells freshly baked bread and homemade jam.

🏕 N 55°10'59'' W 7°36'43''
www.eurocampings.co.uk/103089

---

564 Quigley's Point (Co. Donegal), Donegal · ♿ 📶 iD · 4 A1

- 🏔 Foyleside Caravan & Camping Park
- 📅 17 Mar - 30 Nov
- ☎ +353 (0)74-9383786
- @ info@foylesidecaravanpark.com

1 AILNOPQRST	6
2 EFKOPSVWX	ABD EFGHIK 7
3 AKM	ABEFNQRTU 8
4	9
5 DM	AGHJPR 10

16A CEE
3,6ha 26T(70-90m²) 40P

➊ €25.00
➋ €25.00

🚗 From Londonderry A2 north. At Muff the road becomes the R238, the campsite is on the right side of the road after 8 km. Across from The Point Inn.

💬 Quiet and lovely campsite by the Foyle Baai, with a good connection to Derry (15 km).

🏕 N 55°7'26'' W 7°11'44''
www.eurocampings.co.uk/118447

---

565 Rathdrum (Wicklow), Wicklow · 📶 CC€19 iD · 4 A3

- 🏔 Hidden Valley Holiday Park★★★★
- 🏕 Rathdrum
- 📅 16 Mar - 30 Sep
- ☎ +353 (0)86-7272872
- @ info@irelandholidaypark.com

1 ADJMNOPRST	JNUVX 6
2 BCDFGJKOPRSWX	ABDEFGIJ 7
3 BEFKRSU	ABEFJNQRTUV 8
4 BFHI	BFPQRTU 9
5 EFJMN	ABHIJORZ 10

16A CEE
A90 6ha 135T(100-110m²) 47P

➊ €30.00
➋ €40.00

🚗 Via N11 to Wicklow. At Wicklow follow signs Rathdrum R752. In Rathdrum campsite is signposted.
💬 The campsite is located in a magnificent valley, the Vale of Clara, with waterfalls leading to Avonmore River. In Rathdrum (10-minute walk) you will find pubs with live music, restaurants, cafeterias and shops. Wicklow Mountains and Clara Vale national park are close by and great for a day out.

CC 16/3-23/3 9/4-3/5 8/5-31/5 4/6-28/6 27/8-29/9

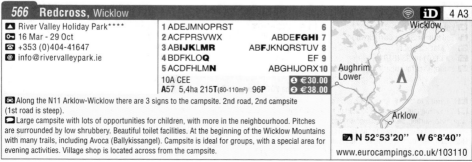

🏕 N 52°56'12'' W 6°13'39''
www.eurocampings.co.uk/111187

---

566 Redcross, Wicklow · 📶 iD · 4 A3

- 🏔 River Valley Holiday Park★★★★
- 📅 16 Mar - 29 Oct
- ☎ +353 (0)404-41647
- @ info@rivervalleypark.ie

1 ADEJMNOPRST	6
2 ACFPRSVWX	ABDEFGHI 7
3 ABIJKLMR	ABFJKNQRSTUV 8
4 BDFKLOQ	EF 9
5 ACDFHLMN	ABGHIJORX 10

10A CEE
A57 5,4ha 215T(80-110m²) 96P

➊ €30.00
➋ €38.00

🚗 Along the N11 Arklow-Wicklow there are 3 signs to the campsite. 2nd road, 2nd campsite (1st road is steep).
💬 Large campsite with lots of opportunities for children, with more in the neighbourhood. Pitches are surrounded by low shrubbery. Beautiful toilet facilities. At the beginning of the Wicklow Mountains with many trails, including Avoca (Ballykissangel). Campsite is ideal for groups, with a special area for evening activities. Village shop is located across from the campsite.

🏕 N 52°53'20'' W 6°8'40''
www.eurocampings.co.uk/103110

567 Renvyle, Galway
3 A2

- ▲ Renvyle Beach C. & C. Park
- ⊙ 1 Apr - 30 Sep
- ☎ +353 (0)95-43462
- @ renvylebeachcaravanpark@gmail.com

1 HKNOPRST	KNPQSWX	6
2 EFGHIMPQSTW	AB	7
3	ABEFNQRV	8
4	J	9
5 D	AHJPR	10
10A CEE	❶ €20.00	
4,5ha 78T 3P	❷ €26.00	

🚗 On N59 turn left at the T-junction direction Tullycross. Follow the signs, the campsite is 6.6 km ahead. Note: steep entrance/exit.

💬 Campsite near the sea. Lovely bay and panoramic views. No dogs allowed during high season.

Aughrus Beg — Rosroe — N59

◤ N 53°36'10'' W 9°59'6''

www.eurocampings.co.uk/116599

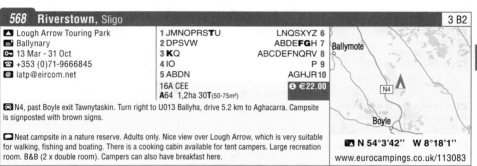

568 Riverstown, Sligo
3 B2

- ▲ Lough Arrow Touring Park
- ✉ Ballynary
- ⊙ 13 Mar - 31 Oct
- ☎ +353 (0)71-9666845
- @ latp@eircom.net

1 JMNOPRSTU	LNQSXYZ	6
2 DPSVW	ABDEFGH	7
3 KQ	ABCDEFNQRV	8
4 IO	P	9
5 ABDN	AGHJR	10
16A CEE	❶ €22.00	
A64 1,2ha 30T(50-75m²)		

🚗 N4, past Boyle exit Tawnytaskin. Turn right to U013 Ballyha, drive 5.2 km to Aghacarra. Campsite is signposted with brown signs.

💬 Neat campsite in a nature reserve. Adults only. Nice view over Lough Arrow, which is very suitable for walking, fishing and boating. There is a cooking cabin available for tent campers. Large recreation room. B&B (2 x double room). Campers can also have breakfast here.

Ballymote — N4 — Boyle

◤ N 54°3'42'' W 8°18'1''

www.eurocampings.co.uk/113083

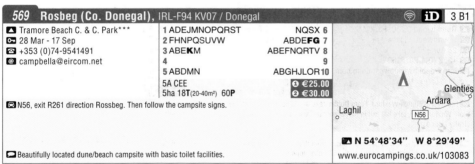

569 Rosbeg (Co. Donegal), IRL-F94 KV07 / Donegal
3 B1

- ▲ Tramore Beach C. & C. Park***
- ⊙ 28 Mar - 17 Sep
- ☎ +353 (0)74-9541491
- @ campbella@eircom.net

1 ADEJMNOPQRST	NQSX	6
2 FHNPQSUVW	ABDEFG	7
3 ABEKM	ABEFNQRTV	8
4		9
5 ABDMN	ABGHJLOR	10
5A CEE	❶ €25.00	
5ha 18T(20-40m²) 60P	❷ €30.00	

🚗 N56, exit R261 direction Rossbeg. Then follow the campsite signs.

💬 Beautifully located dune/beach campsite with basic toilet facilities.

Glenties — Ardara — Laghil — N56

◤ N 54°48'34'' W 8°29'49''

www.eurocampings.co.uk/103083

570 Rosses Point, IRL-F91 TC64 / Sligo
3 B2

- ▲ Greenlands Caravan Park****
- ⊙ 14 Apr - 15 Sep
- ☎ +353 (0)71-9177113
- @ rossespointcvp@eircom.net

1 ADEJMNOPQRST	KNQSX	6
2 AEFGHOPSTVW	ABDEFGHIJK	7
3 BK	ABEFNQRSV	8
4 IOQ		9
5 DMN	AFGHIJNOR	10
10A CEE	❶ €30.00	
2,5ha 80T(40-60m²) 40P	❷ €32.00	

🚗 From Sligo take the N15 as far as exit Rosses Point and then follow the R291 to the end of it.

💬 The campsite is located at an altitude by the sea with a stunning view of Sligo Bay, with a child-friendly beach and safe swimming. High-quality amenities.

Grange — N15 — N16 — Strandhill — N59 — Sligo

◤ N 54°18'26'' W 8°34'9''

www.eurocampings.co.uk/111317

Ireland

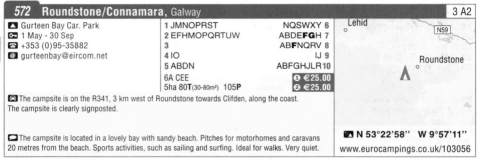

571 Rossnowlagh, Donegal   ⚙ iD   4 A1

- ⛺ Boortree Touring and Campingpark
- 🏕 Rossnowlagh
- 📅 1 Mar - 31 Oct
- ☎ +353 (0)85-1655917
- @ info@rossnowlaghcamping.com

1 ADEJMNOPRST	K	6
2 AEFHPSVW	ABHK	7
3 K	ABEFJNQRTV	8
4 FH		9
5 D	ABGHJR	10
8A CEE	❶ €30.00	
0,5ha 22T(85m²)	❷ €30.00	

🅿 On the N15 halfway between Donegal and Ballyshannon. Brown sign Rossnowlagh on the right side of the road. Drive all the way to the sea.

💬 This campsite, near the sea and sandy beach, opened in 2014. Located near a large recreation park.

N 54°33'55'' W 8°12'45''

www.eurocampings.co.uk/122253

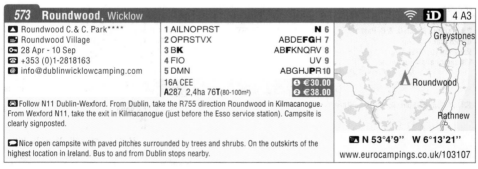

572 Roundstone/Connamara, Galway   3 A2

- ⛺ Gurteen Bay Car. Park
- 📅 1 May - 30 Sep
- ☎ +353 (0)95-35882
- @ gurteenbay@eircom.net

1 JMNOPRST	NQSWXY	6
2 EFHMOPQRTUW	ABDEFGH	7
3	ABFNQRV	8
4 IO	IJ	9
5 ABDN	ABFGHJLR	10
6A CEE	❶ €25.00	
5ha 80T(30-80m²) 105P	❷ €25.00	

🅿 The campsite is on the R341, 3 km west of Roundstone towards Clifden, along the coast. The campsite is clearly signposted.

💬 The campsite is located in a lovely bay with sandy beach. Pitches for motorhomes and caravans 20 metres from the beach. Sports activities, such as sailing and surfing. Ideal for walks. Very quiet.

N 53°22'58'' W 9°57'11''

www.eurocampings.co.uk/103056

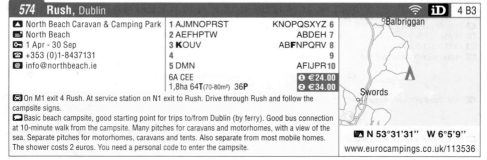

573 Roundwood, Wicklow   📶 iD   4 A3

- ⛺ Roundwood C.& C. Park****
- 🏕 Roundwood Village
- 📅 28 Apr - 10 Sep
- ☎ +353 (0)1-2818163
- @ info@dublinwicklowcamping.com

1 AILNOPRST	N	6
2 OPRSTVX	ABDEFGH	7
3 BK	ABFKNQRV	8
4 FIO	UV	9
5 DMN	ABGHJPR	10
16A CEE	❶ €30.00	
A287 2,4ha 76T(80-100m²)	❷ €38.00	

🅿 Follow N11 Dublin-Wexford. From Dublin, take the R755 direction Roundwood in Kilmacanogue. From Wexford N11, take the exit in Kilmacanogue (just before the Esso service station). Campsite is clearly signposted.

💬 Nice open campsite with paved pitches surrounded by trees and shrubs. On the outskirts of the highest location in Ireland. Bus to and from Dublin stops nearby.

N 53°4'9'' W 6°13'21''

www.eurocampings.co.uk/103107

---

574 Rush, Dublin   📶 iD   4 B3

- ⛺ North Beach Caravan & Camping Park
- 🏕 North Beach
- 📅 1 Apr - 30 Sep
- ☎ +353 (0)1-8437131
- @ info@northbeach.ie

1 AJMNOPRST	KNOPQSXYZ	6
2 AEFHPTW	ABDEH	7
3 KOUV	ABFNPQRV	8
4		9
5 DMN	AFIJPR	10
6A CEE	❶ €24.00	
1,8ha 64T(70-80m²) 36P	❷ €34.00	

🅿 On M1 exit 4 Rush. At service station on N1 exit to Rush. Drive through Rush and follow the campsite signs.

💬 Basic beach campsite, good starting point for trips to/from Dublin (by ferry). Good bus connection at 10-minute walk from the campsite. Many pitches for caravans and motorhomes, with a view of the sea. Separate pitches for motorhomes, caravans and tents. Also separate from most mobile homes. The shower costs 2 euros. You need a personal code to enter the campsite.

N 53°31'31'' W 6°5'9''

www.eurocampings.co.uk/113536

Ireland

575 Salthill, Galway 🛜 iD 3 B3

- 🏕 O'Halloran's
- 🗓 1 May - 30 Sep
- ☎ +353 (0)87-9601770
- @ gilliancondon12@gmail.com

1 ACJMNOPRST	NQS 6
2 AEKMOPSTW	AB 7
3 K	ABCDFNQRUV 8
4	E 9
5 DN	ABFIJLPR 10
12A CEE	❶ €25.00
4ha 65T(50-100m²) 12P	❷ €30.00

🚗 On the N6/M6 direction Galway Centre. Then follow R336 along the coast to Salthill. Entrance opposite service station.

💬 Very neat campsite on the sea. Lightly sloping grounds with separate locations for tents and caravans. Beautiful views. Bus stop at campsite with buses to Galway centre. Check-in from 11.30 am. Wifi not included in the price.

📷 N 53°15'28'' W 9°6'11''
www.eurocampings.co.uk/116606

576 Salthill, Galway 🛜 iD 3 B3

- 🏕 Salthill Caravan and Camping Park
- 🗓 1 Apr - 29 Sep
- ☎ +353 (0)91-523972
- @ info@salthillcaravanpark.com

1 AJMNOPQRST	KMNPQRSTUWXZ 6
2 AEFJKMOPQRSUVW	ABCDEFGHIJ 7
3 AJK	ABCDEFNQRSTUV 8
4	D 9
5 D	AHIJPR 10
10A	❶ €25.00
4ha 70T 83P	❷ €26.00

🚗 From Salthill westward along the coast. After 1 km the campsite is on the left side of the road.

💬 Campsite is near the sea, next to a golf course. Lovely panoramic view.

📷 N 53°15'34'' W 9°6'18''
www.eurocampings.co.uk/113059

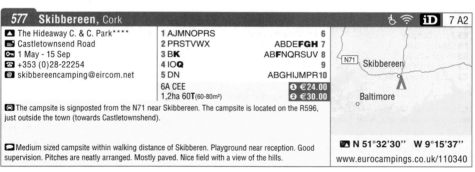

577 Skibbereen, Cork ♿ 🛜 iD 7 A2

- 🏕 The Hideaway C. & C. Park****
- 🏠 Castletownsend Road
- 🗓 1 May - 15 Sep
- ☎ +353 (0)28-22254
- @ skibbereencamping@eircom.net

1 AJMNOPRS	6
2 PRSTVWX	ABDEFGH 7
3 BK	ABFNQRSUV 8
4 IOQ	9
5 DN	ABGHIJMPR 10
6A CEE	❶ €24.00
1,2ha 60T(60-80m²)	❷ €30.00

🚗 The campsite is signposted from the N71 near Skibbereen. The campsite is located on the R596, just outside the town (towards Castletownshend).

💬 Medium sized campsite within walking distance of Skibberen. Playground near reception. Good supervision. Pitches are neatly arranged. Mostly paved. Nice field with a view of the hills.

📷 N 51°32'30'' W 9°15'37''
www.eurocampings.co.uk/110340

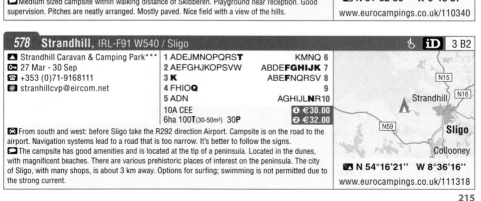

578 Strandhill, IRL-F91 W540 / Sligo ♿ iD 3 B2

- 🏕 Strandhill Caravan & Camping Park***
- 🗓 27 Mar - 30 Sep
- ☎ +353 (0)71-9168111
- @ stranhillcvp@eircom.net

1 ADEJMNOPQRST	KMNQ 6
2 AEFGHJKOPSVW	ABDEFGHIJK 7
3 K	ABEFNQRSV 8
4 FHIOQ	9
5 ADN	AGHIJLNR 10
10A CEE	❶ €30.00
6ha 100T(30-50m²) 30P	❷ €32.00

🚗 From south and west: before Sligo take the R292 direction Airport. Campsite is on the road to the airport. Navigation systems lead to a road that is too narrow. It's better to follow the signs.
💬 The campsite has good amenities and is located at the tip of a peninsula. Located in the dunes, with magnificent beaches. There are various prehistoric places of interest on the peninsula. The city of Sligo, with many shops, is about 3 km away. Options for surfing; swimming is not permitted due to the strong current.

📷 N 54°16'21'' W 8°36'16''
www.eurocampings.co.uk/111318

Ireland

579 Tralee, Kerry

🚴 📶 (CC€19) **iD** | 7 A1

- 🏕 Woodlands Park★★★★
- 🏠 Dan Spring Road
- 📅 1 Feb - 30 Nov
- ☎ +353 (0)66-7121235
- @ woodlandstralee@gmail.com

1 ADEJMNOPRST			6
2 BOPRSVWX		ABDE**FG**HIK	7
3 BE**KU**		ABE**FG**JNQRSTU	8
4 FHIO**PQ**			9
5 ABDMN		ABFGHIJMORV	10
10A CEE		❶ €30.00	
6ha 135T(165m²)		❷ €36.00	

🏕 The campsite is on the N86 Tralee-Dingle, 0.5 km south of Tralee and is also signposted on the N22 from Killarney.

💬 A well maintained and attractive town campsite with views of the woods. Within walking distance of Ireland's largest Aquadome which is open each day until 10:00 pm (large discounts for campsite guests, almost 50%).

(CC) 1/2-29/3 3/4-30/6 1/9-29/11

Ardfert
Tralee | N69
N21
N70 | N22
Castlemaine | N23

⛰ N 52°15'49'' W 9°42'11''

www.eurocampings.co.uk/110253

580 Tramore, IRL-X91 EO99 / Waterford

📶 **iD** | 8 A1

- 🏕 Newtown Cove Caravan Park★★★★
- 🏠 Newtown Cove
- 📅 27 Apr - 30 Sep
- ☎ +353 (0)51-381979
- @ info@newtowncove.com

1 ACDEJMNOPQR**T**		X	6
2 PRSVW		ABDE**FG**HI	7
3 A**KL**		ABE**F**NQRT	8
4 IO**PQ**			9
5 ABDMN		ABGHJ**P**R	10
10A CEE		❶ €31.00	
2,2ha 46T(50-100m²) 56P		❷ €37.00	

🏕 Take the R675 Coast Road from Tramore towards Dungarvan. After approx. 1 km turn left and then there are signs to the campsite.

💬 Beautiful campsite, divided into several grass fields, surrounded by trees. 1 km from the seaside resort of Tramore with its cosy promenade and lovely beach. The toilet facilities include showers but also a bathroom with a bathtub.

Tramore
Dunmore East

⛰ N 52°8'52'' W 7°10'21''

www.eurocampings.co.uk/103101

581 Tuosist/Post Killarney, Kerry

📶 **iD** | 7 A1

- 🏕 Beara Camping
- 🏠 Coornagillagh
- 📅 15 Apr - 15 Oct
- ☎ +353 (0)64-6684287
- @ info@bearacamping.com

1 ADGIKNOPQRS**T**		KNQSX	6
2 EJPRSWXY		ABDE**FG**IJ	7
3 AE**GH**S		ABEFNV	8
4 E		EF	9
5 ADFKN		AIJLPRV	10
8A CEE		❶ €21.50	
2ha 46T(80-120m²) 10P		❷ €26.50	

🏕 From Kenmare N71, take the R571 directly after the bridge, direction Castletownbere. After 12 km the campsite is on the right, clearly signposted.

💬 True nature campsite with lots of privacy, near the sea. Sober amenities, but plenty available. Large space with kitchen for campers; campers can gather around the open fire for that lovely holiday feeling. Five, well-equipped hiker's cabins.

Sneem | Kenmare
N70
N71
Glengarriff

⛰ N 51°49'35'' W 9°43'50''

www.eurocampings.co.uk/109784

582 Westport, Mayo

🚫 🚴 📶 | 3 B2

- 🏕 Westporthouse C. & C. Park★★★
- 📅 25 Apr - 15 Sep
- ☎ +353 (0)98-27766
- @ info@westporthouse.ie

1 DEHKNOPRST		N	6
2 CDFGHPRSTXY		ABDEH	7
3 ABCEL**RT**		ABEFNQRSTUV	8
4 FHIO**PQ**		T	9
5 DHKLN		AFGHIJ**N**PR	10
16A CEE		❶ €30.00	
4ha 155T(max 100m²)		❷ €38.00	

🏕 N5 Castlebar-Westport. Follow the signs in the centre. The recreation park is located to the right at Westport Quay.

💬 The campsite, with good amenities, is located in Westport Country Park. The park offers a lot of recreational opportunities, such as boating, mini train, pub, pedalo, tennis court, etc. Next to the park are possibilities for sea fishing, sailing and walks on the beach. Recreational possibilities for children, both indoor and outdoor. Lovely country estate, worth a visit.

Newport
Lecanvey | Westport | N5
N59

⛰ N 53°48'21'' W 9°32'20''

www.eurocampings.co.uk/101436

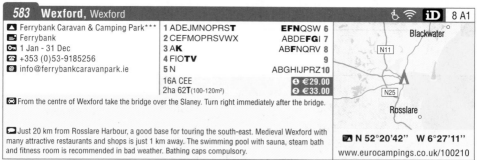

583 Wexford, Wexford   ♿ 🛜 iD   8 A1

🏕 Ferrybank Caravan & Camping Park***
🏠 Ferrybank
🗓 1 Jan - 31 Dec
☎ +353 (0)53-9185256
@ info@ferrybankcaravanpark.ie

1 ADEJMNOPRS**T**	**EFN**QSW 6
2 CEFMOPRSVWX	ABDE**FG**I 7
3 A**K**	AB**F**NQRV 8
4 FIO**TV**	9
5 N	ABGHIJPRZ 10
16A CEE	❶ €29.00
2ha 62**T**(100-120m²)	❷ €33.00

🚗 From the centre of Wexford take the bridge over the Slaney. Turn right immediately after the bridge.

💬 Just 20 km from Rosslare Harbour, a good base for touring the south-east. Medieval Wexford with many attractive restaurants and shops is just 1 km away. The swimming pool with sauna, steam bath and fitness room is recommended in bad weather. Bathing caps compulsory.

📍 N 52°20'42''   W 6°27'11''
www.eurocampings.co.uk/100210

Blackwater · N11 · N25 · Rosslare

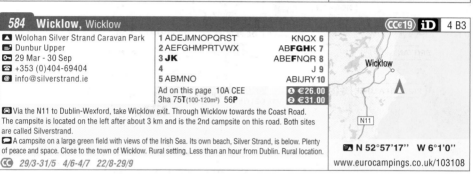

584 Wicklow, Wicklow   (CC€19) iD   4 B3

🏕 Wolohan Silver Strand Caravan Park
🏠 Dunbur Upper
🗓 29 Mar - 30 Sep
☎ +353 (0)404-69404
@ info@silverstrand.ie

1 ADEJMNOPQRST	KNQX 6
2 AEFGHMPRTVWX	AB**FGH**K 7
3 **JK**	ABE**F**NQR 8
4	J 9
5 ABMNO	ABIJRY 10
Ad on this page 10A CEE	❶ €26.00
3ha 75**T**(100-120m²) 56**P**	❷ €31.00

🚗 Via the N11 to Dublin-Wexford, take Wicklow exit. Through Wicklow towards the Coast Road. The campsite is located on the left after about 3 km and is the 2nd campsite on this road. Both sites are called Silverstrand.

💬 A campsite on a large green field with views of the Irish Sea. Its own beach, Silver Strand, is below. Plenty of peace and space. Close to the town of Wicklow. Rural setting. Less than an hour from Dublin. Rural location.

CC 29/3-31/5   4/6-4/7   22/8-29/9

📍 N 52°57'17''   W 6°1'0''
www.eurocampings.co.uk/103108

Wicklow · N11

Ireland

Wolohan Silver Strand Caravan Park

A campsite with pitches on a large field surrounded by shrubs and a magnificent view of the Irish Sea.
It has a private beach for guests.
Wolohan Silver Strand accepts the CampingCard ACSI.

Dunbur Upper • Wicklow • Tel. 0404-69404
E-mail: info@silverstrand.ie • Internet: www.silverstrand.ie

France

Channel

BELGIUM   GERMANY

Nord-
Pas-de-Calais   LUXEMBOURG

Upper Normandy   **HAUTS-DE-FRANCE**

NORMANDY `234`   `223`
Picardy

Lower Normandy   **ÎLE-DE-FRANCE**   **GRAND EST** `408`
Alsace

BRITTANY `279`   `255`   Champagne-
Ardenne   Lorraine

PAYS DE LA LOIRE `315`   **BOURGOGNE-FRANCHE-COMTÉ**

CENTRE-VAL DE LOIRE   `427`   Franche-
Comté   SWITZERLAND
`263`   Bourgogne

Atlantic Ocean

Poitou-Charentes   Limousin   **AUVERGNE-RHÔNE-ALPES** `447`   ITALY

NOUVELLE-AQUITAINE   Auvergne
`355`   Rhône-Alpes

Aquitaine   Midi-Pyrénées   **PROVENCE-ALPES-
CÔTE D'AZUR**

OCCITANIA `475`   `554`   Rivièra-
Côte d'Azur
Provence-Alpes-
Côte d'Azur

SPAIN   Languedoc-
Roussillon

ANDORRA   **CORSICA**
Mediterranean Sea   `592`

CS-WEU

| **CENTRE-VAL-DE-LOIRE** | Current regions |
| Languedoc-Roussillon | Previous regions |

General

France is a member of the EU. The capital city is Paris.

Time

The time in France is one hour ahead of London.

Language

French. You can also get by in English in tourist areas.

Crossing

There are many ferry connections between the United Kingdom, Ireland and France. On page 36, you can see at a glance where the ferries depart and arrive.

Currency

The currency in France is the euro. Approximate exchange rates September 2017: € 1 = £ 0.92. You can exchange money at banks and exchange offices. In general you can pay in France using your debit card. ATMs, called 'distributeur automatique de billets' in French, are widely available in major cities and towns. There's an ATM inside or outside most bank branches, often below an eye-catching sign that says retraite - the French word for "withdrawal".

Credit cards

You can pay almost everywhere by credit card, like Visa, Mastercard/Eurocard, including motorway tolls. You usually have to validate a purchase with a signature and you may sometimes be asked for identification.

Mobile phones

The mobile network works well throughout France, except in some areas in the Alps and the Massif Central. There is a 4G network for mobile internet.

Wifi, internet

You can use wifi networks at more and more public locations, often for free.

Opening times/Public Holidays

Banks

French banks are open from Tuesday to Friday between 9:00 am and 6:00 pm. Banks are open on Saturday mornings.

Shops (including pharmacies)

Shops are open from Tuesday to Saturday until 7:00/8:00 pm. Most shops in country areas are closed between 1:00 and 2:00 pm. Many shops are closed on Monday morning or for the whole day. French pharmacies, easy to recognise by a green cross, are open on weekdays until 7:00 pm.

Post

Post offices are open from Monday to Friday until 6:00 pm and on Saturday until 12:00 pm.

Public holidays

New Year's Day, Easter, 1 May (Labour Day), 8 May (1945 Armistice), Ascension Day, Pentecost, 14 July (Bastille Day), 15 August (The Assumption), 1 November (All Saints), 11 November (1918 Armistice), Christmas Day.

Roads and traffic

Traffic regulations

Remember, all traffic in France drives on the right and overtakes on the left! Headlight deflectors are advisable to prevent annoying oncoming drivers. You can adjust your lights for driving on the right by placing a special sticker on the headlights. If you are from Britain you will need to attach a GB sticker to the rear, unless your number plate incorporates a GB identifier.

Traffic from the right has priority except on main roads. Uphill traffic on narrow mountain roads has priority over descending traffic. You have priority on a roundabout if this is indicated by a triangular sign showing a roundabout. If there is no such sign drivers entering the roundabout will have priority. You must use dipped headlights in poor visibility. Never cross continuous white road markings, not even with one wheel! Take note: children under 10 must always sit in the back.

If you go to France by car, make sure that you have the correct documents with you. See page 18. Furthermore, in France it is compulsory to have the following items in your car:

- Reflective jackets: one for each occupant, these must be kept inside the vehicle within easy reach.
- Warning triangle: compulsory in every vehicle with 4 wheels or more.
- Breathalysers/alcohol test: An alcohol tester (éthylotest or alcootest) is mandatory in any vehicle (including foreign vehicles), but drivers who do not have the test with them will not be fined.

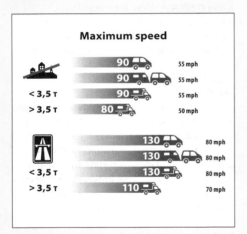

The maximum permitted alcohol level is 0.5 promille. Drivers who have had their driver's license for less than three years are subject to a limit of 0.2 promille.

You must phone hands-free and as of March 2017, it is illegal to drive a car in France using headphones or earphones. The offence is liable to a €90 on-the-spot fine.

Are you taking a bike ride with the children? Please remember that children under the age of 12 must wear a bicycle helmet, even if they are sitting on the back of the bike. The fine for not wearing a helmet is €135.

Roads

France uses the metric system, so distances are measured in kilometres (km) and speeds in kilometres per hour (km/h). 1 mile = 1.609 km and 1 km = 0.621 mile.

You are advised not to drive after dark in rural areas. France does not have any roadside assistance organisations. There are orange emergency phones ('les bornes SOS') along the motorways, which you can use in emergency situations to request breakdown or recovery services ('dépanneur').

Caravans, motorhomes

If your caravan weighs more than 3.5 tonnes lower speed limits apply. Overnight stays in your caravan or motorhome in built up areas and beside the motorway are prohibited, except in specially designated areas and for a maximum of 24 hours. Caravans with a twin axle are generally not permitted on municipal campsites.

Maximum permitted measurements of combined length

Height unlimited, width 2.55 metres and maximum length 18.75 metres (of which the trailer is 12 metres maximum).

Environmental zones

Environmental zones to target air pollution are being introduced in more and more French cities. In cities with an environmental zone, you are only allowed to drive into the city if you have an

environmental sticker on your car. The so-called Crit'Air Ecovignet is only available online via the official website ▶ *www.certificat-air.gouv.fr* ◀. There are 6 different environmental stickers for different vehicles. If you enter an environmental zone without an environmental sticker in your windscreen, you risk a high fine.

Fuel

Euro 95 has been replaced almost totally by E10. Check before your holiday whether E10 is suitable for your vehicle. Superplus 98 is a suitable alternative for euro 95. Diesel and LPG are easily available at the pumps.

Filling stations

Most filling stations on motorways are open 24 hours. Some service stations on 'routes nationales' are also open day and night, but many close at 9:00 pm. Take note that an increasing number of service stations away from motorways are closed on Sunday. Credit cards and most bank cards showing the Maestro logo are accepted at filling stations.

Charging stations

France has many charging stations for electric cars. Especially around Paris, in the larger cities and in the south of France, coverage is good. For the precise location of charging stations, we advise you to check websites like
▶ *www.chargemap.com* ◀,
▶ *www.plugsurfing.com* ◀,
▶ *openchargemap.org* ◀ or one of the many apps.

Tolls

Tolls apply to most French motorways. Blue signs indicate a road leading to a motorway. The indication 'péage' shows that it is a toll road. If you do not wish to pay a toll, follow the green signs which show alternative routes. You can pay the toll by credit card. Some of them can only be paid in cash. Take note that your toll ticket is only valid for 24 hours. More information about toll roads in France: ▶ *www.autoroutes.fr* ◀ (also in English).

Black Saturday
The busiest Saturdays in the summer season are known as 'black Saturdays'. Black Saturdays occur in the last week of July and the first week of August every year.

Emergency numbers
- 112: the national emergency number for fire, police and ambulance
- 17: police
- 18: fire
- 15: ambulance

Camping
France is Europe's biggest camping country. Be sure to reserve early if you want to go to the Ardèche or Dordogne in the interior, or to large seaside resorts. Pitches inland are often more spacious, better equipped and better value than on the coast.

In all swimming pools, proper swimming trunks/costumes are obligatory and women are often required to wear a bathing cap. For hygienic reasons, boxer shorts, Bermuda shorts and other similar clothing is not allowed. On campsites in France you may come across signs 'Inondation par temps de grosse pluie', meaning that the area is prone to flooding during heavy rainfall.

Practical
- Prices for electrical hook-ups are high and can vary from € 1.50 to € 4.50 per day. (These are included in the CampingCard ACSI rate!).
- Make sure you have a world adaptor for electrical appliances.
- Drink bottled (mineral) water in preference to mains water.

Corsica
Most campsites on Corsica are on the coast and are usually well indicated. The roads, especially in the west, are narrow and twisty. French is the official language but a dialect similar to Italian is also spoken. There are few service stations inland! Corsica can be reached by various routes, see page 36 for more information on ferry boat connections.

Hauts-de-France

The Green Fields of Hauts-de-France

Conveniently reached by ferry or tunnel, Hauts-de-France includes Nord-Pas-de-Calais and Picardy and shares a border with Belgium to the north. The landscape is made up of wetlands, forests, hills, hedges, grain fields, beaches, chalk cliffs interspersed with fishing villages and historic mediaeval towns and military monuments.

The old and the new

Amiens, where French kings were crowned, has the largest Gothic cathedral in France. You'll appreciate the beautiful domed basilica in Boulogne-Sur-Mer and the kids will find Nausicaa National Sea Centre fascinating. Explore Boulogne's lovely seafront and nearby Opale Nature Park. Closer to Belgium is Lille: the Old Town extends between the Grand Palace and Rue d'Angleterre, and art enthusiasts will like the Palais des Beaux Art and LaM. The Citadel and old walls of Montreuil-sur-Mer helped inspire novelist Victor Hugo, while the name Dunkirk still resonates today as the location of the greatest evacuation of World War II. Nowadays Dunkirk hosts a huge Carnaval every year, during which the Mayor throws fish at participants.

Other activities

Everywhere you go in Hauts-de-France, you will see monuments to both of the World Wars. The Peronne Museum of the Great War gives an idea of army life, while in Albert you can experience life in the trenches. Tours are available to Thiepval Monument and other notable locations.

The whole family will adore the Baie de la Somme Nature Reserve – look out for birds and seals;

for adrenaline junkies there's kayaking, sailing, walking, riding, and cycling. Walk across Baie with a guide, go on a steam train, or be a knight in Rambures Castle! Visit beautiful Chantilly Castle in Oises Nature Park, near Paris, and the kids will go mad in Park Asterix! Enjoy views over the English Channel at Blanc Nez, or explore the

gardens at Valloires Abbey. Contemplate the Louvre-Lens art installation between Lille and Arras, where timelines and development of art are emphasised.

Our tips

1. See the Flemish Baroque Squares and underground tunnels used for shelter in WWI in Arras

2. La Coupole, the museum located on a former Nazi secret base and underground town

3. Admire the beautiful old towns of Coucy-le-Chateau-Auffrique and Laon

4. Check out Roubaix, home to La Piscine Museum, formerly an Art Deco swimming pool

5. Visit the Scarpe Escaut and De l'Avesnois National Parks

What to eat and drink

Did you know whipped cream was invented here? Other sweets include filled waffles, Amiens macarons, and Lille Merveilleux tart. Savoury dishes include Touquet Fish soup, Flemish stew, Picardy crepes, mussels with fries, and delicious lamb.

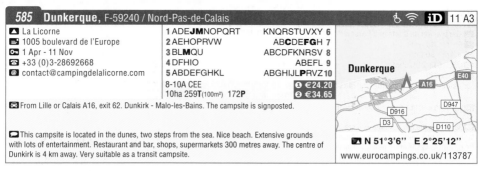

585 Dunkerque, F-59240 / Nord-Pas-de-Calais

🏕 La Licorne
✉ 1005 boulevard de l'Europe
📅 1 Apr - 11 Nov
☎ +33 (0)3-28692668
@ contact@campingdelalicorne.com

1 ADE**JM**NOPQRT	KNQRSTUVXY 6
2 AEHOPRVW	ABC**DEFGH** 7
3 BL**M**QU	ABCDFKNRSV 8
4 DFHIO	ABEFL 9
5 ABDEFGHKL	ABGHIJL**P**RVZ 10

8-10A CEE
10ha 259T(100m²) 172P

💶 €24.20
💶 €34.65

🚗 From Lille or Calais A16, exit 62. Dunkirk - Malo-les-Bains. The campsite is signposted.

💬 This campsite is located in the dunes, two steps from the sea. Nice beach. Extensive grounds with lots of entertainment. Restaurant and bar, shops, supermarkets 300 metres away. The centre of Dunkirk is 4 km away. Very suitable as a transit campsite.

⬧ 11 A3

📍 N 51°3'6'' E 2°25'12''

www.eurocampings.co.uk/113787

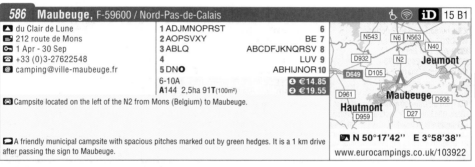

586 Maubeuge, F-59600 / Nord-Pas-de-Calais

🏕 du Clair de Lune
✉ 212 route de Mons
📅 1 Apr - 30 Sep
☎ +33 (0)3-27622548
@ camping@ville-maubeuge.fr

1 ADJMNOPRST	6
2 AOPSVXY	BE 7
3 ABLQ	ABCDFJKNQRSV 8
4	LUV 9
5 DN**O**	ABHIJNOR 10

6-10A
A144 2,5ha 91T(100m²)

💶 €14.85
💶 €19.55

🚗 Campsite located on the left of the N2 from Mons (Belgium) to Maubeuge.

💬 A friendly municipal campsite with spacious pitches marked out by green hedges. It is a 1 km drive after passing the sign to Maubeuge.

⬧ 15 B1

📍 N 50°17'42'' E 3°58'38''

www.eurocampings.co.uk/103922

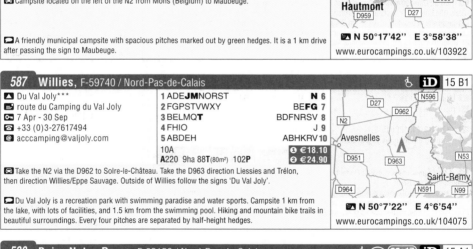

587 Willies, F-59740 / Nord-Pas-de-Calais

🏕 Du Val Joly***
✉ route du Camping du Val Joly
📅 7 Apr - 30 Sep
☎ +33 (0)3-27617494
@ acccamping@valjoly.com

1 ADE**JM**NORST	**N** 6
2 FGPSTVWXY	BE**FG** 7
3 BELMQ**T**	BDFNRSV 8
4 FHIO	J 9
5 ABDEH	ABHKRV 10

10A
A220 9ha 88T(80m²) 102P

💶 €18.10
💶 €24.90

🚗 Take the N2 via the D962 to Solre-le-Château. Take the D963 direction Liessies and Trélon, then direction Willies/Eppe Sauvage. Outside of Willies follow the signs 'Du Val Joly'.

💬 Du Val Joly is a recreation park with swimming paradise and water sports. Campsite 1 km from the lake, with lots of facilities, and 1.5 km from the swimming pool. Hiking and mountain bike trails in beautiful surroundings. Every four pitches are separated by half-height hedges.

⬧ 15 B1

📍 N 50°7'22'' E 4°6'54''

www.eurocampings.co.uk/104075

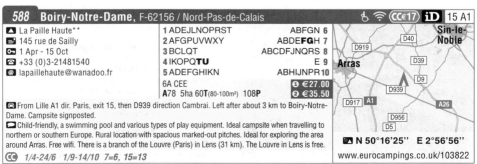

588 Boiry-Notre-Dame, F-62156 / Nord-Pas-de-Calais

🏕 La Paille Haute**
✉ 145 rue de Sailly
📅 1 Apr - 15 Oct
☎ +33 (0)3-21481540
@ lapaillehaute@wanadoo.fr

1 ADEJLNOPRST	ABFGN 6
2 AFGPUVWXY	ABDE**FGH** 7
3 BCLQT	ABCDFJNQRS 8
4 IKOPQ**TU**	E 9
5 ADEFGHIKN	ABHIJNPR 10

6A CEE
A78 5ha 60T(80-100m²) 108P

💶 €27.00
💶 €35.50

🚗 From Lille A1 dir. Paris, exit 15, then D939 direction Cambrai. Left after about 3 km to Boiry-Notre-Dame. Campsite signposted.

💬 Child-friendly, with a swimming pool and various types of play equipment. Ideal campsite when travelling to northern or southern Europe. Rural location with spacious marked-out pitches. Ideal for exploring the area around Arras. Free wifi. There is a branch of the Louvre (Paris) in Lens (31 km). The Louvre in Lens is free.

CC 1/4-24/6 1/9-14/10 7=6, 15=13

⬧ 15 A1

📍 N 50°16'25'' E 2°56'56''

www.eurocampings.co.uk/103822

France

589 Condette, F-62360 / Nord-Pas-de-Calais   ♿ 🛜 iD   10 B3

▲ Caravaning du Château d'Hardelot****	1 ADEJMNOPQRST	6
🏠 21 rue Nouvelle	2 AOPRVX	ABDE**FG**H 7
🕒 1 Apr - 30 Oct	3 AH**KL**	ABCDFJNQRS 8
☎ +33 (0)3-21875959	4 BILO**PQ**	E 9
@ contact@	5 DN	ABHIJO**P**R 10
camping-caravaning-du-chateau.com	10A CEE	❶ €29.60
	1,2ha 70**T**(80-140m²) 25**P**	❷ €40.70

🗺 Via D940 or D119 direction Condette. The campsite is signposted.

💬 Beautifully situated campsite with spacious, marked pitches. Remarkably maintained toilet facilities. Nearby forest and the sandy beach of Hardelot Plage for relaxing walks. Campsite is 800 m from Hardelot Castle with a beautiful park that offers lots of activities (many free of charge), such as the 'Théâtre Elisabethan'.

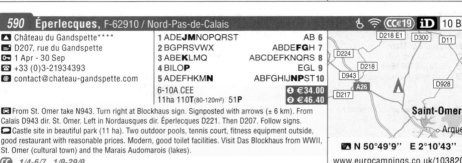

🧭 N 50°38'48''　E 1°37'32''

www.eurocampings.co.uk/113776

---

590 Éperlecques, F-62910 / Nord-Pas-de-Calais   ♿ 🛜 (CC€19) iD   10 B3

▲ Château du Gandspette****	1 ADE**JM**NOPQRST	AB 6
🏠 D207, rue du Gandspette	2 BGPRSVWX	ABDE**FG**H 7
🕒 1 Apr - 30 Sep	3 ABE**KL**MQ	ABCDEFKNQRS 8
☎ +33 (0)3-21934393	4 BILO**P**	EGL 9
@ contact@chateau-gandspette.com	5 ADEFHKM**N**	ABFGHIJ**NP**ST 10
	6-10A CEE	❶ €34.00
	11ha 110**T**(80-120m²) 51**P**	❷ €46.40

🗺 From St. Omer take N943. Turn right at Blockhaus sign. Signposted with arrows (± 6 km). From Calais D943 dir. St. Omer. Left in Nordausques dir. Éperlecques D221. Then D207. Follow signs.

💬 Castle site in beautiful park (11 ha). Two outdoor pools, tennis court, fitness equipment outside, good restaurant with reasonable prices. Modern, good toilet facilities. Visit Das Blockhaus from WWII, St. Omer (cultural town) and the Marais Audomarois (lakes).

CC 1/4-6/7　1/9-29/9

🧭 N 50°49'9''　E 2°10'43''

www.eurocampings.co.uk/103820

---

591 Equihen-Plage, F-62224 / Nord-Pas-de-Calais   🛜 (CC€17) iD   10 B3

▲ Mun. La Falaise***	1 ADE**JM**NOPRST	**ABEFG**HKSTX**Y** 6
🏠 rue Charles Cazin	2 AEHPQTVX	BDEFGH 7
🕒 28 Mar - 7 Nov	3 BELQ	BCD**F**NQS 8
☎ +33 (0)3-21312261	4 IP**Q**	EJ 9
@ camping.equihen.plage@orange.fr	5 D	ABGHIJOR 10
	Ad on this page 10-16A CEE	❶ €26.90
	8ha 95**T**(100-120m²) 242**P**	❷ €37.05

🗺 N1 Boulogne-Abbeville, exit Le Portel/Hardelot or A16 Boulogne-Paris, exit Neuchâtel. From there campsite is signposted.

💬 A large municipal campsite with marked-out pitches which are positioned only 150 metres from the sea. There is plenty of shade. A good base for visiting Boulogne-sur-Mer and Le Touquet-Paris-Plage. With a large, partly covered new pool. Bakery 200 metres from the campsite.

CC 28/3-7/7　26/8-6/11

🧭 N 50°40'15''　E 1°34'18''

www.eurocampings.co.uk/110275

592 Etaples-sur-Mer, F-62630 / Nord-Pas-de-Calais   10 B3

- ▲ La Pinède***
- ✉ 940 chemin Départemental
- 🗓 1 Apr - 15 Nov
- ☎ +33 (0)3-21943575
- @ lapinede.etaples@gmail.com

1 ADE**JM**NOPRS**T**	**X** 6	
2 ABHPVWX	ABDE**FG** 7	
3 ABLQRST	ABCDFJNRSV 8	
4 BCDFH**Q**	BEJV 9	
5 AFGHJM**N**	ABFGHIJORV 10	
6-10A CEE	❶ €24.40	
5ha 68**T**(80-120m²) 46**P**	❷ €35.40	

🚗 From Belgium on the A16 take exit 27 Etaples-Le Touquet D940. After 10 km turn right to British Military Cemetery. Campsite is on the right. From Amiens-Rouen take exit 26. In Etaples head towards Boulogne-sur-Mer, following D940.

💬 On the Canche estuary which flows into the Channel. Beautiful dunes and routes for walks and bike rides. Restaurant nearby. Visit Le Touquet Paris Plage. Peaceful camping area with adequate shade. 2km from sandy beach.

CC 1/4-6/7 27/8-14/11 7=6, 14=12

📍 N 50°31'57'' E 1°37'33''

www.eurocampings.co.uk/111161

---

593 Guines, F-62340 / Nord-Pas-de-Calais   10 B3

- ▲ La Bien Assise*****
- ✉ D231, avenue de la Libération
- 🗓 31 Mar - 29 Sep
- ☎ +33 (0)3-21352077
- @ castels@bien-assise.com

1 ADE**JM**NOPQRST	CDFGH 6	
2 AGPVX	ABDE**FG**H 7	
3 ABE**ILMQ**	ABCDEFJKNOQRSTUV 8	
4 FIO**P**	EL 9	
5 ACDEFHKLMN	ABDFHIJNO**P**R 10	
Ad on this page 10-16A CEE	❶ €36.20	
15ha 149**T**(100-300m²) 66**P**	❷ €46.20	

🚗 From Calais A16, exit 43 to Guines D305. Follow signs in Guines. Site located near roundabout. From Boulonge exit 36 to Guines. From St. Omer take D943 to Ardres, then D231 past Guines. Follow signs to campsite.

💬 Lovely, well maintained castle campsite. Varied surroundings and only 8 km from the coast. The campsite is equipped with modern toilet facilities, a restaurant with an excellent menu, an indoor pool and spacious pitches.

CC 31/3-29/6 3/9-28/9 7=6, 14=12, 21=18

📍 N 50°51'59'' E 1°51'30''

www.eurocampings.co.uk/100234

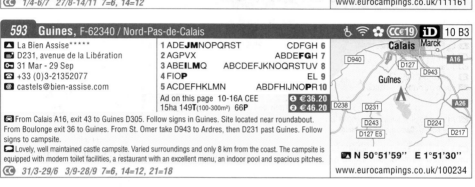

---

594 Licques, F-62850 / Nord-Pas-de-Calais   10 B3

- ▲ Pommiers des Trois Pays****
- ✉ 273 rue du Breuil
- 🗓 15 Mar - 31 Oct
- ☎ +33 (0)3-21350202
- @ contact@pommiers-3pays.com

1 ADE**JM**NOPQRST	CDEFG 6	
2 APSVWX	ABDE**FG**H 7	
3 ABLQT	ABCDEFJKNRSTUV 8	
4 FHIOP	EJU 9	
5 ABDEFGHK**N**	ABFGHIJMPRV 10	
Ad on page 228 16A CEE	❶ €28.90	
A65 2,5ha 36**T**(100-150m²) 35**P**	❷ €36.90	

🚗 From Lille, to Saint-Omer via A26/E15. Exit 2 to Licques. Campsite signposted. From Calais head to Guines. Then D215 to Licques.

💬 The campsite is located in a former apple orchard, with spacious marked-out pitches, situated in Parc Natural Régional des Caps et Marais d'Opale. Licques is just 25 km from the sea, there is a good restaurant with reasonable prices. Open nearly all season. Arrival possible until 10:00 pm.

CC 15/3-6/7 27/8-30/10 7=6

📍 N 50°46'47'' E 1°56'52''

www.eurocampings.co.uk/118070

France

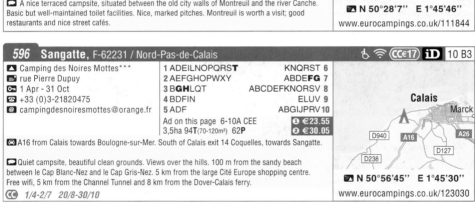

595 Montreuil-sur-Mer, F-62170 / Nord-Pas-de-Calais   📶 iD   10 B3

- ⛰ La Fontaine des Clercs***
- ⛪ 1 rue de l'Eglise
- 🗓 1 Jan - 31 Dec
- ☎ +33 (0)3-21060728
- @ desmarest.mi@wanadoo.fr

1 ADEJMNOPRST		N	6
2 CGPUVX	ABDE	F	7
3 LT	ABCDEFJNRT		8
4 FH	ER		9
5 AD	ABFHIJLPR		10

10A CEE　① €19.50
3ha 76T(80-110m²) 28P　② €23.40

🚗 A16 exit 26 direction Montreuil D939. Before Montreuil on the D349, turn right uphill, directly after the railway. Campsite is signposted.

💬 A nice terraced campsite, situated between the old city walls of Montreuil and the river Canche. Basic but well-maintained toilet facilities. Nice, marked pitches. Montreuil is worth a visit; good restaurants and nice street cafés.

Étaples — A16 — D901 — D939 — Attin — D126
D143 — D918 — D138
Berck — D940 — Conchil-le-Temple — D939

📍 N 50°28'7'' E 1°45'46''
www.eurocampings.co.uk/111844

596 Sangatte, F-62231 / Nord-Pas-de-Calais   ♿ 📶 (CC€17) iD   10 B3

- ⛰ Camping des Noires Mottes***
- ⛪ rue Pierre Dupuy
- 🗓 1 Apr - 31 Oct
- ☎ +33 (0)3-21820475
- @ campingdesnoiresmottes@orange.fr

1 ADEILNOPQRST	KNQRST		6
2 AEFGHOPWXY	ABDE	FG	7
3 BGHLQT	ABCDEFKNORSV		8
4 BDFIN	ELUV		9
5 ADF	ABGIJPRV		10

Ad on this page 6-10A CEE　① €23.55
3,5ha 94T(70-120m²) 62P　② €30.05

🚗 A16 from Calais towards Boulogne-sur-Mer. South of Calais exit 14 Coquelles, towards Sangatte.

💬 Quiet campsite, beautiful clean grounds. Views over the hills. 100 m from the sandy beach between le Cap Blanc-Nez and le Cap Gris-Nez. 5 km from the large Cité Europe shopping centre. Free wifi, 5 km from the Channel Tunnel and 8 km from the Dover-Calais ferry.

CC 1/4-2/7 20/8-30/10

Calais — Marck
D940 — A16 — A26
D238 — D127

📍 N 50°56'45'' E 1°45'30''
www.eurocampings.co.uk/123030

France

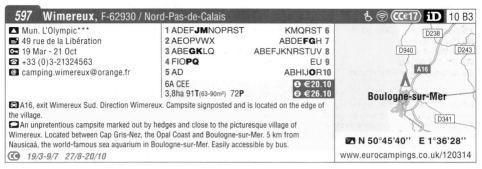

597 Wimereux, F-62930 / Nord-Pas-de-Calais
🚼 📶 (CC€17) iD 10 B3

- ▲ Mun. L'Olympic***
- 🏠 49 rue de la Libération
- 📅 19 Mar - 21 Oct
- ☎ +33 (0)3-21324563
- @ camping.wimereux@orange.fr

1 ADEF**JM**NOPRST	KMQRST 6
2 AEOPVWX	ABDE**FG**H 7
3 ABE**GK**LQ	ABEFJKNRSTUV 8
4 FIO**PQ**	EU 9
5 AD	ABHIJO**R**10
6A CEE	❶ €20.10
3,8ha 91**T**(63-90m²) 72**P**	❷ €26.10

🚗 A16, exit Wimereux Sud. Direction Wimereux. Campsite signposted and is located on the edge of the village.
💬 An unpretentious campsite marked out by hedges and close to the picturesque village of Wimereux. Located between Cap Gris-Nez, the Opal Coast and Boulogne-sur-Mer. 5 km from Nausicaá, the world-famous sea aquarium in Boulogne-sur-Mer. Easily accessible by bus.

🏕 N 50°45'40'' E 1°36'28''

CC 19/3-9/7 27/8-20/10

www.eurocampings.co.uk/120314

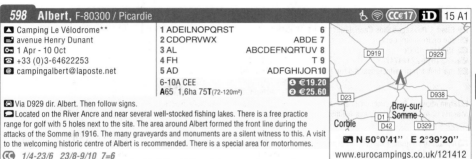

598 Albert, F-80300 / Picardie
🚼 📶 (CC€17) iD 15 A1

- ▲ Camping Le Vélodrome**
- 🏠 avenue Henry Dunant
- 📅 1 Apr - 10 Oct
- ☎ +33 (0)3-64622253
- @ campingalbert@laposte.net

1 ADEILNOPQRST	6
2 CDOPRVWX	ABDE 7
3 AL	ABCDEFNQRTUV 8
4 FH	T 9
5 AD	ADFGHIJOR10
6-10A CEE	❶ €19.20
A65 1,6ha 75**T**(72-120m²)	❷ €25.60

🚗 Via D929 dir. Albert. Then follow signs.
💬 Located on the River Ancre and near several well-stocked fishing lakes. There is a free practice range for golf with 5 holes next to the site. The area around Albert formed the front line during the attacks of the Somme in 1916. The many graveyards and monuments are a silent witness to this. A visit to the welcoming historic centre of Albert is recommended. There is a special area for motorhomes.

🏕 N 50°0'41'' E 2°39'20''

CC 1/4-23/6 23/8-9/10 7=6

www.eurocampings.co.uk/121412

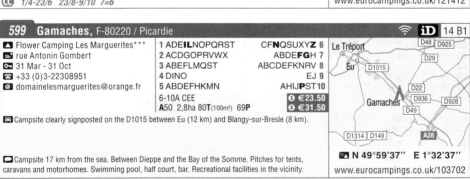

599 Gamaches, F-80220 / Picardie
📶 iD 14 B1

- ▲ Flower Camping Les Marguerites***
- 🏠 rue Antonin Gombert
- 📅 31 Mar - 31 Oct
- ☎ +33 (0)3-22308951
- @ domainelesmarguerites@orange.fr

1 ADE**IL**NOPQRST	CF**N**QSUXY**Z** 6
2 ACDGOPRVWX	ABDE**FG**H 7
3 ABEFLMQST	ABCDEFKNRV 8
4 DINO	EJ 9
5 ABDEFHKMN	AHIJ**P**ST10
6-10A CEE	❶ €23.50
A50 2,8ha 80**T**(100m²) 69**P**	❷ €31.50

🚗 Campsite clearly signposted on the D1015 between Eu (12 km) and Blangy-sur-Bresle (8 km).

💬 Campsite 17 km from the sea. Between Dieppe and the Bay of the Somme. Pitches for tents, caravans and motorhomes. Swimming pool, half court, bar. Recreational facilities in the vicinity.

🏕 N 49°59'37'' E 1°32'37''

www.eurocampings.co.uk/103702

600 Le Crotoy, F-80550 / Picardie
🚼 📶 (CC€17) iD 44

- ▲ Flower Camping Les Aubépines****
- 🏠 rue de la Maye - St. Firmin
- 📅 30 Mar - 4 Nov
- ☎ +33 (0)3-22270134
- @ contact@camping-lesaubepines.com

1 ADE**JM**NOPQRS**T**	ABEFG 6
2 AGHOPVX	ABDE**FG**HK 7
3 A**KL**MQRSTV	ABCDFHJKNPQRSTUV 8
4 **A**BDEFHKLO	ELUV 9
5 ACDEFGJKM**NO**	ABDGHIJN**P**R10
3-10A CEE	❶ €30.00
4ha 74**T**(90-180m²) 122**P**	❷ €39.00

🚗 From A16 exit 23, follow road to Le Crotoy. At Le Crotoy, follow D4 Crotoy/St. Firmin de C. Left at sign for St. Firmin. The campsite is signposted. Do not follow SatNav on last section.
💬 Les Aubépines, a family campsite with a lovely indoor pool, is located in the heart of the Somme bay region, in natural surroundings and 1 km from the beach. A paradise for cyclists and walkers. You can bring your own horse. The campsite can arrange half-board.

🏕 N 50°14'59'' E 1°36'43''

CC 30/3-4/5 14/5-6/7 27/8-31/10

www.eurocampings.co.uk/111128

601 Mers-les-Bains, F-80350 / Picardie
≋ CC€17 iD 44

- ▲ Flower Camping Le Rompval***
- ▤ Lieu dit Blengues
- ☷ 30 Mar - 4 Nov
- ☎ +33 (0)2-35844321
- @ campinglerompval@gmail.com

1	ADEF**JM**NOPQRS**T**	CDFG 6
2	GPVWXY	ABDE**FGH** 7
3	ALQTV	ABCDFGHJNQRSTUV 8
4	BCDLNO**PQ**	BEHLV 9
5	ABDEFGHJM**NO**	ABDGHIJPR10

6-13A CEE ❶ €29.60
3ha 79T(90-100m²) 53P ❷ €40.10

🅰️ A28, exit 2 direction Le Tréport. Follow the D940 (Route d'Eu) direction St. Valery-sur-Somme. Left after 3 km. Signposted. Don't go via Mers-les-Bains with a caravan.

💬 A quietly located Flower campsite for those who appreciate the countryside. Located next to a protected wood less than 1 km from the Falaise. Mers-les-Bains and Tréport are worth a visit. Try ordering a delicious breakfast.

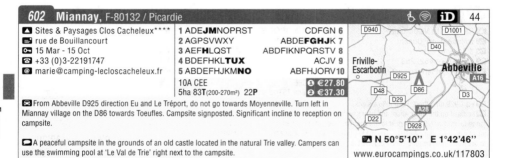

⚓ N 50°4'39'' E 1°24'52''

CC 30/3-7/7 25/8-3/11 7=6, 14=11

www.eurocampings.co.uk/118519

602 Miannay, F-80132 / Picardie
♿ ≋ iD 44

- ▲ Sites & Paysages Clos Cacheleux****
- ▤ rue de Bouillancourt
- ☷ 15 Mar - 15 Oct
- ☎ +33 (0)3-22191747
- @ marie@camping-lecloscacheleux.fr

1	ADE**JM**NOPRST	CDFGN 6
2	AGPSVWXY	ABDE**FGHJ**K 7
3	AEF**H**LQST	ABDFIKNPQRSTV 8
4	BDEFHKL**TUX**	ACJV 9
5	ABDEFHJKM**NO**	ABFHJORV10

10A CEE ❶ €27.80
5ha 83T(200-270m²) 22P ❷ €37.30

🅰️ From Abbeville D925 direction Eu and Le Tréport, do not go towards Moyenneville. Turn left in Miannay village on the D86 towards Toeufles. Campsite signposted. Significant incline to reception on campsite.

💬 A peaceful campsite in the grounds of an old castle located in the natural Trie valley. Campers can use the swimming pool at 'Le Val de Trie' right next to the campsite.

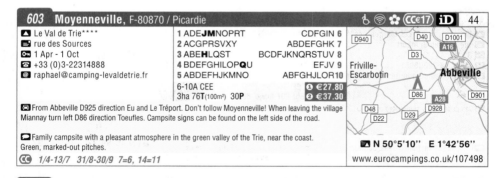

⚓ N 50°5'10'' E 1°42'46''

www.eurocampings.co.uk/117803

603 Moyenneville, F-80870 / Picardie
♿ ≋ ✿ CC€17 iD 44

- ▲ Le Val de Trie****
- ▤ rue des Sources
- ☷ 1 Apr - 1 Oct
- ☎ +33 (0)3-22314888
- @ raphael@camping-levaldetrie.fr

1	ADE**JM**NOPRT	CDFGIN 6
2	ACGPRSVXY	ABDE**FGHK** 7
3	ABE**H**LQST	BCDFJKNQRSTUV 8
4	BDEFGHILOP**QU**	EFJV 9
5	ABDEFHJKMNO	ABFGHJLOR10

6-10A CEE ❶ €27.80
3ha 76T(100m²) 30P ❷ €37.30

🅰️ From Abbeville D925 direction Eu and Le Tréport. Don't follow Moyenneville! When leaving the village Miannay turn left D86 direction Toeufles. Campsite signs can be found on the left side of the road.

💬 Family campsite with a pleasant atmosphere in the green valley of the Trie, near the coast. Green, marked-out pitches.

⚓ N 50°5'10'' E 1°42'56''

CC 1/4-13/7 31/8-30/9 7=6, 14=11

www.eurocampings.co.uk/107498

604 Péronne, F-80200 / Picardie
♿ ≋ CC€17 👫 iD 15 A1

- ▲ Port de Plaisance***
- ▤ route de Paris
- ☷ 1 Mar - 31 Oct
- ☎ +33 (0)3-22841931
- @ contact@camping-plaisance.com

1	ADE**JM**NOPRST	ABFG**NXYZ** 6
2	ACOPVX	ABDE**FG** 7
3	ALQ	ABCDFJNQR 8
4	IO**PQ**	JV 9
5	ABDFHN	ABDFGHJ**NO**PRZ10

10A CEE ❶ €27.20
A56 2ha 82T(80-150m²) 12P ❷ €31.20

🅰️ The campsite is located south of Péronne, on the N17.

💬 This campsite is located a few kilometres from the A1 near a yacht harbour close to Peronne. The grounds are level with a choice of shaded or non-shaded pitches. The area is known for its many historic World War I locations.

⚓ N 49°55'4'' E 2°55'57''

CC 1/3-10/7 28/8-30/10 7=6

www.eurocampings.co.uk/103824

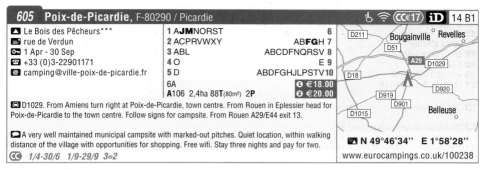

605 Poix-de-Picardie, F-80290 / Picardie
♿ 📶 (CC€17) iD 14 B1

- ⛰ Le Bois des Pêcheurs***
- 🏠 rue de Verdun
- 📅 1 Apr - 30 Sep
- ☎ +33 (0)3-22901171
- @ camping@ville-poix-de-picardie.fr

1 A**JM**NORST		6
2 ACPRVWXY	AB**FG**H	7
3 ABL	ABCDFNQRSV	8
4 O	E	9
5 D	ABDFGHJLPSTV	10
6A	❶ €18.00	
A106 2,4ha 88T(80m²) 2P	❷ €20.00	

🚗 D1029. From Amiens turn right at Poix-de-Picardie, town centre. From Rouen in Eplessier head for Poix-de-Picardie to the town centre. Follow signs for campsite. From Rouen A29/E44 exit 13.

💬 A very well maintained municipal campsite with marked-out pitches. Quiet location, within walking distance of the village with opportunities for shopping. Free wifi. Stay three nights and pay for two.
CC 1/4-30/6 1/9-29/9 3=2

🗺 N 49°46'34'' E 1°58'28''
www.eurocampings.co.uk/100238

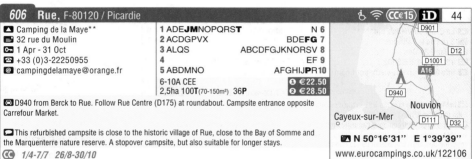

606 Rue, F-80120 / Picardie
♿ 📶 (CC€15) iD 44

- ⛰ Camping de la Maye**
- 🏠 32 rue du Moulin
- 📅 1 Apr - 31 Oct
- ☎ +33 (0)3-22250955
- @ campingdelamaye@orange.fr

1 ADE**JM**NOPQRS**T**	N	6
2 ACDGPVX	BDE**FG**	7
3 ALQS	ABCDFGJKNORSV	8
4	EF	9
5 ABDMNO	AFGHIJ**P**R	10
6-10A CEE	❶ €22.50	
2,5ha 100T(70-150m²) 36P	❷ €28.50	

🚗 D940 from Berck to Rue. Follow Rue Centre (D175) at roundabout. Campsite entrance opposite Carrefour Market.

💬 This refurbished campsite is close to the historic village of Rue, close to the Bay of Somme and the Marquenterre nature reserve. A stopover campsite, but also suitable for longer stays.
CC 1/4-7/7 26/8-30/10

🗺 N 50°16'31'' E 1°39'39''
www.eurocampings.co.uk/122106

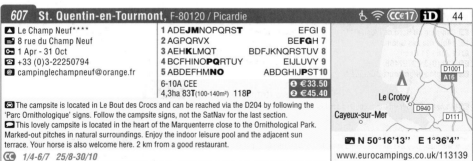

607 St. Quentin-en-Tourmont, F-80120 / Picardie
♿ 📶 (CC€17) iD 44

- ⛰ Le Champ Neuf****
- 🏠 8 rue du Champ Neuf
- 📅 1 Apr - 31 Oct
- ☎ +33 (0)3-22250794
- @ campinglechampneuf@orange.fr

1 ADE**JM**NOPQRS**T**	EFGI	6
2 AGPQRVX	BE**FG**H	7
3 AEH**K**LMQT	BDFJKNQRSTUV	8
4 BCFHINO**PQ**RTUY	EIJLUVY	9
5 ABDEFHM**NO**	ABDGHIJ**P**ST	10
6-10A CEE	❶ €33.50	
4,3ha 83T(100-140m²) 118P	❷ €45.40	

🚗 The campsite is located in Le Bout des Crocs and can be reached via the D204 by following the 'Parc Ornithologique' signs. Follow the campsite signs, not the SatNav for the last section.
💬 This lovely campsite is located in the heart of the Marquenterre close to the Ornithological Park. Marked-out pitches in natural surroundings. Enjoy the indoor leisure pool and the adjacent sun terrace. Your horse is also welcome here. 2 km from a good restaurant.
CC 1/4-6/7 25/8-30/10

🗺 N 50°16'13'' E 1°36'4''
www.eurocampings.co.uk/113139

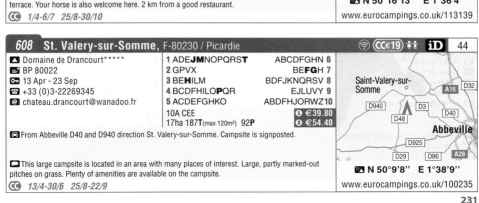

608 St. Valery-sur-Somme, F-80230 / Picardie
📶 (CC€19) 🚻 iD 44

- ⛰ Domaine de Drancourt*****
- 🏠 BP 80022
- 📅 13 Apr - 23 Sep
- ☎ +33 (0)3-22269345
- @ chateau.drancourt@wanadoo.fr

1 ADE**JM**NOPQRS**T**	ABCDFGHN	6
2 GPVX	BE**FG**H	7
3 BE**H**ILM	BDFJKNQRSV	8
4 BCDFHILO**P**QR	EJLUVY	9
5 ACDEFGHKO	ABDFHJORWZ	10
10A CEE	❶ €39.80	
17ha 187T(max 120m²) 92P	❷ €54.40	

🚗 From Abbeville D40 and D940 direction St. Valery-sur-Somme. Campsite is signposted.

💬 This large campsite is located in an area with many places of interest. Large, partly marked-out pitches on grass. Plenty of amenities are available on the campsite.
CC 13/4-30/6 25/8-22/9

🗺 N 50°9'8'' E 1°38'9''
www.eurocampings.co.uk/100235

France

609 Villers-sur-Authie, F-80120 / Picardie ♿ 📶 ⚙ (CC€17) iD 44

▲ Sites & Paysages
Le Val d'Authie*****
🏠 20 route de Vercourt
📅 1 Apr - 30 Sep
☎ +33 (0)3-22299247
@ camping@valdauthie.fr

1 ADE**JM**NOPRS**T**	CDFG 6
2 AGPVX	ABDE**FG**HK 7
3 AE**KL**MQST	BDFJKNPQRSTV 8
4 ILNOR**TUV**	ELV 9
5 ACDEFGHKN	ABFGHIJN**PR**Z10
6-10A	❶ €31.00
7ha 60**T**(100-150m²) 104**P**	❷ €41.00

🚗 D901 Boulogne-Abbeville, exit Nampont, direction Villers-sur-Authie.

💬 This five-star campsite with excellent toilets and many facilities is 10 minutes from the coast, with Marquenterre nature reserve, and from the woods at Crécy. The site is an oasis of peace and has a good restaurant, indoor swimming pool and wellness room. Good cycling options.

CC 1/4-6/7 25/8-29/9 8=7, 14=12

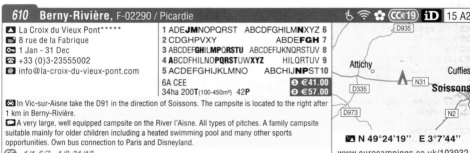

N 50°18'49'' E 1°41'42''

www.eurocampings.co.uk/109606

610 Berny-Rivière, F-02290 / Picardie ♿ 📶 ⚙ (CC€19) iD 15 A2

▲ La Croix du Vieux Pont*****
🏠 8 rue de la Fabrique
📅 1 Jan - 31 Dec
☎ +33 (0)3-23555002
@ info@la-croix-du-vieux-pont.com

| 1 ADE**JM**NOPQRST ABCDFGHILM**N**XYZ 6 |
| 2 CDGHPVXY ABDE**FGH** 7 |
| 3 ABCDEF**GHILMPQRSTU** ABCDEFIJKNQRSTUV 8 |
| 4 ABCDFHILNO**PQRST**UWX**YZ** HILQRTUV 9 |
| 5 ACDEFGHIJKLMNO ABCHIJ**NP**ST10 |
| 6A CEE ❶ €41.00 |
| 34ha 200**T**(100-450m²) 42**P** ❷ €57.00 |

🚗 In Vic-sur-Aisne take the D91 in the direction of Soissons. The campsite is located to the right after 1 km in Berny-Rivière.

💬 A very large, well equipped campsite on the River l'Aisne. All types of pitches. A family campsite suitable mainly for older children including a heated swimming pool and many other sports opportunities. Own bus connection to Paris and Disneyland.

CC 1/1-6/7 1/9-31/12

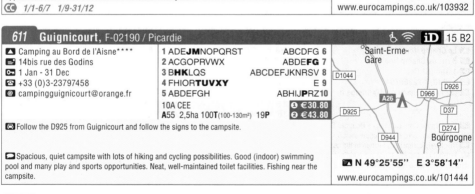

N 49°24'19'' E 3°7'44''

www.eurocampings.co.uk/103932

611 Guignicourt, F-02190 / Picardie ♿ 📶 iD 15 B2

▲ Camping au Bord de l'Aisne****
🏠 14bis rue des Godins
📅 1 Jan - 31 Dec
☎ +33 (0)3-23797458
@ campingguignicourt@orange.fr

| 1 ADE**JM**NOPQRST ABCDFG 6 |
| 2 ACGOPRVWX ABDE**FG** 7 |
| 3 B**HK**LQS ABCDEFJKNRSV 8 |
| 4 FHIOR**TUVXY** E 9 |
| 5 ABDEFGH ABHIJ**PR**Z10 |
| 10A CEE ❶ €30.80 |
| A55 2,5ha 100**T**(100-130m²) 19**P** ❷ €43.80 |

🚗 Follow the D925 from Guignicourt and follow the signs to the campsite.

💬 Spacious, quiet campsite with lots of hiking and cycling possibilities. Good (indoor) swimming pool and many play and sports opportunities. Neat, well-maintained toilet facilities. Fishing near the campsite.

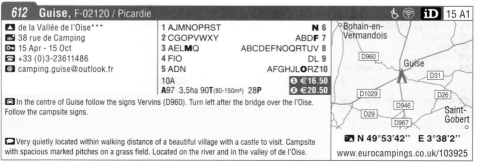

N 49°25'55'' E 3°58'14''

www.eurocampings.co.uk/101444

612 Guise, F-02120 / Picardie ♿ 📶 iD 15 A1

▲ de la Vallée de l'Oise***
🏠 38 rue de Camping
📅 15 Apr - 15 Oct
☎ +33 (0)3-23611486
@ camping.guise@outlook.fr

| 1 AJMNOPRST **N** 6 |
| 2 CGOPVWXY ABD**F** 7 |
| 3 AELMQ ABCDEFNOQRTUV 8 |
| 4 FIO DL 9 |
| 5 ADN AFGHJL**OR**Z10 |
| 10A ❶ €16.50 |
| A97 3,5ha 90**T**(80-150m²) 28**P** ❷ €20.50 |

🚗 In the centre of Guise follow the signs Vervins (D960). Turn left after the bridge over the l'Oise. Follow the campsite signs.

💬 Very quietly located within walking distance of a beautiful village with a castle to visit. Campsite with spacious marked pitches on a grass field. Located on the river and in the valley of de l'Oise.

N 49°53'42'' E 3°38'2''

www.eurocampings.co.uk/103925

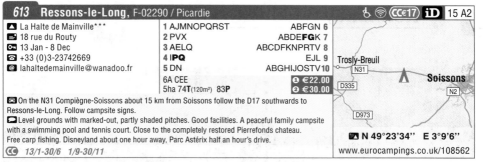

613 Ressons-le-Long, F-02290 / Picardie ♿ 🛜 (CC€17) **iD** 15 A2

- 🏕 La Halte de Mainville***
- 🏠 18 rue du Routy
- 📅 13 Jan - 8 Dec
- ☎ +33 (0)3-23742669
- @ lahaltedemainville@wanadoo.fr

1 AJMNOPQRST	ABFGN	6
2 PVX	ABDE**FGK**	7
3 AELQ	ABCDFKNPRTV	8
4 I**PQ**	EJL	9
5 DN	ABGHIJOSTV	10
6A CEE	❶ €22.00	
5ha 74**T**(120m²) 83**P**	❷ €30.00	

🚗 On the N31 Compiègne-Soissons about 15 km from Soissons follow the D17 southwards to Ressons-le-Long. Follow campsite signs.

🏕 Level grounds with marked-out, partly shaded pitches. Good facilities. A peaceful family campsite with a swimming pool and tennis court. Close to the completely restored Pierrefonds chateau. Free carp fishing. Disneyland about one hour away, Parc Astérix half an hour's drive.

CC 13/1-30/6   1/9-30/11

N 49°23'34''   E 3°9'6''

www.eurocampings.co.uk/108562

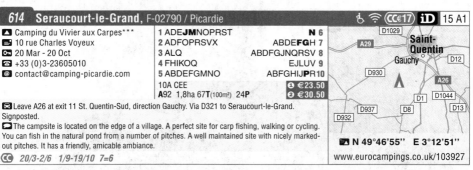

614 Seraucourt-le-Grand, F-02790 / Picardie ♿ 🛜 (CC€17) **iD** 15 A1

- 🏕 Camping du Vivier aux Carpes***
- 🏠 10 rue Charles Voyeux
- 📅 20 Mar - 20 Oct
- ☎ +33 (0)3-23605010
- @ contact@camping-picardie.com

1 ADE**JM**NOPRST	**N**	6
2 ADFOPRSVX	ABDE**FGH**	7
3 ALQ	ABDFGJNQRSV	8
4 FHIKOQ	EJLUV	9
5 ABDEFGMNO	ABFGHIJ**PR**	10
10A CEE	❶ €23.50	
A92 1,8ha 67**T**(100m²) 24**P**	❷ €30.50	

🚗 Leave A26 at exit 11 St. Quentin-Sud, direction Gauchy. Via D321 to Seraucourt-le-Grand. Signposted.

🏕 The campsite is located on the edge of a village. A perfect site for carp fishing, walking or cycling. You can fish in the natural pond from a number of pitches. A well maintained site with nicely marked-out pitches. It has a friendly, amicable ambiance.

CC 20/3-2/6   1/9-19/10 7=6

N 49°46'55''   E 3°12'51''

www.eurocampings.co.uk/103927

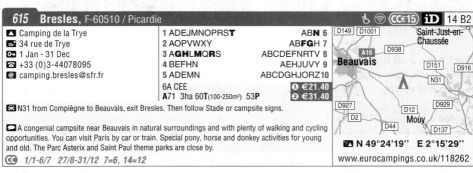

615 Bresles, F-60510 / Picardie ♿ 🛜 (CC€15) **iD** 14 B2

- 🏕 Camping de la Trye
- 🏠 34 rue de Trye
- 📅 1 Jan - 31 Dec
- ☎ +33 (0)3-44078095
- @ camping.bresles@sfr.fr

1 ADEJMNOPRS**T**	AB**N**	6
2 AOPVWXY	AB**FGH**	7
3 A**GHLMQR**S	ABCDEFNRTV	8
4 BEFHN	AEHJUVY	9
5 ADEMN	ABCDGHJORZ	10
6A CEE	❶ €21.40	
A71 3ha 60**T**(100-250m²) 53**P**	❷ €31.40	

🚗 N31 from Compiègne to Beauvais, exit Bresles. Then follow Stade or campsite signs.

🏕 A congenial campsite near Beauvais in natural surroundings and with plenty of walking and cycling opportunities. You can visit Paris by car or train. Special pony, horse and donkey activities for young and old. The Parc Asterix and Saint Paul theme parks are close by.

CC 1/1-6/7   27/8-31/12 7=6, 14=12

N 49°24'19''   E 2°15'29''

www.eurocampings.co.uk/118262

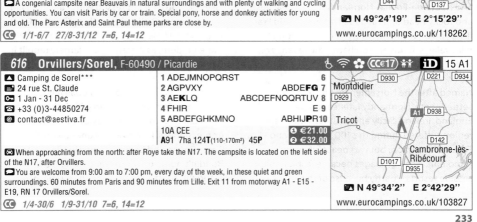

616 Orvillers/Sorel, F-60490 / Picardie ♿ 🛜 ✿ (CC€17) ✹✹ **iD** 15 A1

- 🏕 Camping de Sorel***
- 🏠 24 rue St. Claude
- 📅 1 Jan - 31 Dec
- ☎ +33 (0)3-44850274
- @ contact@aestiva.fr

1 ADEJMNOPQRST		6
2 AGPVXY	ABDE**FG**	7
3 AE**K**LQ	ABCDEFNOQRTUV	8
4 FHIR	E	9
5 ABDEFGHKMNO	ABHIJ**PR**	10
10A CEE	❶ €21.00	
A91 7ha 124**T**(110-170m²) 45**P**	❷ €32.00	

🚗 When approaching from the north: after Roye take the N17. The campsite is located on the left side of the N17, after Orvillers.

🏕 You are welcome from 9:00 am to 7:00 pm, every day of the week, in these quiet and green surroundings. 60 minutes from Paris and 90 minutes from Lille. Exit 11 from motorway A1 - E15 - E19, RN 17 Orvillers/Sorel.

CC 1/4-30/6   1/9-31/10 7=6, 14=12

N 49°34'2''   E 2°42'29''

www.eurocampings.co.uk/103827

Normandy

Darkness and light

Now peaceful, Normandy is strewn with reminders of the region's turbulent past.

Located in north-west France between Brittany and Hauts-de-France, Normandy's long beaches and rocky headlands include traces of World War II. As you drive inland from the coast, among the hills, valleys, farms and orchards, the ravages of war seem a world away.

Named after the Norsemen, or Vikings, who settled there, Normandy later conquered England, Ireland, Sicily and Southern Italy. The region suffered during the 100 Years War and French Revolution, but was peaceful under Napoleon. Fishing villages became fashionable seaside resorts – partly because of the railways.

Historic towns, fashion and painting

Victor Hugo called it the 'city of 100 spires' and walking through Rouen, you will see why: mediaeval houses, imposing churches, the Palais de Justice, and the Gothic 'le Gros Horloge'. Likewise you'll be impressed with Caen, William the Conqueror's city: the castle built in 1060 now houses the Museum of Fine Arts. Le Havre feels more modern, as its centre was largely rebuilt in reinforced precast concrete.

Beach-lovers visit Dieppe and Colleville-sur-Mer, while Deauville is linked with fashion icon Coco Chanel. Normandy is associated with the Impressionists: Pisarro and Monet painted in Caen, Rouen and Le Havre, and Honfleur was Boudin's home town. Eretrat Cliffs and archways along the coast and the Seine Valley still attract painters and nature lovers, while art lovers flock to Monet's Gardens and the Museum of Impressionism at Giverny.

Out in the fresh air

Everyone can enjoy the Norman great outdoors! The region has excellent nature reserves and national parks, such De Marais du Contentin, and Boucles de la Seine includes the castle of Robert the Devil. The kids will go ape in the Corza Zoological Park near Lisieux, with animal safari, walkways and zoo train. If contemplative nature is your thing, you'll appreciate the forests, bog and heathlands of Perche Nature Park.

Food and drink

Fresh air works up an appetite, so try delicious Camembert cheese, apples or cider, or tuck into some seafood – plat du fruits de mer is a local staple. Food festivals abound here: Villers-sur-Mer Scallop and Seafood Festival and Caudebec-en-Caux Cider Festival. Sweet tooth? Visit Maison Du Biscuit factory, Sortosville-en-Beaumont.

Our tips

1. *Experience historic D-Day landing beaches: Omaha, Utah, Juno, Gold and Sword*

2. *Art lover? Visit the Musée du Bocage Normand, Saint-Lo*

3. *Manoir d'Ango near Dieppe, is an example of a Norman 'manoir ferme'*

4. *Cross over to Mont St Michel, the fortified coastal island town*

5. *See the 1000-year-old oak tree known as Chene Chapelle at Allouville-Bellevosse*

617 Fécamp, F-76400 / Haute-Normandie

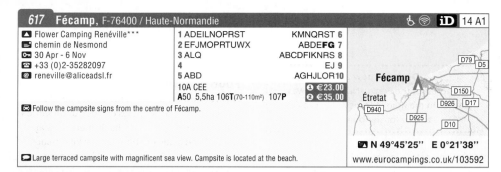

♿ 📶 **iD** 14 A1

- 🏕 Flower Camping Renéville***
- ✉ chemin de Nesmond
- 📅 30 Apr - 6 Nov
- ☎ +33 (0)2-35282097
- @ reneville@aliceadsl.fr

1 ADEILNOPRST	KMNQRST	6
2 EFJMOPRTUWX	ABDE**FG**	7
3 ALQ	ABCDFIKNRS	8
4	EJ	9
5 ABD	AGHJLOR	10
10A CEE	❶ €23.00	
A50 5,5ha 106**T**(70-110m²) 107**P**	❷ €35.00	

🚗 Follow the campsite signs from the centre of Fécamp.

💬 Large terraced campsite with magnificent sea view. Campsite is located at the beach.

📍 **N 49°45'25'' E 0°21'38''**

www.eurocampings.co.uk/103592

---

618 Forges-les-Eaux, F-76440 / Haute-Normandie

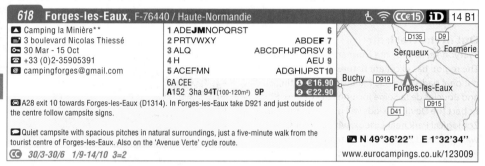

♿ 📶 **(CC€15)** **iD** 14 B1

- 🏕 Camping la Minière**
- ✉ 3 boulevard Nicolas Thiessé
- 📅 30 Mar - 15 Oct
- ☎ +33 (0)2-35905391
- @ campingforges@gmail.com

1 ADE**JM**NOPQRST		6
2 PRTVWXY	ABDE**F**	7
3 ALQ	ABCDFHJPQRSV	8
4 H	AEU	9
5 ACEFMN	ADGHIJPST	10
6A CEE	❶ €16.90	
A152 3ha 94**T**(100-120m²) 9**P**	❷ €22.90	

🚗 A28 exit 10 towards Forges-les-Eaux (D1314). In Forges-les-Eaux take D921 and just outside of the centre follow campsite signs.

💬 Quiet campsite with spacious pitches in natural surroundings, just a five-minute walk from the tourist centre of Forges-les-Eaux. Also on the 'Avenue Verte' cycle route.

CC 30/3-30/6 1/9-14/10 3=2

📍 **N 49°36'22'' E 1°32'34''**

www.eurocampings.co.uk/123009

---

619 Hautot-sur-Mer, F-76550 / Haute-Normandie

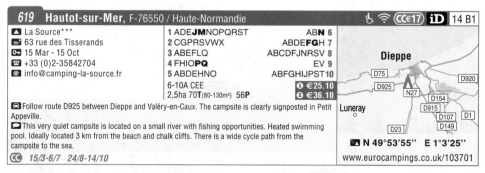

♿ 📶 **(CC€17)** **iD** 14 B1

- 🏕 La Source***
- ✉ 63 rue des Tisserands
- 📅 15 Mar - 15 Oct
- ☎ +33 (0)2-35842704
- @ info@camping-la-source.fr

1 ADE**JM**NOPQRST	AB**N**	6
2 CGPRSVWX	ABDE**FG**H	7
3 ABEFLQ	ABCDFJNRSV	8
4 FHIO**PQ**	EV	9
5 ABDEHNO	ABFGHIJPST	10
6-10A CEE	❶ €25.10	
2,5ha 70**T**(80-130m²) 56**P**	❷ €36.10	

🚗 Follow route D925 between Dieppe and Valéry-en-Caux. The campsite is clearly signposted in Petit Appeville.

💬 This very quiet campsite is located on a small river with fishing opportunities. Heated swimming pool. Ideally located 3 km from the beach and chalk cliffs. There is a wide cycle path from the campsite to the sea.

CC 15/3-6/7 24/8-14/10

📍 **N 49°53'55'' E 1°3'25''**

www.eurocampings.co.uk/103701

---

620 Jumieges, F-76480 / Haute-Normandie

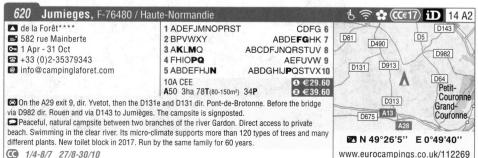

♿ 📶 ✿ **(CC€17)** **iD** 14 A2

- 🏕 de la Forêt****
- ✉ 582 rue Mainberte
- 📅 1 Apr - 31 Oct
- ☎ +33 (0)2-35379343
- @ info@campinglaforet.com

1 ADEFJMNOPRST	CDFG	6
2 BPVWXY	ABDE**FG**HK	7
3 A**KLM**Q	ABCDFJNQRSTUV	8
4 FHIO**PQ**	AEFUVW	9
5 ABDEFHJ**N**	ABDGHIJ**P**QSTVX	10
10A CEE	❶ €29.60	
A50 3ha 78**T**(80-150m²) 34**P**	❷ €39.60	

🚗 On the A29 exit 9, dir. Yvetot, then the D131e and D131 dir. Pont-de-Brotonne. Before the bridge via D982 dir. Rouen and via D143 to Jumièges. The campsite is signposted.

💬 Peaceful, natural campsite between two branches of the river Gardon. Direct access to private beach. Swimming in the clear river. Its micro-climate supports more than 120 types of trees and many different plants. New toilet block in 2017. Run by the same family for 60 years.

CC 1/4-8/7 27/8-30/10

📍 **N 49°26'5'' E 0°49'40''**

www.eurocampings.co.uk/112269

France

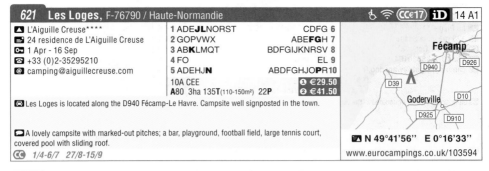

621 Les Loges, F-76790 / Haute-Normandie
♿ 🛜 (CC€17) iD 14 A1

- 🏔 L'Aiguille Creuse★★★★
- 🏠 24 residence de L'Aiguille Creuse
- 🗓 1 Apr - 16 Sep
- ☎ +33 (0)2-35295210
- @ camping@aiguillecreuse.com

1 ADE**JL**NORST	CDFG	**6**
2 GOPVWX	ABE**FG**H	**7**
3 AB**K**LMQT	BDFGIJKNRSV	**8**
4 FO	EL	**9**
5 ADEHJ**N**	ABDFGHJO**P**R	**10**
10A CEE	❶ €29.50	
A80 3ha 135**T**(110-150m²) 22**P**	❷ €41.50	

🏕 Les Loges is located along the D940 Fécamp-Le Havre. Campsite well signposted in the town.

💬 A lovely campsite with marked-out pitches; a bar, playground, football field, large tennis court, covered pool with sliding roof.

CC 1/4-6/7 27/8-15/9

N 49°41'56'' E 0°16'33''

www.eurocampings.co.uk/103594

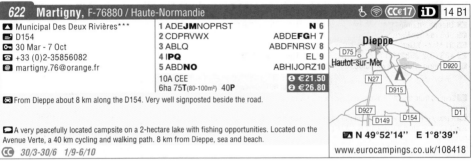

622 Martigny, F-76880 / Haute-Normandie
♿ 🛜 (CC€17) iD 14 B1

- 🏔 Municipal Des Deux Rivières★★★
- 🏠 D154
- 🗓 30 Mar - 7 Oct
- ☎ +33 (0)2-35856082
- @ martigny.76@orange.fr

1 ADE**JM**NOPRST	**N**	**6**
2 CDPRVWX	ABDE**FG**H	**7**
3 ABLQ	ABDFNRSV	**8**
4 **IPQ**	EL	**9**
5 ABD**NO**	ABHIJORZ	**10**
10A CEE	❶ €21.50	
6ha 75**T**(80-100m²) 40**P**	❷ €26.80	

🏕 From Dieppe about 8 km along the D154. Very well signposted beside the road.

💬 A very peacefully located campsite on a 2-hectare lake with fishing opportunities. Located on the Avenue Verte, a 40 km cycling and walking path. 8 km from Dieppe, sea and beach.

CC 30/3-30/6 1/9-6/10

N 49°52'14'' E 1°8'39''

www.eurocampings.co.uk/108418

623 Neufchâtel-en-Bray, F-76270 / Haute-Normandie
♿ 🛜 (CC€15) iD 14 B1

- 🏔 Sainte Claire★★★
- 🏠 19 rue Grande Flandre
- 🗓 1 Apr - 15 Oct
- ☎ +33 (0)2-35930393
- @ fancelot@wanadoo.fr

1 ADEJMNOPQRST		**6**
2 ACGPSVWX	ABDE**FG**	**7**
3	ABCDFNRSV	**8**
4 FH	FJ	**9**
5 ABDEFHKN	ABCDFGHJ**P**R	**10**
6-10A CEE	❶ €17.00	
2,5ha 91**T**(60-180m²) 9**P**	❷ €23.00	

🏕 Well signposted about 1 km from Neufchâtel-en-Bray. Coming from Amiens exit 7 and from Rouen exit 9 on A28/E402 motorway.

💬 The campsite is located in the grounds of a picturesque old farmstead in the shade of apple trees and a few steps from the 'Avenue Verte'. A dream for cyclists and walkers. Campers are welcome after 1:00 pm.

CC 1/4-30/6 1/9-14/10

N 49°44'16'' E 1°25'41''

www.eurocampings.co.uk/113364

624 Pourville-sur-Mer, F-76550 / Haute-Normandie
♿ 🛜 (CC€17) iD 14 B1

- 🏔 Le Marqueval★★★
- 🏠 1210 rue de la Mer
- 🗓 19 Mar - 15 Oct
- ☎ +33 (0)2-35826646
- @ contact@campinglemarqueval.com

1 ADE**JM**NOPQRS**T**	ABFGN	**6**
2 CFGJMOPVWX	BE**FG**H	**7**
3 ABELQT	BDFJNQRSV	**8**
4 BDIN**PQTU**	EFLV	**9**
5 ABDEFGHKMN**O**	ABFGHJ**P**ST	**10**
6A CEE	❶ €28.10	
5ha 85**T**(80-120m²) 210**P**	❷ €40.60	

🏕 Coming from Dieppe well signposted on the D75, follow the campsite signs. Coming from Veules-les-Roses well signposted on the D75.

💬 There are three fishing ponds and a small river on the campsite. 1500 metres from the beach with its lovely chalkstone cliffs. Heated swimming pool. Plenty of cycle paths and footpaths from the campsite to the coast.

CC 19/3-8/7 26/8-14/10

N 49°54'32'' E 1°2'26''

www.eurocampings.co.uk/117291

France

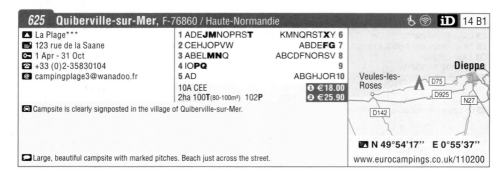

625 Quiberville-sur-Mer, F-76860 / Haute-Normandie — 14 B1

- La Plage***
- 123 rue de la Saane
- 1 Apr - 31 Oct
- +33 (0)2-35830104
- campingplage3@wanadoo.fr

1 ADE**JM**NOPRS**T**	KMNQRST**XY** 6
2 CEHJOPVW	ABDE**FG** 7
3 ABEL**MNQ**	ABCDFNORSV 8
4 IO**PQ**	9
5 AD	ABGHJOR 10
10A CEE	❶ €18.00
2ha 100T(80-100m²) 102P	❷ €25.90

Campsite is clearly signposted in the village of Quiberville-sur-Mer.

Large, beautiful campsite with marked pitches. Beach just across the street.

Veules-les-Roses / Dieppe / D75 / D925 / N27 / D142

N 49°54'17'' E 0°55'37''

www.eurocampings.co.uk/110200

626 St. Aubin-sur-Scie, F-76550 / Haute-Normandie — 14 B1

- Dieppe Vitamín****
- 865 rue des Vertus
- 31 Mar - 1 Oct
- +33 (0)2-35821111
- camping.vitamin@wanadoo.fr

1 ADE**JM**NOPRST	ABEFGH 6
2 GPRVWX	ABDE**FG**H 7
3 ABELQ	ABCDFKNRSV 8
4 BDNO**PQRTU**Y	DEJL 9
5 ADEHO	ABFHIJO**P**R 10
10A CEE	❶ €29.50
A80 5ha 69T(80-120m²) 113P	❷ €40.50

Coming from the D925 direction Dieppe water tower. Coming from Rouen N27. Direction water tower.

A really lovely and well run campsite 3 km from Dieppe centre. The indoor swimming pool is also enjoyable when the weather is not so good. There are various department stores close to the campsite.

CC 31/3-7/7 25/8-30/9

Dieppe / Saint-Nicolas-d'Aliermont / D75 / D925 / D927 / D154 / D1 / D149 / D915

N 49°54'1'' E 1°4'28''

www.eurocampings.co.uk/114953

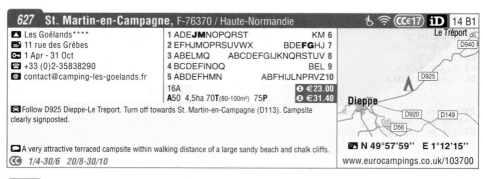

627 St. Martin-en-Campagne, F-76370 / Haute-Normandie — 14 B1

- Les Goélands****
- 11 rue des Grèbes
- 1 Apr - 31 Oct
- +33 (0)2-35838290
- contact@camping-les-goelands.fr

1 ADE**JM**NOPQRST	KM 6
2 EFHJMOPRSUVWX	BDE**FG**HJ 7
3 ABELMQ	ABCDEFGIJKNQRSTUV 8
4 BCDEFINOQ	BEL 9
5 ABDEFHMN	ABFHIJLNPRVZ 10
16A	❶ €23.00
A50 4,5ha 70T(80-100m²) 75P	❷ €31.40

Follow D925 Dieppe-Le Treport. Turn off towards St. Martin-en-Campagne (D113). Campsite clearly signposted.

A very attractive terraced campsite within walking distance of a large sandy beach and chalk cliffs.

CC 1/4-30/6 20/8-30/10

Le Tréport / D940 / D925 / Dieppe / D920 / D149 / D56

N 49°57'59'' E 1°12'15''

www.eurocampings.co.uk/103700

628 St. Pierre-en-Port, F-76540 / Haute-Normandie — 14 A1

- Les Falaises**
- 130 rue du Camping
- 1 Apr - 5 Oct
- +33 (0)2-35295158
- lesfalaises@cegetel.net

1 AJMNOPRST	KM 6
2 EGJMOPVWX	BE**F** 7
3 ABELQ	BDFKNOQRV 8
4 EFI	9
5 DFGHN	AGHIJR 10
10A CEE	❶ €19.90
A50 4,2ha 72T(120-140m²) 98P	❷ €31.40

Take the D79 between Fécamp and St. Valéry. Signposted in St. Pierre-en-Port.

Extremely well located campsite high up on the cliffs and 300 m from the sea. Access to beach via Le Rédillon is very easy. All necessary amenities available.

CC 1/4-6/7 26/8-4/10

D68 / D79 / D17 / D10 / D925 / Fécamp / D150 / Saint-Léonard / D940 / D50 / D131

N 49°48'35'' E 0°29'38''

www.eurocampings.co.uk/103591

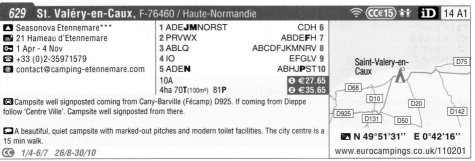

629 St. Valéry-en-Caux, F-76460 / Haute-Normandie   📶 CC€15 ⚥ iD 14 A1

🏕 Seasonova Etennemare★★★
📧 21 Hameau d'Etennemare
📅 1 Apr - 4 Nov
☎ +33 (0)2-35971579
@ contact@camping-etennemare.com

1 ADE**JM**NORST	CDH **6**
2 PRVWX	ABDE**F**H **7**
3 ABLQ	ABCDFJKMNRV **8**
4 IO	EFGLV **9**
5 ADE**N**	ABHJ**P**ST**10**
10A	**①** €27.65
4ha 70**T**(100m²) 81**P**	**②** €35.65

🅿 Campsite well signposted coming from Cany-Barville (Fécamp) D925. If coming from Dieppe follow 'Centre Ville'. Campsite well signposted from there.

💬 A beautiful, quiet campsite with marked-out pitches and modern toilet facilities. The city centre is a 15 min walk.

CC 1/4-6/7 26/8-30/10

◪ **N 49°51'31'' E 0°42'16''**

www.eurocampings.co.uk/110201

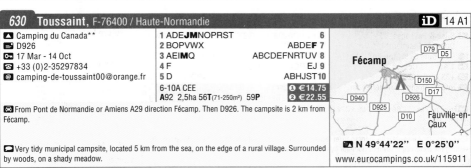

630 Toussaint, F-76400 / Haute-Normandie   iD 14 A1

🏕 Camping du Canada★★
📧 D926
📅 17 Mar - 14 Oct
☎ +33 (0)2-35297834
@ camping-de-toussaint00@orange.fr

1 ADE**JM**NOPRST	**6**
2 BOPVWX	ABDE**F** **7**
3 AEIMQ	ABCDEFNRTUV **8**
4 F	EJ **9**
5 D	ABHJST**10**
6-10A CEE	**①** €14.75
A92 2,5ha 56**T**(71-250m²) 59**P**	**②** €22.55

🅿 From Pont de Normandie or Amiens A29 direction Fécamp. Then D926. The campsite is 2 km from Fécamp.

💬 Very tidy municipal campsite, located 5 km from the sea, on the edge of a rural village. Surrounded by woods, on a shady meadow.

◪ **N 49°44'22'' E 0°25'0''**

www.eurocampings.co.uk/115911

631 Veules-les-Roses, F-76980 / Haute-Normandie   ♿ 📶 ✿ CC€17 ⚥ iD 14 A1

🏕 Seasonova Les Mouettes★★★
📧 avenue Jean Moulin
📅 1 Apr - 15 Oct
☎ +33 (0)2-35976198
@ contact@
 camping-lesmouettes-normandie.com

1 ADE**JM**NOPRST	CDFG **6**
2 EOPRVWX	ABDE**FG**H **7**
3 ABE**H**LQT	ABCDEFJNRSV **8**
4 BDFILNO**PQRTU**	BEV **9**
5 ABDEH	ABGHJ**P**ST**10**
6A CEE	**①** €29.80
3,6ha 122**T**(80-150m²) 45**P**	**②** €37.80

🅿 Campsite well signposted from the centre.

💬 A lovely campsite with marked-out pitches, located 300 m from the beach. A beautiful village with France's shortest river, just 1,100 m long. This is an extremely peaceful campsite with excellent toilet facilities. Heated indoor swimming pool, children's pool and jacuzzi.

CC 1/4-6/7 26/8-14/10

◪ **N 49°52'33'' E 0°48'11''**

www.eurocampings.co.uk/110199

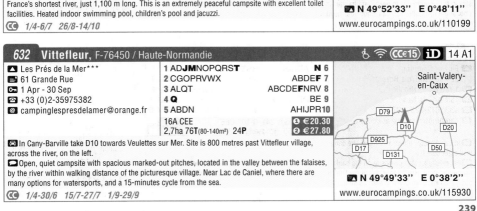

632 Vittefleur, F-76450 / Haute-Normandie   ♿ 📶 CC€15 iD 14 A1

🏕 Les Prés de la Mer★★★
📧 61 Grande Rue
📅 1 Apr - 30 Sep
☎ +33 (0)2-35975382
@ campinglespresdelamer@orange.fr

1 AD**JM**NOPQRS**T**	**N 6**
2 CGOPRVWX	ABDE**F 7**
3 ALQT	ABCDE**F**NRV **8**
4 **Q**	BE **9**
5 ABDN	AHIJPR**10**
16A CEE	**①** €20.30
2,7ha 76**T**(80-140m²) 24**P**	**②** €27.80

🅿 In Cany-Barville take D10 towards Veulettes sur Mer. Site is 800 metres past Vittefleur village, across the river, on the left.

💬 Open, quiet campsite with spacious marked-out pitches, located in the valley between the falaises, by the river within walking distance of the picturesque village. Near Lac de Caniel, where there are many options for watersports, and a 15-minutes cycle from the sea.

CC 1/4-30/6 15/7-27/7 1/9-29/9

◪ **N 49°49'33'' E 0°38'2''**

www.eurocampings.co.uk/115930

France

France

633 Yport, F-76111 / Haute-Normandie 🛜 iD 14 A1

🏕 Le Rivage**
📧 rue André Toutain
📅 1 Apr - 31 Oct
☎ +33 (0)2-35273378
@ contact@camping-lerivage.com

1 ADEJMNORST	KM 6
2 EFGJOPSUVWX	ABDE**FG** 7
3 Q	ABCDFNRV 8
4	EF 9
5 ABD	ABGHJO**P**ST 10
6A	❶ €19.50
A50 2,7ha 90**T**(60-100m²) 18**P**	❷ €29.50

🚗 From Étretat or Fécamp: the campsite is clearly signposted in the centre of Yport.

💬 This terraced campsite on the cliffs with magnificent views as far as Fécamp is located in a picturesque fishing village.

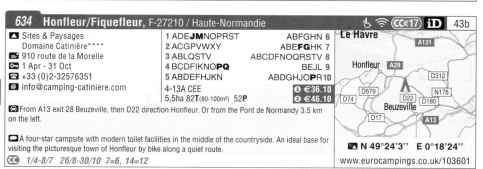

🧭 N 49°44'11'' E 0°18'27''

www.eurocampings.co.uk/110504

634 Honfleur/Fiquefleur, F-27210 / Haute-Normandie ♿ 🛜 CC€17 iD 43b

🏕 Sites & Paysages
　Domaine Catinière****
📧 910 route de la Morelle
📅 1 Apr - 31 Oct
☎ +33 (0)2-32576351
@ info@camping-catiniere.com

1 ADE**JM**NOPRST	AB**FG**HN 6
2 ACGPVWXY	ABE**FG**HK 7
3 ABLQSTV	ABCDFNOQRSTV 8
4 BCDFIKNO**PQ**	BEJL 9
5 ABDEFHJKN	ABDGHJO**P**R 10
4-13A CEE	❶ €36.10
5,5ha 82**T**(80-100m²) 52**P**	❷ €46.10

🚗 From A13 exit 28 Beuzeville, then D22 direction Honfleur. Or from the Pont de Normandy 3.5 km on the left.

💬 A four-star campsite with modern toilet facilities in the middle of the countryside. An ideal base for visiting the picturesque town of Honfleur by bike along a quiet route.

CC 1/4-8/7 26/8-30/10 7=6, 14=12

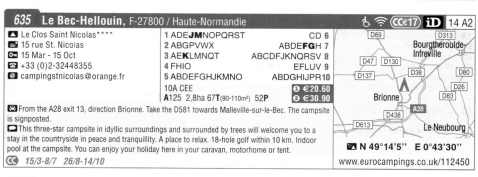

🧭 N 49°24'3'' E 0°18'24''

www.eurocampings.co.uk/103601

635 Le Bec-Hellouin, F-27800 / Haute-Normandie ♿ 🛜 CC€17 iD 14 A2

🏕 Le Clos Saint Nicolas****
📧 15 rue St. Nicolas
📅 15 Mar - 15 Oct
☎ +33 (0)2-32448355
@ campingstnicolas@orange.fr

1 ADE**JM**NOPQRST	CD 6
2 ABGPVWX	ABDE**FG**H 7
3 AE**K**LMNQT	ABCDFJKNQRSV 8
4 FHIO	EFLUV 9
5 ABDEFGHJKMNO	ABDGHIJPR 10
10A CEE	❶ €20.60
A125 2,8ha 67**T**(90-110m²) 52**P**	❷ €30.90

🚗 From the A28 exit 13, direction Brionne. Take the D581 towards Malleville-sur-le-Bec. The campsite is signposted.

💬 This three-star campsite in idyllic surroundings and surrounded by trees will welcome you to a stay in the countryside in peace and tranquillity. A place to relax. 18-hole golf within 10 km. Indoor pool at the campsite. You can enjoy your holiday here in your caravan, motorhome or tent.

CC 15/3-8/7 26/8-14/10

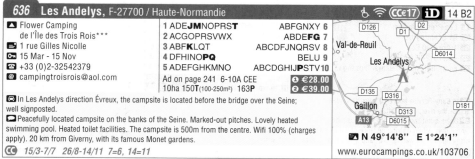

🧭 N 49°14'5'' E 0°43'30''

www.eurocampings.co.uk/112450

636 Les Andelys, F-27700 / Haute-Normandie ♿ 🛜 CC€17 iD 14 B2

🏕 Flower Camping
　de l'Île des Trois Rois***
📧 1 rue Gilles Nicolle
📅 15 Mar - 15 Nov
☎ +33 (0)2-32542379
@ campingtroisrois@aol.com

1 ADE**JM**NOPRS**T**	AB**F**GNXY 6
2 ACGOPRSVWX	ABDE**FG** 7
3 ABF**K**LQT	ABCDFJNQRSV 8
4 DFHINO**PQ**	BELU 9
5 ADEFGHKMNO	ABCDGHIJ**P**STV 10
Ad on page 241 6-10A CEE	❶ €28.00
10ha 150**T**(100-250m²) 163**P**	❷ €39.00

🚗 In Les Andelys direction Évreux, the campsite is located before the bridge over the Seine; well signposted.

💬 Peacefully located campsite on the banks of the Seine. Marked-out pitches. Lovely heated swimming pool. Heated toilet facilities. The campsite is 500m from the centre. Wifi 100% (charges apply). 20 km from Giverny, with its famous Monet gardens.

CC 15/3-7/7 26/8-14/11 7=6, 14=11

🧭 N 49°14'8'' E 1°24'1''

www.eurocampings.co.uk/103706

240

---

637 Marcilly-sur-Eure, F-27810 / Haute-Normandie   ॐ ᯤ (CC€19) ᛉᛉ iD   14 B2

- 🏕 Domaine de Marcilly★★★★
- 🏠 rue de Saint André de l'Eure
- 🕐 1 Jan - 31 Dec
- ☎ +33 (0)2-37484542
- @ domainedemarcilly@wanadoo.fr

1 ADJMNOPRST	AB **6**
2 BGPRVX	A**FGH 7**
3 ELMNQ	ABCDFNOQRTUV **8**
4 INOPQ	EJLV **9**
5 ABD	ABDFGHIJ**P**RV**10**
10A CEE	
	❶ €34.00
A131 15ha 100**T**(100-200m²) 219**P**	❷ €42.00

🚗 Coming from Dreux on the D928 turn left after about 15 km towards Marcilly. Then follow campsite signs. From Annet on the D928 turn right after about 8 km. Follow route as shown above.
🛏 A really lovely campsite in the middle of a wood with lovely marked-out grounds, a wonderful (heated) swimming pool, 2 tennis courts, a large petanque alley. The reception is open 9:00 am -12:00 pm and 2:00 pm -6:00 pm.

(CC) 1/1-30/6 1/9-31/12

Saint-Lubin-des-Joncherets
Dreux
D6154 · D833 · D52 · D16 · D143 · D928 · D11 1 · N12
☑ N 48°49'55'' E 1°19'47''
www.eurocampings.co.uk/117653

---

638 Poses, F-27740 / Haute-Normandie   ॐ ᯤ iD   14 B2

- 🏕 L'île Adeline★★
- 🏠 rue des Masures
- 🕐 1 Apr - 16 Oct
- ☎ +33 (0)2-32254533
- @ info@camping-ile-adeline.com

1 ADE**IL**NOPRS	LN**X 6**
2 ACDGOPVWXY	BE**FG**H **7**
3 ABEJKLQ	ABDFNRV **8**
4 BDFHIN**PQ**	DE **9**
5 ABDEFHKM**N**	ABIJOSTV**10**
6A CEE	
	❶ €18.25
3ha 62**T**(80-140m²) 78**P**	❷ €22.35

🚗 Coming from Pont-de-l'Arche follow the D77; then campsite signs on the left. Coming from Val-de-Reuil follow the D77; then campsite signs on the right.

🛏 If you are looking for nature, water, fun, fishing or want to play golf, the campsite L'île Adeline is the place for you. 1 hour from Paris and 30 minutes from Rouen.

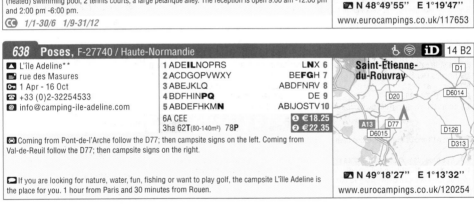

Saint-Étienne-du-Rouvray
D1 · D20 · D6014 · A13 · D77 · D126 · D6015 · D313
☑ N 49°18'27'' E 1°13'32''
www.eurocampings.co.uk/120254

---

639 Bayeux, F-14400 / Basse-Normandie   ॐ ᯤ (CC€17) ᛉᛉ iD   43b

- 🏕 Camping des Bords de l'Aure★★★
- 🏠 boulevard d'Eindhoven
- 🕐 30 Mar - 4 Nov
- ☎ +33 (0)2-31920843
- @ campingmunicipal@mairie-bayeux.fr

1 ADEFJMNOPRST	EFG **6**
2 ACGOPSVWXY	ABD**FG 7**
3 AE**K**LQ	ABCDFNORV **8**
4 FHIO**ST**	EL **9**
5 ADN	ABFGHJPSTZ**10**
6A CEE	
	❶ €20.60
A50 2,5ha 136**T**(80-100m²) 10**P**	❷ €28.30

🚗 From A13 exit Bayeux then on the northern bypass towards Arromanches and Port-en-Bessin. Campsite is well signposted.
🛏 Well maintained campsite within walking distance of the very interesting historic centre of Bayeux. Public swimming pool offers free entrance for campsite guests. 10 km from D-Day beaches. Reception is closed between 12:00 pm and 2:00 pm.

(CC) 30/3-27/5 11/6-17/6 2/9-3/11

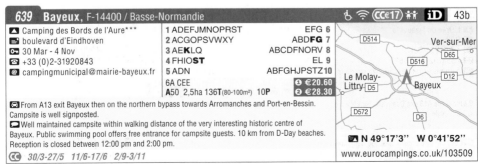

Ver-sur-Mer
Le Molay-Littry
Bayeux
D514 · D65 · D516 · D12 · D5 · D572 · D6
☑ N 49°17'3'' W 0°41'52''
www.eurocampings.co.uk/103509

France

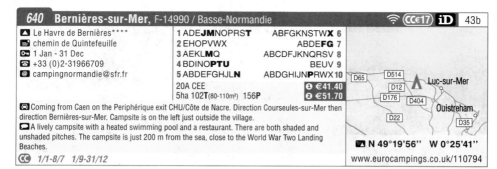

640 Bernières-sur-Mer, F-14990 / Basse-Normandie

🛜 CC17 iD 43b

- 🏕 Le Havre de Bernières****
- 📧 chemin de Quintefeuille
- 📅 1 Jan - 31 Dec
- ☎ +33 (0)2-31966709
- @ campingnormandie@sfr.fr

1 ADEJMNOPRST	ABFGKNSTWX 6
2 EHOPVWX	ABDEFG 7
3 AEKLMQ	ABCDFJKNQRSV 8
4 BDINOPTU	BEUV 9
5 ABDEFGHJLN	ABDGHIJNPRWX 10

20A CEE
5ha 102T(80-110m²) 156P

❶ €41.40
❷ €51.70

🚗 Coming from Caen on the Periphérique exit CHU/Côte de Nacre. Direction Courseules-sur-Mer then direction Bernières-sur-Mer. Campsite is on the left just outside the village.

💬 A lively campsite with a heated swimming pool and a restaurant. There are both shaded and unshaded pitches. The campsite is just 200 m from the sea, close to the World War Two Landing Beaches.

CC 1/1-8/7 1/9-31/12

🧭 N 49°19'56'' W 0°25'41''

www.eurocampings.co.uk/110794

641 Creully, F-14480 / Basse-Normandie

♿ 🛜 CC15 iD 43b

- 🏕 Les Trois Rivières***
- 📧 rue de Tierceville
- 📅 15 Mar - 15 Nov
- ☎ +33 (0)2-31809017
- @ contact@camping-les-3-rivieres.com

1 ADEJMNOPQRST	6
2 CGOPTVWXY	ABDEFGHK 7
3 ALMQ	ABCDEFNRSV 8
4 FIOPQ	EL 9
5 ABDEFHJMN	ABHIJOSTW 10

10A CEE
1,5ha 65T 17P

❶ €20.60
❷ €26.60

🚗 A13 in Caen on Périferique Nord take exit 6. Via D22 to Creully. From Bayeaux D12 to Creully. Campsite is signposted there.

💬 Quiet campsite 500 m from the little town of Creully with its castle, which regularly hosts exhibitions. Ideal for visiting the WWII landing beaches. Bayeux 12 km, Caen 16 km, sea 7 km. Restaurant facilities open at weekends in May, June, September.

CC 15/3-7/7 25/8-14/11 7=6, 14=12

🧭 N 49°17'23'' W 0°31'46''

www.eurocampings.co.uk/114177

642 Deauville/St. Arnoult, F-14800 / Basse-Normandie

♿ 🛜 CC17 iD 43b

- 🏕 La Vallée de Deauville*****
- 📧 rue des Genêts
- 📅 1 Apr - 31 Oct
- ☎ +33 (0)2-31885817
- @ contact@camping-deauville.com

1 ADEFJMNOPRST	ABCDFGHIN 6
2 ACDGOPVWX	ABDEFGH 7
3 ABEKLQT	ABCDFGIJKNRS 8
4 BDIJLNOPQRTUX	EFV 9
5 ABDEFGHJKNO	ABDGHJNPR 10

10A CEE
19ha 105T(80-120m²) 305P

❶ €36.10
❷ €51.35

🚗 From A13 exit Deauville. Direction Caen at roundabouts. Campsite is near the 3rd roundabout.

💬 Large grounds with spacious pitches in natural surroundings. The campsite is near the famous seaside resorts of Deauville and Trouville. New heated leisure pool including indoor swimming pool with jacuzzi. Reception closed from 12:00 pm to 2:00 pm.

CC 1/4-8/7 26/8-30/10

🧭 N 49°19'44'' E 0°5'11''

www.eurocampings.co.uk/103605

643 Deauville/Tourgéville, F-14800 / Basse-Normandie

🛜 iD 43b

- 🏕 L'Orée de Deauville***
- 📧 D27
- 📅 1 Apr - 31 Oct
- ☎ +33 (0)2-31879622
- @ camping-oreedeauville@orange.fr

1 ADEJMNOPQRST	ABFGX 6
2 AGPVWXY	ABDEFGH 7
3 AGKLST	ABCDFNRV 8
4 BDFHILOQ	EVY 9
5 ADEFHJKMNO	ABFGHIJLOR 10

12A CEE
1,5ha 72T(100-130m²) 78P

❶ €27.10
❷ €34.10

🚗 From the A13 exit Deauville. Turn towards Caen at the three roundabouts via the D27. Signposted in Tourgéville.

💬 Cosy family campsite near the well-known seaside resorts of Deauville and Trouville. Well-kept grounds with spacious pitches surrounded by trees and hedges.

🧭 N 49°19'19'' E 0°3'39''

www.eurocampings.co.uk/103603

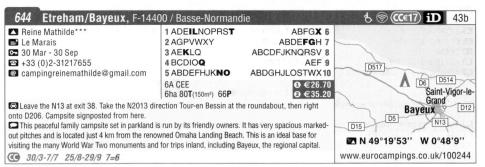

644 Etreham/Bayeux, F-14400 / Basse-Normandie · 📶 ⓦ (CC€17) iD · 43b

🏕 Reine Mathilde***
📧 Le Marais
📅 30 Mar - 30 Sep
☎ +33 (0)2-31217655
@ campingreinemathilde@gmail.com

1	ADE**IL**NOPRS**T**	ABFG**X**	6
2	AGPVWXY	ABDE**FGH**	7
3	AE**K**LQ	ABCDFJKNQRSV	8
4	BCDIO**Q**	AEF	9
5	ABDEFHJK**NO**	ABDGHJLOSTWX	10

6A CEE · ❶ €26.70
6ha 80**T**(150m²) 66**P** · ❷ €35.20

🚗 Leave the N13 at exit 38. Take the N2013 direction Tour-en Bessin at the roundabout, then right onto D206. Campsite signposted from here.
💬 This peaceful family campsite set in parkland is run by its friendly owners. It has very spacious marked-out pitches and is located just 4 km from the renowned Omaha Landing Beach. This is an ideal base for visiting the many World War Two monuments and for trips inland, including Bayeux, the regional capital.
CC 30/3-7/7 25/8-29/9 7=6

🧭 N 49°19'53'' W 0°48'9''
www.eurocampings.co.uk/100244

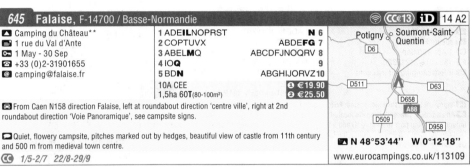

645 Falaise, F-14700 / Basse-Normandie · ⓦ (CC€13) iD · 14 A2

🏕 Camping du Château**
📧 1 rue du Val d'Ante
📅 1 May - 30 Sep
☎ +33 (0)2-31901655
@ camping@falaise.fr

1	ADE**IL**NOPRST	N	6
2	COPTUVX	ABDE**FG**	7
3	ABEL**MQ**	ABCDFJNOQRV	8
4	IO**Q**		9
5	BD**N**	ABGHIJORVZ	10

10A CEE · ❶ €19.90
1,5ha 60**T**(80-100m²) · ❷ €25.50

🚗 From Caen N158 direction Falaise, left at roundabout direction 'centre ville', right at 2nd roundabout direction 'Voie Panoramique', see campsite signs.

💬 Quiet, flowery campsite, pitches marked out by hedges, beautiful view of castle from 11th century and 500 m from medieval town centre.
CC 1/5-2/7 22/8-29/9

🧭 N 48°53'44'' W 0°12'18''
www.eurocampings.co.uk/113109

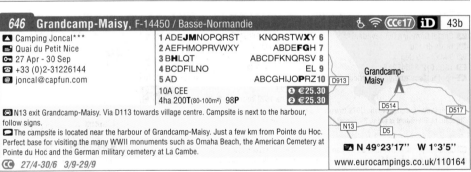

646 Grandcamp-Maisy, F-14450 / Basse-Normandie · 📶 ⓦ (CC€17) iD · 43b

🏕 Camping Joncal***
📧 Quai du Petit Nice
📅 27 Apr - 30 Sep
☎ +33 (0)2-31226144
@ joncal@capfun.com

1	ADE**JM**NOPQRST	KNQRSTW**X**Y	6
2	AEFHMOPRVWXY	ABDE**FGH**	7
3	B**H**LQT	ABCDFKNQRSV	8
4	BCDFILNO	EL	9
5	AD	ABCGHIJO**P**RZ	10

10A CEE · ❶ €25.30
4ha 200**T**(80-100m²) 98**P** · ❷ €25.30

🚗 N13 exit Grandcamp-Maisy. Via D113 towards village centre. Campsite is next to the harbour, follow signs.
💬 The campsite is located near the harbour of Grandcamp-Maisy. Just a few km from Pointe du Hoc. Perfect base for visiting the many WWII monuments such as Omaha Beach, the American Cemetery at Pointe du Hoc and the German military cemetery at La Cambe.
CC 27/4-30/6 3/9-29/9

🧭 N 49°23'17'' W 1°3'5''
www.eurocampings.co.uk/110164

647 Honfleur/Équemauville, F-14600 / Basse-Normandie · 📶 ⓦ (CC€17) iD · 43b

🏕 La Briquerie*****
📧 D62
📅 31 Mar - 30 Sep
☎ +33 (0)2-31892832
@ info@campinglabriquerie.com

1	A**JM**NOPRST	ABEFGHI	6
2	AGOPVWXY	ABDE**FGH**	7
3	BE**IK**LMQST	ABCDFGIJKNRSTUV	8
4	BCDFHIJLNO**PQRTU**	EJL	9
5	ABDEFHJKLM**N**	ABDFGHIJNPQRYZ	10

6-10A · ❶ €34.70
A104 11ha 200**T**(100m²) 250**P** · ❷ €48.20

🚗 From A29 exit 1. Go towards Pont-l'Évêque. Right after 2 km on D579 dir. Honfleur. Third exit at Intermarché to D62. Campsite about 150m on the right.
💬 In easily accessible woodland with large, marked-out pitches. Easy access. 3 km from the sea and the picturesque town of Honfleur. 1 km from a large wood for walks. 100 m from large supermarket. Luxury toilet facilities.
CC 1/4-8/7 26/8-29/9 7=6

🧭 N 49°23'53'' E 0°12'31''
www.eurocampings.co.uk/103600

France

243

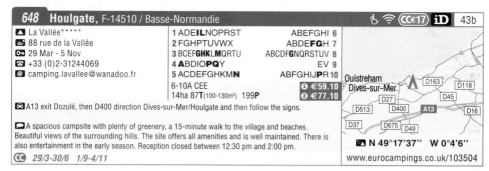

648 Houlgate, F-14510 / Basse-Normandie ♿ 🛜 ⒸⒸ€17 iD 43b

- 🏕 La Vallée*****
- 📧 88 rue de la Vallée
- 📅 29 Mar - 5 Nov
- ☎ +33 (0)2-31244069
- @ camping.lavallee@wanadoo.fr

1 ADE**IL**NOPRST	ABEFGH**I** 6
2 FGHPTUVWX	ABDEF**GH** 7
3 BCEF**GHKLM**QRTU	ABCDF**G**NQRSTUV 8
4 **A**BDIOP**QY**	EV 9
5 ACDEFGHKM**N**	ABFGHIJ**P**R 10

6-10A CEE ❶ €59.10
14ha 87**T**(100-130m²) 199**P** ❷ €77.10

🚗 A13 exit Dozulé, then D400 direction Dives-sur-Mer/Houlgate and then follow the signs.

💬 A spacious campsite with plenty of greenery, a 15-minute walk to the village and beaches. Beautiful views of the surrounding hills. The site offers all amenities and is well maintained. There is also entertainment in the early season. Reception closed between 12:30 pm and 2:00 pm.

ⒸⒸ 29/3-30/6 1/9-4/11

N 49°17'37" W 0°4'6"
www.eurocampings.co.uk/103504

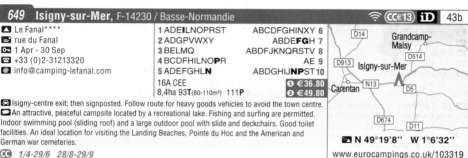

649 Isigny-sur-Mer, F-14230 / Basse-Normandie 🛜 ⒸⒸ€13 iD 43b

- 🏕 Le Fanal****
- 📧 rue du Fanal
- 📅 1 Apr - 30 Sep
- ☎ +33 (0)2-31213320
- @ info@camping-lefanal.com

1 ADE**IL**NOPRST	ABCDFGHINXY 6
2 ADGPVWXY	ABDEF**GH** 7
3 BELMQ	ABDFJKNQRSTV 8
4 BCDFHILNOP**R**	AE 9
5 ADEFGHL**N**	ABDGHIJ**NP**ST 10

16A CEE ❶ €36.80
8,4ha 93**T**(80-110m²) 111**P** ❷ €49.80

🚗 Isigny-centre exit; then signposted. Follow route for heavy goods vehicles to avoid the town centre.

💬 An attractive, peaceful campsite located by a recreational lake. Fishing and surfing are permitted. Indoor swimming pool (sliding roof) and a large outdoor pool with slide and deckchairs. Good toilet facilities. An ideal location for visiting the Landing Beaches, Pointe du Hoc and the American and German war cemeteries.

ⒸⒸ 1/4-29/6 28/8-29/9

N 49°19'8" W 1°6'32"
www.eurocampings.co.uk/103319

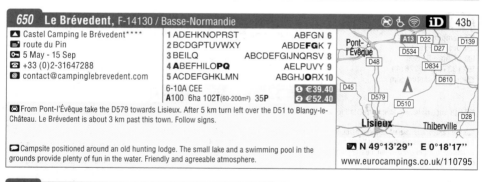

650 Le Brévedent, F-14130 / Basse-Normandie ⊗ ♿ 🛜 iD 43b

- 🏕 Castel Camping le Brévedent****
- 📧 route du Pin
- 📅 5 May - 15 Sep
- ☎ +33 (0)2-31647288
- @ contact@campinglebrevedent.com

1 ADEHKNOPRST	ABFGN 6
2 BCDGPTUVWXY	ABDEF**GK** 7
3 BEILQ	ABCDEFGIJNQRSV 8
4 **A**BEFHILOP**Q**	AELPUVY 9
5 ACDEFGHKLMN	ABGHJ**O**RX 10

6-10A CEE ❶ €39.40
A100 6ha 102**T**(60-200m²) 35**P** ❷ €52.40

🚗 From Pont-l'Évêque take the D579 towards Lisieux. After 5 km turn left over the D51 to Blangy-le-Château. Le Brévedent is about 3 km past this town. Follow signs.

💬 Campsite positioned around an old hunting lodge. The small lake and a swimming pool in the grounds provide plenty of fun in the water. Friendly and agreeable atmosphere.

N 49°13'29" E 0°18'17"
www.eurocampings.co.uk/110795

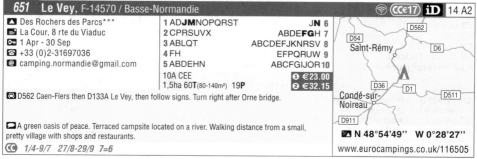

651 Le Vey, F-14570 / Basse-Normandie 🛜 ⒸⒸ€17 iD 14 A2

- 🏕 Des Rochers des Parcs***
- 📧 La Cour, 8 rte du Viaduc
- 📅 1 Apr - 30 Sep
- ☎ +33 (0)2-31697036
- @ camping.normandie@gmail.com

1 AD**JM**NOPQRST	**JN** 6
2 CPRSUVX	ABDEF**GH** 7
3 ABLQT	ABCDEFJKNRSV 8
4 FH	EFPQRUW 9
5 ABDEHN	ABCFGIJOR 10

10A CEE ❶ €23.00
1,5ha 60**T**(80-140m²) 19**P** ❷ €32.15

🚗 D562 Caen-Flers then D133A Le Vey, then follow signs. Turn right after Orne bridge.

💬 A green oasis of peace. Terraced campsite located on a river. Walking distance from a small, pretty village with shops and restaurants.

ⒸⒸ 1/4-9/7 27/8-29/9 7=6

N 48°54'49" W 0°28'27"
www.eurocampings.co.uk/116505

France

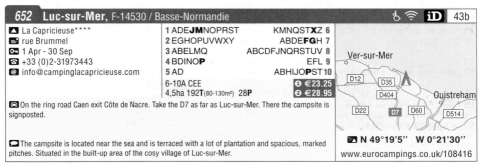

652 Luc-sur-Mer, F-14530 / Basse-Normandie ♿ 📶 **iD** 43b

- ⛰ La Capricieuse****
- 🏠 rue Brummel
- 📅 1 Apr - 30 Sep
- ☎ +33 (0)2-31973443
- @ info@campinglacapricieuse.com

1 ADE**JM**NOPRST	KMNQST**X**Z	6
2 EGHOPUVWXY	ABDE**FG**H	7
3 ABELMQ	ABCDFJNQRSTUV	8
4 BDINO**P**	EFL	9
5 AD	ABHIJO**P**ST	10
6-10A CEE	❶ €23.25	
4,5ha 192**T**(80-130m²) 28**P**	❷ €28.95	

🚗 On the ring road Caen exit Côte de Nacre. Take the D7 as far as Luc-sur-Mer. There the campsite is signposted.

💬 The campsite is located near the sea and is terraced with a lot of plantation and spacious, marked pitches. Situated in the built-up area of the cosy village of Luc-sur-Mer.

📍 N 49°19'5'' W 0°21'30''

www.eurocampings.co.uk/108416

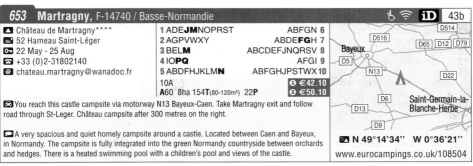

653 Martragny, F-14740 / Basse-Normandie ♿ 📶 **iD** 43b

- ⛰ Château de Martragny****
- 🏠 52 Hameau Saint-Léger
- 📅 22 May - 25 Aug
- ☎ +33 (0)2-31802140
- @ chateau.martragny@wanadoo.fr

1 ADE**JM**NOPRST	ABFGN	6
2 AGPVWXY	ABDE**FG**H	7
3 BEL**M**	ABCDEFJNQRSV	8
4 IO**PQ**	AFGI	9
5 ABDFHJKLM**N**	ABFGHJPSTWX	10
10A	❶ €42.10	
A60 8ha 154**T**(80-120m²) 22**P**	❷ €50.10	

🚗 You reach this castle campsite via motorway N13 Bayeux-Caen. Take Martragny exit and follow road through St-Leger. Château campsite after 300 metres on the right.

💬 A very spacious and quiet homely campsite around a castle. Located between Caen and Bayeux, in Normandy. The campsite is fully integrated into the green Normandy countryside between orchards and hedges. There is a heated swimming pool with a children's pool and views of the castle.

📍 N 49°14'34'' W 0°36'21''

www.eurocampings.co.uk/108504

654 Merville-Franceville-Plage, F-14810 / Basse-Normandie ♿ 📶 ✿ (CC€19) **iD** 43b

- ⛰ Les Peupliers****
- 🏠 allée des Pins
- 📅 1 Apr - 31 Oct
- ☎ +33 (0)2-31240507
- @ contact@camping-peupliers.com

1 ADEF**IL**NOPRST	ABEFGK**N**QV	6
2 ACEGHPVWX	ABE**FG**H	7
3 AE**K**LQT	ABCDFGIJKNQRSTUV	8
4 ABDFHILNO**P**UY	EJL	9
5 ABDEFHJ**N**	ABDGHJN**P**TUV	10
10A CEE	❶ €37.10	
4ha 100**T**(80-200m²) 62**P**	❷ €46.50	

🚗 Drive from Cabourg via the D514 in the direction of Merville. The campsite is located on the left of this road and is signposted.

💬 A peacefully located family campsite with large pitches. Grounds with plenty of flowers, close to Cabourg for all your shopping. Heated outdoor and indoor swimming pool and heated toilet facilities. 300m from the sandy beach. Walking and cycling routes right from the campsite. Reception closed from 12:00 pm to 2:00 pm.

CC 1/4-30/4 22/5-30/6 1/9-30/10

📍 N 49°17'3'' W 0°10'8''

www.eurocampings.co.uk/109961

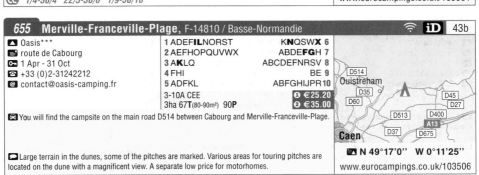

655 Merville-Franceville-Plage, F-14810 / Basse-Normandie 📶 **iD** 43b

- ⛰ Oasis***
- 🏠 route de Cabourg
- 📅 1 Apr - 31 Oct
- ☎ +33 (0)2-31242212
- @ contact@oasis-camping.fr

1 ADEF**IL**NORST	KNQSW**X**	6
2 AEFHOPQUVWX	ABDE**FG**H	7
3 A**K**LQ	ABCDEFNRSV	8
4 FHI	BE	9
5 ADFKL	ABFGHIJPR	10
3-10A CEE	❶ €25.20	
3ha 67**T**(80-90m²) 90**P**	❷ €35.00	

🚗 You will find the campsite on the main road D514 between Cabourg and Merville-Franceville-Plage.

💬 Large terrain in the dunes, some of the pitches are marked. Various areas for touring pitches are located on the dune with a magnificent view. A separate low price for motorhomes.

📍 N 49°17'0'' W 0°11'25''

www.eurocampings.co.uk/103506

France

656 Merville-Franceville-Plage, F-14810 / Basse-Normandie 43b

▲ Seasonova Le Point du Jour★★★★
≣ 75 route de Cabourg
☷ 30 Mar - 4 Nov
☏ +33 (0)2-31242334
@ contact@camping-lepointdujour.com

1	ADEF**JM**NOPRT	EFGKMNPQRSTUVW**X** 6
2	AEFGHOPQUVWX	BE**FG**H 7
3	AFH**K**LQ	ABCDFJKNQRSTU 8
4	ABDEFGHI**J**LNOPQR**TUXYZ**	ELUV 9
5	ABDEFGHJKLNO	ABDGHIJ**N**P**R** 10

10A CEE ① €40.10
2,7ha 88**T** 50**P** ② €49.90

A13 exit 29B Dozulé, direction Cabourg. Then via D514 towards Ouistreham. Campsite signposted. From the west: A13, exit 29 Dozulé, direction Cabourg. Then D514 direction Ouistreham.

Located right by the sea with an indoor swimming pool. Close to Caen and Cabourg with plenty of shops. A cycle path leads from the site to Cabourg. The centre of Merville is a 400 metres walk via the beach. Reception closed 1:00 - 2:00 pm.

CC 30/3-6/7 26/8-31/10

N 49°17'0'' W 0°11'29''

www.eurocampings.co.uk/115977

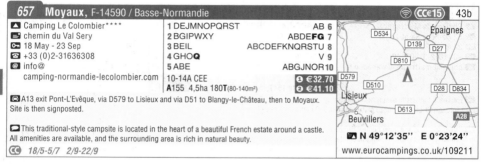

657 Moyaux, F-14590 / Basse-Normandie 43b

▲ Camping Le Colombier★★★★
≣ chemin du Val Sery
☷ 18 May - 23 Sep
☏ +33 (0)2-31636308
@ info@
   camping-normandie-lecolombier.com

1	DEJMNOPQRST	AB 6
2	BGIPWXY	ABDE**FG** 7
3	BEIL	ABCDEFKNQRSTU 8
4	GHO**Q**	V 9
5	ABE	ABGJNOR 10

10-14A CEE ① €32.70
A155 4,5ha 180**T**(80-140m²) ② €41.10

A13 exit Pont-L'Evêque, via D579 to Lisieux and via D51 to Blangy-le-Château, then to Moyaux. Site is then signposted.

This traditional-style campsite is located in the heart of a beautiful French estate around a castle. All amenities are available, and the surrounding area is rich in natural beauty.

CC 18/5-5/7 2/9-22/9

N 49°12'35'' E 0°23'24''

www.eurocampings.co.uk/109211

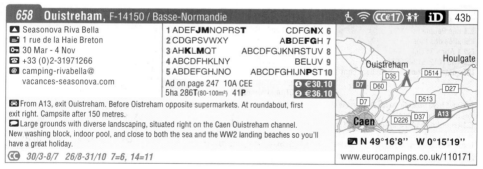

658 Ouistreham, F-14150 / Basse-Normandie 43b

▲ Seasonova Riva Bella
≣ 1 rue de la Haie Breton
☷ 30 Mar - 4 Nov
☏ +33 (0)2-31971266
@ camping-rivabella@
   vacances-seasonova.com

1	ADEF**JM**NOPRS**T**	CDFG**N**X 6
2	CDGPSVWXY	**AB**DE**FG**H 7
3	AH**KLM**QT	ABCDFGJKNRSTUV 8
4	ABCDFHKLNY	BELUV 9
5	ABDEFGHJNO	ABCDFGHIJN**P**S**T** 10

Ad on page 247 10A CEE ① €30.10
5ha 286**T**(80-100m²) 41**P** ② €36.10

From A13, exit Ouistreham. Before Oistreham opposite supermarkets. At roundabout, first exit right. Campsite after 150 metres.

Large grounds with diverse landscaping, situated right on the Caen Ouistreham channel. New washing block, indoor pool, and close to both the sea and the WW2 landing beaches so you'll have a great holiday.

CC 30/3-8/7 26/8-31/10 7=6, 14=11

N 49°16'8'' W 0°15'19''

www.eurocampings.co.uk/110171

659 Port-en-Bessin, F-14520 / Basse-Normandie 43b

▲ Port'Land★★★★
≣ chemin du Castel
☷ 1 Apr - 3 Nov
☏ +33 (0)2-31510706
@ info@camping-portland.fr

1	ADE**IL**NOPRST	ABEFGHN 6
2	DFGOPVWXY	BE**FG**H 7
3	BE**K**LQT	ABCDFJKNQRSTUV 8
4	BDFHILNOP**Q**	EL 9
5	ABDEFGHIJL**O**	ABFGHIJNORVZ 10

16-20A CEE ① €48.80
A60 9ha 151**T**(100-250m²) 128**P** ② €60.80

Take the northern ring road in Bayeux, exit Port-en-Bessin. Follow 'toutes directions' at the roundabout in Port-en-Bessin. The campsite is signposted.

Beautiful landscaped, modern grounds with wide variety of planting. Various water features. View of the sea and the landing beaches of Omaha Beach from the campsite. 600m from Port-en-Bessin and 5 km from Omaha Beach.

N 49°20'47'' W 0°46'24''

www.eurocampings.co.uk/111993

France

France

---

660 Ranville, F-14860 / Basse-Normandie   🛜 iD 43b

🔺 Les Capucines***
📧 rue de la Côte Fleurie, CD37c
🔲 1 Jan - 31 Dec
☎ +33 (0)2-31786982
@ campingdescapucines.14@orange.fr

1 ADE**JM**NORS**T**		6
2 AGPUVWXY	ABDE**FG**H	7
3 AI**K**LU	ABCDFJKNQRSTUV	8
4 IO	DEFGH	9
5 ABDM**O**	ABCFGHJL**P**R	10
10A CEE		❶ €21.40
4ha 187**T**(80-100m²) 25**P**		❷ €30.60

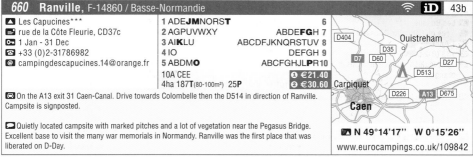

N 49°14'17'' W 0°15'26''

🚗 On the A13 exit 31 Caen-Canal. Drive towards Colombelle then the D514 in direction of Ranville. Campsite is signposted.

💬 Quietly located campsite with marked pitches and a lot of vegetation near the Pegasus Bridge. Excellent base to visit the many war memorials in Normandy. Ranville was the first place that was liberated on D-Day.

www.eurocampings.co.uk/109842

---

661 St. Aubin-sur-Mer, F-14750 / Basse-Normandie   ♿ 🛜 CC€17 iD 43b

🔺 Sandaya La Côte de Nacre*****
📧 17 rue du Général Moulton
🔲 6 Apr - 9 Sep
☎ +33 (0)2-31971445
@ cotedenacre@sandaya.fr

1 ADE**JM**NOPRST	ABCDEFGHI**X**	6
2 GOPVWXY	ABDE**FG**H	7
3 BE**K**LQTU	ABCDEFJKNQRSTUV	8
4 BCDILNO**PQTV**Y		E 9
5 ACDEFGHJL**O**	ABDGHIJNO**P**STVZ	10
Ad on the cover 10A		❶ €52.10
10ha 142**T**(80-120m²) 369**P**		❷ €67.60

N 49°19'33'' W 0°23'26''

🚗 On the Caen ring road exit Côte de Nacre, then via the D7 to Langrune-sur-Mer and St. Aubin-sur-Mer. Campsite is on the D7 and is signposted.

💬 A beautiful parkland campsite with a leisure pool (open air and indoor and heated); sauna, Turkish bath, jacuzzi, restaurant, shopping facilities. Campsite is within walking distance of St. Aubin and 650 m from the beach. All amenities are also open in the early and late seasons.

CC 6/4-6/7 1/9-8/9

www.eurocampings.co.uk/103499

662 Thury-Harcourt, F-14220 / Basse-Normandie

iD 43b

- ⛺ Camping du Traspy***
- 🏠 rue du pont Benoit
- 🕐 1 Apr - 30 Sep
- ☎ +33 (0)2-31299086
- @ contact@campingdutraspy.com

1	ADJMNOPRST	EFGHINUV 6
2	CDGOPUVX	ABDEFGH 7
3	ABEMQST	ABCDFNORST 8
4	FHINO	EJL 9
5	ADEFGHKMN	ABFGHIJPRVWX 10

16A CEE ❶ €21.90
A200 1,7ha 75T(100-200m²) 22P ❷ €28.90

🚗 From the A13 at Caen take the Flers exit. Then take the motorway towards Flers/Alençon, then the D562 to Thury-Harcourt. In Thury-Harcourt first turn left over the bridge after the 'Centre Aquatique'.

💬 A quiet family-run campsite in the wooded area of 'Norman Switzerland' (La Suisse Normande). Just 35 minutes from the landing points.

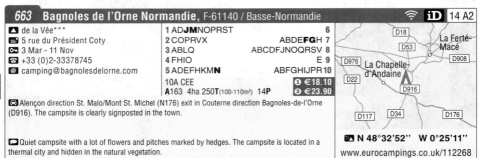

📍 N 48°59'20" W 0°28'8"
www.eurocampings.co.uk/103510

663 Bagnoles de l'Orne Normandie, F-61140 / Basse-Normandie

iD 14 A2

- ⛺ de la Vée***
- 🏠 5 rue du Président Coty
- 🕐 3 Mar - 11 Nov
- ☎ +33 (0)2-33378745
- @ camping@bagnolesdelorne.com

1	ADJMNOPRST	6
2	COPRVX	ABDEFGH 7
3	ABLQ	ABCDFJNOQRSV 8
4	FHIO	E 9
5	ADEFHKMN	ABFGHIJPR 10

10A CEE ❶ €18.10
A163 4ha 250T(100-110m²) 14P ❷ €23.90

🚗 Alençon direction St. Malo/Mont St. Michel (N176) exit in Couterne direction Bagnoles-de-l'Orne (D916). The campsite is clearly signposted in the town.

💬 Quiet campsite with a lot of flowers and pitches marked by hedges. The campsite is located in a thermal city and hidden in the natural vegetation.

📍 N 48°32'52" W 0°25'11"
www.eurocampings.co.uk/112268

664 Barneville-Carteret, F-50270 / Basse-Normandie

iD 13 B2

- ⛺ Les Bosquets***
- 🏠 1 rue du Capitaine Quenault
- 🕐 1 Apr - 15 Oct
- ☎ +33 (0)2-33047362
- @ campinglesbosquetsbarneville@
  orange.fr

1	ADEJMNOPQRST	ABFGKMNQSTWXY 6
2	EHPQVWXY	ABDEFGH 7
3	BEGHKLQT	ABCDFKNQRSV 8
4	BDFILNOPQ	E 9
5	ABDEHNO	ABGHIJOR 10

10A ❶ €24.40
11ha 110T(100-300m²) 221P ❷ €35.60

🚗 The campsite is signposted in Barneville with signs pointing to the beach.

💬 The campsite has spacious pitches in a natural environment. Trees and bushes provide shelter. French family campsite with modern, new (2016) toilet facilities.

📍 N 49°22'0" W 1°45'36"
www.eurocampings.co.uk/110280

665 Baubigny, F-50270 / Basse-Normandie

iD 13 B1

- ⛺ Bel Sito**
- 🏠 L'Église
- 🕐 15 Apr - 15 Sep
- ☎ +33 (0)6-75807280
- @ camping@bel-sito.com

1	AJMNOPQRST	NQSWX 6
2	FHPQUWX	BDEFGH 7
3	AEKL	ABCDEFNRS 8
4	I	JL 9
5	ABDMN	AJOST 10

6-10A CEE ❶ €30.00
6ha 65T(120-300m²) 23P ❷ €41.50

🚗 From Barneville take the D904 direction Cherbourg. After approx. 8 km turn left to Baubigny. The campsite is signposted from there.

💬 Campsite located in a natural dune landscape, 900 m from the beach, looking out over the sea. Not all pitches are marked.

📍 N 49°25'47" W 1°48'17"
www.eurocampings.co.uk/103313

666 Beauvoir, F-50170 / Basse-Normandie ☞ 🎧 (CC€17) iD 43a

- 🏕 Aux Pommiers****
- 📧 28 route du Mont-St-Michel
- 📅 28 Mar - 4 Nov
- ☎ +33 (0)2-33601136
- @ campingauxpommiers@gmail.com

1 ADE**JM**NOPRST	EFGHNX 6		
2 ACGOPRVX	ABDE**FG**H 7		
3 ABELQST	ABCDF**IL**NQRSTUV 8		
4 BCDFHINO**PQ**	EGJV 9		
5 ABCDEFGH**NO**	ABDGHIJPST 10		

Ad on this page 10A CEE
1,8ha 72T(95-105m²) 34P
- ❶ €30.00
- ❷ €42.10

🚐 Via N175 from Avranches direction Pontorson, then via D976 direction Mont-St-Michel. Follow arrows.
💬 A family campsite with a heated and covered swimming pool, only 4 km from Mont St. Michel, which can easily be reached by bike. Also a shuttle bus (charges apply) to Mont St. Michel. Arrival at the campsite from 12:00 hrs.
CC 28/3-7/7 1/9-3/11 7=6

Le Mont-Saint-Michel Avranches Le Val-Saint-Père
☛ N 48°35'47" W 1°30'45"
www.eurocampings.co.uk/107967

Family campsite, 4km from Mont-Saint-Michel and 2.5km from paid shuttles to Mont-Saint-Michel • Covered & heated swimming pool • Wifi • Bike rentals • Bar • Bread • Paid shuttle to Mont-Saint-Michel

28 rte du Mont-St-Michel, 50170 Beauvoir
Tel. 02-33601136 • E-mail: campingauxpommiers@gmail.com
Internet: www.camping-auxpommiers.com

---

667 Bréhal, F-50290 / Basse-Normandie ☞ 🎧 iD 13 B2

- 🏕 La Vanlée***
- 📧 rue des Gabions
- 📅 1 Apr - 15 Oct
- ☎ +33 (0)2-33616380
- @ camping.vanlee@wanadoo.fr

1 AD**JM**NOPRST	ABFGKNQRSTX 6		
2 EFHOPQTVW	ABDE**FG**H 7		
3 ABEF**GJK**LQ	ABCDFNRSV 8		
4 BCDFHLNO	AE 9		
5 ACDEFGHKMN	ABGHIJORZ 10		

10A CEE
11ha 460T(80-100m²) 16P
- ❶ €26.50
- ❷ €34.30

🚐 From Granville, D971 to Bréhal, in Bréhal at roundabout 3/4 left. Drive straight ahead at the traffic lights. D592 as far as St. Martin/Bréhal. Campsite and golf course are signposted.

💬 Family campsite in a natural area in the dunes near the sea, directly on the beach. In the bay of Mont St. Michel. Ideal campsite for children and anyone who loves the sea. Ideal starting point to visit the region.

Granville Saint-Pair-sur-Mer
☛ N 48°54'31" W 1°33'53"
www.eurocampings.co.uk/100260

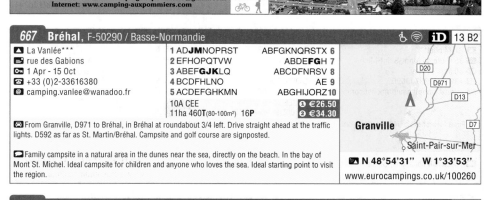

---

668 Breville-sur-Mer, F-50290 / Basse-Normandie ☞ 🎧 (CC€15) iD 13 B2

- 🏕 La Route Blanche****
- 📧 6 la Route Blanche
- 📅 6 Apr - 23 Sep
- ☎ +33 (0)2-33502331
- @ larouteblanche@camping-breville.com

1 ABDE**JM**NOPRS**T**	ABFGHI 6		
2 GHPQVX	ABDE**FG**H 7		
3 ABEJKLQST ABCDEFGIJKNQRSTUV 8			
4 BFGHLNO**PU**	E 9		
5 ACDEFGHJKM**O**	ABGHIJ**NP**ST 10		

Ad on page 250 6-10A CEE
5,5ha 131T(90-120m²) 133P
- ❶ €39.50
- ❷ €53.50

🚐 From Caen on A84 towards Villedieu and Granville (exit 37). Before Granville take D971 towards Cherbourg-Brehal. After 2.5 km at the roundabout exit towards Bréville-sur-Mer, D135. Campsite is well signposted.
💬 Pretty campsite carpeted with flowers less than a kilometre from the sea. Beautiful heated pool. Good toilet facilities. Lots of days out in the area. The campsite has a golf course. Hikers and cyclists will love it here.
CC 6/4-7/7 25/8-22/9

Bréhal Granville
☛ N 48°52'10" W 1°33'50"
www.eurocampings.co.uk/113312

France

---

669 Carentan, F-50500 / Basse-Normandie   ♿ 🛜 (CC€17)   13 B2

▲ Flower Camping Le Haut Dick***	1 DE**JM**NOPRS**T**	CDFGNXY 6
🏕 30 chemin de Grand-Bas Pays	2 ACOPVWXY	ABDE**FG**H 7
⌚ 30 Mar - 30 Sep	3 BELQST	ABCDFNQRSTV 8
☎ +33 (0)2-33421689	4 BDFHIO**PQ**	AEFLUVY 9
@ contact@camping-lehautdick.com	5 ABDFHL	ABDFGHIJ**P**STV 10
	10A CEE	❶ €28.50
	2,5ha 71T(100m²) 29P	❷ €39.00

🚗 First direction Centre Ville. Then the campsite is clearly signposted.

💬 A friendly, peaceful campsite with naturally separated pitches. Right next to the yacht harbour. About a 15-minute walk to the centre. The campsite has a heated swimming pool. The following sights are within a one-hour drive: Mont St. Michel, Cherbourg, Cap de la Hague and the invasion beaches.

(CC) 30/3-31/5 10/6-30/6 1/9-29/9

🗺 N 49°18'36'' W 1°14'21''

www.eurocampings.co.uk/100241

---

670 Courtils, F-50220 / Basse-Normandie   🛜 (CC€17) **iD**   43a

▲ St. Michel***	1 ADE**JM**NOPRS**T**	AB 6
🏕 35 route du Mont-Saint-Michel	2 AGPRVX	ABDE**FG**H 7
⌚ 30 Mar - 4 Nov	3 ABLQT	ABCDEFJNQRSV 8
☎ +33 (0)2-33709690	4 BCDIKLO**P**	ELV 9
@ infos@campingsaintmichel.com	5 ACDFGHM**NO**	ABFGHIJOSTV 10
	6-10A CEE	❶ €28.90
	5,2ha 100T(90-100m²) 53P	❷ €40.40

🚗 From Avranches via D43 direction Mont St. Michel. Campsite is located on the left just after Courtils.

💬 A beautifully floral family campsite with a heated pool. Close to Mont St. Michel, St. Malo and Dinard.

(CC) 30/3-7/7 25/8-3/11 7=6, 14=11

🗺 N 48°37'41'' W 1°24'57''

www.eurocampings.co.uk/101175

---

671 Genêts, F-50530 / Basse-Normandie   ♿ 🛜 (CC€17) **iD**   43a

▲ Les Coques d'Or****	1 ADE**JM**NOPRS**T**	ABCDFGHX 6
🏕 14 rue du Bec d'Andaine	2 AHOPVWX	ABDE**FG**H 7
⌚ 1 Apr - 30 Sep	3 ABELQT	ABCDEFJKNQRSV 8
☎ +33 (0)2-33708257	4 BCDINO**PTUV**	BELUV 9
@ contact@campinglescoquesdor.com	5 ACDEFGHKLM**NO**	ABFGHIJ**NP**ST 10
	6-10A CEE	❶ €30.50
	7,5ha 70T(100-120m²) 98P	❷ €40.90

🚗 At Avranches take exit Granville (D973). Then D911 direction Jullouville. The campsite is just past Genêts, left.

💬 Calm campsite located on the bay of Mont Saint-Michel. Lovely restaurant, full board possible (all meals supplied).

(CC) 1/4-6/7 24/8-29/9

🗺 N 48°41'16'' W 1°29'4''

www.eurocampings.co.uk/103327

672 Les Pieux, F-50340 / Basse-Normandie

� ☐ (CC€17) ♂♀ **iD** 13 B1

- ▲ Le Grand Large*****
- 🛏 route du Grand Large
- 🕒 7 Apr - 23 Sep
- ☎ +33 (0)2-33524075
- @ info@legrandlarge.com

1 ADE**IL**NOPQRST ABCDFGKMNQSWXY 6	
2 EFGHPQVWX ABDE**FG**H 7	
3 BEL**MQST** ABCDEFHJKNPQRSTUV 8	
4 BCDFHIO**PQ**U EL 9	
5 ABDEFHM**N** ABGHIJ**NP**RXZ 10	

Ad on this page 10A CEE
4ha 123**T**(100m²) 100**P**

❶ €42.00
❷ €52.00

🗺 From Valognes, take the D902. In Bricquebec direction Les Pieux. Clearly signposted from Les Pieux.

💬 A family campsite in the dunes of Normandy on the west coast of the Cotentin area and near the British Channel Islands. The campsite is located right by the sea with a wide sandy beach. Pitches marked out by hedges. Lovely partially covered swimming pool with bubble bath.

CC 7/4-6/7 26/8-22/9 7=6, 14=11

🗺 N 49°29'40'' W 1°50'32''

www.eurocampings.co.uk/103311

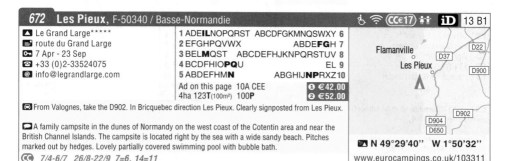

673 Maupertus-sur-Mer, F-50330 / Basse-Normandie

� ☐ ✿ (CC€19) **iD** 13 B1

- ▲ L'Anse du Brick*****
- 🛏 18 Anse du Brick
- 🕒 30 Mar - 15 Sep
- ☎ +33 (0)2-33543357
- @ welcome@anse-du-brick.com

1 ADE**IL**NOPQRST ABEFGHKNOQSX 6	
2 BCEFHJKMPRUVWXY ABDE**FG**H 7	
3 BEF**KLMQT** ABCDEFGHJKNPQRSTUV 8	
4 BCDFILNO**P**U EFJLRU 9	
5 ACDEFGHKLM**N** ABDGHIJNO**PR** 10	

Ad on this page 6-16A CEE
10ha 184**T**(90-150m²) 46**P**

❶ €45.10
❷ €58.10

🗺 From Cherbourg via the D116 towards Bretteville-Barfleur. Follow the D116. Campsite signposted after about 4 km. Attention: difficult to reach via Maupertus, take D116 via Cherbourg.

💬 A lovely campsite with every comfort close to Cherbourg and by the sea. Large pitches on terraces, heated toilet facilities and two swimming pools. Direct access to footpaths and the beach. 30 minutes free wifi daily in the bar.

CC 30/3-5/7 26/8-14/9

🗺 N 49°40'4'' W 1°29'19''

www.eurocampings.co.uk/103308

France

674 Pontaubault, F-50220 / Basse-Normandie

⊚ (CC€17) iD 43a

- △ Vallée de la Séline**
- 🏠 7 rue Maréchal Leclerc
- 🗓 1 Apr - 15 Oct
- ☎ +33 (0)2-33603900
- @ campselune@wanadoo.fr

1 ADEJMNOPRST	X 6
2 AORVX	ABDE**FGH** 7
3 AB**MQ**	ABCDFNRV 8
4	E 9
5 BDHMN	AHJORV 10

Ad on this page 10A CEE ❶ €17.50
1,6ha 70T(100-110m²) 16P ❷ €22.50

🚗 From N175 direction Mont-St-Michel D43. Exit Pontaubault; turn right over the bridge, then the second street to the left.

💬 Small, quiet campsite in a beautiful small village with shops and a restaurant. The campsite is only 15 km from Mont-Saint-Michel.

(CC) 1/4-9/7 27/8-14/10 7=6

🗺 N 48°37'49'' W 1°21'10''

www.eurocampings.co.uk/103334

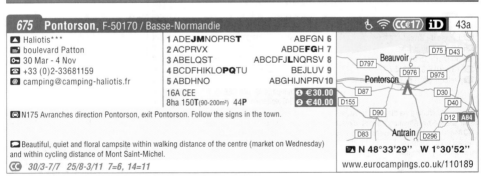

CAMPING VALLÉE DE
LA SÉLUNE ★ ★

Quiet campsite on the border of
Normandy-Brittany and 12 km from
Mont St. Michel.

7 rue Maréchal Leclerc,
50220 Pontaubault • Tel. 02-33603900
E-mail: campselune@wanadoo.fr
Internet: www.campselune.com

675 Pontorson, F-50170 / Basse-Normandie

♿ ⊚ (CC€17) iD 43a

- △ Haliotis***
- 🏠 boulevard Patton
- 🗓 30 Mar - 4 Nov
- ☎ +33 (0)2-33681159
- @ camping@camping-haliotis.fr

1 ADE**JM**NOPRS**T**	ABFGN 6
2 ACPRVX	ABDE**FGH** 7
3 ABELQST	ABCDFJ**L**NQRSV 8
4 BCDFHIKLO**PQ**TU	BEJLUV 9
5 ABDHNO	ABGHIJNPRV 10

16A CEE ❶ €30.00
8ha 150T(90-200m²) 44P ❷ €40.00

🚗 N175 Avranches direction Pontorson, exit Pontorson. Follow the signs in the town.

💬 Beautiful, quiet and floral campsite within walking distance of the centre (market on Wednesday) and within cycling distance of Mont Saint-Michel.

(CC) 30/3-7/7 25/8-3/11 7=6, 14=11

🗺 N 48°33'29'' W 1°30'52''

www.eurocampings.co.uk/110189

676 Ravenoville-Plage, F-50480 / Basse-Normandie

♿ ⊚ ✿ (CC€19) iD 13 B1

- △ Le Cormoran*****
- 🏠 Ravenoville-Plage
- 🗓 31 Mar - 30 Sep
- ☎ +33 (0)2-33413394
- @ lecormoran@wanadoo.fr

1 ADE**IL**NOPQRST	ABEFGKNQSWXY 6
2 AEGHPSVWX	ABDE**FGH**JK 7
3 ABEFG**HIK**LMQR**ST**	ABCDEFJK**LM**NQRSTUV 8
4 BCDFHIKLNOP**QR**TU**XZ**	BEJLVYZ 9
5 ACDEFGHM**NO**	ABDFGHIJMN**NP**STVWXZ 10

Ad on page 253 6-10A CEE ❶ €40.00
8ha 140T(100-150m²) 156P ❷ €49.00

🚗 From St. Mère-Église follow the D15 towards Ravenoville. Then direction Plage. Campsite signposted.

💬 A modern campsite with every comfort and luxury. Located right on Utah Beach by the sea. Spacious marked-out pitches with plenty of greenery and flowers. Ideal base for sightseeing (WW II).

(CC) 31/3-6/7 25/8-29/9 7=6, 14=11

🗺 N 49°27'59'' W 1°14'8''

www.eurocampings.co.uk/101172

France

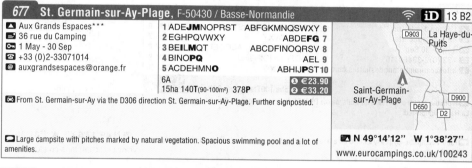

677 St. Germain-sur-Ay-Plage, F-50430 / Basse-Normandie 🛜 iD 13 B2

- ▲ Aux Grands Espaces***
- 🏠 36 rue du Camping
- 🔓 1 May - 30 Sep
- ☎ +33 (0)2-33071014
- @ auxgrandsespaces@orange.fr

1	ADE**JM**NOPRST	ABFGKMNQSWXY	6
2	EGHPQVWXY	ABDE**FG**	7
3	BE**ILM**QT	ABCDFINOQRSV	8
4	BINO**PQ**	AEL	9
5	ACDEHMN**O**	ABHIJ**P**ST	10
6A			
15ha 140**T**(90-100m²) 378**P**		❶ €23.90	
		❷ €33.20	

🚐 From St. Germain-sur-Ay via the D306 direction St. Germain-sur-Ay-Plage. Further signposted.

La Haye-du-Puits — D903

Saint-Germain-sur-Ay-Plage — D900 — D650 — D2

💬 Large campsite with pitches marked by natural vegetation. Spacious swimming pool and a lot of amenities.

🏕 N 49°14'12" W 1°38'27"

www.eurocampings.co.uk/100243

678 St. Jean-de-la-Rivière, F-50270 / Basse-Normandie ♿ 🛜 (CC€17) iD 13 B2

- ▲ Camping du Golf****
- 🏠 43 chemin des Mielles
- 🔓 1 Apr - 30 Sep
- ☎ +33 (0)2-33047890
- @ contact@camping-du-golf.fr

1	ADE**IL**NOPRST	CDFGHKNQWXY	6
2	EFHPQVW	ABDE**FG**H	7
3	BEF**JL**QT	ABCDFGIJKNQRST	8
4	BDFGHINO**PQ**	EV	9
5	ABDEFGHLN**O**	ABDGHIJ**P**ST	10
6A CEE			
3,2ha 90**T**(140-180m²) 59**P**		❶ €32.00	
		❷ €44.00	

🚐 From Barneville-Carteret towards Barneville/St. Jean-de-la-Rivière. Signposted beyond there.

D904 — D902 — D900 — D650 — Saint-Jean-de-la-Rivière — D15 — D903 — La Haye-du-Puits

💬 A family campsite with large pitches, located 500 m from the Normandy Beaches, opposite the Channel Islands of Guernsey and Jersey. Covered and heated swimming pool. Bar, restaurant, pizzeria and shop on site. Plenty of activities available.

🏕 N 49°21'35" W 1°44'55"

www.eurocampings.co.uk/111034

© 1/4-6/7 25/8-29/9

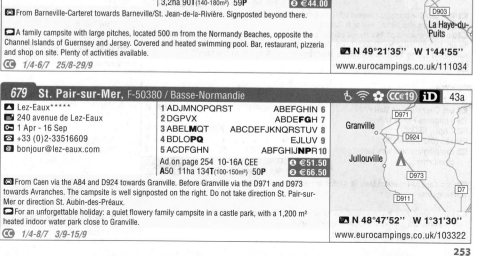

679 St. Pair-sur-Mer, F-50380 / Basse-Normandie ♿ 🛜 ❄ (CC€19) iD 43a

- ▲ Lez-Eaux*****
- 🏠 240 avenue de Lez-Eaux
- 🔓 1 Apr - 16 Sep
- ☎ +33 (0)2-33516609
- @ bonjour@lez-eaux.com

1	ADJMNOPQRST	ABEFGHIN	6
2	DGPVX	ABDE**FG**H	7
3	ABEL**M**QT	ABCDEFJKNQRSTUV	8
4	BDLO**PQ**	EJLUV	9
5	ACDFGHN	ABFGHIJ**NP**R	10
Ad on page 254 10-16A CEE		❶ €51.50	
A50 11ha 134**T**(100-150m²) 50**P**		❷ €66.50	

🚐 From Caen via the A84 and D924 towards Granville. Before Granville via the D971 and D973 towards Avranches. The campsite is well signposted on the right. Do not take direction St. Pair-sur-Mer or direction St. Aubin-des-Préaux.

D971 — Granville — D924 — Jullouville — D973 — D911 — D7

💬 For an unforgettable holiday: a quiet flowery family campsite in a castle park, with a 1,200 m² heated indoor water park close to Granville.

🏕 N 48°47'52" W 1°31'30"

www.eurocampings.co.uk/103322

© 1/4-8/7 3/9-15/9

Château de Lez-Eaux

Les★★★★★ CASTELS

240, avenue de Lez-Eaux
50380
SAINT PAIR SUR MER

☎ +33.2.33.51.66.09

GPS: N48°47'52"
W01°31'30"

www.lez-eaux.com

---

680 St. Symphorien-le-Valois, F-50250 / Basse-Normandie ♿ 🛜 iD 13 B2

🏕 L'Etang des Haizes★★★★
🏠 43 rue Cauticotte
📅 1 Apr - 30 Sep
☎ +33 (0)2-33460116
@ info@campingetangdeshaizes.com

1 ADE**JM**NOPQRST	ABFGH**N**	6
2 DGPVWXY	ABDE**F**GH	7
3 BELQR	ABCDEFGHIKNQRSV	8
4 BDFHILNO**PQ**RU	EFLTV	9
5 ABDEH**NO**	ABHIJ**P**ST	10

10A CEE
A75 4,5ha 100**T**(90-120m²) 60**P**

❶ €37.70
❷ €49.70

🗺 From the centre of La-Haye-du-Puits via the D900E1 direction Valognes. Turn left just outside La Haye. Signposted.

💬 Family campsite, idyllically located on a lake with fishing. The campsite has a lovely swimming pool with water slides.

Picauville
D15
D900
D903
Saint-Germain-
sur-Ay-Plage
D650

📍 N 49°17'59" W 1°32'36"

www.eurocampings.co.uk/100242

---

681 St. Vaast-la-Hougue, F-50550 / Basse-Normandie ♿ 🛜 (CC€17) iD 13 B1

🏕 La Gallouette★★★★
🏠 10 bis rue de la Gallouette
📅 1 Apr - 30 Sep
☎ +33 (0)2-33542057
@ contact@camping-lagallouette.fr

1 ADE**JM**NOPRST	ABFGKNQSTVXY	6
2 EHMPVWX	BDE**FG**H	7
3 BELQT	ABCDEFKNQRSUV	8
4 BDFILOP**Q**	EJZ	9
5 ABDEFH**NO**	ABDFGHIJ**NP**ST	10

10A CEE
3,5ha 110**T**(85-105m²) 68**P**

❶ €31.05
❷ €38.75

🗺 N13 Caen-Cherbourg, at Valognes D902 dir. Quettehou and St. Vaast-la-Hougue. Right at traffic lights, turn right after 300m - Rue de la Galouette.
💬 Quiet site, spacious pitches. Heated outdoor pool, jeu de boules, playground, wifi. 5 min. walk from the sea, harbour and shops. Outings to e.g. Vauban castle on the Tatihou island and Barfleur. Plenty of walking and cycling. Maritime atmosphere. Ideal stopover site: 30 min. from Cherbourg (ferry).
(CC) 1/4-6/7 26/8-29/9

D901
D355
D24
D26
Saint-Vaast-la-
Hougue
D902
D42
D14

📍 N 49°35'4" W 1°16'8"

www.eurocampings.co.uk/111551

---

682 Villedieu-les-Poêles, F-50800 / Basse-Normandie ♿ 🛜 (CC€17) iD 13 B2

🏕 Les Chevaliers de Malte★★★
🏠 2 impasse Pré de la Rose
📅 1 Apr - 15 Oct
☎ +33 (0)2-33594904
@ campingleschevaliersdemalte@
gmail.com

1 ADE**JM**NOPRS**T**	AB**N**	6
2 ACPRVX	ABDE**FG**H	7
3 ABELQST	ABCDFJKNQRSV	8
4 IO**PQ**	EJ	9
5 ABDEFGHJMN	ABFGHJOR	10

8-16A CEE
A100 1,5ha 78**T**(90-100m²) 9**P**

❶ €27.90
❷ €36.90

🗺 From Caen A84 direction Mont St. Michel. In Villedieu take exit 38 towards the centre. Campsite well signposted.

💬 A small campsite in the countryside with marked-out pitches. Located 300 metres from the centre. Copper works, bell-foundry and a typical weekly market.
(CC) 1/4-8/7 26/8-14/10 7=6, 14=11

D38 Percy
D9
Villedieu-les- A84
Poêles
D7
D924 D524
D975
D999 D33
D39

📍 N 48°50'12" W 1°13'2"

www.eurocampings.co.uk/103321

France

Ile-de-France

Central hub of France

The most densely populated region of France, Ile-de-France includes the capital Paris, and is surrounded by Normandy, Pays de la Loire, Centre-Val de Loire, Hauts-de-France, Bourgogne, and Grand Est. Once you leave the city it becomes farming country, with forests and river valleys – the region's name refers to the inland peninsula bordered by the rivers Oise, Seine, Ourcq and Marne. As Il-de-France has been a centre of power for almost 2000 years, the architecture is quite diverse, from simple farmhouses to mediaeval towns and Baroque castles to the 20th century La Défense.

Historic cities and towns

You'll definitely want to see Paris, the iconic Eiffel Tower and Palais du Louvre, take a boat trip along the Seine – or you shop till you drop in Les Halles.

Art history buffs and engineers will be drawn to St-Denis: now a northern suburb of Paris, the magnificent abbey church there is famous for showing the transition from Romanesque to Gothic in architecture. The people of Province re-enact their history on and in the town walls, dungeons and underground vaults during the annual Mediaeval Festival. Other historic locations are Versailles, famous for its palace, Hall of Mirrors and gardens; and experts consider Vaux-le-Vicomte castle near Melun a masterpiece of French Baroque.

Adventurous days out

After you've walked or cycled through the forest at Fontainebleau, visit the enormous castle with its 'horseshoe' stairs. Chateau de Groussay has 9 follies: including a Chinese pagoda, Tatar tent, and a temple in the middle of a labyrinth.

255

The zoo at Thoiry castle is certain to be a hit with the kids, and the historic house has its own attractions. Closer to Paris, museum Marmottan Monet is right beside the Bois du Boulogne, and

Our tips

1. *A day at Disneyland will ensure you are always the best Mum or Dad ever!*
2. *Like art? Visit the Auguste Roden Museum in Meudon*
3. *Learn how to turn wheat into bread the traditional way at Parc du Vexin*
4. *Chill in the big city at the Bois du Vincennes park at the edge of Paris*
5. *Interested in Roman France? Visit the National Museum of Antiquities in St-Germain-En-Laye*

the kids will go nuts in the Jardin d'Acclimatation. If you like horse-riding, boating, swimming and fishing, Parc de la Haute Vallée de Chevreuse is the place to go.

Food and drink

Refuel with Beef Miroton – a type of very slow-cooked beef stew with vegetables. Brie is a local speciality, delicious with baguette. Want something sweet? Try Paris-Brest cake with crème praliné filling. Bon appétit!

683 Maisons-Laffitte, F-78600 / Ile-de-France

🚿 📶 (CC€17) iD 14 B2

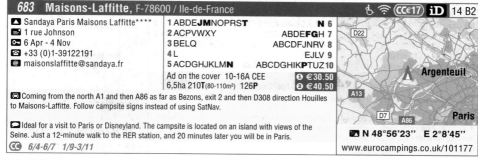

- 🏕 Sandaya Paris Maisons Laffitte★★★★
- 📧 1 rue Johnson
- 📅 6 Apr - 4 Nov
- ☎ +33 (0)1-39122191
- @ maisonslaffitte@sandaya.fr

1 ABDE**JM**NOPRS**T**		**N** 6
2 ACPVWXY	ABDE**FG**H	7
3 BELQ	ABCDFJNRV	8
4 L	EJLV	9
5 ACDGHJKLM**N**	ABCDGHIK**P**TUZ	10

Ad on the cover 10-16A CEE
6,5ha 210T(80-110m²) 126P

❶ €30.50
❷ €40.50

🚗 Coming from the north A1 and then A86 as far as Bezons, exit 2 and then D308 direction Houilles to Maisons-Laffitte. Follow campsite signs instead of using SatNav.

💬 Ideal for a visit to Paris or Disneyland. The campsite is located on an island with views of the Seine. Just a 12-minute walk to the RER station, and 20 minutes later you will be in Paris.

(CC) 6/4-6/7 1/9-3/11

⚑ N 48°56'23'' E 2°8'45''

www.eurocampings.co.uk/101177

---

684 Rambouillet, F-78120 / Ile-de-France

🚿 (CC€17) iD 14 B2

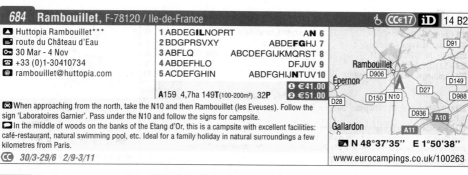

- 🏕 Huttopia Rambouillet★★★
- 📧 route du Château d'Eau
- 📅 30 Mar - 4 Nov
- ☎ +33 (0)1-30410734
- @ rambouillet@huttopia.com

1 ABDEG**IL**NOPRT		**AN** 6
2 BDGPRSVXY	ABDE**FG**HJ	7
3 ABFLQ	ABCDEFGIJKMQRST	8
4 ABDEFHLO	DFJUV	9
5 ACDEFGHIN	ABDFGHIJ**N**TUV	10

A159 4,7ha 149T(100-200m²) 32P

❶ €41.00
❷ €51.00

🚗 When approaching from the north, take the N10 and then Rambouillet (les Eveuses). Follow the sign 'Laboratoires Garnier'. Pass under the N10 and follow the signs for campsite.

💬 In the middle of woods on the banks of the Etang d'Or, this is a campsite with excellent facilities: café-restaurant, natural swimming pool, etc. Ideal for a family holiday in natural surroundings a few kilometres from Paris.

(CC) 30/3-29/6 2/9-3/11

⚑ N 48°37'35'' E 1°50'38''

www.eurocampings.co.uk/100263

---

685 Versailles, F-78000 / Ile-de-France

🚿 📶 (CC€19) iD 14 B2

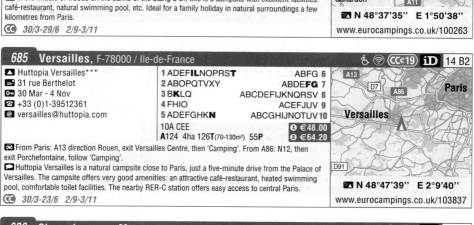

- 🏕 Huttopia Versailles★★★
- 📧 31 rue Berthelot
- 📅 30 Mar - 4 Nov
- ☎ +33 (0)1-39512361
- @ versailles@huttopia.com

1 ADEF**IL**NOPRS**T**		ABFG 6
2 ABOPQTVXY	ABDE**FG**	7
3 B**K**LQ	ABCDEFIJKNQRSV	8
4 FHIO	ACEFJUV	9
5 ADEFGHK**N**	ABCGHIJNOTUV	10

10A CEE
A124 4ha 126T(70-130m²) 55P

❶ €48.00
❷ €64.20

🚗 From Paris: A13 direction Rouen, exit Versailles Centre, then 'Camping'. From A86: N12, then exit Porchefontaine, follow 'Camping'.

💬 Huttopia Versailles is a natural campsite close to Paris, just a five-minute drive from the Palace of Versailles. The campsite offers very good amenities: an attractive café-restaurant, heated swimming pool, comfortable toilet facilities. The nearby RER-C station offers easy access to central Paris.

(CC) 30/3-23/6 2/9-3/11

⚑ N 48°47'39'' E 2°9'40''

www.eurocampings.co.uk/103837

---

686 Champigny-sur-Marne, F-94507 / Ile-de-France

🚿 📶 iD 15 A2

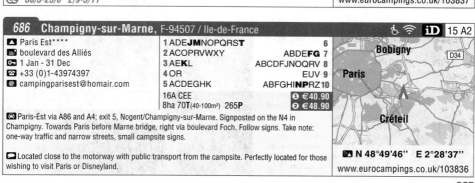

- 🏕 Paris Est★★★★
- 📧 boulevard des Alliés
- 📅 1 Jan - 31 Dec
- ☎ +33 (0)1-43974397
- @ campingparisest@homair.com

1 ADE**JM**NOPQRS**T**		6
2 ACOPRVWXY	ABDE**FG**	7
3 AE**K**L	ABCDFJNOQRV	8
4 OR	EUV	9
5 ACDEGHK	ABFGHI**NP**RZ	10

16A CEE
8ha 70T(40-100m²) 265P

❶ €40.90
❷ €48.90

🚗 Paris-Est via A86 and A4; exit 5, Nogent/Champigny-sur-Marne. Signposted on the N4 in Champigny. Towards Paris before Marne bridge, right via boulevard Foch. Follow signs. Take note: one-way traffic and narrow streets, small campsite signs.

💬 Located close to the motorway with public transport from the campsite. Perfectly located for those wishing to visit Paris or Disneyland.

⚑ N 48°49'46'' E 2°28'37''

www.eurocampings.co.uk/103836

France

687 Paris, F-75016 / Ile-de-France
  ♿ 🛜 (CC€19) **iD** 14 B2

- ⛺ Camping de Paris****
- 🏠 2 allée du Bord de l'Eau
- 📅 1 Jan - 31 Dec
- ☎ +33 (0)1-45243000
- @ paris@camping-indigo.com

1 ADEJMNOPRS**T**		6
2 ABCORVXY	ABDE**FGH**	7
3 ABL	ABDFJKNQRSTU	8
4 IO	BCEV	9
5 ACDEFGHKMN**O**	ABGHIKNOTU	10
10A CEE		❶ €44.80
7ha 313T(80-100m²) 97P		❷ €57.40

🚗 Périphérique Sud exit Porte Maillot. Follow the signs to the campsite and Bagatelle.

💬 Campsite is located in Bois de Boulogne, a beautiful natural park on the Seine. Ideally situated for discovering Paris or the lovely countryside around it. The pitches are spacious and marked out and there are many old trees which provide sufficient shade.

(CC) 7/1-6/4 21/5-14/6 2/9-22/12

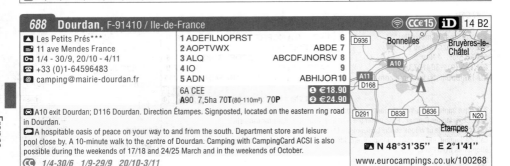

☓ N 48°52'6'' E 2°14'5''

www.eurocampings.co.uk/100265

688 Dourdan, F-91410 / Ile-de-France
  🛜 (CC€15) **iD** 14 B2

- ⛺ Les Petits Prés***
- 🏠 11 ave Mendes France
- 📅 1/4 - 30/9, 20/10 - 4/11
- ☎ +33 (0)1-64596483
- @ camping@mairie-dourdan.fr

1 ADEFILNOPRST		6
2 AOPTVWX	ABDE	7
3 ALQ	ABCDFJNORSV	8
4 IO		9
5 ADN	ABHIJOR	10
6A CEE		❶ €18.90
A90 7,5ha 70T(80-110m²) 70P		❷ €24.90

🚗 A10 exit Dourdan; D116 Dourdan. Direction Étampes. Signposted, located on the eastern ring road in Dourdan.

💬 A hospitable oasis of peace on your way to and from the south. Department store and leisure pool close by. A 10-minute walk to the centre of Dourdan. Camping with CampingCard ACSI is also possible during the weekends of 17/18 and 24/25 March and in the weekends of October.

(CC) 1/4-30/6 1/9-29/9 20/10-3/11

☓ N 48°31'35'' E 2°1'41''

www.eurocampings.co.uk/100268

689 Milly-la-Forêt, F-91490 / Ile-de-France
  ♿ **iD** 15 A3

- ⛺ La Musardière***
- 🏠 route des Grandes Vallées
- 📅 15 Feb - 20 Nov
- ☎ +33 (0)1-64989191
- @ lamusardiere91@orange.fr

1 ADEJMNOPRST	ABFG	6
2 BPQVXY	ABDE**FG**	7
3 BELQU	ABCDFJNORST	8
4 FH	EU	9
5 ADN	AFJS	10
Ad on this page 6A		❶ €26.20
12ha 80T(max 200m²) 187P		❷ €34.80

🚗 D837 Milly-la-Forêt direction Fontainebleau. The campsite is signposted. A6, exit 13 Milly-la-Forêt, follow the arrows.

💬 Campsite near Paris and Fontainebleau, but surrounded by nature. Nature partly determines where you can park your caravan between the trees. Lovely swimming pool. Within walking distance of climbing rocks. Cycling and walking routes.

☓ N 48°23'40'' E 2°30'23''

www.eurocampings.co.uk/103844

690 Monnerville, F-91930 / Ile-de-France

🏕 Le Bois de la Justice***
chemin de Mennessard
7 Feb - 24 Nov
☎ +33 (0)1-64950534
@ boisdelajustice@gmail.com

1 ADE**JM**NOPRS**T**	AB	6
2 BPRTVWXY	ABDE**FG**	7
3 BELQ	ABCDFJNQRS	8
4 IO	EJ	9
5 ADEF**GN**	ABHJOR	10

Ad on this page   6A
A140 5,6ha 30**T**(80-150m²) 126**P**

❸ €25.00
❸ €31.00

🚗 N20 Paris-Orléans, exit Monnerville. Follow the signs 'Camping Bois de la Justice'.

💬 Campsite in a peaceful setting in a wood. Heated pool. Friendly welcome. 2 km from the N20 Paris-Orléans.

CC 1/3-15/6   10/9-30/10

🛰 N 48°19'56''   E 2°2'49''

www.eurocampings.co.uk/103845

🏳 ((€19)) iD 14 B3

Map locations: D24, D21, Étampes, D63, N20, D721, A10, D838, D49, D939, D145, D921, Sermaises, Rouvray-Saint-Denis, D97, D22, D2020

France

691 Villiers-sur-Orge, F-91700 / Ile-de-France

🏕 Paris Beau Village***
1 voie des Prés
1 Jan - 31 Dec
☎ +33 (0)1-60161786
@ contact@campingaparis.com

1 ADEFJMNOPRST	N	6
2 ACPWXY	A**B**DE**FG**H	7
3 BELQ	ABCDEFJKNRSV	8
4 IO**PQR**	EL	9
5 ADHNO	ABFGHIJP**R**V	10

10-16A CEE
2,5ha 124**T**(100-120m²) 52**P**

❸ €27.50
❸ €37.00

🚗 A6 exit 6 Savigny, direction Montlhéry and Gare de Ste Geneviève-des-Bois (D25).
N20 exit Villiers-sur-Orge (D35). Campsite signposted.

💬 Small family campsite located on a quiet little river, close to a big shopping centre (3 km). The pitches are well marked out and the trees offer sufficient shade.

🛰 N 48°39'19''   E 2°18'15''

www.eurocampings.co.uk/103840

🏳 iD 14 B2

Map locations: Limeil-Brévannes, N20, A6, Morsang-sur-Orge, A10, D446, D97, Breuillet

692 Bray-sur-Seine, F-77480 / Ile-de-France

🏕 La Peupleraie**
rue des Pâtures
1 Apr - 31 Oct
☎ +33 (0)1-60671224
@ camping.lapeupleraie@wanadoo.fr

1 A**JM**NOPRS**T**	A**BFGN**XYZ	6
2 ACGHIPVWXY	ABDE**FG**H	7
3 AEF**H**LMQSU	ABCDEFNORSTUV	8
4 I	DEQUVY	9
5 DEFGHKMN	AGHIJP**R**V	10

6A
A60 8ha 140**T**(80-120m²) 138**P**

❸ €19.25
❸ €27.05

🚗 A5 exit 18, then D41 direction Bray-sur-Seine. Signposted before the centre (next to the sports centre).

💬 On the banks of the river Seine, situated beside a large sports complex (with activities for everyone) and within walking distance of a supermarket.

🛰 N 48°24'51''   E 3°14'46''

www.eurocampings.co.uk/113234

🏳 iD 15 A3

Map locations: Montigny-Lencoup, D209, Gouaix, D213, D59 A, D411, D412, A5, Sergines, D606

693 Crécy-la-Chapelle, F-77580 / Ile-de-France ♿ 🛜 iD 15 A2

- ▲ Le Soleil de Crécy***
- 🚩 route de Serbonne
- 📅 1 Apr - 23 Oct
- ☎ +33 (0)1-60435700
- @ reception@campinglesoleil.com

1 ABDEIKNOPRST	AF**N**	6
2 ACGOPSVWXY	ABDE**FG**H	7
3 BE**K**LQ	ABCDFJNQRSV	8
4 **A**BFHILN	EL	9
5 ABDEFHIKN	ABFHIJNPR	10

10A ❶ €34.20
A55 6ha 104**T**(100m²) 42**P** ❷ €34.20

🚗 A4 direction Metz-Nancy. Exit 16, then N34 direction Coulommiers and follow campsite signs. Just after the built up area of Crécy turn right downhill after the bend by the church and the traffic lights.

💬 The campsite is easily accessible and ideally situated for a visit to Disneyland. Regular bus service available. Beautiful, inviting swimming pool.

📷 N 48°51'13" E 2°55'46"
www.eurocampings.co.uk/100266

694 Crèvecoeur-en-Brie, F-77610 / Ile-de-France ♿ 🛜 iD 15 A2

- ▲ Caravaning Des 4 Vents***
- 🚩 22 rue de Beauregard
- 📅 20 Mar - 1 Nov
- ☎ +33 (0)1-64074111
- @ f.george@free.fr

1 ADE**JM**NOPRST	A	6
2 OPVXY	ABDE**FG**H	7
3 BCEFLQ	ABCDFNQRT	8
4	J	9
5 ADEFG	ABGHIJOR	10

6A CEE ❶ €32.00
A114 10ha 200**T**(150-250m²) 56**P** ❷ €44.00

🚗 A4 exit 13. D231 direction Provins till 4.5 km past the obelisk. Then turn right onto C3 towards Crèvecoeur-en-Brie. Then follow signs.

💬 Your own spot in an old orchard. Relaxation and space among the blossom. Just a 15-minute drive to Disneyland Paris and 8 minutes to the Tournan RER station: direct to Paris.

📷 N 48°45'2" E 2°53'50"
www.eurocampings.co.uk/101447

695 Grez-sur-Loing/Fontainebleau, F-77880 / Ile-de-France ♿ 🛜 iD 15 A3

- ▲ Les Prés**
- 🚩 1 chemin des Prés
- 📅 17 Mar - 11 Nov
- ☎ +33 (0)1-64457275
- @ camping-grez@wanadoo.fr

1 ADEJMNOPRS**T**	NX	6
2 ACGPVWX	ABD**FG**K	7
3 AE**KLM**QS	ABCDFJNOQRS	8
4	DQRUV	9
5 BD**N**	ABGHIJL**NPR**	10

Ad on this page 5A ❶ €17.30
A56 6ha 50**T**(100m²) 103**P** ❷ €22.60

🚗 From Fontainebleau take the N7 direction Nemours, village Pavée-du-Roy, turn left after 3 km, follow the campsite signs. On the roundabout direction Grez-sur-Loing.

💬 Well maintained campsite in wooded area; forest, water and historical heritage 400 m away.

📷 N 48°19'3" E 2°41'47"
www.eurocampings.co.uk/103846

696 Jablines, F-77450 / Ile-de-France

♿ 🛜 (CC€19) **iD** 15 A2

- 🏕 International de Jablines***
- 🏖 Base de Loisirs
- 📅 24 Mar - 3 Nov
- ☎ +33 (0)1-60260937
- @ welcome@camping-jablines.com

1 AD**EFJM**NOPRST	LM**N**QRSTW**XYZ** 6
2 ADGHIOPSVWXY	AB**DEFG** 7
3 B**EFGHIKL**M**QT**	ABCDFJKNRSUV 8
4 FH	DELMOQRTUV 9
5 ABCD**N**	ABGHIJ**N**PRZ 10
10A CEE	❶ €32.10
3,5ha 139T(90-100m²) 15P	❷ €44.10

🚗 A104 exit 8 or N3 exit D404 'Base de Plein Air et de Loisirs-Jablines'. Follow signs. The campsite is along the D45.

💬 Lovely, hospitable campsite in natural surroundings of 450 hectares. Marked-out pitches, free wifi, ticket sales and shuttle bus to Disneyland. The largest beach in the Paris region (an enormous lake) for swimming and many types of watersport is next to the campsite. Close to Paris, 9 km from Disneyland and 30 km from Parc Asterix.

CC 24/3-6/7 25/8-2/11

📌 N 48°54'49'' E 2°44'4''

www.eurocampings.co.uk/101178

697 La Rochette, F-77000 / Ile-de-France

♿ 🛜 **iD** 15 A2

- 🏕 Camping La Rochette Etoile***
- 🏖 1 Quai de Seine
- 📅 1 Apr - 8 Oct
- ☎ +33 (0)1-64394812
- @ info@campinglabelleetoile.com

1 AD**EJM**NOPRST	ABF**N** 6
2 ACGPVWXY	ABDE**FGH** 7
3 ABEF**K**LQST	ABCDFNOQRSV 8
4 LO	AEJVY 9
5 ADEGHIKM**N**	ABGHIK**NP**ST 10
6A CEE	❶ €27.00
3,5ha 160T(80-100m²) 27P	❷ €37.00

🚗 From south take RD606 from Fontainebleau direction Melun. From north follow RD606 direction Fontainebleau and in La Rochette at the 'Buffalo Grill' follow campsite signs to banks of the Seine.

💬 Dutch-French owners. Ideal location for day-trips to Paris by train and Disneyland, situated in the heart of an extraordinary historic and cultural heirtage site. Directly on the Seine, on the crossroads of motorways going north-south and east-west.

📌 N 48°31'32'' E 2°40'8''

www.eurocampings.co.uk/101448

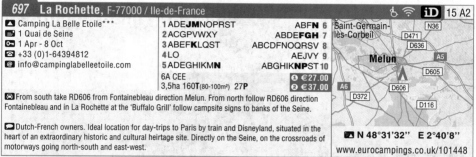

698 Touquin, F-77131 / Ile-de-France

🛜 **iD** 15 A2

- 🏕 Les Etangs Fleuris***
- 🏖 route de la Couture
- 📅 14 Apr - 16 Sep
- ☎ +33 (0)1-64041636
- @ contact@etangs-fleuris.com

1 AD**EJM**NORST	ABFGH**N** 6
2 CGPVWXY	AB**DEFG** 7
3 BELQS	ABCDFJNQRSTV 8
4 **OPQ**	E 9
5 ABDFHN	ABFGHIJ**OR** 10
Ad on this page 10A CEE	❶ €28.00
A100 10ha 123T(100-160m²) 58P	❷ €40.00

🚗 A4, exit 13 direction Provins. Continue to the D231 as far as Touquin and follow the campsite signs.

💬 A lovely campsite with plenty of trees and a swimming pool. Peaceful rural location. Good base for visiting Paris, Disneyland and Parc Asterix (50 minutes). Camping Qualité label.

📌 N 48°43'52'' E 3°2'51''

www.eurocampings.co.uk/107477

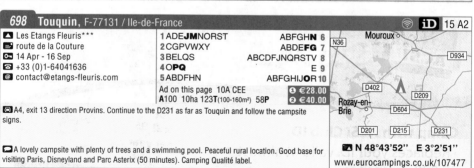

France

699 Veneux-les-Sablons, F-77250 / Ile-de-France

🛜 (CC€19) iD 15 A3

🏕 Les Courtilles du Lido***
📧 chemin du Passeur
📅 20 Mar - 24 Sep
☎ +33 (0)1-60704605
@ lescourtilles-dulido@wanadoo.fr

1 ADE**JM**NOPRST	AB**N** 6
2 CPRVXY	BD**FG**H 7
3 B**IKL**MQT	BDFNQRSV 8
4 O	ADE 9
5 ABDGH**NO**	ABGHIJPR10

Ad on this page 10A CEE
5ha 161**T**(100-300m²) 42**P**

❶ €23.00
❷ €31.00

🚗 From Fontainebleau N6 towards Sens. Exit Veneux-les-Sablons. Left at traffic lights after bridge and follow campsite signs.

🛏 This is the place to relax. Heated swimming pool, tennis, crazy golf. Paris and Fontainebleau within easy reach by train or car. Free internet on the entire campsite. Climbing opportunities in the vicinity.

CC 20/3-1/7 31/8-23/9

Map showing Chailly-en-Bière, Avon, Écuelles with roads D227, D210, A5, D605, D152, D607, D219, A6, D403, D218

📍 N 48°22'59'' E 2°48'6''
www.eurocampings.co.uk/107474

Les Courtilles du Lido
★ ★ ★

A quiet family campsite located near Paris and Fontainebleau. Heated swimming pool, crazy golf, rock climbing, etc. Caravan and tent rental. Wifi throughout the grounds (free).

Chemin du Passeur, 77250 Veneux-les-Sablons
Tel. 01-60704605 • Fax 01-64706265
E-mail: lescourtilles-dulido@wanadoo.fr
Internet: www.les-courtilles-du-lido.fr

Centre-Val de Loire

The granary of France

Follow the Loire upriver through a rich countryside full of forests, lakes, grain fields, meadows and vineyards, and you'll understand why so many French nobles chose to build their castles here. Located in the centre of the country, this region is bordered by Ile-de-France, Bourgogne-France-Comté, Auvergne-Rhone-Alpes, Nouvelle-Aquitaine, Pays de la Loire and Normandy.

Rich history, and simply rich

The combination of a glorious landscape, Renaissance castles, historic towns and landscaped gardens still inspires artists today. The cathedral of Chartres attracts the faithful, while the nearby stained-glass workshop and museum draw artists and artisans. Joan of Arc is the Maid of Orleans, whose bravery prevented England from invading France, and she is celebrated in an annual festival, complete with re-enactments and street theatre. In Tours you can admire the White Tower, the last remaining part of the city's mediaeval defences. In addition to its Gothic cathedral, Tours also has the Gothic Palais Jacques Coeurs, the Berry Museum and beautiful Mediaeval and Renaissance buildings, such as Lallement's Hotel. Music lovers flock to Bourges for the Printemps de Bourges Festival, and the city is also known as the birthplace of French Impressionist painter Berthe Morisot. Admire the spires of the cathedral of St Etienne in Bourge, and if you are interested in life changing history, you'll like the Bertrand Museum.

Other activities

Known as the 'land of a thousand lakes', conservation areas St Mesmin, Brenne Nature

Park draw walkers, hikers and nature lovers. The Loire valley is ideal for hikers and cyclists, but also water sports enthusiasts: with canoeing, kayaking and swimming. The kids will be fascinated about exploring cave dwellings in Loches, or climbing to the treetops near Clinon. Adrenaline junkies enjoy crossing the lake near Sidailles by zipwire. If that's not high enough, take a hot air balloon ride over the Loire Valley. Prefer to keep both feet on the ground? Visit the castles and gardens in Cheverny, Usse and Villandry.

> **Did you know ...?**
> Hollywood actress, singer, musician, songwriter and environmentalist Marion Cotillard grew up in Orléans.

What to eat and drink

Now that you've worked up an appetite, have some paté l'oeuf, meat paste with egg; or some local freshwater fish, accompanied by delicious local wines. Fancy something sweet? Try messepain d'Issodun, a marzipan cake, or Forestine pralines. Local Orléans specialities are vinegar and mustard, both of which add a zing to any dish!

Our tips

1. Visit the town of Azay-le-Rideau, see family-owned Chateau d'Islette
2. Tours Botanic Gardens has activities for kids, and emus, wallabies and tortoises
3. See raptors, seals and other animals at Beauval zoo, Saint-Aignan
4. Is gardening your thing? Check out the Chaumont Garden Festival
5. A whole new level of cuteness: See the mini-chateaux at Amboise

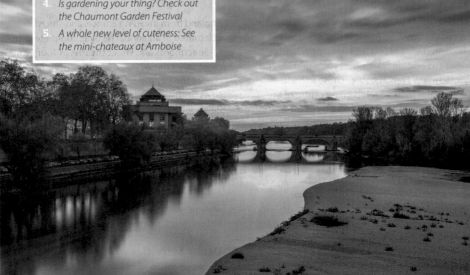

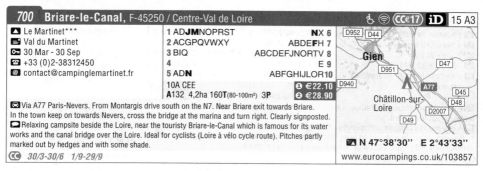

700 Briare-le-Canal, F-45250 / Centre-Val de Loire   ♿ 🛜 (CC€17) iD   15 A3

- ⛰ Le Martinet***
- 🏕 Val du Martinet
- 📅 30 Mar - 30 Sep
- ☎ +33 (0)2-38312450
- @ contact@campinglemartinet.fr

1	ADJMNOPRST	NX	6
2	ACGPQVWXY	ABDEFH	7
3	BIQ	ABCDEFJNORTV	8
4		E	9
5	ADN	ABFGHIJLOR	10

10A CEE   ❶ €22.10
A132   4,2ha 160T(80-100m²)   3P   ❷ €28.90

🚗 Via A77 Paris-Nevers. From Montargis drive south on the N7. Near Briare exit towards Briare. In the town keep on towards Nevers, cross the bridge at the marina and turn right. Clearly signposted.
💬 Relaxing campsite beside the Loire, near the touristy Briare-le-Canal which is famous for its water works and the canal bridge over the Loire. Ideal for cyclists (Loire à vélo cycle route). Pitches partly marked out by hedges and with some shade.
CC 30/3-30/6   1/9-29/9

📍 N 47°38'30''   E 2°43'33''
www.eurocampings.co.uk/103857

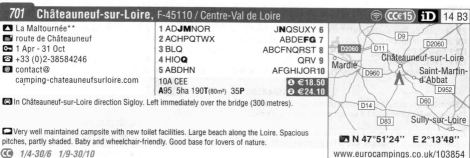

701 Châteauneuf-sur-Loire, F-45110 / Centre-Val de Loire   🛜 (CC€15) iD   14 B3

- ⛰ La Maltournée**
- 🏕 route de Châteauneuf
- 📅 1 Apr - 31 Oct
- ☎ +33 (0)2-38584246
- @ contact@
  camping-chateauneufsurloire.com

1	ADJMNOR	JNQSUXY	6
2	ACHPQTWX	ABDEFG	7
3	BLQ	ABCFNQRST	8
4	HIOQ	QRV	9
5	ABDHN	AFGHIJOR	10

10A CEE   ❶ €18.50
A95   5ha 190T(80m²)   35P   ❷ €24.10

🚗 In Châteauneuf-sur-Loire direction Sigloy. Left immediately over the bridge (300 metres).

💬 Very well maintained campsite with new toilet facilities. Large beach along the Loire. Spacious pitches, partly shaded. Baby and wheelchair-friendly. Good base for lovers of nature.
CC 1/4-30/6   1/9-30/10

📍 N 47°51'24''   E 2°13'48''
www.eurocampings.co.uk/103854

France

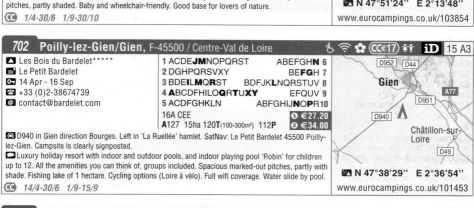

702 Poilly-lez-Gien/Gien, F-45500 / Centre-Val de Loire   ♿ 🛜 ✿ (CC€17) 🚼 iD   15 A3

- ⛰ Les Bois du Bardelet*****
- 🏕 Le Petit Bardelet
- 📅 14 Apr - 16 Sep
- ☎ +33 (0)2-38674739
- @ contact@bardelet.com

1	ACDEJMNOPQRST	ABEFGHN	6
2	DGHPQRSVXY	BEFGH	7
3	BDEILMQRST	BDFJKLNQRSTUV	8
4	ABCDFHILOQRTUXY	EFQUV	9
5	ACDFGHKLN	ABFGHIJNOPR	10

16A CEE   ❶ €27.20
A127   15ha 120T(100-300m²)   112P   ❷ €34.00

🚗 D940 in Gien direction Bourges. Left in 'La Ruellée' hamlet. SatNav: Le Petit Bardelet 45500 Poilly-lez-Gien. Campsite is clearly signposted.
💬 Luxury holiday resort with indoor and outdoor pools, and indoor playing pool 'Robin' for children up to 12. All the amenities you can think of, groups included. Spacious marked-out pitches, partly with shade. Fishing lake of 1 hectare. Cycling options (Loire á vèlo). Full wifi coverage. Water slide by pool.
CC 14/4-30/6   1/9-15/9

📍 N 47°38'29''   E 2°36'54''
www.eurocampings.co.uk/101453

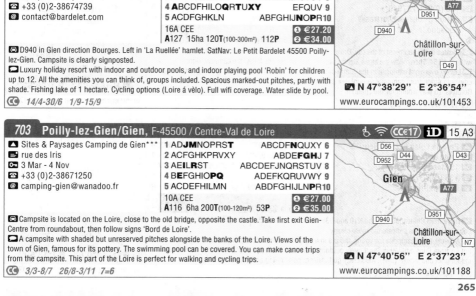

703 Poilly-lez-Gien/Gien, F-45500 / Centre-Val de Loire   ♿ 🛜 (CC€17) iD   15 A3

- ⛰ Sites & Paysages Camping de Gien***
- 🏕 rue des Iris
- 📅 3 Mar - 4 Nov
- ☎ +33 (0)2-38671250
- @ camping-gien@wanadoo.fr

1	ADJMNOPRST	ABCDFNQUXY	6
2	ACFGHKPRVXY	ABDEFGHJ	7
3	AEILRST	ABCDEFJNQRSTUV	8
4	BEFGHIOPQ	ADEFKQRUVWY	9
5	ACDEFHILMN	ABDFGHIJLNPR	10

10A CEE   ❶ €27.00
A116   6ha 200T(100-120m²)   53P   ❷ €35.00

🚗 Campsite is located on the Loire, close to the old bridge, opposite the castle. Take first exit Gien-Centre from roundabout, then follow signs 'Bord de Loire'.
💬 A campsite with shaded and unreserved pitches alongside the banks of the Loire. Views of the town of Gien, famous for its pottery. The swimming pool can be covered. You can make canoe trips from the campsite. This part of the Loire is perfect for walking and cycling trips.
CC 3/3-8/7   26/8-3/11   7=6

📍 N 47°40'56''   E 2°37'23''
www.eurocampings.co.uk/101188

704 Sully/St. Père-sur-Loire, F-45600 / Centre-Val de Loire 📶 (CC€17) iD 14 B3

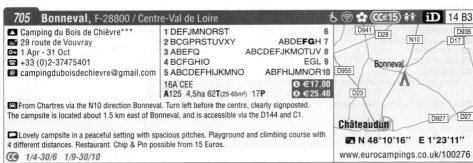

- ▲ Le Jardin de Sully***
- ✉ 1 rue d'Orleans
- ⌕ 1 Jan - 31 Dec
- ☎ +33 (0)2-38671084
- @ info-camping-lejardindesully@orange.fr

1 ADJMNOPQRS	ABFG**N**	6
2 CGHIOPQSVXY	ABDE**FGH**	7
3 AB**IKLMNQ**	ABCDFJLNQRSTUV	8
4 AFHIO**Q**	DEFJQVY	9
5 ABDEFGHN	ABGHIJLN**PRZ**10	
10A CEE	❶ €25.00	
	❷ €30.00	
A123 5ha 80**T**(90-120m²) 32**P**		

🔲 Approaching from Lorris or Bellegarde towards Sully, turn right at the roundabout before the Loire bridge. Campsite indicated.

💬 A very peaceful campsite with spacious pitches and lots of plants. An area rich in nature, right by the Loire. An excellent starting point for light walking and cycling in level surroundings. Various castles, towns and villages with plenty of sights close by. Sully has an attractive centre.

(CC) 1/1-7/7 25/8-31/12 7=6

N 47°46'16'' E 2°21'44''

www.eurocampings.co.uk/103855

705 Bonneval, F-28800 / Centre-Val de Loire ♿ 📶 ✿ (CC€15) ✲✲ iD 14 B3

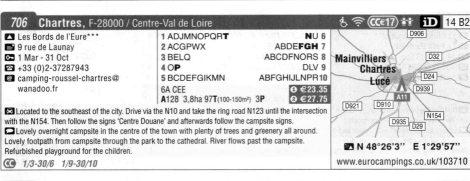

- ▲ Camping du Bois de Chièvre***
- ✉ 29 route de Vouvray
- ⌕ 1 Apr - 31 Oct
- ☎ +33 (0)2-37475401
- @ campingduboisdechievre@gmail.com

1 DEFJMNORST		6
2 BCGPRSTUVXY	ABDE**FGH**	7
3 ABEFQ	ABCDEFJKMOTUV	8
4 BCFGHIO	EGL	9
5 ABCDEFHIJKMNO	ABFHIJMNOR 10	
16A CEE	❶ €17.00	
	❷ €25.40	
A125 4,5ha 62**T**(25-65m²) 17**P**		

🔲 From Chartres via the N10 direction Bonneval. Turn left before the centre, clearly signposted. The campsite is located about 1.5 km east of Bonneval, and is accessible via the D144 and C1.

💬 Lovely campsite in a peaceful setting with spacious pitches. Playground and climbing course with 4 different distances. Restaurant. Chip & Pin possible from 15 Euros.

(CC) 1/4-30/6 1/9-30/10

N 48°10'16'' E 1°23'11''

www.eurocampings.co.uk/100276

706 Chartres, F-28000 / Centre-Val de Loire ♿ 📶 (CC€17) ✲✲ iD 14 B2

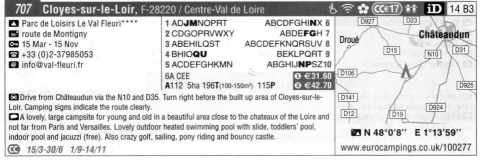

- ▲ Les Bords de l'Eure***
- ✉ 9 rue de Launay
- ⌕ 1 Mar - 31 Oct
- ☎ +33 (0)2-37287943
- @ camping-roussel-chartres@wanadoo.fr

1 ADJMNOPQR**T**	N**U**	6
2 ACGPWX	ABDE**FGH**	7
3 BELQ	ABCDFNORS	8
4 O**P**	DLV	9
5 BCDEFGIKMN	ABFGHIJLNPR 10	
6A CEE	❶ €23.35	
	❷ €27.75	
A128 3,8ha 97**T**(100-150m²) 3**P**		

🔲 Located to the southeast of the city. Drive via the N10 and take the ring road N123 until the intersection with the N154. Then follow the signs 'Centre Douane' and afterwards follow the campsite signs.

💬 Lovely overnight campsite in the centre of the town with plenty of trees and greenery all around. Lovely footpath from campsite through the park to the cathedral. River flows past the campsite. Refurbished playground for the children.

(CC) 1/3-30/6 1/9-30/10

N 48°26'3'' E 1°29'57''

www.eurocampings.co.uk/103710

707 Cloyes-sur-le-Loir, F-28220 / Centre-Val de Loire ♿ 📶 ✿ (CC€17) ✲✲ iD 14 B3

- ▲ Parc de Loisirs Le Val Fleuri****
- ✉ route de Montigny
- ⌕ 15 Mar - 15 Nov
- ☎ +33 (0)2-37985053
- @ info@val-fleuri.fr

1 AD**JM**NOPRT	ABCDFGHI**N**X	6
2 CDGOPRVWXY	ABDE**FGH**	7
3 ABEHILQST	ABCDEFKNQRSUV	8
4 BHIO**QU**	BEKLPQRT	9
5 ACDEFGHKMN	ABGHIJ**NPS**Z10	
6A CEE	❶ €31.60	
	❷ €42.70	
A112 5ha 196**T**(100-150m²) 115**P**		

🔲 Drive from Châteaudun via the N10 and D35. Turn right before the built up area of Cloyes-sur-le-Loir. Camping signs indicate the route clearly.

💬 A lovely, large campsite for young and old in a beautiful area close to the chateaux of the Loire and not far from Paris and Versailles. Lovely outdoor heated swimming pool with slide, toddlers' pool, indoor pool and jacuzzi (free). Also crazy golf, sailing, pony riding and bouncy castle.

(CC) 15/3-30/6 1/9-14/11

N 48°0'8'' E 1°13'59''

www.eurocampings.co.uk/100277

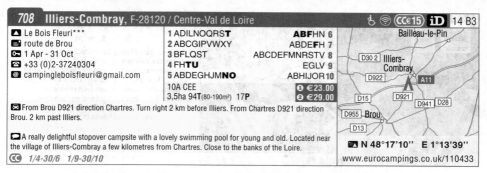

708 Illiers-Combray, F-28120 / Centre-Val de Loire   ♿ 📶 (CCⓔ15) iD   14 B3

🏕 Le Bois Fleuri***
✉ route de Brou
🕐 1 Apr - 31 Oct
☎ +33 (0)2-37240304
@ campingleboisfleuri@gmail.com

1 ADILNOQRS**T**	**ABF**HN	**6**
2 ABCGIPVWXY	ABDE**F**H	**7**
3 BFLQST	ABCDEFMNRSTV	**8**
4 FH**TU**	EGLV	**9**
5 ABDEGHJM**NO**	ABHIJOR	**10**

10A CEE   ❶ €23.00
3,5ha 94T(80-190m²)   17**P**   ❷ €29.00

🚗 From Brou D921 direction Chartres. Turn right 2 km before Illiers. From Chartres D921 direction Brou. 2 km past Illiers.

💬 A really delightful stopover campsite with a lovely swimming pool for young and old. Located near the village of Illiers-Combray a few kilometres from Chartres. Close to the banks of the Loire.

CC 1/4-30/6   1/9-30/10

📷 N 48°17'10''   E 1°13'39''

www.eurocampings.co.uk/110433

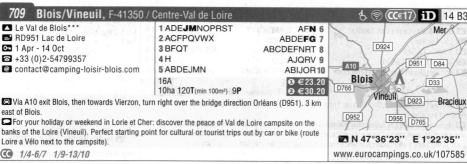

709 Blois/Vineuil, F-41350 / Centre-Val de Loire   ♿ 📶 (CCⓔ17) iD   14 B3

🏕 Le Val de Blois***
✉ RD951 Lac de Loire
🕐 1 Apr - 14 Oct
☎ +33 (0)2-54799357
@ contact@camping-loisir-blois.com

1 ADE**JM**NOPRST	AF**N**	**6**
2 ACFPQVWX	ABDE**FG**	**7**
3 BFQT	ABCDEFNRT	**8**
4 H	AJQRV	**9**
5 ABDEJMN	ABIJOR	**10**

16A   ❶ €23.20
10ha 120T(min 100m²)   9**P**   ❷ €30.20

🚗 Via A10 exit Blois, then towards Vierzon, turn right over the bridge direction Orléans (D951). 3 km east of Blois.

💬 For your holiday or weekend in Lorie et Cher: discover the peace of Val de Loire campsite on the banks of the Loire (Vineuil). Perfect starting point for cultural or tourist trips out by car or bike (route Loire a Vélo next to the campsite).

CC 1/4-6/7   1/9-13/10

📷 N 47°36'23''   E 1°22'35''

www.eurocampings.co.uk/107585

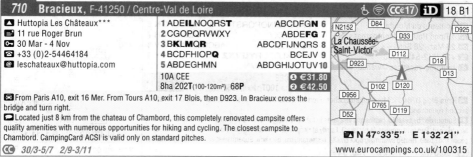

710 Bracieux, F-41250 / Centre-Val de Loire   ♿ 📶 (CCⓔ17) iD   18 B1

🏕 Huttopia Les Châteaux***
✉ 11 rue Roger Brun
🕐 30 Mar - 4 Nov
☎ +33 (0)2-54464184
@ leschateaux@huttopia.com

1 ADE**IL**NOQRS**T**	ABCDF**G**N	**6**
2 CGOPQRVWXY	ABDE**FG**	**7**
3 B**KLM**QR	ABCDFIJNQRS	**8**
4 BCDFHIOP**Q**	BCEJV	**9**
5 ABDEGHMN	ABDGHIJOTUV	**10**

10A CEE   ❶ €31.80
8ha 202T(100-120m²)   68**P**   ❷ €42.50

🚗 From Paris A10, exit 16 Mer. From Tours A10, exit 17 Blois, then D923. In Bracieux cross the bridge and turn right.

💬 Located just 8 km from the chateau of Chambord, this completely renovated campsite offers quality amenities with numerous opportunities for hiking and cycling. The closest campsite to Chambord. CampingCard ACSI is valid only on standard pitches.

CC 30/3-5/7   2/9-3/11

📷 N 47°33'5''   E 1°32'21''

www.eurocampings.co.uk/100315

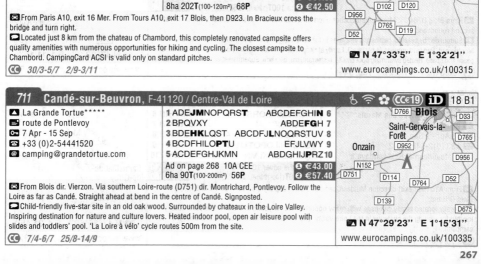

711 Candé-sur-Beuvron, F-41120 / Centre-Val de Loire   ♿ 📶 ✿ (CCⓔ19) iD   18 B1

🏕 La Grande Tortue*****
✉ route de Pontlevoy
🕐 7 Apr - 15 Sep
☎ +33 (0)2-54441520
@ camping@grandetortue.com

1 ADE**JM**NOPQRS**T**	ABCDEFGH**IN**	**6**
2 BPQVXY	ABDE**FG**H	**7**
3 BDE**HK**LQST	ABCDFJLNOQRSTUV	**8**
4 BCDFHILO**PTU**	EFJLVWY	**9**
5 ACDEFGHJKMN	ABDGHIJ**PR**Z	**10**

Ad on page 268 10A CEE   ❶ €43.00
6ha 90T(100-200m²)   56**P**   ❷ €57.40

🚗 From Blois dir. Vierzon. Via southern Loire-route (D751) dir. Montrichard, Pontlevoy. Follow the Loire as far as Candé. Straight ahead at bend in the centre of Candé. Signposted.

💬 Child-friendly five-star site in an old oak wood. Surrounded by chateaux in the Loire Valley. Inspiring destination for nature and culture lovers. Heated indoor pool, open air leisure pool with slides and toddlers' pool. 'La Loire à vélo' cycle routes 500m from the site.

CC 7/4-6/7   25/8-14/9

📷 N 47°29'23''   E 1°15'31''

www.eurocampings.co.uk/100335

France

LA GRANDE TORTUE
★ ★ ★ ★ ★

Well-equipped family campsite. Spacious pitches.
Shop, bar, cafe terrace, restaurant. Entertainment
programme in the high season. Tropical waterpark
with slide, indoor part and separate paddling pool.
Sauna and jacuzzi. Pitches with private sanitary.
Trampolines, rope pyramid and enclosed toddlers'
playground. Caravan and chalet rental. Options for
cycling and hiking in the area.

41120 Candé-sur-Beuvron
Tel. 00 33 (0)2 54441520
E-mail: camping@grandetortue.com
Internet: www.grandetortue.com

---

712 Cheverny, F-41700 / Centre-Val de Loire — 18 B1

- ▲ Sites & Paysages Les Saules****
- 🏠 Les Saules
- 📅 1 Apr - 15 Sep
- ☎ +33 (0)2-54799001
- @ contact@camping-cheverny.com

1 ADE**JM**NOR**T**	ABCDFN	6
2 BGPVXY	ABDE**FG**HK	7
3 BE**IJK**LV	ABDFKNQRSTV	8
4 BFHILO	AJVWZ	9
5 ACDEFGHKMN	ABDGHIJNORZ	10
10A CEE	❶ €38.00	
8ha 164T(100-140m²) 16P	❷ €42.00	

🚗 A10, exit 17 Blois direction Vierzon. From centre Cheverny take direction Château. Campsite on the
right 1.4 km after castle.

💬 The woods around Les Saules offer relaxation. The campsite fits in perfectly with spacious shaded pitches
and well maintained toilets. The friendly ambiance provides the rest. Good walking and cycling opportunities
such as the 'Loire à vélo' cycle route which can be reached from the site. Golf course 2 km away.

CC 1/4-8/7 26/8-14/9 7=6, 14=12

Saint-Gervais-la-Forêt · D923 · D765 · D102 · D120 · D764 · D52 · Contres · D122 · D675 · D956 · D119

⬛ N 47°28'40'' E 1°27'3''

www.eurocampings.co.uk/100337

---

713 Faverolles-sur-Cher, F-41400 / Centre-Val de Loire — 18 B1

- ▲ Couleurs du Monde****
- 🏠 1 Rond Point de Montparnasse
- 📅 26 Mar - 28 Sep
- ☎ +33 (0)2-54320608
- @ touraine-vacances@wanadoo.fr

1 ADE**JM**NOPQRST	ABCDF**GN**	6
2 GOPVXY	ABDE**FG**H	7
3 BELQST	ABCDEFKNQRSV	8
4 FHIKLOPQR**TUVXZ**	ABCELQTVWY	9
5 ACDEFGHKMN	ABDGHIJ**P**RVY	10
6-10A CEE	❶ €29.90	
A60 4ha 100T(120m²) 26P	❷ €39.90	

🚗 From Blois D764 dir. Montrichard/Loches. From Montrichard dir. Faverolles. Campsite on left after
second roundabout.

💬 Surrounded by beautiful castles and vineyards in the Loire Valley. A stone's throw from the historic town of
Montrichard. Parkland grounds (4 hectares). Family atmosphere: 'la douce France'. Hospitable, good facilities,
peace and space. Heated swimming pool on site, restaurant, bar, bike hire. Supermarket within walking distance.

CC 26/3-13/7 31/8-27/9 7=6, 14=12

D139 · D61 · D115 · D62 · Montrichard · D40 · N76 · A85 · D176 · D281 · Saint-Aignan · D764 · D81 · D675

⬛ N 47°20'2'' E 1°11'15''

www.eurocampings.co.uk/107586

---

714 Muides-sur-Loire, F-41500 / Centre-Val de Loire — 14 B3

- ▲ Sandaya Château des Marais*****
- 🏠 27 rue de Chambord
- 📅 13 Apr - 9 Sep
- ☎ +33 (0)2-54870542
- @ chateaudesmarais@sandaya.fr

1 ADE**JM**NOQRST	ABEFHIN	6
2 ABGPVX	ABDEFGH	7
3 BE**HILM**T	ABCDEFNQRSTU	8
4 BCDFHILO**PQTUVX**	EJLVY	9
5 ACDEFGHKLMN	ABFGHIJ**NP**RZ	10
Ad on the cover 10A CEE	❶ €46.10	
8ha 116T(100-120m²) 160P	❷ €63.00	

🚗 From A10 (Mer exit) direction Muides/Chambord. Campsite signposted. Also via D951
Blois-Orléans.

💬 Rurally located family campsite with many opportunities for young and old. Water park! Ideally
located for visiting the chateaux in the Loire Valley. The chateau of Chambord is 500 m from the
campsite.

CC 13/4-6/7 1/9-8/9

Tavers · A10 · Mer · D951 · D2152 · D925 · Saint-Claude-de-Diray · D103 · Vineuil · D33 · D112 · D13

⬛ N 47°39'59'' E 1°31'45''

www.eurocampings.co.uk/103717

715 Nouan-le-Fuzelier, F-41600 / Centre-Val de Loire ♿ 🛜 (CC€15) iD | 18 B1

- ▲ La Grande Sologne***
- 🏕 rue Cauchoix
- 📅 1 Apr - 16 Oct
- ☎ +33 (0)2-54887022
- @ info@campinggrandesologne.com

1 ADE**JM**NOPRT	ABFGHN 6
2 ABCDGOPVWXY	ADEFGH 7
3 BE**GHILMN**PQS	ABCDFKNQRSV 8
4 BDFH!OQ	BEVY 9
5 ABDEFKMN	ABDFGHIJPSTV 10
10A	❶ €25.40
A104 10ha 150T(80-120m²) 28P	❷ €34.40

🚗 From the north A71, exit 3 dir. RD2020. From Orléans follow the RD2020 dir. Vierzon until past the town of Nouan-le-Fuzelier. From the south A71 exit 4 dir. Orléans.
🛏 Friendly family site located around a fish pond; spacious shaded pitches, extensive sports facilities including tennis and swimming pool next to the site. Children's playground, free wifi. Close to the chateaux of the Loire (including Chambord). Various cycling and walking routes.
(CC) 1/4-2/7 20/8-15/10 7=6, 14=11

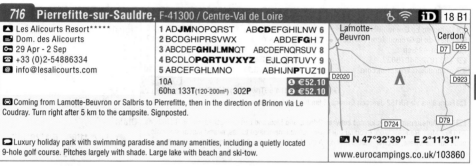

Lamotte-Beuvron · D922 · D923 · A71 · Saint-Viâtre · N20 · D121 · D123 · D724

🌄 N 47°31'58'' E 2°2'12''
www.eurocampings.co.uk/103859

716 Pierrefitte-sur-Sauldre, F-41300 / Centre-Val de Loire ♿ 🛜 iD | 18 B1

- ▲ Les Alicourts Resort*****
- 🏕 Dom. des Alicourts
- 📅 29 Apr - 2 Sep
- ☎ +33 (0)2-54886334
- @ info@lesalicourts.com

1 AD**JM**NOPQRST	ABCDEFGHILNW 6
2 BCDGHIPRSVWX	ABDE**FG**H 7
3 ABCDEF**GHIJLMN**QT	ABCDEFNQRSUV 8
4 BCDLO**PQRTUVXYZ**	EJLQRTUVY 9
5 ABCEFGHLMNO	ABHIJN**P**TUZ 10
10A	❶ €52.10
60ha 133T(120-200m²) 302P	❷ €52.10

🚗 Coming from Lamotte-Beuvron or Salbris to Pierrefitte, then in the direction of Brinon via Le Coudray. Turn right after 5 km to the campsite. Signposted.

🛏 Luxury holiday park with swimming paradise and many amenities, including a quietly located 9-hole golf course. Pitches largely with shade. Large lake with beach and ski-tow.

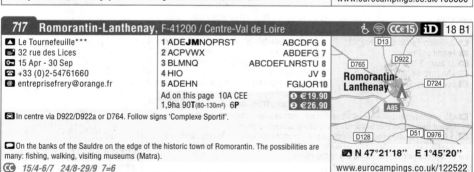

Lamotte-Beuvron · Cerdon · D7 · D65 · D2020 · D923 · D724 · D79

🌄 N 47°32'39'' E 2°11'31''
www.eurocampings.co.uk/103860

717 Romorantin-Lanthenay, F-41200 / Centre-Val de Loire ♿ 🛜 (CC€15) iD | 18 B1

- ▲ Le Tournefeuille***
- 🏕 32 rue des Lices
- 📅 15 Apr - 30 Sep
- ☎ +33 (0)2-54761660
- @ entreprisefrery@orange.fr

1 ADE**JM**NOPRST	ABCDFG 6
2 ACPVWX	ABDEFG 7
3 BLMNQ	ABCDEFLNRSTU 8
4 HIO	JV 9
5 ADEHN	FGIJOR 10
Ad on this page 10A CEE	❶ €19.90
1,9ha 90T(80-130m²) 6P	❷ €26.90

🚗 In centre via D922/D922a or D764. Follow signs 'Complexe Sportif'.

🛏 On the banks of the Sauldre on the edge of the historic town of Romorantin. The possibilities are many: fishing, walking, visiting museums (Matra).
(CC) 15/4-6/7 24/8-29/9 7=6

D13 · D765 · D922 · Romorantin-Lanthenay · D724 · A85 · D128 · D51 · D976

🌄 N 47°21'18'' E 1°45'20''
www.eurocampings.co.uk/122522

718 Salbris, F-41300 / Centre-Val de Loire ♿ 📶 (CC€15) iD 18 B1

- ⛺ Camping de Sologne***
- 🏠 8 alleé de la Sauldre
- 📅 1 Apr - 30 Sep
- ☎ +33 (0)2-54970638
- @ campingdesologne@wanadoo.fr

1 ADFJMNOPQRST	ABNQSX 6	
2 ACDPVWX	ABDEFG 7	
3 ALMQ	ABCDFNRSTUV 8	
4 FHO	EJ 9	
5 ABDEHK	ABHIKNP10	
10A CEE	❶ €23.05	
A105 2ha 85T(60-100m²) 8P	❷ €31.70	

🅰 From Orléans via the N20 towards Vierzon, turn left at Salbris onto the D55 to Pierrefitte. Campsite after 300 metres right.

💬 A beautiful, relaxing campsite by a lake. Located 2 km from the motorway. Restaurants and shops within walking distance of the pleasant and quiet Salbris. Close to a swimming pool.
(CC) 1/4-17/6 1/9-29/9

📍 N 47°25'49'' E 2°3'16''
www.eurocampings.co.uk/103862

---

719 Suèvres, F-41500 / Centre-Val de Loire ♿ 📶 (CC€15) iD 14 B3

- ⛺ Camping La Grenouillère
- 🏠 Chât. de la Grenouillère, RN152
- 📅 14 Apr - 9 Sep
- ☎ +33 (0)2-54878037
- @ grenouillere@capfun.com

1 ADEILNOPRT	ABEFGHIN 6	
2 ABGPVXY	ABDEFGH 7	
3 BDEKLMQT ABCDEFJKLMNQRSTV 8		
4 BDHILNOPQRTU	EJVY 9	
5 ACDEFGHKLN	ABDGHIJOPST10	
10A	❶ €34.10	
A78 11ha 69T(90-150m²) 170P	❷ €45.60	

🅰 From Blois via RN152 direction Orléans. 3 km beyond Suèvres on the left.

💬 This chateau campsite is located between Orléans and Blois and can be reached via the RN152 (via A10 exit Mer). Rural location. Good facilities such as well maintained toilets, heated indoor swimming pool. Bar restaurant, pizzeria, spacious shop. A good base for exploring further in the Loire Valley.
(CC) 14/4-30/6 3/9-8/9

📍 N 47°41'8'' E 1°29'14''
www.eurocampings.co.uk/103716

---

720 Valloire-sur-Cisse, F-41150 / Centre-Val de Loire ♿ 📶 (CC€15) iD 14 B3

- ⛺ Camping-Ferme de Prunay****
- 🏠 Ferme de Prunay
- 📅 31 Mar - 3 Nov
- ☎ +33 (0)2-54700201
- @ contact@prunay.com

1 ADEJMNOPQRST	ABFGN 6	
2 GPVWXY	ABDEFGHIJK 7	
3 BEHLQ ABCDEFGHIKNQRSTUV 8		
4 BDEFHIKO	EJLV 9	
5 ABDEFGHKN	ABDFGHIJORVWX10	
12A CEE	❶ €36.90	
A111 6ha 69T(300-400m²) 32P	❷ €48.70	

🅰 A10, exit Blois direction Angers/Château-Renault. D131 Molineuf - Chambon-sur-Cisse, in Molineuf continue towards Seillac (D135 and D760). Campsite signposted.
💬 Le Prunay' is located in quiet surroundings in the heart of the Loire, close to both castles and countryside. Camping pitches from 300 to 400 m2. Heated pool. Bar/restaurant on site. Campsite is the starting point for several walking and cycling routes.
(CC) 31/3-30/6 18/8-2/11 10=9, 22=21

📍 N 47°33'17'' E 1°10'50''
www.eurocampings.co.uk/110988

---

721 Vendôme, F-41100 / Centre-Val de Loire ♿ 📶 (CC€15) iD 14 B3

- ⛺ Au Coeur de Vendôme***
- 🏠 rue Geoffroy Martel
- 📅 14 Apr - 30 Oct
- ☎ +33 (0)2-54770027
- @ aucoeurdevendome@
  camp-in-ouest.com

1 ADEJMNOPRST	AEFGHN 6	
2 CGOPVWXY	ABDEFGH 7	
3 BLMQT	ABCDFJNRUV 8	
4 FHLOPQ	AEJQRV 9	
5 ADNO	ABDGHIJPR10	
10A CEE	❶ €20.00	
A64 2,5ha 140T(80-100m²) 25P	❷ €25.60	

🅰 Via N10 from north. In Vendôme, turn right at third traffic light Quartier des Grands Prés, then first left and left again. Follow signs to swimming pool and sports centre.

💬 400 m from the centre of historic and cultural town. Located next to N10 on the banks of the River Loir. Suitable for those passing through or staying. Touraine and Loire castles all around the site.
(CC) 14/4-8/7 26/8-29/10 7=6, 14=13

📍 N 47°47'28'' E 1°4'19''
www.eurocampings.co.uk/103715

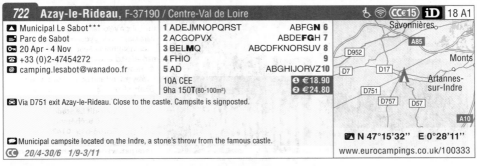

722 Azay-le-Rideau, F-37190 / Centre-Val de Loire

🚲 📶 CC€15 iD 18 A1

- ⛺ Municipal Le Sabot***
- 🏠 Parc de Sabot
- 📅 20 Apr - 4 Nov
- ☎ +33 (0)2-47454272
- @ camping.lesabot@wanadoo.fr

1 ADEJMNOPQRST	ABFG**N** 6
2 ACGOPVX	ABDE**FGH** 7
3 BEL**MQ**	ABCDFKNORSUV 8
4 FHIO	9
5 AD	ABGHIJORV**Z**10
10A CEE	❶ €18.90
9ha 150**T**(80-100m²)	❷ €24.80

🚗 Via D751 exit Azay-le-Rideau. Close to the castle. Campsite is signposted.

💬 Municipal campsite located on the Indre, a stone's throw from the famous castle.

CC 20/4-30/6 1/9-3/11

N 47°15'32'' E 0°28'11''

www.eurocampings.co.uk/100333

723 Ballan-Miré, F-37510 / Centre-Val de Loire

🚲 📶 CC€17 ♿ iD 18 A1

- ⛺ La Mignardière****
- 🏠 22 avenue des Aubépines
- 📅 1 Apr - 12 Sep
- ☎ +33 (0)2-47733100
- @ info@mignardiere.com

1 ADE**JM**NOPQRST	ABE**F**N 6
2 AOPVXY	ABDE**FGH** 7
3 BE**IK**LQ	ABCDEFKNQRSV 8
4 FHIOP**TUXYZ**	BDEJLVY 9
5 ACDEFGKL**O**	ABDGHIJ**P**R10
6-10A CEE	❶ €29.60
3,5ha 118**T**(80-150m²) 47**P**	❷ €37.60

🚗 Via A10 past Tours, take exit 24 Joué-les-Tours, centre direction Ballan-Miré. Right at first traffic lights and follow campsite signs.

💬 A lovely family campsite with good toilet facilities. Heated swimming pool (also covered), tennis. Playground opposite. There is a lake close by for surfing. A good base for cycle trips or visiting the chateaux of the Loire.

CC 1/4-5/7 26/8-11/9 7=6

N 47°21'19'' E 0°38'2''

www.eurocampings.co.uk/100331

France

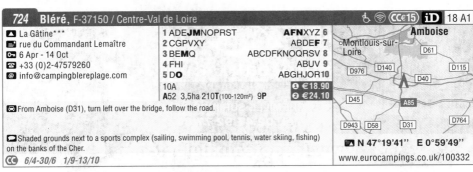

724 Bléré, F-37150 / Centre-Val de Loire

🚲 📶 CC€15 iD 18 A1

- ⛺ La Gâtine***
- 🏠 rue du Commandant Lemaître
- 📅 6 Apr - 14 Oct
- ☎ +33 (0)2-47579260
- @ info@campingblereplage.com

1 ADE**JM**NOPRST	**AFN**XYZ 6
2 CGPVXY	ABDE**F** 7
3 BE**MQ**	ABCDFKNOQRSV 8
4 FHI	ABUV 9
5 D**O**	ABGHJOR10
10A	❶ €18.90
A52 3,5ha 210**T**(100-120m²) 9**P**	❷ €24.10

🚗 From Amboise (D31), turn left over the bridge, follow the road.

💬 Shaded grounds next to a sports complex (sailing, swimming pool, tennis, water skiing, fishing) on the banks of the Cher.

CC 6/4-30/6 1/9-13/10

N 47°19'41'' E 0°59'49''

www.eurocampings.co.uk/100332

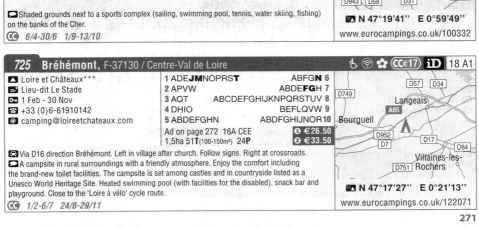

725 Bréhémont, F-37130 / Centre-Val de Loire

🚲 📶 ✿ CC€17 iD 18 A1

- ⛺ Loire et Châteaux***
- 🏠 Lieu-dit Le Stade
- 📅 1 Feb - 30 Nov
- ☎ +33 (0)6-61910142
- @ camping@loireetchateaux.com

1 ADE**JM**NOPRS**T**	ABFG**N** 6
2 APVW	ABDE**FGH** 7
3 AQT	ABCDEFGHIJKNPQRSTUV 8
4 DHIO	BEFLQVW 9
5 ABDEFGHN	ABDFGHIJNOR10
Ad on page 272 16A CEE	❶ €26.50
1,5ha 51**T**(100-150m²) 24**P**	❷ €33.50

🚗 Via D16 direction Bréhémont. Left in village after church. Follow signs. Right at crossroads.

💬 A campsite in rural surroundings with a friendly atmosphere. Enjoy the comfort including the brand-new toilet facilities. The campsite is set among castles and in countryside listed as a Unesco World Heritage Site. Heated swimming pool (with facilities for the disabled), snack bar and playground. Close to the 'Loire à vélo' cycle route.

CC 1/2-6/7 24/8-29/11

N 47°17'27'' E 0°21'13''

www.eurocampings.co.uk/122071

France

726 Chemillé-sur-Indrois, F-37460 / Centre-Val de Loire   ♿ 🛜 ✿ (CC€17) ♟♟ iD 18 B1

▲ Les Coteaux du Lac****
📅 24 Mar - 7 Oct
☎ +33 (0)2-47927783
@ lescoteauxdulac@wanadoo.fr

1	ADE**JM**NOPQRST	ABFGHLM**N**QXY	6
2	DFGHPVWX	ABDE**FG**HK	7
3	BEILQST	ABCDEFINQRSTUV	8
4	BDFHIO**P**R	BEJLQRTUVY	9
5	ABDEFGHKN	ABDFGHIJPR	10

Ad on this page   16A CEE   ❶ €30.00
A83   2,5ha 60T(100-170m²)   37P   ❷ €39.00

🚗 From St. Aignan via the D675 to Nouans, then D760 direction Montrésor and via the D10 to Chemillé. After passing the village cross the bridge and turn right. Follow the signs.

💬 Situated on the shore of a lake. Ideal place for family holidays and for discovering the Châteaux of the Loire. Heated swimming pool, children's toilets, shop, television room. Also: paddle boats, canoes, supervised beach, fishing (carp), bar/restaurant.

CC   24/3-8/7   26/8-6/10   7=6

📷 **N 47°9'28''**   **E 1°9'35''**
www.eurocampings.co.uk/100339

(Map showing: D10, Genillé, D31, D764, D81, Loches, D675, D760, D943, D9, Écueillé, D41)

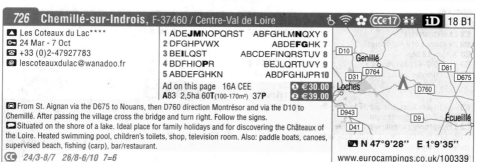
727 Francueil/Chenonceaux, F-37150 / Centre-Val de Loire   ♿ 🛜 (CC€17) iD 18 B1

▲ Le Moulin Fort***
📅 5 May - 30 Sep
☎ +33 (0)2-47238622
@ lemoulinfort@wanadoo.fr

1	ADE**JM**NOPQRST	AF**N**	6
2	CGPVX	ABDE**FG**	7
3	B ILQ	ABCDEFNQRSV	8
4	FHIO**X**		9
5	ACDEFHKMN	ABGHIJ**O**STV	10

Ad on this page 273   6A CEE   ❶ €29.00
A53   3ha 130T(80-100m²)   ❷ €38.00

🚗 From Bléré via the D976, after 6 km turn left towards Chenonceaux. Before you reach the bridge turn right. Clearly signposted.

💬 Well maintained campsite very close to Chenonceaux Castle. Site located on the banks of the River Cher. Good amenities and good leisure opportunities in and around the grounds.

CC   5/5-6/7   27/8-29/9

📷 **N 47°19'35''**   **E 1°5'1''**
www.eurocampings.co.uk/103723

(Map showing: Amboise, D139, D61, D62, D115, D140, Montrichard, D40, N76, D58, D31, D281, A85, D764, D81)

---

728 La Ville-aux-Dames, F-37700 / Centre-Val de Loire ♿ 📶 ⓒⓔ€17 iD 18 A1

- 🏕 Tours Les Acacias★★★
- 📧 rue Berthe Morisot
- 🗓 1 Jan - 31 Dec
- ☎ +33 (0)2-47440816
- @ contact@camplvad.com

1 ADE**JM**NOPRS**T**	N**U** 6	
2 ABCGOPQSVWXY	ABDE**FG**HK 7	
3 BE**K**LQST	ABCDEFJNQRSV 8	
4 DFHIO	EUVW 9	
5 ABDEGHK**N**O	ABCDGHIJPR10	

Ad on this page 10A CEE   ❶ €22.00
3,5ha 88**T**(100-120m²) 20**P**   ❷ €27.00

🚗 A10 exit 21. Accessible from Tours. 6 km direction Montlouis. Clearly signposted.

💬 A quiet and partly shaded campsite where peace and hospitality are the order of the day all year round. Passers-by and longer stayers can enjoy the many opportunities. Route 'Loire à Velo' from the campsite. Free wifi.

ⓒⓒ 1/1-8/7   26/8-31/12 7=6, 14=12

🗺 N 47°24'7''   E 0°46'48''

www.eurocampings.co.uk/100327

---

729 Limeray, F-37530 / Centre-Val de Loire 📶 iD 18 B1

- 🏕 Le Jardin Botanique★★★
- 📧 9B rue de la Rivière
- 🗓 15 Mar - 5 Nov
- ☎ +33 (0)2-47301350
- @ campingjardinbotanique@wanadoo.fr

1 ADE**JM**NOPQRT	ABC**N** 6	
2 AGPVXY	ABE**F**H 7	
3 BELQ	ABDFGJKNQRSTUV 8	
4 FHIO	DELUV 9	
5 ABDEFHJL**NO**	ABFGHIJP**R**10	

Ad on page 274 10A CEE   ❶ €21.60
A65 1,5ha 68**T**(100-200m²) 19**P**   ❷ €30.60

🚗 On the D952 Tours-Blois, exit Limeray. Signposted.

💬 Small campsite where you are hospitably welcomed, located by the N152.

🗺 N 47°26'48''   E 1°2'52''

www.eurocampings.co.uk/108823

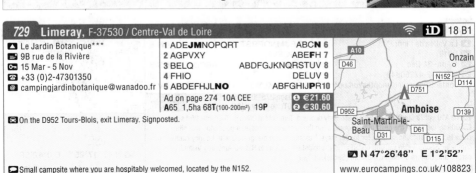

France

France

730 Loches, F-37600 / Centre-Val de Loire
♿ 🛜 CC€17 iD | 18 A1

- 🏕 La Citadelle★★★★
- 🚏 Aristide Briand
- 📅 30 Mar - 5 Oct
- ☎ +33 (0)2-47590591
- @ camping@lacitadelle.com

1 ADEJMNOPQRST	ABEFN	6
2 CGOPVXY	ABDEFGH	7
3 BJKLMQST	ABCDFKNOQRSTU	8
4 BDFHILOPQ	BEJLY	9
5 ABDEFGHKMN	ABDGHIJMPRV	10

Ad on this page 10-20A CEE ❶ €33.50
4ha 115T(50-180m²) 34P ❷ €43.30

🚧 Follow campsite signs in the centre.
🛏 Hospitable campsite on the edge of the historic town of Loches with its interesting castle. Various leisure opportunities. Heated swimming pool, bar/snack/restaurant and good toilet facilities. Low season opening times: 8:00 am - 12:15 pm and 2:00 - 7:30 pm. Discount offered at restaurant and wellness centre in town. Wifi Euro2/day, Euro1/night after 7 nights, and free after 14 nights.

CC 30/3-6/7 25/8-4/10

📷 N 47°7'22'' E 1°0'8''

www.eurocampings.co.uk/101458

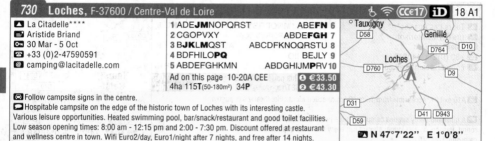

731 Montbazon, F-37250 / Centre-Val de Loire
♿ 🛜 CC€15 iD | 18 A1

- 🏕 La Vallée de l'Indre★★★
- 🚏 D910
- 📅 1 Apr - 31 Dec
- ☎ +33 (0)2-47260643
- @ contact@camping-montbazon.com

1 ADEJMNOPRST	AN	6
2 ACGOPVX	ABDEFGHK	7
3 EILMT	ABCDEFNORS	8
4 FH	EPQRT	9
5 ABDEFHKLNO	ABDGIJPRV	10

Ad on page 275 10A CEE ❶ €24.80
3ha 110T(100-120m²) 12P ❷ €32.30

🚧 Via A10 exit 23 Chambray to D910 in southerly direction. Turn right at Office de Tourisme. Well signposted.
🛏 Quietly located in the heart of the Touraine, on the banks of the Indre. A good stopover site, close to the N910. Also suitable for longer stays. Restaurant and playground with bouncy castles on campsite. Shops within walking distance. In the midst of the Azay le Rideau-Amboise-Villandry-Ussé castles and Honoré de Balzac museum (Saché).

CC 1/4-7/7 25/8-30/12 4=3, 8=6

📷 N 47°17'25'' E 0°42'59''

www.eurocampings.co.uk/100334

la Vallée de l'Indre Camping ***

In the heart of the Vallée des Rois and the Jardins de France

☎ +33 (2) 47 26 06 43 - www.camping-montbazon.com - contact@camping-montbazon.com

---

732 Montlouis-sur-Loire, F-37270 / Centre-Val de Loire   ♿ 🛜 (CC€15) iD 18 A1

🏕 Camping Les Peupliers***
🛏 D751
📅 30 Mar - 21 Oct
☎ +33 (0)2-47508190
@ camping.lespeupliers@wanadoo.fr

1 ADEGJMNOPRST	ABN 6
2 CPSVXY	ABDEFGH 7
3 BLMQ	ABCDEFNRSTUV 8
4 FHIO	EV 9
5 ABDEH	AFHIJORV 10
10A CEE	🔵 €19.10
4ha 72T(100-120m²) 10P	🔵 €24.60

🅿 From Tours via the D751 direction Amboise, well signposted.

💬 This campsite has sunny and shaded pitches. Good amenities.
(CC) 30/3-7/7 25/8-20/10

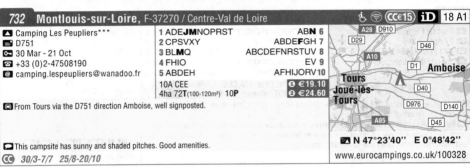

⛵ N 47°23'40'' E 0°48'42''
www.eurocampings.co.uk/100328

---

733 Rillé, F-37340 / Centre-Val de Loire   ♿ iD 18 A1

🏕 Huttopia Rillé***
🛏 Lac de Rillé
📅 7 Apr - 16 Oct
☎ +33 (0)2-47246297
@ rille@huttopia.com

1 ADEGILNOPRST	ABFGNQSXYZ 6
2 BDGIPQX	ABDEFGH 7
3 ABEHLM	ABCDEFGIJKNOQRSTUV 8
4 ABDFHILO	AEJQTU 9
5 ABDEFGHKN	ABFGHIJNTUV 10
16A CEE	🔵 €35.50
A76 4,5ha 69T(100-200m²) 71P	

🅿 In Rillé (from Langeais D57, Château la Vallière D749) take the D49 to Breil. Signposted.

💬 Located in the middle of a wood on the edge of Lake Rillé. Original natural materials were used when laying out the grounds.

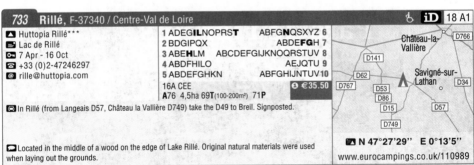

⛵ N 47°27'29'' E 0°13'5''
www.eurocampings.co.uk/110989

---

734 Savonnières, F-37550 / Centre-Val de Loire   ♿ 🛜 (CC€17) iD 18 A1

🏕 La Confluence***
🛏 route du Bray
📅 30 Apr - 30 Sep
☎ +33 (0)2-47500025
@ contact@campinglaconfluence.fr

1 ADEJMNOPRST	N 6
2 ACIOPVWXY	ABDEFG 7
3 BELMQ	ABCDEFGIKNRSTUV 8
4 FH	ABJ 9
5 ADN	AFHIJOR 10
10A CEE	🔵 €23.30
80T(95-100m²) 8P	🔵 €30.10

🅿 Accessible via A58, exit Villandry. Follow direction Villandry/Savonnières. Left after centre. Via D37 exit Savonnières. Right before centre. Well signposted.

💬 La Confluence is located on the banks of the Cher with a view of the village. Spacious pitches. The stalactite caves and mushroom farms in the vicinity are worth a visit. Don't forget to visit Ussé castle (Sleeping Beauty castle) and Villandry with its beautiful gardens.
(CC) 30/4-30/6 1/9-29/9

⛵ N 47°20'59'' E 0°33'0''
www.eurocampings.co.uk/117835

735 St. Avertin, F-37550 / Centre-Val de Loire

♿ ⓦ (CC€17) iD 18 A1

- 🏕 Tours Val de Loire****
- ✉ 61 rue de Rochepinard
- 🗓 2 Feb - 16 Dec
- ☎ +33 (0)2-47278747
- @ contact@campingtoursvaldeloire.fr

1 ADE**JM**NOPRST	N**QSU**	6
2 ACDGOPSVX	ABDEF**GK**	7
3 LMQT	ABCDFNQRS	8
4 HIOP	AFJ	9
5 ABDJN	ABGHIJOR	10
10A CEE		❶ €26.70
A68 2,6ha 90**T**(80-100m²) 24**P**		❷ €34.50

🚗 A10 exit Tours-Sud/St. Avertin. Follow direction Bléré via N76 direction Vierzon. Also A85 exit Bléré (Est) and exit St.Avertin (Ouest). Campsite signposted.

🏕 Near the centre of the art and history city of Tours, this site is located in shaded, well maintained surroundings on the banks of the Cher. A convenient location for visiting the tourist attractions. Swimming pool and playground. The site is located on the cycle route 'La Loire à Vélo'.

(CC) 2/2-30/6 1/9-15/12

📍 N 47°22'15'' E 0°43'25''

www.eurocampings.co.uk/103614

736 Ste Catherine-de-Fierbois, F-37800 / Centre-Val de Loire

♿ ⓦ (CC€19) iD 18 A1

- 🏕 Parc de Fierbois*****
- 🗓 27 Apr - 2 Sep
- ☎ +33 (0)2-47654335
- @ contact@fierbois.com

1 ADEILNOPQRST	ABEFHINX	6
2 ADGHIPVXY	BE**FG**H	7
3 BEF**HI**LMQR	BDFKNQRSTUV	8
4 BDFHILO**PQR**	EJLVY	9
5 ACDEFGHK	ABDGHIJN**O**ST	10
Ad on this page 10A CEE		❶ €55.00
30ha 189**T**(130-150m²) 197**P**		❷ €77.00

🚗 Can be reached via the A10 exit St. Maure (25) and Sorigny (24.1), then Tours. Via the N10, located 16 km south of Montbazon.

🏕 This Castel campsite is located in 30-hectare grounds around a lake that is surrounded by an old wood. The facilities include an indoor heated swimming pool, aquatic park with slides, skate park, bar and restaurant. Many castles and vineyards in the area.

(CC) 27/4-30/6 25/8-1/9

📍 N 47°8'49'' E 0°39'10''

www.eurocampings.co.uk/103618

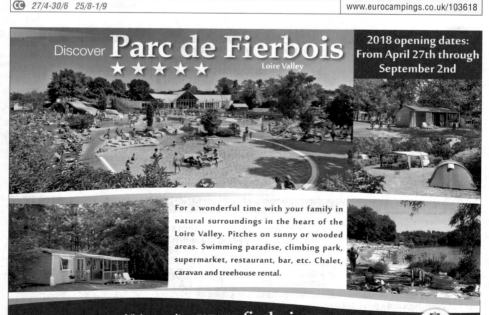

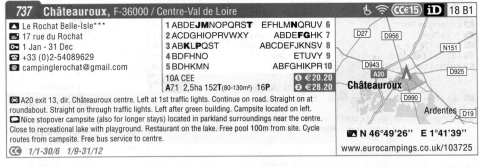

737 Châteauroux, F-36000 / Centre-Val de Loire ♿ 📶 CCE15 iD 18 B1

- ▲ Le Rochat Belle-Isle***
- 🏠 17 rue du Rochat
- 📅 1 Jan - 31 Dec
- ☎ +33 (0)2-54089629
- @ campinglerochat@gmail.com

1 ABDEJMNOPQRST	EFHLMNQRUV 6
2 ACDGHIOPRVWXY	ABDEFGHK 7
3 ABKLPQST	ABCDEFJKNSV 8
4 BDFHNO	ETUVY 9
5 BDHKMN	ABFGHIKPR 10

10A CEE — € 20.20
A71 2,5ha 152T(80-130m²) 16P — € 28.20

🚗 A20 exit 13, dir. Châteauroux centre. Left at 1st traffic lights. Continue on road. Straight on at roundabout. Straight on through traffic lights. Left after green building. Campsite located on left.
💬 Nice stopover campsite (also for longer stays) located in parkland surroundings near the centre. Close to recreational lake with playground. Restaurant on the lake. Free pool 100m from site. Cycle routes from campsite. Free bus service to centre.
CC 1/1-30/6 1/9-31/12

Châteauroux · Ardentes D19 · D27 · D956 · N151 · D943 · A20 · D925 · D990

🏕 N 46°49'26'' E 1°41'39''
www.eurocampings.co.uk/103725

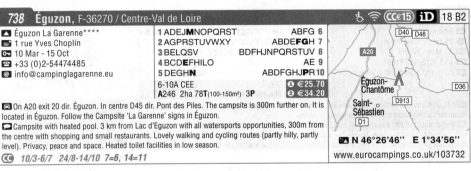

738 Éguzon, F-36270 / Centre-Val de Loire ♿ 📶 CCE15 iD 18 B2

- ▲ Éguzon La Garenne****
- 🏠 1 rue Yves Choplin
- 📅 10 Mar - 15 Oct
- ☎ +33 (0)2-54474485
- @ info@campinglagarenne.eu

1 ADEJMNOPQRST	ABFG 6
2 AGPRSTUVWXY	ABDEFGH 7
3 BELQSV	BDFHJNPQRSTUV 8
4 BCDEFHILO	AE 9
5 DEGHN	ABDFGHJPR 10

6-10A CEE — € 25.70
A246 2ha 78T(100-150m²) 3P — € 34.20

🚗 On A20 exit 20 dir. Éguzon. In centre D45 dir. Pont des Piles. The campsite is 300m further on. It is located in Éguzon. Follow the Campsite 'La Garenne' signs in Éguzon.
💬 Campsite with heated pool. 3 km from Lac d'Eguzon with all watersports opportunities, 300m from the centre with shopping and small restaurants. Lovely walking and cycling routes (partly hilly, partly level). Privacy, peace and space. Heated toilet facilities in low season.
CC 10/3-6/7 24/8-14/10 7=6, 14=11

Éguzon-Chantôme · Saint-Sébastien · D40 · D48 · A20 · D36 · D913 · D1

🏕 N 46°26'46'' E 1°34'56''
www.eurocampings.co.uk/103732

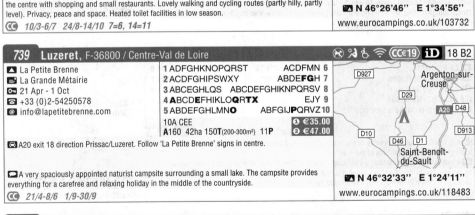

739 Luzeret, F-36800 / Centre-Val de Loire 🚫 🐕 ♿ 📶 CCE19 iD 18 B2

- ▲ La Petite Brenne
- 🏠 La Grande Métairie
- 📅 21 Apr - 1 Oct
- ☎ +33 (0)2-54250578
- @ info@lapetitebrenne.com

1 ADFGHKNOPQRST	ACDFMN 6
2 ACDFGHIPSWXY	ABDEFGH 7
3 ABCEGHLQS	ABCDEFGHIKNPQRSV 8
4 ABCDEFHIKLOQRTX	EJY 9
5 ABDEFGHLMNO	ABFGIJPQRVZ 10

10A CEE — € 35.00
A160 42ha 150T(200-300m²) 11P — € 47.00

🚗 A20 exit 18 direction Prissac/Luzeret. Follow 'La Petite Brenne' signs in centre.

💬 A very spaciously appointed naturist campsite surrounding a small lake. The campsite provides everything for a carefree and relaxing holiday in the middle of the countryside.
CC 21/4-8/6 1/9-30/9

Argenton-sur-Creuse · Saint-Benoît-du-Sault · D927 · D29 · A20 · D48 · D10 · D913 · D46 · D1

🏕 N 46°32'33'' E 1°24'11''
www.eurocampings.co.uk/118483

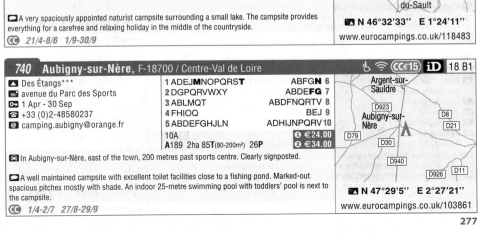

740 Aubigny-sur-Nère, F-18700 / Centre-Val de Loire ♿ 📶 CCE15 iD 18 B1

- ▲ Des Étangs***
- 🏠 avenue du Parc des Sports
- 📅 1 Apr - 30 Sep
- ☎ +33 (0)2-48580237
- @ camping.aubigny@orange.fr

1 ADEJMNOPQRST	ABFGN 6
2 DGPQRVWXY	ABDEFG 7
3 ABLMQT	ABDFNQRTV 8
4 FHIOQ	BEJ 9
5 ABDEFGHJLN	ADHIJNPQRV 10

10A — € 24.00
A189 2ha 85T(80-200m²) 26P — € 34.00

🚗 In Aubigny-sur-Nère, east of the town, 200 metres past sports centre. Clearly signposted.

💬 A well maintained campsite with excellent toilet facilities close to a fishing pond. Marked-out spacious pitches mostly with shade. An indoor 25-metre swimming pool with toddlers' pool is next to the campsite.
CC 1/4-2/7 27/8-29/9

Argent-sur-Sauldre · Aubigny-sur-Nère · D923 · D8 · D21 · D79 · D30 · D940 · D926 · D11

🏕 N 47°29'5'' E 2°27'21''
www.eurocampings.co.uk/103861

France

741 Bannay/Cosne-sur-Loire, F-18300 / Centre-Val de Loire ♿ 📶 (CC€15) iD 19 A1

- ▲ Camping de l'Ile***
- 🏕 Ile de Cosne
- 📅 30 Mar - 28 Oct
- ☎ +33 (0)3-86244843
- @ camping.cosne@orange.fr

1 ADE**JM**NOPQRST	NUV 6
2 ABCFGHIPQRVXY	ABDE**FG**HK 7
3 ABCEF**GIJK**LQR**T**V	ABCDEFNRSTV 8
4 BDHIO**PQ**	BELQRV 9
5 ABDFHIJK	AHIJLOR 10
10A CEE	❸ €18.00
A167 6ha 180T(100m²) 7P	❷ €23.80

🚗 From A77 exit Cosne-sur-Loire then direction Bourges.

💬 Well maintained campsite on the banks of the Loire at walking distance from Cosne-sur-Loire. Spacious camping pitches, largely shaded. Bicycle rental and canoes to enjoy the Loire and the landscape.

(CC) 30/3-7/7 25/8-27/10 7=6, 14=11

N 47°24'30" E 2°55'2"

www.eurocampings.co.uk/100985

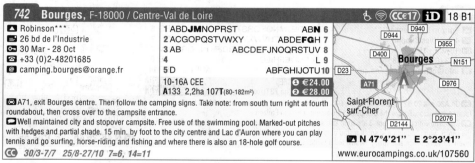

742 Bourges, F-18000 / Centre-Val de Loire ♿ 📶 (CC€17) iD 18 B1

- ▲ Robinson***
- 🏕 26 bd de l'Industrie
- 📅 30 Mar - 28 Oct
- ☎ +33 (0)2-48201685
- @ camping.bourges@orange.fr

1 ABD**JM**NOPRST	AB**N** 6
2 ACGOPQSTVWXY	ABDE**FG**H 7
3 AB	ABCDEFJNOQRSTUV 8
4	L 9
5 D	ABFGHIJOTU 10
10-16A CEE	❸ €24.00
A133 2,2ha 107T(80-182m²)	❷ €28.00

🚗 A71, exit Bourges centre. Then follow the camping signs. Take note: from south turn right at fourth roundabout, then cross over to the campsite entrance.

💬 Well maintained city and stopover campsite. Free use of the swimming pool. Marked-out pitches with hedges and partial shade. 15 min. by foot to the city centre and Lac d'Auron where you can play tennis and go surfing, horse-riding and fishing and where there is also an 18-hole golf course.

(CC) 30/3-7/7 25/8-27/10 7=6, 14=11

N 47°4'21" E 2°23'41"

www.eurocampings.co.uk/107560

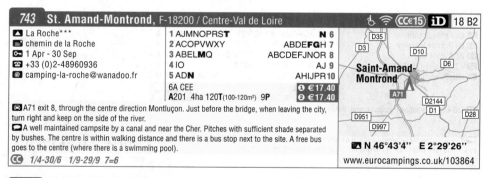

743 St. Amand-Montrond, F-18200 / Centre-Val de Loire ♿ 📶 (CC€15) iD 18 B2

- ▲ La Roche***
- 🏕 chemin de la Roche
- 📅 1 Apr - 30 Sep
- ☎ +33 (0)2-48960936
- @ camping-la-roche@wanadoo.fr

1 AJMNOPRS**T**	**N** 6
2 ACOPVWXY	ABDE**FG**H 7
3 ABEL**MQ**	ABCDEFJNOR 8
4 IO	AJ 9
5 AD**N**	AHIJPR 10
6A CEE	❸ €17.40
A201 4ha 120T(100-120m²) 9P	❷ €17.40

🚗 A71 exit 8, through the centre direction Montluçon. Just before the bridge, when leaving the city, turn right and keep on the side of the river.

💬 A well maintained campsite by a canal and near the Cher. Pitches with sufficient shade separated by bushes. The centre is within walking distance and there is a bus stop next to the site. A free bus goes to the centre (where there is a swimming pool).

(CC) 1/4-30/6 1/9-29/9 7=6

N 46°43'4" E 2°29'26"

www.eurocampings.co.uk/103864

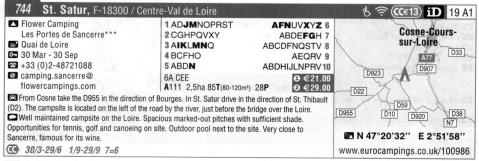

744 St. Satur, F-18300 / Centre-Val de Loire ♿ 📶 (CC€13) iD 19 A1

- ▲ Flower Camping
  Les Portes de Sancerre***
- 🏕 Quai de Loire
- 📅 30 Mar - 30 Sep
- ☎ +33 (0)2-48721088
- @ camping.sancerre@
  flowercampings.com

1 AD**JM**NOPRST	**AFN**UV**XYZ** 6
2 CGHPQVXY	ABDE**FG**H 7
3 A**IKLMN**Q	ABCDFNQSTV 8
4 BCFHO	AEQRV 9
5 ABD**N**	ABDHIJLNPRV 10
6A CEE	❸ €21.00
A111 2,5ha 85T(80-120m²) 28P	❷ €29.00

🚗 From Cosne take the D955 in the direction of Bourges. In St. Satur drive in the direction of St. Thibault (D2). The campsite is located on the left of the road by the river, just before the bridge over the Loire.

💬 Well maintained campsite on the Loire. Spacious marked-out pitches with sufficient shade. Opportunities for tennis, golf and canoeing on site. Outdoor pool next to the site. Very close to Sancerre, famous for its wine.

(CC) 30/3-29/6 1/9-29/9 7=6

N 47°20'32" E 2°51'58"

www.eurocampings.co.uk/100986

France

Brittany

End of the Word

Named after the Britons who fled from the Anglo-Saxon invasion in England, Brittany juts out into the Atlantic, with the English Channel to the north and the Bay of Biscay to the south.

The north coast and hilly west coast are rough and wild, and the south is gentler, with long beaches and beautiful pinkish granite rocks. Inland, forests, heathlands and meadows gradually flatten eastwards.

Brittany has something for everyone. History buffs will be intrigued by mediaeval towns and the ancient sites of Morbihan, water sports enthusiasts will adore the amenities available along the 2500 km stretch of coastline, and need we even mention the culinary delights?

Castles and coastlines

Walk the twisty picturesque mediaeval streets of Rennes, and see Notre Dame Cathedral and the Museum of Fine Art. Picturesque St Malo, on the north coast, is located on a peninsula with amazing coastal views. Explore the town's history on the city walls and the rocky outcrop of Fort National. Further west is Fort la Lotte, a castle perched on the cliffs – the kids will love its towers, dungeons and drawbridge. Brest is on the south-west coast, and while much of the town was rebuilt after World War II, you can still visit the castle, then cross the modern drawbridge to the Tanguy tower.

Other activities

Take a day trip to Ile de Brehat, or visit the restored hamlet of Meneham on the west coast, once a lookout post. The kids won't want to leave Oceanopolis near Brest, which has huge aquariums and adorable otters, and if you are drawn to ancient sites, visit Morbihan, the menhirs at Carnac, and Gavrinis island. Prefer the great wide open? Visit Amorica Nature Park

near Brest, Falaise Plouha with its high cliffs and hidden bays, and Cap Sizun with its ancient watermills. Take to the dancefloor at the annual Interceltique in Lorient.

Breton cuisine: full and rich

The local salted butter is a staple in Galettes and is used for quatre-quart cake, far, Kouign Amann, craquelins, to name but a few. Crepes also originated in Brittany, and fish lovers must try the seafood platters and fish soups. Andouille sausages and pre-salted mutton are also local delicacies, as is the petit gris melon. Wash it all down with Chouchen or Muscadet.

Our tips

1. Visit the museum at Pont Aven, home to the historic school of painting
2. Like crepes? You'll love Gourin, which hosts an annual Festival of Crepes
3. Stroll around the old towns Fougeres, Vité and Dinane
4. Visit the Fisheries Museum at Concarneau
5. Explore the Arthurian connection at Paimpont

745 Ambon, F-56190 / Bretagne

♿ 🛜 (CC€11) iD 42b

- 🏕 Camping de Cromenac'h**
- 🏠 Lieu dit Cromenac'h
- 📅 1 Apr - 31 Oct
- ☎ +33 (0)2-97416747
- @ villagedecromenach@orange.fr

1 ADE**JM**NOPQRST	KNOPQSWXY**Z** 6
2 ABEFHKMPSVWXY	ABDE**FG** 7
3 ALQST	BDEFNORTUV 8
4 FHO	EI 9
5 ADFNO	ABDGIJ**OR**10

Ad on this page 6-10A CEE
1,5ha 94**T**(80-120m²) 39**P**
- ❶ €17.90
- ❷ €25.05

🚗 E60 Vannes-Nantes, exit Muzillac towards Sarzeau. On roundabout by shopping centre take direction Damgan. First roundabout take direction Cromenac'h.

💬 Quiet, simple campsite directly on a small beach. Modern toilet facilities, a few pitches with a view of the sea. Lovely, old chapel directly next to the pitches. Almost level region with walking and cycling paths. Reception closed from 12:00 to 2:00 pm.

(CC) 1/4-6/7 27/8-30/10 21=18

⬛ N 47°31'33'' W 2°31'29''

www.eurocampings.co.uk/122740

France

746 Arradon, F-56610 / Bretagne

♿ 🛜 (CC€15) iD 42b

- 🏕 Camping de l'Allée***
- 🏠 L'Allée
- 📅 31 Mar - 30 Sep
- ☎ +33 (0)2-97440198
- @ contact@camping-allee.com

1 ADE**JM**NOPQRST	ABEFGNOPQRST**XYZ** 6
2 AEKMPTVWXY	ABDE**FGH** 7
3 B**K**LQS	ABCDEFGJKNORSV 8
4 FIO**PQ**	BEIMOQR 9
5 ABDEFHM**O**	ABDGIJ**P**R10

10-15A CEE
124**T**(80-140m²) 40**P**
- ❶ €26.25
- ❷ €36.05

🚗 N165/E60 Nantes-Lorient, exit Vannes Ouest/Arradon. Via D101 and D127 to Arradon just past shopping centre. Follow campsite signs at roundabout.

💬 Peaceful campsite in the green belt between the town and the sea, rugged coastline with many coves and islands in the Gulf of Morbihan. Large level pitches between trees and hedges or open pitches with plenty of sun. Covered pool and heated toilet blocks.

(CC) 31/3-1/7 3/9-29/9

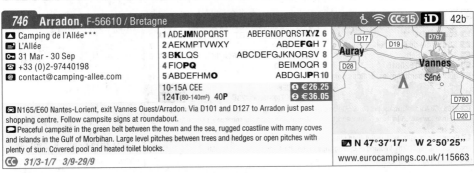

⬛ N 47°37'17'' W 2°50'25''

www.eurocampings.co.uk/115663

747 Arradon, F-56610 / Bretagne

♿ 🛜 ⚙ (CC€17) iD 42b

- 🏕 Sites & Paysages De Penboch****
- 🏠 9 chemin de Penboch
- 📅 7 Apr - 29 Sep
- ☎ +33 (0)2-97447129
- @ camping.penboch@wanadoo.fr

1 ADE**JM**NOPQRST	ABEFGHIKNPQRST**X** 6
2 AEFHKMPVWXY	ABDE**FGH** 7
3 BCE**IK**LQT	ABCDEFGHIJKL**LM**NPQRSTUV 8
4 **A**FHIO**PQ**U	EILMOQRUV 9
5 ABDEFH**O**	ABDGHIJ**NP**RVZ10

10A CEE
3,5ha 117**T**(85-110m²) 81**P**
- ❶ €42.40
- ❷ €54.20

🚗 N165/E60 Vannes-Lorient, exit Vannes-Ouest/Arradon. Via the D101 dir. Arradon, then follow campsite signs or 'Pointe de Penboch'.

💬 Well equipped campsite 300m from north coast of the Golfe Du Morbihan and Grande Randonnée 34. Boat excursions on the Golfe Du Morbihan. Vannes is worth visiting, 8 km by bike. Excellent toilet facilities, lovely indoor swimming pool and heated outdoor pool with slides.

(CC) 7/4-6/7 27/8-22/9

⬛ N 47°37'20'' W 2°48'4''

www.eurocampings.co.uk/103274

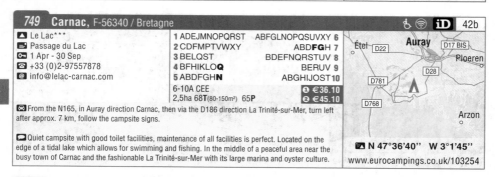

748 Baden/Bourgerel, F-56870 / Bretagne

♿ 🛜 (CC€15) ♦♦ **iD** 42b

🏕 Campéole Penn Mar***
📧 21 route de Port Blanc
📅 30 Mar - 30 Sep
☎ +33 (0)2-97574990
@ pennmar@campeole.com

1	ADEJMNOPQRST	CDFGNOPQRSTUVX	6
2	EFHKMOPVWXY	ABDEFGH	7
3	ADEKLMQT	ABCDEFGHIJNPRSV	8
4	ABCDFHILNO	BCELMNOQR	9
5	ABDEFHMNO	ABDGHIJPTUVWZ	10

10A CEE — ❶ €34.30
6ha 72T(100-150m²) 120P — ❷ €46.50

🚗 N165/E60 Vannes-Lorient, exit Vannes-Ouest/Arradon. Via D101 dir. Baden/Île-aux-Moines. Then follow Île-aux-Moines via D316, campsite on the left.
💬 Family campsite with toilet facilities close to the 'Golfe du Morbihan' with its hundreds of islands, the most famous of which, Île-aux-Moines, is especially worth a visit. Lovely new indoor pool with a fun open-air water playground.
(CC) 30/3-6/7 25/8-29/9

📍 N 47°36'25''   W 2°52'32''
www.eurocampings.co.uk/121610

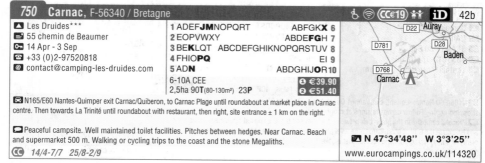

749 Carnac, F-56340 / Bretagne

♿ 🛜 **iD** 42b

🏕 Le Lac***
📧 Passage du Lac
📅 1 Apr - 30 Sep
☎ +33 (0)2-97557878
@ info@lelac-carnac.com

1	ADEJMNOPQRST	ABFGLNOPQSUVXY	6
2	CDFMPTVWXY	ABDFGH	7
3	BELQST	BDEFNQRSTUV	8
4	BFHIKLOQ	BERUV	9
5	ABDFGHN	ABGHIJOST	10

6-10A CEE — ❶ €36.10
2,5ha 68T(80-150m²) 65P — ❷ €45.10

🚗 From the N165, in Auray direction Carnac, then via the D186 direction La Trinité-sur-Mer, turn left after approx. 7 km, follow the campsite signs.

💬 Quiet campsite with good toilet facilities, maintenance of all facilities is perfect. Located on the edge of a tidal lake which allows for swimming and fishing. In the middle of a peaceful area near the busy town of Carnac and the fashionable La Trinité-sur-Mer with its large marina and oyster culture.

📍 N 47°36'40''   W 3°1'45''
www.eurocampings.co.uk/103254

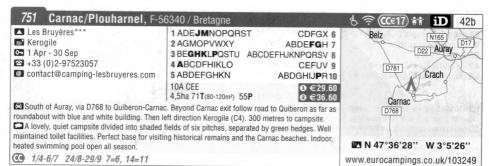

750 Carnac, F-56340 / Bretagne

♿ 🛜 (CC€19) ♦♦ **iD** 42b

🏕 Les Druides***
📧 55 chemin de Beaumer
📅 14 Apr - 3 Sep
☎ +33 (0)2-97520818
@ contact@camping-les-druides.com

1	ADEFJMNOPQRT	ABFGKX	6
2	EOPVWXY	ABDEFGH	7
3	BEKLQT	ABCDEFGHIKNOPQRSTUV	8
4	FHIOPQ	EI	9
5	ADN	ABDGHIJOR	10

6-10A CEE — ❶ €39.90
2,5ha 90T(80-130m²) 23P — ❷ €51.40

🚗 N165/E60 Nantes-Quimper exit Carnac/Quiberon, to Carnac Plage until roundabout at market place in Carnac centre. Then towards La Trinité until roundabout with restaurant, then right, site entrance ± 1 km on the right.

💬 Peaceful campsite. Well maintained toilet facilities. Pitches between hedges. Near Carnac. Beach and supermarket 500 m. Walking or cycling trips to the coast and the stone Megaliths.
(CC) 14/4-7/7 25/8-2/9

📍 N 47°34'48''   W 3°3'25''
www.eurocampings.co.uk/114320

---

751 Carnac/Plouharnel, F-56340 / Bretagne

♿ 🛜 (CC€17) ♦♦ **iD** 42b

🏕 Les Bruyères***
📧 Kerogile
📅 1 Apr - 30 Sep
☎ +33 (0)2-97523057
@ contact@camping-lesbruyeres.com

1	ADEJMNOPQRST	CDFGX	6
2	AGMOPVWXY	ABDEFGH	7
3	BEGHKLPQSTU	ABCDEFHJKNPQRSV	8
4	ABCDFHIKLO	CEFUV	9
5	ABDEFGHKN	ABDGHIJPR	10

10A CEE — ❶ €29.60
4,5ha 71T(80-120m²) 55P — ❷ €36.60

🚗 South of Auray, via D768 to Quiberon-Carnac. Beyond Carnac exit follow road to Quiberon as far as roundabout with blue and white building. Then left direction Kerogile (C4). 300 metres to campsite.
💬 A lovely, quiet campsite divided into shaded fields of six pitches, separated by green hedges. Well maintained toilet facilities. Perfect base for visiting historical remains and the Carnac beaches. Indoor, heated swimming pool open all season.
(CC) 1/4-6/7 24/8-29/9 7=6, 14=11

📍 N 47°36'28''   W 3°5'26''
www.eurocampings.co.uk/103249

France

752 Damgan, F-56750 / Bretagne

♿ 📶 (CC€17) ♟♟ **iD** 42b

🔺 Grand Air Cadu***
🏠 rue de Cadu
🔓 1 Apr - 31 Oct
☎ +33 (0)2-97411730
@ info@campingcadu.com

1	ADE**JM**NOPRST	ABCDFGHKMNOPQRSTVWX**YZ**	6
2	AEHMOPVWX	ABDE**FG**H	7
3	BE**IL**MQT	ABCDEFNRSTUV	8
4	BDFHINO**PQ**	ENOQRTUVWY	9
5	ADFGM**O**	ABDFGHIJM**P**TUV	10

16A CEE · € 29.70
7,8ha 93**T**(100-200m²) 84**P** · € 38.85

🅖 N165/E60 Vannes-Nantes. Exit Damgan or Muzillac, then to Damgan and follow campsite signs.
💬 300 m from the beach with pitches separated by bushes and hedges. Modern and well maintained toilet facilities, heated indoor swimming pool. Beaches nearby. Microclimate due to its proximity to the sea and the many tidal pools. Level area, so fit for walking and cycling. Armbands compulsory everywhere on the campsite. Reception closed 12:00 pm-3:30 pm.

ⒸⒸ 1/4-6/7 1/9-30/10

▲ N 47°31'19'' W 2°35'31''
www.eurocampings.co.uk/116752

753 Erdeven, F-56410 / Bretagne

♿ 📶 (CC€17) **iD** 42b

🔺 Des Mégalithes***
🏠 Kerfelicite, chemin des Saules
🔓 1 May - 23 Sep
☎ +33 (0)2-97556876
@ campingdesmegalithes@orange.fr

1	ADE**JM**NOPQRST	ABFGX	6
2	PVWXY	ABDE**FG**H	7
3	BE**K**LQ	ABCDEFNQRSV	8
4	FH		9
5	ABD**O**	ABDFGHIJPRW	10

10A CEE · € 27.00
5ha 100**T**(90-160m²) 86**P** · € 36.00

🅖 N165/E60 Vannes-Lorient, exit Quiberon/Carnac, D768 direction Quiberon. At the crossroad in Plouharnel turn right to Erdeven via D781. After about 3.5 km turn left.
💬 A quiet, well equipped campsite with small pitches set between hedges and separated from the mobile homes. Megalith park within 500 m. You can go for peaceful bike rides between the site and the sea, or take a trip to Quiberon via the cycle path.

ⒸⒸ 1/5-6/7 25/8-22/9

▲ N 47°37'43'' W 3°8'46''
www.eurocampings.co.uk/103247

754 La Trinité-sur-Mer, F-56470 / Bretagne

♿ 📶 **iD** 42b

🔺 De la Plage****
🚋 44 rue de Kervourden Kervilen
🔓 5 May - 16 Sep
☎ +33 (0)2-97557328
@ camping@camping-plage.com

1	ADE**JM**NOPQRST	ABFGHKNOPQSWX**YZ**	6
2	EHMPVWX	ABDE**FG**H	7
3	B**IKLMQ**	ABCDEFGHIJKNPQRSTU	8
4	**A**BDFHILNO**PQU**	EFLQRUVW	9
5	ACDEFHLM**NO**	ABGHIJ**NP**TUV	10

6-10A CEE · € 47.10
3ha 118**T**(90-110m²) 68**P** · € 56.50

🅖 A11/A81 Paris-Rennes. N24/N166 via Vannes towards Auray, then the D781 direction Carnac as far as exit D186 to La Trinité-sur-Mer. The campsite is signposted in the centre of La Trinité-sur-Mer.

💬 Nice, well equipped family campsite near the beach. Well maintained sanitary facilities. Pitches between trees and hedges. Centre of La Trinité is about 2.5 km away via a path along the coast. Attractive, slightly undulating region, good for bicycle tours to the many prehistoric sites.

▲ N 47°34'32'' W 3°1'44''
www.eurocampings.co.uk/108508

755 La Trinité-sur-Mer, F-56470 / Bretagne

♿ 📶 (CC€17) **iD** 42b

🔺 Kervilor****
🚋 21 Kervilor
🔓 30 Mar - 30 Sep
☎ +33 (0)2-97557675
@ camping.kervilor@wanadoo.fr

1	ADE**IL**NOPQRST	ABCDFGHX	6
2	CMOPVWXY	ABDE**FG**H	7
3	BE**IKLM**QST	ABCDEFIKNQRSTUV	8
4	**A**BCDFHILNO**PQ**RU	EV	9
5	ABCDEFGHM**NO**	ABDGHIJO**P**STZ	10

6-10A · € 41.10
4,7ha 154**T**(80-120m²) 98**P** · € 51.90

🅖 South of Auray. D768 dir. Carnac, then D186 dir. La Trinité then via campsite signposts. Turn left before the centre.
💬 Peaceful campsite in well visited area. Free choice of pitches out of season. Heated indoor pool. Outdoor pool heated from 10 May. 3 km from the famous prehistoric megalith park at Carnac. The centre of La Trinité is 1.5 km away. Market twice weekly, large yacht harbour. The surroundings are wooded and good for cycling and walking.

ⒸⒸ 30/3-11/7 29/8-29/9 7=6, 14=12

▲ N 47°36'8'' W 3°2'12''
www.eurocampings.co.uk/103255

756 Locmariaquer, F-56740 / Bretagne

♿ 🛜 (CC€15) iD 42b

🏠 Lann Brick***
📧 18 Lieu Dit Lann Brick
📅 17 Mar - 31 Oct
☎ +33 (0)2-97573279
@ camping.lannbrick@wanadoo.fr

1 ADE**JM**NOPQRST	ABFGKNOPQSX	6
2 EHMOPVWXY	ABDE**FG**H	7
3 BLQ	ABCDEFHKNOPRSV	8
4 BDEFHINO**PQ**	BDEFRUV	9
5 ABDEFHMN	ABDHIJOST	10

Ad on this page 6-10A CEE ❶ €27.60
1,5ha 39**T**(70-90m²) 69**P** ❷ €36.60

🛣 N165/E60 Nantes/Quimper, exit Crach, via D28 direction Locmariaquer. Towards La Trinité/Carnac. Via D781 direction Locmariaquer, after ± 2 km turn right.
💬 A small, quiet campsite with well maintained toilet facilities located on a headland between the ocean and the Golfe du Morbihan 300 m from the beach. You can walk or cycle on a pathway which covers the entire length of the headland past many prehistoric sights. Reception closed 1:00 pm-2.00 pm.

(CC) 17/3-6/7 27/8-30/10 14=13, 21=19

Auray
D28
Carnac Baden
D768
⛺
🔲 N 47°34'43'' W 2°58'28''
www.eurocampings.co.uk/115680

757 Lomener/Ploemeur, F-56270 / Bretagne

♿ 🛜 iD 42b

🏠 Belle-Plage***
📧 rue de l'Anse du Stole
📅 30 Mar - 30 Sep
☎ +33 (0)2-97567717
@ info@yellohvillage-belle-plage.com

1 ABDEF**JM**NOPRT	CDFGKNOPQRSTVXY**Z**	6
2 AEHMOPSVWXY	ABDE**FG**H	7
3 AB**KL**QT	BDFJNOQRSV	8
4 BCDEFHILNO**X**	BEMNOQRSUV	9
5 ABDEFGHKN	ABGHIJNO**P**STVZ	10

10A CEE ❶ €34.10
4ha 108**T**(80-100m²) 114**P** ❷ €48.10

🛣 N165/E60 Nantes-Quimper. Exit 43 direction Lorient, via D29 direction Larmor Plage, via D152 signs to Kerpape. Campsite entrance is next to Kerpape.

💬 Campsite with flat pitches, right on the beach. Three toilet blocks scattered over the grounds. All beach activities in the immediate vicinity.

D765 Hennebont
D152 D781
Lorient
D33
⛺
🔲 N 47°42'24'' W 3°25'19''
www.eurocampings.co.uk/121626

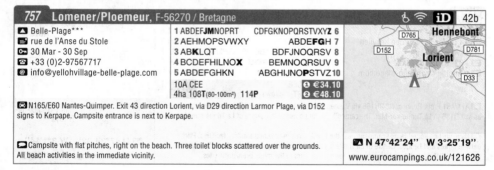

758 Noyal-Muzillac, F-56190 / Bretagne

♿ 🛜 (CC€15) iD 42b

🏠 Moulin de Cadillac****
📧 route de Berric
📅 7 Apr - 16 Sep
☎ +33 (0)2-97670347
@ infos@moulin-cadillac.com

1 ADE**JM**NOPQRST	ABEFGHIN	6
2 ACDPVWXY	ABDE**FG**H	7
3 BDE**IL**MQST	ABCDEFGHJKNOPQRSV	8
4 DFHIKNO**PQ**R	EJ	9
5 ABDFHM**NO**	ABDFGHIJMNO**P**STV	10

16A CEE ❶ €33.70
7ha 129**T**(100-150m²) 86**P** ❷ €43.00

🛣 Between Nantes and Vannes via N165/E60 exit Muzillac, in the centre D5 towards Noyal-Muzillac. Follow the signs of the campsite. Turn left in the centre of Noyal-Muzillac before you reach the church, 4.5 km. Campsite entrance on the right.
💬 Quiet campsite in natural surroundings. A stream flows through the site that used to turn the mill wheel, hence the name. Experienced cyclists can enjoy themselves in undulating landscape.

(CC) 7/4-27/4 2/5-4/5 14/5-18/5 22/5-6/7 1/9-15/9

D775
Questembert
Theix D7 D1
Surzur D153
D20 N165 D5
D139
⛺
🔲 N 47°36'51'' W 2°30'5''
www.eurocampings.co.uk/107922

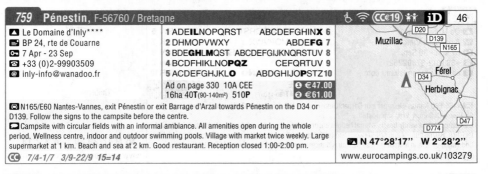

759 Pénestin, F-56760 / Bretagne

♿ 📶 ⓒⓒ€19 ♀♂ iD 46

- ▲ Le Domaine d'Inly****
- ✉ BP 24, rte de Couarne
- 📅 7 Apr - 23 Sep
- ☎ +33 (0)2-99903509
- @ inly-info@wanadoo.fr

1	ADE**IL**NOPQRST	ABCDEFGHIN**X** 6
2	DHMOPVWXY	ABDE**FG** 7
3	BDE**GHLM**QST	ABCDEFGIJKNQRSTUV 8
4	BCDFHIKLNO**PQZ**	CEFQRTUV 9
5	ACDEFGHJKL**O**	ABDGHIJO**P**STZ 10

Ad on page 330 10A CEE

€ €47.00
€ €61.00

16ha 40**T**(90-140m²) 510**P**

🚗 N165/E60 Nantes-Vannes, exit Pénestin or exit Barrage d'Arzal towards Pénestin on the D34 or D139. Follow the signs to the campsite before the centre.

🏕 Campsite with circular fields with an informal ambiance. All amenities open during the whole period. Wellness centre, indoor and outdoor swimming pools. Village with market twice weekly. Large supermarket at 1 km. Beach and sea at 2 km. Good restaurant. Reception closed 1:00-2:00 pm.

ⓒⓒ 7/4-1/7 3/9-22/9 15=14

📷 N 47°28'17'' W 2°28'2''

www.eurocampings.co.uk/103279

760 Ploërmel/Taupont, F-56800 / Bretagne

♿ 📶 ⓒⓒ€15 ♀♂ iD 42b

- ▲ Camping du Lac**
- ✉ Les Belles Rives
- 📅 31 Mar - 14 Oct
- ☎ +33 (0)2-97740122
- @ contact@ camping-du-lac-ploermel.com

1	ADE**JM**NOPQRST	LMN**P**QRSTVWXY 6
2	ADFHPVWXY	BDF**G** 7
3	BEF**HJL**MQRT	BDF**LMN**RTUV 8
4	FHNO	EJMNOPQRTUW 9
5	AEFHN**O**	ABDGIJ**P**STW 10

6-10A

€ €19.50
€ €25.90

2,5ha 92**T**(100-120m²) 24**P**

🚗 N24 Rennes-Quimper, exit Ploërmel/Dinan/St. Malo, follow ring road to Lac au Duc. Campsite is located between the road and the lake and is signposted.

🏕 Family campsite directly on the Lac au Duc. Pitches with a view of the lake. 600 metres from a unique hydrangea garden via a cycle/walking path. 1300 metres from a shopping centre. 15 km cycle route around the lake.

ⓒⓒ 31/3-6/7 25/8-12/10

📷 N 47°56'56'' W 2°25'16''

www.eurocampings.co.uk/112392

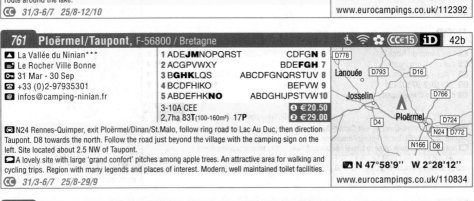

761 Ploërmel/Taupont, F-56800 / Bretagne

♿ 📶 ✿ ⓒⓒ€15 iD 42b

- ▲ La Vallée du Ninian***
- ✉ Le Rocher Ville Bonne
- 📅 31 Mar - 30 Sep
- ☎ +33 (0)2-97935301
- @ infos@camping-ninian.fr

1	ADE**JM**NOPQRST	CDFG**N** 6
2	ACGPVWXY	BDE**FGH** 7
3	B**GHK**LQS	ABCDFGNQRSTUV 8
4	BCDFHIKO	BEFVW 9
5	ABDEFHK**NO**	ABDGHIJPSTVW 10

3-10A CEE

€ €20.50
€ €29.00

2,7ha 83**T**(100-160m²) 17**P**

🚗 N24 Rennes-Quimper, exit Ploërmel/Dinan/St.Malo, follow ring road to Lac Au Duc, then direction Taupont. D8 towards the north. Follow the road just beyond the village with the camping sign on the left. Site located about 2.5 NW of Taupont.

🏕 A lovely site with large 'grand confort' pitches among apple trees. An attractive area for walking and cycling trips. Region with many legends and places of interest. Modern, well maintained toilet facilities.

ⓒⓒ 31/3-6/7 25/8-29/9

📷 N 47°58'9'' W 2°28'12''

www.eurocampings.co.uk/110834

762 Pont-Scorff, F-56620 / Bretagne

♿ 📶 ✿ ⓒⓒ€15 iD 42b

- ▲ Ty Nénez***
- ✉ route de Lorient
- 📅 1 Jan - 31 Dec
- ☎ +33 (0)2-97325116
- @ camping-ty-nenez@wanadoo.fr

1	ADEF**JM**NOPQRST	EFG**N** 6
2	AGOPVWX	ABD**FGH** 7
3	AB**K**LQRT	ABCDFGJKNRSTUV 8
4	FHIO**XZ**	EKU 9
5	ABDEFHM**N**	ABDFGHIJLPVZ 10

8-16A CEE

€ €28.90
€ €39.60

2,5ha 69**T**(100-200m²) 24**P**

🚗 N165 direction Brest, exit Quéven direction Pont-Scorff, 600 metres after zoo turn right. Then follow signs.

🏕 Peacefully located campsite with lovely spacious pitches. Indoor swimming pool with water heated to 30° that is open for the entire season. 1 km to the shops and animal park nearby (500 metres).

ⓒⓒ 1/1-29/6 3/9-31/12

📷 N 47°49'13'' W 3°24'12''

www.eurocampings.co.uk/115686

France

763 Quiberon, F-56170 / Bretagne ♿ 🛜 ✿ (CC€17) 👫 iD 42b

- 🔺 Do Mi Si La Mi***
- 🏠 8 rue de la Vierge
- 📅 31 Mar - 30 Sep
- ☎ +33 (0)2-97502252
- @ camping@domisilami.com

1 ADE**JL**NOPQRST	KNOPQRSW	6
2 EFHJMOPVWX	ABDE**FG**HK	7
3 BCE**K**LQST ABCDEFGHIKNOPRSTUV		8
4 BCFHIO**P**	AELUVW	9
5 ACDEFGHKM**NO**	ABDFGHIJ**P**R	10
10A CEE	❶ €32.00	
5ha 184**T**(80-110m²) 164**P**	❷ €39.00	

🗺 N165/E60 Nantes-Quimper exit Carnac/Quiberon, via D768 direction Quiberon. Turn left after St. Pierre/Quiberon. Well signposted.
💬 Campsite by a sandy beach, natural hedges ensure plenty of shade and privacy. Well maintained toilet facilities. Bar/restaurant and self-service shop (with fresh fruit and vegetables and a meat section). Lightly undulating cycle and footpaths close by. You will receive a surprise if you use the ACSI-DoMi code.

(CC) 31/3-29/6 1/9-29/9

📌 N 47°29'59" W 3°7'13"

www.eurocampings.co.uk/114299

764 Quiberon, F-56170 / Bretagne ♿ 🛜 (CC€17) iD 42b

- 🔺 Flower Camping Le Bois d'Amour****
- 🏠 rue St. Clément
- 📅 30 Mar - 30 Sep
- ☎ +33 (0)2-97501352
- @ camping.boisdamour@ flowercampings.com

1 ADE**IL**NOPRST	CDFGKNOPQRSTUVW**X**	6
2 EHMOPQVWX	ABDE**FG**H	7
3 B**IK**L**MN**PQT	ABCDEFKNQRSV	8
4 BCDFHILN**PQ**	ABCEV	9
5 ABDEFGHL**O**	ABDGHIJPST	10
6-16A CEE	❶ €43.90	
5,5ha 65**T**(60-100m²) 168**P**	❷ €55.90	

🗺 South of Auray, via the D768 to Quiberon. In Quiberon town direction Thalassotherapie or follow the campsite signs.
💬 A good campsite with many facilities, 150m from a flat sandy beach. Noisy near the entrance, quieter at the rear. Located in an old dune area, so plenty of sand and long tent pegs are required. Indoor pool.

(CC) 30/3-29/6 1/9-29/9 7=6

📌 N 47°28'35" W 3°6'15"

www.eurocampings.co.uk/103260

765 Quiberon, F-56170 / Bretagne ♿ 🛜 (CC€17) 👫 iD 42b

- 🔺 Les Joncs du Roch***
- 🏠 rue de l'Aérodrome
- 📅 7 Apr - 22 Sep
- ☎ +33 (0)2-97502437
- @ camping@lesjoncsduroch.com

1 ADEF**JM**NOPQRST	CDFGKNOPQRSTVWXY**Z**	6
2 EHMOPVWX	ABDE**FG**H	7
3 BE**GHKLMN**QT	ABCDEFGKNORSTV	8
4 FHINO	EMNOPQRSUVY	9
5 AD**O**	ABDGHIJ**P**ST	10
10A CEE	❶ €36.40	
2,3ha 105**T**(80-120m²) 53**P**	❷ €47.00	

🗺 N165/E60 Nantes-Quimper, exit Carnac-Quiberon, via D768 to Quiberon. Left just before railway beyond St. Pierre/Quiberon. Follow Aerodrôme and Port-Haligven signs.
💬 Hospitable campsite close to a lovely beach and town. 800m from a supermarket. Large level pitches and renovated toilet facilities (2016). You can watch light aircraft take off and land at the nearby airfield (open from 8:00 am to 6:00 pm). Indoor swimming pool, always heated to 30°C.

(CC) 7/4-6/7 24/8-21/9

📌 N 47°28'45" W 3°6'2"

www.eurocampings.co.uk/115688

766 Rochefort-en-Terre, F-56220 / Bretagne ♿ 🛜 (CC€17) iD 42b

- 🔺 Sites & Paysages Au Gré Des Vents***
- 🏠 2 chemin de Bogeais
- 📅 31 Mar - 30 Sep
- ☎ +33 (0)2-97433752
- @ gredesvents@orange.fr

1 ADE**JM**NOPQRST	CDF**G**N	6
2 OPTVWXY	ABDE**FG**H	7
3 BE**KLM**QS	ABCDFNOQRS	8
4 DFHIO**Q**	BDEJUVW	9
5 ABDEFHJMN**O**	ABDGHIJ**P**STV	10
6-10A CEE	❶ €25.70	
2,5ha 70**T**(85-150m²) 19**P**	❷ €35.20	

🗺 N116 Ploërmel/Vannes exit D775, to Redon, D777 to Rochefort-en-Terre, then to Limerzel, D774, take a right after 800 metres. See campsite signs.
💬 800 metres from one of the most beautiful and characteristic villages in France. Campsite with greenery, large pitches separated by hedges. Modern toilet facilities, paths for walking, cycling and mountain biking. First two hours free wifi.

(CC) 31/3-6/7 26/8-29/9

📌 N 47°41'43" W 2°20'57"

www.eurocampings.co.uk/109047

767 Sarzeau, F-56370 / Bretagne

♿ 🛜 ❄ (CC€15) ⛺ iD 42b

- 🏕 La Ferme de Lann Hoëdic***
- 🏠 rue Jean de la Fontaine
- 📅 31 Mar - 31 Oct
- ☎ +33 (0)2-97480173
- @ contact@camping-lannhoedic.fr

1 ADEJLNOPRST	NOPQRSTX 6
2 HKMPVWXY	ABDEFGH 7
3 BKLQST	ABCDEFGHKNPRSV 8
4 FHIKOTXZ	BEFMOQRUV 9
5 ABDFHJNO	ABDGHIJMNORZ 10
10A CEE	💶 €24.90
3,6ha 106T(100-160m²) 25P	💶 €33.00

🚗 N165 Vannes-Nantes, exit Sarzeau via D20 or D780 (Do not enter Sarzeau). Follow the D20 dir. Port Navalo to roundabout with the Super U supermarket. At the roundabout turn left dir. Roaliguen. Follow the sign to the campsite.

💬 Near the sea, natural campsite with rural charm and 3-star comfort. Beach 800 m, supermarket 2 km, Sarzeau 2.5 km. Coastline with sandy beaches and cliffs. 15 min. free wifi per day. Reception closed 12:00-3:00 pm.

(CC) 31/3-9/7 27/8-30/10 14=13

📍 N 47°30'26'' W 2°45'39''

www.eurocampings.co.uk/112208

---

768 Sarzeau, F-56370 / Bretagne

♿ 🛜 ❄ (CC€17) iD 42b

- 🏕 Manoir de Ker An Poul****
- 🏠 Lieu dit Penvins
- 📅 7 Apr - 23 Sep
- ☎ +33 (0)2-43530433
- @ info@manoirdekeranpoul.com

1 ADEILNOPQRST	ABCDFGHKNPQRSTVX 6
2 EHKMPVWXY	ABDEFGH 7
3 BELR	ABCDFGIKNQRSTUV 8
4 ABCDEFHILNOPQ	ELMOQRUV 9
5 ADEFGHJKO	ABDGHIJOPTU 10
Ad on this page 10-16A CEE	💶 €41.10
6ha 107T(80-130m²) 190P	💶 €52.10

🚗 N165/E60 Vannes-Nantes. Via D780 direction Sarzeau and then the D199, direction Penvins until you see the campsite in the centre of Penvins.

💬 Large but quiet campsite close to the sea. Lots of mobile homes on the grounds, the touring pitches are grouped centrally between two toilet blocks and there is plenty of natural landscaping. Good campsite, particularly for families with children.

(CC) 7/4-7/7 25/8-22/9 7=6

📍 N 47°30'19'' W 2°40'59''

www.eurocampings.co.uk/101185

France

---

769 St. Gildas-de-Rhuys, F-56730 / Bretagne

♿ 🛜 (CC€15) iD 42b

- 🏕 Camping du Menhir****
- 🏠 19 route du clos er bé
- 📅 1 May - 13 Sep
- ☎ +33 (0)2-97452288
- @ campingmenhir@aol.com

1 ADEJMNOPRST	ABFGHX 6
2 HMOPVWXY	ABDEFGH 7
3 BFIKLMQST	ABCDFKNQRSTUV 8
4 BFHINOPQR	EUVW 9
5 ABDEFGHKO	ABDGHIJMOST 10
6A	💶 €35.60
3ha 121T(90-100m²) 54P	💶 €46.80

🚗 N165/E60 Vannes-Nantes, exit direction Sarzeau, then via D20 or D780 direction Port Crouesty until the campsite signs direct you to the left.

💬 Very quiet, comfortable four-star campsite, especially in the low season. Surroundings almost level, sea is nearby in three directions, beach 1 km. Free choice of pitches in the low season. Cycling routes nearby. In the low season not possible to pay by card. Reception closed 12:00-2:00 pm.

(CC) 1/5-30/6 26/8-12/9

📍 N 47°31'44'' W 2°50'51''

www.eurocampings.co.uk/103275

770 Vannes, F-56000 / Bretagne   ♿ 🛜 (CC€17) iD 42b

- 🏕 Flower Camping Le Conleau****
- ✉ 188 avenue Maréchal Juin
- 📅 30 Mar - 30 Sep
- ☎ +33 (0)2-97631388
- @ camping.conleau@
  flowercampings.com

1	ADE**JM**NOPQRS**T**	CDFGNQRSTU	6
2	AEFHLMOPSTVWXY	ABDE**FG**H	7
3	B**K**LQT	ABCDFHJKNOPQRSTUV	8
4	ABDFHILNO**PQ**	ABEJMNQRUV	9
5	ABDEFGHK**O**	ABDFGHIJNPST	10

6A CEE   ❶ €33.10
5ha 104**T**(80-150m²) 87**P**   ❷ €44.10

🗺 N165/E60 Nantes-Lorient exit Vannes Ouest/Arradon. Then Vannes Centre and follow campsite signs, each roundabout has a 'Le Conleau' sign.
💬 Near the sea with well-equipped toilet facilities. Choice of pitches with plenty of sun or shade. 2 km to historical city centre. 500 m from landscaped swimming lake with sea water and small beach. Cycling and walking routes right by the entrance. Reception closed (low season): 12:00-2:30 pm.
(CC) 30/3-6/7 25/8-29/9 7=6

📍 N 47°38'0" W 2°46'48"

www.eurocampings.co.uk/110137

---

771 Arzano, F-29310 / Bretagne   ♿ 🛜 ✿ (CC€13) ⛄ iD 42b

- 🏕 Le Ty Nadan*****
- ✉ route d'Arzano
- 📅 27 Apr - 2 Sep
- ☎ +33 (0)2-98717547
- @ info@tynadan-vacances.fr

1	ADE**JM**NOPQRST	ABEFGHIJ**N**UV	6
2	CFGHPVWXY	BEF**GH**	7
3	BCDEF**GHLMQRTU**	ABCDFGJK**LM**NQRSTUV	8
4	**A**BCDEFHJKLMNNO**PQ**UXYZ	ABCEIJLQRTUV	9
5	ACDEFGHLMNO	ABGHIJN**P**RZ	10

10A CEE   ❶ €50.10
21ha 100**T**(90-200m²) 98**P**   ❷ €65.80

🗺 North of Lorient via the N165/E60 towards Quimperlé, exit Quimperlé-Est. Take the D22 before Quimperlé-centre to Arzano. Head towards Locunolé just before Arzano-centre, or follow the signs.
💬 A family campsite in midst of the countryside. The swimming pools are always heated to minimum of 28° C. There is an obstacle course in the trees. A few kilometres from the Devil's Rocks, well worth a visit.
(CC) 27/4-30/6 31/8-1/9

📍 N 47°54'17" W 3°28'30"

www.eurocampings.co.uk/103244

---

772 Bénodet, F-29950 / Bretagne   ♿ 🛜 iD 41b

- 🏕 Camping Du Letty****
- ✉ chemin de Creisanguer
- 📅 20 Jun - 4 Sep
- ☎ +33 (0)2-98570469
- @ reception@campingduletty.com

1	ADE**JM**NOPQRST	ABEFGHIKNOPQRSUXY	6
2	EFHOPRVX	ABDE**FG**H	7
3	B**CEFKL**MQRU	ABCDEFKNOPQRSTUV	8
4	BCDFHILNO**PQRTUVXYZ**	BDRUV	9
5	ACDEFGHM**NO**	ABGHIJ**NP**RXZ	10

10A CEE   ❶ €48.50
10ha 542**T**(80-150m²) 22**P**   ❷ €66.50

🗺 From Quimper take the D34 to Bénodet. Then follow the campsite signs.

💬 Campsite run by the family itself. Every imaginable comfort. Very well maintained and sound toilet facilities. Spacious, marked pitches. Feels like a park setting! Private sandy beach. Water park with 2 heated pools, 1 outdoor and 1 indoor (even the air is heated), slides, very spacious toddlers' pool full of surprises and next to it is a large panoramic terrace.

📍 N 47°51'54" W 4°5'23"

www.eurocampings.co.uk/109109

---

773 Bénodet, F-29950 / Bretagne   ♿ 🛜 (CC€19) 41b

- 🏕 Camping du Poulquer****
- ✉ 23 rue du Poulquer
- 📅 1 May - 30 Sep
- ☎ +33 (0)2-98570419
- @ contact@campingdupoulquer.com

1	DE**JM**NOPQRT	ABCDFGHIKMNPQSX	6
2	EHPVWXY	ABDE**FG**H	7
3	B**K**LQST	ABCDEFKNRSV	8
4	DFHILNO**PQ**TUVY	E	9
5	ABDEFH**NO**	ABDGHIJNOR	10

6-10A   ❶ €30.80
3ha 148**T**(80-100m²) 38**P**   ❷ €38.20

🗺 From Quimper take the D34 to Bénodet. Continue Bénodet-plage. Turn left at the end of the boulevard. Follow the signs!
💬 Family campsite close to the town and located near Bénodet and its beach. Modern and well maintained toilet facilities. Lovely heated outdoor pool with jacuzzi and slides, also an indoor pool with sliding roof, free hammam, sauna and wellness area with Balneo. Free wifi. Look out for the name of the campsite when you arrive!
(CC) 1/5-10/7 28/8-29/9

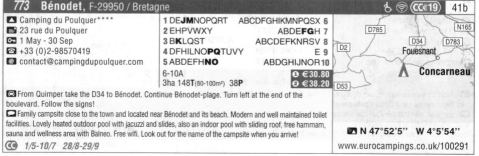

📍 N 47°52'5" W 4°5'54"

www.eurocampings.co.uk/100291

774 Bénodet, F-29950 / Bretagne

  🚿 📶 ⚙️ **iD** | 41b

- 🏕️ Sunêlia L'Escale Saint-Gilles*****
- 🏠 Corniche de la Mer
- 📅 21 Apr - 16 Sep
- ☎ +33 (0)2-98570537
- @ sunelia@stgilles.fr

1 ADE**J**KNOQRST	ACD**E**FGHIKNPQS**X**	6
2 EFHMPVX	ABDE**FG**H	7
3 BE**K**LMQ	ABCDEFJKNQRSV	8
4 BDFHILNO**PQRTUVXZ**	AELUV	9
5 ACDEFGHL**N**	ABGHIJ**NP**SXZ	10
10A		❶ €47.30
11ha 60T(80-100m²) 607P		❷ €60.30

🚗 From Quimper, follow the D34 direction Bénodet. Follow Bénodet-plage. At the end turn left and continue on the esplanade (follow signs).

💬 The campsite is located in the tourist village of Bénodet. Lovely water park with outdoor and indoor pools (even the air is heated, and it can be opened in fine weather). Very nice room for entertainment and wellness with indoor pool, spa, hammam, sauna, jacuzzi and beauty centre.

📍 N 47°51'46'' W 4°5'44''
www.eurocampings.co.uk/103219

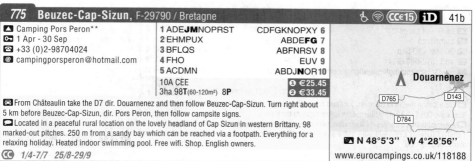

775 Beuzec-Cap-Sizun, F-29790 / Bretagne

  🚿 📶 **CC€15** **iD** | 41b

- 🏕️ Camping Pors Peron**
- 📅 1 Apr - 30 Sep
- ☎ +33 (0)2-98704024
- @ campingporsperon@hotmail.com

1 ADE**JM**NOPRST	CDFGKNOPXY	6
2 EHMPUX	ABDE**FG**	7
3 BFLQS	ABFNRSV	8
4 FHO	EUV	9
5 ACDMN	ABDJ**N**OR	10
10A CEE		❶ €25.45
3ha 98T(60-120m²) 8P		❷ €33.45

🚗 From Châteaulin take the D7 dir. Douarnenez and then follow Beuzec-Cap-Sizun. Turn right about 5 km before Beuzec-Cap-Sizun, dir. Pors Peron, then follow campsite signs.

💬 Located in a peaceful rural location on the lovely headland of Cap Sizun in western Brittany. 98 marked-out pitches. 250 m from a sandy bay which can be reached via a footpath. Everything for a relaxing holiday. Heated indoor swimming pool. Free wifi. Shop. English owners.

CC 1/4-7/7 25/8-29/9

📍 N 48°5'3'' W 4°28'56''
www.eurocampings.co.uk/118188

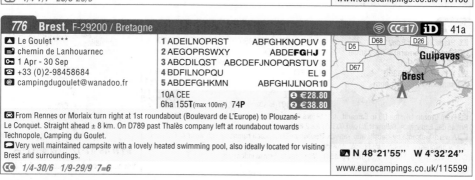

776 Brest, F-29200 / Bretagne

  📶 **CC€17** **iD** | 41a

- 🏕️ Le Goulet****
- 🏠 chemin de Lanhouarnec
- 📅 1 Apr - 30 Sep
- ☎ +33 (0)2-98458684
- @ campingduguoulet@wanadoo.fr

1 ADEILNOPRST	ABFGHKNOPUV	6
2 AEGOPRSWXY	ABDE**FGH**J	7
3 ABCDILQST	ABCDEFJNOPQRSTUV	8
4 BDFILNOPQU	EL	9
5 ABDEFGHKMN	ABFGHIJLNOR	10
10A CEE		❶ €28.80
6ha 155T(max 100m²) 74P		❷ €38.80

🚗 From Rennes or Morlaix turn right at 1st roundabout (Boulevard de L'Europe) to Plouzané-Le Conquet. Straight ahead ± 8 km. On D789 past Thalès company left at roundabout towards Technopole, Camping du Goulet.

💬 Very well maintained campsite with a lovely heated swimming pool, also ideally located for visiting Brest and surroundings.

CC 1/4-30/6 1/9-29/9 7=6

📍 N 48°21'55'' W 4°32'24''
www.eurocampings.co.uk/115599

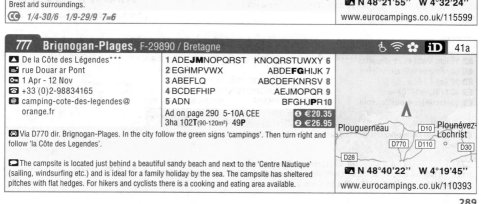

777 Brignogan-Plages, F-29890 / Bretagne

  🚿 📶 ⚙️ **iD** | 41a

- 🏕️ De la Côte des Légendes***
- 🏠 rue Douar ar Pont
- 📅 1 Apr - 12 Nov
- ☎ +33 (0)2-98834165
- @ camping-cote-des-legendes@orange.fr

1 ADE**JM**NOPQRST	KNOQRSTUWXY	6
2 EGHMPVWX	ABDE**FG**HIJK	7
3 ABEFLQ	ABCDEFKNRSV	8
4 BCDEFHIP	AEJMOPQR	9
5 ADN	BFGHJ**P**R	10
Ad on page 290 5-10A CEE		❶ €20.35
3ha 102T(90-120m²) 49P		❷ €26.95

🚗 Via D770 dir. Brignogan-Plages. In the city follow the green signs 'campings'. Then turn right and follow 'la Côte des Legendes'.

💬 The campsite is located just behind a beautiful sandy beach and next to the 'Centre Nautique' (sailing, windsurfing etc.) and is ideal for a family holiday by the sea. The campsite has sheltered pitches with flat hedges. For hikers and cyclists there is a cooking and eating area available.

📍 N 48°40'22'' W 4°19'45''
www.eurocampings.co.uk/110393

De la Côte des Légendes
★ ★ ★

The campsite, located by the sea along a lovely sandy beach, is perfect for a family holiday. Mobile home rental. Extensive focus on the natural surroundings.

Rue Douar ar Pont
29890 Brignogan-Plages
Tel. 02-98834165 • Fax 02-98835994
E-mail: camping-cote-des-legendes@orange.fr
Internet: www.campingcotedeslegendes.com

---

778 Camaret-sur-Mer, F-29570 / Bretagne 🌀 ⚡ (CC€15) iD 41a

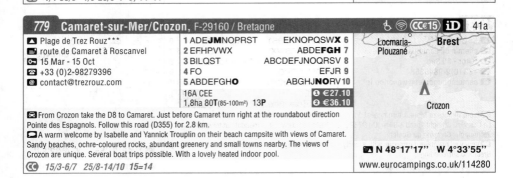

- 🔺 Le Grand Large★★★★
- ✉ Lambézen
- 🕐 30 Mar - 30 Sep
- ☎ +33 (0)2-98279141
- @ contact@campinglegrandlarge.com

1 ADE**JM**NORT	ABFGHKQSX	6
2 EHJPRVX	ABDE**FGH**	7
3 BF**I**LMQ	ABCDEFKNQRSTU	8
4 FIO**P**	EFL	9
5 ACDFHM	ABGHJL**N**OR	10
10A CEE	❶ €27.60	
A50 2,8ha 123T(80-130m²) 30P	❷ €36.20	

Locmaria-Plouzané · **Brest**

Λ

Crozon

📷 From Cozon the D8 to Camaret. Just past Camaret the roundabout to the right, direction Roscanvel/D355 (1.8 km). At Lambézen follow signs to the right.
📷 A campsite that deserves its star rating, very clean and well maintained new toilet facilities including showers and washbasins in the same room. 450 m to the beach with spectacular panoramas of the sea and rocks.

🆑 1/4-30/6 1/9-29/9 7=6, 14=11

📍 N 48°16'51" W 4°33'53"

www.eurocampings.co.uk/103204

---

779 Camaret-sur-Mer/Crozon, F-29160 / Bretagne 🌀 ⚡ (CC€15) iD 41a

- 🔺 Plage de Trez Rouz★★★
- ✉ route de Camaret à Roscanvel
- 🕐 15 Mar - 15 Oct
- ☎ +33 (0)2-98279396
- @ contact@trezrouz.com

1 ADE**JM**NOPRST	EKNOPQSW**X**	6
2 EFHPVWX	ABDE**FGH**	7
3 BILQST	ABCDEFJNOQRSV	8
4 FO	EFJR	9
5 ABDEFGH**O**	ABGHJ**N**ORV	10
16A CEE	❶ €27.10	
1,8ha 80T(85-100m²) 13P	❷ €36.10	

Locmaria-Plouzané · **Brest**

Λ

Crozon

📷 From Crozon take the D8 to Camaret. Just before Camaret turn right at the roundabout direction Pointe des Espagnols. Follow this road (D355) for 2.8 km.
📷 A warm welcome by Isabelle and Yannick Trouplin on their beach campsite with views of Camaret. Sandy beaches, ochre-coloured rocks, abundant greenery and small towns nearby. The views of Crozon are unique. Several boat trips possible. With a lovely heated indoor pool.

🆑 15/3-6/7 25/8-14/10 15=14

📍 N 48°17'17" W 4°33'55"

www.eurocampings.co.uk/114280

---

780 Carantec, F-29660 / Bretagne 🌀 ⚡ iD 41a

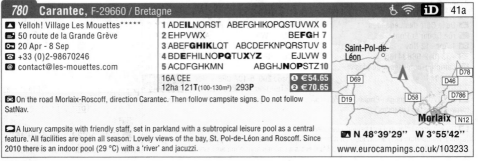

- 🔺 Yelloh! Village Les Mouettes★★★★★
- ✉ 50 route de la Grande Grève
- 🕐 20 Apr - 8 Sep
- ☎ +33 (0)2-98670246
- @ contact@les-mouettes.com

1 ADE**IL**NORST	ABEFGHIKOPQSTUVWX	6
2 EHPVWX	BE**FGH**	7
3 ABEF**GHIK**LQT	ABCDEFKNPQRSTUV	8
4 BDE**F**HILNO**PQ**TUX**YZ**	EJLVW	9
5 ACDFGHKMN	ABGHJ**NOP**STZ	10
16A CEE	❶ €54.65	
12ha 121T(100-130m²) 293P	❷ €70.65	

Saint-Pol-de-Léon

Λ

D69 · D78
D46
D19 · D58 · D786

Morlaix N12

📷 On the road Morlaix-Roscoff, direction Carantec. Then follow campsite signs. Do not follow SatNav.

📷 A luxury campsite with friendly staff, set in parkland with a subtropical leisure pool as a central feature. All facilities are open all season. Lovely views of the bay, St. Pol-de-Léon and Roscoff. Since 2010 there is an indoor pool (29 °C) with a 'river' and jacuzzi.

📍 N 48°39'29" W 3°55'42"

www.eurocampings.co.uk/103233

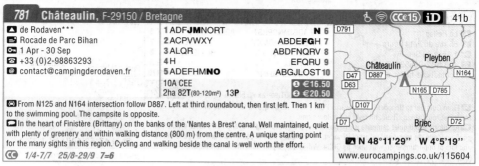

781 Châteaulin, F-29150 / Bretagne
🛜 (CC€15) **iD** 41b

- 🏕 de Rodaven***
- 📧 Rocade de Parc Bihan
- 📅 1 Apr - 30 Sep
- ☎ +33 (0)2-98863293
- @ contact@campingderodaven.fr

1	ADF**JM**NORT		N 6
2	ACPVWXY		ABDEF**GH** 7
3	ALQR		ABDFNQRV 8
4	H		EFQRU 9
5	ADEFHM**NO**		ABGJLOST 10
10A CEE			❶ €16.50
2ha 82T(80-120m²) 13P			❷ €20.50

🚗 From N125 and N164 intersection follow D887. Left at third roundabout, then first left. Then 1 km to the swimming pool. The campsite is opposite.
📍 In the heart of Finistère (Brittany) on the banks of the 'Nantes à Brest' canal. Well maintained, quiet with plenty of greenery and within walking distance (800 m) from the centre. A unique starting point for the many sights in this region. Cycling and walking beside the canal is well worth the effort.

(CC) 1/4-7/7 25/8-29/9 7=6

N 48°11'29" W 4°5'19"
www.eurocampings.co.uk/115604

782 Châteaulin, F-29150 / Bretagne
🛜 (CC€15) **iD** 41b

- 🏕 La Pointe***
- 📧 route de St. Coulitz
- 📅 15 Mar - 15 Oct
- ☎ +33 (0)2-98865153
- @ lapointecamping@aol.com

1	ADE**JM**NOPRST		NX 6
2	ABCPRVWXY		ABDE**FG**HK 7
3	AL		ABCDEFGKNQRSV 8
4	I		RV 9
5	ABDN		ABGHJPR 10
10A			❶ €22.00
2ha 60T(80-120m²)			❷ €27.00

🚗 In Châteaulin take direction Saint-Coulitz, then follow signs.
📍 A modest, quiet and well maintained campsite where kindness, friendliness and hospitality are top of the list. Its central location in Finistère makes this a good campsite for trips out in the region. The centre is within walking distance (1.5 km) along the lovely 'Nantes-Brest' canal, which can also be cycled.

(CC) 15/3-8/7 26/8-14/10 7=6

N 48°11'15" W 4°5'5"
www.eurocampings.co.uk/118417

783 Clohars-Carnoët, F-29360 / Bretagne
🛜 (CC€13) **iD** 41b

- 🏕 Flower Camping Le Kergariou***
- 📧 Kervec
- 📅 1 Apr - 15 Sep
- ☎ +33 (0)2-98715465
- @ camping.lekergariou@wanadoo.fr

1	ADEF**JM**NOPRT	CDFGXY**Z** 6
2	A**MO**PVWXY	ABDE**FG**H 7
3	BCEFLQST	ABDFGNRSTUV 8
4	BDFHIOQ**T**	BEJ 9
5	ADEFH**NO**	ABFGHIJM**P**STVW 10
10A CEE		❶ €23.00
2,7ha 71T(80-150m²) 35P		❷ €31.00

🚗 E60/N165 Lorient-Quimper, exit Kervidanou. Via D16 to Clohars-Carnoët, straight through centre to roundabout. Dir. Doëlan.
📍 Peacefully located campsite with pitches between hedges and several mature trees. Well equipped toilet facilities. Cycling to the nearby small harbours is possible but watch out for some steep roads. Owner is a fervent angler and can inform you of the best places to fish. Indoor heated swimming pool open throughout the season.

(CC) 1/4-13/7 1/9-14/9

N 47°46'58" W 3°35'20"
www.eurocampings.co.uk/112437

784 Clohars-Carnoët/Le Pouldu, F-29360 / Bretagne
🛜 ✿ (CC€17) **iD** 42b

- 🏕 Les Embruns*****
- 📧 2 rue de Philosophe Alain
- 📅 6 Apr - 23 Sep
- ☎ +33 (0)2-98399107
- @ contact@camping-les-embruns.com

1	ADE**JM**NOPQRST	CDFG**HK**MNOPQRSTVWXY**Z** 6
2	AEHMOPVWXY	ABDE**FG**H**IJ**K 7
3	BE**GH**ILMQT	ABCDEFGIJKNQRSTU 8
4	BCDFHIKLNOP**QRTVXZ**	ELMOQRUVZ 9
5	ACDEFGHLMN	ABDEFGHIJMNO**P**RVXZ 10
16A CEE		❶ €46.10
6ha 65T(100-150m²) 105P		❷ €60.10

🚗 E60 Lorient towards Quimperlé. Exit Kervidanou or exit Kergostiou/Quimperlé centre. Via D16 to Clohars-Carnoët, straight through centre, D24 to Le Pouldu. Campsite in the town centre.
📍 Beautiful family campsite in village centre, 250 m from beach. Lovely indoor pool. Many flowers, awarded campsite with most beautiful plants in France. Supermarket open when the campsite is. Restaurant. Excellent toilet facilities, sauna, hamam and beauty salon.

(CC) 6/4-9/7 27/8-22/9 14=12

N 47°46'7" W 3°32'42"
www.eurocampings.co.uk/103242

France

785 Combrit/Sainte-Marine, F-29120 / Bretagne   ♿ 🛜 (CC€17) iD 41b

- ▲ Le Helles***
- 🏠 55 rue du Petit Bourg
- 📅 1 Apr - 30 Sep
- ☎ +33 (0)2-98563146
- @ contact@le-helles.com

1 ADE**JM**NOPRST	ABCDFGKMNPQRSW**X** 6	
2 EGHOPVWXY	ABDE**FGH** 7	
3 B**K**LQST	ABCDEFKNRSV 8	
4 BFHL	E 9	
5 ABDEFGHN	ABDHIJPR 10	
10A	❸ €29.50	
2,7ha 80**T**(90-120m²) 55**P**	❷ €39.50	

🚗 From Quimper to Bénodet. Then towards Pont-l'Abbé via D44. Over the bridge and 1st left to Ste Marine at roundabout. Then 2nd right and follow signs.
💬 An informal and quiet campsite with a heated outdoor swimming pool and new indoor swimming pool, opposite the renowned resort of Bénodet. 300m from a natural beach with fine sand and dunes and lots of opportunities to walk such as GR34. Wifi is free. 600m from Ste Marine harbour.

(CC) 1/4-7/7 26/8-29/9

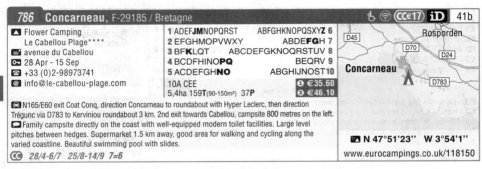

📍 N 47°52'10" W 4°7'42"

www.eurocampings.co.uk/117635

786 Concarneau, F-29185 / Bretagne   ♿ 🛜 (CC€17) iD 41b

- ▲ Flower Camping
  Le Cabellou Plage****
- 🏠 avenue du Cabellou
- 📅 28 Apr - 15 Sep
- ☎ +33 (0)2-98973741
- @ info@le-cabellou-plage.com

1 ADEF**JM**NOPQRST	ABFGHKNOPQSXY**Z** 6	
2 EFGHMOPVWXY	ABDE**FGH** 7	
3 BF**K**LQT	ABCDEFGKNOQRSTUV 8	
4 BCDFHINO**PQ**	BEQRV 9	
5 ACDEFGH**NO**	ABGHIJNOST 10	
10A CEE	❸ €35.60	
5,4ha 159**T**(90-150m²) 37**P**	❷ €46.10	

🚗 N165/E60 exit Coat Conq, direction Concarneau to roundabout with Hyper Leclerc, then direction Trégunc via D783 to Kerviniou roundabout 3 km. 2nd exit towards Cabellou, campsite 800 metres on the left.
💬 Family campsite directly on the coast with well-equipped modern toilet facilities. Large level pitches between hedges. Supermarket 1.5 km away, good area for walking and cycling along the varied coastline. Beautiful swimming pool with slides.

(CC) 28/4-6/7 25/8-14/9 7=6

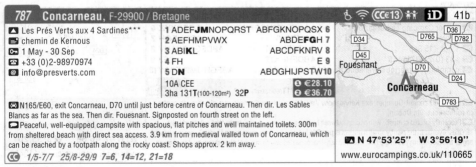

📍 N 47°51'23" W 3°54'1"

www.eurocampings.co.uk/118150

787 Concarneau, F-29900 / Bretagne   ♿ 🛜 (CC€13) 🚻 iD 41b

- ▲ Les Prés Verts aux 4 Sardines***
- 🏠 chemin de Kernous
- 📅 1 May - 30 Sep
- ☎ +33 (0)2-98970974
- @ info@presverts.com

1 ADEF**JM**NOPQRST	ABFGKNOPQSX 6	
2 AEFHMPVWX	ABDE**FGH** 7	
3 AB**IK**L	ABCDFKNRV 8	
4 FH	E 9	
5 D**N**	ABDGHIJPSTW 10	
10A CEE	❸ €28.10	
3ha 131**T**(100-120m²) 32**P**	❷ €36.70	

🚗 N165/E60, exit Concarneau, D70 until just before centre of Concarneau. Then dir. Les Sables Blancs as far as the sea. Then dir. Fouesnant. Signposted on fourth street on the left.
💬 Peaceful, well-equipped campsite with spacious, flat pitches and well maintained toilets. 300m from sheltered beach with direct sea access. 3.9 km from medieval walled town of Concarneau, which can be reached by a footpath along the rocky coast. Shops approx. 2 km away.

(CC) 1/5-7/7 25/8-29/9 7=6, 14=12, 21=18

📍 N 47°53'25" W 3°56'19"

www.eurocampings.co.uk/110665

788 Concarneau, F-29900 / Bretagne   ♿ 🛜 (CC€15) 🚻 iD 41b

- ▲ Les Sables Blancs****
- 🏠 avenue du Dorlett
- 📅 1 Apr - 31 Oct
- ☎ +33 (0)2-98971644
- @ contact@
  camping-lessablesblancs.com

1 ADE**JM**NOPQRST	ABFGKMNOPQRSTVWXY**Z** 6	
2 AEFHMOPUVWXY	ABDE**FGH** 7	
3 BE**K**LQST	ABCDEFGIJKNQRSTUV 8	
4 BDFHLNO**PQ**RUY	EMNOQRTV 9	
5 ABDEFGHKL**NO**	ABDGHIJPR 10	
10-16A CEE	❸ €36.30	
2,9ha 99**T**(80-200m²) 50**P**	❷ €45.30	

🚗 From N165 dir. Concarneau, centre via D70, to roundabout with supermarket, dir. Concarneau. Third to the right to Les Sables Blancs, via 2 roundabouts to sea, until T-junction, then turn right.
💬 Small quiet site with pool and restaurant in middle of countryside. 250m from beach and 15 min. walk from Concarneau, a lovely medieval walled town. Market twice a week in town centre. Modern, heated toilet facilities. Sea views on some pitches.

(CC) 1/4-6/7 25/8-30/10 7=6, 14=12, 21=18

📍 N 47°52'55" W 3°55'43"

www.eurocampings.co.uk/103237

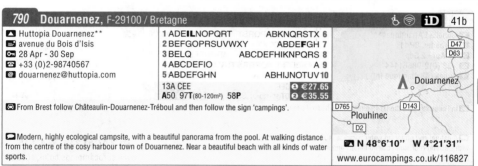

789 Crozon, F-29160 / Bretagne

♿ 📶 iD 41a

- ⛺ Les Pieds Dans L'Eau★★★
- 🏠 'Pratmeur' Saint-Fiacre
- 📅 1 Mar - 31 Oct
- ☎ +33 (0)2-98276243
- @ campinglespiedsdansleau-crozon@orange.fr

1	**AIL**NOPRST	KNQSUX	6
2	EFKPRVXY	ABDE**F**H	7
3	BIL	ABDFNORS	8
4	FH	EQ	9
5	ABDH**O**	ABHJLOST	10

10A ❶ €22.60
2,7ha 100T(100-120m²) 10P ❷ €30.35

🚗 From Crozon, direction Roscanvel. Just before roundabout exit D355 to the right and follow D55 towards 'Ile Longue'. First left after 200m.

💬 Well maintained campsite directly on the sea (no sandy beach) with lots of foliage. Ideal campsite for those seeking peace and quiet, with plenty to see and do in the area.

La Trinité
Brest
Λ
Crozon
Telgruc-sur-Mer

📍 N 48°17'5'' W 4°31'43''
www.eurocampings.co.uk/103205

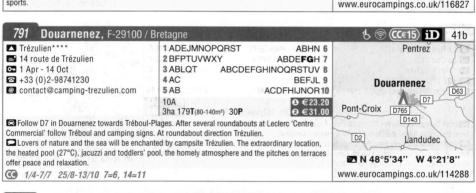

790 Douarnenez, F-29100 / Bretagne

♿ 📶 iD 41b

- ⛺ Huttopia Douarnenez★★
- 🏠 avenue du Bois d'Isis
- 📅 28 Apr - 30 Sep
- ☎ +33 (0)2-98740567
- @ douarnenez@huttopia.com

1	ADE**IL**NOPQRT	ABKNQRSTX	6
2	BEFGOPRSUVWXY	ABDE**F**GH	7
3	BELQ	ABCDEFHIKNPQRS	8
4	ABCDEFIO	A	9
5	ABDEFGHN	ABHIJNOTUV	10

13A CEE ❶ €27.65
A50 97T(80-120m²) 58P ❷ €35.55

🚗 From Brest follow Châteaulin-Douarnenez-Tréboul and then follow the sign 'campings'.

💬 Modern, highly ecological campsite, with a beautiful panorama from the pool. At walking distance from the centre of the cosy harbour town of Douarnenez. Near a beautiful beach with all kinds of water sports.

D47
D63
Λ Douarnenez
D765 D143
Plouhinec
D2

📍 N 48°6'10'' W 4°21'31''
www.eurocampings.co.uk/116827

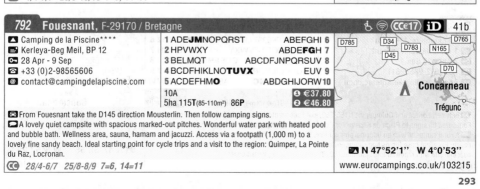

791 Douarnenez, F-29100 / Bretagne

♿ 📶 CC€15 iD 41b

- ⛺ Trézulien★★★★
- 🏠 14 route de Trézulien
- 📅 1 Apr - 14 Oct
- ☎ +33 (0)2-98741230
- @ contact@camping-trezulien.com

1	ADEJMNOPQRST	ABHN	6
2	BFPTUVWXY	ABDE**F**GH	7
3	ABLQT	ABCDEFGHINOQRSTUV	8
4	AC	BEFJL	9
5	AB	ACDFHIJNOR	10

10A ❶ €23.20
3ha 179T(80-140m²) 30P ❷ €31.00

🚗 Follow D7 in Douarnenez towards Tréboul-Plages. After several roundabouts at Leclerc 'Centre Commercial' follow Tréboul and camping signs. At roundabout direction Trézulien.

💬 Lovers of nature and the sea will be enchanted by campsite Trézulien. The extraordinary location, the heated pool (27°C), jacuzzi and toddlers' pool, the homely atmosphere and the pitches on terraces offer peace and relaxation.

CC 1/4-7/7 25/8-13/10 7=6, 14=11

Pentrez
Douarnenez
D63
Pont-Croix D765 D7
D143
D2 Landudec

📍 N 48°5'34'' W 4°21'8''
www.eurocampings.co.uk/114288

---

792 Fouesnant, F-29170 / Bretagne

♿ 📶 CC€17 iD 41b

- ⛺ Camping de la Piscine★★★★
- 🏠 Kerleya-Beg Meil, BP 12
- 📅 28 Apr - 9 Sep
- ☎ +33 (0)2-98565606
- @ contact@campingdelapiscine.com

1	ADE**JM**NOPQRST	ABEFGHI	6
2	HPVWXY	ABDE**FG**H	7
3	BELMQT	ABCDFJNPQRSUV	8
4	BCDFHIKLNO**TUVX**	EUV	9
5	ACDEFHM**O**	ABDGHIJORW	10

10A ❶ €37.80
5ha 115T(85-110m²) 86P ❷ €46.80

🚗 From Fouesnant take the D145 direction Mousterlin. Then follow camping signs.

💬 A lovely quiet campsite with spacious marked-out pitches. Wonderful water park with heated pool and bubble bath. Wellness area, sauna, hamam and jacuzzi. Access via a footpath (1,000 m) to a lovely fine sandy beach. Ideal starting point for cycle trips and a visit to the region: Quimper, La Pointe du Raz, Locronan.

CC 28/4-6/7 25/8-8/9 7=6, 14=11

D785 D34 D783 N165 D765
D45 D70
Λ **Concarneau**
Trégunc

📍 N 47°52'1'' W 4°0'53''
www.eurocampings.co.uk/103215

793 Fouesnant, F-29170 / Bretagne ♿ 📶 ✿ iD 41b

- ⛺ Kost Ar Moor***
- 🏕 Pointe de Mousterlin
- 📅 30 Apr - 10 Sep
- ☎ +33 (0)2-98560416
- @ contact@camping-fouesnant.com

1 ADE**IL**NOPQRST	ABFGKNPQS**XY** 6
2 DEHPRVVWXY	ABDE**FGH** 7
3 BE**KL**ST	ABCDFINQRSTUV 8
4 BDFHIO**PQ**	BEIUV 9
5 ACDEFGH**NO**	ABHJ**P**ST 10

10A
3,5ha 100T(100-150m²) 66P

❶ €30.30
❷ €39.90

🚗 From Fouesnant D145 direction Mousterlin. Drive to the end and follow the arrows.

💬 Quiet campsite with spacious, shady pitches. Close to a very nice beach and situated in a nature reserve. Playfully landscaped swimming pool with balneo bath.

D785 · D45 · D783 · D70
Pont-l'Abbé · Trégunc

📷 N 47°51'5" W 4°2'8"
www.eurocampings.co.uk/111590

794 Fouesnant, F-29170 / Bretagne ⊗ ♿ 📶 ✿ iD 41b

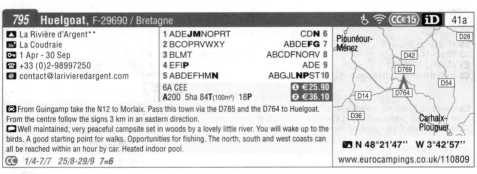

- ⛺ Sunêlia L'Atlantique****
- 🏕 Kerbader, BP 11
- 📅 27 Apr - 2 Sep
- ☎ +33 (0)2-98561444
- @ sunelia@latlantique.fr

1 ADEHKNOPQRST	ABCDFGHIKNQSX 6
2 EGHPVWXY	ABDE**FGH** 7
3 BE**FILM**QR	ABCDEFIKLNQRS 8
4 ABDFHILNO**PQRST**UV**XYZ**	AEFLUVY 9
5 ACDEFGHKN	ABFGHIJ**NP**ST 10

6-10A CEE
9ha 120T(90-120m²) 333P

❶ €46.00
❷ €56.00

🚗 In Fouesnant take the D145 direction Kerbader. Follow the campsite signs.

💬 A natural and protected water paradise, 400 metres from sandy beach. Three heated pools - one with a sliding roof - with balneotherapy and solarium. Wellness area with sauna, hammam, fitness and beauty centre.

D785 · D34 · D45 · D783 · N165 · D70
Concarneau · Trégunc

📷 N 47°51'23" W 4°1'15"
www.eurocampings.co.uk/100290

795 Huelgoat, F-29690 / Bretagne ♿ 📶 (CC€15) iD 41a

- ⛺ La Rivière d'Argent**
- 🏕 La Coudraie
- 📅 1 Apr - 30 Sep
- ☎ +33 (0)2-98997250
- @ contact@larivieredargent.com

1 ADE**JM**NOPRT	CD**N** 6
2 BCOPRVWXY	ABDE**FG** 7
3 BLMT	ABCDFNORV 8
4 EFI**P**	ADE 9
5 ABDEFH**M**N	ABGJL**NP**ST 10

6A CEE
A200 5ha 84T(100m²) 18P

❶ €25.90
❷ €36.10

🚗 From Guingamp take the N12 to Morlaix. Pass this town via the D785 and the D764 to Huelgoat. From the centre follow the signs 3 km in an eastern direction.

💬 Well maintained, very peaceful campsite set in woods by a lovely little river. You will wake up to the birds. A good starting point for walks. Opportunities for fishing. The north, south and west coasts can all be reached within an hour by car. Heated indoor pool.

CC 1/4-7/7 25/8-29/9 7=6

Plounéour-Ménez · D28 · D42 · D769 · D54 · D14 · D764 · D36 · Carhaix-Plouguer

📷 N 48°21'47" W 3°42'57"
www.eurocampings.co.uk/110809

796 La Forêt-Fouesnant, F-29940 / Bretagne ♿ 📶 ✿ (CC€17) iD 41b

- ⛺ De Kérantérec****
- 🏕 1 route de Saint Laurent
- 📅 7 Apr - 23 Sep
- ☎ +33 (0)2-98569811
- @ info@camping-keranterec.com

1 ADE**JM**NOPQRST	ABCFGHKMNOPQRSTVWXY**Z** 6
2 AEFHMOPTUVWXY	ABDE**FGH** 7
3 BEF**KL**MQT	CDEFHIKNPQRSTU 8
4 BCDFHILNO**PQ**U	EJMOQRUV 9
5 ABDEFGH**NO**	ABDGHIJMNORW 10

10-15A
6,5ha 110T(90-150m²) 138P

❶ €36.20
❷ €46.20

🚗 Between Lorient and Quimper via N165-E60, exit Fouesnant/Concarneau, via D44 direction Fouesnant till signs to Plage de Kerleven or Port La Forêt. Well signposted.

💬 A rural campsite with an informal atmosphere. Right by the sea and direct access to the sandy beach. Excellent base for visiting Quimper-Concarneau and surroundings. Environmentally friendly, peaceful site with renewed toilet facilities (2016) and interesting, varied coast.

CC 7/4-7/7 25/8-22/9

D34 · D783 · D45 · D765 · D782 · D24 · Fouesnant · N165 · Concarneau

📷 N 47°53'55" W 3°57'22"
www.eurocampings.co.uk/111037

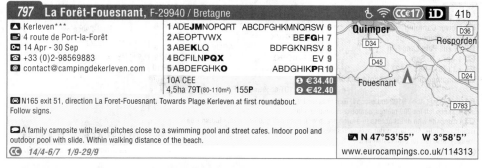

797 La Forêt-Fouesnant, F-29940 / Bretagne

♿ 🛜 (CC€17) iD 41b

▲ Kerleven***
🏠 4 route de Port-la-Forêt
🗓 14 Apr - 30 Sep
☎ +33 (0)2-98569883
@ contact@campingdekerleven.com

1	ADE**JM**NOPQRT	ABCDFGHKMNQRSW	6
2	AEOPTVWX	BE**FG**H	7
3	ABE**KL**Q	BDFGKNRSV	8
4	BCFILN**PQX**	EV	9
5	ABDEFGHK**O**	ABDGHIK**P**R	10
10A CEE			

4,5ha 79**T**(80-110m²) 155**P**
- ① €34.40
- ② €42.40

🚗 N165 exit 51, direction La Foret-Fouesnant. Towards Plage Kerleven at first roundabout. Follow signs.

💬 A family campsite with level pitches close to a swimming pool and street cafes. Indoor pool and outdoor pool with slide. Within walking distance of the beach.

CC 14/4-6/7 1/9-29/9

Quimper
Rosporden
Fouesnant
D36 D34 D45 D24 D783

⚓ N 47°53'55'' W 3°58'5''
www.eurocampings.co.uk/114313

798 Landéda, F-29870 / Bretagne

♿ 🛜 (CC€17) iD 41a

▲ Des Abers****
🏠 Plage de St. Marguerite
🗓 28 Apr - 30 Sep
☎ +33 (0)2-98049335
@ camping-des-abers@wanadoo.fr

1	ADE**JM**NOPRST	KMNOPQSUWXY	6
2	EFHOPQRUVWX	ABDE**FG**H	7
3	BEFLQ	ABCDE**F**NQRS	8
4	ADEFHI**PZ**	BELUV	9
5	ACDFGHM**N**	ABDGHIJN**P**R	10
10A			

5,5ha 154**T**(90-120m²) 26**P**
- ① €22.00
- ② €29.30

🚗 From Lannilis follow green 'campsites' signs through Landéda. 1.7 km past Landéda follow camping signs.

💬 Hubert and his team offer you a warm welcome in French, German or English to their lovely campsite positioned right on a sandy beach. Panoramic views of the ocean and countless small islands which are accessible at low tide. A wonderful site for an extended stay.

CC 28/4-6/7 1/9-29/9 14=12

Plouguerneau
Ploudalmézeau
D28 D68 D168 D26 D13

⚓ N 48°35'36'' W 4°36'9''
www.eurocampings.co.uk/103203

France

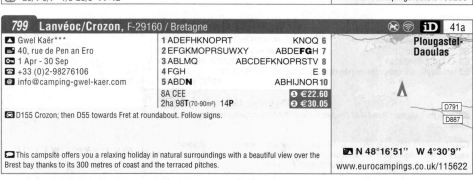

799 Lanvéoc/Crozon, F-29160 / Bretagne

🚫 🛜 iD 41a

▲ Gwel Kaër***
🏠 40, rue de Pen an Ero
🗓 1 Apr - 30 Sep
☎ +33 (0)2-98276106
@ info@camping-gwel-kaer.com

1	ADEFHKNOPRT	KNOQ	6
2	EFGKMOPRSUWXY	ABDE**FG**H	7
3	ABLMQ	ABCDEFKNOPRSTV	8
4	FGH	E	9
5	ABD**N**	ABHIJNOR	10
8A CEE			

2ha 98**T**(70-90m²) 14**P**
- ① €22.60
- ② €30.05

🚗 D155 Crozon; then D55 towards Fret at roundabout. Follow signs.

💬 This campsite offers you a relaxing holiday in natural surroundings with a beautiful view over the Brest bay thanks to its 300 metres of coast and the terraced pitches.

Plougastel-Daoulas
D791 D887

⚓ N 48°16'51'' W 4°30'9''
www.eurocampings.co.uk/115622

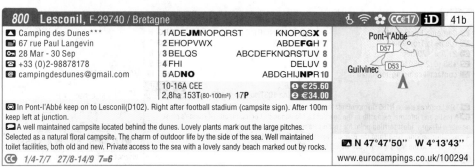

800 Lesconil, F-29740 / Bretagne

♿ 🛜 ❄ (CC€17) iD 41b

▲ Camping des Dunes***
🏠 67 rue Paul Langevin
🗓 28 Mar - 30 Sep
☎ +33 (0)2-98878178
@ campingdesdunes@gmail.com

1	ADE**JM**NOPQRST	KNOPQS**X**	6
2	EHOPVWX	ABDE**FG**H	7
3	BELQS	ABCDEFKNQRSTUV	8
4	FHI	DELUV	9
5	AD**NO**	ABDGHIJN**P**R	10
10-16A CEE			

2,8ha 153**T**(80-100m²) 17**P**
- ① €25.60
- ② €34.00

🚗 In Pont-l'Abbé keep on to Lesconil(D102). Right after football stadium (campsite sign). After 100m keep left at junction.

💬 A well maintained campsite located behind the dunes. Lovely plants mark out the large pitches. Selected as a natural floral campsite. The charm of outdoor life by the side of the sea. Well maintained toilet facilities, both old and new. Private access to the sea with a lovely sandy beach marked out by rocks.

CC 1/4-7/7 27/8-14/9 7=6

Pont-l'Abbé
Guilvinec
D57 D53

⚓ N 47°47'50'' W 4°13'43''
www.eurocampings.co.uk/100294

801 Lesconil, F-29740 / Bretagne   ♿ 🛜 (CC€15) iD   41b

🏕 Flower Camping
de la Grande Plage***
🏠 71 rue Paul Langevin
📅 1 Apr - 15 Sep
☎ +33 (0)2-98878827
@ campinggrandeplage@hotmail.com

1	ADE**JM**NOPQRST	ABFGHIKNPQS**X** 6
2	EHOPRVX	ABDE**FG**H 7
3	BLQ	ABCDFKNOQRSV 8
4	BFHIO**PQ**	ACEUVX 9
5	ADEFHKN	ABDGHIJO**P**R 10
10A CEE		❶ €26.00
2,5ha 110**T**(80-120m²)	39**P**	❷ €33.00

🚗 From Pont-l'Abbé D102 to Lesconil. Turn right past the football stadium and skating park (camping signs). Keep left for 200 metres, campsite is another 1 km.
🏖 A campsite with direct access to a large beach with sand and granite rocks. Modern well maintained toilet facilities, water park with slides and bubble bath and a snack bar with takeaway meals. It also has its own restaurant.

(CC) 1/4-30/6 1/9-14/9 7=6

Pont-l'Abbé
D57 D2
Penmarch D53

⛺ **N 47°47'52" W 4°13'44"**
www.eurocampings.co.uk/110757

---

802 Lesconil, F-29740 / Bretagne   ♿ 🛜 iD   41b

🏕 Les Sables Blancs**
🏠 21 Keralouet
📅 1 Apr - 30 Sep
☎ +33 (0)2-98878479
@ sriviere@magic.fr

1	A**JM**NOPQRST	KNQRSTV 6
2	HOPRVWXY	ABDE**FG** 7
3	B**I**LQRS	ABCDEFJNQRV 8
4		DEL 9
5	ADEFGH**NO**	ABFGJ**N**PR 10
6-10A		❶ €14.60
2,2ha 80**T**(80-100m²)	16**P**	❷ €19.30

🚗 From Pont-l'Abbé to Plobannalec/Lesconil. Turn left after roundabout. Straight ahead at next roundabout, over the bridge to the left, turn left three times. Campsite signposted.

🏖 Campsite with family atmosphere and beautiful, large pitches in quiet natural surroundings. Modern, well-maintained toilet facilities, heated when the outside temperature drops. The traditional crepes are delicious and generous.

D57 D2 Pont-l'Abbé D34
Penmarch

⛺ **N 47°48'22" W 4°12'22"**
www.eurocampings.co.uk/115627

---

803 Lesconil/Plobannalec, F-29740 / Bretagne   ♿ 🛜 iD   41b

🏕 Yelloh! Village L'Océan Breton*****
📅 10 Apr - 4 Sep
☎ +33 (0)2-98822389
@ info@yellohvillage-loceanbreton.com

1	ABDE**JL**NOPQRST	ABCDEFGHIN 6
2	BCFGLOPRVX	ABDE**FG**H 7
3	BDE**H**LMQT	ABCDEFJKNQRSTUV 8
4	BCDFHILNO**PQ**RTX**Z**	AEJUVY 9
5	ACDEFGHKN	ABFGHIJNO**P**S**T** 10
10A		❶ €45.90
12ha 68**T**(100-170m²)	192**P**	❷ €59.90

🚗 Follow the D102 from Pont-l'Abbé direction Lesconil/Plobannalec. Campsite signposted beyond Plobannalec.

🏖 Le Manoir is a 19th-century estate surrounded by a river with a protected park, all of which ensures a special ambiance in a microclimate. All 4-star facilities are available from the opening date onwards. Our team will welcome you in English, Dutch or German.

Plonéour-Lanvern D34
D57
Penmarch

⛺ **N 47°48'45" W 4°13'17"**
www.eurocampings.co.uk/103221

---

804 Locronan, F-29180 / Bretagne   ♿ 🛜 (CC€15) iD   41b

🏕 Camping Locronan***
🏠 rue de la Troménie
📅 21 Apr - 29 Sep
☎ +33 (0)2-98918776
@ contact@camping-locronan.fr

1	ADE**JM**NOPRS	CDFG 6
2	BHPUVX	BD**FG** 7
3	B**G**LM	BDFINRSV 8
4	FH	ADE 9
5	AD**N**	ABHJOST 10
10A CEE		❶ €20.00
A160 2ha 103**T**(90-130m²)	19**P**	❷ €38.80

🚗 Take Locronan exit on N165 Quimper/Brest then follow campsite signs after 15 km when entering Locronan.
🏖 A rustic and informal campsite in the heart of La Montagne de Locronan, one of France's most beautiful villages. Ideal starting point for visiting Pointe Bretagne. Indoor heated swimming pool. A mecca for walking: GR38 and the Bois du Névet. Lovely views of the Baie de Douarnenez from site. You can walk to the Montagne for sea views. Free wifi.

(CC) 21/4-6/7 24/8-28/9 7=6

D887
D63
D7
Douarnenez
D143 Plogonnec N165
D765 D39
D784

⛺ **N 48°5'46" W 4°11'53"**
www.eurocampings.co.uk/117563

805 Loctudy, F-29750 / Bretagne

▲ Les Hortensias***
▩ 38 rue des Tulipes
☉ 1 Apr - 30 Sep
☎ +33 (0)2-98874664
@ hortensias@camping-loctudy.com

1	ADE**JM**NOPQRST	ABCDFGKNOPQSW**XY** 6
2	EHMOPVXY	ABDE**FG** 7
3	BELQST	ABCDEFGKNRSV 8
4	BFO**PU**	BDEV 9
5	ABDEFGHM**O**	ABDHIJ**PR** 10

6-10A CEE — ☉ €26.00
2ha 63**T**(80-110m²) 57**P** — ☉ €34.50

🚘 From Pont-L'Abbé direction Loctudy. Right before the chapel, straight on through traffic lights. 1 km further, site is on left.
🗩 Quiet family campsite 300 m from the sea in the south of the Finistère. This campsite welcomes families to an enormous area where nature is preserved. Heated indoor swimming pool with sliding roof from 2017.
© 1/4-6/7 27/8-29/9

Plonéour-Lanvern
D2 D785 D34
D57
D53

▲ N 47°48'47'' W 4°10'54''
www.eurocampings.co.uk/115629

---

806 Milizac, F-29290 / Bretagne

▲ Camping de la Récré****
▩ Le Lac des 3 Curés
☉ 1 Jan - 31 Dec
☎ +33 (0)2-98079217
@ campingdelarecre@orange.fr

1	ADEG**JM**NOPQRST	EFGH**N** 6
2	ABDGPRSUWXY	ABDE**FGH** 7
3	ABCDEIQ**RT**	ABCDEFGHINOPQRSV 8
4	BCDFHNOQ	EFJLV 9
5	ABDEFMNO	AFGHIJNPRZ 10

Ad on this page 10A CEE — ☉ €20.00
5,5ha 102**T** 44**P** — ☉ €33.00

🚘 From Brest Nord on the D26 exit 'Les Trois Curés'.

🗩 A very attractive campsite in a peaceful location. Ideal for families as the campsite forms part of a lovely amusement park. Well located for visiting Brest and the surroundings.
© 1/1-30/6 1/9-31/12

D28
D168 D26 D13 D788
D68
D5
D67
Plouzané **Guipavas** **Brest**

▲ N 48°28'32'' W 4°31'37''
www.eurocampings.co.uk/121351

---

807 Morgat, F-29160 / Bretagne

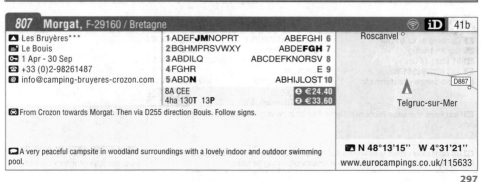

▲ Les Bruyères***
▩ Le Bouis
☉ 1 Apr - 30 Sep
☎ +33 (0)2-98261487
@ info@camping-bruyeres-crozon.com

1	ADEF**JM**NOPRT	ABEFGHI 6
2	BGHMPRSVWXY	ABDE**FGH** 7
3	ABDILQ	ABCDEFKNORSV 8
4	FGHR	E 9
5	ABD**N**	ABHIJLOST 10

8A CEE — ☉ €24.40
4ha 130**T** 13**P** — ☉ €33.60

🚘 From Crozon towards Morgat. Then via D255 direction Bouis. Follow signs.

🗩 A very peaceful campsite in woodland surroundings with a lovely indoor and outdoor swimming pool.

Roscanvel °
D887
Telgruc-sur-Mer

▲ N 48°13'15'' W 4°31'21''
www.eurocampings.co.uk/115633

808 Névez, F-29920 / Bretagne ⚿ 📶 (CC€17) iD 41b

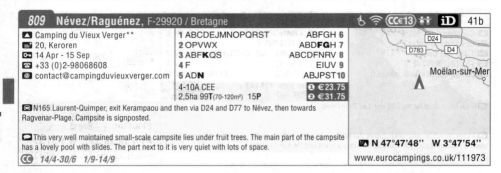

- 🏕 Sandaya Les 2 Fontaines****
- 🏠 Feunteun Vihan
- 📅 13 Apr - 9 Sep
- ☎ +33 (0)2-98068191
- @ 2fontaines@sandaya.fr

1 ADEF**JM**NOPRT	ABCDFGHIX	6
2 HMPVWXY	BE**FG**H	7
3 BEF**HJLMQ**R	BDFNQRSV	8
4 BCDFHILNO**Q**	ACEJ	9
5 ACDEFGH	ABDGHIJO**P**STZ	10

Ad on the cover 10A CEE
6,5ha 56T(100-140m²) 247P
❶ €43.20
❷ €55.20

🚗 N165/E60 Lorient-Quimper, exit Kerampaou, via D24 and D77 direction Névez centre, church at roundabout. Direction Raguénez, left after 3 km. Campsite well signposted.

💬 Good family campsite. Lovely large pitches with plenty of foliage. Nice walking path along the rugged coast, small roads in the area undulate, but are excellent for cycling tours. 900 metres to the coast.

(CC) 13/4-6/7 1/9-8/9

Concarneau D24 D4
D783
Moëlan-sur-Mer
Λ

📍 N 47°47'58" W 3°47'25"

www.eurocampings.co.uk/108411

809 Névez/Raguénez, F-29920 / Bretagne ⚿ 📶 (CC€13) 🚹🚺 iD 41b

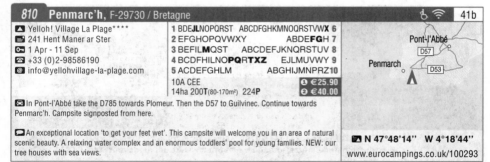

- 🏕 Camping du Vieux Verger**
- 🏠 20, Keroren
- 📅 14 Apr - 15 Sep
- ☎ +33 (0)2-98068608
- @ contact@campingduvieuxverger.com

1 ABCDEJMNOPQRST	ABFGH	6
2 OPVWX	ABD**FG**H	7
3 ABF**KQ**S	ABCDFNRV	8
4 F	EIUV	9
5 AD**N**	ABJPST	10

4-10A CEE
2,5ha 99T(70-120m²) 15P
❶ €23.75
❷ €31.75

🚗 N165 Laurent-Quimper, exit Kerampaou and then via D24 and D77 to Névez, then towards Ragvenar-Plage. Campsite is signposted.

💬 This very well maintained small-scale campsite lies under fruit trees. The main part of the campsite has a lovely pool with slides. The part next to it is very quiet with lots of space.

(CC) 14/4-30/6 1/9-14/9

D24
D783 D4
Moëlan-sur-Mer
Λ

📍 N 47°47'48" W 3°47'54"

www.eurocampings.co.uk/111973

810 Penmarc'h, F-29730 / Bretagne ⚿ 📶 41b

- 🏕 Yelloh! Village La Plage****
- 🏠 241 Hent Maner ar Ster
- 📅 1 Apr - 11 Sep
- ☎ +33 (0)2-98586190
- @ info@yellohvillage-la-plage.com

1 BDE**JL**NOPQRST ABCDFGHKMNOQRSTVW**X**		6
2 EFGHOPQVWXY	ABDE**FG**H	7
3 BEFIL**M**QST ABCDEFJKNQRSTUV		8
4 BCDFHILNO**PQ**R**TXZ**	EJLMUVWY	9
5 ACDEFGHLM	ABGHIJMNPRZ	10

10A CEE
14ha 200T(80-170m²) 224P
❶ €25.90
❷ €40.00

🚗 In Pont-l'Abbé take the D785 towards Plomeur. Then the D57 to Guilvinec. Continue towards Penmarc'h. Campsite signposted from here.

💬 An exceptional location 'to get your feet wet'. This campsite will welcome you in an area of natural scenic beauty. A relaxing water complex and an enormous toddlers' pool for young families. NEW: our tree houses with sea views.

Pont-l'Abbé
D57
Penmarch D53
Λ

📍 N 47°48'14" W 4°18'44"

www.eurocampings.co.uk/100293

811 Plomeur, F-29120 / Bretagne ⚿ 📶 ✿ iD 41b

- 🏕 Camping de La Torche***
- 🏠 Roz An Tremen
- 📅 31 Mar - 14 Oct
- ☎ +33 (0)2-98586282
- @ info@campingdelatorche.fr

1 ADEJ**M**NOPRST	CDFGQSX	6
2 HPQVWXY	ABDE**FG**H	7
3 BELQST	ABCDEFNQRSV	8
4 BDILNO	EFJLUV	9
5 ABDFGHMNO	ABHIJLOSTV	10

6-10A CEE
4ha 92T(80-100m²) 58P
❶ €28.90
❷ €37.90

🚗 From Plomeur direction Pointe de la Torche. Turn left at the small campsite sign. Campsite on the right.

💬 The campsite is nearest to the famous surfing spot of 'La Torche'. Warm and friendly welcome. Possibility to fly your model airplanes, with demonstrations during the season.

Plonéour-Lanvern
D2
D57 D785
Penmarch
Λ

📍 N 47°49'58" W 4°19'33"

www.eurocampings.co.uk/103220

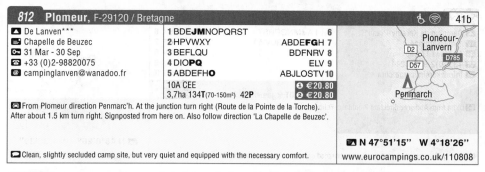

812 Plomeur, F-29120 / Bretagne   ♿ 🛜   41b

- ⛺ De Lanven***
- 🏕 Chapelle de Beuzec
- 📅 31 Mar - 30 Sep
- ☎ +33 (0)2-98820075
- @ campinglanven@wanadoo.fr

1 BDE**JM**NOPQRST		6
2 HPVWXY	ABDE**FG**H	7
3 BEFLQU	BDFNRV	8
4 DIO**PQ**	ELV	9
5 ABDEFH**O**	ABJLOSTV	10
10A CEE		€ €20.80
3,7ha 134T(70-150m²) 42P		€ €20.80

🚐 From Plomeur direction Penmarc'h. At the junction turn right (Route de la Pointe de la Torche). After about 1.5 km turn right. Signposted from here on. Also follow direction 'La Chapelle de Beuzec'.

💬 Clean, slightly secluded camp site, but very quiet and equipped with the necessary comfort.

📷 N 47°51'15''   W 4°18'26''

www.eurocampings.co.uk/110808

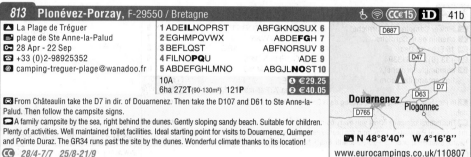

813 Plonévez-Porzay, F-29550 / Bretagne   ♿ 🛜 (CC€15) **iD** 41b

- ⛺ La Plage de Tréguer
- 🏕 plage de Ste Anne-la-Palud
- 📅 28 Apr - 22 Sep
- ☎ +33 (0)2-98925352
- @ camping-treguer-plage@wanadoo.fr

1 ADE**IL**NOPRST	ABFGKNQSUX	6
2 EGHMPQVWX	ABDE**FG**H	7
3 BEFLQST	ABFNORSUV	8
4 FILNO**PQ**U	ADE	9
5 ABDEFGHLMNO	ABGJL**NO**ST	10
10A		€ €29.25
6ha 272T(90-130m²) 121P		€ €40.05

🚐 From Châteaulin take the D7 in dir. of Douarnenez. Then take the D107 and D61 to Ste Anne-la-Palud. Then follow the campsite signs.

💬 A family campsite by the sea, right behind the dunes. Gently sloping sandy beach. Suitable for children. Plenty of activities. Well maintained toilet facilities. Ideal starting point for visits to Douarnenez, Quimper and Pointe Duraz. The GR34 runs past the site by the dunes. Wonderful climate thanks to its location!

CC 28/4-7/7   25/8-21/9

📷 N 48°8'40''   W 4°16'8''

www.eurocampings.co.uk/110807

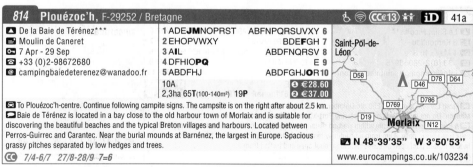

814 Plouézoc'h, F-29252 / Bretagne   ♿ 🛜 (CC€13) 🚻 **iD** 41a

- ⛺ De la Baie de Térénez***
- 🏕 Moulin de Caneret
- 📅 7 Apr - 29 Sep
- ☎ +33 (0)2-98672680
- @ campingbaiedeterenez@wanadoo.fr

1 ADE**JM**NOPRST	ABFNPQRSUVXY	6
2 EHOPVWXY	BDE**FG**H	7
3 A**I**L	ABDFNQRSV	8
4 DFHIO**PQ**	E	9
5 ABDFHJ	ABDFGHJ**OR**	10
10A		€ €28.60
2,3ha 65T(100-140m²) 19P		€ €37.00

🚐 To Plouézoc'h-centre. Continue following campsite signs. The campsite is on the right after about 2.5 km.

💬 Baie de Térénez is located in a bay close to the old harbour town of Morlaix and is suitable for discovering the beautiful beaches and the typical Breton villages and harbours. Located between Perros-Guirrec and Carantec. Near the burial mounds at Barnénez, the largest in Europe. Spacious grassy pitches separated by low hedges and trees.

CC 7/4-6/7   27/8-28/9   7=6

📷 N 48°39'35''   W 3°50'53''

www.eurocampings.co.uk/103234

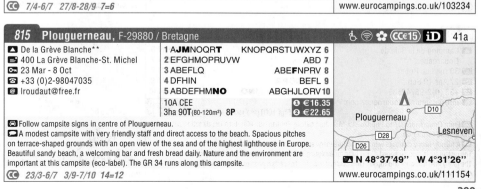

815 Plouguerneau, F-29880 / Bretagne   ♿ 🛜 ✿ (CC€15) **iD** 41a

- ⛺ De la Grève Blanche**
- 🏕 400 La Grève Blanche-St. Michel
- 📅 23 Mar - 8 Oct
- ☎ +33 (0)2-98047035
- @ lroudaut@free.fr

1 A**JM**NOQR**T**	KNOPQRSTUWXYZ	6
2 EFGHMOPRUVW	ABD	7
3 ABEFLQ	ABE**F**NPRV	8
4 DFHIN	BEFL	9
5 ABDEFHM**NO**	ABGHJLORV	10
10A CEE		€ €16.35
3ha 90T(80-120m²) 8P		€ €22.65

🚐 Follow campsite signs in centre of Plouguerneau.

💬 A modest campsite with very friendly staff and direct access to the beach. Spacious pitches on terrace-shaped grounds with an open view of the sea and of the highest lighthouse in Europe. Beautiful sandy beach, a welcoming bar and fresh bread daily. Nature and the environment are important at this campsite (eco-label). The GR 34 runs along this campsite.

CC 23/3-6/7   3/9-7/10   14=12

📷 N 48°37'49''   W 4°31'26''

www.eurocampings.co.uk/111154

France

816 Plouhinec, F-29780 / Bretagne — iD 41b

- ▲ Camping de Kersiny-Plage**
- ✉ 1 rue Nominoé
- 🗓 14 May - 17 Sep
- ☎ +33 (0)2-98708244
- @ info@kersinyplage.com

1	AJMNOPRST	KNOPQSX 6
2	EFHMPRUVWXY	BF 7
3	AL	ABCDFNRV 8
4	F	EJ 9
5	DMO	ABHIJPST 10
8A CEE		
1,9ha 80T(80-100m²) 6P		❶ €19.65
		❷ €30.05

D784 from Audierne direction Plouhinec. Follow the campsite signs there.

Very quiet, located directly by the sea, terraced campsite. Clean sanitary facilities.

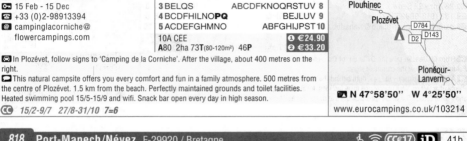

N 48°0'26" W 4°30'29"
www.eurocampings.co.uk/115641

817 Plozévet, F-29710 / Bretagne — iD 41b

- ▲ Flower Camping La Corniche***
- ✉ chemin de la Corniche
- 🗓 15 Feb - 15 Dec
- ☎ +33 (0)2-98913394
- @ campinglacorniche@flowercampings.com

1	ADEJMNOPQRST	ABFGX 6
2	FGOPRVWXY	ABEFGHK 7
3	BELQS	ABCDFKNOQRSTUV 8
4	BCDFHILNOPQ	BEJLUV 9
5	ACDEFGHMNO	ABFGHIJPST 10
10A CEE		
A80 2ha 73T(80-120m²) 46P		❶ €24.90
		❷ €33.20

In Plozévet, follow signs to 'Camping de la Corniche'. After the village, about 400 metres on the right.

This natural campsite offers you every comfort and fun in a family atmosphere. 500 metres from the centre of Plozévet. 1.5 km from the beach. Perfectly maintained grounds and toilet facilities. Heated swimming pool 15/5-15/9 and wifi. Snack bar open every day in high season.

CC 15/2-9/7 27/8-31/10 7=6

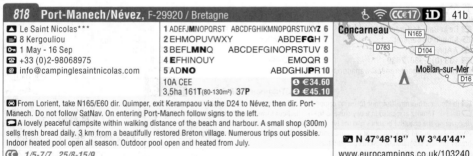

N 47°58'50" W 4°25'50"
www.eurocampings.co.uk/103214

818 Port-Manech/Névez, F-29920 / Bretagne — iD 41b

- ▲ Le Saint Nicolas***
- ✉ 8 Kergouliou
- 🗓 1 May - 16 Sep
- ☎ +33 (0)2-98068975
- @ info@campinglesaintnicolas.com

1	ADEFJMNOPQRST	ABCDFGHIKMNOPQRSTUXYZ 6
2	EHMOPUVWXY	ABDEFGH 7
3	BEFLMNQ	ABCDEFGINOPRSTUV 8
4	EFHINOUY	EMOQR 9
5	ADNO	ABDGHIJPR 10
10A CEE		
3,5ha 161T(80-130m²) 37P		❶ €34.60
		❷ €45.10

From Lorient, take N165/E60 dir. Quimper, exit Kerampaou via the D24 to Névez, then dir. Port-Manech. Do not follow SatNav. On entering Port-Manech follow signs to the left.

A lovely peaceful campsite within walking distance of the beach and harbour. A small shop (300m) sells fresh bread daily. 3 km from a beautifully restored Breton village. Numerous trips out possible. Indoor heated pool open all season. Outdoor pool open and heated from July.

CC 1/5-7/7 25/8-15/9

N 47°48'18" W 3°44'44"
www.eurocampings.co.uk/103240

819 Poullan-sur-Mer/Douarnenez, F-29100 / Bretagne — iD 41b

- ▲ Camping de la Baie de Douarnenez****
- ✉ 30 rue Luc Robet
- 🗓 27 Apr - 9 Sep
- ☎ +33 (0)2-98742639
- @ info@camping-douarnenez.com

1	ADEFJMNOPRST	ABEFGHN 6
2	PVX	ABDEFGH 7
3	BEILMQ	ABCDFNRS 8
4	ILNOPQ	AEFLU 9
5	ACDEFGHLMNO	ABGHJNPR 10
10A		
A70 5,5ha 100T(100-150m²) 101P		❶ €36.90
		❷ €42.90

From Douarnenez D7 to Poullan-sur-Mer. Just before Poullan-sur-Mer, turn left direction campsite. Signposted further on.

A friendly family campsite with plenty of greenery, spacious pitches and a lovely indoor swimming pool. The restaurant is recommended. Good base for exploring the beautiful surroundings, including by bike. The lovely little harbours and rugged cliffs contrast with sandy beaches and are a unique area for birdwatchers.

CC 27/4-6/7 26/8-8/9

N 48°4'54" W 4°24'24"
www.eurocampings.co.uk/103211

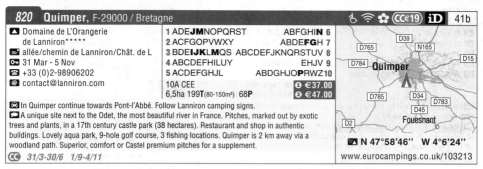

820 Quimper, F-29000 / Bretagne ♿ 📶 ❀ CC€19 iD 41b

Domaine de L'Orangerie de Lanniron***
allée/chemin de Lanniron/Chât. de L
31 Mar - 5 Nov
☎ +33 (0)2-98906202
@ contact@lanniron.com

1 ADEJMNOPQRST ABFGHIN 6
2 ACFGOPVWXY ABDEFGH 7
3 BDEIJKLMQS ABCDEFJKNQRSTUV 8
4 ABCDEFHILUY EHJV 9
5 ACDEFGHJL ABDGHJOPRWZ 10
10A CEE ❶ €37.00
6,5ha 199T(80-150m²) 68P ❷ €47.00

In Quimper continue towards Pont-l'Abbé. Follow Lanniron camping signs.
A unique site next to the Odet, the most beautiful river in France. Pitches, marked out by exotic trees and plants, in a 17th century castle park (38 hectares). Restaurant and shop in authentic buildings. Lovely aqua park, 9-hole golf course, 3 fishing locations. Quimper is 2 km away via a woodland path. Superior, comfort or Castel premium pitches for a supplement.
CC 31/3-30/6 1/9-4/11

N 47°58'46'' W 4°6'24''
www.eurocampings.co.uk/103213

821 Raguénès/Névez, F-29920 / Bretagne ♿ 📶 CC€17 iD 41b

Airotel Le Raguénès Plage**
19 rue des Îles
20 Apr - 1 Oct
☎ +33 (0)2-98068069
@ leraguenesplage@orange.fr

1 ADEJMNOPQRST ABCDFGHIKMNOPQSWXY 6
2 EFHMPVWXY ABDEFGH 7
3 BELQS CDEFIKNOQRSTUV 8
4 BCDFHILNOPQRT EUV 9
5 ACDEFGHJLNO ABDGHIJPR 10
6-15A CEE ❶ €40.70
7ha 218T(90-140m²) 105P ❷ €50.80

N165 Lorient-Quimper, exit Kerampaou and via D24/D77 to Névez. Then direction Raguénès-Plage. Well indicated after 3 km.
A lovely, luxurious campsite close to the sea. Choose a pitch with plenty of or little shade. There are a couple of nice walking and cycling routes close by. A lovely sandy beach 300 m away via a footpath. Indoor pool heated all season, outdoor pool heated from the end of May. Sea views from 15 of the pitches.
CC 20/4-9/7 27/8-30/9 7=6, 14=12

N 47°47'36'' W 3°48'3''
www.eurocampings.co.uk/108505

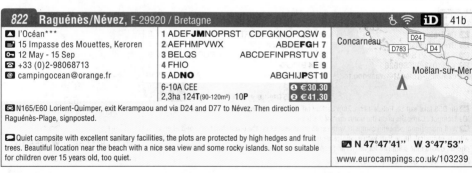

822 Raguénès/Névez, F-29920 / Bretagne ♿ 📶 iD 41b

l'Océan*
15 Impasse des Mouettes, Keroren
12 May - 15 Sep
☎ +33 (0)2-98068713
@ campingocean@orange.fr

1 ADEFJMNOPRST CDFGKNOPQSW 6
2 AEFHMPVWX ABDEFGH 7
3 BELQS ABCDEFINPRSTUV 8
4 FHIO E 9
5 ADNO ABGHIJPST 10
6-10A CEE ❶ €30.30
2,3ha 124T(90-120m²) 10P ❷ €41.30

N165/E60 Lorient-Quimper, exit Kerampaou and via D24 and D77 to Névez. Then direction Raguénès-Plage, signposted.

Quiet campsite with excellent sanitary facilities, the plots are protected by high hedges and fruit trees. Beautiful location near the beach with a nice sea view and some rocky islands. Not so suitable for children over 15 years old, too quiet.

N 47°47'41'' W 3°47'53''
www.eurocampings.co.uk/103239

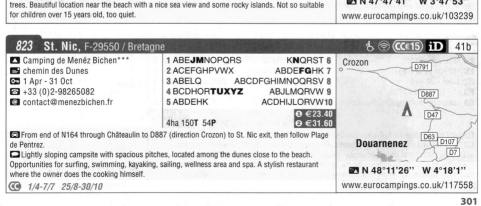

823 St. Nic, F-29550 / Bretagne ♿ 📶 CC€15 iD 41b

Camping de Menéz Bichen*
chemin des Dunes
1 Apr - 31 Oct
☎ +33 (0)2-98265082
@ contact@menezbichen.fr

1 ABEJMNOPQRS KNQRST 6
2 ACEFGHPVWX ABDEFGHK 7
3 ABELQ ABCDFGHIMNOQRSV 8
4 BCDHORTUXYZ ABJLMQRVW 9
5 ABDEHK ACDHIJLORVW 10
❶ €23.40
4ha 150T 54P ❷ €31.60

From end of N164 through Châteaulin to D887 (direction Crozon) to St. Nic exit, then follow Plage de Pentrez.
Lightly sloping campsite with spacious pitches, located among the dunes close to the beach. Opportunities for surfing, swimming, kayaking, sailing, wellness area and spa. A stylish restaurant where the owner does the cooking himself.
CC 1/4-7/7 25/8-30/10

N 48°11'26'' W 4°18'1''
www.eurocampings.co.uk/117558

France

824 St. Pol-de-Léon, F-29250 / Bretagne ♿ 🛜 ✿ (CC€17) iD 41a

- ⛺ Ar Kleguer****
- 📧 avenue de la Mer
- 📅 31 Mar - 23 Sep
- ☎ +33 (0)2-98691881
- @ info@camping-ar-kleguer.com

1 ADEJMNOQRST	ABEFHKNOQRSTWXYZ 6
2 EFGHPUVWX	ABDEFGHK 7
3 BCEFIKLMQS	ABCDFGHIJNQRS 8
4 BDFIKOPQV	EJKLUV 9
5 ABCDEHJLM	ABDGHJLOPST 10

Ad on this page 10A
5,5ha 132T(90-120m²) 50P
- ❶ €32.45
- ❷ €43.65

🗺 On the D58, take exit St. Pol-de-Léon and follow 'camping' and 'plage' signs. Don't use SatNav from Roscoff or Landivisian.
💬 Unique location, luxury 4-star campsite with lovely views of the bay of Morlaix and the many islands near St. Pol-de-Léon. Restaurant within walking distance. Spacious modern toilet facilities and a lovely indoor pool. The subtropical plants growing on the site will delight you. 5 km from the lovely town of Roscoff.

CC 31/3-6/7 27/8-22/9

Saint-Pol-de-Léon △ Carantec
D10 D58
D69 D46
D19 D769

📷 N 48°41'26'' W 3°58'3''
www.eurocampings.co.uk/103235

Ar Kleguer ★ ★ ★

The campsite is just 5 km from the Roscoff ferry.

Wonderful location with immediate access to the sea. Heated outdoor swimming pool with 2 large slides. New: an indoor swimming pool. New: spacious and heated bathroom facilities. Wi-Fi throughout the campsite (for a fee). Free Wi-Fi point.

**Avenue de la Mer
29250 St. Pol-de-Léon
Tel. 02-98691881
E-mail: info@camping-ar-kleguer.com
Internet: www.camping-ar-kleguer.com**

825 St. Pol-de-Léon, F-29250 / Bretagne ♿ 🛜 (CC€15) iD 41a

- ⛺ De Trologot***
- 📧 Grève du Man
- 📅 1 May - 30 Sep
- ☎ +33 (0)2-98690626
- @ camping-trologot@wanadoo.fr

1 ADEJMNOPQRT	ABFGKNOQSUWXY 6
2 EHJMPVX	ABDEFGH 7
3 BLQT	ABCDFNOPRSV 8
4 BFIOQ	E 9
5 ABDHJNO	ABHJOSTX 10

10A CEE
2,5ha 85T(80-100m²) 15P
- ❶ €24.50
- ❷ €32.75

🗺 On D58 take exit St. Pol-de-Léon. Turn SatNav off. Follow 'camping' and 'plage' signs. Then follow 'De Trologot'. Campsite is on the north east of the town.
💬 Well maintained, peaceful campsite with excellent amenities on the coast. Near St. Pol-de-Léon with its cathedral, Île de Batz with exotic gardens and Roscoff with its ferries. Extra service: special pitches outside the campsite for arrival and departure outside reception opening times.

CC 1/5-8/7 26/8-29/9 7=6, 14=12

Roscoff
Saint-Pol-de-Léon △
D58
D788 D46
D19 D58

📷 N 48°41'36'' W 3°58'10''
www.eurocampings.co.uk/114302

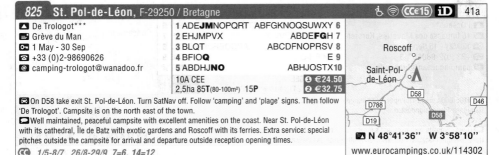

826 Telgruc-sur-Mer, F-29560 / Bretagne ♿ 🛜 (CC€15) iD 41b

- ⛺ Armorique****
- 📧 112 rue de la Plage
- 📅 1 Apr - 30 Sep
- ☎ +33 (0)2-98277733
- @ contact@campingarmorique.com

1 ADEJMNOPRT	ABFGHX 6
2 FGHMPUVWXY	ABDEFGH 7
3 BLQS	ABCDEFNQRSV 8
4 FHILNOQ	EFJ 9
5 ABDEFHMN	ABDGHIJNOR 10

10A CEE
A130 3ha 100T(80-120m²) 39P
- ❶ €26.55
- ❷ €35.15

🗺 D887 from Châteaulin to Crozon. Campsite is clearly marked in Telgruc.
💬 Peaceful terraced campsite with heated swimming pool (approx. 27°C), children's pool and water slide (12 m) with unique views over the bay of Douarnenez. Sandy beaches within 700 m. The campsite is run by an enthusiastic couple with a passion for hygiene (toilets cleaned 3 times a day). Park-like entrance. In the centre of unspoiled scenery. The campsite is easily accessible.

CC 1/4-7/7 25/8-29/9 7=6

Crozon
Telgruc-sur-Mer △
N165
D791
D887
D47
D63

📷 N 48°13'32'' W 4°22'17''
www.eurocampings.co.uk/103207

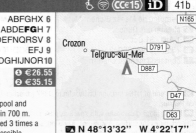

827 Telgruc-sur-Mer, F-29560 / Bretagne   ♿ 📶 ✿ (CC€15) iD   41b

- Sites & Paysages Le Panoramic****
- 130 route de la Plage le Penker
- 1 May - 16 Sep
- +33 (0)2-98277841
- info@camping-panoramic.com

1 ADE**JM**NOPRST	ABFGQRSTUVX	6
2 FPRUVX	BE**FG**H	7
3 BL**MQ**	BDEFNOQRSTUV	8
4 FHIOU	EHLUV	9
5 ABDEFGHKLM**NO**	ABDFGHJNORV	10
10A CEE		❶ €27.60
A70 4ha 127T(100-160m²) 43P		❷ €35.60

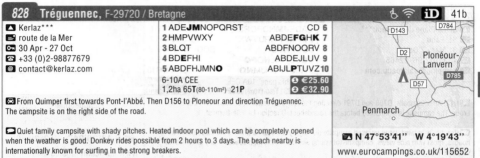

N165 — Crozon ○ Telgruc-sur-Mer — D791 — D887 — D47 — D63

From Châteaulin, the D887, direction Crozon. In Telgruc continue straight ahead. The campsite is signposted.
A peaceful family campsite with plenty of privacy. Views of Douarnenez Bay in the middle of the regional nature park of Armorique. 500 m from a lovely sandy beach. Plenty of opportunities for taking walks. The heated swimming pool is open from 1 June.

(CC) 1/5-7/7 25/8-15/9 7=6

N 48°13'25'' W 4°22'21''
www.eurocampings.co.uk/103206

828 Tréguennec, F-29720 / Bretagne   ♿ 📶 iD   41b

- Kerlaz***
- route de la Mer
- 30 Apr - 27 Oct
- +33 (0)2-98877679
- contact@kerlaz.com

1 ADE**JM**NOPQRST	CD	6
2 HMPVWXY	ABDE**FGH**K	7
3 BLQT	ABDFNOQRV	8
4 BD**E**FHI	ABDEJLUV	9
5 ABDFHJMN**O**	ABIJL**P**TUVZ	10
6-10A CEE		❶ €25.60
1,2ha 65T(80-110m²) 21P		❷ €32.90

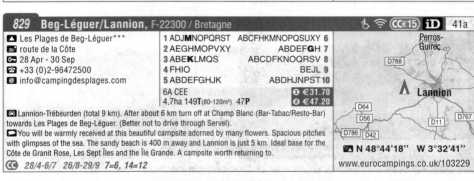

D143 — D784 — D2 — Plonéour-Lanvern — D785 — D57 — Penmarch ○

From Quimper first towards Pont-l'Abbé. Then D156 to Ploneour and direction Tréguennec. The campsite is on the right side of the road.

Quiet family campsite with shady pitches. Heated indoor pool which can be completely opened when the weather is good. Donkey rides possible from 2 hours to 3 days. The beach nearby is internationally known for surfing in the strong breakers.

N 47°53'41'' W 4°19'43''
www.eurocampings.co.uk/115652

829 Beg-Léguer/Lannion, F-22300 / Bretagne   ♿ 📶 (CC€15) iD   41a

- Les Plages de Beg-Léguer***
- route de la Côte
- 28 Apr - 30 Sep
- +33 (0)2-96472500
- info@campingdesplages.com

1 ADJ**M**NOPQRST	ABCFHKMNOPQSUXY	6
2 AEGHMOPVXY	ABDEFGH	7
3 ABE**K**LMQS	ABCDFKNOQRSV	8
4 FHIO	BEJL	9
5 ABDEFGHJK	ABDHJNPST	10
6A CEE		❶ €31.70
4,7ha 149T(80-120m²) 47P		❷ €47.20

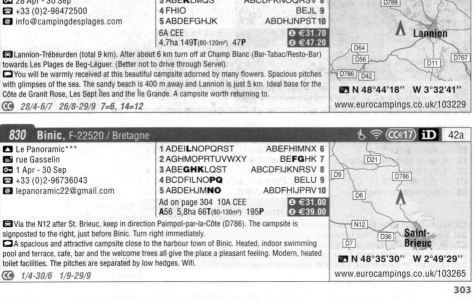

Perros-Guirec ○ — D788 — Lannion — D64 — D56 — D11 — D767 — D786 — D42

Lannion-Trébeurden (total 9 km). After about 6 km turn off at Champ Blanc (Bar-Tabac/Resto-Bar) towards Les Plages de Beg-Léguer. (Better not to drive through Servel).
You will be warmly received at this beautiful campsite adorned by many flowers. Spacious pitches with glimpses of the sea. The sandy beach is 400 m away and Lannion is just 5 km. Ideal base for the Côte de Granit Rose, Les Sept Îles and the Île Grande. A campsite worth returning to.

(CC) 28/4-6/7 26/8-29/9 7=6, 14=12

N 48°44'18'' W 3°32'41''
www.eurocampings.co.uk/103229

830 Binic, F-22520 / Bretagne   ♿ 📶 (CC€17) iD   42a

- Le Panoramic***
- rue Gasselin
- 1 Apr - 30 Sep
- +33 (0)2-96736043
- lepanoramic22@gmail.com

1 ADE**IL**NOPQRST	ABEFHIMNX	6
2 AGHMOPRTUVWXY	BE**FG**HK	7
3 ABE**GHK**LQST	ABCDFIJKNRSV	8
4 BCDFILNO**PQ**	BELU	9
5 ABDEHJM**NO**	ABDFHIJPRV	10
Ad on page 304 10A CEE		❶ €31.00
A56 5,8ha 66T(80-130m²) 195P		❷ €39.00

D21 — D9 — D786 — D6 — N12 — D36 — D7 — Saint-Brieuc

Via the N12 after St. Brieuc, keep in direction Paimpol-par-la-Côte (D786). The campsite is signposted to the right, just before Binic. Turn right immediately.
A spacious and attractive campsite close to the harbour town of Binic. Heated, indoor swimming pool and terrace, cafe, bar and the welcome trees all give the place a pleasant feeling. Modern, heated toilet facilities. The pitches are separated by low hedges. Wifi.

(CC) 1/4-30/6 1/9-29/9

N 48°35'30'' W 2°49'29''
www.eurocampings.co.uk/103265

Le Panoramic ★ ★ ★

- Ideal family campsite
- Indoor swimming pool with aquapark
- Entertainment in high season
- 500m from sandy beach and port from Binic
- Mobile home rental
- Wifi

**Rue Gasselin, 22520 Binic
Tel. 02-96736043
E-mail: lepanoramic22@gmail.com
Internet: www.lepanoramic.net**

---

831 Erquy, F-22430 / Bretagne   ♿ 🛜 **iD** 42a

🔺 de La Plage de St. Pabu***
🏠 St. Pabu
📅 31 Mar - 7 Oct
☎ +33 (0)2-96722465
@ camping@saintpabu.com

1 ADE**JM**NOPQRST	KNQSWXY	6
2 EFGHPQRUVWX	ABDE**FG**H	7
3 BEF**K**LQT	BCDFNRSTUV	8
4 BCDFHILNO**PQ**	E	9
5 ACDEFGHJM**NO**	ABGHIJOR	10

Ad on this page 10A CEE
5,5ha 331T(80-110m²) 39P
❶ €27.40
❷ €36.00

🗺 N12. After Lamballe, D768 and D791 direction Pléneuf-Val-André. At St. Alban D17a direction Erquy. The campsite is signposted before the roundabout. Direction La Ville-Berneuf.

💬 Beautifully located, large terraced campsite directly by the sea. All pitches are surrounded by hedges, most with nice views. Campsite for young and old. In the high season many activities for children. Free wifi.

Les-Sables-d'Or-les-Pins
Pléneuf-Val-André D34 D786
Planguenoual D13 D17
D791 D768

📍 N 48°36'24'' W 2°29'48''
www.eurocampings.co.uk/103268

Côtes d'Armor
Bretagne

Located in a green and tranquil area, with immediate access to the beach with various options for sports and water sports.

GPS: N 48°36'24'' W 2°29'48''

St. Pabu, 22430 Erquy • Tel. 02-96722465 • Fax 02-96728717
E-mail: camping@saintpabu.com • Internet: www.saintpabu.com

---

832 Erquy, F-22430 / Bretagne   ♿ 🛜 (CC€17) ♂♀ **iD** 42a

🔺 Des Hautes Grées***
🏠 123 rue St. Michel les Hôpitaux
📅 1 Apr - 1 Oct
☎ +33 (0)2-96723478
@ hautesgrees@wanadoo.fr

1 ADE**JM**NOPQRST	ABFGKNOPQRSTVXY**Z**	6
2 EGHJMOPRSVX	ABDE**FG**HJK	7
3 ABEF**GHJK**LQ	ABCDFHINOQRSV	8
4 ABCDEFHILNORTV**X**	EL	9
5 ABDEFGJKM**NO**	ABDGHIJL**P**RVW	10

10A CEE
3,5ha 177T(80-98m²) 33P
❶ €29.60
❷ €39.40

🗺 Campsite located east of Erquy. At roundabout south-west of Erquy, where the D781 becomes the D34, direction 'Les Hôpitaux'. Then follow signs.
💬 Quiet, well maintained family campsite. Spaciously appointed, generous pitches, lots of flowers. Heated pool, 400 m from the beach. Close to fishing harbour, good base for anglers. Ideal for young families, but also for people seeking some peace and quiet in the low seasons.

CC 1/4-7/7 25/8-30/9

Pléneuf-Val-André D34
D786 D17 D13 D794

📍 N 48°38'31'' W 2°25'27''
www.eurocampings.co.uk/113338

833 Erquy, F-22430 / Bretagne ♿ 📶 (CC€13) ⚥ iD 42a

- 🏠 Les Roches***
- 🏢 rue Pierre Vergos
- 📅 1 Apr - 30 Sep
- ☎ +33 (0)2-96723290
- @ jessica.lesroches@gmail.com

1 ADEJMNOPQRST	X 6
2 FGHMOPRSUVWXY	ABDEFGH 7
3 ABCEFHIKLQST	ABCDFJKNRSV 8
4 BDFIOQ	EL 9
5 ABDFGMNO	ABDGHIJNPR 10

6-10A CEE ❶ €22.20
A60 3ha 175T(80-120m²) 18P ❷ €28.20

🅲 Campsite located between Erquy and Pléneuf-Val-André, D786. Follow signs, well indicated.

💬 In the middle of farmland, this peaceful campsite is 900 m from the sea. The grounds are surrounded by tall hedges. Plenty of shelter from the wind. Lovely pitches with panoramic views of the sea. Modern toilet facilities provided. Free wifi.

CC 1/4-7/7 25/8-29/9

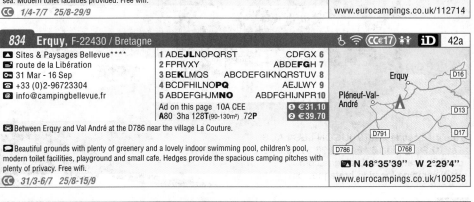

📍 N 48°36'37'' W 2°28'33''

www.eurocampings.co.uk/112714

---

834 Erquy, F-22430 / Bretagne ♿ 📶 (CC€17) ⚥ iD 42a

- 🏠 Sites & Paysages Bellevue****
- 🏢 route de la Libération
- 📅 31 Mar - 16 Sep
- ☎ +33 (0)2-96723304
- @ info@campingbellevue.fr

1 ADEJLNOPQRST	CDFGX 6
2 FPRVXY	ABDEFGH 7
3 BEKLMQS	ABCDEFGIKNQRSTUV 8
4 BCDFHILNOPQ	AEJLWY 9
5 ABDEFGHJMNO	ABDFGHIJNPR 10

Ad on this page 10A CEE ❶ €31.10
A80 3ha 128T(90-130m²) 72P ❷ €39.70

🅲 Between Erquy and Val André at the D786 near the village La Couture.

💬 Beautiful grounds with plenty of greenery and a lovely indoor swimming pool, children's pool, modern toilet facilities, playground and small cafe. Hedges provide the spacious camping pitches with plenty of privacy. Free wifi.

CC 31/3-6/7 25/8-15/9

📍 N 48°35'39'' W 2°29'4''

www.eurocampings.co.uk/100258

A magnificent 3-hectare terrain on a higher altitude, with an indoor heated swimming pool, toddlers' pool, modern toilet facilities and playground. Hedges provide the spacious pitches with plenty of privacy. Free wifi.

Route de la Libération, 22430 Erquy
Tel. 02-96723304
E-mail: info@campingbellevue.fr
Internet: www.campingbellevue.fr

---

835 Jugon-les-Lacs, F-22270 / Bretagne ♿ 📶 (CC€17) iD 42a

- 🏠 Au Bocage du Lac****
- 🏢 rue du Bocage
- 📅 7 Apr - 15 Sep
- ☎ +33 (0)2-96316016
- @ contact@campinglacbretagne.com

1 ADJMNOPRT	ABEFGHINQRSTX 6
2 ADGIPVXY	ABDEFGH 7
3 ABEFHILMQR	ABCDEFKNOQRSV 8
4 EFILNOPQR	EIJLQUV 9
5 ACDEFGHKN	ABFGHIJLNOSTVZ 10

Ad on page 306 10A CEE ❶ €31.50
7ha 183T(100-180m²) 58P ❷ €42.50

🅲 N176 exit Jugon-les-Lacs. The campsite is clearly signposted and is on the Jugon-les-Lacs to Mégrit road (D52).

💬 A pleasant rural family campsite with safe direct access to a 70-hectare lake. A paradise for anglers. For those who like lazing around there is a heated indoor and outdoor swimming pool with a slide and a toddlers' pool.

CC 7/4-30/6 1/9-14/9

📍 N 48°24'6'' W 2°19'0''

www.eurocampings.co.uk/111728

Camping Qualité
Au Bocage du Lac ★★★★ Bretagne

Rue du Bocage 22270 JUGON-LES-LACS
Tél. 02.96.31.60.16 / Fax 02.96.31.75.04
contact@campinglacbretagne.com
www.camping-location-bretagne.com

CAMPING Qualité
L'ENGAGEMENT QUALITÉ PARTAGÉ PAR TOUS

---

836 Lancieux, F-22770 / Bretagne ♿ 📶 **iD** 43a

🏕 Le Villeu***
✉ rue des Bénédictins
🗓 1 Apr - 30 Sep
☎ +33 (0)2-96862167
@ camping.levilleu@orange.fr

1 ADE**JM**NOPRST	NQRSTX	6
2 HMPVWX	ABDE**FG**H	7
3 ABE**HK**LMQ	ABCDEFGKNQRSV	8
4 BFHNO**PX**	ELV	9
5 ABDEFHJM**NO**	ABHIJLOSTW	10
10A CEE	❶ €24.90	
5ha 140**T**(90-110m²) 35**P**	❷ €29.50	

🗺 Via the reservoir at Dinard D168, then D603. In St. Briac over a bridge. Then D786, through Lancieux to a windmill: turn right, drive downhill and straight ahead over the crossroads. Campsite on the left.

💬 A lovely campsite with hedges and trees. Each small plot contains 4 pitches. The campsite is close to a protected dune area with unique beach. Renovated toilet facilities, fishing lake, multi-sports ground: basketball, tennis, football, handball and volleyball.

Saint-Malo
Dinard
D16 D786 D19 D13 D794 D2 D17 D768 N176 D792

📍 N 48°35'54'' W 2°9'25''
www.eurocampings.co.uk/111485

---

837 Lanloup/Paimpol, F-22580 / Bretagne ♿ 📶 (CC€17) ⚤ **iD** 42a

🏕 Le Neptune****
✉ Ker Guistin
🗓 2 Apr - 5 Oct
☎ +33 (0)2-96223335
@ contact@leneptune.com

1 ADE**IL**NOPQRST	CDOUX	6
2 GHJMOPRVWXY	ABDE**FG**H	7
3 BE**KL**Q	BDFJNOQRSTUV	8
4 BCDFHIKNO**P**	EJL	9
5 ACDEFHKM**NO**	ABDGHIJLN**PR**	10
Ad on page 307 10A CEE	❶ €31.50	
A59 1,5ha 57**T**(80-120m²) 22**P**	❷ €42.00	

🗺 From Plouha direction Lanloup. Follow signs for campsite.

💬 A hospitable natural campsite with a heated indoor swimming pool. Pleasantly small-scale. Pitches with plenty of privacy. 1 hour free wifi per day.

CC 2/4-6/7 25/8-4/10

Paimpol
D786 D7 D6 D21
Étables-sur-Mer

📍 N 48°42'49'' W 2°58'1''
www.eurocampings.co.uk/100255

838 Lantic, F-22410 / Bretagne

(CC€13) iD 42a

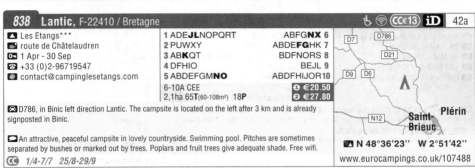

Les Etangs***
route de Châtelaudren
1 Apr - 30 Sep
+33 (0)2-96719547
contact@campinglesetangs.com

1 ADE**JL**NOPQRT	ABFG**NX** 6
2 PUWXY	ABDE**FG**HK 7
3 AB**K**QT	BDFNORS 8
4 DFHIO	BEJL 9
5 ABDEFGM**NO**	ABDFHIJOR 10
6-10A CEE	❶ €20.50
2,1ha 65T(60-108m²) 18P	❷ €27.80

D786, in Binic left direction Lantic. The campsite is located on the left after 3 km and is already signposted in Binic.

An attractive, peaceful campsite in lovely countryside. Swimming pool. Pitches are sometimes separated by bushes or marked out by trees. Poplars and fruit trees give adequate shade. Free wifi.

CC *1/4-7/7 25/8-29/9*

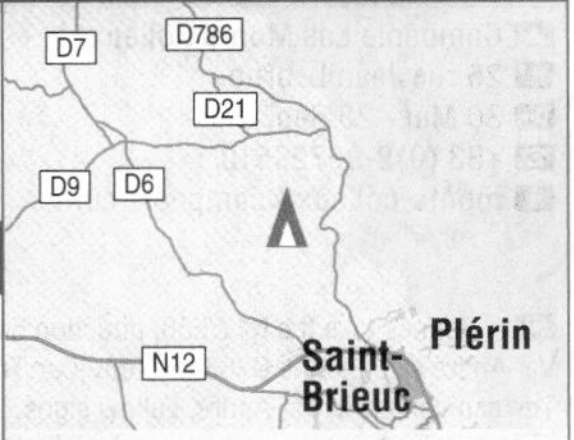

N 48°36'23" W 2°51'42"
www.eurocampings.co.uk/107488

839 Loudéac, F-22600 / Bretagne

(CC€15) iD 13 A3

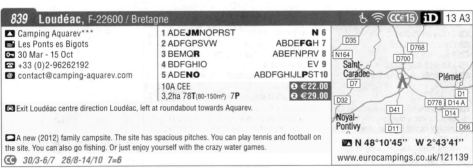

Camping Aquarev***
Les Ponts es Bigots
30 Mar - 15 Oct
+33 (0)2-96262192
contact@camping-aquarev.com

1 ADE**JM**NOPRST	**N** 6
2 ADFGPSVW	ABDE**FG**H 7
3 BEMQ**R**	ABEFNPRV 8
4 BDFGHIO	EV 9
5 ADE**NO**	ABDFGHIJL**P**ST 10
10A CEE	❶ €22.00
3,2ha 78T(80-150m²) 7P	❷ €29.00

Exit Loudéac centre direction Loudéac, left at roundabout towards Aquarev.

A new (2012) family campsite. The site has spacious pitches. You can play tennis and football on the site. You can also go fishing. Or just enjoy yourself with the crazy water games.

CC *30/3-6/7 26/8-14/10 7=6*

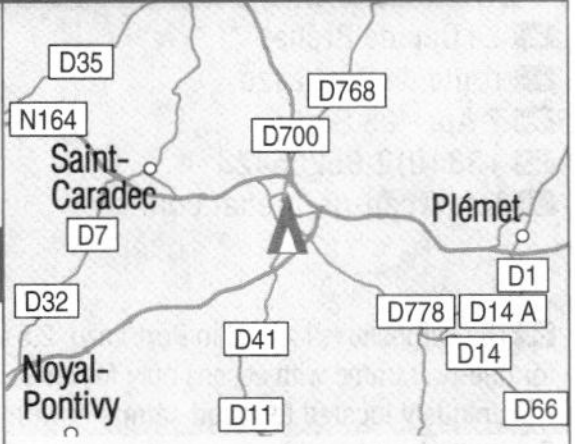

N 48°10'45" W 2°43'41"
www.eurocampings.co.uk/121139

840 Matignon, F-22550 / Bretagne

(CC€13) iD 42a

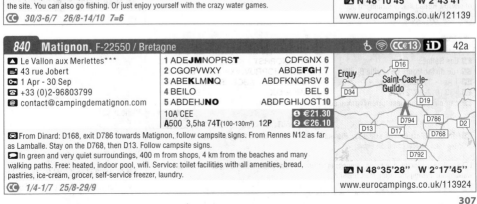

Le Vallon aux Merlettes***
43 rue Jobert
1 Apr - 30 Sep
+33 (0)2-96803799
contact@campingdematignon.com

1 ADE**JM**NOPRS**T**	CDFGNX 6
2 CGOPVWXY	ABDE**FG**H 7
3 ABE**K**LM**N**Q	ABDFKNQRSV 8
4 BEILO	BEL 9
5 ABDEHJ**NO**	ABDFGHIJOST 10
10A CEE	❶ €21.30
A500 3,5ha 74T(100-130m²) 12P	❷ €26.10

From Dinard: D168, exit D786 towards Matignon, follow campsite signs. From Rennes N12 as far as Lamballe. Stay on the D768, then D13. Follow campsite signs.

In green and very quiet surroundings, 400 m from shops, 4 km from the beaches and many walking paths. Free: heated, indoor pool, wifi. Service: toilet facilities with all amenities, bread, pastries, ice-cream, grocer, self-service freezer, laundry.

CC *1/4-1/7 25/8-29/9*

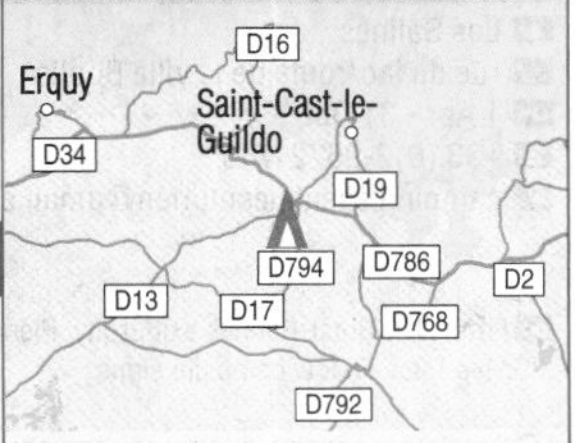

N 48°35'28" W 2°17'45"
www.eurocampings.co.uk/113924

France

841 Pléboulle, F-22550 / Bretagne
   🔥 ⌖ (CC€11) ♦♦ iD 42a

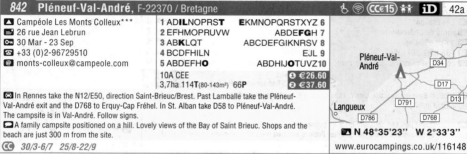

🏕 Le Frêche à l'Âne***
📧 Le Bourg, 6 rue du Champ St. Paul
📅 1 Apr - 31 Oct
☎ +33 (0)2-96410872
@ info@camping-frechealane.com

1 ADE**JM**NOPQRST	X	6
2 FGOPUVWXY	ABDE**FG**HIJK	7
3 ABC**KL**Q	BDFGHNRSV	8
4 FHI**Q**	BEU	9
5 ABDFJN**O**	ABDGHIJOSTZ	10
6-10A CEE	❶ €16.10	
2ha 66**T**(100-200m²) 13**P**	❷ €19.70	

🚗 Coming from Matignon. D786 direction Fréhel, turn left onto D16. Follow signs.

💬 Welcoming, hospitable campsite in the middle of the green Breton countryside. Lovely sandy beaches nearby plus tourist attractions such as Cap Fréhel, Fort de Latte, Dinan.
(CC) 1/4-7/7 25/8-30/10

📷 N 48°36'32'' W 2°20'13''
www.eurocampings.co.uk/119063

842 Pléneuf-Val-André, F-22370 / Bretagne
   🔥 ⌖ (CC€15) ♦♦ iD 42a

🏕 Campéole Les Monts Colleux***
📧 26 rue Jean Lebrun
📅 30 Mar - 23 Sep
☎ +33 (0)2-96729510
@ monts-colleux@campeole.com

1 AD**IL**NOPRS**T**	E**KM**NOPQRSTXYZ	6
2 EFHMOPRUVW	ABDE**FG**H	7
3 AB**KL**QT	ABCDEFGIKNRSV	8
4 BCDFHILN	EJL	9
5 ABDEFH**O**	ABDHIJ**O**TUVZ	10
10A CEE	❶ €26.60	
3,7ha 114**T**(80-143m²) 66**P**	❷ €37.60	

🚗 In Rennes take the N12/E50, direction Saint-Brieuc/Brest. Past Lamballe take the Pléneuf-Val-André exit and the D768 to Erquy-Cap Fréhel. In St. Alban take D58 to Pléneuf-Val-André. The campsite is in Val-André. Follow signs.
💬 A family campsite positioned on a hill. Lovely views of the Bay of Saint Brieuc. Shops and the beach are just 300 m from the site.
(CC) 30/3-6/7 25/8-22/9

📷 N 48°35'23'' W 2°33'3''
www.eurocampings.co.uk/116148

843 Plouézec/Paimpol, F-22470 / Bretagne
   🔥 ⌖ (CC€17) iD 42a

🏕 Le Cap de Bréhat****
📧 route de Port Lazo
📅 7 Apr - 23 Sep
☎ +33 (0)2-96206428
@ info@cap-de-brehat.com

1 ACDEF**IL**NOPRST	CDFGKNPQSUW**XYZ**	6
2 EFGJMPRSUVX	ABDE**FG**HK	7
3 BCE**KL**MQSTUV	ABCDFHIJKNQRSTUV	8
4 DEFGHIO**P**	BE	9
5 ABCDEFGHJKM**NO**	ABDFGHIJO**P**ST	10
16A CEE	❶ €32.70	
A55 5ha 95**T**(80-110m²) 51**P**	❷ €42.20	

🚗 The campsite is located in Port-Lazo, 2.5 km from the D786. Follow the signs carefully; also the signs for one-way traffic with access only for residents and the campsite. (In other words, ignore the No Entry!)
💬 Uniquely located terraced campsite with unforgettable views of the sea and the Isle de Bréhat. Oyster beds at low tide. Direct access to sea and the GR34. Pitches are well secluded and offer plenty of privacy. Heated indoor swimming pool.
(CC) 7/4-7/7 25/8-22/9 7=6

📷 N 48°45'35'' W 2°57'44''
www.eurocampings.co.uk/103261

844 Plurien/Sables d'Or-les-Pins, F-22240 / Bretagne
   🔥 ⌖ (CC€13) iD 42a

🏕 Les Salines
📧 rue du lac/route de la ville Boulin
📅 1 Apr - 31 Oct
☎ +33 (0)2-96721740
@ campinglessalinesplurien@gmail.com

1 ADJLNOPRST	KMNOPQRSTVW**XYZ**	6
2 CEGHIMOPRUVWXY	ABDE**FG**HIJK	7
3 AB**HK**LQ	ABCDEFGHKNOPRSUV	8
4 AE**F**HIO**X**	BDELUVW	9
5 ABDHJM**O**	ABDGHIJ**O**STV	10
6A CEE	❶ €16.10	
4,2ha 150**T** 17**P**	❷ €22.00	

🚗 From N12 Brest-Rennes exit Erquy, Pléneuf-Val-André. 2 km before Erquy exit Cap Fréhel, Sables d'Or-les-Pins. Follow campsite signs.

💬 Spaciously appointed terraced campsite in natural surroundings. Close to lagoon area. Beautiful walking and cycling trips from the campsite.
(CC) 1/4-7/7 25/8-30/10

📷 N 48°37'55'' W 2°24'49''
www.eurocampings.co.uk/115593

845 Pordic, F-22590 / Bretagne

⛵ 📶 (CC€15) iD · 42a

- 🏔 Les Madières***
- 🏠 Le Vau-Madec
- 🔓 9 Apr - 21 Oct
- ☎ +33 (0)2-96790248
- @ campinglesmadieres@wanadoo.fr

1 ADEJ**M**NOPRST	ABNQSTUVX	6
2 AFGHJMOPVWXY	ABDE**FGH**	7
3 ABELQ	ABCDFJNOPRSV	8
4 FHIO	DEL	9
5 ABDEFGHJ**NO**	ABDFGHIJLPR	10

10A CEE · 🔌 €25.70
A79 2ha 75**T**(90-300m²) 13**P** · 🔌 €35.70

🚗 N12, after Plérin exit Les Rampes to Pordic. D786 to Pordic. In Pordic follow centre, then 'campings' signs. Well signposted.

💬 Beautifully appointed and well maintained site with renovated toilet facilities (2014). Relaxing atmosphere in park-like surroundings. Lovely pool in Spanish style. Attractive small restaurant. Natural layout of the grounds, no permanent pitches. Very suitable for hikers. 10 minutes from sea. Free wifi.

CC 9/4-30/6 1/9-20/10

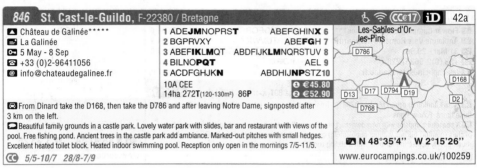

🧭 N 48°34'58'' W 2°48'17''

www.eurocampings.co.uk/103266

---

846 St. Cast-le-Guildo, F-22380 / Bretagne

⛵ 📶 (CC€17) iD · 42a

- 🏔 Château de Galinée*****
- 🏠 La Galinée
- 🔓 5 May - 8 Sep
- ☎ +33 (0)2-96411056
- @ info@chateaudegalinee.fr

1 ADEJ**M**NOPRS**T**	ABEFGHIN**X**	6
2 BGPRVXY	ABE**FGH**	7
3 ABEF**IKLMQ**T	ABDFIJK**LM**NQRSTUV	8
4 BILNO**PQT**	AEL	9
5 ACDFGHJK**N**	ABDHIJ**NP**STZ	10

10A CEE · 🔌 €45.80
14ha 272**T**(120-130m²) 86**P** · 🔌 €52.90

🚗 From Dinard take the D168, then take the D786 and after leaving Notre Dame, signposted after 3 km on the left.

💬 Beautiful family grounds in a castle park. Lovely water park with slides, bar and restaurant with views of the pool. Free fishing pond. Ancient trees in the castle park add ambiance. Marked-out pitches with small hedges. Excellent heated toilet block. Heated indoor swimming pool. Reception only open in the mornings 7/5-11/5.

CC 5/5-10/7 28/8-7/9

🧭 N 48°35'4'' W 2°15'26''

www.eurocampings.co.uk/100259

France

---

847 St. Cast-le-Guildo, F-22380 / Bretagne

⛵ 📶 (CC€19) 👫 iD · 42a

- 🏔 Le Chatelet*****
- 🏠 rue des Nouettes
- 🔓 16 Apr - 14 Sep
- ☎ +33 (0)2-96419633
- @ lechateletcamping@gmail.com

1 ADE**JM**NOPRS**T**	CDFGKNOPQRST**XY**	6
2 EFHMPRUVWXY	ABDE**FGH**IJ	7
3 ABE**GHK**LQ	ABCDFGJKNPQRSTUV	8
4 BCDEFHILNO**PQXZ**	BEL	9
5 ACDFGHM**N**	ABDGHIJ**P**STZ	10

8A CEE · 🔌 €41.70
9ha 105**T**(80-120m²) 171**P** · 🔌 €52.70

🚗 D786, first drive to Matignon. Then, D13 to St. Cast-le-Guildo. After supermarket and garage, turn left dir. 'le Port'. Campsite is signposted. Avoid driving through the centre of St. Cast-le-Guildo.

💬 Lush campsite with beautiful sea views and unique location. Fine sandy beach nearby. Large pool with cover, surrounded by terraces. Fishing lake, friendly clubhouse with bar. Many activities. Pitches are marked by trees, hedges and bushes.

CC 16/4-7/7 25/8-13/9

🧭 N 48°38'14'' W 2°16'10''

www.eurocampings.co.uk/101446

---

848 St. Quay-Portrieux, F-22410 / Bretagne

⛵ 📶 (CC€17) iD · 42a

- 🏔 Bellevue***
- 🏠 68 boulevard du Littoral
- 🔓 19 Apr - 18 Sep
- ☎ +33 (0)2-96704184
- @ campingbellevue22@orange.fr

1 ADE**JL**NOPRST	ABFGKNQSTXY	6
2 EFHKMPRTUVWX	ABDE**FGH**	7
3 BEKLQ	ABCDFKNOPQRSTUV	8
4 FO	EL	9
5 ABDFMN**O**	ABGHIJLMPST	10

6A CEE · 🔌 €25.00
4ha 151**T**(80-120m²) 17**P** · 🔌 €33.00

🚗 From Étables-sur-Mer follow the D786 dir. Paimpol, 50 metres after the second roundabout to the right. Exit Centre Ville. Continue straight to the beach and Casino. Turn left, continue straight and follow signs.

💬 Uniquely located terraced site, lovely views of the sea. Swimming pool and paddling pool. Nearby walks along the coast. St. Quay-Portieux is a lively resort. Sunny grounds with a few trees. Hedges provide shelter from the wind. Free wifi.

CC 19/4-6/7 27/8-17/9

🧭 N 48°39'47'' W 2°50'41''

www.eurocampings.co.uk/100257

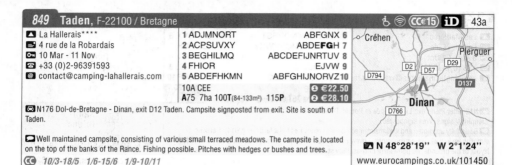

849 Taden, F-22100 / Bretagne

🚭 🛜 (CC€15) iD 43a

- 🏕 La Hallerais★★★★
- 📧 4 rue de la Robardais
- 📅 10 Mar - 11 Nov
- ☎ +33 (0)2-96391593
- @ contact@camping-lahallerais.com

1 ADJMNORT	ABFGNX 6
2 ACPSUVXY	ABDEFGH 7
3 BEGHILMQ	ABCDEFIJNRTUV 8
4 FHIOR	EJVW 9
5 ABDEFHKMN	ABFGHIJNORVZ 10

10A CEE ❸ €22.50
A75 7ha 100T(84-133m²) 115P ❷ €28.10

🛣 N176 Dol-de-Bretagne - Dinan, exit D12 Taden. Campsite signposted from exit. Site is south of Taden.

💬 Well maintained campsite, consisting of various small terraced meadows. The campsite is located on the top of the banks of the Rance. Fishing possible. Pitches with hedges or bushes and trees.

CC 10/3-18/5 1/6-15/6 1/9-10/11

📍 N 48°28'19'' W 2°1'24''

www.eurocampings.co.uk/101450

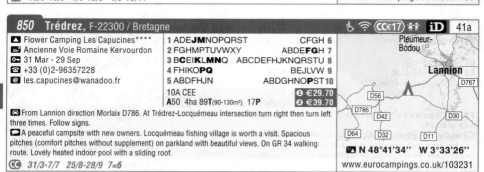

850 Trédrez, F-22300 / Bretagne

🚭 🛜 (CC€17) ✸✸ iD 41a

- 🏕 Flower Camping Les Capucines★★★★
- 📧 Ancienne Voie Romaine Kervourdon
- 📅 31 Mar - 29 Sep
- ☎ +33 (0)2-96357228
- @ les.capucines@wanadoo.fr

1 ADEJMNOPQRST	CFGH 6
2 FGHMPTUVWXY	ABDEFGH 7
3 BCEIKLMNQ	ABCDEFHJKNQRSTU 8
4 FHIKOPQ	BEJLVW 9
5 ABDFHJN	ABDGHNOPST 10

10A CEE ❸ €29.70
A50 4ha 89T(90-130m²) 17P ❷ €39.70

🛣 From Lannion direction Morlaix D786. At Trédrez-Locquémeau intersection turn right then turn left three times. Follow signs.

💬 A peaceful campsite with new owners. Locquémeau fishing village is worth a visit. Spacious pitches (comfort pitches without supplement) on parkland with beautiful views. On GR 34 walking route. Lovely heated indoor pool with a sliding roof.

CC 31/3-7/7 25/8-28/9 7=6

📍 N 48°41'34'' W 3°33'26''

www.eurocampings.co.uk/103231

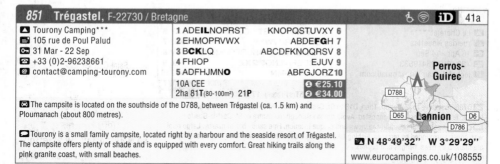

851 Trégastel, F-22730 / Bretagne

🚭 🛜 iD 41a

- 🏕 Tourony Camping★★★
- 📧 105 rue de Poul Palud
- 📅 31 Mar - 22 Sep
- ☎ +33 (0)2-96238661
- @ contact@camping-tourony.com

1 ADEILNOPRST	KNOPQSTUVXY 6
2 EHMOPRVWX	ABDEFGH 7
3 BCKLQ	ABCDFKNOQRSV 8
4 FHIOP	EJUV 9
5 ADFHJMNO	ABFGJORZ 10

10A CEE ❸ €25.10
2ha 81T(80-100m²) 21P ❷ €34.00

🛣 The campsite is located on the southside of the D788, between Trégastel (ca. 1.5 km) and Ploumanach (about 800 metres).

💬 Tourony is a small family campsite, located right by a harbour and the seaside resort of Trégastel. The campsite offers plenty of shade and is equipped with every comfort. Great hiking trails along the pink granite coast, with small beaches.

📍 N 48°49'32'' W 3°29'29''

www.eurocampings.co.uk/108555

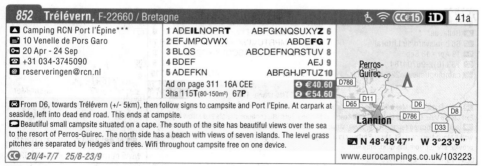

852 Trélévern, F-22660 / Bretagne

🚭 🛜 (CC€15) iD 41a

- 🏕 Camping RCN Port l'Épine★★★
- 📧 10 Venelle de Pors Garo
- 📅 20 Apr - 24 Sep
- ☎ +31 034-3745090
- @ reserveringen@rcn.nl

1 ADEILNOPRT	ABFGKNQSUXYZ 6
2 EFJMPQVWX	ABDEFG 7
3 BLQS	ABCDEFNQRSTUV 8
4 BDEF	AEJ 9
5 ADEFKN	ABFGHJPTUZ 10

Ad on page 311 16A CEE ❸ €40.60
3ha 115T(80-150m²) 67P ❷ €54.60

🛣 From D6, towards Trélévern (+/- 5km), then follow signs to campsite and Port l'Epine. At carpark at seaside, left into dead end road. This ends at campsite.
💬 Beautiful small campsite situated on a cape. The south of the site has beautiful views over the sea to the resort of Perros-Guirec. The north side has a beach with views of seven islands. The level grass pitches are separated by hedges and trees. Wifi throughout campsite free on one device.

CC 20/4-7/7 25/8-23/9

📍 N 48°48'47'' W 3°23'9''

www.eurocampings.co.uk/103223

France

RCN PORT L'EPINE

Amazing location in Breton where the park is located on the coast of the Atlantic Ocean. Camping pitches with stunning sea view.

CAMPING - MOBILE HOME – CHALETS – HEATED SWIMMING POOL

📞 +31 85 0400 700   🌐 www.rcn.fr

---

853 **Trélévern**, F-22660 / Bretagne   ♿ 📶 (CC€15) 🚹🚺 **iD** 41a

🏕 Seasonova les 7 îles***
🏠 Port L'Epine
📅 30 Mar - 12 Oct
☎ +33 (0)2-96917311
@ contact@camping-trelevern.com

1 ADE**JM**NOPRST	EFGKNOPQXY**Z** 6
2 EFGHJKPQRVW	BE**FG**H 7
3 ALQ	ABCDFNORV 8
4 FIO	BC 9
5 ABDEFHJL**N**	ABDGHJO**P**RZ10
10A CEE	€ €26.60
2,8ha 127**T**(80-140m²) 11**P**	€ €36.10

🚗 From Lannion direction Trélévern via D38. In Trélévern follow signs Le Palud or Port L'Epine until the beach.
🏕 This long campsite is located directly on the coast and has a beautiful view over the 'Les 7 Îles' island group. The Côte le Granit Rose and Perros Guirec are nearby. The campsite has its own restaurant with fish specialities.
(CC) 1/4-6/7 26/8-11/10 7=6

Perros-Guirec / D788 / D11 / D65 / **Lannion** D786 / D6 / D33 / D8

🏕 N 48°48'54'' W 3°22'59''
www.eurocampings.co.uk/122569

---

854 **Cancale**, F-35260 / Bretagne   📶 **iD** 43a

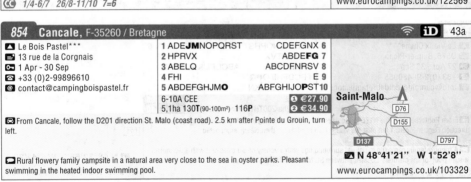

🏕 Le Bois Pastel***
🏠 13 rue de la Corgnais
📅 1 Apr - 30 Sep
☎ +33 (0)2-99896610
@ contact@campingboispastel.fr

1 ADE**JM**NOPQRST	CDEFGNX 6
2 HPRVX	ABDE**FG** 7
3 ABELQ	ABCDFNRSV 8
4 FHI	E 9
5 ABDEFGHJM**O**	ABFGHIJO**P**ST10
6-10A CEE	€ €27.90
5,1ha 130**T**(90-100m²) 116**P**	€ €34.90

🚗 From Cancale, follow the D201 direction St. Malo (coast road). 2.5 km after Pointe du Grouin, turn left.

🏕 Rural flowery family campsite in a natural area very close to the sea in oyster parks. Pleasant swimming in the heated indoor swimming pool.

Saint-Malo / D76 / D155 / D137 / D797

🏕 N 48°41'21'' W 1°52'8''
www.eurocampings.co.uk/103329

---

855 **Dinard**, F-35800 / Bretagne   ♿ 📶 **iD** 43a

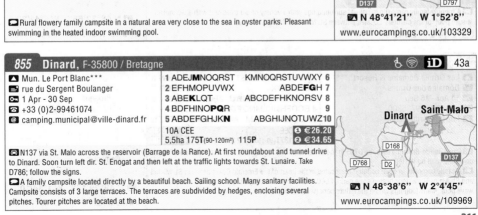

🏕 Mun. Le Port Blanc***
🏠 rue du Sergent Boulanger
📅 1 Apr - 30 Sep
☎ +33 (0)2-99461074
@ camping.municipal@ville-dinard.fr

1 ADE**JM**NOQRST	KMNOQRSTUVWXY 6
2 EFHMOPUVWX	ABDE**FG**H 7
3 ABE**K**LQT	ABCDEFHKNORSV 8
4 BDFHINO**PQ**R	9
5 ABDEFGHJK**N**	ABGHIJNOTUWZ10
10A CEE	€ €26.20
5,5ha 175**T**(90-120m²) 115**P**	€ €34.65

🚗 N137 via St. Malo across the reservoir (Barrage de la Rance). At first roundabout and tunnel drive to Dinard. Soon turn left dir. St. Enogat and then left at the traffic lights towards St. Lunaire. Take D786; follow the signs.
🏕 A family campsite located directly by a beautiful beach. Sailing school. Many sanitary facilities. Campsite consists of 3 large terraces. The terraces are subdivided by hedges, enclosing several pitches. Tourer pitches are located at the beach.

Dinard Saint-Malo / D168 / D137 / D768 / D2

🏕 N 48°38'6'' W 2°4'45''
www.eurocampings.co.uk/109969

856 Dinard/St.Lunaire, F-35800 / Bretagne   ♿ 📶 (CC€17) iD 43a

- 🏕 La Touesse***
- 🏠 171 rue de la ville Gehan
- 📅 1 Apr - 6 Oct
- ☎ +33 (0)2-99466113
- @ camping.la.touesse@wanadoo.fr

1 ADE**JM**NORST	ABEFGHIKNOPQST**X** 6	
2 EHMOPVWXY	ABDE**FG**H 7	
3 ABD**K**LQT	ABCDFHJNRSTUV 8	
4 BDFHINO**PQT**UY	EILV 9	
5 ABDEFGHJKM**NO**	ABCDGHIJ**N**P**R**10	

Ad on this page 5-10A CEE   ❶ €35.40
3ha 80T(90-120m²) 93P   ❷ €45.50

🅿 N137 via St. Malo over barrage. 1st roundabout with viaducts dir. Dinard. On dual carriageway after 500 metres 2nd exit left dir. St. Énogat. After 300 metres left at 1st traffic lights dir. St. Lunaire. Stay on D786. Follow signs.
🛏 Intimate, sheltered site with leisure and covered pool. Nice restaurant with terrace. 300 m from sea, lovely sandy beach. Pitches divided by hedges and trees into tiny fields. Close to historic town of Dinard.
(CC) 1/4-6/7   25/8-5/10

N 48°37'51" W 2°5'3"

www.eurocampings.co.uk/103271

857 Dol-de-Bretagne, F-35120 / Bretagne   📶 (CC€15) iD 43a

- 🏕 Le Vieux Chêne****
- 🏠 D576, Baguer-Pican
- 📅 27 Apr - 30 Sep
- ☎ +33 (0)2-99480955
- @ info@camping-doldebretagne.com

1 ADE**IL**NOPRST	ABFGHIN 6	
2 ADGPTVX	ABDE**FG**H 7	
3 ABEILMQ	ABCDFIJKNQRSTUV 8	
4 BCDFHILO**PQ**	EJ 9	
5 ACDEFGHJKN	ABFGHIJOT10	

10A CEE   ❶ €40.00
A80 12ha 200T(100-115m²) 34P   ❷ €53.10

🅿 From Pontorson take the N176 in the direction of Dol-de-Bretagne. Exit Dol-de-Bretagne-Est. D576 direction Baguer-Pican. 1 km past the village turn right. From then clearly signposted.

🛏 A friendly family campsite in natural surroundings with a variety of old trees and with a wonderful leisure pool for the children. Located between St. Malo and Mont-St-Michel.
(CC) 27/4-5/7   2/9-29/9

N 48°32'58" W 1°41'2"

www.eurocampings.co.uk/103335

858 Epiniac/Dol-de-Bretagne, F-35120 / Bretagne   📶 ❀ (CC€19) iD 43a

- 🏕 Les Ormes Domaine & Resort*****
- 🏠 Domaine des Ormes
- 📅 14 Apr - 16 Sep
- ☎ +33 (0)2-99735300
- @ info@lesormes.com

1 ADE**JM**NOPQRST	ABEFGHIN 6	
2 BDGIPVX	BDE**FG** 7	
3 ABEF**GHIJKLMQRU**	ABCDFJKNQRSV 8	
4 BCDFHIJKLMNO**PQR**	EGIJTUVW 9	
5 ACDEFGHJKLM	ABDGHIJ**NO**P**S**TYZ10	

6-10A CEE   ❶ €63.40
200ha 137T(80-150m²) 212P   ❷ €75.00

🅿 From Dol-de-Bretagne take the D795 in the direction of Combourg. The campsite is located 7 km down the road on the left.
🛏 A castle campsite in open countryside located in the heart of the Emerald Coast between St. Michel and St. Malo. The indoor heated aqua park (4,000 m²) welcomes both young and old. Do not miss the wave pool. Many lodgings within the nature park (woods, forest).
(CC) 14/4-5/7   1/9-15/9   7=6

N 48°29'15" W 1°44'10"

www.eurocampings.co.uk/103337

France

859 La Chapelle-aux-Filtzméens, F-35190 / Bretagne

♿ 📶 (CC€19) iD 13 B2

- ▲ Domaine du Logis*****
- 📅 30 Mar - 1 Oct
- ☎ +33 (0)2-99452545
- @ domainedulogis@wanadoo.fr

1 ABDEILNOPQRST	ABFGHNUV	6
2 BCFGPRSVWXY	ABCDEFGH	7
3 ABCEILQRST	ABCDEFGIJKNQRSTUV	8
4 BCDFHILOPQRTU	EUVW	9
5 ABEFGHKLNO	ABCDHIJPQRZ	10

16A CEE   € 33.00
8ha 180T(80-125m²) 192P   € 39.00

🚗 4 km east of the N137 Rennes-St.-Malo. On the D13 between St.-Domineuc and Combourg.
💬 This quiet campsite is located in the grounds of a 15th-century castle. In the converted barn you will find a restaurant, bar and a shop with fresh croissants and bread every morning. During the day you can have fun in the heated pool, in the evening in the club house with games and billiards. There is also a BMX course for the young (at heart).
CC 30/3-7/7   25/8-30/9   7=6

Plouasne   D20   Montreuil-sur-Ille
▲ N 48°22'55''   W 1°50'5''
www.eurocampings.co.uk/112420

---

860 St. Coulomb/La Guimorais, F-35350 / Bretagne

📶 ✿ (CC€17) iD 43a

- ▲ Des Chevrets***
- 📅 30/3 - 12/10, 27/10 - 3/11
- ☎ +33 (0)2-99890190
- @ contact@campingdeschevrets.fr

1 ADEJMNOPRST	KNOPQSWXY	6
2 EHPQUVX	ABDEFGH	7
3 ABEILQT	BCDFKNRSUV	8
4 BDFINO	E	9
5 ABCDEFGHKLMN	ABGHIJNPST	10

6A CEE   € 28.10
13ha 254T(80-100m²) 376P   € 31.30

🚗 From Cancale via the D201 direction St. Malo. In La Guimorais turn right. The campsite is to the right of the D201 and is clearly signposted.
💬 A peaceful, floral campsite with pitches marked out by plants. This site has a unique location: on high dunes with direct access to the beach and lovely views over the bay. There is a good restaurant for gourmets.
CC 30/3-8/7   26/8-11/10   27/10-2/11

Saint-Malo   D76   D155
▲ N 48°41'24''   W 1°56'30''
www.eurocampings.co.uk/103332

France

861 St. Jouan-des-Guérêts, F-35430 / Bretagne

📶 iD 43a

- ▲ Yelloh! Village Le P'tit Bois*****
- 🚉 St. Malo
- 📅 13 Apr - 16 Sep
- ☎ +33 (0)2-99211430
- @ contact@ptitbois.com

1 ADEILNOPRST	ABEFGHI	6
2 AGPRVX	ABDEFGH	7
3 ABEILMQST	ABCDFJKNOQRSTUV	8
4 BDILNOPQU	ELV	9
5 ACDEFGHJKMN	ABGHIJNPTUZ	10

10A CEE   € 50.00
A50 6ha 70T(80-120m²) 208P   € 64.00

🚗 Leave the N137 between Châteauneuf and St. Malo at the second exit St. Jouan-des-Guérêts and 'Centre Commercial'. Campsite is clearly signposted in the village.
💬 Pleasant, quiet campsite, with plenty of flowers in a green environment. On the edge of the town of St. Malo. Close to Dinard, Mont St. Michel, Cap Frehel, la Pointe de Grouin and the walled town in the city of St. Malo. Heated indoor swimming pool with jacuzzi. Tennis, crazy golf and free wifi in the low season.

Saint-Malo   Dinard
▲ N 48°36'36''   W 1°59'13''
www.eurocampings.co.uk/100261

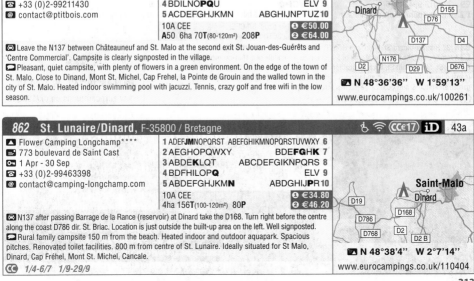

862 St. Lunaire/Dinard, F-35800 / Bretagne

♿ 📶 (CC€17) iD 43a

- ▲ Flower Camping Longchamp****
- 🚉 773 boulevard de Saint Cast
- 📅 1 Apr - 30 Sep
- ☎ +33 (0)2-99463398
- @ contact@camping-longchamp.com

1 ADEJMNOPQRST	ABEFGHIKMNOPQRSTUVWXY	6
2 AEGHOPQWXY	BDEFGHK	7
3 ABDEKLQT	ABCDEFGIKNPQRS	8
4 BDFHILOPQ	ELV	9
5 ABDEFGHJKMN	ABDGHIJPR	10

10A CEE   € 34.80
4ha 156T(100-120m²) 80P   € 46.20

🚗 N137 after passing Barrage de la Rance (reservoir) at Dinard take the D168. Turn right before the centre along the coast D786 dir. St. Briac. Location is just outside the built-up area on the left. Well signposted.
💬 Rural family campsite 150 m from the beach. Heated indoor and outdoor aquapark. Spacious pitches. Renovated toilet facilities. 800 m from centre of St. Lunaire. Ideally situated for St Malo, Dinard, Cap Fréhel, Mont St. Michel, Cancale.
CC 1/4-6/7   1/9-29/9

Saint-Malo   Dinard
▲ N 48°38'4''   W 2°7'14''
www.eurocampings.co.uk/110404

863 St. Malo, F-35400 / Bretagne

🛜 (CC€17) **iD** 43a

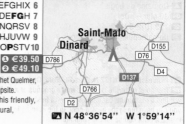

- 🏔 Domaine de La Ville Huchet★★★★
- 🏕 rte de la Passagère
- 📅 7 Apr - 23 Sep
- ☎ +33 (0)2-99811183
- @ info@lavillehuchet.com

1 ADE**JL**NOPQRST	ABEFGHIX	6
2 AGOPRX	ABDE**FG**H	7
3 ABE**I**LQST	ABCDFKNQRSV	8
4 ABCDILNO**PQ**	EHJUVW	9
5 ABDEFGHJKM**N**	ABDGHJO**P**STV	10

Ad on this page 6-10A CEE ❶ €39.50
A50 6,4ha 102T(100-120m²) 96P ❷ €49.10

Saint-Malo
Dinard

D786 D155
D76
D4
D137
D766
D2

🗺 N 48°36'54'' W 1°59'14''

📶 N137 from Rennes to St. Malo, firstly direction 'centre ville'. At the roundabout exit La Ville Huchet Quelmer, straight ahead at the next roundabout then turn 100 metres to the right under the bridge to the campsite.

💬 You can discover the Brittany region, the ancient city of Intra Muros, Saint-Malo from this friendly, peaceful family camping with its indoor pool (28°C). You will experience unforgettable, natural, culinary and historical richness.

(CC) 7/4-6/7 1/9-22/9

www.eurocampings.co.uk/103333

864 Tinténiac, F-35190 / Bretagne

♿ 🛜 (CC€17) **iD** 13 B2

- 🏔 Domaine Les Peupliers★★★
- 🏕 21, La Besnelais
- 📅 1 Apr - 1 Oct
- ☎ +33 (0)2-99454975
- @ contact@domainelespeupliers.fr

1 AD**JM**NORT	ABN	6
2 ACGPVWX	ABDE**FG**	7
3 BE**G**LMQ	ABCDEFNQR	8
4 HIO**PQ**	EIJ	9
5 ABCDFHJKLMNO	ABGHIJM**PR**	10

Ad on this page 6A CEE ❶ €25.50
A50 5ha 36T(100-130m²) 62P ❷ €34.30

Combourg D794
D2
D795
D137
D68 D20
D70 D27
D21
D72 Gévezé Melesse

🗺 N 48°18'34'' W 1°49'19''

📶 N137 Rennes-Dinard/St. Malo, exit Hédé/Tinténiàc. Campsite is south of Tinténiàc.

💬 A family campsite in a natural area of 5 hectares in the middle of a 16th-century estate. Close to Rennes, St. Malo, Mont St. Michel. Ideal for families and senior citizens. Opportunities for walking (canal d'Ille et Rance), fishing and various trips out. Lake, swimming pool, tennis courts, various games and pitch & putt golf. Large pitches screened by hedges.

(CC) 1/4-6/7 26/8-30/9 7=6, 14=12

www.eurocampings.co.uk/103338

France

Pays de la Loire

Glorious coast and river valleys

Rough, rocky, marshy and hilly, Pays de la Loire in western France is situated between Normandy, Brittany and the Bay of Biscay. Glorious beaches and salt flats adorn the coast. Inland are orchards, fields, heathlands, and forests. This is the 'garden of France'.

So much living history

The Loire valley is famous for its castles: Chambord park is the size of Paris; Chenonceaux is built over the river on elegant yet functional arches; Sully-sur-Loire is like a fairy-tale illustration. And can you imagine living in a cave? There are labyrinthine troglodyte dwellings inside the hills that have windows and doors. Visit Troo, and listen carefully according to legend, a cave dweller had a very talkative wife, he asked the devil to take her away, but she talked so much the devil dropped her down a well. They say she's still down there, babbling away …

The villages of Montsoreau and Vouvant are famous throughout France: Montsoreau as the setting for the novel 'La Dame De Montsoreau', and Vouvant for its castle and Romanesque church. Explore the castles of the Dukes of Brittany in the port city of Nantes, and science fiction fans will like the Jules Verne Museum – the writer was born here. Le Mans is famous for its 24-hour endurance motor race event, but did you know there are also Roman baths there?

Day Excursions

Check out the local market on a day trip to Guerande, which is also the centre of the salt flats. Nearby is La Briere Nature Park, where you can learn about traditional agriculture and conservation activities. Regional Park Loire-Anjou-Touraine includes Foutevrand Abbey, linked with the Plantagenet dynasty. Theme park Puy de Fou is a hit with kids – complete with re-

enactments of gladiator trials and Viking battles, how cool is that?

Food and drink

To refuel: try Rillette Sarthoises, local cheeses, salt marsh veal or other local meat covered with beurre-blanc sauce. Alternatively, tuck into a plat du fruit de mer, or sample savoury crepes – sweet crepes are also available, as are brioches, niniches, and local pyramid-shaped sweets known as berlingots. Tipples include Cointreau, pommeau de Maine, and wines.

Our tips

1. *The fantastic blend of science fiction, art and imagination at Machines de l'Ile, Nantes*
2. *On your bike! Follow the river Loire, or go to Ile d'Yeu, a paradise for cyclists*
3. *Laze on the beach and visit the marina at St-Jean-de-Monts*
4. *Like a good movie? Check out the La-Roche-sur-Yon Film Festival*
5. *Sample local cheeses and fresh fish at the Guerande Saturday market*

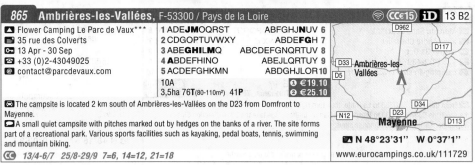

865 Ambrières-les-Vallées, F-53300 / Pays de la Loire

🌐 CC €15 iD 13 B2

- ⛺ Flower Camping Le Parc de Vaux***
- 📧 35 rue des Colverts
- 📅 13 Apr - 30 Sep
- ☎ +33 (0)2-43049025
- @ contact@parcdevaux.com

1 ADE**JM**OQRST	ABFGHJ**N**UV	6
2 CDGOPTUVWXY	ABDE**F**G**H**	7
3 ABE**GHILM**Q	ABCDEFGNQRTUV	8
4 **A**BDEFHINO	ABEJLQRTUY	9
5 ACDEFGHKMN	ABDGHJLOR	10
10A		❶ €19.10
3,5ha 76**T**(80-110m²) 41**P**		❷ €25.10

🚗 The campsite is located 2 km south of Ambrières-les-Vallées on the D23 from Domfront to Mayenne.

💬 A small quiet campsite with pitches marked out by hedges on the banks of a river. The site forms part of a recreational park. Various sports facilities such as kayaking, pedal boats, tennis, swimming and mountain biking.

CC 13/4-6/7 25/8-29/9 7=6, 14=12, 21=18

📍 N 48°23'31'' W 0°37'1''

www.eurocampings.co.uk/111729

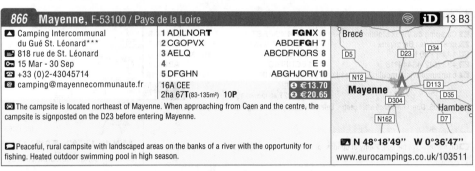

866 Mayenne, F-53100 / Pays de la Loire

🌐 iD 13 B3

- ⛺ Camping Intercommunal du Gué St. Léonard***
- 📧 818 rue de St. Léonard
- 📅 15 Mar - 30 Sep
- ☎ +33 (0)2-43045714
- @ camping@mayennecommunaute.fr

1 ADILNOR**T**	**FGN**X	6
2 CGOPVX	ABDE**F**G**H**	7
3 AELQ	ABCDFNORS	8
4	E	9
5 DFGHN	ABGHJORV	10
16A CEE		❶ €13.70
2ha 67**T**(83-135m²) 10**P**		❷ €20.65

🚗 The campsite is located northeast of Mayenne. When approaching from Caen and the centre, the campsite is signposted on the D23 before entering Mayenne.

💬 Peaceful, rural campsite with landscaped areas on the banks of a river with the opportunity for fishing. Heated outdoor swimming pool in high season.

📍 N 48°18'49'' W 0°36'47''

www.eurocampings.co.uk/103511

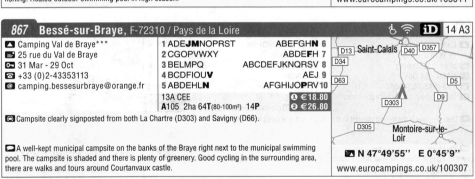

867 Bessé-sur-Braye, F-72310 / Pays de la Loire

♿ 🌐 iD 14 A3

- ⛺ Camping Val de Braye***
- 📧 25 rue du Val de Braye
- 📅 31 Mar - 29 Oct
- ☎ +33 (0)2-43353113
- @ camping.bessesurbraye@orange.fr

1 ADE**JM**NOPRST	ABEFG**H**N	6
2 CGOPVWXY	ABDE**F**H	7
3 BELMPQ	ABCDEFJKNQRSV	8
4 BCDFIOU**V**	AEJ	9
5 ABDEHL**N**	AFGHIJO**P**RV	10
13A CEE		❶ €18.80
A105 2ha 64**T**(80-100m²) 14**P**		❷ €26.80

🚗 Campsite clearly signposted from both La Chartre (D303) and Savigny (D66).

💬 A well-kept municipal campsite on the banks of the Braye right next to the municipal swimming pool. The campsite is shaded and there is plenty of greenery. Good cycling in the surrounding area, there are walks and tours around Courtanvaux castle.

📍 N 47°49'55'' E 0°45'9''

www.eurocampings.co.uk/100307

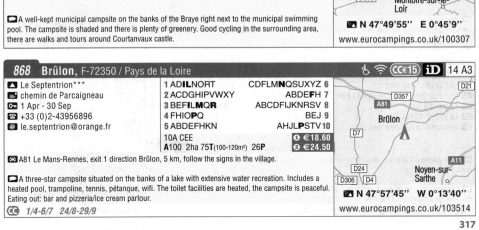

868 Brûlon, F-72350 / Pays de la Loire

♿ 🌐 CC €15 iD 14 A3

- ⛺ Le Septentrion***
- 📧 chemin de Parcaigneau
- 📅 1 Apr - 30 Sep
- ☎ +33 (0)2-43956896
- @ le.septentrion@orange.fr

1 AD**IL**NORT	CDFLM**NQ**SUXYZ	6
2 ACDGHIPVWXY	ABDE**F**H	7
3 BEF**IL**M**Q**R	ABCDFIJKNRSV	8
4 FHIO**PQ**	BEJ	9
5 ABDEFHKN	AHJL**P**STV	10
10A CEE		❶ €18.60
A100 2ha 75**T**(100-120m²) 26**P**		❷ €24.50

🚗 A81 Le Mans-Rennes, exit 1 direction Brûlon, 5 km, follow the signs in the village.

💬 A three-star campsite situated on the banks of a lake with extensive water recreation. Includes a heated pool, trampoline, tennis, pétanque, wifi. The toilet facilities are heated, the campsite is peaceful. Eating out: bar and pizzeria/ice cream parlour.

CC 1/4-6/7 24/8-29/9

📍 N 47°57'45'' W 0°13'40''

www.eurocampings.co.uk/103514

France

869 Fresnay-sur-Sarthe, F-72130 / Pays de la Loire 🕭 🛜 iD 14 A3

- 🏕 Mun. du Sans Souci***
- 🏠 allée André Chevalier
- 📅 1 Apr - 31 Oct
- ☎ +33 (0)2-43973287
- @ camping-fresnay@wanadoo.fr

1 ADEJMNOPQRST	ABFGNUV	6
2 CGPRVWXY	ABDEFGH	7
3 ABEFILMQV	ABCDFNRSTUV	8
4 FHILO	EJQR	9
5 ABDMN	ABGHIJLPR	10
10A CEE		❶ €13.30
2ha 75T(80-120m²) 7P		❷ €16.70

🚗 From the north via D338 to La Hutte, then turn right via D310 to Fresnay-sur-Sarthe. From the south via D338 and D39 to Fresnay-sur-Sarthe. In the village take the D310 direction Sillé-la-Guillaume. Then follow the campsite signs.

💬 Quietly situated municipal campsite on the green banks of the river Sarthe.

📍 N 48°16'57'' E 0°0'58''

www.eurocampings.co.uk/103608

870 La Chartre-sur-le-Loir, F-72340 / Pays de la Loire 🕭 🛜 iD 14 A3

- 🏕 Camping du Vieux Moulin***
- 🏠 chemin des Bergivaux
- 📅 1 Mar - 30 Nov
- ☎ +33 (0)2-43444118
- @ campingduvieuxmoulin72@gmail.com

1 AJMNOPRST	ABFGNX	6
2 CDGIOPVWXY	ABDEFG	7
3 ABELQS	ABCDFNQRSV	8
4 BCDFHIO	AEUV	9
5 ABDEFGHKN	ABFGHIJPR	10
10A CEE		❶ €24.50
2,5ha 82T(80-120m²) 19P		❷ €29.30

🚗 Via D305. Direction Poncé after centre. Left immediately after bridge. Clearly signposted.

💬 On the banks of the Loir. Plenty of options for cycling, walking, fishing and just enjoying the peace and the open air.

📍 N 47°43'58'' E 0°34'17''

www.eurocampings.co.uk/101186

871 La Flèche, F-72200 / Pays de la Loire 🕭 🛜 CC€13 iD 14 A3

- 🏕 Camping Municipal de la Route d'Or****
- 🏠 allée du Camping
- 📅 1 Mar - 31 Oct
- ☎ +33 (0)2-43945590
- @ info@camping-laroutedor.com

1 ADEJMNOPRST	ABNUXY	6
2 CPSVXY	ABDEFGH	7
3 BELMQR	ABCDEFJNORSUV	8
4 BNO	EKQR	9
5 ADN	ABFGHJLOR	10
10A CEE		❶ €18.00
4ha 190T(80-100m²) 10P		❷ €23.20

🚗 The campsite is clearly signposted in the village and is located at the river.

💬 Ideal location in the heart of town but still in greenery, on the banks of the Loir. Spacious pitches, everything is available for your dream holiday! Cycle routes, canoeing/kayaking, recreation, archery...

CC 1/3-7/7 1/9-30/10 7=6

📍 N 47°41'42'' W 0°4'46''

www.eurocampings.co.uk/100303

872 Marçon, F-72340 / Pays de la Loire 🕭 🛜 CC€15 iD 14 A3

- 🏕 Le Lac des Varennes***
- 🏠 route du Port Gauthier/Saint Lezin
- 📅 1 Apr - 29 Oct
- ☎ +33 (0)2-43441372
- @ contact@lacdesvarennes.com

1 ADJMNOPRST	JLNQRSTU	6
2 CDGHPVWXY	BEFGH	7
3 AFLMQRU	ABCDFJKNQRSV	8
4 BCDFIL	AEJMOPQRTV	9
5 ABDEFGH	ABHIJPST	10
10A CEE		❶ €21.10
7ha 170T(100-300m²) 80P		❷ €27.10

🚗 Drive via the D305 to Marçon. In the centre pass the Post Office/Town Hall (on the left). Follow the road. Signposted.

💬 This peaceful and spacious campsite borders both a large lake and the Loir. There is plenty of countryside around with footpaths and fishing on the site.

CC 1/4-7/7 25/8-28/10 7=6, 14=12, 21=17

📍 N 47°42'45'' E 0°29'58''

www.eurocampings.co.uk/103611

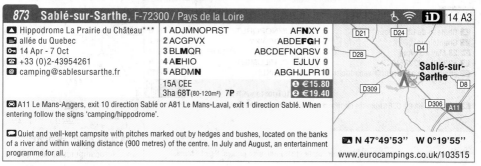

873 Sablé-sur-Sarthe, F-72300 / Pays de la Loire 🚲 🛜 iD 14 A3

- 🏕 Hippodrome La Prairie du Château***
- 🏠 allée du Quebec
- 🗓 14 Apr - 7 Oct
- ☎ +33 (0)2-43954261
- @ camping@sablesursarthe.fr

1 ADJMNOPRST	AFNXY	6	
2 ACGPVX	ABDEFGH	7	
3 BLMQR	ABCDEFNQRSV	8	
4 AEHIO	EJLUV	9	
5 ABDMN	ABGHJLPR	10	
15A CEE		❶ €15.80	
3ha 68T(80-120m²) 7P		❷ €19.40	

🅰A11 Le Mans-Angers, exit 10 direction Sablé or A81 Le Mans-Laval, exit 1 direction Sablé. When entering follow the signs 'camping/hippodrome'.

💬Quiet and well-kept campsite with pitches marked out by hedges and bushes, located on the banks of a river and within walking distance (900 metres) of the centre. In July and August, an entertainment programme for all.

🏕 N 47°49'53" W 0°19'55"

www.eurocampings.co.uk/103515

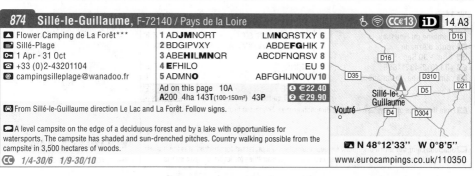

874 Sillé-le-Guillaume, F-72140 / Pays de la Loire 🚲 🛜 CC€13 iD 14 A3

- 🏕 Flower Camping de La Forêt***
- 🏠 Sillé-Plage
- 🗓 1 Apr - 31 Oct
- ☎ +33 (0)2-43201104
- @ campingsilleplage@wanadoo.fr

1 ADJMNORT	LMNQRSTXY	6	
2 BDGIPVXY	ABDEFGHIK	7	
3 ABEHILMNQR	ABCDFNQRSV	8	
4 EFHILO	EU	9	
5 ADMNO	ABFGHIJNOUV	10	
Ad on this page 10A		❶ €22.40	
A200 4ha 143T(100-150m²) 43P		❷ €29.90	

🅰From Sillé-le-Guillaume direction Le Lac and La Forêt. Follow signs.

💬A level campsite on the edge of a deciduous forest and by a lake with opportunities for watersports. The campsite has shaded and sun-drenched pitches. Country walking possible from the campsite in 3,500 hectares of woods.

CC 1/4-30/6 1/9-30/10

🏕 N 48°12'33" W 0°8'5"

www.eurocampings.co.uk/110350

France

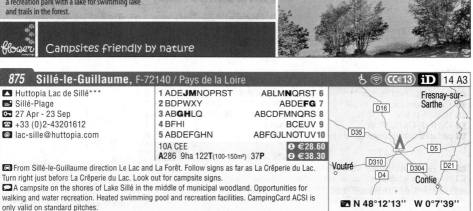

875 Sillé-le-Guillaume, F-72140 / Pays de la Loire 🚲 🛜 CC€13 iD 14 A3

- 🏕 Huttopia Lac de Sillé***
- 🏠 Sillé-Plage
- 🗓 27 Apr - 23 Sep
- ☎ +33 (0)2-43201612
- @ lac-sille@huttopia.com

1 ADEJMNOPRST	ABLMNQRST	6	
2 BDPWXY	ABDEFG	7	
3 ABGHLQ	ABCDFMNQRS	8	
4 BFHI	BCEUV	9	
5 ABDEFGHN	ABFGJLNOTUV	10	
10A CEE		❶ €28.60	
A286 9ha 122T(100-150m²) 37P		❷ €38.30	

🅰From Sillé-le-Guillaume direction Le Lac and La Forêt. Follow signs as far as La Crêperie du Lac. Turn right just before La Crêperie du Lac. Look out for campsite signs.
💬A campsite on the shores of Lake Sillé in the middle of municipal woodland. Opportunities for walking and water recreation. Heated swimming pool and recreation facilities. CampingCard ACSI is only valid on standard pitches.

CC 27/4-5/7 26/8-22/9

🏕 N 48°12'13" W 0°7'39"

www.eurocampings.co.uk/111323

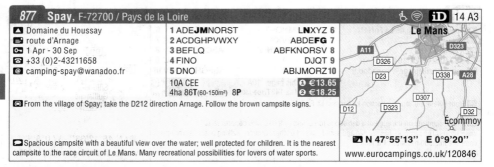

876 Sillé-le-Philippe, F-72460 / Pays de la Loire ♿ 🛜 ✿ iD 14 A3

- 🏰 Château de Chanteloup*****
- 📧 Chanteloup
- 📅 28 May - 31 Aug
- ☎ +33 (0)2-43275107
- @ chanteloup.souffront@wanadoo.fr

1 ADEJMNOPQRST	ABFGN	6
2 BDFGIOPWXY	ABDEFGH	7
3 ABEKLQST	ABCDEFGIKNQRSV	8
4 ABCDFHILOPQR	AIPV	9
5 ABDFGHKLN	ABHIJLOPR	10
10A		❶ €43.90
21ha 110T(100-200m²) 11P		❷ €58.90

Accessible via the D301 from the north and the south. The campsite is signposted on this road.

Beautiful, quiet campsite by a 19th century castle (1815) with large estates. Near Le Mans.

N 48°6'17" E 0°20'26"

www.eurocampings.co.uk/103610

877 Spay, F-72700 / Pays de la Loire ♿ 🛜 iD 14 A3

- 🏰 Domaine du Houssay
- 📧 route d'Arnage
- 📅 1 Apr - 30 Sep
- ☎ +33 (0)2-43211658
- @ camping-spay@wanadoo.fr

1 ADEJMNORST	LNXYZ	6
2 ACDGHPVWXY	ABDEFG	7
3 BEFLQ	ABFKNORSV	8
4 FINO	DJQT	9
5 DNO	ABIJMORZ	10
10A CEE		❶ €13.65
4ha 86T(60-150m²) 8P		❷ €18.25

From the village of Spay; take the D212 direction Arnage. Follow the brown campsite signs.

Spacious campsite with a beautiful view over the water; well protected for children. It is the nearest campsite to the race circuit of Le Mans. Many recreational possibilities for lovers of water sports.

N 47°55'13" E 0°9'20"

www.eurocampings.co.uk/120846

878 Tuffé, F-72160 / Pays de la Loire ♿ 🛜 ✿ (CC€15) ♦♦ iD 14 A3

- 🏰 du Lac****
- 📧 route de Prévelles
- 📅 7 Apr - 7 Oct
- ☎ +33 (0)2-43938834
- @ campingdulac.tuffe@orange.fr

1 ADEFJMNOPRST	ABCDFGLNQSTXYZ	6
2 CDGHIOPRVWXY	BEFGHK	7
3 ABEGHILMQU	ABDFGJKNQRSV	8
4 BDFHILOP	EJLQTUV	9
5 ABDHNO	ABDFGHIJPST	10
6A CEE		❶ €22.40
A82 4ha 115T(85-200m²) 23P		❷ €29.70

Follow the D323 to Connerré, then via the D33 to Tuffé and follow the 'Base de Loisirs' camping signs. Camping du Lac is next door.

This fine municipal campsite with an indoor swimming pool, fishpond and plenty of recreational opportunities is located in lovely natural surroundings. Well worth a visit!

(CC) 7/4-7/7 25/8-6/10 7=6, 14=12, 21=18

N 48°7'6" E 0°30'36"

www.eurocampings.co.uk/100274

---

879 Yvré-l'Evêque, F-72530 / Pays de la Loire ♿ 🛜 ✿ (CC€17) iD 14 A3

- 🏰 Camping Le Pont Romain****
- 📧 allée des Ormeaux
- 📅 16 Mar - 11 Nov
- ☎ +33 (0)2-43822539
- @ contact@campinglepontromain.fr

1 ADEGJMNOPRT	ABFG	6
2 AGOPRSVWXY	ABDEFGH	7
3 BILQ	ABCDFJKNQRSTUV	8
4 FHIPQ	ACEJ	9
5 ABDENO	ABDFGHIJOR	10
16A CEE		❶ €28.60
A65 2,5ha 67T(80-150m²) 17P		❷ €37.00

From E50/A11, at exit 6 head south to the A28. On A28, exit 23 Le Mans-Centre.

This campsite is located in a natural oasis a few kilometres from the centre of the art and history town of Le Mans. A convenient location for visiting the tourist attractions. The campsite has a swimming pool, toddlers' pool, activity room and snack bar with terrace to guarantee you a pleasant stay.

(CC) 16/3-30/6 1/9-10/11

N 48°1'8" E 0°16'46"

www.eurocampings.co.uk/118235

France

880 Angers, F-49000 / Pays de la Loire

♿ 📶 (CC€15) iD 17 B1

- ▲ Camping d'Angers-Lac de Maine****
- ⊟ avenue du Lac de Maine
- ☎ 23 Mar - 28 Oct
- ☎ +33 (0)2-41730503
- @ info@campingangers.com

1 ADE**JM**NOPQRST	ABLM**N**QRSTUV 6
2 ADGHOPRVWXY	ABDE**FGH** 7
3 BEFLQ	ABCDEFGJKNQRSTUV 8
4 FHO**PQU**	CEU 9
5 ADGHJN	ABGHIJNOR 10

10A CEE €30.10
4ha 146T(67-136m²) 17P €39.90

Clearly signposted in Angers. Via Lac de Maine.
In the heart of the Anjou in an unusual location: close to a famous historical town in the heart of 100-hectare area abundant in water. 1 hour from famous tourist towns, surrounded by renowned vineyards. Area of good living, gastronomy, heritage and a lovely climate. Recreation ground. Offers opportunities for sailing, swimming, swing golf, fishing. Bus stops 300 m from the campsite.
(CC) 23/3-5/7 26/8-27/10

Montreuil-Juigné
A11
D323
Angers
D111 D4
D751 A87 D748

◤ N 47°27'17" W 0°35'47"
www.eurocampings.co.uk/109214

---

881 Brain-sur-l'Authion, F-49800 / Pays de la Loire

♿ 📶 (CC€15) iD 18 A1

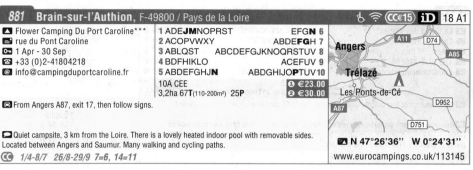

- ▲ Flower Camping Du Port Caroline***
- ⊟ rue du Pont Caroline
- ☎ 1 Apr - 30 Sep
- ☎ +33 (0)2-41804218
- @ info@campingduportcaroline.fr

1 ADE**JM**NOPQRST	EFG**N** 6
2 ACOPVWXY	ABDE**FGH** 7
3 ABLQST	ABCDEFGJKNOQRSTUV 8
4 BDFHIKLO	ACEFUV 9
5 ABDEFGHJ**N**	ABDGHIJO**P**TUV 10

10A CEE €23.00
3,2ha 67T(110-200m²) 25P €30.00

From Angers A87, exit 17, then follow signs.

Quiet campsite, 3 km from the Loire. There is a lovely heated indoor pool with removable sides. Located between Angers and Saumur. Many walking and cycling paths.
(CC) 1/4-8/7 26/8-29/9 7=6, 14=11

Angers
A11 D74
A85
Trélazé
Les Ponts-de-Cé
D952
A87
D751

◤ N 47°26'36" W 0°24'31"
www.eurocampings.co.uk/113145

---

882 Brissac-Quincé, F-49320 / Pays de la Loire

♿ 📶 ✿ (CC€17) iD 18 A1

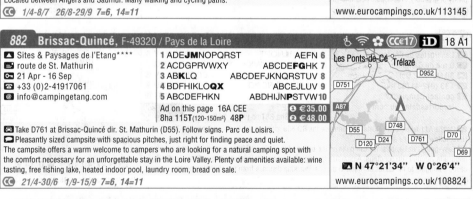

- ▲ Sites & Paysages de l'Etang****
- ⊟ route de St. Mathurin
- ☎ 21 Apr - 16 Sep
- ☎ +33 (0)2-41917061
- @ info@campingetang.com

1 ADE**JM**NOPQRST	AEFN 6
2 ACDGPRVWXY	ABCDE**FG**HK 7
3 AB**K**LQ	ABCDEFJKNQRSTUV 8
4 BDFHIKLO**QX**	ABCEJLUV 9
5 ABCDEFHKN	ABDHIJN**P**STVW 10

Ad on this page 16A CEE €35.00
8ha 115T(120-150m²) 48P €48.00

Take D761 at Brissac-Quincé dir. St. Mathurin (D55). Follow signs. Parc de Loisirs.
Pleasantly sized campsite with spacious pitches, just right for finding peace and quiet.
The campsite offers a warm welcome to campers who are looking for a natural camping spot with the comfort necessary for an unforgettable stay in the Loire Valley. Plenty of amenities available: wine tasting, free fishing lake, heated indoor pool, laundry room, bread on sale.
(CC) 21/4-30/6 1/9-15/9 7=6, 14=11

Les Ponts-de-Cé Trélazé
D952
D751
A87
D55 D748
D120 D24 D761 D70
D69

◤ N 47°21'34" W 0°26'4"
www.eurocampings.co.uk/108824

France

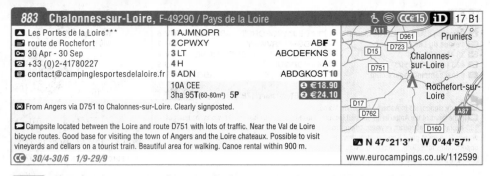

883 Chalonnes-sur-Loire, F-49290 / Pays de la Loire
⚐ 🛜 (CC€15) iD 17 B1

🏕 Les Portes de la Loire***	1 AJMNOPR	6
🛏 route de Rochefort	2 CPWXY	AB**F** 7
🕒 30 Apr - 30 Sep	3 LT	ABCDEFKNS 8
☎ +33 (0)2-41780227	4 H	A 9
@ contact@campinglesportesdelaloire.fr	5 ADN	ABDGKOST 10
	10A CEE	❶ €18.90
	3ha 95**T**(60-80m²) 5**P**	❷ €24.10

🚗 From Angers via D751 to Chalonnes-sur-Loire. Clearly signposted.

💬 Campsite located between the Loire and route D751 with lots of traffic. Near the Val de Loire bicycle routes. Good base for visiting the town of Angers and the Loire chateaux. Possible to visit vineyards and cellars on a tourist train. Beautiful area for walking. Canoe rental within 900 m.

⚐ 30/4-30/6 1/9-29/9

N 47°21'3'' W 0°44'57''
www.eurocampings.co.uk/112599

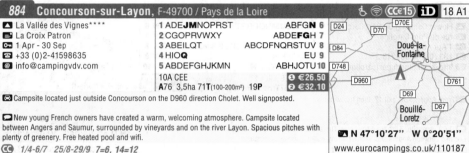

884 Concourson-sur-Layon, F-49700 / Pays de la Loire
⚐ 🛜 (CC€15) iD 18 A1

🏕 La Vallée des Vignes****	1 ADE**JM**NOPRST	ABFG**N** 6
🛏 La Croix Patron	2 CGOPRVWXY	ABDE**FG**H 7
🕒 1 Apr - 30 Sep	3 ABEILQT	ABCDFNQRSTUV 8
☎ +33 (0)2-41598635	4 HIO**Q**	EU 9
@ info@campingvdv.com	5 ABDEFGHJKMN	ABHJOTU 10
	10A CEE	❶ €26.50
	A76 3,5ha 71**T**(100-200m²) 19**P**	❷ €32.10

🚗 Campsite located just outside Concourson on the D960 direction Cholet. Well signposted.

💬 New young French owners have created a warm, welcoming atmosphere. Campsite located between Angers and Saumur, surrounded by vineyards and on the river Layon. Spacious pitches with plenty of greenery. Free heated pool and wifi.

⚐ 1/4-6/7 25/8-29/9 7=6, 14=12

N 47°10'27'' W 0°20'51''
www.eurocampings.co.uk/110187

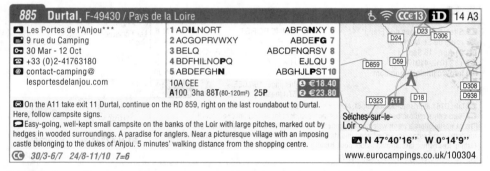

885 Durtal, F-49430 / Pays de la Loire
⚐ 🛜 (CC€13) iD 14 A3

🏕 Les Portes de l'Anjou***	1 AD**IL**NORT	ABFG**N**XY 6
🛏 9 rue du Camping	2 ACGOPRVWXY	ABDE**FG** 7
🕒 30 Mar - 12 Oct	3 BELQ	ABCDFNQRSV 8
☎ +33 (0)2-41763180	4 BDFHILNO**PQ**	EJLQU 9
@ contact-camping@	5 ABDEFGH**N**	ABGHJL**P**ST 10
lesportesdelanjou.com	10A CEE	❶ €18.40
	A100 3ha 88**T**(80-120m²) 25**P**	❷ €23.80

🚗 On the A11 take exit 11 Durtal, continue on the RD 859, right on the last roundabout to Durtal. Here, follow campsite signs.

💬 Easy-going, well-kept small campsite on the banks of the Loir with large pitches, marked out by hedges in wooded surroundings. A paradise for anglers. Near a picturesque village with an imposing castle belonging to the dukes of Anjou. 5 minutes' walking distance from the shopping centre.

⚐ 30/3-6/7 24/8-11/10 7=6

N 47°40'16'' W 0°14'9''
www.eurocampings.co.uk/100304

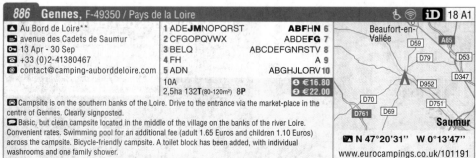

886 Gennes, F-49350 / Pays de la Loire
⚐ 🛜 iD 18 A1

🏕 Au Bord de Loire**	1 ADE**JM**NOPQRST	**ABFH**N 6
🛏 avenue des Cadets de Saumur	2 CFGOPQVWX	ABDE**FG** 7
🕒 13 Apr - 30 Sep	3 BELQ	ABCDEFGNRSTV 8
☎ +33 (0)2-41380467	4 FH	A 9
@ contact@camping-auborddeloire.com	5 ADN	ABGHJLORV 10
	10A	❶ €16.80
	2,5ha 132**T**(80-120m²) 8**P**	❷ €22.00

🚗 Campsite is on the southern banks of the Loire. Drive to the entrance via the market-place in the centre of Gennes. Clearly signposted.

💬 Basic, but clean campsite located in the middle of the village on the banks of the river Loire. Convenient rates. Swimming pool for an additional fee (adult 1.65 Euros and children 1.10 Euros) across the campsite. Bicycle-friendly campsite. A toilet block has been added, with individual washrooms and one family shower.

N 47°20'31'' W 0°13'47''
www.eurocampings.co.uk/101191

887 Les Rosiers-sur-Loire, F-49350 / Pays de la Loire
🚾 🛜 (CC€15) iD 18 A1

- 🏕 Yelloh! Village Les Voiles d'Anjou****
- 🏠 6 rue Sainte Baudruche
- 🗓 1 Apr - 1 Oct
- ☎ +33 (0)2-41519433
- @ contact@camping-valdeloire.com

1	ADE**IL**NOPRT	ABEFG 6
2	APVWXY	ABDE**FG**H 7
3	ABE**FI**LMQRST	ABCDEFKNQRSTUV 8
4	ABCDFHILNO**PQTU**	AEZ 9
5	ABDEGHJMN	ABGHIJPRV 10

10A

4,5ha 111**T**(100-130m²) 53**P**

💶 €29.00
💶 €43.00

🗺 Via D952. Towards Beaufort at the traffic lights in the village. Follow signs. Campsite well signposted.
🛏 In the UNESCO heritage site of the Loire, with its beautiful chateaux, 500m from a lively village.
Two swimming pools, one outdoor and one indoor with a lovely terrace. New toilet facilities.
Playground, bike rental, sightly furnished restaurant with room for music and theatre. Many options
for cycling and walking in the vicinity.

CC 1/4-30/6 1/9-30/9 7=6

📍 N 47°21'32'' W 0°13'32''

www.eurocampings.co.uk/100324

888 Montjean-sur-Loire/Mauges, F-49570 / Pays de la Loire
🚾 🛜 (CC€15) 👫 iD 17 B1

- 🏕 Flower Camping La Promenade***
- 🏠 quai des Mariniers
- 🗓 1 Apr - 17 Oct
- ☎ +33 (0)2-41390268
- @ contact@campinglapromenade.com

1	ADE**JM**NOPQRST	ABFG**N**V 6
2	CHOPVWXY	ABDE**FG**HK 7
3	ABLQ	ABCDEFGINQRSTUV 8
4	BCDFHILNO**PQ**	BCEQRUV 9
5	ABDEFGHJN	ABDGHIJLPRV 10

10A

3ha 150**T**(85-125m²) 34**P**

💶 €22.50
💶 €29.50

🗺 From Angers to the D751. Follow this as far as Montjean-sur-Loire. Campsite well signposted.
🛏 Near a small village in the middle of Anjou on the banks of the Loire. In the area between Angers
and Nantes, famous for the unusual Corniche Angevine. Plenty of walking and cycling possibilities.
Spacious marked-out pitches, lovely swimming pool, new toilet facilities, snack bar and hospitable
owners.

CC 1/4-7/7 25/8-16/10 7=6, 14=12

📍 N 47°23'31'' W 0°52'13''

www.eurocampings.co.uk/113163

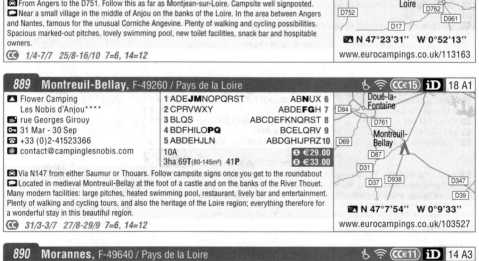

889 Montreuil-Bellay, F-49260 / Pays de la Loire
🚾 🛜 (CC€15) iD 18 A1

- 🏕 Flower Camping
  Les Nobis d'Anjou****
- 🏠 rue Georges Girouy
- 🗓 31 Mar - 30 Sep
- ☎ +33 (0)2-41523366
- @ contact@campinglesnobis.com

1	ADE**JM**NOPQRST	ABN**U**X 6
2	CPRVWXY	ABDE**FG**H 7
3	BLQS	ABCDEFKNQRST 8
4	BDFHILO**PQ**	BCELQRV 9
5	ABDEHJLN	ABDGHIJPRZ 10

10A

3ha 69**T**(80-145m²) 41**P**

💶 €29.00
💶 €33.00

🗺 Via N147 from either Saumur or Thouars. Follow campsite signs once you get to the roundabout
🛏 Located in medieval Montreuil-Bellay at the foot of a castle and on the banks of the River Thouet.
Many modern facilities: large pitches, heated swimming pool, restaurant, lively bar and entertainment.
Plenty of walking and cycling tours, and also the heritage of the Loire region; everything therefore for
a wonderful stay in this beautiful region.

CC 31/3-3/7 27/8-29/9 7=6, 14=12

📍 N 47°7'54'' W 0°9'33''

www.eurocampings.co.uk/103527

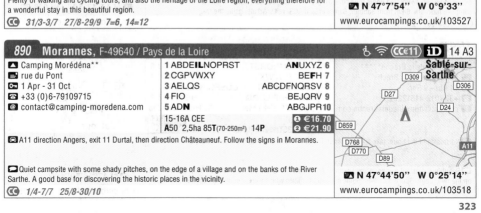

890 Morannes, F-49640 / Pays de la Loire
🚾 🛜 (CC€11) iD 14 A3

- 🏕 Camping Morédéna**
- 🏠 rue du Pont
- 🗓 1 Apr - 31 Oct
- ☎ +33 (0)6-79109715
- @ contact@camping-moredena.com

1	ABDE**IL**NOPRST	A**N**UXYZ 6
2	CGPVWXY	BE**F**H 7
3	AELQS	ABCDFNQRSV 8
4	FIO	BEJQRV 9
5	AD**N**	ABGJPR 10

15-16A CEE

A50 2,5ha 85**T**(70-250m²) 14**P**

💶 €16.70
💶 €21.90

🗺 A11 direction Angers, exit 11 Durtal, then direction Châteauneuf. Follow the signs in Morannes.

🛏 Quiet campsite with some shady pitches, on the edge of a village and on the banks of the River
Sarthe. A good base for discovering the historic places in the vicinity.

CC 1/4-7/7 25/8-30/10

📍 N 47°44'50'' W 0°25'14''

www.eurocampings.co.uk/103518

France

891 Rochefort-sur-Loire, F-49190 / Pays de la Loire ♿ 📶 ❄ (CC€13) iD 17 B1

🔺 Seasonova Les Plages de Loire***
🚸 route de Savennières
📅 31 Mar - 30 Nov
☎ +33 (0)2-41685591
@ contact@
camping-lesplagesdeloire.com

1 ADE**JM**NOPQRST	ABEFG**J**N**U** 6
2 ACDFGHOPVWXY	ABDE**FGH** 7
3 AILQTV	ABCDEFNQRSV 8
4 ABCDEFHI**TUVXZ**	ABCDEQUZ 9
5 ABDEFH**J**N**O**	ABDGHJO**P**R 10

10A CEE ❶ €19.00
6ha 116**T**(80-140m²) 23**P** ❷ €24.20

🚗 Via the A11 to N160 direction Les Ponts-de-Cé. Rochefort is indicated here on the D751. A87 exit 23 direction Denée, D160, D123, D751.

💬 A new campsite designed by a landscape architect and very attractively laid out. Close to all the amenities in the village and positioned by a small river.

(CC) 31/3-7/7 29/8-29/11 7=6, 14=11

📍 N 47°21'37'' W 0°39'24''

www.eurocampings.co.uk/113153

892 Saumur, F-49400 / Pays de la Loire ♿ 📶 (CC€17) iD 18 A1

🔺 Flower Camping L'Ile d'Offard*****
🚸 boulevard de Verden
📅 17 Mar - 28 Oct
☎ +33 (0)2-41403000
@ iledoffard@flowercampings.com

1 ADE**JM**NOPRT	ABFG**N**UV 6
2 ACFGOPRVWX	ABDE**FGH** 7
3 BE**K**LMQT	ABCDEFGJNQRSTUV 8
4 A**B**FHLNO**PTUVX**	AEFQRV 9
5 ACDEFHJKL**N**	ABDFGHJNPRV 10

10A CEE ❶ €36.00
4,5ha 187**T**(100-120m²) 141**P** ❷ €48.00

🚗 The campsite is on an island in the Loire opposite Saumur castle. Easily accessible via the N152, D947 or N147.

💬 The campsite is located in a verdant 4.5-hectare park between both banks of the Loire. 15-minute walk from the centre of Saumur, where a number of events are organised throughout the year. An exceptional location. Vineyards, culture and tradition. CampingCard ACSI is valid for comfort pitches, not for privilege pitches.

(CC) 17/3-29/6 1/9-27/10 7=6

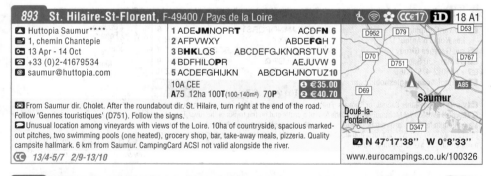

📍 N 47°15'36'' W 0°3'52''

www.eurocampings.co.uk/103524

893 St. Hilaire-St-Florent, F-49400 / Pays de la Loire ♿ 📶 ❄ (CC€17) iD 18 A1

🔺 Huttopia Saumur****
🚸 1, chemin Chantepie
📅 13 Apr - 14 Oct
☎ +33 (0)2-41679534
@ saumur@huttopia.com

1 ADE**JM**NOPR**T**	ACDF**N** 6
2 AFPVWXY	ABDE**FGH** 7
3 B**HK**LQS	ABCDEFGJKNQRSTUV 8
4 BDFHILO**PR**	AEJUVW 9
5 ACDEFGHIJKN	ABCDGHJNOTUZ 10

10A CEE ❶ €35.00
A75 12ha 100**T**(100-140m²) 70**P** ❷ €40.70

🚗 From Saumur dir. Cholet. After the roundabout dir. St. Hilaire, turn right at the end of the road. Follow 'Gennes touristiques' (D751). Follow the signs.

💬 Unusual location among vineyards with views of the Loire. 10ha of countryside, spacious marked-out pitches, two swimming pools (one heated), grocery shop, bar, take-away meals, pizzeria. Quality campsite hallmark. 6 km from Saumur. CampingCard ACSI not valid alongside the river.

(CC) 13/4-5/7 2/9-13/10

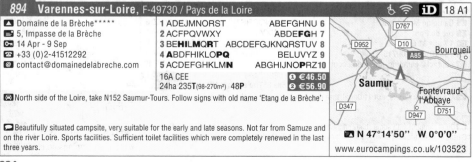

📍 N 47°17'38'' W 0°8'33''

www.eurocampings.co.uk/100326

894 Varennes-sur-Loire, F-49730 / Pays de la Loire ♿ 📶 iD 18 A1

🔺 Domaine de la Brèche*****
🚸 5, Impasse de la Brèche
📅 14 Apr - 9 Sep
☎ +33 (0)2-41512292
@ contact@domainedelabreche.com

1 ADEJMNORST	ABEFGHNU 6
2 ACFPQVWXY	ABDE**FGH** 7
3 BE**HILMQR**T	ABCDEFGJKNQRSTUV 8
4 A**B**DFHIKLO**PQ**	BELUVYZ 9
5 ACDEFGHKLM**N**	ABGHIJNO**P**RZG 10

16A CEE ❶ €46.50
24ha 235**T**(98-270m²) 48**P** ❷ €56.90

🚗 North side of the Loire, take N152 Saumur-Tours. Follow signs with old name 'Etang de la Brèche'.

💬 Beautifully situated campsite, very suitable for the early and late seasons. Not far from Samuze and on the river Loire. Sports facilities. Sufficient toilet facilities which were completely renewed in the last three years.

📍 N 47°14'50'' W 0°0'0''

www.eurocampings.co.uk/103523

895 Assérac, F-44410 / Pays de la Loire   ♿ 🛜 (CC€13) ♦♦ **iD** 46

- 🏠 Camping Du Domaine De Pont Mahé***
- 📧 13 rue Pont-Mahé
- 📅 31 Mar - 13 Oct
- ☎ +33 (0)2-40017498
- @ contact@pont-mahe.com

1 ADE**JM**NOPQRST	CDFGKNPQRSTXY	6
2 BEHMOPVWX	ABE**FG**	7
3 ALQS	ABCDFNRSV	8
4 BCDFHILNOPQ	ABEJ	9
5 ABEFGH**NO**	ABDFHIJPSTV	10

Ad on this page   10A CEE   ❶ €32.60
1,5ha 34**T**(90-120m²)   53**P**   ❷ €42.60

🗺 N165 Nantes-Lorient exit La Roche Bernard, dir. Guérande as far as Assérac. In the centre drive towards Pont-Mahe. Campsite is located on the right in the centre of this small village.
🏖 Small family campsite near the sea with pitches separated by hedges and well maintained toilet facilities. The pitches behind the toilet block are quieter. Special coast with bay that you can walk across during low tide. Reception closed from 1:00 p.m. to 2:00 p.m.
CC 31/3-6/7   1/9-12/10

Damgan   La Porte-Garel
D34   D315   D33   D83   D774

🗺 N 47°26'50''   W 2°27'0''
www.eurocampings.co.uk/112344

France

---

896 Assérac, F-44410 / Pays de la Loire   ♿ 🛜 (CC€17) **iD** 46

- 🏠 Le Moulin de l'Eclis****
- 📧 5 bis rue de la Plage, Pont Mahé
- 📅 1 Apr - 4 Nov
- ☎ +33 (0)2-40017669
- @ info@camping-leclis.com

1 ADE**JM**NOPRST	ABCFGHIKNPQSWXY	6
2 EFHMOPVWXY	ABDE**FG**H	7
3 AE**H**LQS	ABCDEFGHIJKNPQRSTUV	8
4 BCDFHILNO**PUVXYZ**	EJNQRUV	9
5 ACDEFGHJK**O**	ABDGHIJN**P**TUVZ	10

16A CEE   ❶ €41.60
3,8ha 79**T**(90-140m²)   97**P**   ❷ €53.60

🗺 N165/E60 Nantes-Vannes, after La Roche-Bernard dir. Guérande/La Baule as far as Herbignac, then to Assérac. In centre at roundabout (with houses in middle) dir. Pont-Mahé and follow signs.
🏖 Site with covered and open pools. Some pitches have sea views. Shellfish can be dug from the sand. Good cycling and walking. Luxurious toilet facilities with Eco label. Kite surfing centre. Restaurant. Reception closed 12:00-2:00 pm. Wifi free out of season.
CC 1/4-3/5   22/5-6/7   3/9-3/11

N165   D139   D34   D83   Herbignac   D33
Saint-Lyphard
La Turballe   D774   D47

🗺 N 47°26'41''   W 2°27'2''
www.eurocampings.co.uk/116755

---

897 Batz-sur-Mer, F-44740 / Pays de la Loire   ♿ 🛜 (CC€17) **iD** 46

- 🏠 Flower Camping Les Paludiers****
- 📧 rue Nicolas Appert
- 📅 30 Mar - 30 Sep
- ☎ +33 (0)2-40601728
- @ paludiers@flowercampings.com

1 ADE**JM**NOPQRS**T**	ABCDFIKMNOQRSTWXY**Z**	6
2 EHMOPQVWXY	BE**FG**H	7
3 BEF**IK**LQT	ABCDEFGIJKNOQRS	8
4 BCDEFHILNO**PQ**	BCELMOQRUV	9
5 ABDEFGHJKM**O**	ABDFGHIJMPSTVW	10

10A CEE   ❶ €37.10
8ha 120**T**(80-120m²)   152**P**   ❷ €49.60

🗺 Nantes-Lorient N165, via N171 direction St. Nazaire. Then follow Guérande, before Guérande turn onto the D774 at roundabout to Le Croisic and Batz-sur-Mer, then turn left just past Batz village.
🏖 Located on a neck of land about 500m wide on a headland, close to La Baule. Pitches separated by hedges and 100m from a the beach. A trip through salt marshes on car-free roads is possible. Reception closed 12:00-3:00 pm.
CC 31/3-6/7   25/8-29/9   7=6

D774   D47   D45   La Baule-Escoublac

🗺 N 47°16'42''   W 2°29'31''
www.eurocampings.co.uk/111513

898 Guémené-Penfao, F-44290 / Pays de la Loire ⊚ (CC€15) iD 13 B3

- 🏕 Flower Camping L'Hermitage★★★
- 🏠 46 avenue du Paradis
- 🗓 1 Apr - 15 Oct
- ☎ +33 (0)2-40792348
- @ camping.hermitage@orange.fr

1	AJMNOPRT	ABFGHN 6
2	BCOPRVXY	ABDEFH 7
3	AELMNQT	ABCDFHNRV 8
4	EFHILNOP	BDEFJU 9
5	ABDEFGHMN	ABGHJLOTU 10

Ad on this page 6A CEE ❶ €22.50
2,8ha 55T(36-70m²) 35P ❷ €31.00

🚗 Redon-Châteaubriant, exit Guémené-Penfao. Campsite signposted.

💬 A pleasant and informal campsite in natural surroundings with three rivers.

CC 1/4-7/7 25/8-14/10 7=6

N 47°37'33" W 1°49'8"
www.eurocampings.co.uk/113922

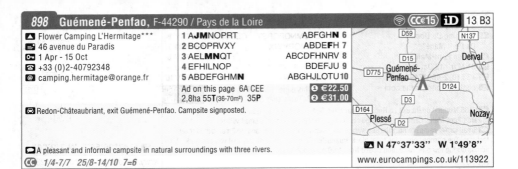

BRETAGNE L'Hermitage ★★★

Open from 01/04 until 15/10 - 90 PITCHES

SEBASTIEN ET HELENE MERVAILLE
46 avenue du Paradis
44290 Guémené-Penfao
Tel. 02-40792348
E-mail: camping.hermitage@orange.fr
Internet: www.campinglhermitage.com

Campsites friendly by nature

899 Guérande, F-44350 / Pays de la Loire ♿ ⊚ (CC€13) iD 46

- 🏕 Camping La Fontaine★★★
- 🏠 rte de Saint Molf -D233- Kersavary
- 🗓 14 Apr - 30 Sep
- ☎ +33 (0)2-40249619
- @ lafontaine.guerande@orange.fr

1	ADEJLNOPQRST	ABFG 6
2	AMOPVWXY	ABDEFGH 7
3	ALQ	ABCDEFGIKNQRSTUV 8
4	BCDFH	AE 9
5	ADEHM	ABDIJPR 10

8-10A CEE ❶ €24.90
2,5ha 80T(100-150m²) 36P ❷ €30.90

🚗 Nantes E60 and N171 dir. St. Nazaire, N171 dir. Guérande. Then past several roundabouts to Vannes, then D233 dir. St. Molf, campsite signs after 500 metres.
💬 A campsite in the countryside. Pitches min. 100 m², in the sun or half-shaded. Comfortable, modern toilet facilities but not sheltered from the wind, heated swimming pools 100 m². Well located for visits to historic Guérande and nearby salt marshes. Reception closed from 12:30 pm to 2:30 pm.

CC 14/4-6/7 25/8-29/9

La Baule-Escoublac

N 47°20'57" W 2°26'3"
www.eurocampings.co.uk/120789

900 Guérande, F-44350 / Pays de la Loire ♿ ⊚ (CC€19) ♛♙ iD 46

- 🏕 Domaine de Léveno★★★★
- 🏠 Lieu dit Léveno
- 🗓 7 Apr - 23 Sep
- ☎ +33 (0)2-40247930
- @ domaine.leveno@wanadoo.fr

1	ADEJMNOPRST	ABCDFGHIX 6
2	ABMPVWXY	ABDEFGH 7
3	BCDEIKLMQS	ABCDEFGIJKLMNOQRSTUV 8
4	BCDFHIKLNOPQRV	AEJUV 9
5	ACDEFGHJKLMNO	ABDGHIJNOPSZ 10

Ad on page 330 10A ❶ €47.10
10ha 74T(100-250m²) 475P ❷ €63.10

🚗 N165 Nantes-Lorient. Exit La Roche-Bernard. Direction Guérande/La Baule via D774. At roundabout (near Guérande) with Super Leclerc supermarket follow signs. Site 1 km beyond supermarket.
💬 Large luxurious site, pitches around toilet block, separated from mobile homes by trees and bushes. Well located for visiting medieval Guerande and the salt marshes. Shops and hypermarket 1.8 km. Reception closed between 1:30 and 2:30 pm. Excellent restaurant.

CC 7/4-1/7 3/9-22/9 15=14

Guérande

Saint-Nazaire

N 47°20'0" W 2°23'26"
www.eurocampings.co.uk/109840

901 Guérande, F-44350 / Pays de la Loire  46

- Le Domaine de Bréhadour****
- route du Bréhadour
- 7 Apr - 23 Sep
- +33 (0)2-40176515
- info@domainedebrehadour.com

1	ADE**JL**NOPQRST	CDFGH	6
2	ABMPTVWXY	ABDE**FG**	7
3	B**GHJ**LMQT	ABCDEFGKNQRSTV	8
4	BCDFHKNO**P**	EFUV	9
5	ABDEFGHJKM	ABDFGHIJMO**P**TUV	10

6-10A CEE ❶ €33.10
8ha 124**T**(100-150m²) 136**P** ❷ €38.60

🚐 Nantes-Vannes via N165/E60 exit Guérande/La Baule, at roundabout near Guérande follow signs Bréhadour.
💬 Good, comfortable campsite with a number of sheltered pitches between trees and hedges, a number of other pitches are more open and have more sun, close to the medieval town of Guérande. About 10 minutes from the beaches of La Turballe or the more crowded La Baule by car. Reception closed between 12.30 and 3:00 pm.

CC 7/4-7/7 25/8-22/9 7=6

🔳 N 47°20'32'' W 2°25'4''

www.eurocampings.co.uk/103281

902 La Baule, F-44500 / Pays de la Loire 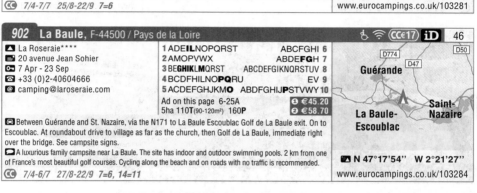 46

- La Roseraie****
- 20 avenue Jean Sohier
- 7 Apr - 23 Sep
- +33 (0)2-40604666
- camping@laroseraie.com

1	ADE**IL**NOPQRST	ABCFGHI	6
2	AMOPVWX	ABDE**FG**H	7
3	BE**GHIKLM**QRST	ABCDEFGIKNQRSTUV	8
4	BCDFHILNO**PQ**RU	EV	9
5	ACDEFGHJKM**O**	ABDFGHIJ**P**STVWY	10

Ad on this page 6-25A ❶ €45.20
5ha 110**T**(90-120m²) 160**P** ❷ €58.70

🚐 Between Guérande and St. Nazaire, via the N171 to La Baule Escoublac Golf de La Baule exit. On to Escoublac. At roundabout drive to village as far as the church, then Golf de La Baule, immediate right over the bridge. See campsite signs.
💬 A luxurious family campsite near La Baule. The site has indoor and outdoor swimming pools. 2 km from one of France's most beautiful golf courses. Cycling along the beach and on roads with no traffic is recommended.

CC 7/4-6/7 27/8-22/9 7=6, 14=11

🔳 N 47°17'54'' W 2°21'27''

www.eurocampings.co.uk/103284

903 La Bernerie-en-Retz, F-44760 / Pays de la Loire  46

- Les Écureuils****
- 24 ave Gilbert Burlot
- 30 Mar - 29 Sep
- +33 (0)2-40827695
- camping.les-ecureuils@wanadoo.fr

1	ADE**IL**NOPQRST	ABCDFGHIKMNOPQRSTW	6
2	AEHMOPVWXY	ABDE**FG**H	7
3	BDEF**KL**MQST	ABCDEFKNOQRSTUV	8
4	BCDFHLNO**P**	BEJLMOQRUVW	9
5	ADEFGHJM	ABDGHIJNO**P**STV	10

10A ❶ €42.80
5,5ha 155**T**(80-110m²) 158**P** ❷ €50.80

🚐 Ring road Nantes-West, exit Noirmoutier/Pornic via D13 dir. Noirmoutier. Exit La Bernerie-en-Retz dir. centre. After 400 metres (50 metres before the railway line) right, then immediately left.
💬 350 m from the sea and the centre of La Bernerie-en-Retz. A beautiful sandy beach and cycle routes. New toilet facilities. Pets maximum 10 kg allowed on camping pitches. Attractive village with a lovely beach. Reception closed from 12:30 to 2:00 pm.

CC 30/3-7/7 26/8-28/9

🔳 N 47°5'3'' W 2°2'14''

www.eurocampings.co.uk/108424

904 La Plaine-sur-Mer, F-44770 / Pays de la Loire ♿ 📶 ✿ (CC€17) 👫 iD 46

- La Tabardière★★★★
- 2 rte d.l. Tabardière
- 14 Apr - 22 Sep
- +33 (0)2-40215883
- info@camping-la-tabardiere.com

1 ADE**JM**NOPQRST	ABCDFGHX	6
2 AMPTUVWXY	ABDE**FGH**	7
3 BE**GHIK**LMQTU	ABCDEFGKNOQRSTUV	8
4 BCDFHILNO**PQR**	EFJUV	9
5 ACDEFGHJM**O**	ABDFGHIJMNPSTW	10

Ad on this page 6-10A CEE ❶ €40.20
6ha 148**T**(90-110m²) 114**P** ❷ €51.20

🚗 D213 St. Nazaire-Pornic, take the exit La Plaine-sur-Mer/Pornic-Ouest. Subsequently, take the D13 towards La Plaine-sur-Mer until you see the signs to the campsite.
💬 A pleasant and peaceful campsite with well maintained toilet facilities. There is a choice of pitches either on the level terraces or large open pitches higher up the campsite. The swimming pool is always heated to 28°C. Reception closed between 12:30 and 2:00 pm.
CC 14/4-8/7 26/8-21/9 7=6, 14=11, 21=17

Tharon-Plage
Pornic
D5 D213 D86 D751 D13

📷 N 47°8'27'' W 2°9'12''
www.eurocampings.co.uk/103291

La Tabardière ★ ★ ★

• Heated swimming pool • Water slide, paddling pool • Bar, snacks, shops • Miniature golf • Play area
Wooden chalet and caravan rental (2-8 persons)

2 rte d.l. Tabardière
44770 La Plaine-sur-Mer
Tel. 02-40215883 • Fax 02-40210268
E-mail: info@camping-la-tabardiere.com   www.camping-la-tabardiere.com

---

905 La Plaine-sur-Mer, F-44770 / Pays de la Loire ♿ 📶 (CC€17) 👫 iD 46

- Le Ranch★★★★
- chemin des Hautes Raillères
- 31 Mar - 30 Sep
- +33 (0)2-40215262
- info@camping-le-ranch.com

1 ADE**JM**NOPQRST	ABEFGHX	6
2 AHMPVWXY	ABDE**FGH**	7
3 BDE**HK**LMQS	ABCDFIKNQRSV	8
4 BCDEFHILNO**PQ**	EJMNOQRUVWY	9
5 ABDEFGHJM**NO**	ABDGHIJO**P**STVW	10

Ad on this page 10A ❶ €41.70
3,5ha 85**T**(90-100m²) 104**P** ❷ €55.70

🚗 South of St. Nazaire via D213, La Route Bleu, exit La Plaine-sur-Mer and Tharon-Plage. Via D96 to La Plaine-sur-Mer and follow campsite signs. (SatNav unreliable in immediate vicinity.)
💬 Quiet, well maintained campsite with pitches between hedges and shade-giving trees. 800m from the beach. Open-air and covered swimming pools. Wifi free on the entire site outside high season. Reception closed 12:00-2:00 pm. Arrival possible until 11:00 pm.
CC 31/3-6/7 27/8-29/9 14=13

Saint-Brevin-les-Pins
Pornic
D86 D213 D5 D751 D13

📷 N 47°9'17'' W 2°9'55''
www.eurocampings.co.uk/113898

Dream, share, enjoy!

AT 800 METERS FROM THE SEA
LA PLAINE-SUR-MER (44)
www.camping-le-ranch.com

Camping ★★★★
Le Ranch

France

906 La Turballe, F-44420 / Pays de la Loire

⛺ La Falaise★★★★
✉ 1 boulevard de Belmont
📅 30 Mar - 28 Oct
☎ +33 (0)2-40233253
@ info@camping-de-la-falaise.com

1 ADEF**JM**NOPQRST	CDFGKNOPQRSTVWXY**Z**	6
2 AEFHMOPQVWXY	ABDE**FG**H	7
3 ACE**KM**QS	CDEFGHIJKNPQRST	8
4 FH	EMNOPQRUVWYZ	9
5 ADEFHJM**O**	ABCDFGHIJNPR	10

Ad on this page 10A CEE ❶ €37.10
3ha 63T(100-130m²) 85P ❷ €50.50

🚗 N165/E60 Vannes-Nantes, exit Guérande/La Baule. Via D774 as far as Guérande, via D99 to La Turballe, follow campsite signs or Super U on D99 when entering village.
🏕 Directly at beach. Luxury toilet facilities. Indoor pool. Pitches divided by hedges. Located on edge of village, 400m from supermarket. 10 pitches with sea views. Please book in May and June. Reception closed 12:30-1:30 pm. CampingCard ACSI rate includes children up to 4 years.
CC 30/3-6/7 26/8-27/10

D83
D774
Λ Guérande
D45
Λ La Baule-Escoublac
📷 N 47°21'13'' W 2°31'4''
www.eurocampings.co.uk/121449

France

907 Le Croisic, F-44490 / Pays de la Loire

⛺ de l'Océan Village et Spa★★★★★
✉ route de la Maison Rouge
📅 7 Apr - 23 Sep
☎ +33 (0)2-40230769
@ camping-ocean@wanadoo.fr

1 ADE**JM**NOPRST	ABEFGHIKNOPQRSTWXY**Z**	6
2 AEHKMOPVWXY	ABDE**FG**H	7
3 BCDE**GHJ**LMQS	ABCDEFGIJKNQRSTUV	8
4 BCDFHILNO**PQR** TUVXYZ	EIUV	9
5 ACDEFGHJLM**O**	ABDGHIJO**P**R	10

Ad on page 330 10A ❶ €57.10
7,5ha 60T(90-120m²) 340P ❷ €75.10

🚗 N165-E60 to Nantes, and N171 to Guérande. Before Guérande head towards Le Croisic (D774) at the roundabout. Just before centre of Le Croisic follow signs.
🏕 Campsite close to Le Croisic with outdoor leisure pool and super deluxe indoor pool with wellness centre. The small town with attractive harbour is within walking distance. Salt marshes between headland and Guérande. Just 800m from a supermarket. Reception closed 12:30-2:00 pm.
CC 7/4-1/7 3/9-22/9 15=14

D774
Λ La Baule-Escoublac
📷 N 47°17'51'' W 2°32'7''
www.eurocampings.co.uk/110312

908 Les Moutiers-en-Retz, F-44760 / Pays de la Loire

⛺ Flower Camping Les Brillas★★★
✉ Le Bois des Tréans
📅 6 Apr - 30 Sep
☎ +33 (0)2-40827978
@ info@campinglesbrillas.com

1 ADE**JL**NOPQRST	CDFGNPQSX	6
2 AFGHMOPVWXY	ABDE**FG**H	7
3 BF**K**LQST	ABCDEFNQRSTUV	8
4 BCDFHIKLNO**PQ**	AEUVW	9
5 ABDEFGHJK**O**	ABDFGHIJLPSTVX	10

Ad on page 331 10A ❶ €31.20
4,5ha 53T(82-278m²) 134P ❷ €43.20

🚗 From ring Nantes-West, exit Noirmoutier/Pornic, continue towards Noirmoutier/Pornic as far as Les Moutiers-en-Retz village, then follow campsite signs.
🏕 A campsite with a choice of pitches between hedges or on an open field. Well maintained toilets. All amenities open from early May. Peaceful and close to a small town and the sea. Centre for farming oysters and mussels. Reception closed 12:00-2:00 pm. Bar/restaurant open weekends out of season.
CC 6/4-6/7 1/9-29/9

D86
D213
D5
Pornic
D751
D13
D758 Machecoul
📷 N 47°4'30'' W 2°0'27''
www.eurocampings.co.uk/117210

---

909 Mesquer, F-44420 / Pays de la Loire ♿ 📶 iD 46

- 🏕 Le Château du Petit Bois***
- 🏠 1820 rte de Kerlagadec
- 📅 29 Mar - 30 Sep
- ☎ +33 (0)2-40426877
- @ info@campingdupetitbois.com

1 ADE**JM**NOPQRST	ABFGHIX	6
2 BMOPVWXY	ABDE**FG**H	7
3 BE**GHKL**QS	ABCDEFKNQRSV	8
4 BCDFHILNO**PQ**	EUV	9
5 ADEFGHJKMN	ABHIJPRW	10

10A CEE
10ha 126T(100-130m²) 106P ❶ €30.60 ❷ €41.80

🚗 N165/E60 Nantes-Vannes via exit Guérande/Pénestin. Via D774 direction Guérande and the D52 via St. Molf to Mesquer and Piriac, located on the D52.

💬 Peaceful campsite 1 km from the village and 1.5 km from the sea. The pitches are located to the rear among old pine trees. There are a few sunny pitches near the toilet blocks on the central field. The surrounding area is virtually flat and ideal for cycle tours.

Pénestin · D34
D315
D83
D47
D774
Guérande

📍 N 47°23'49'' W 2°28'19''
www.eurocampings.co.uk/101456

---

910 Nantes, F-44300 / Pays de la Loire ♿ 📶 ❀ (CC€19) iD 17 B1

- 🏕 Nantes Camping*****
- 🏠 21 boulevard du Petit Port
- 📅 1 Jan - 31 Dec
- ☎ +33 (0)2-40744794
- @ nantes-camping@nge-nantes.fr

1 ADE**JM**NOPRST	EH**N**	6
2 ABCGOPRSVXY	BEGH	7
3 ABDI**KL**Q	BDFJKNQRSTUV	8
4 DFHIO**V**	AEFJV	9
5 ABDEFGHKL	ABCHIJNPRVZ	10

16A CEE
A50 8,5ha 83T(100-200m²) 78P ❶ €41.10 ❷ €49.55

🚗 Take N39 Nantes from the ring road north, exit Porte de la Chapelle. Direction Nantes Centre. Campsite signposted and located at roundabout.

💬 Nantes Camping is located in grounds covering 8.5 hectares and is a natural campsite, a few minutes from the centre of Nantes.

ⓒ 1/1-13/7 3/9-31/12

N137 A11
N165 N137
D751
Nantes
Saint-Sébastien-sur-Loire
D74
D59

📍 N 47°14'36'' W 1°33'24''
www.eurocampings.co.uk/116002

France

---

911 Nort-sur-Erdre, F-44390 / Pays de la Loire   🚿 📶 CC€15 iD 13 B3

🏕 Seasonova Port Mulon***
🚏 rue des Mares Noires
📅 1 Apr - 31 Oct
☎ +33 (0)2-40722357
@ contact@camping-portmulon.com

1 ABDE**JM**NOPRST	AB**NUX** 6
2 BCGPVXY	ABDE**FG** 7
3 AFL	ABCDFHIKNPRSTUV 8
4 FGH	BEJQV 9
5 ADEH	ABDFHIJ**P**RV 10
10A CEE	① €19.00
2ha 100T(88-347m²) 12P	② €24.20

🚗 Direction Sucé-sur-Erdre. Follow 'camping' on the left.

💬 A pleasant, refurbished campsite with many opportunities for the water enthusiast. Modern toilet facilities. Located by a river and close to a marina.

CC 1/4-7/7 27/8-30/10 7=6

Saffré   D33   D121   D178   D164   D16   D31   Casson   D537   D69   Sucé-sur-Erdre   A11

🏕 N 47°25'42''   W 1°29'51''
www.eurocampings.co.uk/116003

---

912 Piriac-sur-Mer, F-44420 / Pays de la Loire   🚿 📶 CC€15 iD 46

🏕 Parc du Guibel***
🚏 route de Kerdrien
📅 1 Apr - 30 Sep
☎ +33 (0)2-40235267
@ camping@parcduguibel.com

1 ADE**JM**NOPQRST	ABEFGHINOPQSVWX 6
2 BHMPVWXY	ABDE**FG**H 7
3 BE**GH**ILQ	CDEFKNORSTUV 8
4 BCDFHILNO**PQ**	EJ 9
5 ACDEFGHJLN	ABFGHIJORZ 10
10A CEE	① €29.35
14ha 300T(100-200m²) 138P	② €40.10

🚗 N165/E60 Nantes-Vannes. Guérande/La Baule exit. Via D774 direction Guérande and via D52 to St. Molf and Piriac-sur-Mer. Campsite located on the D52.
💬 Lovely wooded site with marked-out pitches among pine trees. You will be assigned a quiet pitch if you wish. Comfortable toilet facilities. Nice heated indoor and outdoor pools, you can swim from inside to outside. Peaceful almost level surroundings 1,200 m from a quiet beach and village 3.5 km away.

CC 1/4-14/7 1/9-29/9

D192   D83   La Turballe   D774   D47   **Guérande**   D45

🏕 N 47°23'10''   W 2°30'36''
www.eurocampings.co.uk/109841

---

913 Pornic, F-44210 / Pays de la Loire   🚿 📶 CC€19 iD 46

🏕 La Boutinardière****
🚏 23 rue de la Plage de la Boutinard.
📅 7 Apr - 23 Sep
☎ +33 (0)2-40820568
@ info@laboutinardiere.com

1 ADE**JM**NOPQRST	ABEFGHIKNOPQRSTWXY 6
2 AEHMOPVWXY	ABDE**FG**H 7
3 BCDE**HIKLM**QRST	ABCDEFGHIJKNOQRSTUV 8
4 BCDFHILNO**PQRTU**V**XZ**	BCEIJLMOQRUV 9
5 ACDEFGHJKLM**O**	ABDFGHIJNO**P**ST 10
Ad on page 330 6-10A CEE	① €53.10
8ha 100T(80-120m²) 320P	② €67.60

🚗 Take the exit La Boutinardière/La Rogére at the D13 between Pornic and Bourgneuf-en-Retz, west of Nantes. Follow the signs to the campsite.
💬 Family campsite with well maintained toilet facilities. The pitches are separated by hedges. 200 m from the sea with a sheltered sandy beach between two cliffs. Open air swimming pool 400 m², indoor pool 300 m² with sauna, steam bath and beauty centre, good restaurant. Reception closed from 12:30 to 2:00 pm.

CC 6/5-8/5 13/5-18/5 21/5-6/7 2/9-22/9 15=14

Saint-Michel-Chef-Chef   D58   D86   **Pornic**   D751   D5   D13   D758

🏕 N 47°5'52''   W 2°3'7''
www.eurocampings.co.uk/109671

914 Pornic, F-44210 / Pays de la Loire

  ♿ 🛜 ❀ (CC€17) iD 46

▲ Le Patisseau★★★★
🏠 29 rue du Patisseau
🗓 7 Apr - 23 Sep
☎ +33 (0)2-40821039
@ contact@lepatisseau.com

1	ADE**IL**NOPQRST	ABEFGHIX	6
2	ABMOPUVWXY	ABDE**FGH**	7
3	BDEF**K**LQT ABCDEFGIJKNQRSTUV		8
4	BCDFHILNO**PQ**RTUY**Z** BEJLUVWZ		9
5	ACDEFGHJKL**O** ABDFGHIJN**P**STV		10

10A CEE   ❶ €45.20
4,5ha 67**T**(80-120m²) 130**P**   ❷ €59.20

🗺 South of St. Nazaire via the D213 as far as the Pornic/Le Clion-sur-Mer exit. Follow the campsite signs at the roundabout towards Le Clion-sur-Mer.
💬 Lovely site with luxurious heated toilet facilities and indoor swimming pool. 300 m² outdoor pool. Great restaurant. The site is located in a green belt close to Pornic. Marked footpaths, a sports complex and cycle tracks nearby. Category 1 and 2 dogs are not permitted. Reception closed 12:30-2:00 pm.
© 7/4-6/7   1/9-22/9 7=6, 14=12, 21=18

🖼 N 47°7'8''   W 2°4'23''
www.eurocampings.co.uk/101457

---

915 Pornichet, F-44380 / Pays de la Loire

  ♿ 🛜 (CC€17) ⚤ iD 46

▲ Du Bugeau★★★
🏠 33 avenue de Loriettes
🗓 7 Apr - 30 Sep
☎ +33 (0)2-40610202
@ campingdubugeau@wanadoo.fr

1	ADE**JM**NOPRST CDFKNOPQRSTVX		6
2	AEHOPVWXY	ABDE**FGH**	7
3	B**K**LQ	ABCDEFKNQRSV	8
4	BDFHIO	ELMOQR	9
5	ABDEFGHJ**NO** ABDGHIJPST		10

Ad on this page 10A   ❶ €35.10
2ha 61**T**(70-95m²) 57**P**   ❷ €47.60

🗺 Via the D92 from St. Nazaire dir. La Baule and Pornichet. At roundabout with Carrefour supermarket, dir. St. Sébastien. Turn left before the church, 400 metres further, entrance on the left.
💬 Quiet campsite close to the beach. Divided into small fields separated by hedges, with several trees between the pitches providing shade. The large promenade with its well-known half-moon beach is 1 km away. Approx. 1 km from supermarket, 700 metres from the beach.
© 7/4-6/7   26/8-29/9

🖼 N 47°15'10''   W 2°19'10''
www.eurocampings.co.uk/103286

CAMPING DU BUGEAU
★ ★ ★
(CC) **Open from April 7th to September 30th**

44380 Pornichet
Tel. 0033-2-40610202
www.campingdubugeau.com

---

916 Préfailles, F-44770 / Pays de la Loire

  ♿ 🛜 (CC€17) iD 46

▲ Eléovic★★★★
🏠 route de la pointe Saint-Gildas
🗓 30 Mar - 30 Sep
☎ +33 (0)2-40216160
@ contact@camping-eleovic.com

1	ADE**IL**NOPQRST CDFGKMNPQRSTVW		6
2	AEFHJMPTUVWXY	ABDE**FGH**	7
3	BE**HK**LQ	ABCDFKNQRSTV	8
4	BCDFHILNO**PR** BCEMOPQRVW		9
5	ABDEFGHJKLMNABCDGHIJNO**P**TUV		10

Ad on page 333 10A CEE   ❶ €38.20
56**T**(80-130m²) 97**P**   ❷ €49.20

🗺 D213 St. Nazaire-Pornic exit La Plaine-sur-Mer/Préfailles. Via D96 head towards Préfailles until you see campsite signs.
💬 Campsite in Préfailles (Loire-Atlantique) with shady and sunny marked-out pitches. View of and direct access to the sea. 900m from shops and close to cycling and walking routes. Enjoy the indoor heated pool, warm all year round, and its hydromassage beds. Spacious and extensive toilet facilities with washing facilities.
© 30/3-3/5   13/5-17/5   22/5-5/7   3/9-29/9

🖼 N 47°7'58''   W 2°13'53''
www.eurocampings.co.uk/122869

France

France

917 St. Brévin-les-Pins, F-44250 / Pays de la Loire   ♿ 🛜 (CC€17) iD   46

- 🏕 La Courance***
- ✉ 110, avenue Marechal Foch
- 📅 1 Jan - 31 Dec
- ☎ +33 (0)2-40272291
- @ info@campinglacourance.fr

1 ADEJMNOPQRST	CDFKNPQRSTWX	6
2 ABEFHIOPQTVWXY	ABDEFGH	7
3 AFLQT	BDFJNRV	8
4 BCDFHINP	EJMOQR	9
5 ABEFGHJK	ABDGHIJNPTUV	10
10A		❶ €36.00
4ha 61T(80-120m²) 143P		❷ €47.00

🚗 D213 St. Nazaire/Pornic exit St. Brévin L'Ocean, follow signs L'Ocean and Casino to roundabout west of D213. Follow signs to campsite.

💬 Campsite right on the coast, located between two village centres. Pitches are in a pine forest with lots of trees, plenty of shade and shelter, but some problems with satellite TV reception. Supermarket less than 1 km away. Good-value restaurant on the other side of the street. The campsite is open all year round.

CC 1/1-6/7 1/9-31/12

Saint-Nazaire

D47   N171   D277   D86   D5   D213

🖼 N 47°14'17" W 2°10'14"
www.eurocampings.co.uk/115011

918 St. Brévin-les-Pins, F-44250 / Pays de la Loire   ♿ 🛜 (CC€19) ♙♙ iD   46

- 🏕 Le Fief*****
- ✉ 57 chemin du Fief
- 📅 31 Mar - 23 Sep
- ☎ +33 (0)2-40272386
- @ camping@lefief.com

1 ADEJMNOPQRST	ABEFGHIKMNOPQRSTXYZ	6
2 AEHMOPVWXY	ABDEFGH	7
3 BDEFLMQR	ABCDEFGIJKNQRSTUV	8
4 BCDFHIJLNOPQRTUVXYZ	EJLMOPQRUVY	9
5 ACDEFGHJLO	ABDFGHIJNOPSTZ	10
Ad on page 334 8-10A CEE		❶ €52.00
7ha 127T(80-130m²) 246P		❷ €70.00

🚗 South of St. Nazaire via the D213, exit D5 then Casino. Follow St. Brevin-l'Océan and campsite signs.

💬 A family campsite 900 m from the beach, between the two village centres of St. Brévin-les-Pins with a market 3 times a week. Own restaurant with very reasonable prices. Beautiful outdoor and indoor swimming pools. CampingCard ACSI only for touring pitches, not for seasonal pitches. Larger motorhomes are permitted.

CC 31/3-3/5 14/5-17/5 22/5-6/7 2/9-22/9

Saint-Nazaire   Saint-Brevin-les-Pins

N171   D5   D86   D213

🖼 N 47°14'7" W 2°10'3"
www.eurocampings.co.uk/103288

919 St. Julien-de-Concelles, F-44450 / Pays de la Loire   ♿ 🛜 (CC€17) iD   17 B1

- 🏕 du Chêne***
- ✉ 1 route du Lac
- 📅 30 Mar - 14 Oct
- ☎ +33 (0)2-40541200
- @ contact@campingduchene.fr

1 ABDEJMNOPRST	CDFGNQRSTXY	6
2 ADGIOPSVWXY	BEFGH	7
3 ABFKLMQ	ABDFGKNOQRSV	8
4 FHOP	BELTUVW	9
5 ADEFHNO	ABFGHIJLPRV	10
10A CEE		❶ €23.50
2,5ha 70T(70-150m²) 29P		❷ €29.40

🚗 Exit 44 Porte du Vignoble direction St. Julien-de-Concelles.

💬 The campsite has a friendly atmosphere and is located between the Loire and several vineyards, on the edge of a lake. This is a lovely natural area for complete relaxation.

CC 30/3-7/7 26/8-13/10

La Chapelle-sur-Erdre

Nantes

D723   D751   A11   D23   D115   D37   D763

🖼 N 47°14'57" W 1°22'17"
www.eurocampings.co.uk/118204

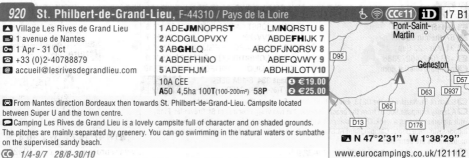

920 St. Philbert-de-Grand-Lieu, F-44310 / Pays de la Loire ♿ 🛜 CCE11 iD 17 B1

🏕 Village Les Rives de Grand Lieu
📧 1 avenue de Nantes
🗓 1 Apr - 31 Oct
☎ +33 (0)2-40788879
@ accueil@lesrivesdegrandlieu.com

1 ADE**JM**NOPRS**T**	LM**N**QRSTU 6
2 ACDGILOPVXY	ABDE**FH**IJK 7
3 AB**GH**LQ	ABCDFJNQRSV 8
4 ABDEFHINO	ABEFQVWY 9
5 ADEFHJM	ABDHIJLOTV10

10A CEE ❶ €19.00
A50 4,5ha 100T(100-200m²) 58P ❷ €25.00

🚗 From Nantes direction Bordeaux then towards St. Philbert-de-Grand-Lieu. Campsite located between Super U and the town centre.
💬 Camping Les Rives de Grand Lieu is a lovely campsite full of character and on shaded grounds. The pitches are mainly separated by greenery. You can go swimming in the natural waters or sunbathe on the supervised sandy beach.
CC 1/4-9/7 28/8-30/10

📍 N 47°2'31" W 1°38'29"
www.eurocampings.co.uk/121112

921 Ste Reine-de-Bretag./Pontchât., F-44160 / Pays de la Loire ♿ 🛜 CCE15 👫 iD 46

🏕 Camping Le Deffay****
📧 D33
🗓 26 Apr - 30 Sep
☎ +33 (0)2-40880057
@ campingledeffay@gmail.com

1 ADEILNOPQRST	CDFGNQS 6
2 ADGPUVWXY	ABCDE**FG**H 7
3 B**KL**MQST	ABCDFKNQRSTUV 8
4 FHIO**PQ**R	EJTVYZ 9
5 ABDEFGHJL**NO**	ABDFGHIJN**P**STW10

10-16A CEE ❶ €30.90
13ha 171T(100-150m²) 52P ❷ €39.70

🚗 N165/E60 Nantes-Vannes, exit Pontchâteau at the roundabout before the town direction Ste Reine-de-Bretagne or Calvaire via D33. Campsite clearly signposted.
💬 Deffay, a lovely 18th-century family estate. Pitches surrounded by flowering bushes and greenery, a number of them with a view of the ponds. Four-star comfort and tranquillity. Toilet facilities renovated in 2017.
CC 26/4-6/7 27/8-29/9

📍 N 47°26'28" W 2°9'36"
www.eurocampings.co.uk/103280

922 Aubigny, F-85430 / Pays de la Loire

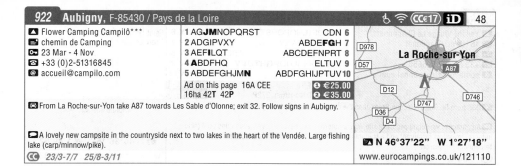

♿ 📶 ⓒⓒ€17 iD 48

- ⛺ Flower Camping Campilô***
- 🏕 chemin de Camping
- 🗓 23 Mar - 4 Nov
- ☎ +33 (0)2-51316845
- @ accueil@campilo.com

1 AG**JM**NOPQRST	CDN	6
2 ADGIPVXY	ABDE**FG**H	7
3 AE**FI**LQT	ABCDEFNPRT	8
4 **A**BDFHQ	ELTUV	9
5 ABDEFGHJM**N**	ABDFGHIJPTUV	10

Ad on this page 16A CEE   ⓵ €25.00
16ha 42**T** 42**P**   ⓶ €35.00

🚗 From La Roche-sur-Yon take A87 towards Les Sable d'Olonne; exit 32. Follow signs in Aubigny.

💬 A lovely new campsite in the countryside next to two lakes in the heart of the Vendée. Large fishing lake (carp/minnow/pike).

ⓒⓒ 23/3-7/7   25/8-3/11

La Roche-sur-Yon
D978 / D57 / A87 / D12 / D36 / D4 / D747 / D746

📷 N 46°37'22''   W 1°27'18''

www.eurocampings.co.uk/121110

France

923 Barbâtre, F-85630 / Pays de la Loire

♿ 📶 ⓒⓒ€17 iD 47

- ⛺ Sandaya Domaine Le Midi****
- 🏕 rue du Camping
- 🗓 13 Apr - 23 Sep
- ☎ +33 (0)2-51396374
- @ midi@originalcamping.com

1 ADE**JM**NOPQRST	ABEFGKNPQSW**X**Y	6
2 BEHPQTVWXY	ABDE**FG**H	7
3 ABEFILMQST	ABCDEFKNRSV	8
4 ABCDFHLNO**PQX**	AEJUV	9
5 ABCDE**N**	ABDGHJN**P**TU	10

Ad on the cover 16A CEE   ⓵ €40.20
13ha 207**T**(80-200m²) 199**P**   ⓶ €50.20

🚗 Direction Noirmoutier. Left at 3rd roundabout after bridge. Follow signs to 'Du Midi' campsite.

💬 This lovely campsite in the dunes has direct access to the beach and has an indoor and an outdoor pool, tennis court and a multi-sports pitch. In the vicinity you will find many beautiful sandy beaches and cycle routes. Various historic towns and villages in the area.

ⓒⓒ 13/4-6/7   26/8-22/9

Noirmoutier-en-l'Île
D948 / D758 / D51 / D59 / D38

📷 N 46°56'43''   W 2°11'7''

www.eurocampings.co.uk/115010

924 Brem-sur-Mer, F-85470 / Pays de la Loire

♿ 📶 ⓒⓒ€17 iD 48

- ⛺ L'Océan****
- 🏕 17 rue du Brandais
- 🗓 7 Apr - 4 Nov
- ☎ +33 (0)2-51905916
- @ locean@cybelevacances.com

1 AD**JM**NOPRST	ABEFGHIMNQS**X**	6
2 HPQVX	ABDE**FG**H	7
3 BEFLQST	ABCDEFKNOQRSTV	8
4 ABCDFHILNO**PQRY**	BEUV	9
5 ACEFGHJK**N**	ABHIJ**P**TUZ	10

16A   ⓵ €36.00
7ha 79**T**(90-120m²) 459**P**   ⓶ €46.00

🚗 Via D38 from Bretignolles-sur-Mer follow road to Les Sables d'Olonne. In Brem-sur-Mer follow signs.

💬 A large, welcoming family campsite, close to the sea. There is a water park of 1,000 m² with slides, wellness area and a toddlers' pool on the campsite. Many activities in the surroundings such as local markets and a climbing park.

ⓒⓒ 14/5-7/7   1/9-3/11

D6 / D12 / D32 / D160 / D80
Olonne-sur-Mer

📷 N 46°36'4''   W 1°50'39''

www.eurocampings.co.uk/116040

925 Brem-sur-Mer, F-85470 / Pays de la Loire ⊗ (CC€17) iD 48

- 🔺 Yelloh! Village Le Chaponnet****
- 🏠 16 rue du Chaponnet
- 📅 14 Apr - 15 Sep
- ☎ +33 (0)2-51905556
- @ contact@le-chaponnet.com

1 ADEIL NOPQRST	ABEFGHNQSX	6
2 HOPQVWXY	ABDEFGH	7
3 ABELMQT	ABCDEFKNRSV	8
4 BCDFHILNOPQRTUVY	EUV	9
5 ADEFGHJK	ABDGHIJNPTV	10

10A CEE ❶ €41.90
6ha 90T(100-120m²) 272P ❷ €51.70

🚗 D38 from St. Gilles direction Brem, then the one-way street on the right.

Saint-Gilles-Croix-de-Vie

💬 An attractive well equipped campsite with an international flavour. Lovely swimming pool (also indoors), excellent restaurant and a favourable position by the ocean. This campsite is pleasant throughout the season.

ⓒⓒ 14/4-6/7 2/9-14/9

📍 N 46°36'15'' W 1°49'57''
www.eurocampings.co.uk/103365

---

926 Brétignolles-sur-Mer, F-85470 / Pays de la Loire ⊗ ✿ (CC€15) iD 48

- 🔺 La Trévillière****
- 🏠 rue de Bellevue
- 📅 30 Mar - 29 Sep
- ☎ +33 (0)2-51330505
- @ info@chadotel.com

1 ADEIL NOPQRST	ABCDFHQSX	6
2 PRVXY	ABDEFGH	7
3 BEFILQ	ABCDEFKNQRSUV	8
4 BCDFHILNOPQ	DEJLUV	9
5 ABDEFGHJKLMN	ABDGHIJPST	10

10A CEE ❶ €36.00
3,2ha 69T(100-130m²) 101P ❷ €43.00

🚗 From St. Gilles-Croix-de-Vie take the D38 in the direction of Brétignolles. Overhead campsite sign on bend after 8 km, indicating left.

Saint-Hilaire-de-Riez

💬 A modestly sized campsite with shaded pitches on the edge of the village.

ⓒⓒ 30/3-12/7 30/8-28/9

📍 N 46°38'10'' W 1°51'30''
www.eurocampings.co.uk/107470

---

927 Brétignolles-sur-Mer, F-85470 / Pays de la Loire ♿ ⊗ iD 48

- 🔺 Les Marsouins***
- 🏠 15 rue du Prégneau
- 📅 1 Apr - 15 Oct
- ☎ +33 (0)2-51901457
- @ marsouins.85@wanadoo.fr

1 ADEIL NOPQRST	ABEFGHMNQSXY	6
2 HOPQVXY	ABDEFGH	7
3 ABEILQT	ABCDEFKNORSTV	8
4 BCDFHILNOPQRTU	EK	9
5 ABDEFGHJKM	ABFGHIJLPTU	10

10A CEE ❶ €33.00
6ha 95T(100-140m²) 208P ❷ €42.00

🚗 From Brétignolles take the D38 direction St. Gilles. Turn left 700 metres after roundabout (tourist office).

Saint-Gilles-Croix-de-Vie

Saint-Hilaire-de-Riez

💬 Typically French, cosy campsite. Flat with paths and fields. With some vegetation both in the shady and sunnier areas. Within walking distance of the sea.

📍 N 46°37'58'' W 1°51'52''
www.eurocampings.co.uk/103363

---

928 Chaillé-les-Marais, F-85450 / Pays de la Loire ⊗ (CC€13) iD 17 B2

- 🔺 L'Île Cariot***
- 🏠 rue du 8 mai
- 📅 1 Apr - 30 Sep
- ☎ +33 (0)2-51567527
- @ camping.ilecariot@gmail.com

1 ADEIL NOPRT	ABFG	6
2 PVXY	ABDEFGH	7
3 ABELQRS	ABCDEFJNRV	8
4 BCDFHIO	BEJQV	9
5 ABDEHJK	ABDGHIJOSTV	10

Ad on page 337 10A CEE ❶ €19.00
4,5ha 38T(70-120m²) 12P ❷ €26.40

🚗 From the D25, signposted in the village of Chaillé-les-Marais.

Luçon

Charron Marans Vix

💬 A friendly campsite with spacious pitches in the countryside of the 'Marais Poitevin'. Exploration tours from the campsite in a canoe (free). All amenities. Swimming pool from 15 June. Bikes for hire. Free wifi zone.

ⓒⓒ 1/4-6/7 25/8-29/9 7=6, 14=11

📍 N 46°23'31'' W 1°1'10''
www.eurocampings.co.uk/116043

L'Île Cariot ★ ★ ★

Friendly family campsite with spacious pitches in a green area near the 'Venise Verte'. From the campsite, venture out on an exploratory canoe expedition in the Marais Poitevin (free). Go crab-fishing, treasure-hunting or enjoy a mussel evening in the high season. Bicycle rental. Caravans and mobile home rental. Free wifi zone.

Rue du 8 mai · 85450 Chaillé-les-Marais
Tel. 02-51567527
E-mail: camping.ilecariot@gmail.com
www.camping-chaille-les-marais.com

France

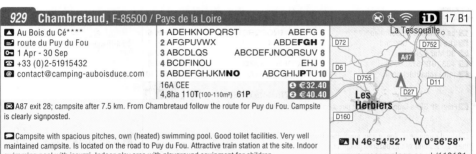

929 Chambretaud, F-85500 / Pays de la Loire
⊗ ♿ 🛜 **iD** 17 B1

- ⛰ Au Bois du Cé****
- 🏠 route du Puy du Fou
- 📅 1 Apr - 30 Sep
- ☎ +33 (0)2-51915432
- @ contact@camping-auboisduce.com

1 ADEHKNOPQRST	ABEFG	6
2 AFGPUVWX	ABDE**FGH**	7
3 ABCDLQS	ABCDEFJNOQRSUV	8
4 BCDFINOU	EHJ	9
5 ABDEFGHJKM**NO**	ABCGHIJ**P**RZTU	10

16A CEE ❶ €32.40
4,8ha 110T(100-110m²) 61P ❷ €40.40

🚗 A87 exit 28; campsite after 7.5 km. From Chambretaud follow the route for Puy du Fou. Campsite is clearly signposted.

💬 Campsite with spacious pitches, own (heated) swimming pool. Good toilet facilities. Very well maintained campsite. Is located on the road to Puy du Fou. Attractive train station at the site. Indoor swimming pool with jacuzzi. Indoor play area with playground equipment for children.

📍 N 46°54'52'' W 0°56'58''
www.eurocampings.co.uk/113161

---

930 Coëx, F-85220 / Pays de la Loire
🛜 (CC€15) **iD** 48

- ⛰ Camping RCN La Ferme du Latois****
- 🏠 D40
- 📅 6 Apr - 24 Sep
- ☎ +31 034-3745090
- @ reserveringen@rcn.nl

1 ACD**IL**NOPQRST	ABFGHN	6
2 DGPVWXY	ABDE**FG**HK	7
3 ABE**HKL**Q**R**T	ABCDEFIKNQRSV	8
4 **A**BCDEFHILO	CEUV	9
5 ACDEFGHKLMN	ABDFGHIJM**P**RZ	10

Ad on this page 6-16A CEE ❶ €41.00
21ha 164T(110-250m²) 34P ❷ €53.50

🚗 Coëx, take the D40 in the direction of Brétignolles-sur-Mer. Signposted.

💬 A lovely farm campsite with very varied vegetation and a pond. Large pitches and lovely fields with ample privacy.

CC 6/4-7/7 25/8-23/9

📍 N 46°40'36'' W 1°46'8''
www.eurocampings.co.uk/110057

931 Damvix, F-85420 / Pays de la Loire · 🦽 📶 (CC€15) iD · 17 B2

- ⛺ Camping des Conches***
- 🏕 route du Grand Port
- 📅 1 Apr - 15 Oct
- ☎ +33 (0)2-51871706
- @ campingdesconches@orange.fr

1 ADE**JM**NOPRST	AB**N**XZ	6
2 CGPVXY	ABD**E**F**H**	7
3 BLMQS	ABCDEFHNORSV	8
4 BFGHO	BE**U**VY	9
5 DEF**H**J**N**	ABDGHIJ**P**RV	10
10A CEE	❶ €20.20	
2,1ha 72**T**(80-120m²) 17**P**	❷ €26.60	

🚗 From Fontenay-le-Comte direction Niort. Then direction Maillezais, then to Damvix. Campsite signposted in Damvix village.

💬 A friendly campsite, quietly located in 'Marais de Poitevin' in the peaceful village of Damvix. Ideal for cycling and trips out in the surrounding area.

CC 1/4-29/6 1/9-14/10

🧭 N 46°18'46'' W 0°43'57''
www.eurocampings.co.uk/121806

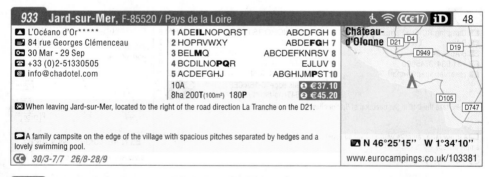

932 Givrand/St.Gilles-Croix-de-Vie, F-85800 / Pays de la Loire · 🦽 📶 (CC€15) iD · 47

- ⛺ Le Domaine de Beaulieu****
- 🏕 rue du Parc - Givrand
- 📅 30 Mar - 29 Sep
- ☎ +33 (0)2-51330505
- @ info@chadotel.com

1 AD**JM**NOPQRST	ABEFGH**N**	6
2 OPRVWX	ABDE**FGH**K	7
3 BE**IKLM**QT	ABCDEFNRSV	8
4 BCDFHILNO**PQ**	DEJLUV	9
5 ACDEFGHKLM	ABDHIJ**O**P**ST**	10
6A CEE	❶ €33.60	
8ha 127**T**(100-125m²) 183**P**	❷ €41.60	

🚗 From St. Gilles-Croix-de-Vie: D38 direction Les Sables-d'Olonne. Located on the left after 3 km.

💬 Good campsite on fine, green, maintained level grounds. The swimming pool and restaurant are the main features of this peaceful campsite.

CC 30/3-12/7 30/8-28/9

🧭 N 46°40'16'' W 1°54'13''
www.eurocampings.co.uk/103359

933 Jard-sur-Mer, F-85520 / Pays de la Loire · 🦽 📶 (CC€17) iD · 48

- ⛺ L'Océano d'Or*****
- 🏕 84 rue Georges Clémenceau
- 📅 30 Mar - 29 Sep
- ☎ +33 (0)2-51330505
- @ info@chadotel.com

1 ADE**IL**NOPQRST	ABCDFGH	6
2 HOPRVWXY	ABDE**FGH**	7
3 BE**L**MQ	ABCDEFKNRSV	8
4 BCDILNO**PQR**	EJLUV	9
5 ACDEFGHJ	ABGHIJM**P**ST	10
10A	❶ €37.10	
8ha 200**T**(100m²) 180**P**	❷ €45.20	

🚗 When leaving Jard-sur-Mer, located to the right of the road direction La Tranche on the D21.

💬 A family campsite on the edge of the village with spacious pitches separated by hedges and a lovely swimming pool.

CC 30/3-7/7 26/8-28/9

🧭 N 46°25'15'' W 1°34'10''
www.eurocampings.co.uk/103381

934 Jard-sur-Mer, F-85520 / Pays de la Loire · 📶 (CC€15) iD · 48

- ⛺ La Ventouse****
- 🏕 18bis rue Pierre Curie
- 📅 31 Mar - 30 Sep
- ☎ +33 (0)2-51335865
- @ info@campinglaventouse.com

1 ADE**IL**NOPRT	ABFG	6
2 BEOPQTUXY	ABDE**FGH**	7
3 BE**L**QT	ABCDFKNORSV	8
4 BDIO	BCELUV	9
5 ABDEFHN**O**	ABDGHIJO**P**T	10
10A	❶ €27.50	
5,5ha 113**T**(80-100m²) 65**P**	❷ €41.50	

🚗 In Jard-sur-Mer follow signs 'campings' and then signs 'Parfums d'Eté'.

💬 The charm of bush-camping on a campsite. Lovely location in a forest within walking distance of the sea and the touristic Jard-sur-Mer. Good amenities and renovated toilet facilities. Free wifi zone.

CC 31/3-6/7 25/8-29/9

🧭 N 46°24'45'' W 1°34'53''
www.eurocampings.co.uk/111354

935 L'Épine, F-85740 / Pays de la Loire

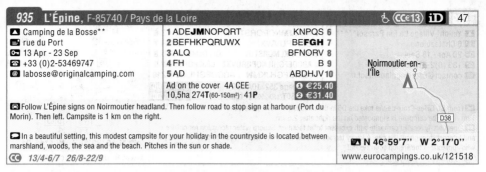

 ♿ (CC€13) iD 47

- ⛺ Camping de la Bosse**
- 🏠 rue du Port
- 📅 13 Apr - 23 Sep
- ☎ +33 (0)2-53469747
- @ labosse@originalcamping.com

1 ADE**JM**NOPQRT	KNPQS	6
2 BEFHKPQRUWX	BE**FGH**	7
3 ALQ	BFNORV	8
4 FH	B	9
5 AD	ABDHJV	10
Ad on the cover 4A CEE	❶ € 25.40	
10,5ha 274T(60-150m²) 41P	❷ € 31.40	

🗺 Follow L'Épine signs on Noirmoutier headland. Then follow road to stop sign at harbour (Port du Morin). Then left. Campsite is 1 km on the right.

💬 In a beautiful setting, this modest campsite for your holiday in the countryside is located between marshland, woods, the sea and the beach. Pitches in the sun or shade.

(CC) 13/4-6/7 26/8-22/9

Noirmoutier-en-l'Île

D38

📍 N 46°59'7" W 2°17'0"

www.eurocampings.co.uk/121518

936 La Barre-de-Monts, F-85550 / Pays de la Loire

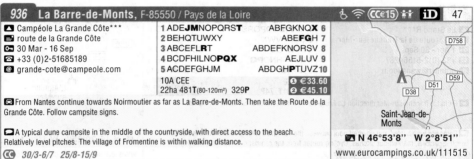

 ♿ 📶 (CC€15) 🚻 iD 47

- ⛺ Campéole La Grande Côte***
- 🏠 route de la Grande Côte
- 📅 30 Mar - 16 Sep
- ☎ +33 (0)2-51685189
- @ grande-cote@campeole.com

1 ADE**JM**NOPQRS**T**	ABFGKNQ**X**	6
2 BEHQTUWXY	ABE**FGH**	7
3 ABCEFL**R**T	ABDEFKNORSV	8
4 BCDFHILNO**PQX**	AEJLUV	9
5 ACDEFGHJM	ABDGH**P**TUVZ	10
10A CEE	❶ € 33.60	
22ha 481T(80-120m²) 329P	❷ € 45.10	

🗺 From Nantes continue towards Noirmoutier as far as La Barre-de-Monts. Then take the Route de la Grande Côte. Follow campsite signs.

💬 A typical dune campsite in the middle of the countryside, with direct access to the beach. Relatively level pitches. The village of Fromentine is within walking distance.

(CC) 30/3-6/7 25/8-15/9

D758
D59
D51
D38
Saint-Jean-de-Monts

📍 N 46°53'8" W 2°8'51"

www.eurocampings.co.uk/111515

937 La Barre-de-Monts, F-85550 / Pays de la Loire

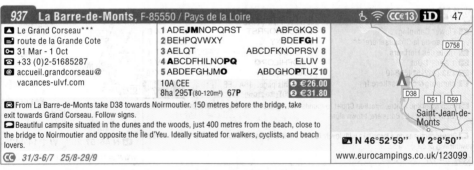

 ♿ 📶 (CC€13) iD 47

- ⛺ Le Grand Corseau***
- 🏠 route de la Grande Cote
- 📅 31 Mar - 1 Oct
- ☎ +33 (0)2-51685287
- @ accueil.grandcorseau@ vacances-ulvf.com

1 ADE**JM**NOPQRST	ABFGKQS	6
2 BEHPQVWXY	BDE**FGH**	7
3 AELQT	ABCDFKNOPRSV	8
4 **A**BCDFHILNO**PQ**	ELUV	9
5 ABDEFGHJM**O**	ABDGHO**P**TUZ	10
10A CEE	❶ € 26.00	
8ha 295T(80-120m²) 67P	❷ € 31.80	

🗺 From La Barre-de-Monts take D38 towards Noirmoutier. 150 metres before the bridge, take exit towards Grand Corseau. Follow signs.

💬 Beautiful campsite situated in the dunes and the woods, just 400 metres from the beach, close to the bridge to Noirmoutier and opposite the Île d'Yeu. Ideally situated for walkers, cyclists, and beach lovers.

(CC) 31/3-6/7 25/8-29/9

D758
D38
D51
D59
Saint-Jean-de-Monts

📍 N 46°52'59" W 2°8'50"

www.eurocampings.co.uk/123099

938 La Boissière-de-Montaigu, F-85600 / Pays de la Loire

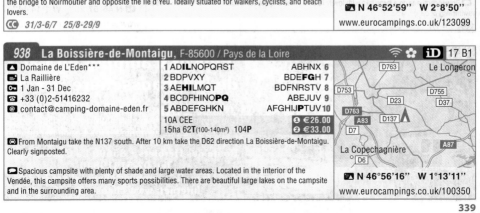

 📶 ✿ iD 17 B1

- ⛺ Domaine de L'Eden***
- 🏠 La Raillière
- 📅 1 Jan - 31 Dec
- ☎ +33 (0)2-51416232
- @ contact@camping-domaine-eden.fr

1 AD**IL**NOPQRST	ABHNX	6
2 BDPVXY	BDE**FGH**	7
3 AE**HI**LMQT	BDFNRSTV	8
4 BCDFHINO**PQ**	ABEJUV	9
5 ABDEFGHKN	AFGHIJ**P**TUV	10
10A CEE	❶ € 26.00	
15ha 62T(100-140m²) 104P	❷ € 33.00	

🗺 From Montaigu take the N137 south. After 10 km take the D62 direction La Boissière-de-Montaigu. Clearly signposted.

💬 Spacious campsite with plenty of shade and large water areas. Located in the interior of the Vendée, this campsite offers many sports possibilities. There are beautiful large lakes on the campsite and in the surrounding area.

D763 Le Longeron
D753
D755
D23
D37
D763
A83
D137
D7
A87
La Copechagnière
D6

📍 N 46°56'16" W 1°13'11"

www.eurocampings.co.uk/100350

939 La Chapelle-Hermier, F-85220 / Pays de la Loire

♿ 📶 ✿ (CC€17) iD | 48

- ▲ Yelloh! Village Le Pin Parasol*****
- 🏕 6 Châteaulong
- 📅 20 Apr - 16 Sep
- ☎ +33 (0)2-51346472
- @ contact@campingpinparasol.fr

1 ADE**JM**NOPQRST	ABEFGHIN**Q**SXYZ 6
2 DFHIPUVWX	BE**FGH** 7
3 BDEF**HKLMQR**STUV	DEFGIJKNQRSTU 8
4 **A**BCDEFGHILNO**PQ**RUV**XZ**	CEJLPQRTUVW 9
5 ABDEFGHJKM**N**	ABCDFGHIJ**NP**RZ10

Ad on page 352 10A CEE
21ha 230**T**(150-250m²) 138**P**

❶ €48.00
❷ €58.00

🚗 From St. Gilles-Croix-de-Vie take the D6 in the direction of Coëx. Follow the road as far as the D21. Turn right. The campsite is signposted on the right after 2.5 km.

💬 A beautifully located campsite with excellent toilet facilities. Superb water recreation for children, and Internet throughout the site. A lovely terrace with extraordinary views. A campsite for the camper who appreciates the French countryside!

CC 20/4-6/7 1/9-15/9

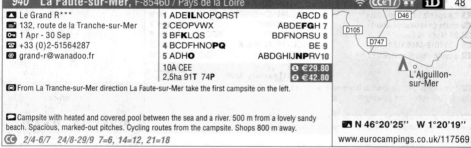

🏴 N 46°39'56'' W 1°45'21''

www.eurocampings.co.uk/109362

---

940 La Faute-sur-Mer, F-85460 / Pays de la Loire

📶 (CC€17) ⚤ iD | 48

- ▲ Le Grand R***
- 🏕 132, route de la Tranche-sur-Mer
- 📅 1 Apr - 30 Sep
- ☎ +33 (0)2-51564287
- @ grand-r@wanadoo.fr

1 ADE**IL**NOPQRST	ABCD 6
2 CEOPVWX	ABDE**FGH** 7
3 BF**KL**QS	BDFNORSU 8
4 BCDFHNO**PQ**	BE 9
5 ADH**O**	ABDGHIJ**NP**RV10

10A CEE
2,5ha 91**T** 74**P**

❶ €29.80
❷ €42.80

🚗 From La Tranche-sur-Mer direction La Faute-sur-Mer take the first campsite on the left.

💬 Campsite with heated and covered pool between the sea and a river. 500 m from a lovely sandy beach. Spacious, marked-out pitches. Cycling routes from the campsite. Shops 800 m away.

CC 2/4-6/7 24/8-29/9 7=6, 14=12, 21=18

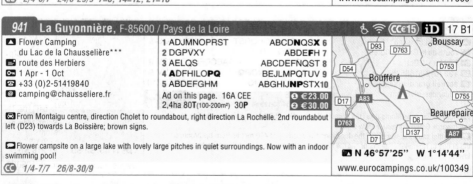

🏴 N 46°20'25'' W 1°20'19''

www.eurocampings.co.uk/117569

---

941 La Guyonnière, F-85600 / Pays de la Loire

♿ 📶 (CC€15) iD | 17 B1

- ▲ Flower Camping
  du Lac de la Chausselière***
- 🏕 route des Herbiers
- 📅 1 Apr - 1 Oct
- ☎ +33 (0)2-51419840
- @ camping@chausseliere.fr

1 ADJMNOPRST	ABCD**N**QS**X** 6
2 DGPVXY	ABDE**FH** 7
3 AELQS	ABCDEFNQST 8
4 **A**DFHILO**PQ**	BEJLMPQTUV 9
5 ABDEFGHM	ABGHIJ**NP**STX10

Ad on this page. 16A CEE
2,4ha 80**T**(100-200m²) 30**P**

❶ €23.00
❷ €30.00

🚗 From Montaigu centre, direction Cholet to roundabout, right direction La Rochelle. 2nd roundabout left (D23) towards La Boissière; brown signs.

💬 Flower campsite on a large lake with lovely large pitches in quiet surroundings. Now with an indoor swimming pool!

CC 1/4-7/7 26/8-30/9

🏴 N 46°57'25'' W 1°14'44''

www.eurocampings.co.uk/100349

France

942 La Tranche-sur-Mer, F-85360 / Pays de la Loire ◦ ⚕ 🛜 iD 48

- ▲ Baie d'Aunis Camping****
- 📧 10 rue du Pertuis Breton
- ⌚ 20 Apr - 15 Sep
- ☎ +33 (0)2-51274736
- @ info@camping-baiedaunis.com

1 ADEJKNOPQRST	ABFGKMNQRSTWXYZ	6
2 EHOPQVWXY	ABDEFGH	7
3 ABELQ	ABCDEFJKNOQRSV	8
4 BCDFHIO	EJL	9
5 ADEFGHKLMN	ABGHIJNPRZ	10

10A CEE   ❶ €37.70
2,5ha 130T(80-100m²) 19P   ❷ €54.90

🚗 From La Roche-sur-Yon take the D747. In La Tranche follow 'Centre Ville'. Then campsite signs.

💬 Sunny campsite on the edge of the village with lots of vegetation and trees offering a lot of shade. At the back of the campsite is an exit to the beautiful sandy beach.

Les Portes-en-Ré

🧭 N 46°20'46'' W 1°25'56''

www.eurocampings.co.uk/103384

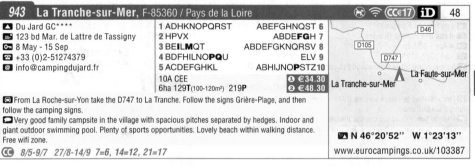

943 La Tranche-sur-Mer, F-85360 / Pays de la Loire ◦ ⊗ 🛜 (CC€17) iD 48

- ▲ Du Jard GC****
- 📧 123 bd Mar. de Lattre de Tassigny
- ⌚ 8 May - 15 Sep
- ☎ +33 (0)2-51274379
- @ info@campingdujard.fr

1 ADHKNOPQRST	ABEFGHNQST	6
2 HPVX	ABDEFGH	7
3 BEILMQT	ABDEFGKNQRSV	8
4 BDFHILNOPQU	ELV	9
5 ACDEFGHKL	ABHIJNOPSTZ	10

10A CEE   ❶ €34.30
6ha 129T(100-120m²) 219P   ❷ €48.30

🚗 From La Roche-sur-Yon take the D747 to La Tranche. Follow the signs Grière-Plage, and then follow the camping signs.

💬 Very good family campsite in the village with spacious pitches separated by hedges. Indoor and giant outdoor swimming pool. Plenty of sports opportunities. Lovely beach within walking distance. Free wifi zone.

CC 8/5-9/7 27/8-14/9 7=6, 14=12, 21=17

La Faute-sur-Mer
La Tranche-sur-Mer

🧭 N 46°20'52'' W 1°23'13''

www.eurocampings.co.uk/103387

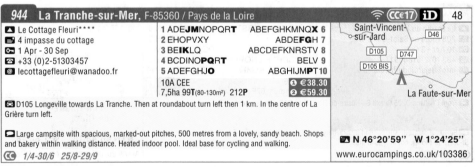

944 La Tranche-sur-Mer, F-85360 / Pays de la Loire 🛜 (CC€17) iD 48

- ▲ Le Cottage Fleuri****
- 📧 4 impasse du cottage
- ⌚ 1 Apr - 30 Sep
- ☎ +33 (0)2-51303457
- @ lecottagefleuri@wanadoo.fr

1 ADEJMNOPQRT	ABEFGHKMNQX	6
2 EHOPVXY	ABDEFGH	7
3 BEIKLQ	ABCDEFKNRSTV	8
4 BCDINOPQRT	BELV	9
5 ADEFGHJO	ABGHIJMPT	10

10A CEE   ❶ €38.30
7,5ha 99T(80-130m²) 212P   ❷ €59.30

🚗 D105 Longeville towards La Tranche. Then at roundabout turn left then 1 km. In the centre of La Grière turn left.

💬 Large campsite with spacious, marked-out pitches, 500 metres from a lovely, sandy beach. Shops and bakery within walking distance. Heated indoor pool. Ideal base for cycling and walking.

CC 1/4-30/6 25/8-29/9

Saint-Vincent-sur-Jard
La Faute-sur-Mer

🧭 N 46°20'59'' W 1°24'25''

www.eurocampings.co.uk/103386

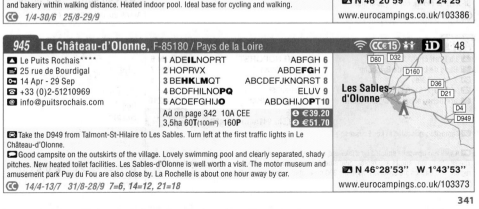

945 Le Château-d'Olonne, F-85180 / Pays de la Loire 🛜 (CC€15) ♟♟ iD 48

- ▲ Le Puits Rochais****
- 📧 25 rue de Bourdigal
- ⌚ 14 Apr - 29 Sep
- ☎ +33 (0)2-51210969
- @ info@puitsrochais.com

1 ADEILNOPRT	ABFGH	6
2 HOPRVX	ABDEFGH	7
3 BEHKLMQT	ABCDEFJKNQRST	8
4 BCDFHILNOPQ	ELUV	9
5 ACDEFGHIJO	ABDGHIJOPT	10

Ad on page 342 10A CEE   ❶ €39.20
3,5ha 60T(100m²) 160P   ❷ €51.70

🚗 Take the D949 from Talmont-St-Hilaire to Les Sables. Turn left at the first traffic lights in Le Château-d'Olonne.

💬 Good campsite on the outskirts of the village. Lovely swimming pool and clearly separated, shady pitches. New heated toilet facilities. Les Sables-d'Olonne is well worth a visit. The motor museum and amusement park Puy du Fou are also close by. La Rochelle is about one hour away by car.

CC 14/4-13/7 31/8-28/9 7=6, 14=12, 21=18

Les Sables-d'Olonne

🧭 N 46°28'53'' W 1°43'53''

www.eurocampings.co.uk/103373

France

Le Puits Rochais
★ ★ ★ ★

Modern campsite in the Vendée near a sandy beach. It has spacious and separated pitches with some shade and every comfort required. There is a new playground, multi-purpose sports field and a heated swimming pool with a slide.

25 rue de Bourdigal • 85180 Le Château-d'Olonne
Tel. 02-51210969 • Fax 02-51236220
E-mail: info@puitsrochais.com
Internet: www.puitsrochais.com

---

946 **Le Château-d'Olonne**, F-85180 / Pays de la Loire 🛜 (CC€15) iD 48

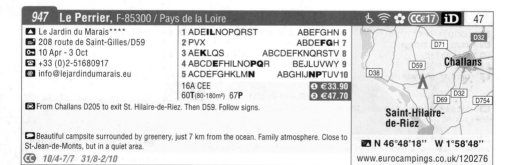

🔺 Les Fosses Rouges****
🏠 8 rue des Fosses Rouges
📅 4 Apr - 30 Sep
☎ +33 (0)2-51951795
@ info@camping-lesfossesrouges.com

1 ADE**JM**NOPQRST	CDFG 6
2 OPVXY	ABDE**FGH** 7
3 ABF**ILM**QS	ABCDFNRS 8
4 NO**PQ**	DEVY 9
5 ABCDFHM**NO**	ABDGHIJOP**R**V10

10A
3,5ha 162T(75-120m²) 78P

❶ €25.20
❷ €31.20

🔀 From Talmont-St-Hilaire take the D949 direction Les Sables. Follow signs to the left at first traffic lights 7 km further on.

💬 Friendly family campsite close to the fine sandy beaches of Les Sables-d'Olonnes. Indoor swimming pool, bar and entertainment room. Ideal as base for walking and cycling trips. Free wifi zone at the bar.

CC 4/4-6/7 24/8-29/9

Les Sables-d'Olonne

🔀 N 46°28'46'' W 1°44'28''

www.eurocampings.co.uk/114393

---

947 **Le Perrier**, F-85300 / Pays de la Loire ♿ 🛜 ❄ (CC€17) iD 47

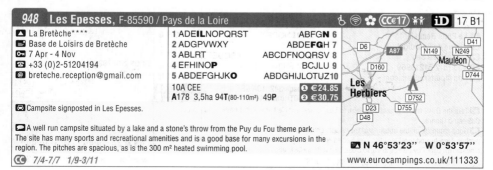

🔺 Le Jardin du Marais****
🏠 208 route de Saint-Gilles/D59
📅 10 Apr - 3 Oct
☎ +33 (0)2-51680917
@ info@lejardindumarais.eu

1 ADE**IL**NOPQRST	ABEFGHN 6
2 PVX	ABDE**FGH** 7
3 AE**K**LQS	ABCDEFKNQRSTV 8
4 ABCD**E**FHILNO**PQ**R	BEJLUVWY 9
5 ACDEFGHKLM**N**	ABGHIJ**NP**TUV10

16A CEE
60T(80-180m²) 67P

❶ €33.90
❷ €47.70

🔀 From Challans D205 to exit St. Hilaire-de-Riez. Then D59. Follow signs.

💬 Beautiful campsite surrounded by greenery, just 7 km from the ocean. Family atmosphere. Close to St-Jean-de-Monts, but in a quiet area.

CC 10/4-7/7 31/8-2/10

Challans

Saint-Hilaire-de-Riez

🔀 N 46°48'18'' W 1°58'48''

www.eurocampings.co.uk/120276

---

948 **Les Epesses**, F-85590 / Pays de la Loire ♿ 🛜 ❄ (CC€17) 🚻 iD 17 B1

🔺 La Bretèche****
🏠 Base de Loisirs de Bretèche
📅 7 Apr - 4 Nov
☎ +33 (0)2-51204194
@ breteche.reception@gmail.com

1 ADE**IL**NOPQRST	ABFG**N** 6
2 ADGPVWXY	ABDE**FGH** 7
3 ABLRT	ABCDFNOQRSV 8
4 EFHINO**P**	BCJLU 9
5 ABDEFGHJK**O**	ABDGHIJLOTUZ10

10A CEE
A178 3,5ha 94T(80-110m²) 49P

❶ €24.85
❷ €30.75

🔀 Campsite signposted in Les Epesses.

💬 A well run campsite situated by a lake and a stone's throw from the Puy du Fou theme park. The site has many sports and recreational amenities and is a good base for many excursions in the region. The pitches are spacious, as is the 300 m² heated swimming pool.

CC 7/4-7/7 1/9-3/11

Mauléon

Les Herbiers

🔀 N 46°53'23'' W 0°53'57''

www.eurocampings.co.uk/111333

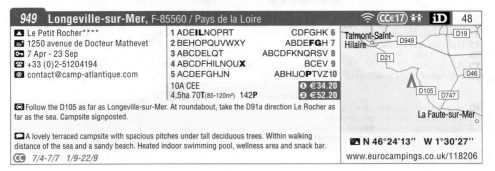

949 Longeville-sur-Mer, F-85560 / Pays de la Loire 📶 (CC€17) ♦♦ iD 48

- 🏕 Le Petit Rocher****
- ✉ 1250 avenue de Docteur Mathevet
- 📅 7 Apr - 23 Sep
- ☎ +33 (0)2-51204194
- @ contact@camp-atlantique.com

1 ADE**IL**NOPRT	CDFGHK **6**	
2 BEHOPQUVWXY	ABDE**FG**H **7**	
3 ABCDELQT	ABCDFKNQRSV **8**	
4 ABCDFHILNOU**X**	BCEV **9**	
5 ACDEFGHJN	ABHIJO**P**TVZ**10**	
10A CEE		💶 €34.20
4,5ha 70**T**(85-120m²) 142**P**		💶 €52.20

🚗 Follow the D105 as far as Longeville-sur-Mer. At roundabout, take the D91a direction Le Rocher as far as the sea. Campsite signposted.

💬 A lovely terraced campsite with spacious pitches under tall deciduous trees. Within walking distance of the sea and a sandy beach. Heated indoor swimming pool, wellness area and snack bar.

CC 7/4-7/7 1/9-22/9

N 46°24'13"   W 1°30'27"

www.eurocampings.co.uk/118206

950 Maché, F-85190 / Pays de la Loire 🚲 📶 iD 48

- 🏕 Val de Vie***
- ✉ 5 rue du Stade
- 📅 1 May - 30 Sep
- ☎ +33 (0)2-51602102
- @ campingvaldevie@bbox.fr

1 AD**JM**NOPQRST	ABN**Q**S**X**YZ **6**	
2 DPRVWX	ABDE**F**H **7**	
3 AE**KLM**QST	ABCDEFKNRSTUV **8**	
4 BDFHZ	EUV **9**	
5 ADEHN	ABFGHIJ**P**RZ**10**	
Ad on this page 10A CEE		💶 €25.40
2,2ha 78**T**(100-150m²) 30**P**		💶 €34.30

🚗 D948 Aizenay-Challans. Signposted in the village of Maché. Then follow the D40 in the direction of Brem-sur-Mer.

💬 Beautiful open campsite with very friendly owner. Just a little further inland from the coast, but beautifully situated in the Valley of the river Vie.

N 46°45'11"   W 1°41'9"

www.eurocampings.co.uk/110644

951 Noirmoutier-en-l'Île, F-85330 / Pays de la Loire 🚲 📶 (CC€17) iD 47

- 🏕 Huttopia Noirmoutier***
- ✉ 23, allée des Sableaux
- 📅 13 Apr - 23 Sep
- ☎ +33 (0)2-51390624
- @ noirmoutier@huttopia.com

1 ADE**IL**NOPRS**T**	KNPQSWXY **6**	
2 BEFHJPQWXY	ABDE**FG**H **7**	
3 ABFLQ	ABCDFINQRSV **8**	
4 BCDFHL	ARUV **9**	
5 ABDEFJN	ABCDGHJNOTU**10**	
10A CEE		💶 €32.10
12ha 386**T**(80-100m²) 100**P**		💶 €42.00

🚗 From Nantes direction Noirmoutier. Via the bridge to the island towards Noirmoutier-en-l'Île. Then follow Plage des Sableaux from centre.

💬 A campsite by the sea alongside the beach at Les Sableaux in a pine forest. Uniquely situated on the island of Noirmoutier. Direct beach access in several places. Quality amenities. CampingCard ACSI is only valid for standard pitches.

CC 13/4-22/6 27/8-22/9

N 46°59'49"   W 2°13'14"

www.eurocampings.co.uk/117132

France

952 Notre-Dame-de-Riez, F-85270 / Pays de la Loire 🛜 ✿ (CC€17) iD 47

- 🏔 Domaine des Renardières★★★
- 🏠 13 chemin du chêne vert
- 📅 1 Apr - 30 Sep
- ☎ +33 (0)2-51551417
- @ campinglesrenardieres@orange.fr

1	**AIL**NOPQRST	ABEFG**N**	6
2	B**PQVXY**	ABDE**FGH**	7
3	AB**EKLQ**	BDEFKMNORSTV	8
4	ABCDFHILNO**PQ**	EUV	9
5	ABDEFGHM**N**	ABDFGHIJ**P**TUVZ	10

10A		❶ €25.00
3,5ha 80**T**(90-130m²) 75**P**		❷ €35.00

🚗 Challans direction Sable d'Olonne (8 km), first intersection after the level crossing (right). In Notre-Dame-de-Riez sharp turn to the right. Signposted.
💬 A beautiful campsite for the whole season. Covered saltwater pool (always 27°C), fine toilet facilities, spacious pitches. Excellent motorhome pitches in park-like surroundings. More than worth a visit. Bicycles for hire.
ⓒⓒ 1/4-13/7 1/9-29/9

Challans
D51 / D948 / D59 / D69 / D754 / D38 / D94 / Saint-Hilaire-de-Riez / D32 / D6

📷 **N 46°45'18'' W 1°53'53''**
www.eurocampings.co.uk/103350

---

953 Olonne-sur-Mer, F-85340 / Pays de la Loire 🛜 iD 48

- 🏔 la Gachère★★★★
- 🏠 Les Granges
- 📅 1 Apr - 30 Sep
- ☎ +33 (0)2-51226582
- @ contact@camping-gachere.com

1	ADE**JM**NOPQRST	ABEFGN	6
2	B**HPQVXY**	ABDE**FGH**	7
3	B**ELMQS**	CDEFKNPRSV	8
4	BCDFHINO**PQ**R	EFLUVY	9
5	ABDEFGHJK**N**	ABHIJN**P**V	10

10A CEE		❶ €31.90
4,8ha 106**T** 98**P**		❷ €38.30

🚗 From Brem-sur-Mer, take the road to Les Sables d'Olonne via the Forêt d'Olonne. Campsite is clearly signposted.

💬 Beautiful campsite in the woods and dunes with an exit to the ocean with a beautiful beach.

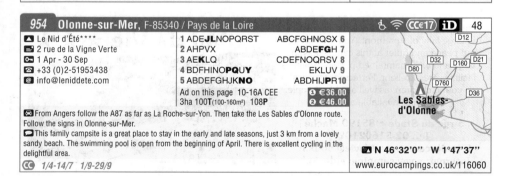

D12 / D32 / D38 / D160 / Olonne-sur-Mer / D36

📷 **N 46°35'25'' W 1°49'57''**
www.eurocampings.co.uk/108831

---

954 Olonne-sur-Mer, F-85340 / Pays de la Loire ♿ 🛜 (CC€17) iD 48

- 🏔 Le Nid d'Été★★★★
- 🏠 2 rue de la Vigne Verte
- 📅 1 Apr - 30 Sep
- ☎ +33 (0)2-51953438
- @ info@leniddete.com

1	ADE**JL**NOPQRST	ABCFGHNQSX	6
2	A**HPVX**	ABDE**FGH**	7
3	A**EKLQ**	CDEFNOQRSV	8
4	BDFHINO**PQU**Y	EKLUV	9
5	ABDEFGHJK**NO**	ABDHIJ**P**R	10

Ad on this page 10-16A CEE		❶ €36.00
3ha 100**T**(100-160m²) 108**P**		❷ €46.00

🚗 From Angers follow the A87 as far as La Roche-sur-Yon. Then take the Les Sables d'Olonne route. Follow the signs in Olonne-sur-Mer.
💬 This family campsite is a great place to stay in the early and late seasons, just 3 km from a lovely sandy beach. The swimming pool is open from the beginning of April. There is excellent cycling in the delightful area.
ⓒⓒ 1/4-14/7 1/9-29/9

D12 / D32 / D160 / D21 / D80 / D760 / D36 / Les Sables-d'Olonne

📷 **N 46°32'0'' W 1°47'37''**
www.eurocampings.co.uk/116060

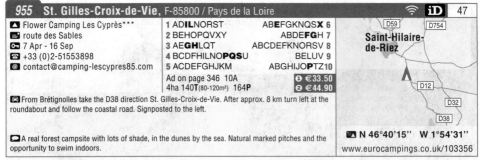

955 St. Gilles-Croix-de-Vie, F-85800 / Pays de la Loire — 📶 iD 47

- 🏕 Flower Camping Les Cyprès***
- 🏡 route des Sables
- 🗓 7 Apr - 16 Sep
- ☎ +33 (0)2-51553898
- @ contact@camping-lescypres85.com

1 AD**IL**NORST	AB**E**FGKNQS**X**	6
2 BEHOPQVXY	ABDE**FGH**	7
3 AE**GH**LQT	ABCDEFKNORSV	8
4 BCDFHILNO**PQS**U	BELUV	9
5 ACDEFGHJKM	ABGHIJO**P**TZ	10

Ad on page 346 10A ❶ €33.50
4ha 140**T**(80-120m²) 164**P** ❷ €44.90

🚗 From Brétignolles take the D38 direction St. Gilles-Croix-de-Vie. After approx. 8 km turn left at the roundabout and follow the coastal road. Signposted to the left.

💬 A real forest campsite with lots of shade, in the dunes by the sea. Natural marked pitches and the opportunity to swim indoors.

📍 N 46°40'15'' W 1°54'31''
www.eurocampings.co.uk/103356

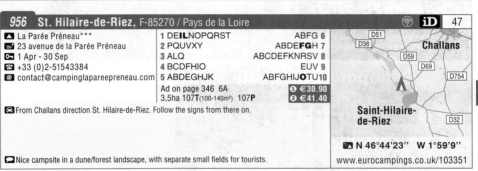

956 St. Hilaire-de-Riez, F-85270 / Pays de la Loire — 📶 iD 47

- 🏕 La Parée Préneau***
- 🏡 23 avenue de la Parée Préneau
- 🗓 1 Apr - 30 Sep
- ☎ +33 (0)2-51543384
- @ contact@campinglapareepreneau.com

1 DE**IL**NOPQRST	ABFG	6
2 PQUVXY	ABDE**FGH**	7
3 ALQ	ABCDEFKNRSV	8
4 BCDFHIO	EUV	9
5 ABDEGHJK	ABFGHIJ**O**TU	10

Ad on page 346 6A ❶ €30.90
3,5ha 107**T**(100-140m²) 107**P** ❷ €41.40

🚗 From Challans direction St. Hilaire-de-Riez. Follow the signs from there on.

💬 Nice campsite in a dune/forest landscape, with separate small fields for tourists.

📍 N 46°44'23'' W 1°59'9''
www.eurocampings.co.uk/103351

957 St. Hilaire-de-Riez, F-85270 / Pays de la Loire — 📶 (CC€17) iD 47

- 🏕 La Plage****
- 🏡 106 av. de la Pège
- 🗓 1 Apr - 30 Sep
- ☎ +33 (0)2-51543393
- @ campinglaplage@campingscollinet.com

1 AD**JM**NOPRST	ABEFGHKNQSX	6
2 EHPQVX	ABDE**FGH**	7
3 ABE**KLMP**Q	ABCDEFKNORSV	8
4 ABCDHILNO**PQ**U	AEFKL	9
5 ABDEFGHJKMN	ABDGHIJOTU	10

Ad on this page 10A ❶ €34.10
5,5ha 46**T**(100-120m²) 239**P** ❷ €47.00

🚗 Take the D38 around St. Hilaire as far as the roundabout (Fina service station). Then take the D123 in the direction of La Pège. Signposted after 4.5 km.
💬 A large campsite with many facilities on a coastal road. Deciduous and conifer trees alternate with bushes, quiet avenues and busier sections at the entrance to the campsite. Cycle tracks in area and lovely swimming pool (also covered).

CC 1/4-7/7 31/8-29/9

📍 N 46°44'43'' W 2°0'36''
www.eurocampings.co.uk/103348

France

Flower Camping Les Cyprès
★ ★ ★

The Les Cyprès campsite is a lovely wooded/dune campsite with a family-oriented and lively atmosphere. With a heated indoor swimming pool and outdoor swimming pool. Perfectly located: 400m from the beach and dunes, near cycling options by the coast and only 3 km from the centre of Saint-Gilles-Croix-de-Vie.

Route des Sables
85800 St. Gilles-Croix-de-Vie
Tel. 02-51553898
E-mail: contact@camping-lescypres85.com
Internet: www.camping-lescypres85.com

Camping Côté Plage
★ ★ ★

Camping Côté Plage is located 200m from the beach of Parée-du-Jonc, in the heart of the Saint-Jean-de-Monts forest. It has room for caravans and canvas tents in natural surroundings and with a warm and friendly atmosphere. With a beautiful outdoor swimming pool (with a water slide), heated from May to mid-September and with sports facilities and entertainment in summer.

Chemin de la Parée du Jonc
85160 St. Jean-de-Monts
Tel: 02-51588658
info@campingcoteplage.com
www.campingcoteplage.com

Camping La Parée Préneau
★ ★ ☆

Camping La Parée Préneau is located near the Saint-Hilaire-de-Riez bath resort and heartily welcomes you into a family-oriented ambiance. Large and shaded pitches for tents and caravans and close to bicycle routes. You and your children are sure to have a lovely time playing, relaxing or reading. With two heated swimming pools, one with an indoor jacuzzi. Day and evening entertainment. Located 900m from the sea.

23 avenue de la Parée Préneau
85270 St. Hilaire-de-Riez
Tel: 02-51543384
contact@campinglapareepreneau.com
www.campinglapareepreneau.com

958 St. Hilaire-de-Riez, F-85270 / Pays de la Loire

🏕 La Plage de Riez***
✉ avenue des Mimosas
🕐 1 Apr - 30 Sep
☎ +33 (0)2-51543659
@ riez85@free.fr

1 ADE**IL**NOPQRST	ABFGKN**X** 6	
2 BEHPQVXY	ABDE**FG**H 7	
3 AELQT	ABCDEFKNRSTV 8	
4 BCDFHIO**PQX**	EUVY 9	
5 ABDEFGHJKM	ABDFGHIJL**P**UV10	

Ad on this page 6A CEE
11ha 289T(80-140m²) 142P

❶ €37.00
❷ €48.00

🚗 From Nantes: direction La Roche-sur-Yon via Route Départementale, then Challans, St. Hilaire-de-Riez/St. Gilles-Croix-de-Vie and direction Sion-sur-L'Ocean (not towards centre).
💬 You will be camping 'with your feet in the water' at this friendly and hospitable campsite in the middle of woods and with direct access to the beach. Extensive network of cycle paths, including one to Sion where you can go shopping.
ⓒⓒ 1/4-30/6 1/9-29/9

🛰 N 46°43'22'' W 1°58'46''
www.eurocampings.co.uk/116064

Saint-Hilaire-de-Riez
D38 D59 D69 D754 D32 D6 D12

🆔 47

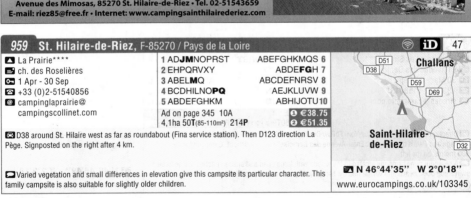

959 St. Hilaire-de-Riez, F-85270 / Pays de la Loire

🏕 La Prairie****
✉ ch. des Roselières
🕐 1 Apr - 30 Sep
☎ +33 (0)2-51540856
@ campinglaprairie@
    campingscollinet.com

1 AD**JM**NOPRST	ABEFGHKMQS 6	
2 EHPQRVXY	ABDE**FG**H 7	
3 ABEL**MQ**	ABCDEFNRSV 8	
4 BCDHILNO**PQ**	AEJKLUVW 9	
5 ABDEFGHKM	ABHIJOTU10	

Ad on page 345 10A
4,1ha 50T(85-110m²) 214P

❶ €38.75
❷ €51.35

🚗 D38 around St. Hilaire west as far as roundabout (Fina service station). Then D123 direction La Pège. Signposted on the right after 4 km.

💬 Varied vegetation and small differences in elevation give this campsite its particular character. This family campsite is also suitable for slightly older children.

Challans
D51 D38 D59 D69
Saint-Hilaire-de-Riez
D32

🛰 N 46°44'35'' W 2°0'18''
www.eurocampings.co.uk/103345

🆔 47

960 St. Hilaire-de-Riez, F-85270 / Pays de la Loire

🏕 Le Clos des Pins****
✉ ch. des Roselières
🕐 1 Apr - 30 Sep
☎ +33 (0)2-51543262
@ campingleclosdespins@
    campingscollinet.com

1 AD**JM**NOQRST	ABEFGH 6	
2 QTUVXY	BE**FG**H 7	
3 ABE**KL**	BDFKNRSV 8	
4 BCDFHILNO**PQ**	BEF 9	
5 ABDEFGHJKM	ABHIJOTU10	

Ad on page 345 10A CEE
4,1ha 50T(80-100m²) 179P

❶ €34.10
❷ €47.00

🚗 D38 around St. Hilaire west as far as roundabout (Fina service station). Then direction La Pège. Signposted on the right after 4 km.

💬 Campsite situated in the dunes, but not far from the coast. The swimming pool is central. A campsite for young and old.

Challans
D51 D38 D59 D69
Saint-Hilaire-de-Riez
D32

🛰 N 46°44'52'' W 2°0'3''
www.eurocampings.co.uk/103346

🆔 47

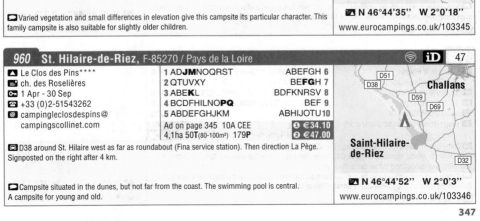

France

961 St. Hilaire-de-Riez, F-85270 / Pays de la Loire ⓦ iD 47

- △ Les Écureuils****
- ▤ 100 avenue de la Pège
- ⊙ 28 Apr - 3 Sep
- ☎ +33 (0)2-51543371
- @ info@camping-aux-ecureuils.com

1 ADJMNOPQRST	ABEFGHKNQSX 6
2 EHOPQVX	ABDEFGH 7
3 ABELMQ	ABCDEFKNRSTV 8
4 BCDFHILNOPQRUV	EHL 9
5 ABDEFGHJKN	ABHIJMOR10
Ad on this page 6A	❶ €44.70
4,5ha 32T(110-160m²) 294P	❷ €59.50

🚗 D38 around St. Hilaire-de-Riez, then D123 direction La Pège. Campsite sign after 4 km.

💬 Campsite on the coast road but still quiet. Separate fields for the tourist camper.

D51 Challans
D38
Saint-Jean-de- D59
Monts D69
△
Saint-Hilaire-de-Riez
D32

🔲 N 46°44'41'' W 2°0'35''

www.eurocampings.co.uk/116062

Les Écureuils ★ ★ ★

Les Écureuils campsite is located a mere 300m from the magnificent sandy beach of 'la Pège'. The campsite's beautiful swimming pool ensures cool refreshment and is suitable for both young and old. The pitches are large (140m²) and toilet facilities excellent. Do you prefer renting? That's also an option. Welcome to Les Écureuils.

100 avenue de la Pège, 85270 St. Hilaire-de-Riez
Tel. 02-51543371 • Fax 02-51226908
E-mail: info@camping-aux-ecureuils.com
Internet: www.camping-aux-ecureuils.com

---

962 St. Jean-de-Monts, F-85164 / Pays de la Loire ♿ ⓦ (CC€15) ⚥ iD 47

- △ Campéole Les Sirènes***
- ▤ 71 avenue des Demoiselles
- ⊙ 30 Mar - 30 Sep
- ☎ +33 (0)2-51580131
- @ sirenes@campeole.com

1 ADJMNOPQRST	ABFG 6
2 BHPQWXY	ABDEFG 7
3 ABEKLQT	ABCDEFKNRS 8
4 BCDFHLN	EJLUV 9
5 ABCDEJO	ABDGHIJPTUZ10
10A CEE	❶ €35.60
15ha 280T(min 90m²) 177P	❷ €47.10

🚗 Direction Nantes/La Roche-sur-Yon. Follow Challans and St. Jean-de-Monts. Then Le Bourg, La Plage and Palais des congrès. Enter Avenue des Demoiselle at roundabout. Campsite located 500 metres on the left.

💬 A beautiful dune campsite located in the woods with large open and shaded pitches. Large heated swimming pool. Beach and village nearby. Many cycling and walking opportunities.

©© 30/3-6/7 25/8-29/9

D948
Challans
D51 D753
D59
△ D69
D38
Saint-Hilaire-de-Riez

🔲 N 46°46'49'' W 2°3'18''

www.eurocampings.co.uk/116068

---

963 St. Jean-de-Monts, F-85160 / Pays de la Loire ♿ ⓦ (CC€15) ⚥ iD 47

- △ Campéole Plage
  des Tonnelles - Dornier****
- ▤ 18 route de la Tonnelle
- ⊙ 13 Apr - 16 Sep
- ☎ +33 (0)2-51588116
- @ plage-tonnelles@campeole.com

1 ADEJMNOPQRST	ABFGK 6
2 BEHOQTWX	ABDEFGH 7
3 ABEFIKLQRTU	ABCDEFGIKNORSV 8
4 BCDFHILNORTU	BCEJLUV 9
5 ACDEF	ABDGHJOTUZ10
10A CEE	❶ €34.80
25ha 200T(70-110m²) 291P	❷ €46.30

🚗 Coming from Nantes, direction Noirmoutier/Challans/St. Jean-de-Monts at the first roundabout in St. Jean-de-Monts, continue towards D38 Notre Dame-de-Monts/Noirmoutier. Turn left at the Tonnelles roundabout and follow campsite signs.

💬 A dune campsite with outdoor pool in sheltered surroundings. Access to the beach via a gate and through the dunes. Shop in immediate vicinity. Fitness room and sauna with jacuzzi. Walking and cycling.

©© 13/4-6/7 25/8-15/9

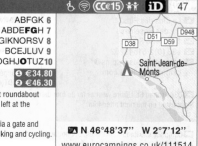

D948
D51 D59
D38
Saint-Jean-de-Monts
△

🔲 N 46°48'37'' W 2°7'12''

www.eurocampings.co.uk/111514

964 St. Jean-de-Monts, F-85160 / Pays de la Loire · 47

- ▲ Côté Plage***
- chemin de la Parée du Jonc
- 1 Apr - 17 Sep
- ☎ +33 (0)2-51588658
- @ info@campingcoteplage.com

1 ADE**IL**NORT	ABFGHKQS **6**
2 EHPQVX	ABDE**FG** **7**
3 AFLQT	ABCDEFKNRTV **8**
4 BCDFHINO**PQ**R	EUV **9**
5 ACDEFGHJKM	ABHIJOTU**10**
Ad on page 346 **10A**	❶ €35.40
124**T** 126**P**	❷ €45.70

From Challans direction St. Jean-de-Monts. Follow the signs from there on.

A friendly campsite with splendid facilities near a lovely sandy beach.

N 46°48'25'' W 2°6'49''

www.eurocampings.co.uk/116065

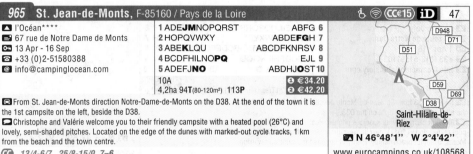

965 St. Jean-de-Monts, F-85160 / Pays de la Loire · 47

- ▲ l'Océan****
- 67 rue de Notre Dame de Monts
- 13 Apr - 16 Sep
- ☎ +33 (0)2-51580388
- @ info@campinglocean.com

1 ADE**JM**NOPQRST	ABFG **6**
2 HOPQVWXY	ABDE**FGH** **7**
3 ABE**K**LQU	ABCDFKNRSV **8**
4 BCDFHILNO**PQ**	EJL **9**
5 ADEFJ**NO**	ABDHJ**O**ST**10**
10A	❶ €34.20
4,2ha 94**T**(80-120m²) 113**P**	❷ €42.20

From St. Jean-de-Monts direction Notre-Dame-de-Monts on the D38. At the end of the town it is the 1st campsite on the left, beside the D38.

Christophe and Valérie welcome you to their friendly campsite with a heated pool (26°C) and lovely, semi-shaded pitches. Located on the edge of the dunes with marked-out cycle tracks, 1 km from the beach and the town centre.

CC 13/4-6/7 25/8-15/9 7=6

N 46°48'1'' W 2°4'42''

www.eurocampings.co.uk/108568

France

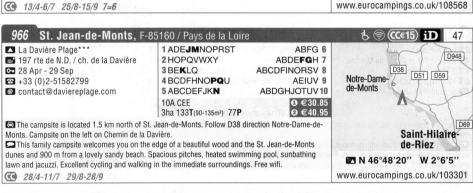

966 St. Jean-de-Monts, F-85160 / Pays de la Loire · 47

- ▲ La Davière Plage***
- 197 rte de N.D. / ch. de la Davière
- 28 Apr - 29 Sep
- ☎ +33 (0)2-51582799
- @ contact@daviereplage.com

1 ADE**JM**NOPRST	ABFG **6**
2 HOPQVWXY	ABDE**FGH** **7**
3 BE**K**LQ	ABCDFINORSV **8**
4 BCDFHNO**PQ**U	AEIUV **9**
5 ABCDEFJK**N**	ABDGHJOTUV**10**
10A CEE	❶ €30.85
3ha 133**T**(90-135m²) 77**P**	❷ €40.95

The campsite is located 1.5 km north of St. Jean-de-Monts. Follow D38 direction Notre-Dame-de-Monts. Campsite on the left on Chemin de la Davière.

This family campsite welcomes you on the edge of a beautiful wood and the St. Jean-de-Monts dunes and 900 m from a lovely sandy beach. Spacious pitches, heated swimming pool, sunbathing lawn and jacuzzi. Excellent cycling and walking in the immediate surroundings. Free wifi.

CC 28/4-11/7 29/8-28/9

N 46°48'20'' W 2°6'5''

www.eurocampings.co.uk/103301

967 St. Jean-de-Monts, F-85160 / Pays de la Loire · 47

- ▲ La Yole****
- chemin des Bosses
- 7 Apr - 22 Sep
- ☎ +33 (0)2-51586717
- @ contact@la-yole.com

1 ADE**IL**NOPQRST	ABEFGHN **6**
2 PQVXY	ABDE**FGH** **7**
3 BE**K**LMQ	ABCDEFGIJKNQRSUV **8**
4 BDFGHILNO**PQ**RUY	AEUV **9**
5 ACDEFGHJKLM	ABDGHIJ**P**TVZ**10**
	❶ €41.90
9ha 172**T**(90-150m²) 320**P**	❷ €55.30

From St. Hilaire take the D38B north-west as far as Le Pissot. Then take the D38, signposted to the left after 4 km. Or from St. Jean-de-Monts direction St. Hilaire 6 km on the right.

A well organised campsite just near the coast with varied landscaping and playgrounds. Playfully designed swimming pool.

CC 7/4-13/7 31/8-21/9 7=6, 14=11

N 46°45'23'' W 2°0'27''

www.eurocampings.co.uk/103340

La Yole ★ ★ ★ ★

- Every modern convenience • Disabled bathroom facilities • Wifi • Bicycle rental • Wonderful indoor and outdoor swimming pool • Horseback riding 1 km away • Beach 2 km away

85160 St. Jean-de-Monts
Tel. 02-51586717 • Fax 02-51590535
E-mail: contact@la-yole.com
Internet: www.vendee-camping.eu

---

968 St. Jean-de-Monts, F-85160 / Pays de la Loire ⟨♿ 📶 CC€17 iD⟩ 47

- ▲ Le Bois Joly****
- 📧 46 route de Notre Dame
- 📅 1 Apr - 16 Sep
- ☎ +33 (0)2-51591163
- @ info@camping-leboisjoly.com

1 ADEI**L**NOPQRST	ABEFGHI	6
2 HOPSVWXY	ABDE**FGH**	7
3 ABDEF**K**LQT	ABCDEFGJKNORSTUV	8
4 BCDFHILNO**Q**U	BEFUV	9
5 ADEFJKM**O**	ABDGHIJ**NOP**TZ	10
10A CEE		❶ €43.20
7,5ha 171**T**(80-110m²) 201**P**		❷ €53.20

🚗 Take the D38 from St. Jean-de-Monts direction Notre-Dame-de-Monts. The campsite is located on the edge of the village, right on the D38.

💬 Pleasant campsite with spacious pitches. Heated toilet facilities. Outdoor and indoor swimming pool (expansion in 2017), new bar/restaurant. Free wifi point. Walking distance from St. Jean-de-Monts. Beautiful beach nearby. Plenty of options for cycling and walking.

CC 1/4-30/6 1/9-15/9

Saint-Jean-de-Monts
D51 D948 D753 D59 D38 D69

🧭 N 46°47'59'' W 2°4'28''
www.eurocampings.co.uk/103300

---

969 St. Jean-de-Monts, F-85169 / Pays de la Loire ⟨♿ 📶 CC€17 iD⟩ 47

- ▲ Les Amiaux****
- 📧 223 rte Notre Dame de Monts
- 📅 2 May - 30 Sep
- ☎ +33 (0)2-51582222
- @ accueil@amiaux.fr

1 ADE**IL**NOPQRS**T**	ABEFGH	6
2 HOPVWXY	ABDE**FGH**	7
3 ABDE**K**LMQR	ABCDEFNRSTUV	8
4 BCDFHILNO**PQ**RU	EILUV	9
5 ACDEFJM**N**	ABHJ**P**TUZ	10
10A CEE		❶ €39.10
16ha 300**T**(100-120m²) 244**P**		❷ €47.30

🚗 From St. Jean-de-Monts, the D38 in northerly direction to Noirmoutier. The campsite is directly on the D38.

💬 Large four-star campsite with spacious separated pitches. Many facilities are available, including a small supermarket (open until August), a fitness room and a large indoor swimming pool with water slides. 700 m from a lovely beach. Next to a cycle path and a wood, perfect for lovely walks.

CC 5/5-30/6 31/8-29/9

D948 D38 D51 D59

Saint-Hilaire-de-Riez

🧭 N 46°48'28'' W 2°6'17''
www.eurocampings.co.uk/103305

---

970 St. Julien-des-Landes, F-85150 / Pays de la Loire ⟨♿ 📶 CC€15 iD⟩ 48

- ▲ Flower Camping La Bretonnière****
- 📅 7 Apr - 30 Sep
- ☎ +33 (0)2-51466244
- @ info@la-bretonniere.com

1 ADE**JM**NOPQRST	ABCFGNQS**X**YZ	6
2 D**H**PWXY	ABDE**FGH**	7
3 ADEFKL**M**Q	ABCDFKNOQRSV	8
4 **A**BDE**F**HILO**PQ**	ACEJPQRTUV	9
5 ABDEFGHJMN	ABDGHIJO**P**R	10
Ad on page 352 12A CEE		❶ €34.20
5,5ha 119**T**(140-200m²) 34**P**		❷ €45.20

🚗 From Angers take the A87 in the direction of Cholet, Roche-sur-Yonne. Here continue to Sables d'Olonne. At the exit La Mothe-Achard / St. Julien drive in the direction of St. Gilles.

💬 A beautiful campsite located in the countryside around a former farmhouse with its own fish pond and large pitches.

CC 7/4-6/7 25/8-29/9

Coëx D6 Aizenay
D12 D978 D57
D32 D160
L'Île-d'Olonne D21

🧭 N 46°38'39'' W 1°43'57''
www.eurocampings.co.uk/110408

971 St. Julien-des-Landes, F-85150 / Pays de la Loire ⚹ 🤶 ✿ (CC€19) iD 48

- ▲ La Garangeoire*****
- 🏠 4 May - 24 Sep
- ☎ +33 (0)2-51466539
- @ info@garangeoire.com

1 ADEJLNOPQRST	ABFGHNSXYZ 6
2 DGHPQVXY	ABDEFGH 7
3 BEFGHIKLMNQRSTV	ABCDEFIJKLNQRSTU 8
4 ABCDEFHIJKLNOPQTUXZ	AEJLPQRTUVWY 9
5 ACDEFGHKLMNO	ABCDGHIJNOQTUZ 10

Ad on page 352 12A CEE
20ha 174T(120-180m²) 216P
❶ €45.20
❷ €57.45

🚗 On the N160 Les Sables d'Olonne - La Roche-sur-Yon, at La Mothe-Achard take the D12 in the direction of St. Julien-des-Landes. Located to the right after 3 km on the D21 in the direction of La Chapelle.
🛏 A large castle campsite on a beautiful wooded estate. Paths criss-cross woods and fields. An international campsite including for teenagers. Horse and pony riding also in early and late seasons. Sandy beach on campsite.
CC 4/5-29/6 1/9-23/9

Aizenay D6
Givrand D978
L'Aiguillon-sur-Vie
Vairé D57 D760
D80 D32 D160 D21 D12

📍 N 46°39'39'' W 1°42'56''

www.eurocampings.co.uk/103366

---

972 St. Julien-des-Landes, F-85150 / Pays de la Loire ⚹ 🤶 iD 48

- ▲ Village de la Guyonnière*****
- 🏳 La Guyonnière
- 🏠 26 May - 17 Sep
- ☎ +33 (0)2-51466259
- @ info@laguyonniere.com

1 ADEJMNOPQRST	ABCDFGHINQSXYZ 6
2 ADFGHPRUVWXYY	ABDEFGHK 7
3 ABEFGHLMQTV	ABCDFKNQRSTV 8
4 ABCDFHIKLNOPQTUVXYZ	CEFJKLPQRTUVW 9
5 ACDEFGHJKLMN	ABFGHIJMNPSTZ 10

Ad on page 352 10A CEE
30ha 192T(150-300m²) 133P
❶ €48.00
❷ €64.00

🚗 A83 Nantes-Bordeaux/La Rochelle exit D763 La Roche-sur-Yon. Or A87 Angers-Cholet/La Roche-sur-Yon. Follow N160 Sables-d'Olonne. At the exit continue to La Mothe-Achard/St. Julien.

🛏 An excellent campsite, very spacious pitches in beautiful natural surroundings. The lovely indoor pool is open all season. Fishing at the campsite is a challenge right on the large Lac du Jaunay. A trusted address and highly recommended. Entertainment team throughout the season.

Saint-Gilles-Croix-de-Vie Aizenay
D6
D12 D978 D57
D32 D160
D80 D21

📍 N 46°39'0'' W 1°45'0''

www.eurocampings.co.uk/103360

---

973 St. Julien-des-Landes, F-85150 / Pays de la Loire 🤶 (CC€17) iD 48

- ▲ Yelloh! Village Château La Forêt****
- 🏠 4 May - 5 Sep
- ☎ +33 (0)2-51466211
- @ camping@chateaulaforet.com

1 ADEJMNOPQRST	ABEFGHNQX 6
2 BDFGIPVXY	ABDEFGHK 7
3 ABCEFGHILMQRST	BDFHKNQRSTU 8
4 ABCDFHIKLNOPQUXYZ	ACEJLPQRTUV 9
5 ABDEFGHJLN	ABDFGHIJNOPTVZ 10

Ad on this page 10A
50ha 150T(100-140m²) 110P
❶ €42.20
❷ €54.20

🚗 D12 La Chaize-Giraud direction St. Julien-des-Landes. Then pass the church and turn left onto the D55. Signposted.
🛏 Château La Forêt is a lovely international campsite on a 50-hectare estate. The site opens on 28/4 and most amenities, such as the swimming pool, can be used immediately. The campsite is up to full strength from 13/5. Well worth a visit!
CC 4/5-6/7 26/8-4/9

Coëx Aizenay D6
D978 D57
D32 D160 D12
L'Île-d'Olonne D21

📍 N 46°38'36'' W 1°42'41''

www.eurocampings.co.uk/103361

France

Vendée - France

Le Pin Parasol ★★★★

Le Pin Parasol is one of the prettiest outdoor hotels between land and sea: 50 metres from Lake Jaunay and 10 minutes from the Vendée beaches. Rediscover the joys of life in the magnificent open air in the heart of a fishing area. Enjoy our heated water park with >2500 m², 5 swimming pools and 5 slides, 2 with rubber tyres. With entertainment, a mini club, plenty of activities on site and nearby, and with services and high-end amenities! New in 2018! New district near Pin Parasol: the Nature & Sens area. A 9-ha oasis of tranquillity with plenty of comfort and options: lovely accommodation, a pond, wellness centre, botanical garden, 2500 m² sensory aquatic room, services and great activities.

Châteaulong, 85220 La Chapelle-Hermier
Tel : +33 (0)2 51 34 64 72
contact@campingpinparasol.fr
www.campingpinparasol.fr

Flower Camping ★★★★
La Bretonnière

A charming campsite with a family-oriented ambiance in the countryside and just 15 minutes from the ocean. Beautiful and large pitches, entertainment for young and old, excellent toilet facilities, lovely swimming pool, new water playground for young children and free wifi. The Magaud family guarantees hospitality and friendliness.

85150 St.Julien-des-Landes
Tel : +33 (0)2 51 46 62 44
Fax : +33 (0)2 51 46 61 36
info@la-bretonniere.com
www.la-bretonniere.com

Campings
du Lac du Jaunay

4 campsites
around Lake Jaunay

10 minutes from the magnificent beaches of the Atlantic Ocean!

Camping Village ★★★
de la Guyonnière

A beautiful campsite with exceptionally large pitches. The perfect campsite for young and old. A campsite where anything is possible, from angling, cycling and swimming in an (indoor) heated pool with a spectacular 65-metre long rapids, to enjoying a delicious meal in the restaurant. New toilet facilities. There is always something to do for children and the space and quiet at this lovely campsite ensure a carefree holiday, also in spring and autumn. Entertainment during the entire opening period. With a wellness centre. Free wifi throughout the entire grounds. New swimming pool complex (2018)!

La Guyonnière, 85150 St.Julien-des-Landes
Tel : +33 (0)2 51 46 62 59 Fax : +33 (0)2 51 46 62 89
info@laguyonniere.com
www.camping-guyonniere.com

Castel Camping ★★★★★
La Garangeoire

The campsite with international style provides all you could wish for. The numerous activities organised by the entertainment team guarantee great fun. There is always something to do, especially for children. Options include angling, riding, swimming, archery and tennis. The large country estate ensures peace and quiet in the green oasis. The campsite is known for its restaurant with extensive menu, where you can enjoy French cuisine in a delightful location.

85150 St.Julien-des-Landes
Tel : +33 (0)2 51 46 65 39
Fax : +33 (0)2 51 46 69 85
info@garangeoire.com
www.camping-la-garangeoire.com

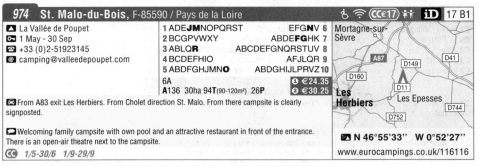

974 St. Malo-du-Bois, F-85590 / Pays de la Loire

♿ 🛜 ⒸⒸ€17 ♂♀ iD 17 B1

- 🏕 La Vallée de Poupet
- 📅 1 May - 30 Sep
- ☎ +33 (0)2-51923145
- @ camping@valleedepoupet.com

1	ADE**JM**NOPQRST	EFG**N**V	6
2	BCGPVWXY	ABDE**FG**HK	7
3	ABLQ**R**	ABCDEFGNQRSTUV	8
4	BCDEFHIO	AFJLQR	9
5	ABDFGHJMN**O**	ABDGHIJLPRVZ	10
6A		€ €24.35	
A136 30ha 94**T**(90-120m²) 26**P**		€ €30.25	

From A83 exit Les Herbiers. From Cholet direction St. Malo. From there campsite is clearly signposted.

Welcoming family campsite with own pool and an attractive restaurant in front of the entrance. There is an open-air theatre next to the campsite.

ⒸⒸ 1/5-30/6 1/9-29/9

N 46°55'33'' W 0°52'27''

www.eurocampings.co.uk/116116

975 St. Martin-Lars-en-Ste-Hermine, F-85210 / Pays de la Loire

♨ ♿ 🛜 ✿ ⒸⒸ€19 iD 17 B2

- 🏕 Le Colombier****
- 📅 1 Apr - 1 Oct
- ☎ +33 (0)2-51278384
- @ lecolombier.nat@wanadoo.fr

1	ADE**JM**NOPQRST	ABFG**N**	6
2	BCDGPTVWXY	ABDE**FG**K	7
3	ABELQRS	ABEFKNQRS	8
4	BCDFHIKOR**TUVX**	CEJL	9
5	ABDEFHJKN	ABDGHIJM**NP**TUVZ	10
6-16A CEE		€ €29.20	
A70 50ha 112**T**(120-200m²) 79**P**		€ €38.20	

From Noirt take the N148 to Ste Hermine, D8 through Thiré. In Thiré left onto D10 to St. Martin-Lars. Marked with small signs from here.

A well maintained naturist campsite with excellent toilet facilities. Large swimming pool, spacious pitches and a lively atmosphere in the bar and restaurant.

ⒸⒸ 1/4-7/7 25/8-30/9

N 46°35'52'' W 0°58'9''

www.eurocampings.co.uk/103530

France

976 St. Michel-en-l'Herm, F-85580 / Pays de la Loire

♿ 🛜 ⒸⒸ€17 iD 17 B2

- 🏕 La Dive****
- 🏠 12 route de la Mer
- 📅 1 Apr - 30 Sep
- ☎ +33 (0)2-51302694
- @ camping-la-dive@wanadoo.fr

1	ADE**IL**NOPQRST	ABFGHI	6
2	OPVWXY	ABDE**FG**H	7
3	BDEF**GHI**LQT	ABCDEFGKNQRST	8
4	BCDE**F**HKNO**PRTU**	BCEJUV	9
5	ABDEFGHJK**O**	ABDGHIJMP**S**TVZ	10
10A CEE		€ €33.40	
9ha 85**T** 173**P**		€ €44.70	

In St. Michel-en-l'Herm direction l'Aiguillon-sur-Mer. Right at end of village and follow campsite signs.

A lovely campsite between land and sea. 5 minutes from the lovely sandy beaches and close to the 'Vénise Verte'. Bar, small shop and a beautiful jacuzzi and sauna. Wonderful atmosphere.

ⒸⒸ 1/4-13/7 1/9-29/9

N 46°20'57'' W 1°14'53''

www.eurocampings.co.uk/121240

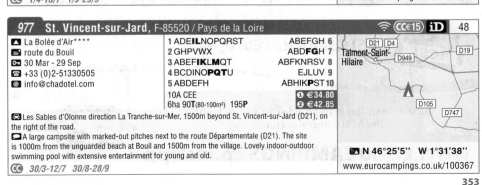

977 St. Vincent-sur-Jard, F-85520 / Pays de la Loire

🛜 ⒸⒸ€15 iD 48

- 🏕 La Bolée d'Air****
- 🏠 route du Bouil
- 📅 30 Mar - 29 Sep
- ☎ +33 (0)2-51330505
- @ info@chadotel.com

1	ADE**IL**NOPQRST	ABEFGH	6
2	GHPVWX	ABD**FG**H	7
3	ABEF**IKLM**QT	ABFKNRSV	8
4	BCDINO**PQT**U	EJLUV	9
5	ABDEFH	ABHIK**P**ST	10
10A CEE		€ €34.80	
6ha 90**T**(80-100m²) 195**P**		€ €42.85	

Les Sables d'Olonne direction La Tranche-sur-Mer, 1500m beyond St. Vincent-sur-Jard (D21), on the right of the road.

A large campsite with marked-out pitches next to the route Départementale (D21). The site is 1000m from the unguarded beach at Bouil and 1500m from the village. Lovely indoor-outdoor swimming pool with extensive entertainment for young and old.

ⒸⒸ 30/3-12/7 30/8-28/9

N 46°25'5'' W 1°31'38''

www.eurocampings.co.uk/100367

978 Talmont-St-Hilaire, F-85440 / Pays de la Loire ♿ 🛜 iD 48

▲ Yelloh! Village Le Littoral★★★★★
🏠 Le Porteau
📅 7 Apr - 15 Sep
☎ +33 (0)2-51220464
@ info@campinglelittoral.com

1 ADE**IL**NOPQRST	ABEFGHINO	6
2 BEJMOPQVWXY	ABDE**FGH**	7
3 ABDE**HK**LQT	ABCDEFJKNOQRSTUV	8
4 **A**BCDFHILNO**PQ**U	ELV	9
5 ABCDEFGHJKLM**N**	ABFGHIJ**NOP**TUZ	10
10A CEE	❶ €53.20	
9ha 60T(80-100m²) 349P	❷ €69.20	

🗺 D949 from Talmont-St-Hilaire to Les Sables-d'Olonne, turn left just past the racecourse. Signposted.

💬 A lovely family campsite with plenty of comfort and all facilities within walking distance of the ocean. Wonderful heated leisure pool and indoor pool. Bar, restaurant and small supermarket open all season. Walking and cycling routes from the campsite. Five minutes from Sables d'Olonne.

Les Sables-d'Olonne

📷 N 46°27'7'' W 1°42'6''
www.eurocampings.co.uk/100366

979 Vendrennes, F-85250 / Pays de la Loire 🛜 (CC€15) iD 17 B1

▲ de la Motte★★★★
🏠 La Motte
📅 1 Jan - 21 Dec
☎ +33 (0)2-51635967
@ contact@camping-lamotte.com

1 ADE**JM**NOPQRST	ABFGHN	6
2 AOPVXY	ABDE**FG**	7
3 AEQS	ABCDEFJNRV	8
4 BCDFHIKNO**PQ**U	EJL	9
5 ABDEFGHJMN	ABDHIJOR	10
Ad on this page 16A CEE	❶ €24.20	
3ha 43T(100-140m²) 79P	❷ €29.80	

🗺 From the A83 or A87 take the Les Essarts exit, then the D160 towards Cholet. Campsite signposted in the village of Vendrennes.

💬 This friendly campsite with large pitches in the interior of the Vendée guarantees relaxation and space. Right next to the A83/A87 motorways.

© 1/1-9/7 27/8-20/12

Saint-Fulgent Les Herbiers

📷 N 46°49'38'' W 1°7'2''
www.eurocampings.co.uk/120278

Nouvelle-Aquitaine

Largest region in France

Mention Bordeaux, and full-bodied red wine is the first thing to come to mind. Comprising the former departments of Poitou-Charentes, Limousin en Aquitaine, with diversity of landscape, historic cities, picturesque villages and fabulous coastal resorts, there's so much more to Nouvelle-Aquitaine. Located in the south-west corner of France, the fabulous beaches of the Atlantic coast to the west give way to hills, pine forests, vineyards and farms, and wetlands fed by the rivers of the area, with the Pyrenees Mountains in the south marking the border with Spain.

Living history

Here, every town you visit has reminders of past settlers. Admire the serene Roman Palais Galais in Bordeaux, or see the mediaeval Porte Cailhau, from which there's a great view over Ponte de Pierre, and enjoy the light on the 'water mirror' at Place de la Bourse. You'll feel like you've gone back in time at the ancient Roman remains and Vesunna Gallo-Roman Museum at Périgieux. Browse the shops of La Rochelle, with its Old Town and Old Harbour, and the kids will just want to dive right into the Aquarium! Dress in red and white for the Festival of Bayonne, and when you need a break, stop at the Musée Basque.

Activities on land and water

Naturally the long coastline and high mountains attract adrenaline junkies – surfers, wind-surfers and kayakers love the sea and lakes, and true adventurers go rafting and canyoning on the rushing mountain streams. Art lovers will be blown away by the replicated ancient paintings of animals at the Caves of Lascaux.

For nature lovers: Marais Poitevin, south of La Rochelle, is part agricultural, part coastal and part marsh; Millevaches, with lovely valleys and gorges that you can walk, ride or cycle, and Lake

Our tips

1. *Visit picturesque Carennac in the Dordogne valley*
2. *For the chocoholics: Chocolate Days Festival in Bayonne*
3. *See the story of Durandal, the sword of Roland, told on horseback at Rocomadour*
4. *Enjoy a great family day and evening out in Futuroscope near Poitiers*
5. *Explore the salt flats and sample a bowl of mussels from the wall on Ile de Re*

Vassiviere; and there is the richly forested Landes de Gascogne. Don't forget your camera!

What to eat and drink

If you like to eat well, Nouvelle Aquitaine is paradise. In addition to wine, the region produces Cognac and Armagnac. Local specialities include Bayonne ham and Chicken Basquaise, oysters, mussels, goat's cheese, truffles and acorn bread, and sweet Charantais melon. And you know you want to visit the Museum of Macarons at Montmorillan …

980 Ars-en-Ré, F-17590 / Poitou-Charentes 📶 (CC€17) iD 45b

- ⛺ Camp du Soleil***
- 🚩 route de la Plage
- 📅 2 Apr - 30 Sep
- ☎ +33 (0)5-46294062
- @ contact@campdusoleil.com

1 ADE**IL**NOPQRST	ABFG	6
2 EPQVWXY		7
3 BLQ	BDFGIJKNQRSV	8
4 HO**P**	EV	9
5 ABDEFGHJK	ABGHIJMNPTUZ	10

Ad on this page 10A CEE	❶ €48.10
2ha 67**T**(70-120m²) 88**P**	❷ €67.70

🗺 After tollbridge D735 towards Ars-en-Ré. At Ars on D735, signposted to left.

💬 A peaceful family campsite with pitches marked out by hedges with and without shade. At walking distance from a lovely beach and the welcoming harbour town of Ars-en-Ré. All amenities and with a bar and restaurant. Bicycles for rent. Free wifi on the whole site.

CC 2/4-6/7 26/8-29/9

Saint-Clément-des-Baleines   Loix

🧭 N 46°12'14'' W 1°31'13''
www.eurocampings.co.uk/103392

Camp du Soleil ★ ★ ★

Magnificent family campsite with sunny and shaded areas, within walking distance of a lovely sandy beach and the friendly Ars-en-Ré seaport town. Plenty of facilities, which include a bar and small restaurant. Bicycle rental. Free wifi throughout the entire grounds. Mobile home rental.

Route de la Plage, 17590 Ars-en-Ré
Tel. 05-46294062 • Fax 05-46294174
E-mail: contact@campdusoleil.com
Internet: www.campdusoleil.com

CAMPING Qualité

France

---

981 Aytré/La Rochelle, F-17440 / Poitou-Charentes 📶 (CC€19) iD 45b

- ⛺ Les Sables****
- 🚩 chemin du Pontreau
- 📅 1 Apr - 14 Oct
- ☎ +33 (0)5-46454030
- @ camping_les_sables@yahoo.fr

1 ADE**IL**NORT	ABEFGHIKNQS	6
2 EHPRVWX	ABDE**FGH**	7
3 ABDE**GH**LMQR	ABCDFIKNORSV	8
4 BDILMO**PRS TVW**	ELV	9
5 ABDEFGHJK	ABGHIKNPR	10

6A CEE	❶ €35.20
5,5ha 298**T**(100-140m²) 94**P**	❷ €46.30

🗺 N137 La Rochelle-Rochefort. Exit Aytré (D939). Turn right at the roundabout. At the following roundabout third exit left onto the D937. Turn left at the second traffic lights. Follow the signs 'La Plage'.
💬 A wonderful family campsite with every amenity. Spacious pitches separated by hedges. Sandy beach within walking distance. Heated indoor swimming pool. Free wifi throughout the site. Close to La Rochelle.

CC 1/4-30/6 1/9-13/10

D735 D9 N11
La Rochelle Aytré
D109
D137
D5

🧭 N 46°6'59'' W 1°7'10''
www.eurocampings.co.uk/103399

---

982 Boyardville, F-17190 / Poitou-Charentes 📶 (CC€15) iD 49

- ⛺ Les Saumonards**
- 🚩 route des Saumonards
- 📅 1 Apr - 15 Oct
- ☎ +33 (0)5-46472320
- @ campingmunicipal.
  stgeorgesdoleron@wanadoo.fr

1 ADEF**JM**NOPQRS**T**	QS	6
2 BEHQWXY	ABDE**FGH**	7
3 A**K**LQ	ABCDEFNRSV	8
4 FH	BF	9
5 ADEFGHJ	AIOTU	10

5A CEE	❶ €26.60
267**T**(60-120m²) 2**P**	❷ €35.00

🗺 From the viaduct towards Dolus and then Boyardville. Over the bridge in Boyardville. Campsite shown as 'Municipal'.

💬 A peaceful campsite in pine woods with access to the beach.

CC 1/4-30/6 1/9-14/10 7=6

Saint-Denis-d'Oléron   Châtelaillon-Plage
Saint-Georges-d'Oléron
Saint-Pierre-d'Oléron   Port-des-Barques

🧭 N 45°58'42'' W 1°14'28''
www.eurocampings.co.uk/116517

983 Châtelaillon-Plage, F-17340 / Poitou-Charentes — CCe19 iD 45b

- Camping Au Port-Punay***
- allée Bernard Moreau, Les Boucholeur
- 4 May - 23 Sep
- +33 (0)5-17810000
- contact@camping-port-punay.com

1 ADE**IL**NOPRS**T**	ABFGKMNQSXY	6
2 EHOPQRVWXY	BE**FGH**	7
3 ABLQ	ABCDEFGIKNOQRSTUV	8
4 ABDHILNO**PQ**U	EFUV	9
5 ABCDEFGHKM**NO**	ABDGHIJM**NP**RVZ	10
10A CEE	❶ €43.20	
3ha 116**T**(100m²) 41**P**	❷ €55.70	

N137 La Rochelle-Rochefort, exit D109 Châtelaillon-Plage. First left at the second roundabout. Follow 'Les Boucholeurs' then follow campsite signs.

A friendly campsite, partly under trees and 200m from a sandy beach. Heated swimming pool. Excellent toilet facilities and large pitches. Starting point for visiting the islands Ré and Aix, situated between La Rochelle and Rochefort. Châtelaillon can be visited by bike. The site has an Ecolabel.

CC 4/5-6/7 25/8-22/9

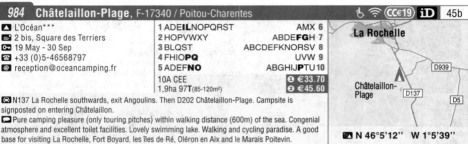

N 46°3'18" W 1°5'0"

www.eurocampings.co.uk/103403

984 Châtelaillon-Plage, F-17340 / Poitou-Charentes — CCe19 iD 45b

- L'Océan***
- 2 bis, Square des Terriers
- 19 May - 30 Sep
- +33 (0)5-46568797
- reception@oceancamping.fr

1 ADE**IL**NOPQRST	AMX	6
2 HOPVWXY	ABDE**FGH**	7
3 BLQST	ABCDEFKNORSV	8
4 FHIO**PQ**	UVW	9
5 ADEF**NO**	ABGHIJ**P**TU	10
10A CEE	❶ €33.70	
1,9ha 97**T**(85-120m²)	❷ €45.60	

N137 La Rochelle southwards, exit Angoulins. Then D202 Châtelaillon-Plage. Campsite is signposted on entering Châtelaillon.

Pure camping pleasure (only touring pitches) within walking distance (600m) of the sea. Congenial atmosphere and excellent toilet facilities. Lovely swimming lake. Walking and cycling paradise. A good base for visiting La Rochelle, Fort Boyard, les îles de Ré, Oléron en Aix and le Marais Poitevin.

CC 19/5-1/7 26/8-29/9 7=6

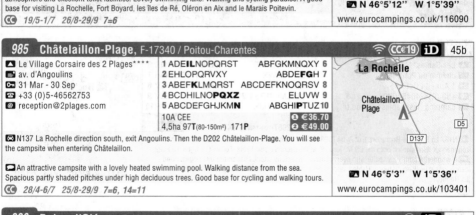

N 46°5'12" W 1°5'39"

www.eurocampings.co.uk/116090

985 Châtelaillon-Plage, F-17340 / Poitou-Charentes — CCe19 iD 45b

- Le Village Corsaire des 2 Plages****
- av. d'Angoulins
- 31 Mar - 30 Sep
- +33 (0)5-46562753
- reception@2plages.com

1 ADE**IL**NOPQRST	ABFGKMNQXY	6
2 EHLOPQRVXY	ABDE**FGH**	7
3 ABEF**KL**MQRST	ABCDEFKNOQRSV	8
4 BCDHILNO**PQXZ**	ELUVW	9
5 ABCDEFGHJKM**N**	ABGHI**P**TUZ	10
10A CEE	❶ €36.70	
4,5ha 97**T**(80-150m²) 171**P**	❷ €49.00	

N137 La Rochelle direction south, exit Angoulins. Then the D202 Châtelaillon-Plage. You will see the campsite when entering Châtelaillon.

An attractive campsite with a lovely heated swimming pool. Walking distance from the sea. Spacious partly shaded pitches under high deciduous trees. Good base for cycling and walking tours.

CC 28/4-6/7 25/8-29/9 7=6, 14=11

N 46°5'3" W 1°5'36"

www.eurocampings.co.uk/103401

986 Dolus-d'Oléron, F-17550 / Poitou-Charentes — iD 49

- Huttopia Oléron Les Chênes Verts****
- 9 Passe de l'Ecuissière
- 1 Jun - 11 Sep
- +33 (0)5-46753288
- oleron-chenesverts@huttopia.com

1 ADEF**IL**NOPR**T**	KNPQRST	6
2 BEKPQUY	ABDE**FGH**	7
3 BEF**KL**Q**R**	ABCDEFGHIKNQRS	8
4 BDFHI	FV	9
5 ABDEFGHJMN	ABHJNOTU	10
10A CEE	❶ €35.00	
4ha 105**T** 45**P**	❷ €46.20	

Follow Dolus from the viaduct. Turn left at roundabout at Intermarché, then straight ahead. Then signposted.

Nature friendly campsite situated in a forest by the sea. Campsite has great attention to nature. All buildings are made of wood.

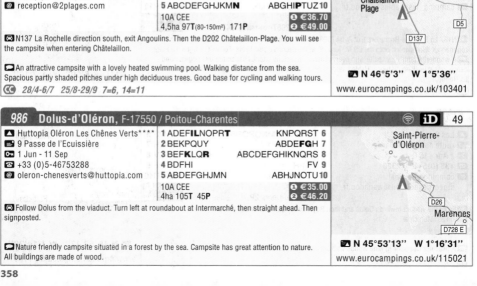

N 45°53'13" W 1°16'31"

www.eurocampings.co.uk/115021

987 Fouras, F-17450 / Poitou-Charentes
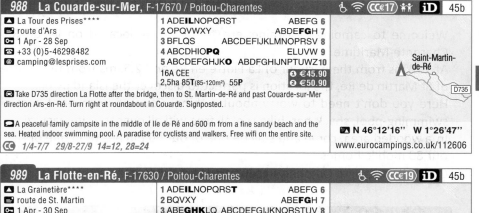

▲ Municipal Le Cadoret***   ⚲ ⚡ ♿ (CC€15) iD 49

- ⌂ boulevard de Chaterny
- 📅 1 Jan - 31 Dec
- ☎ +33 (0)5-46821919
- @ campingcadoret@fouras-les-bains.fr

1 ADE**JM**NOPRT	ABFGHKMNQRSTW	6
2 AEHOPRVWXY	ABDE**FG**H	7
3 ABE**K**LQT	ABCDEFJKNPRSTV	8
4 BCDFHINO**PQ**	ELUVW	9
5 ABDEFHJKM**NO**	ABHIJPTUVZ	10

6-10A   ❶ €31.40
7,6ha 300T(40-130m²) 198P   ❷ €40.80

🗺 From La Rochelle to Rochefort. Exit Fouras (D937). Turn to the right after 2 km. Turn to the right at the first junction. Signposted.
💬 Le Cadoret campsite welcomes in quiet and cosy style. Situated on the coast, in a forested, park-like area, 500 m from the city centre. The numerous pitches are located in partial shade, or in the sun closer to the sea, both are marked out and have a grassy surface for maximum comfort.
(CC) 1/1-29/6   3/9-31/12

📷 N 45°59'35''   W 1°5'14''

www.eurocampings.co.uk/103410

---

988 La Couarde-sur-Mer, F-17670 / Poitou-Charentes
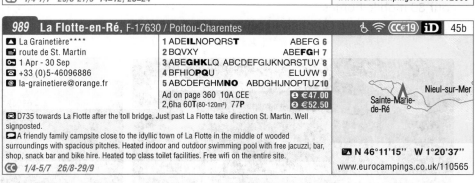

▲ La Tour des Prises****   ♿ ⚲ (CC€17) ♟♟ iD 45b

- ⌂ route d'Ars
- 📅 1 Apr - 28 Sep
- ☎ +33 (0)5-46298482
- @ camping@lesprises.com

1 ADE**IL**NOPQRST	ABEFG	6
2 OPQVWXY	ABDE**FG**H	7
3 BFLQS	ABCDEFIJKLMNOPRSV	8
4 ABCDHIO**PQ**	ELUVW	9
5 ABCDEFGHJK**O**	ABDFGHIJNPTUVWZ	10

16A CEE   ❶ €45.90
2,5ha 85T(85-120m²) 55P   ❷ €50.90

🗺 Take D735 direction La Flotte after the bridge, then to St. Martin-de-Ré and past Couarde-sur-Mer direction Ars-en-Ré. Turn right at roundabout in Couarde. Signposted.

💬 A peaceful family campsite in the middle of Ile de Ré and 600 m from a fine sandy beach and the sea. Heated indoor swimming pool. A paradise for cyclists and walkers. Free wifi on the entire site.
(CC) 1/4-7/7   29/8-27/9   14=12, 28=24

📷 N 46°12'16''   W 1°26'47''

www.eurocampings.co.uk/112606

---

989 La Flotte-en-Ré, F-17630 / Poitou-Charentes
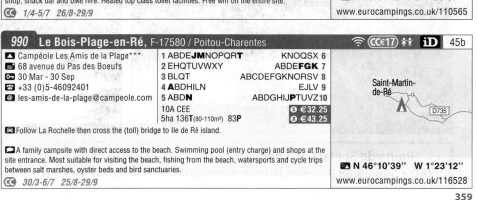

▲ La Grainetière****   ♿ ⚲ (CC€19) iD 45b

- ⌂ route de St. Martin
- 📅 1 Apr - 30 Sep
- ☎ +33 (0)5-46096886
- @ la-grainetiere@orange.fr

1 ADE**IL**NOPQRS**T**	ABEFG	6
2 BQVXY	ABE**FG**H	7
3 ABE**GHK**LQ	ABCDEFGIJKNQRSTUV	8
4 BFHIO**PQ**U	ELUVW	9
5 ABCDEFGHM**NO**	ABDGHIJNOPTUZ	10

Ad on page 360   10A CEE   ❶ €47.00
2,6ha 60T(80-120m²) 77P   ❷ €52.50

🗺 D735 towards La Flotte after the toll bridge. Just past La Flotte take direction St. Martin. Well signposted.
💬 A friendly family campsite close to the idyllic town of La Flotte in the middle of wooded surroundings with spacious pitches. Heated indoor and outdoor swimming pool with free jacuzzi, bar, shop, snack bar and bike hire. Heated top class toilet facilities. Free wifi on the entire site.
(CC) 1/4-5/7   26/8-29/9

📷 N 46°11'15''   W 1°20'37''

www.eurocampings.co.uk/110565

---

990 Le Bois-Plage-en-Ré, F-17580 / Poitou-Charentes

▲ Campéole Les Amis de la Plage***   ⚲ (CC€17) ♟♟ iD 45b

- ⌂ 68 avenue du Pas des Boeufs
- 📅 30 Mar - 30 Sep
- ☎ +33 (0)5-46092401
- @ les-amis-de-la-plage@campeole.com

1 ABDE**JM**NOPQR**T**	KNOQSX	6
2 EHQTUVWXY	ABDE**FGK**	7
3 BLQT	ABCDEFGKNORSV	8
4 **A**BDHILN	EJLV	9
5 ABD**N**	ABDGHIJ**P**TUVZ	10

10A CEE   ❶ €32.25
5ha 136T(80-110m²) 83P   ❷ €43.25

🗺 Follow La Rochelle then cross the (toll) bridge to Ile de Ré island.

💬 A family campsite with direct access to the beach. Swimming pool (entry charge) and shops at the site entrance. Most suitable for visiting the beach, fishing from the beach, watersports and cycle trips between salt marshes, oyster beds and bird sanctuaries.
(CC) 30/3-6/7   25/8-29/9

📷 N 46°10'39''   W 1°23'12''

www.eurocampings.co.uk/116528

France

Welcome to camping La Grainetière ****, ideally located on Ile de Ré, Charente-Maritime.

At 1.5kms from the harbour of La Flotte en Ré and 2.5kms from the centre of St Martin de Ré, the location is perfect to discover the island by bike.

Here you don't need to worry about a thing! Covered-uncovered heated swimming-pool, snack-bar, bike rental, free wifi all over the site, jacuzzi...

In a wooded area, come and stay on one of our 50 pitches or in one of our 80 mobile homes.

Open from April to October. Reservations are advised.

Route de St Martin - Chemin des Essarts - 17630 La Flotte en Ré
0033.546.09.68.86 www.la-grainetiere.com la-grainetiere@orange.fr

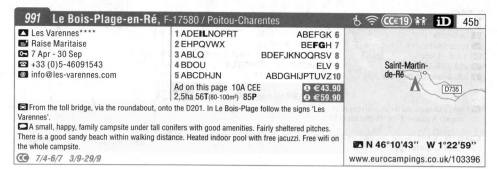

991 Le Bois-Plage-en-Ré, F-17580 / Poitou-Charentes   ♿ 📶 (CC€19) 🚻 iD   45b

🏕 Les Varennes****
📧 Raise Maritaise
📅 7 Apr - 30 Sep
📞 +33 (0)5-46091543
@ info@les-varennes.com

1 ADE**IL**NOPRT	ABEFGK 6
2 EHPQVWX	BE**FG**H 7
3 ABLQ	BDEFJKNOQRSV 8
4 BDOU	ELV 9
5 ABCDHJN	ABDGHIJPTUVZ 10

Ad on this page 10A CEE   ❶ €43.90
2,5ha 56T(80-100m²) 85P   ❷ €59.90

Saint-Martin-de-Ré   ⛺   D735

🚗 From the toll bridge, via the roundabout, onto the D201. In Le Bois-Plage follow the signs 'Les Varennes'.

💬 A small, happy, family campsite under tall conifers with good amenities. Fairly sheltered pitches. There is a good sandy beach within walking distance. Heated indoor pool with free jacuzzi. Free wifi on the whole campsite.

📍 N 46°10'43"   W 1°22'59"

www.eurocampings.co.uk/103396

CC 7/4-6/7 3/9-29/9

France

Les Varennes ★ ★ ★ ★

Family campsite with sunny and shaded areas, 300m from a sandy beach and 500m from Le Bois-Plage. Located in a tranquil area. Entirely modernised and heated indoor and outdoor swimming pool with free jacuzzi. With every comfort and facility required. Mobile home rental. Free wifi throughout the entire campsite.

Raise Maritaise, 17580 Le Bois-Plage-en-Ré
Tel. 05-46091543 • Fax 05-46094727
E-mail: info@les-varennes.com
Internet: www.les-varennes.com

992 Le Château-d'Oléron, F-17480 / Poitou-Charentes   ♿ 📶 (CC€17) iD   49

🏕 Airotel Oléron****
📧 19 avenue de la Libération
📅 1 Apr - 30 Sep
📞 +33 (0)5-46476182
@ info@camping-airotel-oleron.com

1 ADF**JM**NOPRST	ABFGN**X** 6
2 DPRVWXY	ABDE**FG**H 7
3 BEF**GHKLM**Q**R**	ABCDEFJNORSV 8
4 BCDFHILNO**PQ**	BEJLUV 9
5 ABDEFGHJKLM**NO**	ABHIJM**NP**RV 10

10A CEE   ❶ €38.00
7,4ha 123T(80-150m²) 196P   ❷ €54.40

Saint-Pierre-d'Oléron   🏕   D26   D728 E

🚗 Direction Le Château beyond bridge, then left towards centre. Follow signs by 'Crédit Agricole'.

💬 Campsite close to the centre of Château-d'Oléron. Perfect for horse lovers. With a swimming pool and other sports opportunities.

📍 N 45°52'57"   W 1°12'24"

www.eurocampings.co.uk/103418

CC 1/4-7/7 25/8-29/9 7=6, 14=11, 21=17

993 Le Château-d'Oléron, F-17480 / Poitou-Charentes ♿ 📶 (CC€17) iD 49

🔺 La Brande*****
🚩 route des Huîtres
📅 1 Apr - 4 Nov
☎ +33 (0)5-46476237
@ info@camping-labrande.com

1 ADEF**IL**NOPRST	CEFGHKNQSX	6
2 EGHPQRVWXY	ABDE**FGH**	7
3 BE**IKLMNPQR**	ABCDEFIK**LMN**OQRSTU	8
4 **A**BCDEFHILNO**PQT**UV	EJLUVW	9
5 ABDEFGHJKLM	ABGHJOTUV	10

10A — ❸ €49.00
5,5ha 109T(100-200m²) 90P — ❷ €69.00

🔳 From Le Château take the coastal road Route des Huitres in a north-westerly direction.
The campsite is located to the left after about 3 km.

📗 A family campsite located in a rural area 300 metres from the sea. Indoor heated swimming pool with slide. Free wifi hot spot.

CC 1/4-6/7 27/8-3/11

Saint-Pierre-d'Oléron °

📷 N 45°54'15" W 1°12'55"

www.eurocampings.co.uk/103417

994 Le Château-d'Oleron/La Gaconn., F-17480 / Poitou-Charentes ♿ 📶 (CC€15) iD 49

🔺 Le Fief Melin***
🚩 rue des Alizés
📅 1 May - 30 Sep
☎ +33 (0)5-46476085
@ lefiefmelin@wanadoo.fr

1 ADEF**JM**NOPQRST	CDPQRSTX	6
2 OPRVX	ABDE**F**	7
3 BEF**KLQT**	ABCDFNORV	8
4 BCDFHINO**Q**	ELUV	9
5 ADEFGH**NO**	ABHJMP**R**	10

10A CEE — ❸ €35.60
3ha 81T(82-130m²) 30P — ❷ €42.90

🔳 From the bridge towards Le Château, then direction Dolus to La Gaconnière, follow Rue des Illexés 400 metres on the right.

📗 A peacefully located campsite with a lovely indoor swimming pool. 1 km from the beach.

CC 1/5-7/7 25/8-29/9 8=7

Saint-Pierre-d'Oléron °

📷 N 45°53'37" W 1°12'52"

www.eurocampings.co.uk/110929

995 Le Grand-Village-Plage, F-17370 / Poitou-Charentes 📶 (CC€17) iD 49

🔺 Camping-Club Les Pins****
🚩 6 allée des Pins
📅 15 Mar - 15 Nov
☎ +33 (0)5-46475013
@ contact@lespinsdoleron.com

1 ABDEF**JM**NOPQRST	AMNQSX	6
2 BHQTVWXY	ABDE**FGH**	7
3 B**K**LQ	ABCDEFGIKNQRSTU	8
4 BCDFHILNO	BCEV	9
5 ADEFGHJM	ABGHIJ**P**TU	10

10A CEE — ❸ €42.00
6ha 70T(80-100m²) 100P — ❷ €59.00

🔳 From viaduct straight on at 1st roundabout, 2nd roundabout direction Grand-Village, 3rd roundabout direction Centreville-Plage, 4th roundabout straight on. Campsite then signposted.

📗 A campsite located in pine woods. Friendly reception, every comfort provided. Swimming lake with sandy beach.

CC 15/3-7/7 25/8-14/11 7=6

Saint-Pierre-d'Oléron °

La Tremblade °

📷 N 45°51'44" W 1°14'26"

www.eurocampings.co.uk/114372

996 Les Mathes, F-17570 / Poitou-Charentes ♿ 📶 (CC€17) iD 49

🔺 La Palombière***
🚩 1551 route de la Fouasse
📅 1 Apr - 15 Oct
☎ +33 (0)5-46226925
@ camping.lapalombiere@wanadoo.fr

1 A**JM**NOPQRST	ABFGM**N**	6
2 BOPSWXY	ABDE**FGH**	7
3 ABEF**K**LQRS	ABCDEFGIJNRSV	8
4 BDFHO	BEJUVW	9
5 ABDEFGHJK**NO**	ABDFGHIJ**P**TVZ	10

6-10A CEE — ❸ €36.70
9,5ha 218T(100-200m²) 65P — ❷ €46.70

🔳 Take exit 35 on the A10 at Saintes direction Royan N150. Then follow La Palmyre signs. Direction Les Mathes at the large roundabout. Campsite signposted at the next roundabout.
📗 A campsite idyllically situated in the woods with luxurious toilet facilities and just 3 km from the sandy beaches of the Côte Sauvage. An ideal base for interesting trips out. Restaurant and optical fibre wifi available (for a fee).

CC 1/4-2/7 27/8-14/10

Saint-Sulpice-de-Royan °

📷 N 45°43'24" W 1°10'27"

www.eurocampings.co.uk/114212

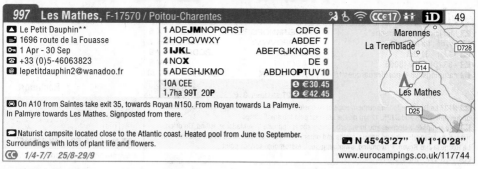

997 Les Mathes, F-17570 / Poitou-Charentes — iD 49

- ▲ Le Petit Dauphin**
- 🚩 1696 route de la Fouasse
- 📅 1 Apr - 30 Sep
- ☎ +33 (0)5-46063823
- @ lepetitdauphin2@wanadoo.fr

1 ADE**JM**NOPQRST	CDFG 6
2 HOPQVWXY	ABDEF 7
3 **IJK**L	ABEFGJKNQRS 8
4 NO**X**	DE 9
5 ADEGHJKMO	ABDHIO**P**TUV 10
10A CEE	€ €30.45
1,7ha 99T 20P	€ €42.45

On A10 from Saintes take exit 35, towards Royan N150. From Royan towards La Palmyre. In Palmyre towards Les Mathes. Signposted from there.

Naturist campsite located close to the Atlantic coast. Heated pool from June to September. Surroundings with lots of plant life and flowers.

CC 1/4-7/7 25/8-29/9

Marennes
La Tremblade — D728
D14
Les Mathes
D25

▲ N 45°43'27'' W 1°10'28''

www.eurocampings.co.uk/117744

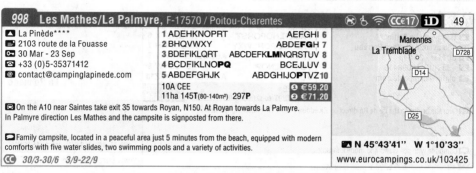

998 Les Mathes/La Palmyre, F-17570 / Poitou-Charentes — iD 49

- ▲ La Pinède****
- 🚩 2103 route de la Fouasse
- 📅 30 Mar - 23 Sep
- ☎ +33 (0)5-35371412
- @ contact@campinglapinede.com

1 ADEHKNOPRT	AEFGHI 6
2 BHQVWXY	ABDE**FGH** 7
3 BDEFIKLQRT	ABCDEFK**LM**NQRSTUV 8
4 BCDFIKLNO**PQ**	BCEJLUV 9
5 ABDEFGHJK	ABDGHIJO**P**TVZ 10
10A CEE	€ €59.20
11ha 145T(80-140m²) 297P	€ €71.20

On the A10 near Saintes take exit 35 towards Royan, N150. At Royan towards La Palmyre. In Palmyre direction Les Mathes and the campsite is signposted from there.

Family campsite, located in a peaceful area just 5 minutes from the beach, equipped with modern comforts with five water slides, two swimming pools and a variety of activities.

CC 30/3-30/6 3/9-22/9

Marennes
La Tremblade — D728
D14
D25

▲ N 45°43'41'' W 1°10'33''

www.eurocampings.co.uk/103425

999 Loix (Île de Ré), F-17111 / Poitou-Charentes — iD 45b

- ▲ Flower Camping Les Ilates****
- 🚩 route du Grouin
- 📅 31 Mar - 30 Sep
- ☎ +33 (0)5-46290543
- @ camping.les.ilates@
  flowercampings.com

1 ADE**JM**NOPR**T**	ABFG 6
2 PVWX	ABDE**FG**H 7
3 BFLMQT	ABCDEFKNQRSTU 8
4 BDLNO**P**U	ABEJLVW 9
5 ABDEFGHJKN	ABGHIJNO**P**R 10
10A CEE	€ €46.00
69T(90-115m²) 134P	€ €65.00

Follow the D102 almost to Loix. Then well signposted.

A large campsite with separate camping pitches. Lovely swimming pool and sports opportunities.

CC 31/3-29/6 1/9-29/9 7=6

Sainte-Marie-de-Ré

▲ N 46°13'35'' W 1°25'34''

www.eurocampings.co.uk/117890

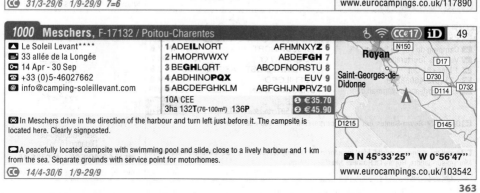

1000 Meschers, F-17132 / Poitou-Charentes — iD 49

- ▲ Le Soleil Levant****
- 🚩 33 allée de la Longée
- 📅 14 Apr - 30 Sep
- ☎ +33 (0)5-46027662
- @ info@camping-soleillevant.com

1 ADE**IL**NORT	AFHMNXY**Z** 6
2 HMOPRVWXY	ABDE**FGH** 7
3 BE**GH**LQRT	ABCDFNORSTU 8
4 ABDHINO**PQX**	EUV 9
5 ABCDEFGHKLM	ABFGHIJN**P**RVZ 10
10A CEE	€ €35.70
3ha 132T(76-100m²) 136P	€ €45.90

In Meschers drive in the direction of the harbour and turn left just before it. The campsite is located here. Clearly signposted.

A peacefully located campsite with swimming pool and slide, close to a lively harbour and 1 km from the sea. Separate grounds with service point for motorhomes.

CC 14/4-30/6 1/9-29/9

N150
Royan — D17
Saint-Georges-de-Didonne — D730
D114 — D732
D1215 — D145

▲ N 45°33'25'' W 0°56'47''

www.eurocampings.co.uk/103542

1001 Port-des-Barques, F-17730 / Poitou-Charentes
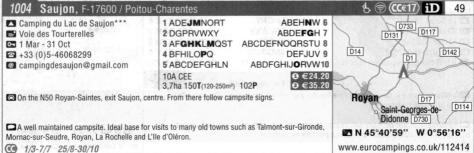
⌃ ✿ (CC€15) iD 49

▲ Municipal de la Garenne***	1 ADE**JM**NOPQRST	AFKNQRSTX 6
🏠 av. de l'Ile Madame	2 EHOPQVWXY	ABDE**FG**H 7
📅 1 Mar - 31 Oct	3 BEL**MQT**	ABCDFNORSV 8
☎ +33 (0)5-46848066	4 **A**BCDIN	EJV 9
@ camping@ville-portdesbarques.fr	5 ADEFGHK**N**	ABDHIJO**P**TUVZ10
	10A CEE	❶ €22.40
	7ha 242T(83-130m²) 31P	❷ €31.40

🚗 N137 La Rochelle to the southern edge of Rochefort (becomes the D733). Right after Charente bridge onto D238 and D125. 12 km on the left, just past the small village.

💬 This campsite welcomes you in superb surroundings opposite 'l'Ile Madame' island. On offer: fishing, watersports, visiting special sights and other activities. Ideally situated by the sea between La Rochelle and Royan. Playground, swimming pool. Motorhome service point.

(CC) 1/3-7/7 26/8-30/10

▲ N 45°56'53'' W 1°5'45''
www.eurocampings.co.uk/100387

1002 Rivedoux-Plage, F-17940 / Poitou-Charentes
⌃ (CC€17) ⚥ iD 45b

▲ Campéole Le Platin***	1 ADE**IL**NOPQRS**T**	KNQRSTX 6
🏠 125 avenue Gustave Perreau	2 AEFHOPQRSWXY	ABDE**FG**H 7
📅 30 Mar - 23 Sep	3 ABLT	ABCDEFGKNRSV 8
☎ +33 (0)5-46098410	4 BCDHILNO**P**	EFLUVW 9
@ platin@campeole.com	5 DHN	ABDFGHIJ**P**TUVZ10
	10A CEE	❶ €31.10
	3,7ha 139T(60-171m²) 106P	❷ €44.50

🚗 Over the bridge to the Île de Ré direction Rivedoux-Plage. Thereafter signposted.

💬 Campsite with sea views and modest facilities.

(CC) 30/3-6/7 25/8-22/9

▲ N 46°9'35'' W 1°15'59''
www.eurocampings.co.uk/116537

1003 Royan, F-17200 / Poitou-Charentes
♿ ⌃ (CC€17) ⚥ iD 49

▲ Campéole Clairefontaine****	1 ADE**JM**NOPRS**T**	ABFGKMNSTX 6
🏠 16 rue du Colonel Lachaud	2 EHOPRWXY	ABDE**FG**H 7
📅 30 Mar - 30 Sep	3 BE**KLMT**	ABCDEFGIKNOQRS 8
☎ +33 (0)5-46390811	4 BCDILNO**PQ**	EFJ 9
@ clairefontaine@campeole.com	5 ADEFGHJ	ABDGHIJ**N**P**R**Z10
	10A CEE	❶ €41.10
	5ha 124T(80-100m²) 119P	❷ €58.90

🚗 A10, near Saintes take exit 35 direction Royan (N150). In Royan drive in the direction of Pontaillac (west of Royan). From there the campsite is clearly signposted.

💬 A lovely camping ground in natural surroundings yet still close to shops, restaurants, the beach and providing everything you could need for an enjoyable holiday.

(CC) 30/3-6/7 25/8-29/9

▲ N 45°37'52'' W 1°3'0''
www.eurocampings.co.uk/103434

1004 Saujon, F-17600 / Poitou-Charentes
♿ ⌃ (CC€17) iD 49

▲ Camping du Lac de Saujon***	1 ADE**JM**NORT	ABEH**N**W 6
🏠 Voie des Tourterelles	2 DGPRVWXY	ABDE**FG**H 7
📅 1 Mar - 31 Oct	3 AF**GHKLM**QST	ABCDEFNOQRSTU 8
☎ +33 (0)5-46068299	4 BFHILO**PQ**	DEFJUV 9
@ campingdesaujon@gmail.com	5 ABCDEFGHLN	ABDFGHIJ**O**RVW10
	10A CEE	❶ €24.40
	3,7ha 150T(120-250m²) 102P	❷ €35.20

🚗 On the N50 Royan-Saintes, exit Saujon, centre. From there follow campsite signs.

💬 A well maintained campsite. Ideal base for visits to many old towns such as Talmont-sur-Gironde, Mornac-sur-Seudre, Royan, La Rochelle and L'Ile d'Oléron.

(CC) 1/3-7/7 25/8-30/10

▲ N 45°40'59'' W 0°56'16''
www.eurocampings.co.uk/112414

1005 St. Augustin-sur-Mer, F-17570 / Poitou-Charentes ⚹ 📶 (CC€19) iD 49

- ⛰ Le Logis du Breuil★★★★
- 🏠 36 rue du Centre
- 📅 5 May - 30 Sep
- ☎ +33 (0)5-46232345
- @ info@logis-du-breuil.com

1	ADE**JM**NOPQRST	EFGHIX 6
2	BOPUVWXY	ABDE**FG**H 7
3	BDE**KLMQ**R	ABCDFGIK**LM**NOQRSTUV 8
4	I**OPQ**U	EIJLV 9
5	ACDEFGHKL**NO**	ABDGHIJ**O**TUW 10

10A CEE	❶ €35.20
9ha 390T(150-250m²) 67P	❷ €50.45

🚗 On the A10 at Saintes take exit 35 towards Royan, N150. At Royan follow dir. St. Palais as far as the St. Augustin exit. Indicated from there.

💬 Located in the heart of the Arvert peninsula. Enjoy the friendly, rural atmosphere on a spacious pitch (approx. 200 sq.m.) in a woodland setting. With the ocean close by you can also enjoy the beach and sea. The surroundings are also well worth the effort. A holiday just made for relaxing.

(CC) 5/5-14/6 1/9-29/9

🗺 N 45°40'32" W 1°5'42"

www.eurocampings.co.uk/103422

1006 St. Clément-des-Baleines, F-17590 / Poitou-Charentes ⚹ 📶 (CC€19) iD 45b

- ⛰ La Plage★★★★
- 🏠 408 rue du Chaume
- 📅 13 Apr - 16 Sep
- ☎ +33 (0)5-46294262
- @ info@la-plage.com

1	ADE**JM**NOPQRT	ABF**G**KNOQRSTWXYZ 6
2	EHOPVX	ABDE**FG**H 7
3	BE**KLMQ**	ABCDEFGJKNOQRSV 8
4	BCDHINO**PRTVX**	BEKV 9
5	ABDEFGHJKL**N**	ABDGHIJNPTU 10

Ad on this page 10A CEE

	❶ €52.00
30T 109P	❷ €64.20

🚗 On Ile de Ré follow D735 past Ars-en-Ré. Follow signs 'Phare des B'. After St. Clément-des-Baleines campsite is clearly indicated.

💬 Sunny campsite behind the dunes with an attractive beach. Lovely, heated pool and many amenities. Wellness facility with sauna and hamam. Free wifi throughout the campsite.

(CC) 13/4-30/6 1/9-15/9

🗺 N 46°14'28" W 1°33'12"

www.eurocampings.co.uk/108571

France

1007 St. Clément-des-Baleines, F-17590 / Poitou-Charentes ⚹ 📶 ✿ (CC€19) ⚹⚹ iD 45b

- ⛰ Les Baleines★★★
- 🏠 Le Gillieux
- 📅 28 Apr - 22 Sep
- ☎ +33 (0)5-46294076
- @ contact@camping-lesbaleines.com

1	ADE**IL**NOPQRST	KNOQRSTWXY 6
2	EHKMOPQUVWXY	ABDE**FG**H 7
3	ABKLQ	ABCDEFKNQRSV 8
4	BFHO	BEFVWZ 9
5	ABCDEFHJ**N**	ABDGHIJOQTUVZ 10

10A CEE	❶ €43.00
4,6ha 157T(80-140m²) 26P	❷ €54.00

🚗 From the bridge direction 'Phare des Baleines' (± 30 km). Turn left before 'Le Phare' car park (signposted) in the Rue du Chaume and Rue de la Madeleine, then straight ahead to the campsite.

💬 Camping in a nature reserve with spacious pitches and direct access to the beach (50 metres). All amenities with top-notch toilet facilities. Views of the bay and Phare des Baleines. European Eco label. Electrical car for rent. Free wifi zone.

(CC) 28/4-6/7 1/9-21/9

🗺 N 46°14'23" W 1°33'35"

www.eurocampings.co.uk/112067

1008 St. Georges-d'Oléron, F-17190 / Poitou-Charentes ♿ 🛜 (CC€17) iD | 49

🏕 Le Suroit****
🍴 1720 rue Ponthézières
🗓 1 Apr - 30 Sep
☎ +33 (0)5-46470725
@ info@camping-lesuroit.com

1 ADE**JM**NOPRST	ABCDFGHIKNQSXY	6
2 EHJPQRTUVWXY	ABDE**FGH**	7
3 BDE**KLQ**	ABCDEFIJ**L**NORSTV	8
4 BCDHILNO**QU**	EUVZ	9
5 ABDEFGHKLM**NO**	ABHIJMP**Q**TUVZ	10

10A CEE		❶ €38.00
5ha 226**T**(80-130m²) 40**P**		❷ €57.00

🗺 From the bridge N734 as far as St. Gilles. Campsite on the left 3 km further on.

💬 Friendly four-star campsite with an attractive restaurant and an indoor pool with three water slides. Located close to the sea. Wifi.

(CC) 1/4-6/7 26/8-29/9

🧭 N 45°56'53'' W 1°22'22''
www.eurocampings.co.uk/108515

1009 St. Georges-de-Didonne, F-17110 / Poitou-Charentes ⊗ ♿ 🛜 (CC€15) iD | 49

🏕 Ideal Camping***
🍴 16 avenue de Suzac
🗓 2 May - 9 Sep
☎ +33 (0)5-46052904
@ info@ideal-camping.com

1 ADEFHKNORT	ABFGHIKNQSWX	6
2 BEHOPQSVWXY	ABDE**FGH**	7
3 BCFLQ	ABCDEFNORV	8
4 FHINO**PQU**	E	9
5 ACDEFGHIJKLM**O**	ABGHIJ**P**TU	10

6-10A		❶ €41.50
8ha 400**T**(90-100m²) 105**P**		❷ €45.90

🗺 Drive on the D25 from Royan to St. Georges-de-Didonne. The campsite is signposted before the centre of St. Georges-de-Didonne.

💬 Very well maintained campsite near the sea (300 m). Beautiful heated leisure pool. 2 km from St. Georges de Didonne. A peaceful campsite with plenty of sports and games for children.

(CC) 2/5-1/7 25/8-8/9

🧭 N 45°35'6'' W 0°59'7''
www.eurocampings.co.uk/108539

1010 St. Jean-d'Angely, F-17400 / Poitou-Charentes ♿ 🛜 (CC€15) ⚦ iD | 17 B2

🏕 Val de Boutonne***
🍴 56 quai Bernouët
🗓 1 Apr - 30 Sep
☎ +33 (0)5-46322616
@ campingvaldeboutonne@gmail.com

1 AD**JM**NOPRS**T**	AF**N**QUVXYZ	6
2 ACDGPRVWXY	ABDE**FGH**	7
3 AELQ	ABCDEFNORTUV	8
4 OPQ	ADEJPQRTUV	9
5 ABD**NO**	ABGHIJ**N**PRV	10

10A CEE		❶ €19.50
1,9ha 99**T**(95-120m²) 49**P**		❷ €26.50

🗺 A10 exit 34 direction St. Jean-d'Angely (Ouest). The campsite is very clearly signposted.

💬 Campsite with plenty of shade located in the centre of St. Jean-d'Angly. Well maintained, close to the river and a large lake in quiet surroundings. An old town well worth a visit, also suitable as a base for visiting historic towns.

(CC) 1/4-6/7 27/8-29/9 7=6

🧭 N 45°56'55'' W 0°32'11''
www.eurocampings.co.uk/103535

1011 St. Just-Luzac, F-17320 / Poitou-Charentes ⊗ ♿ 🛜 ✿ iD | 49

🏕 Camping Séquoia Parc*****
🍴 La Josephtrie
🗓 5 May - 5 Sep
☎ +33 (0)5-46855555
@ info@sequoiaparc.com

1 ADEHKNOPQR**T**	AB**E**FGHIOX	6
2 GPVXY	ABDE**FGH**	7
3 BEF**GHLM**Q	ABCDEFJKNQRSTUV	8
4 BCDHIKLNO**PQRTUVXZ**	CEJLUVY	9
5 ACDEFGHLMN**O**	ABGHIJ**N**PSTXY	10

10A CEE		❶ €59.00
45ha 226**T**(140m²) 375**P**		❷ €77.00

🗺 Via Paris to Bordeaux on the A10. Take the exit direction Ile d'Oléron, the D728, at Saintes. Follow this road as far as exit on the right to the campsite past St. Just-Luzac.

💬 This campsite is set in castle grounds 5 km from the child-friendly beach at Marennes. Here, there are more than enough opportunities for an enjoyable holiday in rural surroundings. Entertainment all year round. It has a large, fun swimming complex.

🧭 N 45°48'39'' W 1°3'41''
www.eurocampings.co.uk/108789

1012 St. Palais-sur-Mer, F-17420 / Poitou-Charentes ♿ 🛜 (CC€17) iD 49

🏕 Des Deux Plages****
📧 41 avenue des Acacias
📅 1 Apr - 30 Sep
☎ +33 (0)5-46231142
@ contact@campingdes2plages.fr

1 ADE**IL**NOPQRST	ABFGMNQRSTUVW**X** 6	
2 HMOPSVWXY	ABDE**FGH** 7	
3 B**K**LQRSV	ABCDFKNQRSV 8	
4 DILNO**PQTUX**	ELUV 9	
5 ABDEFGHJLM**NO**	ABDHIJN**P**TU 10	
10A CEE	⊙ €43.20	
3ha 70T(80-140m²) 60P	⊙ €56.70	

🚗 From the A10 near Saintes, take exit 35 to Royan. At large roundabout near Royan direction St. Palais. Campsite well signposted in the centre.

💬 A very peaceful campsite overlooking 2 beaches in the distance (600 m). Lovely pitches on a flat site near the centre of St Palais-sur-Mer.

CC 1/5-7/7 1/9-29/9

📌 N 45°38'45'' W 1°4'48''

www.eurocampings.co.uk/121652

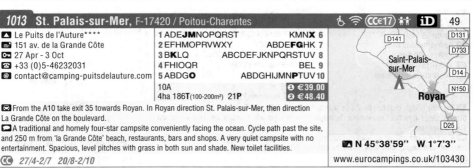

1013 St. Palais-sur-Mer, F-17420 / Poitou-Charentes ♿ 🛜 (CC€17) 🚻 iD 49

🏕 Le Puits de l'Auture****
📧 151 av. de la Grande Côte
📅 27 Apr - 3 Oct
☎ +33 (0)5-46232031
@ contact@camping-puitsdelauture.com

1 ADE**JM**NOPQRST	KMN**X** 6	
2 EFHMOPRVWXY	ABDE**FGH**K 7	
3 B**K**LQ	ABCDEFJKNPQRSTUV 8	
4 FHIOQR	BEL 9	
5 ABDG**O**	ABDGHIJMN**P**TUV 10	
10A	⊙ €39.00	
4ha 186T(100-200m²) 21P	⊙ €48.40	

🚗 From the A10 take exit 35 towards Royan. In Royan direction St. Palais-sur-Mer, then direction La Grande Côte on the boulevard.

💬 A traditional and homely four-star campsite conveniently facing the ocean. Cycle path past the site, and 250 m from 'la Grande Côte' beach, restaurants, bars and shops. A very quiet campsite with no entertainment. Spacious, level pitches with grass in both sun and shade. New toilet facilities.

CC 27/4-2/7 20/8-2/10

📌 N 45°38'59'' W 1°7'3''

www.eurocampings.co.uk/103430

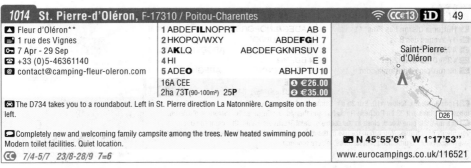

1014 St. Pierre-d'Oléron, F-17310 / Poitou-Charentes 🛜 (CC€13) iD 49

🏕 Fleur d'Oléron**
📧 1 rue des Vignes
📅 7 Apr - 29 Sep
☎ +33 (0)5-46361140
@ contact@camping-fleur-oleron.com

1 ABDEF**IL**NOPR**T**	AB 6	
2 HKOPQVWXY	ABDE**FGH** 7	
3 A**K**LQ	ABCDEFGKNRSUV 8	
4 HI	E 9	
5 ADE**O**	ABHJPTU 10	
16A CEE	⊙ €26.00	
2ha 73T(90-100m²) 25P	⊙ €35.00	

🚗 The D734 takes you to a roundabout. Left in St. Pierre direction La Natonnière. Campsite on the left.

💬 Completely new and welcoming family campsite among the trees. New heated swimming pool. Modern toilet facilities. Quiet location.

CC 7/4-5/7 23/8-28/9 7=6

📌 N 45°55'6'' W 1°17'53''

www.eurocampings.co.uk/116521

1015 St. Pierre-d'Oléron, F-17310 / Poitou-Charentes 🛜 (CC€15) iD 49

🏕 La Perroche Plage***
📧 18 rue du Renclos (la Perroche)
📅 25 Mar - 1 Oct
☎ +33 (0)5-46753733
@ laperroche@oleron-camping.eu

1 ADF**JM**NOPRST	KMNOPQRSTUVXY 6	
2 EHKPQVWXY	ABDE**FGH** 7	
3 BE**K**LQT	ABCDEFHNORSV 8	
4 H**TU**	BEUVW 9	
5 ABDM**NO**	ABDGHJOTUV 10	
6-10A CEE	⊙ €31.30	
1,8ha 70T(80-100m²) 33P	⊙ €42.30	

🚗 After the bridge direction Grand Village Plage, then turn right and follow the coast road. Located to the left after 8 km. 3 km before La Cotinière.

💬 A small, peaceful family campsite with direct access to the dunes and the sea. Opportunities for many watersports. 2 minutes from La Cotinière. Take advantage of the wellness area (jacuzzi, sauna).

CC 25/3-7/7 25/8-30/9

📌 N 45°54'6'' W 1°18'9''

www.eurocampings.co.uk/103415

1016 St. Pierre-d'Oléron, F-17310 / Poitou-Charentes ⅍ 🛜 CC€17 iD 49

- ▲ Le Sous Bois***
- 🏕 avenue des Pins, La Cotinière
- ⊙ 1 Apr - 31 Oct
- ☎ +33 (0)5-46472246
- @ resa.lesousbois@orange.fr

1 ABDEF**JM**NOPRST	KNX	6
2 BEHJKOPVWXY	ABDE**FGH**	7
3 AELQ	ABCDEFNQRSV	8
4 BCDHINO**TUX**	BEJLUV	9
5 D**O**	ABHJM**P**UV	10
10A CEE	❶ €34.50	
2,5ha 139**T**(80-130m²) 48**P**	❷ €37.50	

🚗 From the bridge direction St. Pierre. In St. Pierre direction La Cotinière. In La Cotinière direction L'Ileau. Signposted thereafter.

💬 A small, friendly campsite in the countryside. Located next to fishing village La Cotinière. The peaceful atmosphere is especially appealing!

CC 1/4-30/6 1/9-30/10

Saint-Georges-d'Oléron
Saint-Pierre-d'Oléron
D26

⬛ N 45°55'23'' W 1°20'29''

www.eurocampings.co.uk/112580

1017 St. Trojan-les-Bains, F-17370 / Poitou-Charentes ⅍ 🛜 CC€17 iD 49

- ▲ Camping St-Tro'Park****
- 🏕 36 avenue des Bris
- ⊙ 15 Apr - 30 Sep
- ☎ +33 (0)5-46760047
- @ info@st-tro-park.com

1 ADEF**IL**NOPQRST	ABFGMNPQRST**X**	6
2 BHQTVWXY	ABDE**FGH**	7
3 BE**K**LQ	ABCDEFKNORSTUV	8
4 BDEFHILN**PRTUV**	EHJUV	9
5 ACDEFGHM**NO**	ABEGHIJ**P**TUV	10
10A CEE	❶ €35.00	
4ha 99**T**(80-120m²) 115**P**	❷ €50.60	

🚗 From the bridge, direction St. Pierre 'autres directions', follow St. Trojan as far as the harbour. Straight ahead at harbour roundabout. Turn right at roundabout with fountain. Keep left at junction. Then signposted.

💬 A peaceful campsite in wooded surroundings. The site has a heated swimming pool, jacuzzi, hammam and sauna. Toilet facilities for the disabled. Wifi.

CC 15/4-30/6 1/9-29/9

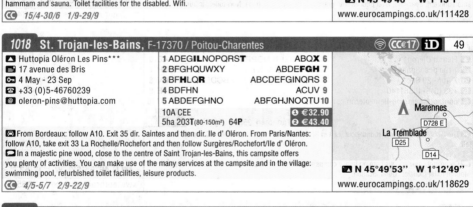

Marennes
D26
D728 E
La Tremblade
D25
D14

⬛ N 45°49'46'' W 1°13'1''

www.eurocampings.co.uk/111428

1018 St. Trojan-les-Bains, F-17370 / Poitou-Charentes 🛜 CC€17 iD 49

- ▲ Huttopia Oléron Les Pins***
- 🏕 17 avenue des Bris
- ⊙ 4 May - 23 Sep
- ☎ +33 (0)5-46760239
- @ oleron-pins@huttopia.com

1 ADEG**IL**NOPQRST	ABQ**X**	6
2 BFGHQUWXY	ABDE**FGH**	7
3 BF**H**LQR	ABCDEFGINQRS	8
4 BDFHN	ACUV	9
5 ABDEFGHNO	ABFGHJNOQTU	10
10A CEE	❶ €32.90	
5ha 203**T**(80-150m²) 64**P**	❷ €43.40	

🚗 From Bordeaux: follow A10. Exit 35 dir. Saintes and then dir. Ile d' Oléron. From Paris/Nantes: follow A10, take exit 33 La Rochelle/Rochefort and then follow Surgères/Rochefort/Ile d' Oléron.

💬 In a majestic pine wood, close to the centre of Saint Trojan-les-Bains, this campsite offers you plenty of activities. You can make use of the many services at the campsite and in the village: swimming pool, refurbished toilet facilities, leisure products.

CC 4/5-5/7 2/9-22/9

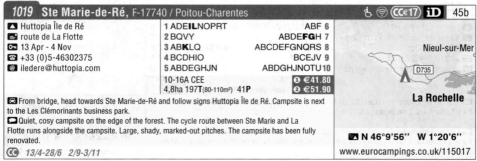

Marennes
D728 E
La Tremblade
D25
D14

⬛ N 45°49'53'' W 1°12'49''

www.eurocampings.co.uk/118629

1019 Ste Marie-de-Ré, F-17740 / Poitou-Charentes ⅍ 🛜 CC€17 iD 45b

- ▲ Huttopia Île de Ré
- 🏕 route de La Flotte
- ⊙ 13 Apr - 4 Nov
- ☎ +33 (0)5-46302375
- @ iledere@huttopia.com

1 ADEI**L**NOPRT	ABF	6
2 BQVY	ABDE**FGH**	7
3 AB**K**LQ	ABCDEFGNQRS	8
4 BCDHIO	BCEJV	9
5 ABDEGHJN	ABDGHJNOTU	10
10-16A CEE	❶ €41.80	
4,8ha 197**T**(80-110m²) 41**P**	❷ €51.90	

🚗 From bridge, head towards Ste Marie-de-Ré and follow signs Huttopia Île de Ré. Campsite is next to the Les Clémorinants business park.

💬 Quiet, cosy campsite on the edge of the forest. The cycle route between Ste Marie and La Flotte runs alongside the campsite. Large, shady, marked-out pitches. The campsite has been fully renovated.

CC 13/4-28/6 2/9-3/11

Nieul-sur-Mer
D735
La Rochelle

⬛ N 46°9'56'' W 1°20'6''

www.eurocampings.co.uk/115017

1020 Vaux-sur-Mer, F-17640 / Poitou-Charentes

        🚻 📶 (CC€17) **iD** | 49

⬛ Flower Camping Le Nauzan-Plage****	1 AD**EJM**NOPQRT	ABEFGMNX 6
📧 39 ave de Nauzan Plage	2 EHOPRVWXY	ABDE**FG**H 7
📅 1 Apr - 30 Sep	3 ABEF**KLMN**ST	ABCDEFJKNQRSUV 8
☎ +33 (0)5-46382913	4 BCDILNO**PQ**	CEJL 9
@ contact@campinglenauzanplage.com	5 ACDEFGHJK	ABDGHIJ**P**R 10

Ad on this page 10A CEE	➊ €46.90
4,5ha 137**T**(90-160m²) 100**P**	➋ €62.85

🚗 From the A10 near Saintes take exit 35 towards Royan, N150. At Royan dir. Vaux-sur-Mer. Campsite well signposted in Vaux.
🛏 Located 450m from the beach, this 4-star campsite offers you all the ingredients of an enjoyable stay. All amenities are available on site or in the immediate surroundings. Horse riding, sailing, swimming, fishing, walking and cycling are just some of the possibilities. There are plenty of interesting sights in the vicinity.

(CC) 1/4-14/7 1/9-29/9 7=6

📷 N 45°38'34" W 1°4'20"
www.eurocampings.co.uk/100389

A camping with excellent toilet facilities. Free hot water. Spacious pitches on grassland. Plenty of facilities and located 450m from a lovely sandy beach in a bay. Just a few kilometres from Royan. The recommended price for 2 persons. A discount applies in the early and late season. Open from April 1st. Booking recommended in July and August!

39 ave de Nauzan Plage, 17640 Vaux-sur-Mer
Tel. 05 46 38 29 13 • Fax 05 46 38 18 43
E-mail: contact@campinglenauzanplage.com
Internet: www.campinglenauzanplage.com

France

1021 Airvault, F-79600 / Poitou-Charentes

        🚻 📶 (CC€19) **iD** | 18 A1

⬛ de Courte Vallée***	1 AD**EJM**NOPQRST	AB**N** 6
📧 rue Courte Vallée	2 GPRVWXY	ABDE**FG**H 7
📅 1 Mar - 31 Oct	3 ALQ	ABCDFNQRV 8
☎ +33 (0)5-49647065	4 FHIOQ	DE 9
@ camping@caravanningfrance.com	5 ABDEFHKN	ABCDFHIJPRV 10

Ad on this page 13-16A CEE	➊ €30.00
A102 3,5ha 65**T**(110-130m²) 3**P**	➋ €36.00

🚗 From Thouars take the D938. Then take the D725-bis as far as Airvault. In the village follow the campsigns 'de Courte Vallée'.
🛏 Campsite is located in the Thouet valley close to the medieval town of Airvault and the Loire valley. The site is characterised by the high level of maintenance. Excellent toilets, swimming pool. Wifi and lovely outside cafe. The English family is hospitable and will do a lot to offer you a wonderful holiday.

(CC) 1/3-14/7 1/9-30/10

📷 N 46°49'59" W 0°8'53"
www.eurocampings.co.uk/101196

1022 Bois Vert/Com. du Tallud, F-79200 / Poitou-Charentes ♿ 🛜 (CC€17) iD 18 A1

- 🏕 Le Bois Vert★★★★
- 🏢 14 rue de Boisseau
- 🗓 2 Apr - 26 Oct
- ☎ +33 (0)5-49647843
- @ campingboisvert@orange.fr

| 1 ADE**JM**NOPRST | ABF**N** 6 |
| 2 CGPRSVWXY | ABDE**FGH** 7 |
| 3 ABLMQ   ABCDEFGHIJKNPQRSTUV 8 |
| 4 DFHIO | AEL 9 |
| 5 ABDEFGHJKMN**O**   ABDFHIJM**NP**TU 10 |

16A CEE   ❶ €28.50
A139 3ha 88T(70-130m²) 18P   ❷ €38.50

🚗 From Niort take the D743 as far as the southwest edge of Parthenay, then turn left onto the D949bis, over the bridge and immediately right.

💬 Medium-sized campsite on a lake and a river with opportunities for fishing. Close to the medieval town of Parthenay. Well marked-out cycling and walking paths.

CC 2/4-5/7 23/8-25/10 7=6

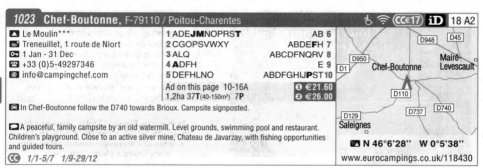

🧭 N 46°38'30'' W 0°16'3''

www.eurocampings.co.uk/103529

1023 Chef-Boutonne, F-79110 / Poitou-Charentes ♿ 🛜 (CC€17) iD 18 A2

- 🏕 Le Moulin★★★
- 🏢 Treneuillet, 1 route de Niort
- 🗓 1 Jan - 31 Dec
- ☎ +33 (0)5-49297346
- @ info@campingchef.com

1 ADE**JM**NOPRS**T**	AB 6
2 CGOPSVWXY	ABDE**FH** 7
3 ALQ	ABCDFNQRV 8
4 **A**DFH	E 9
5 DEFHLNO	ABDFGHIJ**P**ST 10

Ad on this page 10-16A   ❶ €21.60
1,2ha 37T(40-150m²) 7P   ❷ €26.00

🚗 In Chef-Boutonne follow the D740 towards Brioux. Campsite signposted.

💬 A peaceful, family campsite by an old watermill. Level grounds, swimming pool and restaurant. Children's playground. Close to an active silver mine, Chateau de Javarzay, with fishing opportunities and guided tours.

CC 1/1-5/7 1/9-29/12

🧭 N 46°6'28'' W 0°5'38''

www.eurocampings.co.uk/118430

1024 Coulon, F-79510 / Poitou-Charentes ♿ 🛜 ✿ (CC€17) iD 17 B2

- 🏕 Flower Camping La Venise Verte★★★★
- 🏢 178 route des Bords de Sèvre
- 🗓 1 Apr - 15 Oct
- ☎ +33 (0)5-49359036
- @ accueil@camping-laveniseverte.fr

1 ADE**IL**NOPRST	ABF**NX** 6
2 ABCPRVWXY	ABDE**FGH** 7
3 ABELQ	ABCDEFKNQRSTUV 8
4 ABDEFHIO	BEJQVW 9
5 ABDEFHJKMNO	ABDEGHIJORZ 10

10A CEE   ❶ €30.90
2,2ha 97T(80-187m²) 23P   ❷ €44.90

🚗 From Niort direction Coulon (D9), then from Coulon D123 direction Irleau. Campsite on this road.
💬 A campsite 2 km from Coulon, in the heart of the Marais Poitevin. Lovely cycling and walking trips are possible. 97 pitches, large swimming pool, restaurant and many recreational opportunities. The campsite has been awarded the European Eco label, thanks to the sustainable tourism that is practised here. A lovely campsite for a relaxing stay.

CC 1/4-9/7 27/8-14/10

🧭 N 46°18'54'' W 0°36'33''

www.eurocampings.co.uk/113003

1025 St. Hilaire-la-Palud, F-79210 / Poitou-Charentes
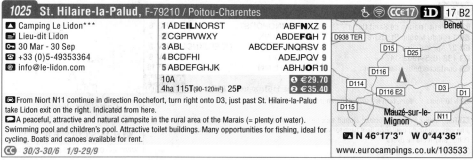

▲ Camping Le Lidon***
≡ Lieu-dit Lidon
30 Mar - 30 Sep
☎ +33 (0)5-49353364
@ info@le-lidon.com

CC€17 iD 17 B2

1 ADE**IL**NORST	ABF**N**XZ	6
2 CGPRVWXY	ABDE**FG**H	7
3 ABL	ABCDEFJNQRSV	8
4 BCDFHI	ADEJPQV	9
5 ABDEFGHJK	ABHJ**OR**	10
10A		€29.70
4ha 115T(90-120m²) 25P		€35.40

From Niort N11 continue in direction Rochefort, turn right onto D3, just past St. Hilaire-la-Palud take Lidon exit on the right. Indicated from here.
A peaceful, attractive and natural campsite in the rural area of the Marais (= plenty of water). Swimming pool and children's pool. Attractive toilet buildings. Many opportunities for fishing, ideal for cycling. Boats and canoes available for rent.
CC 30/3-30/6 1/9-29/9

Benet · D938 TER · D15 · D25 · D116 · D114 · D116 E2 · D3 · D1 · D115 · Mauzé-sur-le-Mignon · N11

N 46°17'3" W 0°44'36"
www.eurocampings.co.uk/103533

1026 Chalandray, F-86190 / Poitou-Charentes
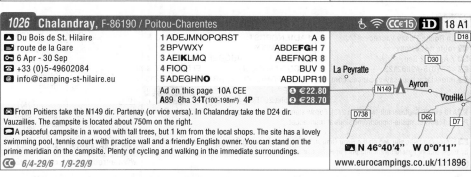

▲ Du Bois de St. Hilaire
≡ route de la Gare
6 Apr - 30 Sep
☎ +33 (0)5-49602084
@ info@camping-st-hilaire.eu

CC€15 iD 18 A1

1 ADEJMNOPQRST	A	6
2 BPVWXY	ABDE**FG**H	7
3 AEI**K**LMQ	ABEFNQR	8
4 FIOQ	BUV	9
5 ADEGHN**O**	ABDIJPR	10
Ad on this page 10A CEE		€22.80
A89 8ha 34T(100-198m²) 4P		€28.70

From Poitiers take the N149 dir. Partenay (or vice versa). In Chalandray take the D24 dir. Vauzailles. The campsite is located about 750m on the right.
A peaceful campsite in a wood with tall trees, but 1 km from the local shops. The site has a lovely swimming pool, tennis court with practice wall and a friendly English owner. You can stand on the prime meridian on the campsite. Plenty of cycling and walking in the immediate surroundings.
CC 6/4-29/6 1/9-29/9

D18 · D30 · La Peyratte · N149 · Ayron · Vouillé · D738 · D62 · D7

N 46°40'4" W 0°0'11"
www.eurocampings.co.uk/111896

1027 Couhé, F-86700 / Poitou-Charentes
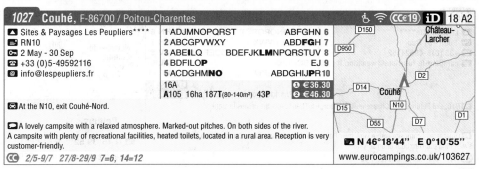

▲ Sites & Paysages Les Peupliers****
≡ RN10
2 May - 30 Sep
☎ +33 (0)5-49592116
@ info@lespeupliers.fr

CC€19 iD 18 A2

1 ADJMNOPQRST	ABFGHN	6
2 ABCGPVWXY	ABD**FG**H	7
3 ABEILQ	BDEFJK**LM**NPQRSTUV	8
4 BDFILO**P**	EJ	9
5 ACDGHM**NO**	ABDGHIJ**P**R	10
16A		€36.30
A105 16ha 187T(80-140m²) 43P		€46.30

At the N10, exit Couhé-Nord.

A lovely campsite with a relaxed atmosphere. Marked-out pitches. On both sides of the river. A campsite with plenty of recreational facilities, heated toilets, located in a rural area. Reception is very customer-friendly.
CC 2/5-9/7 27/8-29/9 7=6, 14=12

D150 · Château-Larcher · D950 · D14 · D2 · Couhé · D15 · N10 · D55 · D7 · D1

N 46°18'44" E 0°10'55"
www.eurocampings.co.uk/103627

1028 Ingrandes, F-86220 / Poitou-Charentes   ♿ 🛜 ⓒⒸ€19 ♀♂ iD 18 A1

- 🏕 Le Petit Trianon de Saint Ustre****
- 🏠 1 rue du Moulin St. Ustre
- 📅 27 Apr - 30 Sep
- ☎ +33 (0)5-49026147
- @ contact@petit-trianon.com

1 ADJMNOPQRST	ABFG	6
2 AFGPTVWXY	ABDEFGH	7
3 ABEILQT	CDEFJKNQRSTUV	8
4 BDFHIOU	AEHIKLV	9
5 ABDGHLMN	ABFGHJNOPST	10
10A		❶ €33.80
A80 7ha 116T(120-150m²) 38P		❷ €43.00

🚗 N10 Tours-Poitiers, turn left before Ingrandes, follow the signs.

🛏 This family campsite is located around a castle in a rural setting, and has spacious pitches and a heated swimming pool. Excellent base for visiting Roman churches, castles, Futuroscope and the Poitou and Touraine rivers.

ⓒⓒ 27/4-6/7 27/8-29/9 7=6

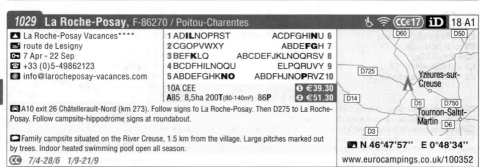

📌 N 46°53'16'' E 0°35'13''

www.eurocampings.co.uk/103620

1029 La Roche-Posay, F-86270 / Poitou-Charentes   ♿ 🛜 ⓒⒸ€17 iD 18 A1

- 🏕 La Roche-Posay Vacances****
- 🏠 route de Lesigny
- 📅 7 Apr - 22 Sep
- ☎ +33 (0)5-49862123
- @ info@larocheposay-vacances.com

1 ADILNOPRST	ACDFGHINU	6
2 CGOPVWXY	ABDEFGH	7
3 BEFKLQ	ABCDEFJKLNOQRSV	8
4 BCDFHILNOQU	ELPQRUVY	9
5 ABDEFGHKNO	ABDFHJNOPRVZ	10
10A CEE		❶ €39.30
A85 8,5ha 200T(80-140m²) 86P		❷ €51.30

🚗 A10 exit 26 Châtellerault-Nord (km 273). Follow signs fo La Roche-Posay. Then D275 to La Roche-Posay. Follow campsite-hippodrome signs at roundabout.

🛏 Family campsite situated on the River Creuse, 1.5 km from the village. Large pitches marked out by trees. Indoor heated swimming pool open all season.

ⓒⓒ 7/4-28/6 1/9-21/9

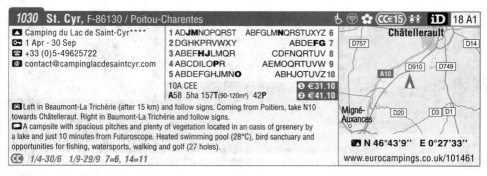

📌 N 46°47'57'' E 0°48'34''

www.eurocampings.co.uk/100352

1030 St. Cyr, F-86130 / Poitou-Charentes   ♿ 🛜 ♻ ⓒⒸ€15 ♀♂ iD 18 A1

- 🏕 Camping du Lac de Saint-Cyr****
- 📅 1 Apr - 30 Sep
- ☎ +33 (0)5-49625722
- @ contact@campinglacdesaintcyr.com

1 ADJMNOPQRST	ABFGLMNQRSTUXYZ	6
2 DGHKPRVWXY	ABDEFG	7
3 ABEFHJLMQR	CDFNQRTUV	8
4 ABCDILOPR	AEMOQRTUVW	9
5 ABDEFGHJMNO	ABHJOTUVZ	10
10A CEE		❶ €31.10
A58 5ha 157T(90-120m²) 42P		❷ €41.10

🚗 Left in Beaumont-La Trichérie (after 15 km) and follow signs. Coming from Poitiers, take N10 towards Châtelleraut. Right in Baumont-La Trichérie and follow signs.

🛏 A campsite with spacious pitches and plenty of vegetation located in an oasis of greenery by a lake and just 10 minutes from Futuroscope. Heated swimming pool (28°C), bird sanctuary and opportunities for fishing, watersports, walking and golf (27 holes).

ⓒⓒ 1/4-30/6 1/9-29/9 7=6, 14=11

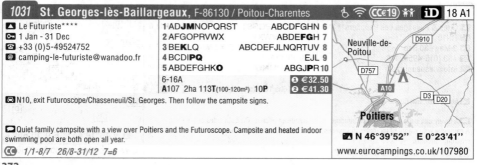

📌 N 46°43'9'' E 0°27'33''

www.eurocampings.co.uk/101461

1031 St. Georges-lès-Baillargeaux, F-86130 / Poitou-Charentes   ♿ 🛜 ⓒⒸ€19 ♀♂ iD 18 A1

- 🏕 Le Futuriste****
- 📅 1 Jan - 31 Dec
- ☎ +33 (0)5-49524752
- @ camping-le-futuriste@wanadoo.fr

1 ADJMNOPQRST	ABCDFGHN	6
2 AFGOPRVWX	ABDEFGH	7
3 BEKLQ	ABCDEFJLNQRTUV	8
4 BCDIPQ	EJL	9
5 ABDEFGHKO	ABGJPR	10
6-16A		❶ €32.50
A107 2ha 113T(100-120m²) 10P		❷ €41.30

🚗 N10, exit Futuroscope/Chasseneuil/St. Georges. Then follow the campsite signs.

🛏 Quiet family campsite with a view over Poitiers and the Futuroscope. Campsite and heated indoor swimming pool are both open all year.

ⓒⓒ 1/1-8/7 26/8-31/12 7=6

📌 N 46°39'52'' E 0°23'41''

www.eurocampings.co.uk/107980

1032 Bignac, F-16170 / Poitou-Charentes
CC€17 iD 18 A2

Marco de Bignac***
2 chemin de la Résistance
1 Feb - 30 Nov
+33 (0)5-45217841
info@marcodebignac.com

1 ABDEJMNOPQRST AN 6
2 ADOPVWXY ABDE**F**GH 7
3 AEFLMQ ABCDFGHIJNQRSV 8
4 DFHK CEV 9
5 ABDFHLN ABDHIJOR 10
6A ❶ €29.30
A50 8ha 84T(100m²) 3P ❷ €37.80

Leave the RN10 at the sign for La Touche D'Anais. Follow the 'Vars', 'Bignac' and then 'Camping Marco de Bignac' signs.
An idyllic and relaxing campsite located by a beautiful fishing lake. Shady and sunny pitches. Renovated and heated toilet facilities. Swimming pool, sports facilities and restaurant with waterside seating.
1/2-7/7 25/8-29/11 7=6

N 45°47'51" E 0°3'47"
www.eurocampings.co.uk/114341

1033 Condac, F-16700 / Poitou-Charentes
CC€13 iD 18 A2

Le Réjallant***
1 Jan - 31 Dec
+33 (0)9-83882906
camping@lerejallant.fr

1 ADEJMNOPQRST ABF 6
2 CDPRSVWXY ABDE**FG** 7
3 ABLQST BDFJNRSTUV 8
4 BFHN EJV 9
5 ABDEFHJMN ABDFGHIJPST 10
10A CEE ❶ €21.80
A113 2ha 70T(80-150m²) 39P ❷ €27.60

Coudac village is 50 km south of Poitiers. Follow Coudac signs direction 'Aire de Réjallant'.

Located in the Charente, 150 metres from the river which bears its name, you can enjoy a holiday in the countryside throughout the year. 50 km from Futuroscope and Cognac.
1/1-30/6 1/9-31/12 7=6

N 46°0'54" E 0°12'46"
www.eurocampings.co.uk/116084

1034 Confolens, F-16500 / Poitou-Charentes
CC€13 iD 18 A2

des Ribières***
route de St. Germain de Confolens
1 Apr - 1 Oct
+33 (0)5-45853527
camping-les-ribieres@orange.fr

1 ADE**JM**NOPRST **N** 6
2 CPSVWXY ABDE**FG**H 7
3 ABL ABFNOP 8
4 FH BQ 9
5 ADN AFGHJPRW 10
16A CEE ❶ €21.00
2,3ha 119T(80-250m²) 2P ❷ €28.60

In Confolens direction St. Germain. Campsite on left of road after 500 metres.

Quiet campsite on the Vienne (and on the D95), 5 minutes walk from Confolens centre. Excellent base for walking and cycling in the peaceful Charente region. The area has many culinary options.
1/4-30/6 1/9-30/9

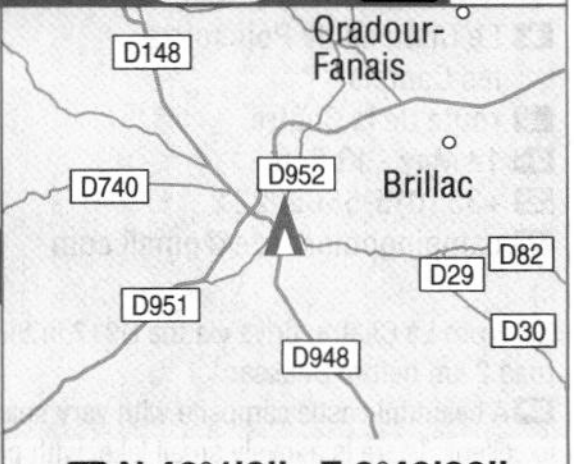

N 46°1'9" E 0°40'30"
www.eurocampings.co.uk/116508

1035 Eymouthiers/Montbron, F-16220 / Poitou-Charentes
CC€19 iD 18 A2

Castel Camping
Les Gorges du Chambon****
861, rue de la Tardoire
1 May - 15 Sep
+33 (0)5-45707170
info@
camping-gorgesduchambon.com

1 ADE**JM**NOPRS**T** ABFGJ**N**U 6
2 CFGHPTVWXY ABDE**FG**H 7
3 BF**HIK**LMQS ABCDEFHJKNQRSTV 8
4 BCDFHILO**P** AEIJLQUW 9
5 ABDEFGHKLMN ABDFGHIJ**OP**ST 10
10A CEE ❶ €39.40
A139 28ha 109T(132-300m²) 30P ❷ €52.40

N10 Poitiers-Angoulême, in Mansle turn left on the D6 direction La Rochefoucauld and Montbron. Signposted in Montbron. Turn left in La Tricherie, take the D163 (follow the signs).
This castle campsite is located in the middle of unspoilt countryside on the borders of the Dordogne and the Charente. Attractively landscaped with plenty of space. Heated swimming pool and restaurant.
1/5-30/6 1/9-14/9

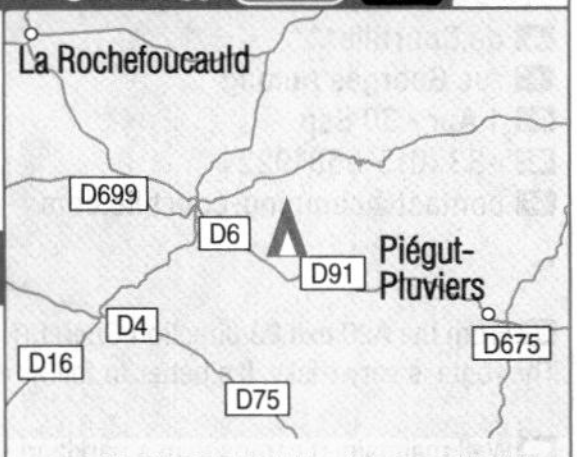

N 45°38'39" E 0°32'27"
www.eurocampings.co.uk/100392

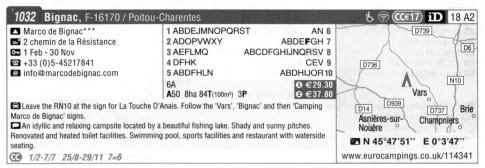

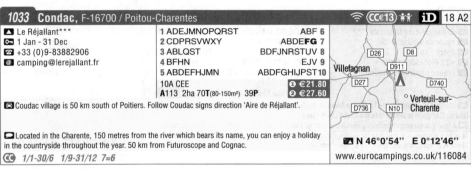

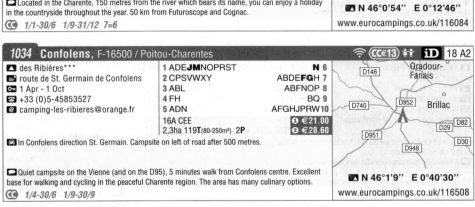

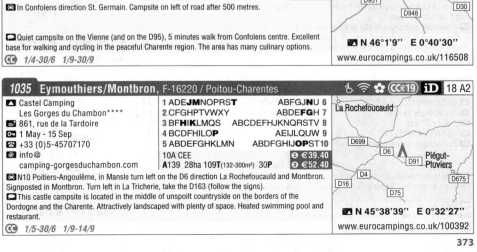

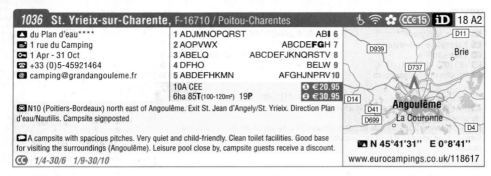

1036 St. Yrieix-sur-Charente, F-16710 / Poitou-Charentes ⚓ 🛜 ✿ (CC€15) iD 18 A2

- ⛺ du Plan d'eau****
- 🏕 1 rue du Camping
- 📅 1 Apr - 31 Oct
- ☎ +33 (0)5-45921464
- @ camping@grandangouleme.fr

1 ADJMNOPQRST	ABI 6
2 AOPVWX	ABCDE**FG**H 7
3 ABELQ	ABCDEFJKNQRSTV 8
4 DFHO	BELW 9
5 ABDEFHKMN	AFGHJNPRV 10
10A CEE	❶ €20.95
6ha 85T(100-120m²) 19P	❷ €30.95

🛣 N10 (Poitiers-Bordeaux) north east of Angoulême. Exit St. Jean d'Angely/St. Yrieix. Direction Plan d'eau/Nautilis. Campsite signposted

💬 A campsite with spacious pitches. Very quiet and child-friendly. Clean toilet facilities. Good base for visiting the surroundings (Angoulême). Leisure pool close by, campsite guests receive a discount.

(CC) 1/4-30/6 1/9-30/10

🗺 N 45°41'31'' E 0°8'41''

www.eurocampings.co.uk/118617

1037 Boussac, F-23600 / Limousin 🏹⚓ 🛜 ✿ (CC€19) 🚻 iD 18 B2

- ⛺ Creuse Nature Naturiste****
- 🏕 route de Bétête, D15
- 📅 1 Apr - 15 Oct
- ☎ +33 (0)5-55651801
- @ creuse.nature@wanadoo.fr

1 ADEFG**JM**NOPQRST	AEFN 6
2 BDGPRSVXY	ABDE**FG**H 7
3 AE**K**LQ**R**V	ABEFNQRTUV 8
4 BCDEFHIO**TUX**	ACDEFJLU 9
5 ABDEFGHKMN	ABDFGHIJMN**P**TVWZ 10
10A	❶ €34.50
A350 19ha 120T(80-160m²) 32P	❷ €41.50

🛣 Boussac is located in the La Châtre-Montluçon-Guéret triangle. In Boussac via the D15 direction Bétête. Campsite is beside this road, well signposted.

💬 A lovely naturist campsite in a woodland setting. Heated indoor pool and sauna. Good facilities and spacious pitches. A lovely area for walking and cycling. French, English, German and Dutch spoken. There is a restaurant and fresh bread every morning.

(CC) 1/4-6/7 24/8-14/10

🗺 N 46°20'57'' E 2°11'11''

www.eurocampings.co.uk/103865

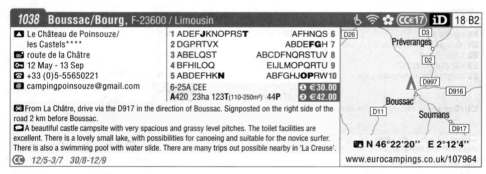

1038 Boussac/Bourg, F-23600 / Limousin ⚓ 🛜 ✿ (CC€17) iD 18 B2

- ⛺ Le Château de Poinsouze/
  les Castels**
- 🏕 route de la Châtre
- 📅 12 May - 13 Sep
- ☎ +33 (0)5-55650221
- @ campingpoinsouze@gmail.com

1 ADEF**J**KNOPRS**T**	AFHNQS 6
2 DGPRTVX	ABDE**FG**H 7
3 ABELQST	ABCDFNQRSTUV 8
4 BFHILOQ	EIJLMOPQRTU 9
5 ABDEFHK**N**	ABFGHJ**OP**RW 10
6-25A CEE	❶ €30.00
A420 23ha 123T(110-250m²) 44P	❷ €42.00

🛣 From La Châtre, drive via the D917 in the direction of Boussac. Signposted on the right side of the road 2 km before Boussac.

💬 A beautiful castle campsite with very spacious and grassy level pitches. The toilet facilities are excellent. There is a lovely small lake, with possibilities for canoeing and suitable for the novice surfer. There is also a swimming pool with water slide. There are many trips out possible nearby in 'La Creuse'.

(CC) 12/5-3/7 30/8-12/9

🗺 N 46°22'20'' E 2°12'4''

www.eurocampings.co.uk/107964

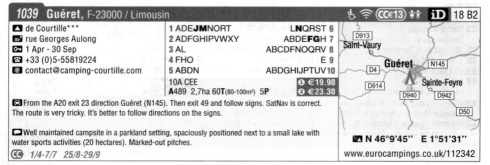

1039 Guéret, F-23000 / Limousin ⚓ 🛜 (CC€13) 🚻 iD 18 B2

- ⛺ de Courtille***
- 🏕 rue Georges Aulong
- 📅 1 Apr - 30 Sep
- ☎ +33 (0)5-55819224
- @ contact@camping-courtille.com

1 ADE**JM**NORT	LNQRST 6
2 ADFGHIPVWXY	ABDE**FG**H 7
3 AL	ABCDFNOQRV 8
4 FHO	E 9
5 ABDN	ABDGHIJPTUV 10
10A CEE	❶ €19.90
A489 2,7ha 60T(80-100m²) 5P	❷ €23.30

🛣 From the A20 exit 23 direction Guéret (N145). Then exit 49 and follow signs. SatNav is correct. The route is very tricky. It's better to follow directions on the signs.

💬 Well maintained campsite in a parkland setting, spaciously positioned next to a small lake with water sports activities (20 hectares). Marked-out pitches.

(CC) 1/4-7/7 25/8-29/9

🗺 N 46°9'45'' E 1°51'31''

www.eurocampings.co.uk/112342

France

1040 Bonnac-la-Côte, F-87270 / Limousin   ♿ 🔊 (CCє19) **iD** 18 B2

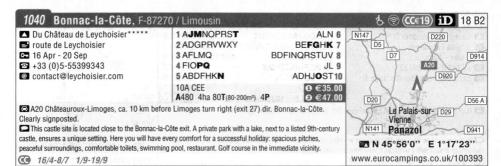

⛺ Du Château de Leychoisier*****	1 AJMNOPRST	ALN 6
🏕 route de Leychoisier	2 ADGPRVWXY	BEFGHK 7
⏰ 16 Apr - 20 Sep	3 AFLMQ	BDFINQRSTUV 8
☎ +33 (0)5-55399343	4 FIOPQ	JL 9
@ contact@leychoisier.com	5 ABDFHKN	ADHJOST 10

| 10A CEE | | ❶ €35.00 |
| A480 4ha 80T(80-200m²) 4P | | ❷ €47.00 |

🅰 A20 Châteauroux-Limoges, ca. 10 km before Limoges turn right (exit 27) dir. Bonnac-la-Côte. Clearly signposted.

🅿 This castle site is located close to the Bonnac-la-Côte exit. A private park with a lake, next to a listed 9th-century castle, ensures a unique setting. Here you will have every comfort for a successful holiday: spacious pitches, peaceful surroundings, comfortable toilets, swimming pool, restaurant. Golf course in the immediate vicinity.

CC 16/4-8/7 1/9-19/9

N 45°56'0'' E 1°17'23''

www.eurocampings.co.uk/100393

1041 Cognac-la-Forêt, F-87310 / Limousin   ♿ 🔊 (CCє15) **iD** 18 A2

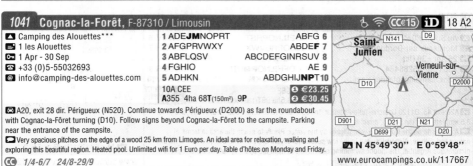

⛺ Camping des Alouettes***	1 ADEJMNOPRT	ABFG 6
🏕 1 les Alouettes	2 AFGPRVWXY	ABDEF 7
⏰ 1 Apr - 30 Sep	3 ABFLQSV	ABCDEFGINRSUV 8
☎ +33 (0)5-55032693	4 FGHIO	AE 9
@ info@camping-des-alouettes.com	5 ADHKN	ABDGHIJNPT 10

| 10A CEE | | ❶ €23.25 |
| A355 4ha 68T(150m²) 9P | | ❷ €30.45 |

🅰 A20, exit 28 dir. Périgueux (N520). Continue towards Périgueux (D2000) as far the roundabout with Cognac-la-Fôret turning (D10). Follow signs beyond Cognac-la-Fôret to the campsite. Parking near the entrance of the campsite.

🅿 Very spacious pitches on the edge of a wood 25 km from Limoges. An ideal area for relaxation, walking and exploring this beautiful region. Heated pool. Unlimited wifi for 1 Euro per day. Table d'hôtes on Monday and Friday.

CC 1/4-6/7 24/8-29/9

N 45°49'30'' E 0°59'48''

www.eurocampings.co.uk/117667

1042 Limoges, F-87280 / Limousin   ♿ 🔊 (CCє15) **iD** 18 B2

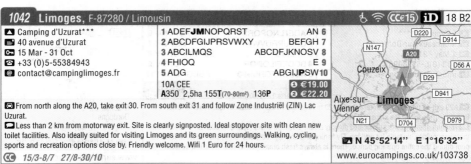

⛺ Camping d'Uzurat***	1 ADEFJMNOPQRST	AN 6
🏕 40 avenue d'Uzurat	2 ABCDFGIJPRSVWXY	BEFGH 7
⏰ 15 Mar - 31 Oct	3 ABCILMQS	ABCDFJKNOSV 8
☎ +33 (0)5-55384943	4 FHIOQ	E 9
@ contact@campinglimoges.fr	5 ADG	ABGIJPSW 10

| 10A CEE | | ❶ €19.00 |
| A350 2,5ha 155T(70-80m²) 136P | | ❷ €22.20 |

🅰 From north along the A20, take exit 30. From south exit 31 and follow Zone Industriël (ZIN) Lac Uzurat.

🅿 Less than 2 km from motorway exit. Site is clearly signposted. Ideal stopover site with clean new toilet facilities. Also ideally suited for visiting Limoges and its green surroundings. Walking, cycling, sports and recreation options close by. Friendly welcome. Wifi 1 Euro for 24 hours.

CC 15/3-8/7 27/8-30/10

N 45°52'14'' E 1°16'32''

www.eurocampings.co.uk/103738

1043 St. Léonard-de-Noblat, F-87400 / Limousin   ♿ 🔊 (CCє11) **iD** 18 B2

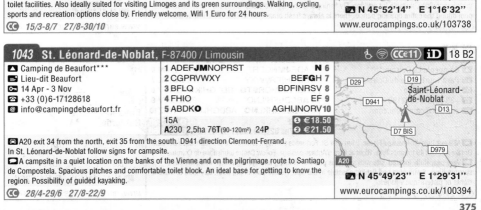

⛺ Camping de Beaufort***	1 ADEFJMNOPRST	N 6
🏕 Lieu-dit Beaufort	2 CGPRVWXY	BEFGH 7
⏰ 14 Apr - 3 Nov	3 BFLQ	BDFINRSV 8
☎ +33 (0)6-17128618	4 FHIO	EF 9
@ info@campingdebeaufort.fr	5 ABDKO	AGHIJNORV 10

| 15A | | ❶ €18.50 |
| A230 2,5ha 76T(90-120m²) 24P | | ❷ €21.50 |

🅰 A20 exit 34 from the north, exit 35 from the south. D941 direction Clermont-Ferrand. In St. Léonard-de-Noblat follow signs for campsite.

🅿 A campsite in a quiet location on the banks of the Vienne and on the pilgrimage route to Santiago de Compostela. Spacious pitches and comfortable toilet block. An ideal base for getting to know the region. Possibility of guided kayaking.

CC 28/4-29/6 27/8-22/9

N 45°49'23'' E 1°29'31''

www.eurocampings.co.uk/100394

France

1044 St. Pardoux, F-87250 / Limousin

♿ 🛜 (CC€15) iD 18 B2

- 🏕 Camping Fréaudour★★★★
- 🏠 Site de Freaudour
- 📅 5 Mar - 4 Nov
- ☎ +33 (0)5-55765722
- @ camping.freaudour@orange.fr

1 ADE**JM**NOPRS**T**	ALM**N**SW**XYZ** 6	
2 ABDFGHIOPTVWXY	ABDE**FGH** 7	
3 AEF**GHL**QTV	ABCDFKNQRSV 8	
4 BDFHINO**PQX**	EJLUV 9	
5 ABDEFHJN	ABDGIJOR 10	

10-16A CEE   ❶ €20.00
A375   4,5ha 103T(80-150m²)   30P   ❷ €28.00

🚗 Take the A20 in the direction of Limoges. Exit 25 Lac de St. Pardoux, then 'Site de Fréaudour'.

📷 By the lake (Lac de Saint-Pardoux) in wooded surroundings with First Aid post and a supervised swimming area. Lovely outdoor swimming pool on the grounds.

(CC) 5/3-7/7   25/8-3/11   7=6, 14=11

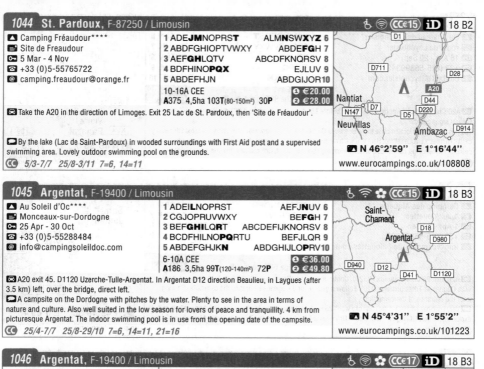

📍 N 46°2'59''   E 1°16'44''

www.eurocampings.co.uk/108808

1045 Argentat, F-19400 / Limousin

♿ 🛜 ✿ (CC€15) iD 18 B3

- 🏕 Au Soleil d'Oc★★★★
- 🏠 Monceaux-sur-Dordogne
- 📅 25 Apr - 30 Oct
- ☎ +33 (0)5-55288484
- @ info@campingsoleildoc.com

1 ADEIL**N**OPRST	AEF**J**NUV 6	
2 CGJOPRUVWXY	BEF**G**H 7	
3 BEF**GHIL**Q**R**T	ABCDEFIJKNORSV 8	
4 BCDFHILNO**PQ**RTU	BEFJLQR 9	
5 ABDEFGHJKN	ABDGHIJLO**P**RV 10	

6-10A CEE   ❶ €36.00
A186   3,5ha 99T(120-140m²)   72P   ❷ €49.80

🚗 A20 exit 45. D1120 Uzerche-Tulle-Argentat. In Argentat D12 direction Beaulieu, in Laygues (after 3.5 km) left, over the bridge, direct left.

📷 A campsite on the Dordogne with pitches by the water. Plenty to see in the area in terms of nature and culture. Also well suited in the low season for lovers of peace and tranquillity. 4 km from picturesque Argentat. The indoor swimming pool is in use from the opening date of the campsite.

(CC) 25/4-7/7   25/8-29/10   7=6, 14=11, 21=16

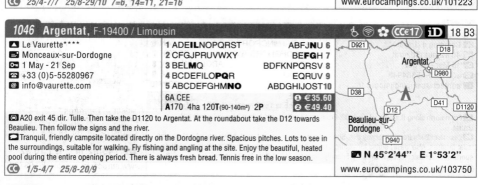

📍 N 45°4'31''   E 1°55'2''

www.eurocampings.co.uk/101223

1046 Argentat, F-19400 / Limousin

♿ 🛜 ✿ (CC€17) iD 18 B3

- 🏕 Le Vaurette★★★★
- 🏠 Monceaux-sur-Dordogne
- 📅 1 May - 21 Sep
- ☎ +33 (0)5-55280967
- @ info@vaurette.com

1 ADEIL**N**OPQRST	ABFJNU 6	
2 CFGJPRUVWXY	BEF**G**H 7	
3 BEL**MQ**	BDFKNPQRSV 8	
4 BCDEFILO**PQ**R	EQRUV 9	
5 ABCDEFGHM**NO**	ABDGHIJOST 10	

6A CEE   ❶ €35.60
A170   4ha 120T(90-140m²)   2P   ❷ €49.40

🚗 A20 exit 45 dir. Tulle. Then take the D1120 to Argentat. At the roundabout take the D12 towards Beaulieu. Then follow the signs and the river.

📷 Tranquil, friendly campsite located directly on the Dordogne river. Spacious pitches. Lots to see in the surroundings, suitable for walking. Fly fishing and angling at the site. Enjoy the beautiful, heated pool during the entire opening period. There is always fresh bread. Tennis free in the low season.

(CC) 1/5-4/7   25/8-20/9

📍 N 45°2'44''   E 1°53'2''

www.eurocampings.co.uk/103750

1047 Aubazine, F-19190 / Limousin

♿ 🛜 (CC€15) ⛲ iD 18 B3

- 🏕 Campéole Le Coiroux★★★★
- 🏠 Parc Touristique du Coiroux
- 📅 27 Apr - 30 Sep
- ☎ +33 (0)5-55272196
- @ coiroux@campeole.com

1 ADE**JM**NOPRT	ABFGLM**N** 6	
2 BDGHIPRVWXY	BEF**GH**K 7	
3 BEF**IJ**LMQR**STU**	BDFGHIKNPQRSV 8	
4 **A**BCDEFHILNO	BCEJLUV 9	
5 ACDEFGHKL**NO**	ABDGHIJN**P**RVWXZ 10	

10A CEE   ❶ €31.70
A450   7ha 62T(100-200m²)   114P   ❷ €42.50

🚗 A89 exit Tulle dir. Beaulieu-Figeac. 2 km after St. Fortunade turn right towards Centre Touristique Coiroux. Or take A20 exit 49 towards Tulle. Right at Gare d'Aubazine village. Follow Centre touristique de Coiroux.

📷 Very peacefully located .site with spacious pitches. Walking and cycling routes in the wooded surroundings. Swimming and fishing possible in the lake. Heated swimming pool. Day trips to historic sights or picturesque villages.

(CC) 27/4-6/7   25/8-29/9

📍 N 45°11'10''   E 1°42'26''

www.eurocampings.co.uk/103746

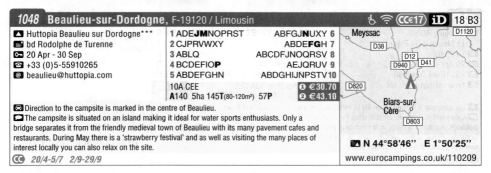

1048 Beaulieu-sur-Dordogne, F-19120 / Limousin   CC€17 iD 18 B3

- ▲ Huttopia Beaulieu sur Dordogne***
- ▣ bd Rodolphe de Turenne
- ▣ 20 Apr - 30 Sep
- ☎ +33 (0)5-55910265
- @ beaulieu@huttopia.com

1 ADE**JM**NOPRST	ABFG**J**N**UXY** 6
2 CJPRVWXY	ABDE**FG**H 7
3 ABLQ	ABCDFJNOQRSV 8
4 BCDEFIO**P**	AEJQRUV 9
5 ABDEFGHN	ABDGHIJNPSTV 10
10A CEE	❶ €30.70
A140 5ha 145**T**(80-120m²) 57**P**	❷ €43.10

🅟 Direction to the campsite is marked in the centre of Beaulieu.
💬 The campsite is situated on an island making it ideal for water sports enthusiasts. Only a bridge separates it from the friendly medieval town of Beaulieu with its many pavement cafes and restaurants. During May there is a 'strawberry festival' and as well as visiting the many places of interest locally you can also relax on the site.
CC 20/4-5/7 2/9-29/9

N 44°58'46'' E 1°50'25''
www.eurocampings.co.uk/110209

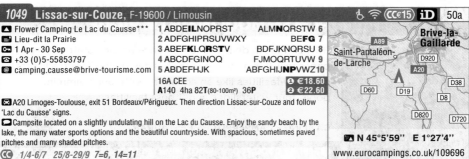

1049 Lissac-sur-Couze, F-19600 / Limousin   CC€15 iD 50a

- ▲ Flower Camping Le Lac du Causse***
- ▣ Lieu-dit la Prairie
- ▣ 1 Apr - 30 Sep
- ☎ +33 (0)5-55853797
- @ camping.causse@brive-tourisme.com

1 ABDE**IL**NOPRST	ALMN**QRST**W 6
2 ADFGHIPRSUVWXY	BE**FG** 7
3 ABEF**KLQRST**V	BDFJKNQRSU 8
4 ABCDFGINOQ	FJMOQRTUVW 9
5 ABDEFHJK	ABFGHIJ**NP**VWZ 10
16A CEE	❶ €18.60
A140 4ha 82**T**(80-100m²) 36**P**	❷ €22.60

🅟 A20 Limoges-Toulouse, exit 51 Bordeaux/Périgueux. Then direction Lissac-sur-Couze and follow 'Lac du Causse' signs.
💬 Campsite located on a slightly undulating hill on the Lac du Causse. Enjoy the sandy beach by the lake, the many water sports options and the beautiful countryside. With spacious, sometimes paved pitches and many shaded pitches.
CC 1/4-6/7 25/8-29/9 7=6, 14=11

N 45°5'59'' E 1°27'4''
www.eurocampings.co.uk/109696

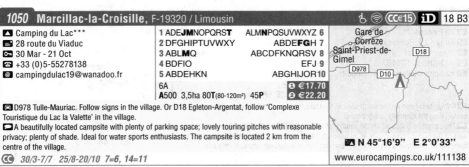

1050 Marcillac-la-Croisille, F-19320 / Limousin   CC€15 iD 18 B3

- ▲ Camping du Lac***
- ▣ 28 route du Viaduc
- ▣ 30 Mar - 21 Oct
- ☎ +33 (0)5-55278138
- @ campingdulac19@wanadoo.fr

1 ADE**JM**NOPQR**ST**	ALMN**P**QSUVWXYZ 6
2 DFGHIPTUVWXY	ABDE**FG**H 7
3 ABL**MQ**	ABCDFKNQRSV 8
4 BDFIO	EFJ 9
5 ABDEHKN	ABGHIJOR 10
6A	❶ €17.70
A500 3,5ha 80**T**(80-120m²) 45**P**	❷ €22.20

🅟 D978 Tulle-Mauriac. Follow signs in the village. Or D18 Egleton-Argentat, follow 'Complexe Touristique du Lac la Valette' in the village.
💬 A beautifully located campsite with plenty of parking space; lovely touring pitches with reasonable privacy; plenty of shade. Ideal for water sports enthusiasts. The campsite is located 2 km from the centre of the village.
CC 30/3-7/7 25/8-20/10 7=6, 14=11

N 45°16'9'' E 2°0'33''
www.eurocampings.co.uk/111138

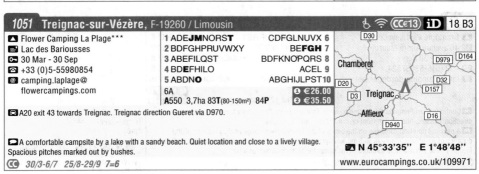

1051 Treignac-sur-Vézère, F-19260 / Limousin   CC€13 iD 18 B3

- ▲ Flower Camping La Plage***
- ▣ Lac des Bariousses
- ▣ 30 Mar - 30 Sep
- ☎ +33 (0)5-55980854
- @ camping.laplage@flowercampings.com

1 ADE**JM**NORS**T**	CDFGLNUVX 6
2 BDFGHPRUVWXY	BE**FG**H 7
3 ABEFILQST	BDFKNO**P**QRS 8
4 BD**E**FHILO	ACEL 9
5 ABD**N**O	ABGHIJLPST 10
6A	❶ €26.00
A550 3,7ha 83**T**(80-150m²) 84**P**	❷ €35.50

🅟 A20 exit 43 towards Treignac. Treignac direction Gueret via D970.
💬 A comfortable campsite by a lake with a sandy beach. Quiet location and close to a lively village. Spacious pitches marked out by bushes.
CC 30/3-6/7 25/8-29/9 7=6

N 45°33'35'' E 1°48'48''
www.eurocampings.co.uk/109971

France

1052 Belvès, F-24170 / Aquitaine

♿ 📶 ⚙ (CC€17) iD 50a

- ▲ Camping RCN
- Le Moulin de la Pique*****
- 📮 La Pique
- 📅 20 Apr - 2 Oct
- ☎ +33 (0)34-3745090
- @ reserveringen@rcn.nl

1 ADE**IL**NOPQRST	ABFGHIJLNX 6
2 CDGPVXY	ABDE**FG**H 7
3 ABEF**GHIKLMQRT**	ABCDFIJKNQRSTUV 8
4 ABCDEFILOR	ACEI 9
5 ABDEFGHLMN	ABDFGHIJPQRZ10

Ad on this page 10A CEE
A50 10ha 170**T**(80–140m²) 86**P**

❶ €55.95
❷ €68.45

📍 The campsite is located on the D710 Fumel-Belvès. About 2 km south of Belvès. Clearly signposted.
💬 A very well maintained, child-friendly five-star campsite located on an estate with 18th-century buildings. Aquaparc la Pique with swimming pools and 3 water slides. Plenty of trips out in the Dordogne Périgord Noir, with its many castles and historic towns. Canoe trips on the Dordogne every week for guests. paved motorhome pitches.

(CC) 20/4-30/6 25/8-1/10

Le Buisson-de-Cadouin D703

D53 D710 D60

D2 D660

📍 N 44°45'43" E 1°0'51"

www.eurocampings.co.uk/100468

RCN LE MOULIN DE LA PIQUE

RCN Le Moulin de la Pique was once an old estate with a paper mill. It is now a modern holiday park offering all sorts of luxury facilities like an aquapark with four swimming pools, four waterslides and fitness facilities.

CAMPING – CAMPERPITCH - RESTAURANT

☎ +31 85 0400 700   🌐 www.rcn.fr

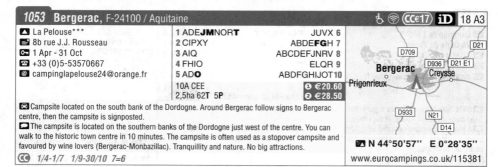

1053 Bergerac, F-24100 / Aquitaine

♿ 📶 (CC€17) iD 18 A3

- ▲ La Pelouse***
- 📮 8b rue J.J. Rousseau
- 📅 1 Apr - 31 Oct
- ☎ +33 (0)5-53570667
- @ campinglapelouse24@orange.fr

1 ADE**JM**NOR**T**	JUVX 6
2 CIPXY	ABDE**FG**H 7
3 AIQ	ABCDEFJNRV 8
4 FHIO	ELQR 9
5 AD**O**	ABDFGHIJOT10

10A CEE
2,5ha 62**T** 5**P**

❶ €20.60
❷ €28.50

📍 Campsite located on the south bank of the Dordogne. Around Bergerac follow signs to Bergerac centre, then the campsite is signposted.
💬 The campsite is located on the southern banks of the Dordogne just west of the centre. You can walk to the historic town centre in 10 minutes. The campsite is often used as a stopover campsite and favoured by wine lovers (Bergerac-Monbazillac). Tranquillity and nature. No big attractions.

(CC) 1/4-1/7 1/9-30/10 7=6

D709 D21

D936 D21 E1

Bergerac Creysse

Prigonrieux

D933 N21

D14

📍 N 44°50'57" E 0°28'35"

www.eurocampings.co.uk/115381

1054 Brantôme, F-24310 / Aquitaine

♿ 📶 (CC€15) ⛸ iD 18 A3

- ▲ Brantôme Peyrelevade***
- 📮 46 avenue André Maurois
- 📅 28 Apr - 30 Sep
- ☎ +33 (0)5-53057524
- @ info@camping-dordogne.net

1 ADE**JM**NOPRST	ABFGJ**NU** 6
2 CGHIPVWXY	ABDE**FG**H 7
3 BE**GHLM**QT	ABCDEFGHJKNQRSTUV 8
4 FHO	AE 9
5 ABDEFH**NO**	ABCDFGHIJPSTV10

10A CEE
A200 4ha 127**T**(100–200m²) 23**P**

❶ €33.10
❷ €43.70

📍 Continue from Perigueux/Brantôme towards Thiviers. From Angoulême towards centre then direction Thiviers. About 1 km from centre. Follow campsite signs.
💬 A peaceful parkland campsite on the banks of the Dronne river. Large pitches within walking distance of Brantôme. Plenty of walking and cycling opportunities, swimming pool and good toilet facilities. Free wifi available throughout the campsite, faster internet for a fee.

(CC) 28/4-4/7 25/8-29/9 7=6, 14=12, 21=18

D707

D675

Brantôme

D106

D78 D939

Tocane-Saint-Apre

📍 N 45°21'39" E 0°39'38"

www.eurocampings.co.uk/113144

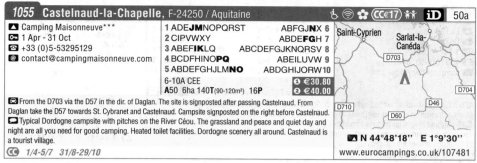

1055 Castelnaud-la-Chapelle, F-24250 / Aquitaine · ⚷ 🛜 ✿ (CC€17) ⚲ iD · 50a

- ▲ Camping Maisonneuve***
- ☎ 1 Apr - 31 Oct
- 🖷 +33 (0)5-53295129
- @ contact@campingmaisonneuve.com

1 ADE**JM**NOPQRST	AB**F**G**J**N**X**	6
2 CIPVWXY	ABDE**FG**H	7
3 ABEF**IK**LQ	ABCDEFGJKNQRSV	8
4 BCDFHINO**PQ**	ABEILUVW	9
5 ABDEFGHJLM**NO**	ABDGHIJORW	10
6-10A CEE	➊ €30.80	
A50 6ha 140T(90-120m²) 16P	➋ €40.00	

🔲 From the D703 via the D57 in the dir. of Daglan. The site is signposted after passing Castelnaud. From Daglan take the D57 towards St. Cybranet and Castelnaud. Campsite signposted on the right before Castelnaud.
💬 Typical Dordogne campsite with pitches on the River Céou. The grassland and peace and quiet day and night are all you need for good camping. Heated toilet facilities. Dordogne scenery all around. Castelnaud is a tourist village.
(CC) 1/4-5/7 31/8-29/10

N 44°48'18" E 1°9'30"

www.eurocampings.co.uk/107481

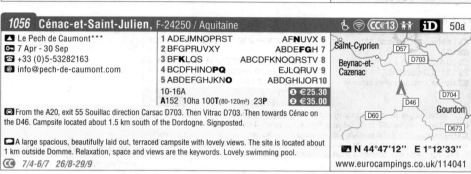

1056 Cénac-et-Saint-Julien, F-24250 / Aquitaine · ⚷ 🛜 (CC€13) ⚲ iD · 50a

- ▲ Le Pech de Caumont***
- ☎ 7 Apr - 30 Sep
- 🖷 +33 (0)5-53282163
- @ info@pech-de-caumont.com

1 ADE**J**MNOPRST	AF**N**UVX	6
2 BFGPRUVXY	ABDE**FG**H	7
3 BF**KL**QS	ABCDF**K**NOQRSTV	8
4 BCDFHINO**PQ**	EJLQRUV	9
5 ABDEFGHJKN**O**	ABDGHIJOR	10
10-16A	➊ €25.30	
A152 10ha 100T(80-120m²) 23P	➋ €35.00	

🔲 From the A20, exit 55 Souillac direction Carsac D703. Then Vitrac D703. Then towards Cénac on the D46. Campsite located about 1.5 km south of the Dordogne. Signposted.

💬 A large spacious, beautifully laid out, terraced campsite with lovely views. The site is located about 1 km outside Domme. Relaxation, space and views are the keywords. Lovely swimming pool.
(CC) 7/4-6/7 26/8-29/9

N 44°47'12" E 1°12'33"

www.eurocampings.co.uk/114041

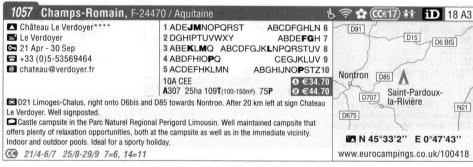

1057 Champs-Romain, F-24470 / Aquitaine · ⚷ 🛜 ✿ (CC€17) ⚲ iD · 18 A3

- ▲ Château Le Verdoyer****
- 🏠 Le Verdoyer
- ☎ 21 Apr - 30 Sep
- 🖷 +33 (0)5-53569464
- @ chateau@verdoyer.fr

1 ADE**JM**NOPQRST	ABCDFGHLN	6
2 DGHIPTUVWXY	ABDE**FG**H	7
3 ABE**KL**MQ	ABCDFGJKLNPQRSTUV	8
4 ABDFHIO**PQ**	CEGJKLUV	9
5 ACDEFHKLMN	ABGHIJNO**P**STZ	10
10A CEE	➊ €34.70	
A307 25ha 109T(100-150m²) 75P	➋ €44.70	

🔲 D21 Limoges-Chalus, right onto D6bis and D85 towards Nontron. After 20 km left at sign Chateau Le Verdoyer. Well signposted.
💬 Castle campsite in the Parc Naturel Regional Perigord Limousin. Well maintained campsite that offers plenty of relaxation opportunities, both at the campsite as well as in the immediate vicinity. Indoor and outdoor pools. Ideal for a sporty holiday.
(CC) 21/4-6/7 25/8-29/9 7=6, 14=11

N 45°33'2" E 0°47'43"

www.eurocampings.co.uk/100418

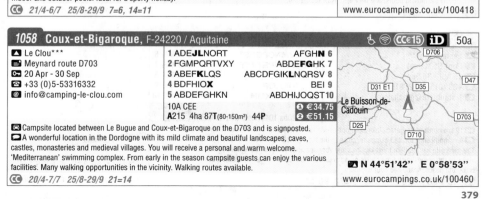

1058 Coux-et-Bigaroque, F-24220 / Aquitaine · ⚷ 🛜 (CC€15) iD · 50a

- ▲ Le Clou***
- 🏠 Meynard route D703
- ☎ 20 Apr - 30 Sep
- 🖷 +33 (0)5-53316332
- @ info@camping-le-clou.com

1 ADE**J**LNORT	AFGH**N**	6
2 FGMPQRTVXY	ABDE**FG**HK	7
3 ABEF**KL**QS	ABCDFGIK**L**NQRSH	8
4 BDFHIO**X**	BEI	9
5 ABDEFGHKN	ABDHIJOQST	10
10A CEE	➊ €34.75	
A215 4ha 87T(80-150m²) 44P	➋ €51.15	

🔲 Campsite located between Le Bugue and Coux-et-Bigaroque on the D703 and is signposted.
💬 A wonderful location in the Dordogne with its mild climate and beautiful landscapes, caves, castles, monasteries and medieval villages. You will receive a personal and warm welcome. 'Mediterranean' swimming complex. From early in the season campsite guests can enjoy the various facilities. Many walking opportunities in the vicinity. Walking routes available.
(CC) 20/4-7/7 25/8-29/9 21=14

N 44°51'42" E 0°58'53"

www.eurocampings.co.uk/100460

France

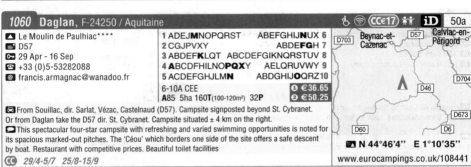

1059 Daglan, F-24250 / Aquitaine
♿ 📶 (CC€15) **iD** 50a

- 🏕 La Peyrugue***
- 🛏 D57
- 📅 1 Apr - 1 Oct
- ☎ +33 (0)5-53284026
- @ camping@peyrugue.com

1 ADEJMNOPRT	AF**N**	6
2 BFGPRUVXY	BE**FGH**	7
3 BEF**GK**LQRV	BDEFGNPQRST	8
4 BCDFHIO**PQ**	AHJL	9
5 ABDEFGHKMN	ABDHIJLPR	10
6-10A CEE	➊ €38.90	
A83 5ha 78T(95-160m²) 14P	➋ €52.90	

🚗 A20 Limoges-Toulouse, exit 55 Souillac, D820 dir. Gourdon, then D673 dir. Gourdon, turn right D801 dir. Gourdon. Through Gourdon and again the D673 dir. Fumel. D6, D46, D60 and D57 through Daglan dir. St. Cybranet.
💬 Emmy and Philip Cappetti have turned this site into one of the most attractive family sites. The pitches are spacious and well maintained. Walking, cycling and canoeing close by. In the middle of the scenic area of the Dordogne.
(CC) 1/4-13/7 31/8-30/9

⬛ N 44°45'9" E 1°11'15"
www.eurocampings.co.uk/110888

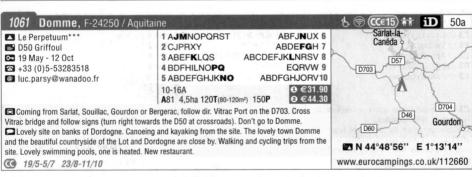

1060 Daglan, F-24250 / Aquitaine
♿ 📶 (CC€17) ⚤ **iD** 50a

- 🏕 Le Moulin de Paulhiac****
- 🛏 D57
- 📅 29 Apr - 16 Sep
- ☎ +33 (0)5-53282088
- @ francis.armagnac@wanadoo.fr

1 ADEJMNOPQRST	ABEFGHIJ**N**UX	6
2 CGJPVXY	ABDE**FGH**	7
3 ABDEF**KL**QT	ABCDEFGIKNQRSTUV	8
4 **A**BCDFHILNO**PQX**Y	AELQRUVWY	9
5 ACDEFGHJLM**N**	ABDGHIJ**O**QRZ	10
6-10A CEE	➊ €36.65	
A85 5ha 160T(100-120m²) 32P	➋ €50.25	

🚗 From Souillac, dir. Sarlat, Vézac, Castelnaud (D57). Campsite signposted beyond St. Cybranet. Or from Daglan take the D57 dir. St. Cybranet. Campsite situated ± 4 km on the right.
💬 This spectacular four-star campsite with refreshing and varied swimming opportunities is noted for its spacious marked-out pitches. The 'Céou' which borders one side of the site offers a safe descent by boat. Restaurant with competitive prices. Beautiful toilet facilities
(CC) 29/4-5/7 25/8-15/9

⬛ N 44°46'4" E 1°10'35"
www.eurocampings.co.uk/108441

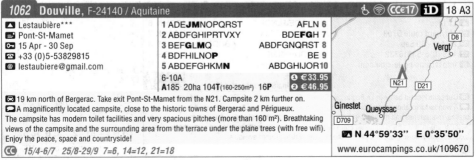

1061 Domme, F-24250 / Aquitaine
♿ 📶 (CC€15) ⚤ **iD** 50a

- 🏕 Le Perpetuum***
- 🛏 D50 Griffoul
- 📅 19 May - 12 Oct
- ☎ +33 (0)5-53283518
- @ luc.parsy@wanadoo.fr

1 A**J**MNOPQRST	ABF**J**NUX	6
2 CJPRXY	ABDE**FGH**	7
3 ABEF**K**LQS	ABCDEFJKL**N**RSV	8
4 BDFHILNO**PQ**	EQRVW	9
5 ABDEFGHJK**NO**	ABDFGHJORV	10
10-16A	➊ €31.90	
A81 4,5ha 120T(80-120m²) 150P	➋ €44.30	

🚗 Coming from Sarlat, Souillac, Gourdon or Bergerac, follow dir. Vitrac Port on the D703. Cross Vitrac bridge and follow signs (turn right towards the D50 at crossroads). Don't go to Domme.
💬 Lovely site on banks of Dordogne. Canoeing and kayaking from the site. The lovely town Domme and the beautiful countryside of the Lot and Dordogne are close by. Walking and cycling trips from the site. Lovely swimming pools, one is heated. New restaurant.
(CC) 19/5-5/7 23/8-11/10

⬛ N 44°48'56" E 1°13'14"
www.eurocampings.co.uk/112660

1062 Douville, F-24140 / Aquitaine
♿ 📶 (CC€17) **iD** 18 A3

- 🏕 Lestaubière***
- 🛏 Pont-St-Mamet
- 📅 15 Apr - 30 Sep
- ☎ +33 (0)5-53829815
- @ lestaubiere@gmail.com

1 ADE**JM**NOPQRST	AFLN	6
2 ABDFGHIPRTVXY	BDE**FGH**	7
3 BEF**GLMQ**	ABDFGNQRST	8
4 BDFHILNO**P**	BE	9
5 ABDEFGHKM**N**	ABDGHIJOR	10
6-10A	➊ €33.95	
A185 20ha 104T(160-250m²) 16P	➋ €46.95	

🚗 19 km north of Bergerac. Take exit Pont-St-Mamet from the N21. Campsite 2 km further on.
💬 A magnificently located campsite, close to the historic towns of Bergerac and Périgueux. The campsite has modern toilet facilities and very spacious pitches (more than 160 m²). Breathtaking views of the campsite and the surrounding area from the terrace under the plane trees (with free wifi). Enjoy the peace, space and countryside!
(CC) 15/4-6/7 25/8-29/9 7=6, 14=12, 21=18

⬛ N 44°59'33" E 0°35'50"
www.eurocampings.co.uk/109670

France

1063 Groléjac, F-24250 / Aquitaine

  📶 🛜 CC€13 ⚤ iD 50a

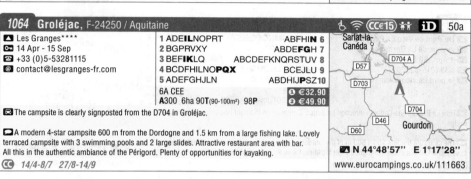

- ▲ Camping du Lac de Groléjac***
- 🏠 Le Roc Percé
- 🗓 28 Apr - 22 Sep
- ☎ +33 (0)5-53594870
- @ contact@
  camping-dulac-dordogne.com

1 ADE**JM**NOPQRST	ABFL**NX** 6
2 DGHPRVXY	ABDE**FG**H 7
3 BEFLMNQS	ABCDFIKNQRSV 8
4 ABCD**E**FHINOP**X**	BEJUV 9
5 ABDEFGHJKM**NO**	ABGHIJOR 10

10A CEE
A80 3ha 96T(90-120m²) 32P
❶ €24.50
❷ €33.40

Sarlat-la-Canéda

🚗 From Groléjac centre in the direction of Gourdon. Campsite is signposted after 2 km.

🛏 This campsite is located on Groléjac lake and exudes peace and quiet. A restaurant and a beautiful pool will complete your holiday. A really homely campsite, with a welcoming atmosphere and lots of space.

CC 28/4-30/6 1/9-21/9 7=6

📍 N 44°48'7'' E 1°17'41''

www.eurocampings.co.uk/122540

1064 Groléjac, F-24250 / Aquitaine

  📶 🛜 CC€15 ⚤ iD 50a

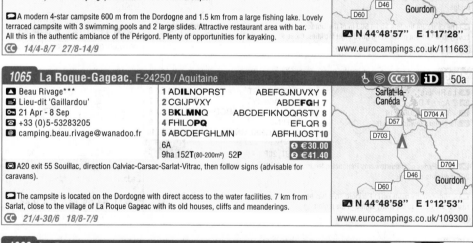

- ▲ Les Granges****
- 🗓 14 Apr - 15 Sep
- ☎ +33 (0)5-53281115
- @ contact@lesgranges-fr.com

1 ADE**IL**NOPRT	ABF**HI**N 6
2 BGPRVXY	ABDE**FG**H 7
3 BEF**IK**LQ	ABCDEFKNQRSTUV 8
4 BCDFHILNOP**PQX**	BCEJLU 9
5 ADEFGHJLN	ABDHIJ**P**SZ 10

6A CEE
A300 6ha 90T(90-100m²) 98P
❶ €32.90
❷ €49.90

Sarlat-la-Canéda

🚗 The campsite is clearly signposted from the D704 in Groléjac.

🛏 A modern 4-star campsite 600 m from the Dordogne and 1.5 km from a large fishing lake. Lovely terraced campsite with 3 swimming pools and 2 large slides. Attractive restaurant area with bar. All this in the authentic ambiance of the Périgord. Plenty of opportunities for kayaking.

CC 14/4-8/7 27/8-14/9

📍 N 44°48'57'' E 1°17'28''

www.eurocampings.co.uk/111663

1065 La Roque-Gageac, F-24250 / Aquitaine

  📶 🛜 CC€13 iD 50a

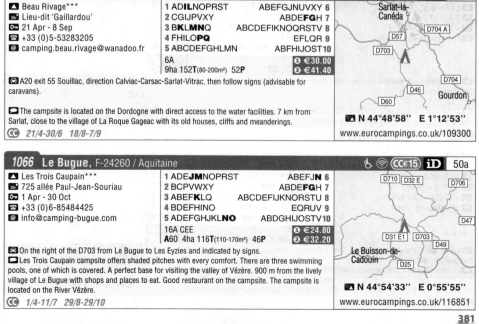

- ▲ Beau Rivage***
- 🏠 Lieu-dit 'Gaillardou'
- 🗓 21 Apr - 8 Sep
- ☎ +33 (0)5-53283205
- @ camping.beau.rivage@wanadoo.fr

1 AD**IL**NOPRST	ABEFGJNUVXY 6
2 CGIJPVXY	ABDE**FG**H 7
3 B**KLMN**Q	ABCDEFIKNOQRSTUV 8
4 FHILO**PQ**	EFLQR 9
5 ABCDEFGHLMN	ABFHIJOST 10

6A
9ha 152T(80-200m²) 52P
❶ €30.00
❷ €41.40

Sarlat-la-Canéda

🚗 A20 exit 55 Souillac, direction Calviac-Carsac-Sarlat-Vitrac, then follow signs (advisable for caravans).

🛏 The campsite is located on the Dordogne with direct access to the water facilities. 7 km from Sarlat, close to the village of La Roque Gageac with its old houses, cliffs and meanderings.

CC 21/4-30/6 18/8-7/9

📍 N 44°48'58'' E 1°12'53''

www.eurocampings.co.uk/109300

1066 Le Bugue, F-24260 / Aquitaine

  📶 🛜 CC€15 iD 50a

- ▲ Les Trois Caupain***
- 🏠 725 allée Paul-Jean-Souriau
- 🗓 1 Apr - 30 Oct
- ☎ +33 (0)6-85484425
- @ info@camping-bugue.com

1 ADE**JM**NOPRST	ABEF**J**N 6
2 BCPVWXY	ABDE**FG**H 7
3 ABEF**K**LQ	ABCDEFIJKNORSTU 8
4 BDEFHINO	EQRUV 9
5 ADEFGHJKL**NO**	ABDGHIJOSTV 10

16A CEE
A60 4ha 116T(110-170m²) 46P
❶ €24.80
❷ €32.20

Le Buisson-de-Cadouin

🚗 On the right of the D703 from Le Bugue to Les Eyzies and indicated by signs.
🛏 Les Trois Caupain campsite offers shaded pitches with every comfort. There are three swimming pools, one of which is covered. A perfect base for visiting the valley of Vézère. 900 m from the lively village of Le Bugue with shops and places to eat. Good restaurant on the campsite. The campsite is located on the River Vézère.

CC 1/4-11/7 29/8-29/10

📍 N 44°54'33'' E 0°55'55''

www.eurocampings.co.uk/116851

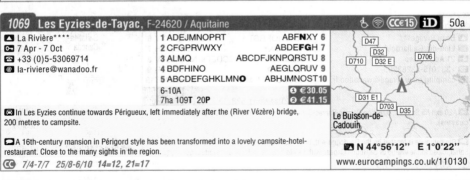

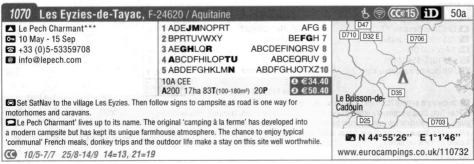

1067 Le Bugue, F-24260 / Aquitaine

 ⚡ 📶 (CC€13) 👫 iD 50a

- 🏕 Rocher de la Granelle***
- ✉ La Borie
- 📅 12 Apr - 17 Sep
- ☎ +33 (0)5-53072432
- @ info@lagranelle.com

1 ADEJ**M**NOPRST	AFH**N**	6
2 BCFGIPSVXY	ABDE**FGH**	7
3 BE**LMQ**	BDFKNRSV	8
4 BDILNO**PQ**	AELQRV	9
5 ABDEFGHJM**NO**	ABDFGHIJL**P**STV	10

10A CEE   ❶ €25.80
A131 7,5ha 102T(80-150m²) 54P   ❷ €33.80

🗺 Campsite located on the south side of Le Bugue on the D31E direction Le Buisson and is well signposted.

💬 Peaceful family campsite with its own typical French ambiance. You can swim in the River Vézère or in the swimming pool with slide. The Périgord-Noir region is renowned for its sumptuous gastronomy, caves and castles. Extensive sports facilities, attractive pitches.

CC 12/4-7/7 25/8-16/9 7=6, 18=15

▪ N 44°54'42'' E 0°55'0''

www.eurocampings.co.uk/103640

1068 Le Buisson-de-Cadouin, F-24480 / Aquitaine

 ⚡ 📶 (CC€15) iD 50a

- 🏕 Du Pont de Vicq En Périgord***
- ✉ avenue de La Dordogne
- 📅 1 Apr - 30 Oct
- ☎ +33 (0)5-53220173
- @ le.pont.de.vicq@wanadoo.fr

1 ADEJ**M**NOPQRST	ABFG**N**UX	6
2 CQWXY	ABDE**FG**H	7
3 B**K**LQS	ABCDEFJKNRSV	8
4 BDFHLNO**PQ**	EFLQRUVW	9
5 ADEFGHK**NO**	ABFGHJLOSTW	10

10A CEE   ❶ €25.10
5,5ha 130T(100-110m²) 30P   ❷ €31.70

🗺 Fom Le Buisson-de-Cadouin direction Le Bugue. Campsite on the right just before the Dordogne bridge.

💬 The campsite borders about 500 m of the Dordogne bank and has a heated swimming pool. Lovely, marked-out pitches and good toilet facilities. Close to the lovely town of Le Buisson.

CC 1/4-7/7 27/8-29/10 7=6, 15=13

▪ N 44°51'13'' E 0°54'38''

www.eurocampings.co.uk/118568

1069 Les Eyzies-de-Tayac, F-24620 / Aquitaine

 ⚡ 📶 (CC€15) iD 50a

- 🏕 La Rivière****
- 📅 7 Apr - 7 Oct
- ☎ +33 (0)5-53069714
- @ la-riviere@wanadoo.fr

1 ADEJMNOPRT	ABF**N**XY	6
2 CFGPRVWXY	ABDE**FG**H	7
3 ALMQ	ABCDFJKNPQRSTU	8
4 BDFHINO	AEGLQRUV	9
5 ABCDEFGHKLMN**O**	ABHJMNOST	10

6-10A   ❶ €30.05
7ha 109T 20P   ❷ €41.15

🗺 In Les Eyzies continue towards Périgueux, left immediately after the (River Vézère) bridge, 200 metres to campsite.

💬 A 16th-century mansion in Périgord style has been transformed into a lovely campsite-hotel-restaurant. Close to the many sights in the region.

CC 7/4-7/7 25/8-6/10 14=12, 21=17

▪ N 44°56'12'' E 1°0'22''

www.eurocampings.co.uk/110130

1070 Les Eyzies-de-Tayac, F-24620 / Aquitaine

 ⚡ 📶 (CC€15) iD 50a

- 🏕 Le Pech Charmant***
- 📅 10 May - 15 Sep
- ☎ +33 (0)5-53359708
- @ info@lepech.com

1 ADE**JM**NOPRT	AFG	6
2 BPRTUVWXY	BEF**GH**	7
3 AE**GHLQR**	ABCDEFINQRSV	8
4 **A**BCDFHILOP**TU**	ABCEQRUV	9
5 ABDEFGHKLM**N**	ABDFGHJOTXZ	10

10A CEE   ❶ €34.40
A200 17ha 83T(100-180m²) 20P   ❷ €50.40

🗺 Set SatNav to the village Les Eyzies. Then follow signs to campsite as road is one way for motorhomes and caravans.

💬 Le Pech Charmant' lives up to its name. The original 'camping à la ferme' has developed into a modern campsite but has kept its unique farmhouse atmosphere. The chance to enjoy typical 'communal' French meals, donkey trips and the outdoor life make a stay on this site well worthwhile.

CC 10/5-7/7 25/8-14/9 14=13, 21=19

▪ N 44°55'26'' E 1°1'46''

www.eurocampings.co.uk/110732

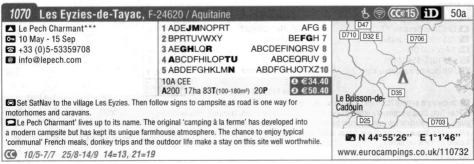

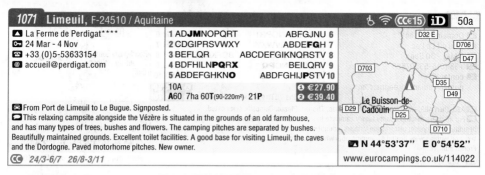

1071 Limeuil, F-24510 / Aquitaine

🏕 La Ferme de Perdigat★★★★
📅 24 Mar - 4 Nov
☎ +33 (0)5-53633154
@ accueil@perdigat.com

	1	ADE**JM**NOPQRT	ABFGJNU	6
	2	CDGIPRSVWXY	ABDE**FGH**	7
	3	BEFLQR	ABCDEFGIKNQRSTV	8
	4	BDFHILN**PQRX**	BEILQRV	9
	5	ABDEFGHKN**O**	ABDFGHIJ**P**STV	10

10A
A60 7ha 60**T**(90-220m²) 21**P**

❶ €27.90
❷ €39.40

🚗 From Port de Limeuil to Le Bugue. Signposted.
💬 This relaxing campsite alongside the Vézère is situated in the grounds of an old farmhouse, and has many types of trees, bushes and flowers. The camping pitches are separated by bushes. Beautifully maintained grounds. Excellent toilet facilities. A good base for visiting Limeuil, the caves and the Dordogne. Paved motorhome pitches. New owner.

CC 24/3-6/7 26/8-3/11

🏔 N 44°53'37" E 0°54'52"
www.eurocampings.co.uk/114022

50a

1072 Limeuil/Alles-sur-Dordogne, F-24480 / Aquitaine

🏕 Le Port de Limeuil★★★★
🚩 D31
📅 27 Apr - 24 Sep
☎ +33 (0)5-53632976
@ leportdelimeuil@orange.fr

	1	ADE**JM**NOPRST	ABFGJNUX	6
	2	CGJPQVXY	ABDE**FGH**	7
	3	BEF**G**LMQS	ABCDEFIJKNQRSTV	8
	4	BDFHIO**PQ**U	ABEILQRUV	9
	5	ACDEFGHJKM**NO**	ABDFGHIJO**P**ST	10

6-10A CEE
7ha 90**T**(100-200m²) 75**P**

❶ €35.40
❷ €45.50

🚗 From Le Bugue follow the D31 dir. Limeuil. Campsite is signposted in plenty of time.
💬 Port de Limeuil campsite is located where the Dordogne and Vézère rivers converge, and on the other side from Limeuil, one of France's most beautiful villages. The site has its own 400m beach for swimming and fishing and canoes can be rented. The site has a shop, bar and snack bar. Wifi and tennis are free. Swimming pool and heated jacuzzi. Paved motorhome pitches.

CC 27/4-5/7 26/8-23/9

🏔 N 44°52'47" E 0°53'9"
www.eurocampings.co.uk/103645

50a

1073 Montignac, F-24290 / Aquitaine

🏕 Le Moulin du Bleufond-Lascaux★★★
🚩 avenue Aristide Briand
📅 1 Apr - 15 Oct
☎ +33 (0)5-53518395
@ info@bleufond.com

	1	ADE**JM**NOPQRST	ABFG**N**UV	6
	2	CGPRVWXY	BEF**GH**	7
	3	BE**I**LMQ	BDFJNPRSTUV	8
	4	**E**FGHIO**PQTU**	ELUVWZ	9
	5	ABDEFGHJKN**O**	ABDGHIJNOQTUV	10

10A CEE
A66 1,3ha 81**T**(70-120m²) 23**P**

❶ €32.45
❷ €44.45

🚗 On the A89 exit Thenon, dir. Montignac/Lascaux. In Montignac direction Valojoux Sergeac. Follow the signs.
💬 You will receive a warm welcome on this comfortable rural campsite, located 2 minutes from Lascaux. Heated toilets and the swimming pool is also heated. The site is within walking distance of the village, where you can do all your shopping. Plenty of sights in the immediate vicinity. An ideal location for visiting the Lascaux caves.

CC 1/4-6/7 27/8-14/10

🏔 N 45°3'36" E 1°9'31"
www.eurocampings.co.uk/111880

50a

1074 Montignac/Lascaux, F-24290 / Aquitaine

🏕 La Fage★★★★
🚩 La Chapelle-Aubareil
📅 7 Apr - 7 Oct
☎ +33 (0)5-53507650
@ contact@camping-lafage.com

	1	ADE**JM**NOPRT	CDFG	6
	2	BGPVWXY	ABDE**FGH**	7
	3	ABCELQRST	ABCDEFKNQRSV	8
	4	**AE**FHILNOPQ	AEJLY	9
	5	ABCDEFGHKM	ABGHJMPRVZ	10

10A
2,5ha 61**T**(80-150m²) 25**P**

❶ €31.50
❷ €38.50

🚗 On the D704 after 8 km between Montignac and Sarlat, south of the Lascaux caves. Then follow campsite signs.

💬 The campsite is located between Montignac and Sarlat, close to the caves at Lascaux and les Eyzies and the many beautiful castles in the Dordogne. Definitely worth a visit.

CC 7/4-7/7 25/8-6/10

🏔 N 45°1'4" E 1°11'17"
www.eurocampings.co.uk/117556

50a

France

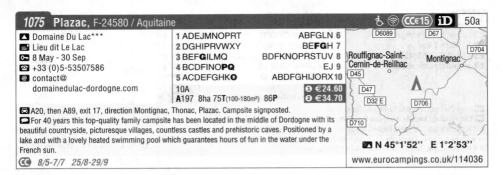

1075 Plazac, F-24580 / Aquitaine
  🚲 ⓦ (CC€15) iD 50a

- 🏠 Domaine Du Lac***
- 🏕 Lieu dit Le Lac
- 📅 8 May - 30 Sep
- ☎ +33 (0)5-53507586
- @ contact@
  domainedulac-dordogne.com

1 ADEJMNOPRT	ABFGLN	6
2 DGHIPRVWXY	BEF**FG**H	7
3 BEF**G**ILMQ	BDFKNOPRSTUV	8
4 BCDFINO**PQ**	EJ	9
5 ACDEFGHK**O**	ABDFGHIJORX	10
10A		❶ €24.60
A197 8ha 75T(100-180m²) 86P		❷ €34.70

🚗 A20, then A89, exit 17, direction Montignac, Thonac, Plazac. Campsite signposted.

💬 For 40 years this top-quality family campsite has been located in the middle of Dordogne with its beautiful countryside, picturesque villages, countless castles and prehistoric caves. Positioned by a lake and with a lovely heated swimming pool which guarantees hours of fun in the water under the French sun.

(CC) 8/5-7/7 25/8-29/9

📍 N 45°1'52'' E 1°2'53''

www.eurocampings.co.uk/114036

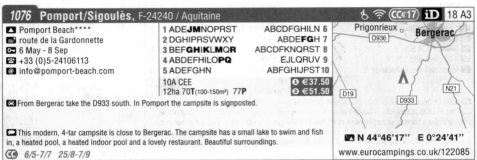

1076 Pomport/Sigoulès, F-24240 / Aquitaine
  🚲 ⓦ (CC€17) iD 18 A3

- 🏠 Pomport Beach****
- 🏕 route de la Gardonnette
- 📅 6 May - 8 Sep
- ☎ +33 (0)5-24106113
- @ info@pomport-beach.com

1 ADE**JM**NOPRST	ABCDFGHILN	6
2 DGHIPRSVWXY	ABDE**FG**H	7
3 BEF**GHIKLM**QR	ABCDFKNQRST	8
4 ABDEFHILO**PQ**	EJLQRUV	9
5 ADEFGHN	ABFGHIJPST	10
10A CEE		❶ €37.50
12ha 70T(100-150m²) 77P		❷ €51.50

🚗 From Bergerac take the D933 south. In Pomport the campsite is signposted.

💬 This modern, 4-tar campsite is close to Bergerac. The campsite has a small lake to swim and fish in, a heated pool, a heated indoor pool and a lovely restaurant. Beautiful surroundings.

(CC) 6/5-7/7 25/8-7/9

📍 N 44°46'17'' E 0°24'41''

www.eurocampings.co.uk/122085

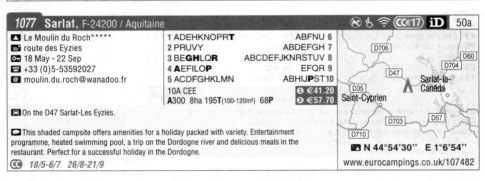

1077 Sarlat, F-24200 / Aquitaine
  ⊗ 🚲 ⓦ (CC€17) iD 50a

- 🏠 Le Moulin du Roch*****
- 🏕 route des Eyzies
- 📅 18 May - 22 Sep
- ☎ +33 (0)5-53592027
- @ moulin.du.roch@wanadoo.fr

1 ADEHKNOPR**T**	ABFNU	6
2 PRUVY	ABDEFGH	7
3 BE**GHL**QR	ABCDEFJKNRSTUV	8
4 **A**EFILO**P**	EFQR	9
5 ACDFGHKLMN	ABHIJ**P**ST	10
10A CEE		❶ €41.20
A300 8ha 195T(100-120m²) 68P		❷ €57.70

🚗 On the D47 Sarlat-Les Eyzies.

💬 This shaded campsite offers amenities for a holiday packed with variety. Entertainment programme, heated swimming pool, a trip on the Dordogne river and delicious meals in the restaurant. Perfect for a successful holiday in the Dordogne.

(CC) 18/5-6/7 26/8-21/9

📍 N 44°54'30'' E 1°6'54''

www.eurocampings.co.uk/107482

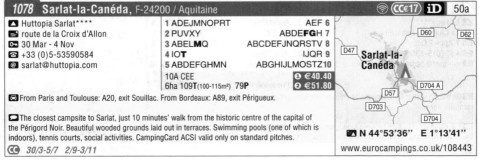

1078 Sarlat-la-Canéda, F-24200 / Aquitaine
  ⓦ (CC€17) iD 50a

- 🏠 Huttopia Sarlat****
- 🏕 route de la Croix d'Allon
- 📅 30 Mar - 4 Nov
- ☎ +33 (0)5-53590584
- @ sarlat@huttopia.com

1 ADEJMNOPRT	AEF	6
2 PUVXY	ABDE**FG**H	7
3 ABEL**MQ**	ABCDEFJNQRSTV	8
4 IO**T**	IJQR	9
5 ABDEFGHMN	ABGHIJLMOSTZ	10
10A CEE		❶ €40.40
6ha 109T(100-115m²) 79P		❷ €51.80

🚗 From Paris and Toulouse: A20, exit Souillac. From Bordeaux: A89, exit Périgueux.

💬 The closest campsite to Sarlat, just 10 minutes' walk from the historic centre of the capital of the Périgord Noir. Beautiful wooded grounds laid out in terraces. Swimming pools (one of which is indoors), tennis courts, social activities. CampingCard ACSI valid only on standard pitches.

(CC) 30/3-5/7 2/9-3/11

📍 N 44°53'36'' E 1°13'41''

www.eurocampings.co.uk/108443

France

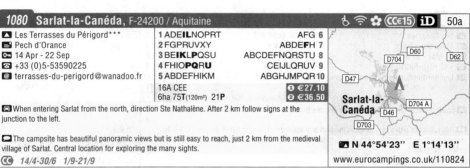

1079 Sarlat-la-Canéda, F-24200 / Aquitaine

⚐ Les Acacias***
🏠 avenue-de-la-Canéda
📅 12 Apr - 30 Sep
☎ +33 (0)5-53310850
@ camping-acacias@wanadoo.fr

  ♿ 🛜 (CC€15) **iD** 50a

1	ADE**IL**NOPRT	ABEF **6**
2	BFGOPRTUVXY	ABDE**FG**HI **7**
3	BE**K**LQ	ABCDEFJKNRSV **8**
4	FHINOPUY	EQRUV **9**
5	ABDEFGHN	ADGHJMOSTV **10**
	10A	❶ €32.20
	A123 4ha 102T(80-150m²) **20P**	❷ €46.20

🚧 In Sarlat direction Cahors, exit La Canéda. Campsite signposted.

💬 A compact French campsite in the centre of La Canéda. Located in the heart of the loveliest tourist sights. Within cycling distance of Sarlat for those who prefer to leave the car behind. Even inexperienced walkers can easily walk the 2.5 km to the centre. There is a bus stop near the campsite. Modern toilet facilities. Free wifi point. Heated indoor swimming pool with jacuzzi.

(CC) 12/4-5/7 23/8-29/9 21=20

N 44°51'27'' E 1°14'15''

www.eurocampings.co.uk/111594

1080 Sarlat-la-Canéda, F-24200 / Aquitaine

⚐ Les Terrasses du Périgord***
🏠 Pech d'Orance
📅 14 Apr - 22 Sep
☎ +33 (0)5-53590225
@ terrasses-du-perigord@wanadoo.fr

  ♿ 🛜 ✿ (CC€15) **iD** 50a

1	ADE**IL**NOPRT	AFG **6**
2	FGPRUVXY	ABDE**F**H **7**
3	BE**IKLP**QSU	ABCDEFNQRSTU **8**
4	FHIO**PQRU**	CEIJLQRUV **9**
5	ABDEFHIKM	ABGHJMPQR **10**
	16A CEE	❶ €27.10
	6ha 75T(120m²) **21P**	❷ €36.50

🚧 When entering Sarlat from the north, direction Ste Nathalène. After 2 km follow signs at the junction to the left.

💬 The campsite has beautiful panoramic views but is still easy to reach, just 2 km from the medieval village of Sarlat. Central location for exploring the many sights.

(CC) 14/4-30/6 1/9-21/9

N 44°54'23'' E 1°14'13''

www.eurocampings.co.uk/110824

France

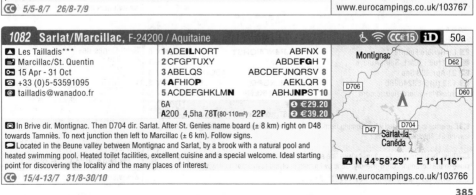

1081 Sarlat/Carsac, F-24200 / Aquitaine

⚐ Le Plein Air des Bories***
🏠 Les Bories
📅 5 May - 8 Sep
☎ +33 (0)5-53281567
@ contact@camping-desbories.com

  ♿ 🛜 (CC€15) **iD** 50a

1	ADE**JM**NORT	ACDFJNUXY **6**
2	CGHPQVWXY	BDE**F**H **7**
3	BELMQS	BDFKNORSV **8**
4	BCDFHILNO**PQ**	EQR **9**
5	ABDEFGHK**O**	ABGHJ**O**ST **10**
	6-16A	❶ €29.00
	A75 3ha 80T(100-120m²) **30P**	❷ €38.50

🚧 On the A20 exit Souillac, direction Sarlat via D703. Left past Calviac towards 'Vallée de la Dordogne'. Go under the railway bridge in Carsac and take the second left. Follow the signs.

💬 A really quietly located campsite. Suitable for families. Hidden away in wooded countryside and located right by the River Dordogne it is an ideal spot to enjoy peace and watersports. The swimming pool can be covered over.

(CC) 5/5-8/7 26/8-7/9

N 44°49'59'' E 1°16'5''

www.eurocampings.co.uk/103767

1082 Sarlat/Marcillac, F-24200 / Aquitaine

⚐ Les Tailladis***
🏠 Marcillac/St. Quentin
📅 15 Apr - 31 Oct
☎ +33 (0)5-53591095
@ tailladis@wanadoo.fr

  ♿ 🛜 (CC€15) **iD** 50a

1	ADE**IL**NORT	ABFNX **6**
2	CFGPTUXY	ABDE**FG**H **7**
3	ABELQS	ABCDEFJNQRSV **8**
4	**A**FHIO**P**	AEKLQR **9**
5	ACDEFGHKLM**N**	ABHJ**NP**ST **10**
	6A	❶ €29.20
	A200 4,5ha 78T(80-110m²) **22P**	❷ €39.20

🚧 In Brive dir. Montignac. Then D704 dir. Sarlat. After St. Genies name board (± 8 km) right on D48 towards Tamniès. To next junction then left to Marcillac (± 6 km). Follow signs.

💬 Located in the Beune valley between Montignac and Sarlat, by a brook with a natural pool and heated swimming pool. Heated toilet facilities, excellent cuisine and a special welcome. Ideal starting point for discovering the locality and the many places of interest.

(CC) 15/4-13/7 31/8-30/10

N 44°58'29'' E 1°11'16''

www.eurocampings.co.uk/103766

1083 Sarlat/Ste Nathalène, F-24200 / Aquitaine

 ♿ 🛜 (CC€17) iD 50a

- 🏔 La Palombière*****
- 📅 7 Apr - 23 Sep
- ☎ +33 (0)5-53594234
- @ contact@lapalombiere.fr

1	ADE**IL**NOPRT	ABFGHI	6
2	FGPRUVWXY	ABE**FG**H	7
3	BEFILMQ	BFGJKNPQRSTU	8
4	FHILNOPR**TUXY**	EJLV	9
5	ACDEFGHLM**NO**	ABHJM**N**PSTZ	10
10A CEE		❶ €38.50	
A250 6,5ha 68T(100-110m²) 70P		❷ €58.10	

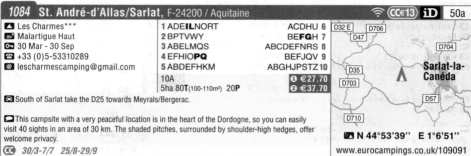

D60 · D704 · D62 · D165 · D703 · D704 A · D57 · D57

Sarlat-la-Canéda

🅰 A20 exit Souillac, D704 dir. Sarlat. Turn right in Rouffiac, D47 Carlux-Sarlat. 8 km from Sarlat in Ste Nathalène.

💬 An entrance that gives camping guests a wonderful feeling at this beautiful and enchanting site located on a hillside. The reception and excellent restaurant built in Perigord style offer a warm welcome. The stunning views and beautifully maintained grounds, with sports areas, will please everyone. New as of 2016: indoor leisure pool.

(CC) 7/4-8/7 27/8-22/9

📍 N 44°54'23'' E 1°17'31''

www.eurocampings.co.uk/100465

1084 St. André-d'Allas/Sarlat, F-24200 / Aquitaine

 🛜 (CC€13) iD 50a

- 🏔 Les Charmes***
- 🏕 Malartigue Haut
- 📅 30 Mar - 30 Sep
- ☎ +33 (0)5-53310289
- @ lescharmescamping@gmail.com

1	ADE**IL**NORT	ACDHU	6
2	BPTVWY	BE**FG**H	7
3	ABELMQS	ABCDEFNRS	8
4	EFHIO**PQ**	BEFJQV	9
5	ABDEFHKM	ABGHJPSTZ	10
10A		❶ €27.70	
5ha 80T(100-110m²) 20P		❷ €37.70	

D32 E · D706 · D47 · D704 · D35 · D703 · D57 · D710

Sarlat-la-Canéda

🅰 South of Sarlat take the D25 towards Meyrals/Bergerac.

💬 This campsite with a very peaceful location is in the heart of the Dordogne, so you can easily visit 40 sights in an area of 30 km. The shaded pitches, surrounded by shoulder-high hedges, offer welcome privacy.

(CC) 30/3-7/7 25/8-29/9

📍 N 44°53'39'' E 1°6'51''

www.eurocampings.co.uk/109091

1085 St. Antoine-d'Auberoche, F-24330 / Aquitaine

 ♿ 🛜 (CC€13) 🚻 iD 18 A3

- 🏔 La Pélonie***
- 🏕 La Pélonie
- 📅 16 Apr - 10 Oct
- ☎ +33 (0)5-53075578
- @ info@campinglapelonie.com

1	ADEJ**M**NOPRST	ABCDFHI	6
2	AGPSUVXY	ABDE**FG**H	7
3	BCE**GH**LQ**R**S	ABCDFIJKNQRSUV	8
4	ADFHILNO**PQ**	E	9
5	ABDEFGHLM**N**	ABDFGHIJLNPSTV	10
10A CEE		❶ €24.50	
A200 3ha 71T(100-120m²) 29P		❷ €34.50	

Trélissac · Boulazac · D5 · A89 · D710 · D6089 · D67 · Rouffignac-Saint-Cernin-de-Reilhac · D45

🅰 On the D6089 (don't take the A road) Brive-Périgueux, 5 km past Fossemagne on the right side, turn in and continue for 200 metres, or coming from Périgueux 5 km past St. Pierre on the left.

💬 Lovely family campsite, well maintained. Located in the countryside, in the heart of Dordogne, 15 km from Périgueux. Suitable for discovering tourist sights in Dordogne. Two heated pools (1 covered) and various water slides. Wifi free in the low season.

(CC) 16/4-9/7 27/8-9/10

📍 N 45°7'54'' E 0°55'43''

www.eurocampings.co.uk/100421

1086 St. Antoine-de-Breuilh, F-24230 / Aquitaine

 ♿ 🛜 (CC€17) 🚻 iD 18 A3

- 🏔 La Rivière Fleurie***
- 🏕 180 rue T. Cart, Saint Aulaye
- 📅 21 Apr - 23 Sep
- ☎ +33 (0)5-53248280
- @ info@la-riviere-fleurie.com

1	ADE**JM**NOPQRS**T**	ABFG**N**X	6
2	CPRVWXY	ABDE**FG**H	7
3	ABEIL**M**	ABCDEFGNRSTV	8
4	BDFHILNO**PQ**	BEHLQRUV	9
5	ABDEFGHKL**N**	ABDHIJOTUV	10
10A CEE		❶ €29.60	
2,4ha 66T(100-200m²) 28P		❷ €39.20	

Saint-Genès-de-Castillon · D708 · D20 · D21 · Le Fleix · D936 · Sainte-Foy-la-Grande · Pineuilh · D672 · D708 E3

🅰 Campsite is signposted when coming from St. Foy on the D936 direction Bordeaux, and when leaving St. Antoine-de Breuilh.

💬 Quiet, beautiful, quality campsite with fine spacious pitches in a family atmosphere. Campsite is close to the Dordogne. Child-friendly. Good swimming pool and restaurant. Lovely surroundings.

(CC) 21/4-8/7 26/8-22/9 7=6, 14=12, 21=18

📍 N 44°49'44'' E 0°7'21''

www.eurocampings.co.uk/111174

France

1087 St. Astier, F-24110 / Aquitaine
♿ 📶 (CC€13) **iD** 18 A3

- ⛺ Le Pontet***
- 🏠 Lieu dit Le Pontet (D41)
- 📅 2 Apr - 15 Sep
- ☎ +33 (0)5-53541422
- @ mail.lepontet@gmail.com

1 ADE**JM**NOPRST	AF**J**N	6
2 ACGIPVWXY	BE**FG**	7
3 AEFILQ	ABCDFNOQRSV	8
4 FHIO**PQ**	BEU	9
5 ADEFHKN	ABHIJ**P**RV	10
6A CEE		

A250 3ha 142**T**(100-120m²) 17**P**
💶 €22.30
💶 €24.30

🚗 N89 Périgueux-Bordeaux or A89 direction Bordeaux, exit 14 direction St. Astier. In Quatre Routes turn right in the direction of St. Astier, take the D41 (3 km).

💬 An unpretentious, well maintained campsite beside River L'Isle in a parkland setting and within walking distance of St. Astier. A lovely base to explore the countryside. Suitable for anglers and outdoor sports enthusiasts.

CC 2/4-7/7 25/8-14/9

🏔 N 45°8'49" E 0°32'0"

www.eurocampings.co.uk/100419

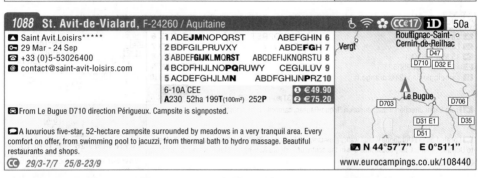

1088 St. Avit-de-Vialard, F-24260 / Aquitaine
♿ 📶 ✿ (CC€17) **iD** 50a

- ⛺ Saint Avit Loisirs*****
- 📅 29 Mar - 24 Sep
- ☎ +33 (0)5-53026400
- @ contact@saint-avit-loisirs.com

1 ADE**JM**NOPQRST	ABEFGHIN	6
2 BDFGILPRUVXY	ABDE**FGH**	7
3 ABDEF**GIJKLMQRST**	ABCDEFIJKNQRSTU	8
4 BCDFHIJLNO**PQR**UWY	CEGIJLUV	9
5 ACDEFGHJLM**N**	ABDFGHIJNP**R**V	10
6-10A CEE		

A230 52ha 199**T**(100m²) 252**P**
💶 €49.90
💶 €75.20

🚗 From Le Bugue D710 direction Périgueux. Campsite is signposted.

💬 A luxurious five-star, 52-hectare campsite surrounded by meadows in a very tranquil area. Every comfort on offer, from swimming pool to jacuzzi, from thermal bath to hydro massage. Beautiful restaurants and shops.

CC 29/3-7/7 25/8-23/9

🏔 N 44°57'7" E 0°51'1"

www.eurocampings.co.uk/108440

1089 St. Crépin-Carlucet/Sarlat, F-24590 / Aquitaine
♿ 📶 (CC€17) **iD** 50a

- ⛺ Les Peneyrals*****
- 🏠 Le Poujol
- 📅 5 May - 12 Sep
- ☎ +33 (0)5-53288571
- @ camping.peneyrals@wanadoo.fr

1 ADE**IL**NOR**T**	ABCFGHN	6
2 PRUVX	ABDE**FG**H	7
3 BEF**ILMQR**T	ABCDEFJKNQRSV	8
4 BEFHILNO**PQ**	EFLQRUV	9
5 ACDEFGHKLM**N**	ABGHIJM**NP**STZ	10
10A		

A260 13ha 117**T**(100-120m²) 65**P**
💶 €42.40
💶 €64.00

🚗 A20 exit Brive or Souillac, dir. Salignac/Sarlat. Campsite signposted. Located 12 km north of Sarlat.
💬 The site is 12 km from the medieval town of Sarlat and blends well into the surroundings. The heated pools (1 indoor), paddling pool and toilet facilities ensure every comfort, even in the early and late season. Excellent restaurant and café with Belgian beers. A hospitable welcome and peaceful surroundings. Free wifi in May, June and September.

CC 5/5-7/7 25/8-11/9 14=12, 21=18

🏔 N 44°57'28" E 1°16'20"

www.eurocampings.co.uk/103756

1090 St. Léon-sur-Vézère, F-24290 / Aquitaine
♿ 📶 ✿ (CC€19) **iD** 50a

- ⛺ Le Paradis*****
- 🏠 La Rebayrolle
- 📅 1 Apr - 20 Oct
- ☎ +33 (0)5-53507264
- @ le-paradis@perigord.com

1 ADE**JM**NOPQRST	ABCDFG**J**NU	6
2 CGPRVXY	BE**FGH**	7
3 BELMQ	BDFGJKNPQRSTUV	8
4 BCD**EFILNOPQ**TUV**X**	AEJLQRUVWYZ	9
5 ACEFHJLM**NO**	ABDGHIJNPQRZ	10
10A CEE		

A71 8ha 144**T**(80-200m²) 50**P**
💶 €40.90
💶 €59.90

🚗 The campsite is located on the D706 Montignac-Les Eyzies (do not turn off towards the village St. Léon). Follow the signs.
💬 A very luxurious campsite on the banks of the Vézère. Spacious pitches surrounded by lovely vegetation. Many historic sights in the immediate vicinity. Plenty of sports opportunities and entertainment. Very clean and comfortable toilet facilities.

CC 1/4-7/7 1/9-19/10

🏔 N 45°0'6" E 1°4'17"

www.eurocampings.co.uk/103752

France

1091 Thiviers, F-24800 / Aquitaine   ♿ 🛜 (CC€15) ✸ iD 18 A3

🏕 Le Repaire***
🏕 Le Repaire
🗓 1 Apr - 1 Nov
☎ +33 (0)5-53526975
@ contact@camping-le-repaire.fr

1 ADEJMNOPRST	CDFN 6
2 DGIPVWXY	ABDEFGH 7
3 BLMQ	CDEFHNQRV 8
4 BCDFHIOQ	EJUV 9
5 ADEHNO	ABCDGHIJOTUV 10
6A	❶ €25.00
A250 8ha 80T(100-150m²) 20P	❷ €33.00

🛣 N21 Limoges-Périgueux, at the second traffic lights (large intersection) in Thiviers turn left onto the D707 in the direction of Lanouaille. Follow the signs.

💬 A beautiful, park-like campsite within walking distance of a village. Lovely swimming pool and close to a lake with opportunities for swimming (1 km).
CC 1/4-14/7 1/9-31/10 7=6, 14=11

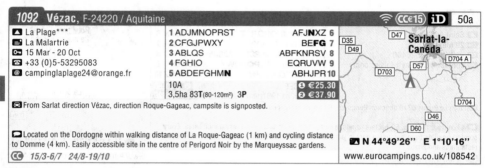
N 45°24'47'' E 0°55'56''
www.eurocampings.co.uk/107467

1092 Vézac, F-24220 / Aquitaine   🛜 (CC€15) iD 50a

🏕 La Plage***
🏕 La Malartrie
🗓 15 Mar - 20 Oct
☎ +33 (0)5-53295083
@ campinglaplage24@orange.fr

1 ADJMNOPRST	AFJNXZ 6
2 CFGJPWXY	BEFG 7
3 ABLQS	ABFKNRSV 8
4 FGHIO	EQRUVW 9
5 ABDEFGHMN	ABHJPR 10
10A	❶ €25.30
3,5ha 83T(80-120m²) 3P	❷ €37.90

🛣 From Sarlat direction Vézac, direction Roque-Gageac, campsite is signposted.

💬 Located on the Dordogne within walking distance of La Roque-Gageac (1 km) and cycling distance to Domme (4 km). Easily accessible site in the centre of Perigord Noir by the Marqueyssac gardens.
CC 15/3-6/7 24/8-19/10

N 44°49'26'' E 1°10'16''
www.eurocampings.co.uk/108542

1093 Vézac, F-24220 / Aquitaine   ♿ 🛜 (CC€15) ✸ iD 50a

🏕 Les Deux Vallées***
🏕 La Gare
🗓 14 Mar - 7 Oct
☎ +33 (0)5-53295355
@ contact@campingles2vallees.com

1 ACDEJMNOPRST	ABFN 6
2 FPQVWXY	ABDEFGH 7
3 ABEKLQ	ABCDFJNRSV 8
4 ABFHILOPQ	EQRUV 9
5 ABDFHKLMN	ABDGHJPQR 10
10A CEE	❶ €33.10
A76 3,3ha 94T(90-160m²) 16P	❷ €46.50

🛣 On the D57 from Sarlat, turn right just after Vézac sign. Campsite is marked.
💬 A beautiful, relaxed campsite in stunning countryside west of Sarlat, with views of Beynac Castle. 'La Roque Gageac', Domme, Castelnau and the river Dordogne are all close by, making it an ideal place for exploring. The region is well known for its excellent cuisine and good wine. Free wifi. Heated toilet facilities.
CC 14/3-6/7 24/8-6/10 16=14

N 44°50'8'' E 1°9'30''
www.eurocampings.co.uk/103770

1094 Vitrac, F-24200 / Aquitaine   ♿ 🛜 (CC€19) iD 50a

🏕 Domaine de Soleil Plage*****
🏕 Plage De Caudon
🗓 7 Apr - 30 Sep
☎ +33 (0)5-53283333
@ info@soleilplage.fr

1 ABDEJLNORT	ABCDFGHIJNUX 6
2 CFGHJKPQRVXY	ABDEFGH 7
3 BEILMQTU	ABCDEFGIJKNQRSTU 8
4 BCDFHILOPQRUX	EFLQRUV 9
5 ABCDEFGHKLMO	ABFGHIJMPRZ 10
16A	❶ €42.70
A100 6ha 106T(80-120m²) 97P	❷ €58.70

🛣 The campsite is located on the D703 and is signposted at Vitrac and Montfort.

💬 Beautifully located on the Dordogne river, this campsite is split up into two parts. With its excellent leisure pool and spacious pitches this campsite exudes space. Centrally located reception, bar and restaurant have been nicely integrated into the valley. Has its own boat rental and multisports grounds.
CC 7/4-5/7 30/8-29/9

N 44°49'28'' E 1°15'11''
www.eurocampings.co.uk/103771

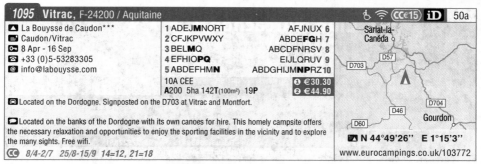

1095 Vitrac, F-24200 / Aquitaine

♿ 📶 ⓒⓒ€15 iD 50a

- ⛺ La Bouysse de Caudon***
- ✉ Caudon/Vitrac
- 📅 8 Apr - 16 Sep
- ☎ +33 (0)5-53283305
- @ info@labouysse.com

1 ADE**JM**NORT	AFJNUX 6
2 CFJKPVWXY	ABDE**FG**H 7
3 BEL**MQ**	ABCDFNRSV 8
4 EFHIO**PQ**	EIJLQRUV 9
5 ABDEFHM**N**	ABDGHIJM**N**PRZ 10

10A CEE   **①** €30.30
A200   5ha 142T(100m²)   19P   **②** €44.90

🚗 Located on the Dordogne. Signposted on the D703 at Vitrac and Montfort.

💬 Located on the banks of the Dordogne with its own canoes for hire. This homely campsite offers the necessary relaxation and opportunities to enjoy the sporting facilities in the vicinity and to explore the many sights. Free wifi.

ⓒⓒ 8/4-2/7   25/8-15/9   14=12, 21=18

🗺 N 44°49'26''   E 1°15'3''

www.eurocampings.co.uk/103772

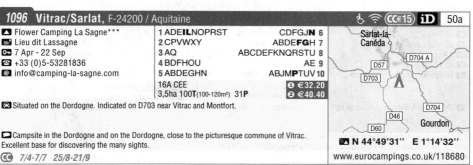

1096 Vitrac/Sarlat, F-24200 / Aquitaine

♿ 📶 ⓒⓒ€15 iD 50a

- ⛺ Flower Camping La Sagne***
- ✉ Lieu dit Lassagne
- 📅 7 Apr - 22 Sep
- ☎ +33 (0)5-53281836
- @ info@camping-la-sagne.com

1 ADE**IL**NOPRST	CDFGJ**N** 6
2 CPVWXY	ABDE**FG**H 7
3 AQ	ABCDEFKNQRSTU 8
4 BDFHOU	AE 9
5 ABDEGHN	ABJM**P**TUV 10

16A CEE   **①** €32.20
3,5ha 100T(100-120m²)   31P   **②** €40.40

🚗 Situated on the Dordogne. Indicated on D703 near Vitrac and Montfort.

💬 Campsite in the Dordogne and on the Dordogne, close to the picturesque commune of Vitrac. Excellent base for discovering the many sights.

ⓒⓒ 7/4-7/7   25/8-21/9

🗺 N 44°49'31''   E 1°14'32''

www.eurocampings.co.uk/118680

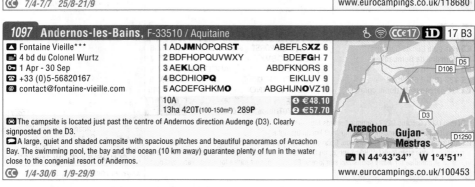

1097 Andernos-les-Bains, F-33510 / Aquitaine

♿ 📶 ⓒⓒ€17 iD 17 B3

- ⛺ Fontaine Vieille***
- ✉ 4 bd du Colonel Wurtz
- 📅 1 Apr - 30 Sep
- ☎ +33 (0)5-56820167
- @ contact@fontaine-vieille.com

1 AD**JM**NOPQRS**T**	ABEFLS**XZ** 6
2 BDFHOPQUVWXY	BDE**FG**H 7
3 AE**K**LQR	ABDFKNORS 8
4 BCDHIO**PQ**	EIKLUV 9
5 ACDEFGHKM**O**	ABGHIJN**O**VZ 10

10A   **①** €48.10
13ha 420T(100-150m²)   289P   **②** €57.70

🚗 The campsite is located just past the centre of Andernos direction Audenge (D3). Clearly signposted on the D3.

💬 A large, quiet and shaded campsite with spacious pitches and beautiful panoramas of Arcachon Bay. The swimming pool, the bay and the ocean (10 km away) guarantee plenty of fun in the water close to the congenial resort of Andernos.

ⓒⓒ 1/4-30/6   1/9-29/9

🗺 N 44°43'34''   W 1°4'51''

www.eurocampings.co.uk/100453

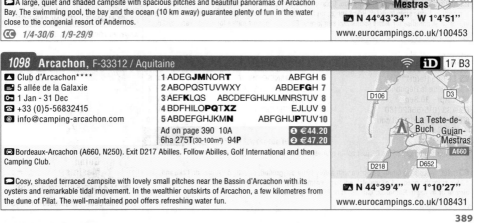

1098 Arcachon, F-33312 / Aquitaine

📶 iD 17 B3

- ⛺ Club d'Arcachon****
- ✉ 5 allée de la Galaxie
- 📅 1 Jan - 31 Dec
- ☎ +33 (0)5-56832415
- @ info@camping-arcachon.com

1 ADEG**JM**NOR**T**	ABFGH 6
2 ABOPQSTUVWXY	ABDE**FG**H 7
3 AEF**K**LQS ABCDEFGHIJKLMNRSTUV 8	
4 BDFHILO**PQ**T**XZ**	EJLUV 9
5 ABDEFGHJKM**N**	ABFGHIJ**P**TUV 10

Ad on page 390   10A   **①** €44.20
6ha 275T(30-100m²)   94P   **②** €47.20

🚗 Bordeaux-Arcachon (A660, N250). Exit D217 Abilles. Follow Abilles, Golf International and then Camping Club.

💬 Cosy, shaded terraced campsite with lovely small pitches near the Bassin d'Arcachon with its oysters and remarkable tidal movement. In the wealthier outskirts of Arcachon, a few kilometres from the dune of Pilat. The well-maintained pool offers refreshing water fun.

🗺 N 44°39'4''   W 1°10'27''

www.eurocampings.co.uk/108431

France

Club d'Arcachon ★ ★ ★ ★

You'll find all the comforts required for an unforgettable holiday in the heart of a beautiful Norwegian spruce forest, close to the town centre and beaches. Located near the Dune du Pyla, the ocean and Le Bassin with its splendid beaches. On the heights of Arcachon in the Quartier des Abatilles. 275 pitches on a hilly and overgrown terrain. With separate areas for families, couples and young people. With a swimming pool complex (open in April, subject to change), playground, barbecue area, entertainment for young and older children (in July and August). Open all year. Heated toilet block. Near the centre and the beach (about 20 minutes on foot).

5 allée de la Galaxie, 33312 Arcachon · Tel. 05-56832415 · Fax 05-57522851
E-mail: info@camping-arcachon.com · Internet: www.camping-arcachon.com

---

1099 Audenge, F-33980 / Aquitaine

♿ 📶 (CC€17) iD · 17 B3

- ▲ Le Braou***
- ✉ 26 route de Bordeaux
- 📅 1 Apr - 30 Sep
- ☎ +33 (0)5-56269003
- @ info@camping-audenge.com

1 ADE**JM**NOPRS**T**	AB**F**X	6
2 AOPQVWXY	ABDE**FG**	7
3 AEF**KLMQ**	ABCDEFNORSTV	8
4 BCDFHIL	BDEJK	9
5 ADEFGHJKM**N**	ABFGHIJPTUV	10
6A	❶ €34.60	
90T(66-180m²) 106P	❷ €40.60	

🚗 D3 Biganos-Andernos. In Audenge right at second roundabout. Campsite 700 metres on the right.

💬 A peaceful campsite with very large pitches and a lovely swimming pool. Ideal for cycling and walking tours or trips out to Arcachon, Bordeaux, the ocean or the Dune of Pilat.

ⓒⓒ 1/4-13/7 31/8-29/9

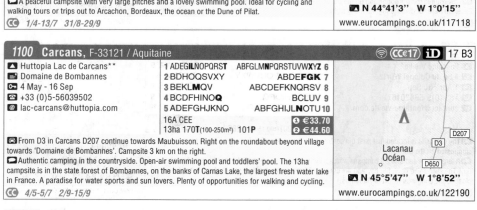

Arcachon
Gujan-Mestras
D5 · D1250 · D216 · A660 · D652 · D3 · A63

📷 N 44°41'3'' W 1°0'15''

www.eurocampings.co.uk/117118

1100 Carcans, F-33121 / Aquitaine

📶 (CC€17) iD · 17 B3

- ▲ Huttopia Lac de Carcans**
- ✉ Domaine de Bombannes
- 📅 4 May - 16 Sep
- ☎ +33 (0)5-56039502
- @ lac-carcans@huttopia.com

1 ADEG**I**LNOPQRS**T**	ABF**G**LM**N**PQRSTUVW**XYZ**	6
2 BDHOQSVXY	ABDE**FGK**	7
3 BEKL**MQV**	ABCDEFKNQRSV	8
4 BCDFHINO**Q**	BCLUV	9
5 ADEFGHJKNO	ABFGHIJL**N**OTU	10
16A CEE	❶ €33.70	
13ha 170T(100-250m²) 101P	❷ €44.60	

🚗 From D3 in Carcans D207 continue towards Maubuisson. Right on the roundabout beyond village towards 'Domaine de Bombannes'. Campsite 3 km on the right.
💬 Authentic camping in the countryside. Open-air swimming pool and toddlers' pool. The 13ha campsite is in the state forest of Bombannes, on the banks of Carnas Lake, the largest fresh water lake in France. A paradise for water sports and sun lovers. Plenty of opportunities for walking and cycling.

ⓒⓒ 4/5-5/7 2/9-15/9

Lacanau Océan
D207 · D3 · D650

📷 N 45°5'47'' W 1°8'52''

www.eurocampings.co.uk/122190

1101 Cassy-Lanton, F-33138 / Aquitaine

♿ 📶 (CC€17) iD · 17 B3

- ▲ Le Coq Hardi***
- ✉ 3 av. de la République
- 📅 1 Apr - 30 Sep
- ☎ +33 (0)5-56820180
- @ violesgalyon@aol.com

1 AD**JM**NOPQRST	AFH**X**	6
2 DFGHOPQVWXY	ABDE**FGH**	7
3 BEFI**KLMQ**	BDFNRSTV	8
4 BCDFHIO**PQ**	DEJV	9
5 ABDFGH**N**	AGIJN**PV**	10
10A	❶ €35.90	
8ha 330T(100-120m²) 106P	❷ €46.40	

🚗 Campsite on right of the D3 just south of Andernos in Cassy. Well signposted.

💬 Quiet, welcoming family campsite with a very large playground, directly on Arcachon Lake and 10 km from the ocean. Well maintained, large swimming pool with slides, spacious pitches. Trips by bicycle or by car to Bordeaux, Cap Jerret or Pilat are possible.

ⓒⓒ 1/4-30/6 1/9-29/9

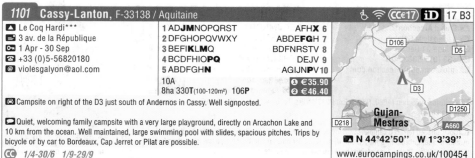

Gujan-Mestras
D106 · D5 · D3 · D1250 · D218 · A660

📷 N 44°42'50'' W 1°3'39''

www.eurocampings.co.uk/100454

1102 Créon, F-33670 / Aquitaine

♿ 📶 CC€17 iD 17 B3

🏕 Bel-Air***
🏠 150 Route Départementale 671
📅 15 Jan - 15 Dec
☎ +33 (0)5-56230190
@ info@camping-bel-air.com

1 ADE**JM**NOPRST	AF 6
2 AGOPVWXY	ABDE**FGH** 7
3 BE**GH**ILQS	BDFJNRV 8
4 FHIO**P**	E 9
5 ADEFGHN	ABDFHIJOR 10

5-10A ❶ € 23.00
A102 3,5ha 62T(80-90m²) 37P ❷ € 29.70

🗺 The campsite is located on the D671 between Bordeaux and Créon, 2 km before Créon.

💬 Perfectly maintained and quiet family campsite close to Bordeaux with a bus connection to the centre from the campsite. Swimming pool, heated toilet facilities, bar and small restaurant. Free wifi point.

CC 15/1-6/7 27/8-14/12

N 44°47'2'' W 0°22'16''

www.eurocampings.co.uk/103552

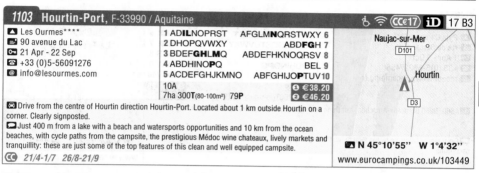

1103 Hourtin-Port, F-33990 / Aquitaine

♿ 📶 CC€17 iD 17 B3

🏕 Les Ourmes****
🏠 90 avenue du Lac
📅 21 Apr - 22 Sep
☎ +33 (0)5-56091276
@ info@lesourmes.com

1 AD**IL**NOPRST	AFGLMN**QR**STWXY 6
2 DHOPQVWXY	ABD**FG**H 7
3 BDEF**GH**L**MQ**	ABDEFHKNOQRSV 8
4 ABDHINO**PQ**	BEL 9
5 ACDEFGHJKMNO	ABFGHIJO**P**TUV 10

10A ❶ € 38.20
7ha 300T(80-100m²) 79P ❷ € 46.20

🗺 Drive from the centre of Hourtin direction Hourtin-Port. Located about 1 km outside Hourtin on a corner. Clearly signposted.

💬 Just 400 m from a lake with a beach and watersports opportunities and 10 km from the ocean beaches, with cycle paths from the campsite, the prestigious Médoc wine chateaux, lively markets and tranquillity: these are just some of the top features of this clean and well equipped campsite.

CC 21/4-1/7 26/8-21/9

N 45°10'55'' W 1°4'32''

www.eurocampings.co.uk/103449

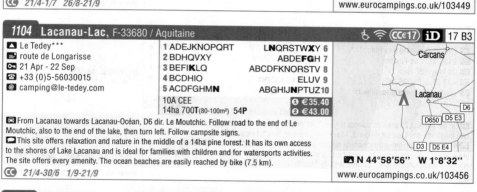

1104 Lacanau-Lac, F-33680 / Aquitaine

♿ 📶 CC€17 iD 17 B3

🏕 Le Tedey***
🏠 route de Longarisse
📅 21 Apr - 22 Sep
☎ +33 (0)5-56030015
@ camping@le-tedey.com

1 ADEJKNOPQRT	LN**QR**STW**XY** 6
2 BDHQVXY	ABDE**FGH** 7
3 BEFI**K**LQ	ABCDFKNORSTV 8
4 BCDHIO	ELUV 9
5 ACDFGHM**N**	ABGHIJ**NP**TUZ 10

10A CEE ❶ € 35.40
14ha 700T(80-100m²) 54P ❷ € 43.00

🗺 From Lacanau towards Lacanau-Océan, D6 dir. Le Moutchic. Follow road to the end of Le Moutchic, also to the end of the lake, then turn left. Follow campsite signs.

💬 This site offers relaxation and nature in the middle of a 14ha pine forest. It has its own access to the shores of Lake Lacanau and is ideal for families with children and for watersports activities. The site offers every amenity. The ocean beaches are easily reached by bike (7.5 km).

CC 21/4-30/6 1/9-21/9

N 44°58'56'' W 1°8'32''

www.eurocampings.co.uk/103456

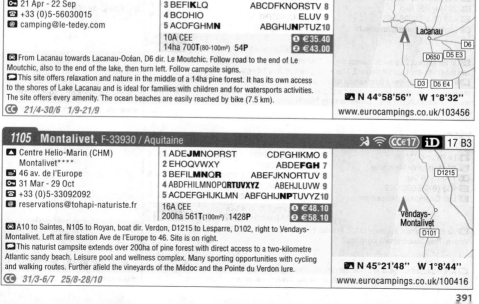

1105 Montalivet, F-33930 / Aquitaine

⛹ 📶 CC€17 iD 17 B3

🏕 Centre Helio-Marin (CHM) Montalivet****
🏠 46 av. de l'Europe
📅 31 Mar - 29 Oct
☎ +33 (0)5-33092092
@ reservations@tohapi-naturiste.fr

1 ADE**JM**NOPRST	CDFGHIKMO 6
2 EHOQVWXY	ABDE**FGH** 7
3 BEFIL**MN**QR	ABEFJKNORTUV 8
4 ABDFHILMNOPQ**RTUVXYZ**	ABEHJLUVW 9
5 ACDEFGHIJKLMN	ABFGHIJ**NP**TUVYZ 10

16A CEE ❶ € 48.10
200ha 561T(100m²) 1428P ❷ € 58.10

🗺 A10 to Saintes, N105 to Royan, boat dir. Verdon, D1215 to Lesparre, D102, right to Vendays-Montalivet. Left at fire station Ave de l'Europe to 46. Site is on right.

💬 This naturist campsite extends over 200ha of pine forest with direct access to a two-kilometre Atlantic sandy beach. Leisure pool and wellness complex. Many sporting opportunities with cycling and walking routes. Further afield the vineyards of the Médoc and the Pointe du Verdon lure.

CC 31/3-6/7 25/8-28/10

N 45°21'48'' W 1°8'44''

www.eurocampings.co.uk/100416

France

391

1106 Montalivet-les-Bains, F-33930 / Aquitaine

⊚ CC€17 ⚤ **iD** 17 B3

- ▲ Campéole Médoc Plage★★★★
- ✉ av. de l'Europe
- ☷ 27 Apr - 16 Sep
- ☎ +33 (0)5-56093345
- @ medoc-plage@campeole.com

1 ADEJMNOPQRST	ABFGHIQRSX 6
2 OPQVWXY	ABDEFGH 7
3 BEFLMQT	ABCDEFKNORSV 8
4 ABCDHILNO	ACELUV 9
5 ABDEFGHJ	ABGHIJMOVZ 10
10-16A CEE	❶ €34.80
30ha 393T(100-120m²) 512P	❷ €46.70

🗺 From D101 in Vendays direction Montalivet (D102). Just before Montalivet-les-Bains (D102) left at filling station. Campsite on left after 800m, well indicated.

💬 A large well equipped campsite with a number of sporting opportunities 700 m from the beach.
CC 27/4-6/7 25/8-15/9

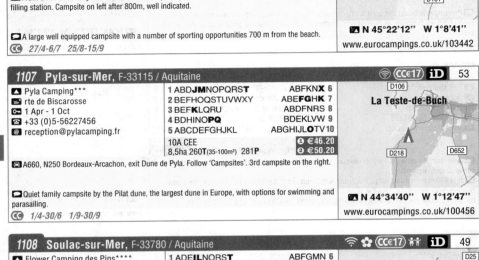

■ N 45°22'12'' W 1°8'41''
www.eurocampings.co.uk/103442

1107 Pyla-sur-Mer, F-33115 / Aquitaine

⊚ CC€17 **iD** 53

- ▲ Pyla Camping★★★
- ✉ rte de Biscarosse
- ☷ 1 Apr - 1 Oct
- ☎ +33 (0)5-56227456
- @ reception@pylacamping.fr

1 ABDJMNOPQRST	ABFKNX 6
2 BEFHOQSTUVWXY	ABEFGHK 7
3 BEFKLQRU	ABDFNRS 8
4 BDHINOPQ	BDEKLVW 9
5 ABCDEFGHJKL	ABGHIJLOTV 10
10A CEE	❶ €46.20
8,5ha 260T(35-100m²) 281P	❷ €50.20

🗺 A660, N250 Bordeaux-Arcachon, exit Dune de Pyla. Follow 'Campsites'. 3rd campsite on the right.

💬 Quiet family campsite by the Pilat dune, the largest dune in Europe, with options for swimming and parasailing.
CC 1/4-30/6 1/9-30/9

■ N 44°34'40'' W 1°12'47''
www.eurocampings.co.uk/100456

1108 Soulac-sur-Mer, F-33780 / Aquitaine

⊚ ✿ CC€17 ⚤ **iD** 49

- ▲ Flower Camping des Pins★★★★
- ✉ 213 Passe de Formose
- ☷ 28 May - 30 Sep
- ☎ +33 (0)5-56098252
- @ contact@campingdespins.fr

1 ADEILNORST	ABFGMN 6
2 BHQRTUVWXY	ABDEFGH 7
3 BEFLQR	ABCDEFSTV 8
4 BCDLNOPQ	BCEV 9
5 ABDEFGKNO	ABDFHIJNPTV 10
6A CEE	❶ €40.20
3,4ha 66T(90-100m²) 84P	❷ €53.20

🗺 On the A10 exit 25 towards Saintes Royan. Take ferry across the Gironde to Le Verdon. In Soulac take the Route-des-Lacs southbound. After leaving built-up area 1st right, 2nd left.
💬 A campsite located in a quiet natural setting, away from the bustle of everyday life. The 3.4-hectare grounds are 2 minutes from the Atlantic with a wide beach. It has a new swimming pool and modern energy-efficient toilet facilities. Environmentally friendly campsite.
CC 28/5-1/7 27/8-29/9

■ N 45°28'58'' W 1°7'38''
www.eurocampings.co.uk/115025

1109 Soulac-sur-Mer, F-33780 / Aquitaine

♿ ⊚ **iD** 49

- ▲ Le Palace★★★★
- ✉ bd Marsan de Montbrun
- ☷ 7 Apr - 16 Sep
- ☎ +33 (0)5-56098022
- @ info@camping-palace.com

1 ADEILNOPRT	ABCDFGHIKMNQSX 6
2 BEHPQVXY	ABDEFGH 7
3 BDEFILMQR	ABCDEFGKNQRSTUV 8
4 BCDFILNOPQRTV	EJLUVW 9
5 ACDEFGHLMNO	ABGHIJNOV 10
Ad on page 330 10A CEE	❶ €46.20
16ha 185T(88-220m²) 324P	❷ €64.20

🗺 Via Paris direction Bordeaux (A10). At Saintes exit 35 direction Royan. Then take the ferry to Le Verdon. Then Soulac, clearly signposted.

💬 Well-equipped campsite in a pine and deciduous forest, with plenty of mimosa, and the beach 400 metres away. With beautiful pitches and lots of privacy. Children can go to the Bambi-Club.

■ N 45°30'6'' W 1°7'55''
www.eurocampings.co.uk/103436

1110 Soulac-sur-Mer, F-33780 / Aquitaine   ♿ 📶 (CC€17) iD 49

- ▲ Les Lacs*****
- 🏠 126 route des Lacs
- 📅 7 Apr - 31 Oct
- ☎ +33 (0)5-56097663
- @ info@camping-les-lacs.com

1 ADE**JM**NOPQRST	AEFGHIMNX	6
2 HPQVWXY	ABDE**FGH**	7
3 ABEILQR	ABCDEFJKNQRSTUV	8
4 **A**CDEIKLNO**PQX**	EJUVW	9
5 ACDEFGHKLMN	ABDFGHIJN**P**TUVWZ	10

10A CEE
5,8ha 98T(102-170m²) 192P
❶ €38.20
❷ €49.20

🚗 From Bordeaux: Rocade exit 7. Then N215 Le Verdon or D2 Pauillac along the D101. From the boat: first to Soulac then direction L'Amélie. Follow Route des Lacs. On the left outside the built up area.

💬 This campsite offers everything you could wish for on a holiday near the ocean. In addition you can enjoy two lovely swimming pools, one of them indoors and heated. Ideally located for trips out.

CC 7/4-14/7 1/9-30/10

📍 N 45°29'0'' W 1°7'8''

www.eurocampings.co.uk/109672

1111 Soulac-sur-Mer, F-33780 / Aquitaine   ♿ 📶 (CC€17) iD 49

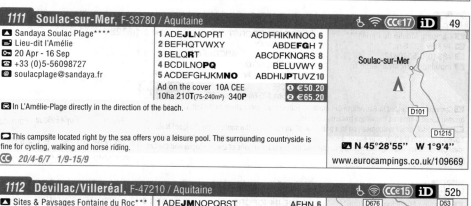

- ▲ Sandaya Soulac Plage****
- 🏠 Lieu-dit l'Amélie
- 📅 20 Apr - 16 Sep
- ☎ +33 (0)5-56098727
- @ soulacplage@sandaya.fr

1 ADE**JL**NOPRT	ACDFHIKMNOQ	6
2 BEFHQTVWXY	ABDE**FG**H	7
3 BEL**QRT**	ABCDFKNQRS	8
4 BCDILNO**PQ**	BELUVWY	9
5 ACDEFGHJKM**NO**	ABDHIJ**P**TUVZ	10

Ad on the cover 10A CEE
10ha 210T(75-240m²) 340P
❶ €50.20
❷ €65.20

🚗 In L'Amélie-Plage directly in the direction of the beach.

💬 This campsite located right by the sea offers you a leisure pool. The surrounding countryside is fine for cycling, walking and horse riding.

CC 20/4-6/7 1/9-15/9

📍 N 45°28'55'' W 1°9'4''

www.eurocampings.co.uk/109669

1112 Dévillac/Villeréal, F-47210 / Aquitaine   ♿ 📶 (CC€15) iD 52b

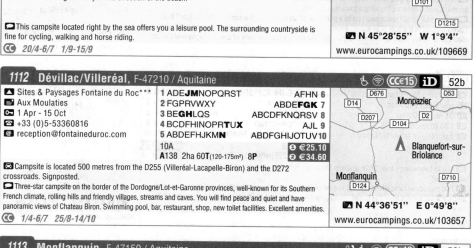

- ▲ Sites & Paysages Fontaine du Roc***
- 🏠 Aux Moulaties
- 📅 1 Apr - 15 Oct
- ☎ +33 (0)5-53360816
- @ reception@fontaineduroc.com

1 ADE**JM**NOPQRST	AFHN	6
2 FGPRVWXY	ABDE**FGK**	7
3 BE**GH**LQS	ABCDFKNQRSV	8
4 BCDFHINOPR**TUX**	AJL	9
5 ABDEFHJKM**N**	ABDFGHIJOTUV	10

10A
A138 2ha 60T(120-175m²) 8P
❶ €25.10
❷ €34.60

🚗 Campsite is located 500 metres from the D255 (Villeréal-Lacapelle-Biron) and the D272 crossroads. Signposted.

💬 Three-star campsite on the border of the Dordogne/Lot-et-Garonne provinces, well-known for its Southern French climate, rolling hills and friendly villages, streams and caves. You will find peace and quiet and have panoramic views of Chateau Biron. Swimming pool, bar, restaurant, shop, new toilet facilities. Excellent amenities.

CC 1/4-6/7 25/8-14/10

📍 N 44°36'51'' E 0°49'8''

www.eurocampings.co.uk/103657

1113 Monflanquin, F-47150 / Aquitaine   ⛹ ♿ 📶 (CC€19) iD 52b

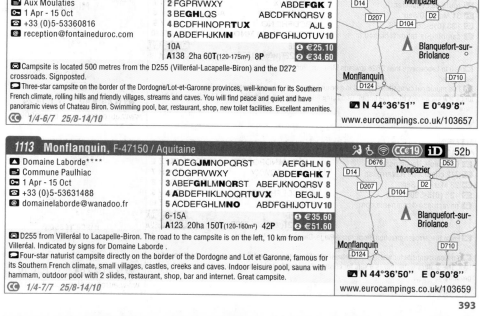

- ▲ Domaine Laborde****
- 🏠 Commune Paulhiac
- 📅 1 Apr - 15 Oct
- ☎ +33 (0)5-53631488
- @ domainelaborde@wanadoo.fr

1 ADEG**JM**NOPQRST	AEFGHLN	6
2 CDGPRVWXY	ABDE**FGH**K	7
3 ABEF**GH**LM**NQR**ST	ABEFJKNOQRSV	8
4 **A**BDEFHIKLNOQRT**UVX**	BEGJL	9
5 ACDEFGHLM**NO**	ABDFGHIJOTUV	10

6-15A
A123 20ha 150T(120-160m²) 42P
❶ €35.60
❷ €51.60

🚗 D255 from Villeréal to Lacapelle-Biron. The road to the campsite is on the left, 10 km from Villeréal. Indicated by signs for Domaine Laborde.

💬 Four-star naturist campsite directly on the border of the Dordogne and Lot et Garonne, famous for its Southern French climate, small villages, castles, creeks and caves. Indoor leisure pool, sauna with hammam, outdoor pool with 2 slides, restaurant, shop, bar and internet. Great campsite.

CC 1/4-7/7 25/8-14/10

📍 N 44°36'50'' E 0°50'8''

www.eurocampings.co.uk/103659

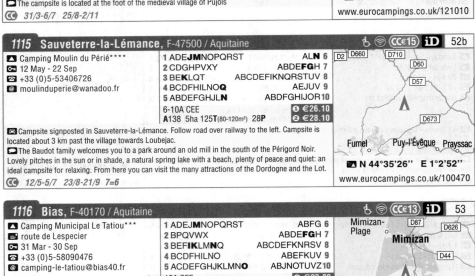

1114 Pujols, F-47300 / Aquitaine

♿ 📶 CCε15 iD 52b

🔺 Lot & Bastides à Pujols***
🏠 allée de Malbentre
📅 31 Mar - 3 Nov
☎ +33 (0)5-53368679
@ contact@camping-lot-et-bastides.fr

1 ADE**JM**NOPQRS**T**	ABFN 6
2 OPVWX	ABDE**FG**H 7
3 BF**KL**Q	ABCDEFGIJKNQRSTU 8
4 **A**BCDFHILO**PU**	AEJUVW 9
5 ABDEFGHJKMNO	ABDFGHIJPRV10

16A CEE ❶ €23.10
A64 12ha 83T(115-140m²) 30P ❷ €31.10

🅿 On the N21 from the north direction Villeneuve-sur-Lot (D661) at first roundabout. Follow Bordeaux then Pujols signs. Then follow Piscine de Malbentre and/or campsite.

💬 The campsite is located at the foot of the medieval village of Pujols

CC 31/3-6/7 25/8-2/11

🔺 N 44°23'41'' E 0°41'13''
www.eurocampings.co.uk/121010

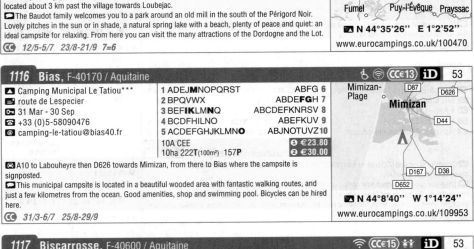

1115 Sauveterre-la-Lémance, F-47500 / Aquitaine

♿ 📶 CCε15 iD 52b

🔺 Camping Moulin du Périé****
📅 12 May - 22 Sep
☎ +33 (0)5-53406726
@ moulinduperie@wanadoo.fr

1 ADE**JM**NOPQRST	ALN 6
2 CDGHPVXY	ABDE**FG**H 7
3 BE**K**LQT	ABCDEFIKNQRSTUV 8
4 BCDFHILNO**Q**	AEJUV 9
5 ABDEFGHJL**N**	ABDFGHIJOR10

6-10A CEE ❶ €26.10
A138 5ha 125T(80-120m²) 28P ❷ €28.10

🅿 Campsite signposted in Sauveterre-la-Lémance. Follow road over railway to the left. Campsite is located about 3 km past the village towards Loubejac.

💬 The Baudot family welcomes you to a park around an old mill in the south of the Périgord Noir. Lovely pitches in the sun or in shade, a natural spring lake with a beach, plenty of peace and quiet: an ideal campsite for relaxing. From here you can visit the many attractions of the Dordogne and the Lot.

CC 12/5-5/7 23/8-21/9 7=6

🔺 N 44°35'26'' E 1°2'52''
www.eurocampings.co.uk/100470

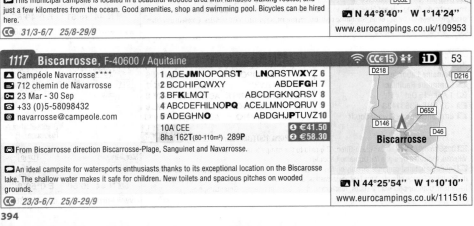

1116 Bias, F-40170 / Aquitaine

📶 CCε13 iD 53

🔺 Camping Municipal Le Tatiou***
🏠 route de Lespecier
📅 31 Mar - 30 Sep
☎ +33 (0)5-58090476
@ camping-le-tatiou@bias40.fr

1 ADE**JM**NOPQRST	ABFG 6
2 BPQVWX	ABDE**FG**H 7
3 BEF**IK**LMNQ	ABCDEFKNRSV 8
4 BCDFHILNO	ABEFKUV 9
5 ACDEFGHJKLMN**O**	ABJNOTUVZ10

10A CEE ❶ €23.80
10ha 222T(100m²) 157P ❷ €30.00

🅿 A10 to Labouheyre then D626 towards Mimizan, from there to Bias where the campsite is signposted.

💬 This municipal campsite is located in a beautiful wooded area with fantastic walking routes, and just a few kilometres from the ocean. Good amenities, shop and swimming pool. Bicycles can be hired here.

CC 31/3-6/7 25/8-29/9

🔺 N 44°8'40'' W 1°14'24''
www.eurocampings.co.uk/109953

1117 Biscarrosse, F-40600 / Aquitaine

📶 CCε15 ♟ iD 53

🔺 Campéole Navarrosse****
🏠 712 chemin de Navarrosse
📅 23 Mar - 30 Sep
☎ +33 (0)5-58098432
@ navarrosse@campeole.com

1 ADE**JM**NOPQRS**T**	LNQRSTWXYZ 6
2 BCDHIPQWXY	ABDE**FG**H 7
3 BF**K**LMQT	ABCDFGKNQRSV 8
4 ABCDEFHILNO**PQ**	ACEJLMNOPQRUV 9
5 ADEGHN**O**	ABDGHJ**P**TUVZ10

10A CEE ❶ €41.50
8ha 162T(80-110m²) 289P ❷ €58.30

🅿 From Biscarrosse direction Biscarrosse-Plage, Sanguinet and Navarrosse.

💬 An ideal campsite for watersports enthusiasts thanks to its exceptional location on the Biscarrosse lake. The shallow water makes it safe for children. New toilets and spacious pitches on wooded grounds.

CC 23/3-6/7 25/8-29/9

🔺 N 44°25'54'' W 1°10'10''
www.eurocampings.co.uk/111516

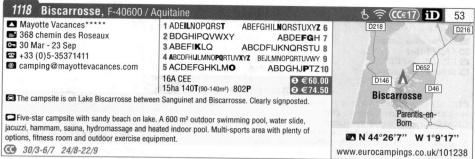

1118 Biscarrosse, F-40600 / Aquitaine

CC€17 iD 53

Mayotte Vacances*****
368 chemin des Roseaux
30 Mar - 23 Sep
+33 (0)5-35371411
camping@mayottevacances.com

1	ADE**IL**NOPQRS**T**	ABEFGHIL**N**QRSTUXY**Z**	6
2	BDGHIPQVWXY	ABDE**FG**H	7
3	ABEFI**K**LQ	ABCDFIJKNQRSTU	8
4	ABCDFHI**J**LMNO**PQ**RTUV**XYZ**	BEJLMNOPQRTUVWY	9
5	ACDEFGHKLM**O**	ABDGHJ**P**TZ	10

16A CEE
15ha 140T(90-140m²) 802P
❶ €60.00
❷ €74.50

The campsite is on Lake Biscarrosse between Sanguinet and Biscarrosse. Clearly signposted.

Five-star campsite with sandy beach on lake. A 600 m² outdoor swimming pool, water slide, jacuzzi, hammam, sauna, hydromassage and heated indoor pool. Multi-sports area with plenty of options, fitness room and outdoor exercise equipment.

CC 30/3-6/7 24/8-22/9

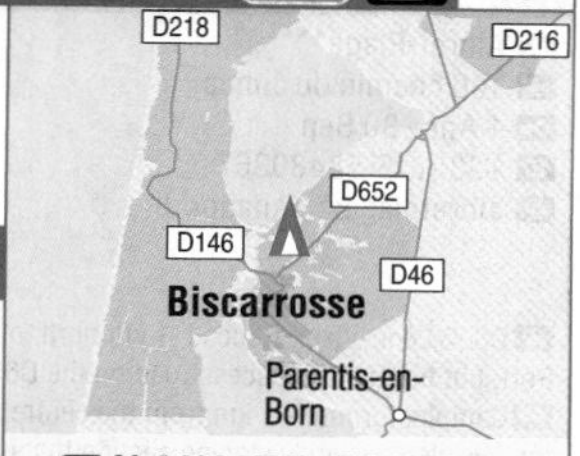

N 44°26'7" W 1°9'17"
www.eurocampings.co.uk/101238

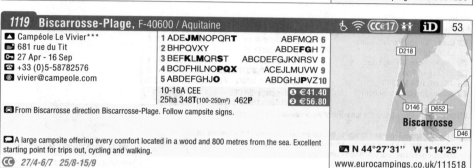

1119 Biscarrosse-Plage, F-40600 / Aquitaine

CC€17 iD 53

Campéole Le Vivier***
681 rue du Tit
27 Apr - 16 Sep
+33 (0)5-58782576
vivier@campeole.com

1	ADE**JM**NOPQR**T**	ABFMQR	6
2	BHPQVXY	ABDE**FG**H	7
3	BEF**KLM**QR**S**T	ABCDEFGJKNRSV	8
4	BCDFHILNO**PQX**	ACEJLMUVW	9
5	ABDEFGHJ**O**	ABDGHJ**P**VZ	10

10-16A CEE
25ha 348T(100-250m²) 462P
❶ €41.40
❷ €56.80

From Biscarrosse direction Biscarrosse-Plage. Follow campsite signs.

A large campsite offering every comfort located in a wood and 800 metres from the sea. Excellent starting point for trips out, cycling and walking.

CC 27/4-6/7 25/8-15/9

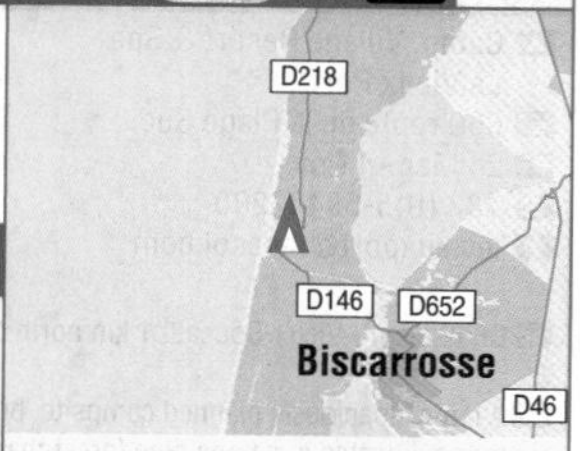

N 44°27'31" W 1°14'25"
www.eurocampings.co.uk/111518

1120 Biscarrosse-Plage, F-40600 / Aquitaine

CC€15 iD 53

Campéole Plage Sud***
230 rue des Bécasses
30 Mar - 14 Oct
+33 (0)5-58782124
plagesud@campeole.com

1	ADE**JL**NOPQRS**T**	ABFG	6
2	BPQVWXY	ABDE**FG**H	7
3	ABE**K**LQSTU	ABCDEFGIKNRSV	8
4	BCDFHILNO**PQ**U	BCEJLUVWY	9
5	ADEFGHL**O**	ABDFGHK**P**TUVZ	10

6-16A CEE
35ha 491T(70-110m²) 472P
❶ €42.40
❷ €57.60

From Biscarrosse direction Biscarrosse-Plage. Follow 'Plage-Sud' campsite signs.

A large campsite in a shaded wood. 800 metres from the sea and from the lively resort of Biscarrosse-Plage. Lovely heated swimming pool and water slide. Campsite completely renovated. Plenty of walking and cycling opportunities in the area.

CC 30/3-6/7 25/8-13/10

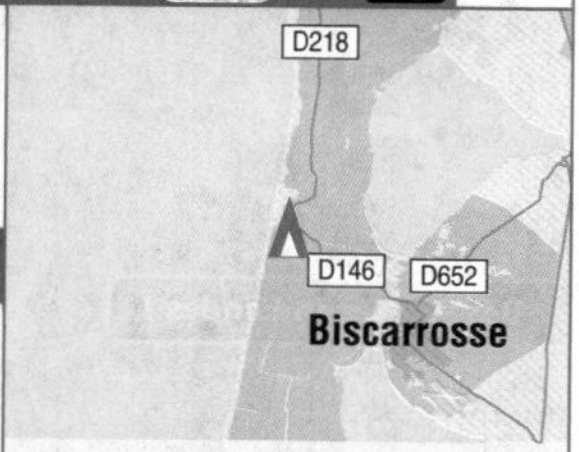

N 44°26'29" W 1°14'44"
www.eurocampings.co.uk/111517

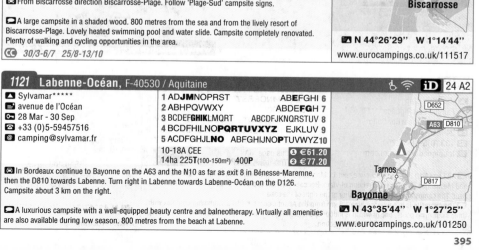

1121 Labenne-Océan, F-40530 / Aquitaine

iD 24 A2

Sylvamar*****
avenue de l'Océan
28 Mar - 30 Sep
+33 (0)5-59457516
camping@sylvamar.fr

1	AD**JM**NOPRST	AB**E**FGHI	6
2	ABHPQVWXY	ABDE**FG**H	7
3	BCDEF**GHIK**LMQRT	ABCDFJKNQRSTUV	8
4	BCDFHILNO**PQRTUVXYZ**	EJKLUV	9
5	ACDFGHJL**NO**	ABFGHIJNO**P**TUVWYZ	10

10-18A CEE
14ha 225T(100-150m²) 400P
❶ €61.20
❷ €77.20

In Bordeaux continue to Bayonne on the A63 and the N10 as far as exit 8 in Bénesse-Maremne, then the D810 towards Labenne. Turn right in Labenne towards Labenne-Océan on the D126. Campsite about 3 km on the right.

A luxurious campsite with a well-equipped beauty centre and balneotherapy. Virtually all amenities are also available during low season. 800 metres from the beach at Labenne.

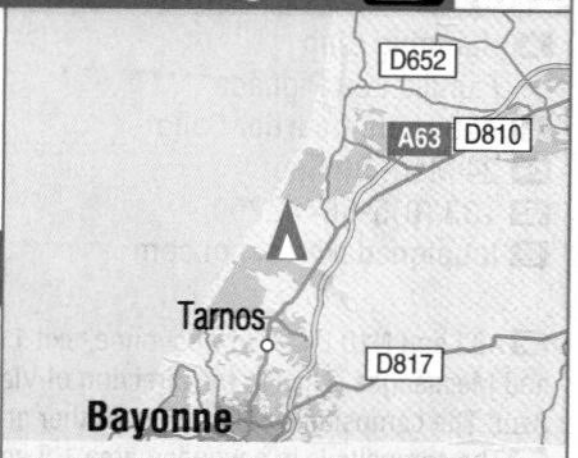

N 43°35'44" W 1°27'25"
www.eurocampings.co.uk/101250

France

1122 Messanges, F-40660 / Aquitaine

 ♿ 📶 (CC€15) iD 53

- 🏕 Albret-Plage***
- 🏠 100 chemin du Junca
- 📅 1 Apr - 30 Sep
- ☎ +33 (0)5-58480367
- @ albretplage@wanadoo.fr

1 ADJMNOQRST	KMNQR 6
2 BEHOPQRSVWXY	ABDEFGH 7
3 BEKLQ	ABCDEFKNORSV 8
4 BDFHINOPQ	EJK 9
5 ACDEFGHJLMNO	ABDFGHIJNOPTUVWZ 10

6A CEE   ❶ €28.50
6ha 117T(80-100m²) 241P   ❷ €35.90

🅿 D652 Léon-Vieux-Boucau, 1 km north of Vieux-Boucau. The campsite is situated next to Le Vieux Port, but has its own access road on the D652.

💬 Camping grounds 1 km from the centre of Vieux Boucau. The campsite is predominantly level but there is also a slightly sloping section that set in a pine forest. There is direct access to the Atlantic Ocean (300 metres). The swimming section of the beach has lifeguards.

CC 1/4-30/6   1/9-29/9

N 43°47'47''   W 1°24'4''
www.eurocampings.co.uk/100510

1123 Messanges, F-40660 / Aquitaine

 ♿ 📶 ✿ (CC€19) iD 53

- 🏕 Camp. Village Resort & Spa Le Vieux Port*****
- 🏠 850 route de la Plage Sud
- 📅 24 Mar - 4 Nov
- ☎ +33 (0)5-58482200
- @ levieuxport@resasol.com

1 ADJMNOPRST	ABEFGHIKMNQSX 6
2 BEHOPQRTVXY	ABDEFGHK 7
3 BDEFGHIKLMNQST	CDEFJKLMNQRSTUV 8
4 BDFHIJLNOPQRSTUVWXYZ	ABCEJKLUVW 9
5 ACDEFGHJLMNO	ABFGHIKLNPTVYZ 10

Ad on this page 6A CEE   ❶ €79.00
30ha 400T(100-120m²) 1120P   ❷ €92.80

🅿 D652 Léon - Vieux-Boucau, 1 km north of Vieux-Boucau. Well signposted.

💬 A large, spaciously planned campsite, but still peaceful as many of the facilities are near the reception. Located in a large pine forest that is divided into coloured zones, each with its own toilet facilities. Large leisure pool with heated swimming pool and slides.

CC 24/3-27/3   2/4-23/6   1/9-3/11

N 43°47'52''   W 1°24'4''
www.eurocampings.co.uk/103479

1124 Messanges, F-40660 / Aquitaine

 ♿ 📶 ✿ iD 53

- 🏕 Camping Club Famille Lou Pignada*****
- 🏠 460 route Quartier Caliot
- 📅 24 Mar - 30 Sep
- ☎ +33 (0)5-58482200
- @ loupignada@resasol.com

1 ADGJMNOPRST	ABEFGHI 6
2 BPQRVXY	ABDEFGH 7
3 BDEFKLMNQT	CDEFKNQRSTUV 8
4 BCDFHIKLNOPQRTUVXYZ	BEJKLUV 9
5 ACDEFGHLMO	ABGHIJNPVWZ 10

Ad on this page 6A   ❶ €72.00
8ha 10T(80-100m²) 482P   ❷ €85.80

🅿 A63 and N10 Bordeaux-Bayonne, exit 11 Magescq. In the centre continue in the direction of Azur and Messanges. Then in the direction of Vieux-Boucau. Turn left approx. 1.5 km before the centre of Azur. The campsite is 600 metres further at the right of the road.

💬 The campsite is in a wooded area 1.5 km from the Atlantic coast. It has a swimming complex with three swimming pools, one of which is indoor and heated (open from early May until late September), a fine restaurant and shop with a wide selection.

N 43°47'51''   W 1°22'55''
www.eurocampings.co.uk/103477

1125 Messanges, F-40660 / Aquitaine — 53 iD

- ▲ La Côte★★★★
- ▤ 361 chemin de la Côte
- ⌖ 1 Apr - 30 Sep
- ☎ +33 (0)5-58489494
- @ info@campinglacote.com

1 ADJMNOPRST	AFG	6
2 PVXY	ABDEFGH	7
3 BEFKLQ	CDEFKNQRSTUV	8
4 FHIOPU	EIKLUV	9
5 ABDFGMNO	ABDGHIJNPTUVW	10
6A	❶ €34.20	
3,5ha 113T(100-130m²) 55P	❷ €43.40	

🚗 In Bordeaux follow Bayonne A63 and D810 as far as exit 11 Magescq. In Magescq centre dir. Azur and Messanges. Then dir. Vieux-Boucau, D652. 2 km past centre of Messanges on the right.
🏕 A campsite on level ground with spacious shaded pitches. Ideal for families thanks to the playground, lovely swimming pool with toddlers' pool and bubble bath. The swimming complex is open from 15 May. Just 1 km to the Atlantic beaches.
CC 1/4-3/7 27/8-29/9

📍 N 43°48'1'' W 1°23'30''
www.eurocampings.co.uk/103478

1126 Messanges, F-40660 / Aquitaine — 53 iD

- ▲ Le Domaine de la Marina★★★★
- ▤ 400 route de la Plage Sud
- ⌖ 1 May - 16 Sep
- ☎ +33 (0)5-58482200
- @ domainedelamarina@resasol.com

1 ADJMNOPRT	CDFGIQTUV	6
2 HPQVWX	ABDEFGH	7
3 BEFGHIKLMQRT	ABCDEFKNQRSTU	8
4 BDTUVXZ	ELUV	9
5 ACDFGHJLN	ABHIKPVZ	10
Ad on page 396 8A CEE	❶ €51.00	
8ha 11T(100m²) 323P	❷ €64.10	

🚗 1 km north from Vieux-Boucau, near campsite Le Vieux Port.

🏕 Campsite with rental facilities on road to 'le Vieux Port'. Near sandy beaches. Well guarded. Pitches with little shadow. Next to a tiny holiday resort (mini golf, bouncy caslte, karts).Campers are allowed to participate in animation on 'Le Vieux Port' for free, but not the swimming pool.

📍 N 43°47'49'' W 1°23'44''
www.eurocampings.co.uk/111418

1127 Messanges, F-40660 / Aquitaine — 53 iD

- ▲ Les Acacias★★★
- ▤ 101 chemin du Houdin
- ⌖ 25 Mar - 15 Oct
- ☎ +33 (0)5-58480178
- @ lesacacias@lesacacias.com

1 ADEJMNOPRST		6
2 PQSVWXY	ABDEFGH	7
3 BEKLQ	ABCDFKNQRSTUV	8
4 BDFHILPQ	EFJKLV	9
5 ACDFGMNO	ABDFGHIJPTUVWZ	10
6-10A CEE	❶ €26.50	
3,4ha 74T(90-120m²) 56P	❷ €33.70	

🚗 A63 and N10 Bordeaux-Bayonne to exit 11 Magescq. Then direction Azur and Messanges. Then direction Vieux-Boucau. Left at roundabout 2 km before Messanges centre (Quartier Caliot road). Campsite 1 km further on the left.
🏕 Friendly family campsite about 2 km from the Atlantic coast. Although you are here in Les Landes, you will not be camping among pine trees. However there is sufficient shade. Very well maintained toilet facilities.
CC 25/3-6/7 25/8-14/10

📍 N 43°47'54'' W 1°22'33''
www.eurocampings.co.uk/101247

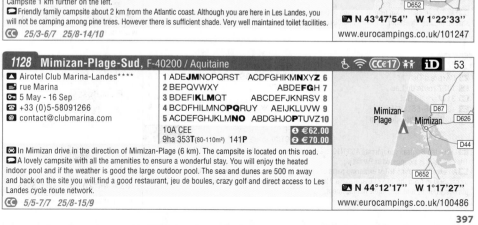

1128 Mimizan-Plage-Sud, F-40200 / Aquitaine — 53 iD

- ▲ Airotel Club Marina-Landes★★★★
- ▤ rue Marina
- ⌖ 5 May - 16 Sep
- ☎ +33 (0)5-58091266
- @ contact@clubmarina.com

1 ADEJMNOPQRST	ACDFGHIKMNXYZ	6
2 BEPQVWXY	ABDEFGH	7
3 BDEFIKLMQT	ABCDEFJKNRSV	8
4 BCDFHILMNOPQRUY	AEIJKLUVW	9
5 ACDEFGHJKLMNO	ABDGHJOPTUVZ	10
10A CEE	❶ €62.00	
9ha 353T(80-110m²) 141P	❷ €70.00	

🚗 In Mimizan drive in the direction of Mimizan-Plage (6 km). The campsite is located on this road.
🏕 A lovely campsite with all the amenities to ensure a wonderful stay. You will enjoy the heated indoor pool and if the weather is good the large outdoor pool. The sea and dunes are 500 m away and back on the site you will find a good restaurant, jeu de boules, crazy golf and direct access to Les Landes cycle route network.
CC 5/5-7/7 25/8-15/9

📍 N 44°12'17'' W 1°17'27''
www.eurocampings.co.uk/100486

France

1129 Moliets-Plage, F-40660 / Aquitaine   ♿ 🛜 (CCE17) iD 53

- ⛺ Le Saint Martin****
- 🏠 2655 avenue de l'Océan
- 📅 1 Apr - 28 Oct
- ☎ +33 (0)5-58485230
- @ contact@camping-saint-martin.fr

1 ADJ**M**NOPQRST	A**E**FGKM**N**QRS	6	
2 EFHPQTUVWXY	ABDE**FG**H	7	
3 BEF**K**LQ	CDFJKNRSTUV	8	
4 BCDFHILNO**PTUX**	BEFJKLUVW	9	
5 ACDEGHJLM**O**	ABDFGHIJ**NP**TUVYZ	10	

15A CEE
18ha 450T(80-150m²) 173P
❶ €50.40
❷ €56.70

🚗 From Bordeaux direction Bayonne over the A63 and N10. Take exit 'Castets' then direction Léon. Turn left just before the centre of Léon towards Messanges. In Moliets take the road to Moliets-Plage. Last campsite before the ocean.

🛏 The campsite has direct access to the Atlantic. You can use the outdoor pool, the heated indoor pool, sauna and bubble bath for free in the low season. Wifi is also free in this period.

CC 1/4-29/6 3/9-27/10

📍 N 43°51'9" W 1°23'13"

www.eurocampings.co.uk/103475

1130 Ondres, F-40440 / Aquitaine   ♿ 🛜 ✿ (CCE17) ♂♀ iD 24 A2

- ⛺ Du Lac*****
- 🏠 518 rue de Janin
- 📅 2 Mar - 31 Oct
- ☎ +33 (0)5-59452845
- @ contact@camping-du-lac.fr

1 ABD**I**LNOR**T**	ABFGI**N**	6	
2 ACDOPQTUVWX	ABDE**FG**H	7	
3 BL**MN**QT	ABCDEFGIJKNQRSTUV	8	
4 BCDHILO**TUVX**Y	AEJLUV	9	
5 ADEFHJL**NO**	ABDGHIJNPVZ	10	

10A CEE
3ha 60T(100-120m²) 66P
❶ €47.20
❷ €61.20

🚗 In Bordeaux direction Bayonne A63 as far as exit 7. Then take D810. Stay on D810 till about 1 km before Ondres centre. Take the road to the left to Ondres-Plage. Left at the 1st roundabout and follow the signs.

🛏 The touring pitches are between the swimming pool and a lovely little lake. The seasonal pitches are on another part of the campsite. Flemish-French owners.

CC 2/3-6/7 27/8-30/10

📍 N 43°33'56" W 1°27'12"

www.eurocampings.co.uk/110443

1131 Ondres, F-40440 / Aquitaine   ♿ 🛜 (CCE15) iD 24 A2

- ⛺ Lou Pignada****
- 🏠 741 avenue de la Plage
- 📅 28 Apr - 30 Sep
- ☎ +33 (0)5-59453065
- @ info@camping-loupignada.com

1 ADEF**JM**NOPQRST	ABFG	6	
2 ABPQVXY	ABDE**FG**H	7	
3 BEFLQ	ABCDFKNSV	8	
4 BDFHINO**PQ**U	EJUV	9	
5 ADEFGHJL**O**	ABHIJ**NP**TUV	10	

10A CEE
4,5ha 93T(80-120m²) 89P
❶ €43.20
❷ €51.20

🚗 A63 Bordeaux-Bayonne to exit 7. Then follow D810 till 1 km before Ondres centre. Then left to Ondres-Plage. Campsite 3 km on the left.

🛏 Family campsite 2 km from the beach of Ondres-Plage. Heated swimming pool. Spacious and shaded pitches. Hossegor, Bayonne and Biarritz are nearby.

CC 28/4-7/7 25/8-29/9

📍 N 43°34'10" W 1°27'39"

www.eurocampings.co.uk/100516

1132 Parentis-en-Born, F-40160 / Aquitaine   ♿ 🛜 (CCE13) iD 53

- ⛺ L'Arbre d'Or****
- 🏠 1037 route du Lac
- 📅 31 Mar - 30 Oct
- ☎ +33 (0)5-58784156
- @ contact@arbre-dor.com

1 ADEJMNOPQRST	ABCDF**N**OXYZ	6	
2 PQVWXY	ABDE**FG**H	7	
3 BE**K**LQ	ABCDEFKNQRSV	8	
4 BCDFHILNO**PU**Y	EFJLRVW	9	
5 ABDEFGHJKLM**NO**	ABDGHIJO**P**TUV	10	

10A CEE
5ha 109T(90-120m²) 101P
❶ €29.90
❷ €40.75

🚗 Leave the Bordeaux motorway A63/N10 in Liposthey and drive towards Parentis (D43). The campsite is signposted in Parentis.

🛏 An excellent campsite for exploring parts of Landes in the early or late season on foot, by bike or by car. 500 m from the lake of Biscarrosse. Heated indoor swimming pool with jacuzzi and spacious pitches. Friendly and hospitable management.

CC 31/3-6/7 25/8-29/10 14=13

📍 N 44°20'46" W 1°5'35"

www.eurocampings.co.uk/100482

1133 Sanguinet, F-40460 / Aquitaine ♿ 🛜 (CC€15) ♀♂ iD 53

- ⛺ Campéole Le Lac de Sanguinet***
- 📧 526 rue de Pinton
- 📅 30 Mar - 30 Sep
- ☎ +33 (0)5-58827080
- @ lac-sanguinet@campeole.com

1 ADE**JM**NOPQRS**T**	ABFGL**N**QRSTUVX**Y** 6
2 DHIPQVWXY	BEF**GH** 7
3 BFLQTU	BDFGKNRSV 8
4 BCDFHILNO**PQX**Y	EFJLMNOPQRT 9
5 ABDEFGHJKN**O**	ABDGHJMP**V**Z 10

10A CEE — ❶ €40.30
10,6ha 147**T**(80-150m²) 193**P** — ❷ €56.40

🚗 A10, exit Arcachon. Follow d'Arcachon road. Exit Mios/Biscarrosse, then direction Sanguinet. Campsite in Sanguinet by the lake. Signposted.
💬 Family campsite near the welcoming village of Sanguinet in the heart of the Landes forests. Quiet location on the shore of one of the most beautiful and largest lakes in Europe. Direct access to a sandy beach.
CC 30/3-6/7 25/8-29/9

N 44°28'53'' W 1°5'36''
www.eurocampings.co.uk/114301

1134 Sanguinet, F-40460 / Aquitaine ♿ 🛜 (CC€17) iD 53

- ⛺ Les Grands Pins*****
- 📧 1039 avenue de Losa
- 📅 31 Mar - 16 Sep
- ☎ +33 (0)5-58786174
- @ info@campinglesgrandspins.com

1 ADE**JM**NOPRS**T**	ABCDFGHL**N**QRSTUX**Y** 6
2 DHIPQVWXY	ABDE**FG** 7
3 ABDEF**KLM**Q	ABCDEFIJKNPRSV 8
4 BCDFHILO**PQ**	EMOPQTUV 9
5 ACDEGHJKL**NO**	ABDGHJ**P**VZ 10

10A CEE — ❶ €49.50
8ha 65**T**(80-130m²) 431**P** — ❷ €70.80

🚗 The campsite is located in Sanguinet. Clearly signposted and positioned by a lake.

💬 Campsite on sandy beach of Lake Sanguinet for a successful holiday in Landes. Outdoor pool and heated indoor pool. Various types of water recreation. Network of cycle paths.
CC 31/3-30/6 1/9-15/9

N 44°29'2'' W 1°5'24''
www.eurocampings.co.uk/100987

1135 St. Girons-Plage, F-40560 / Aquitaine ♿ 🛜 (CC€17) ♀♂ iD 53

- ⛺ Campéole Les Tourterelles***
- 📧 route de la Plage
- 📅 30 Mar - 30 Sep
- ☎ +33 (0)5-58479312
- @ tourterelles@campeole.com

1 AD**JM**NOPRS**T**	ABFGIKMQ 6
2 BEFHOPQTUVWXY	ABDE**FG**H 7
3 BDEFLQRT	ABCDFKNRSV 8
4 **A**BCDHLNO**PQU**X	AEFKLMUV 9
5 ADEFGHJ	ABDFGHIJ**NP**VZ 10

10-16A CEE — ❶ €42.70
20ha 460**T**(80-150m²) 302**P** — ❷ €56.90

🚗 In Bordeaux dir. Bayonne on the A63 and the N10 as far as exit 12 Castets. In Castets centre continue towards Linxe and St. Girons. Then towards St. Girons-Plage till almost at the beach. Campsite on the right.
💬 Campsite in Les Landes in a pine forest with two direct entrances to the beach. Spacious heated swimming facilities with a large paddling pool. Large camping pitches with space for an extra tent (must be paid for). Ideal location for surfers.
CC 30/3-6/7 25/8-29/9

N 43°57'16'' W 1°21'24''
www.eurocampings.co.uk/115029

1136 St. Girons-Plage, F-40560 / Aquitaine ♿ 🛜 (CC€19) iD 53

- ⛺ Eurosol****
- 📧 4756 route de la Plage
- 📅 8 May - 23 Sep
- ☎ +33 (0)5-58479014
- @ contact@camping-eurosol.com

1 ADF**IL**NOPRT	ACDFI 6
2 BPQTVXY	ABE**FG**H 7
3 BEF**IL**MQST	CDFKNQRSTUV 8
4 BCDFHILO**Q**	ABCEJKLMUVW 9
5 ACDEFGHJLM**NO**	ABDFGHIJ**L**PTUWZ 10

10A CEE — ❶ €42.30
18ha 322**T**(70-120m²) 180**P** — ❷ €59.30

🚗 In Bordeaux take dir. Bayonne A63 and N10 as far as exit 12 (Castets); in Castets centre keep in dir. Linxe and St. Girons. Then dir. St. Girons-Plage. Campsite located 5 km on the left of the road (D42).
💬 Located in an area with hills, run by French-Dutch management. At the reception there is a small square with a bar/restaurant and shop and swimming pools, one of which is indoors. You will camp under coniferous trees 600 m from the ocean.
CC 8/5-1/7 25/8-22/9 14=12, 21=17

N 43°57'6'' W 1°21'7''
www.eurocampings.co.uk/108472

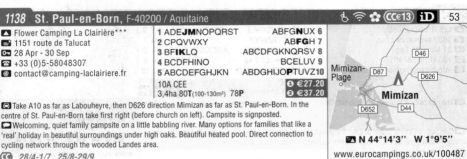

1137 St. Michel-Escalus, F-40550 / Aquitaine   ♿ 🛜 CC€15 iD   53

- 🏕 Huttopia Landes Sud***
- 🏠 450 route Léon
- 📅 4 May - 23 Sep
- ☎ +33 (0)5-58902630
- @ lac-leon@huttopia.com

1 ADE**IL**NOPR**T**	ABF	6
2 ABCPQVXY	ABDE**FG**	7
3 BFLQ	ABCDFNQRS	8
4 BCDIO	ACJV	9
5 ABDEFGHJK	ABGHJNOTU	10
10A	❶ €32.30	
133**T**(60-150m²) 46**P**	❷ €42.60	

🚗 From Bordeaux: A63, exit 12 (8 km).

🏕 Camp in Les Landes close to Le Lac Léon, a few kilometres from the ocean on completely renovated grounds in the middle of a beautiful forest. Enjoy the heated pools, grab a bite to eat at the Pizza Grill, play some beach volleyball, little ones will love the new playground... A new Huttopia destination, suitable for discovering the Les Landes heritage during a 100% natural stay!

CC 4/5-5/7 26/8-22/9

Vieux-Boucau-les-Bains

🧭 N 43°52'46'' W 1°14'5''

www.eurocampings.co.uk/122964

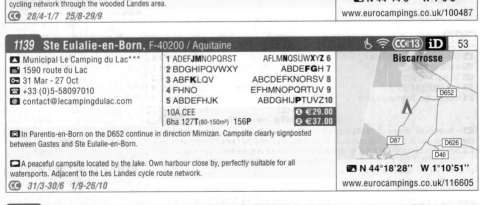

1138 St. Paul-en-Born, F-40200 / Aquitaine   ♿ 🛜 ✿ CC€13 iD   53

- 🏕 Flower Camping La Clairière***
- 🏠 1151 route de Talucat
- 📅 28 Apr - 30 Sep
- ☎ +33 (0)5-58048307
- @ contact@camping-laclairiere.fr

1 ADE**JM**NOPQRST	ABFG**N**UX	6
2 CPQVWXY	ABF**GH**	7
3 BF**IK**LQ	ABCDFGKNQRSV	8
4 BCDFHINO	BCELUV	9
5 ABCDEFGHJKN	ABDGHIJO**P**TUVZ	10
10A CEE	❶ €27.20	
3,4ha 80**T**(100-130m²) 78**P**	❷ €37.20	

🚗 Take A10 as far as Labouheyre, then D626 direction Mimizan as far as St. Paul-en-Born. In the centre of St. Paul-en-Born take first right (before church on left). Campsite is signposted.

🏕 Welcoming, quiet family campsite on a little babbling river. Many options for families that like a 'real' holiday in beautiful surroundings under high oaks. Beautiful heated pool. Direct connection to cycling network through the wooded Landes area.

CC 28/4-1/7 25/8-29/9

Mimizan-Plage

Mimizan

🧭 N 44°14'3'' W 1°9'5''

www.eurocampings.co.uk/100487

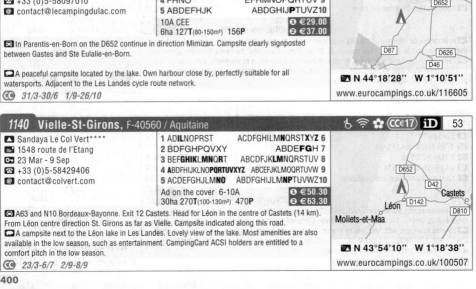

1139 Ste Eulalie-en-Born, F-40200 / Aquitaine   ♿ 🛜 CC€13 iD   53

- 🏕 Municipal Le Camping du Lac***
- 🏠 1590 route du Lac
- 📅 31 Mar - 27 Oct
- ☎ +33 (0)5-58097010
- @ contact@lecampingdulac.com

1 ADEF**JM**NOPQRST	AFLMNQSUW**XYZ**	6
2 BDGHIPQVWXY	ABDE**FG**H	7
3 ABF**K**LQV	ABCDEFKNORSV	8
4 FHNO	EFHMNOPQRTUV	9
5 ABDEFHJK	ABDGHIJ**P**TUVZ	10
10A CEE	❶ €29.00	
6ha 127**T**(80-150m²) 156**P**	❷ €37.00	

🚗 In Parentis-en-Born on the D652 continue in direction Mimizan. Campsite clearly signposted between Gastes and Ste Eulalie-en-Born.

🏕 A peaceful campsite located by the lake. Own harbour close by, perfectly suitable for all watersports. Adjacent to the Les Landes cycle route network.

CC 31/3-30/6 1/9-26/10

Biscarrosse

🧭 N 44°18'28'' W 1°10'51''

www.eurocampings.co.uk/116605

1140 Vielle-St-Girons, F-40560 / Aquitaine   ♿ 🛜 ✿ CC€17 iD   53

- 🏕 Sandaya Le Col Vert****
- 🏠 1548 route de l'Etang
- 📅 23 Mar - 9 Sep
- ☎ +33 (0)5-58429406
- @ contact@colvert.com

1 AD**I**LNOPRST	ACDFGHILMNQRST**XYZ**	6
2 BDFGHPQVXY	ABDE**FG**H	7
3 BEF**GHIK**LMNQRT	ABCDFJK**LM**NQRSTUV	8
4 A**B**DFHIJKLNO**PQRTUVXYZ**	ABCEFJKLMOQRTUVW	9
5 ACDEFGHJLM**NO**	ABDFGHIJLM**NP**TUVWZ	10
Ad on the cover 6-10A	❶ €50.30	
30ha 270**T**(100-130m²) 470**P**	❷ €63.30	

🚗 A63 and N10 Bordeaux-Bayonne. Exit 12 Castets. Head for Léon in the centre of Castets (14 km). From Léon centre direction St. Girons as far as Vielle. Campsite indicated along this road.

🏕 A campsite next to the Léon lake in Les Landes. Lovely view of the lake. Most amenities are also available in the low season, such as entertainment. CampingCard ACSI holders are entitled to a comfort pitch in the low season.

CC 23/3-6/7 2/9-8/9

Castets

Léon

Moliets-et-Maa

🧭 N 43°54'10'' W 1°18'38''

www.eurocampings.co.uk/100507

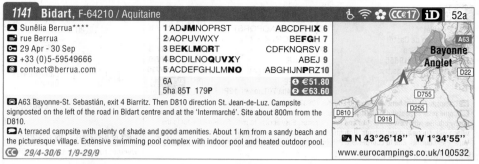

1141 Bidart, F-64210 / Aquitaine
52a

- ⛺ Sunêlia Berrua★★★★
- 🏠 rue Berrua
- 📅 29 Apr - 30 Sep
- ☎ +33 (0)5-59549666
- @ contact@berrua.com

1	ADJMNOPRST	ABCDFHIX 6
2	AOPUVWXY	BEFGH 7
3	BEKLMQRT	CDFKNQRSV 8
4	BCDILNOQUVXY	ABEJ 9
5	ACDEFGHJLMNO	ABGHIJNPRZ 10
6A		❶ €51.80
5ha 85T 179P		❷ €63.60

🚗 A63 Bayonne-St. Sebastián, exit 4 Biarritz. Then D810 direction St. Jean-de-Luz. Campsite signposted on the left of the road in Bidart centre and at the 'Intermarché'. Site about 800m from the D810.

💬 A terraced campsite with plenty of shade and good amenities. About 1 km from a sandy beach and the picturesque village. Extensive swimming pool complex with indoor pool and heated outdoor pool.

CC 29/4-30/6 1/9-29/9

📐 N 43°26'18'' W 1°34'55''

www.eurocampings.co.uk/100532

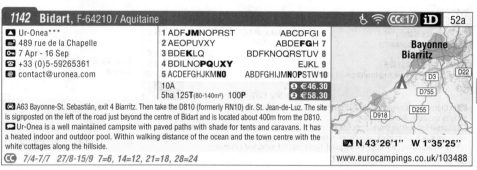

1142 Bidart, F-64210 / Aquitaine
52a

- ⛺ Ur-Onea★★★
- 🏠 489 rue de la Chapelle
- 📅 7 Apr - 16 Sep
- ☎ +33 (0)5-59265361
- @ contact@uronea.com

1	ADFJMNOPRST	ABCDFGI 6
2	AEOPUVXY	ABDEFGH 7
3	BDEKLQ	BDFKNOQRSTUV 8
4	BDILNOPQUXY	EJKL 9
5	ACDEFGHJKMNO	ABDFGHIJMNOPSTW 10
10A		❶ €46.30
5ha 125T(80-140m²) 100P		❷ €58.30

🚗 A63 Bayonne-St. Sebastián, exit 4 Biarritz. Then take the D810 (formerly RN10) dir. St. Jean-de-Luz. The site is signposted on the left of the road just beyond the centre of Bidart and is located about 400m from the D810.

💬 Ur-Onea is a well maintained campsite with paved paths with shade for tents and caravans. It has a heated indoor and outdoor pool. Within walking distance of the ocean and the town centre with the white cottages along the hillside.

CC 7/4-7/7 27/8-15/9 7=6, 14=12, 21=18, 28=24

📐 N 43°26'1'' W 1°35'25''

www.eurocampings.co.uk/103488

France

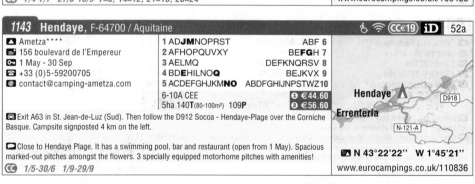

1143 Hendaye, F-64700 / Aquitaine
52a

- ⛺ Ametza★★★★
- 🏠 156 boulevard de l'Empereur
- 📅 1 May - 30 Sep
- ☎ +33 (0)5-59200705
- @ contact@camping-ametza.com

1	ADJMNOPRST	ABF 6
2	AFHOPQUVXY	BEFGH 7
3	AELMQ	DEFKNQRSV 8
4	BDEHILNOQ	BEJKVX 9
5	ACDEFGHJKMNO	ABDFGHIJNPSTWZ 10
6-10A CEE		❶ €44.60
5ha 140T(80-100m²) 109P		❷ €56.60

🚗 Exit A63 in St. Jean-de-Luz (Sud). Then follow the D912 Socoa - Hendaye-Plage over the Corniche Basque. Campsite signposted 4 km on the left.

💬 Close to Hendaye Plage. It has a swimming pool, bar and restaurant (open from 1 May). Spacious marked-out pitches amongst the flowers. 3 specially equipped motorhome pitches with amenities!

CC 1/5-30/6 1/9-29/9

📐 N 43°22'22'' W 1°45'21''

www.eurocampings.co.uk/110836

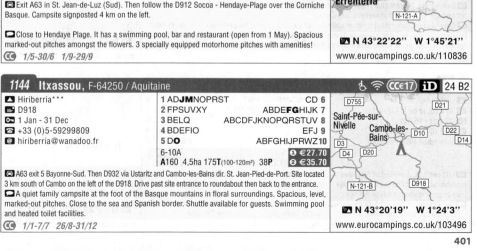

1144 Itxassou, F-64250 / Aquitaine
24 B2

- ⛺ Hiriberria★★★
- 🏠 D918
- 📅 1 Jan - 31 Dec
- ☎ +33 (0)5-59299809
- @ hiriberria@wanadoo.fr

1	ADJMNOPRST	CD 6
2	FPSUVXY	ABDEFGHIJK 7
3	BELQ	ABCDFJKNOPQRSTUV 8
4	BDEFIO	EFJ 9
5	DO	ABFGHIJPRWZ 10
6-10A		❶ €27.70
A160 4,5ha 175T(100-120m²) 38P		❷ €35.70

🚗 A63 exit 5 Bayonne-Sud. Then D932 via Ustaritz and Cambo-les-Bains dir. St. Jean-Pied-de-Port. Site located 3 km south of Cambo on the left of the D918. Drive past site entrance to roundabout then back to the entrance.

💬 A quiet family campsite at the foot of the Basque mountains in floral surroundings. Spacious, level, marked-out pitches. Close to the sea and Spanish border. Shuttle available for guests. Swimming pool and heated toilet facilities.

CC 1/1-7/7 26/8-31/12

📐 N 43°20'19'' W 1°24'3''

www.eurocampings.co.uk/103496

1145 Lestelle-Bétharram, F-64800 / Aquitaine ⚿ 🛜 ⒸⒸ€13 iD 54

- ▲ Le Saillet***
- 🏠 rue Soum de Castet
- 🗓 1 May - 30 Sep
- ☎ +33 (0)5-59719865
- @ le-saillet@orange.fr

1 ADE**JM**NOPQRST	AJ**N**UV 6
2 CFGOPVX	ABDE**FGH** 7
3 BELMQ	ABCDFHNOPRV 8
4 FHI**X**	JQRUV 9
5 DEFHJ**NO**	ABDGHIJLMORVW 10
10A CEE	❶ €20.50
A320 4ha 70T(100m²) 12P	❷ €26.30

🅿 Campsite located between Pau and Lourdes (D937). Signposted in village.
💬 Come relax in peaceful surroundings where you can hear the rushing water. Spacious shaded and sunny pitches with view of the river and Pre-Pyrenees. Easy access to river. 5 minutes' walk to the village with shops and restaurants. Beautiful walking and cycling options from the site, via the Voie Verte Pau-Lourdes. Bus to Lourdes and Pau (bus stop on village square). Free wifi.

ⒸⒸ 1/5-9/7 27/8-29/9 7=6, 14=10

📍 N 43°7'46'' W 0°12'24''

www.eurocampings.co.uk/110842

·1146 Oloron-Ste-Marie, F-64400 / Aquitaine ⚿ 🛜 ⒸⒸ€17 ⚐⚐ iD 24 B2

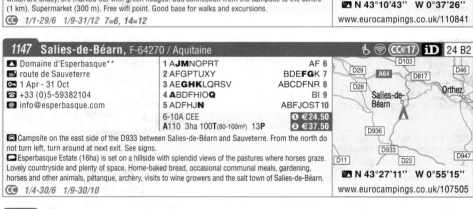

- ▲ Pyrénées Nature***
- 🏠 chemin de Lagravette
- 🗓 1 Jan - 31 Dec
- ☎ +33 (0)5-59391126
- @ camping.pyrenees.nature@gmail.com

1 ADE**JM**NOPRST	N 6
2 CFGOPVWY	ABDE**F**H 7
3 BELQ	ABCDFJNQRST 8
4 F	J 9
5 ABDEFHJMN**O**	ABDGHIJLOTUVW 10
10A CEE	❶ €23.10
A280 3,5ha 110T(80-130m²) 20P	❷ €27.10

🅿 In Oloron on the ringroad, follow signs 'poids lourds' towards Zaragoza or Col du Sampart. Follow signs to campsite. Avoid the centre.
💬 Situated just outside Oloron, this site still offers you all the relaxation you need. Pitches, many of which are shady, are marked out with green hedges. Bus connection from the campsite to the centre (1 km). Supermarket (300 m). Free wifi point. Good base for walks and excursions.

ⒸⒸ 1/1-29/6 1/9-31/12 7=6, 14=12

📍 N 43°10'43'' W 0°37'26''

www.eurocampings.co.uk/110841

1147 Salies-de-Béarn, F-64270 / Aquitaine ⚿ 🛜 ⒸⒸ€17 iD 24 B2

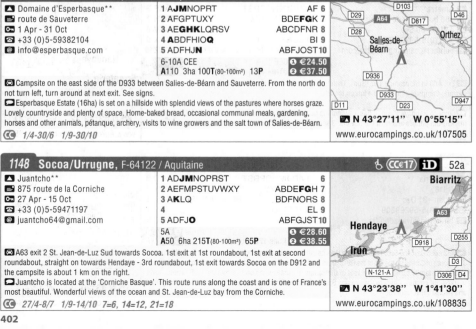

- ▲ Domaine d'Esperbasque**
- 🏠 route de Sauveterre
- 🗓 1 Apr - 31 Oct
- ☎ +33 (0)5-59382104
- @ info@esperbasque.com

1 A**JM**NOPRT	AF 6
2 AFGPTUXY	BDE**FGK** 7
3 AE**GHK**LQRSV	ABCDFNR 8
4 **A**BDFHIO**Q**	BI 9
5 ADFHJ**N**	ABFJOST 10
6-10A CEE	❶ €24.50
A110 3ha 100T(80-100m²) 13P	❷ €37.50

🅿 Campsite on the east side of the D933 between Salies-de-Béarn and Sauveterre. From the north do not turn left, turn around at next exit. See signs.
💬 Esperbasque Estate (16ha) is set on a hillside with splendid views of the pastures where horses graze. Lovely countryside and plenty of space. Home-baked bread, occasional communal meals, gardening, horses and other animals, pétanque, archery, visits to wine growers and the salt town of Salies-de-Béarn.

ⒸⒸ 1/4-30/6 1/9-30/10

📍 N 43°27'11'' W 0°55'15''

www.eurocampings.co.uk/107505

1148 Socoa/Urrugne, F-64122 / Aquitaine ⚿ ⒸⒸ€17 iD 52a

- ▲ Juantcho**
- 🏠 875 route de la Corniche
- 🗓 27 Apr - 15 Oct
- ☎ +33 (0)5-59471197
- @ juantcho64@gmail.com

1 AD**JM**NOPRST	6
2 AEFMPSTUVWXY	ABDE**FG**H 7
3 A**K**LQ	BDFNORS 8
4	EL 9
5 ADFJ**O**	ABFGJST 10
5A	❶ €28.60
A50 6ha 215T(80-100m²) 65P	❷ €38.55

🅿 A63 exit 2 St. Jean-de-Luz Sud towards Socoa. 1st exit at 1st roundabout, 1st exit at second roundabout, straight on towards Hendaye - 3rd roundabout, 1st exit towards Socoa on the D912 and the campsite is about 1 km on the right.
💬 Juantcho is located at the 'Corniche Basque'. This route runs along the coast and is one of France's most beautiful. Wonderful views of the ocean and St. Jean-de-Luz bay from the Corniche.

ⒸⒸ 27/4-8/7 1/9-14/10 7=6, 14=12, 21=18

📍 N 43°23'38'' W 1°41'30''

www.eurocampings.co.uk/108835

1149 St. Jean-de-Luz, F-64500 / Aquitaine ♿ 🛜 (CC€17) iD 52a

- ▲ Atlantica★★★★
- 🏠 15 ch. de Miquelenia-Quartier Acotz
- 📅 28 Mar - 1 Oct
- ☎ +33 (0)5-59477244
- @ atlantica@cielavillage.com

1 ADJMNOPRT	ABFGI 6
2 AEOPTUVWXY	ABDEFGH 7
3 BEIKLQ	DFNQRSTUV 8
4 BDHILNOPQRTUX	ABEKLVW 9
5 ABDEFGHJKNO	ABDGHIJLNPST 10
Ad on this page 6A	❶ €42.00
3,5ha 51T(80-120m²) 134P	❷ €55.00

🚗 A63 Bayonne-St. Sebastián, exit 3 St. Jean-de-Luz (Nord). D810 (formerly N10) direction Bayonne. Continue 1 km and take exit 'Acotz-plages'.

💬 You could not tell by looking at the entrance how lovely this campsite is. Hidden behind a hedge and a small wall is a lovely, heated swimming pool. An extended reception building houses a games room and a restaurant.

CC 28/3-6/7 26/8-30/9

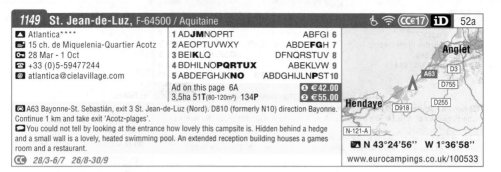

🧭 N 43°24'56" W 1°36'58"

www.eurocampings.co.uk/100533

France

1150 St. Jean-de-Luz, F-64500 / Aquitaine ♿ 🛜 (CC€17) iD 52a

- ▲ Bord de Mer★★★
- 🏠 71, chemin d'Erromardie
- 📅 31 Mar - 4 Nov
- ☎ +33 (0)5-59262461
- @ bord-de-mer64@orange.fr

1 AJMNOPRST	KMNPQX 6
2 AEFHMOPRVWX	ABEFGH 7
3 A	ABCDFNRSV 8
4	9
5 ABDEFGHJKO	ABDGHJPR 10
10A	❶ €37.20
1ha 62T(90-120m²)	❷ €53.20

🚗 A63 Bayonne-St. Sébastian, exit St. Jean-de-Luz (Nord). Then direction St. Jean-de-Luz on the D810 (formerly RN10). Just over 1 km turn right to Plage Erromardie. Follow road ± 2 km to the campsite on the left.

💬 A campsite with access to the beach at Erromardie. Borders the beach over a distance of 300 m. Stunning views of the ocean and mountains from the campsite. Less than 2 km from the centre of St. Jean-de-Luz.

CC 31/3-6/7 25/8-3/11

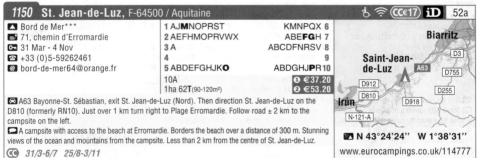

🧭 N 43°24'24" W 1°38'31"

www.eurocampings.co.uk/114777

1151 St. Jean-de-Luz, F-64500 / Aquitaine ♿ 🛜 (CC€15) iD 52a

- ▲ Flower Camping
  La Ferme Erromardie★★★★
- 🏠 40 chemin Erromardie
- 📅 17 Mar - 6 Oct
- ☎ +33 (0)5-59263426
- @ contact@camping-erromardie.com

1 ADEFJMNOPRST	CDFGKMNOPQX 6
2 AEHJKMOPVWXY	ABDEFGH 7
3 BFKLQ	CDEFKNOQRSV 8
4 BDHILNOY	CEUVW 9
5 ABDFGHJLNO	ABDEGHIJPSTZ 10
16A	❶ €38.20
2ha 110T(70-120m²) 55P	❷ €47.20

🚗 A63 Bordeaux-Bayonne-San Sébastian, exit 3 St. Jean-de-Luz Nord. Then direction St. Jean-de-Luz centre and after ± 1 km turn right to Plage Erromardie. Campsite then signposted.

💬 A campsite in three separate parts on the Plage d'Erromardie. Stretches out along the beach for a length of 300 m. The distance from some of the pitches to the sea is sometimes only 20 to 50 m. The grounds are about 2 km from the centre of St. Jean-de-Luz.

CC 17/3-6/7 25/8-5/10 7=6, 14=12, 21=18

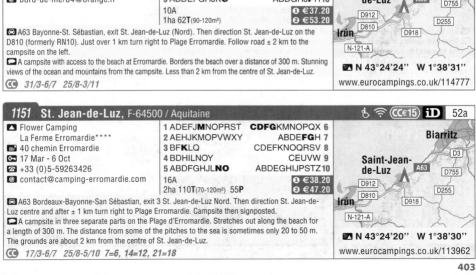

🧭 N 43°24'20" W 1°38'30"

www.eurocampings.co.uk/113962

1152 St. Jean-de-Luz, F-64500 / Aquitaine ♿ 🛜 (CC€15) iD | 52a

- 🏕 Inter-Plages★★★★
- 🏠 305 route des Plages-Acotz
- 🗓 1 Apr - 30 Sep
- ☎ +33 (0)5-59265694

1 A**I**LNOPR**T**	ABFKMNOPQS	6
2 AEFHJMPRSUVX	ABDE**F**H	7
3 B**K**LQ	BDEFJKNORSTUV	8
4 IO	EJUV	9
5 ACDEFGKM**NO**	AGHIJ**O**TUV	10

6-10A ❶ €42.90
1,5ha 63**T**(20-100m²) 28**P** ❷ €60.90

🚗 Bayonne - St. Jean-de-Luz motorway. Exit 3 St. Jean-de-Luz Nord towards Bayonne on the RD 810 to the Plages 'Acotz'. After entering the quartier Acotz turn left and follow this road to the campsite.

💬 As its name suggests, the site is located between two beaches. You will have a beautiful panoramic view of the Atlantic ocean. It is 3 km to St. Jean-de-Luz from the campsite. The pool is heated.

(CC) 1/4-20/6 18/9-29/9

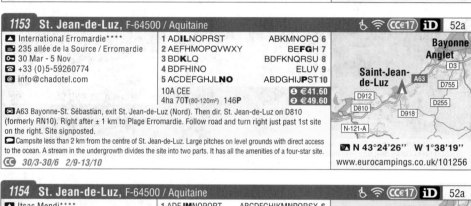

📍 N 43°24'54'' W 1°37'36''
www.eurocampings.co.uk/103491

1153 St. Jean-de-Luz, F-64500 / Aquitaine ♿ 🛜 (CC€17) iD | 52a

- 🏕 International Errormardie★★★★
- 🏠 235 allée de la Source / Erromardie
- 🗓 30 Mar - 5 Nov
- ☎ +33 (0)5-59260774
- @ info@chadotel.com

1 AD**I**LNOPRST	ABKMNOPQ	6
2 AEFHMOPQVWXY	BE**FG**H	7
3 BD**K**LQ	BDFKNQRSU	8
4 BDFHINO	ELUV	9
5 ACDEFGHJL**NO**	ABDGHIJ**P**ST	10

10A CEE ❶ €41.60
4ha 70**T**(80-120m²) 146**P** ❷ €49.60

🚗 A63 Bayonne-St. Sébastian, exit St. Jean-de-Luz (Nord). Then dir. St. Jean-de-Luz on D810 (formerly RN10). Right after ± 1 km to Plage Erromardie. Follow road and turn right just past 1st site on the right. Site signposted.

💬 Campsite less than 2 km from the centre of St. Jean-de-Luz. Large pitches on level grounds with direct access to the ocean. A stream in the undergrowth divides the site into two parts. It has all the amenities of a four-star site.

(CC) 30/3-30/6 2/9-13/10

📍 N 43°24'26'' W 1°38'19''
www.eurocampings.co.uk/101256

1154 St. Jean-de-Luz, F-64500 / Aquitaine ♿ 🛜 (CC€17) iD | 52a

- 🏕 Itsas Mendi★★★★
- 🏠 115 chemin de Duhartia-Acotz
- 🗓 22 Mar - 4 Nov
- ☎ +33 (0)5-59265650
- @ itsas@wanadoo.fr

1 ADE**JM**NOPQRT	ABCDFGHIKMNPQRSX	6
2 AEFHOPTUVXY	ABDE**FG**H	7
3 BDEF**K**LMQT	ABCDEFJKNQRSV	8
4 BCDFHILMNO**PQT**UXY	EKLUVW	9
5 ACDEFGHJLMN**O**	ABDGHIJ**N**PRVZ	10

Ad on this page 10A CEE ❶ €48.00
9ha 230**T**(80-100m²) 415**P** ❷ €59.20

🚗 N10 Bayonne-St. Jean-de-Luz. 3 km north of St. Jean-de-Luz exit 'Acötz-plages' (A63, exit 3 north).
💬 Come with family and friends and enjoy this campsite with its spacious shaded and half-shaded pitches separated by bushes and trees and 500 m from the Basque coast. There is a leisure pool in the middle of the campsite with a toddlers' pool, waterfalls, steam baths, slides, lawns and an indoor heated swimming pool with a jacuzzi.

(CC) 22/3-30/6 1/9-3/11 7=6, 14=12, 21=18

📍 N 43°24'50'' W 1°37'0''
www.eurocampings.co.uk/101257

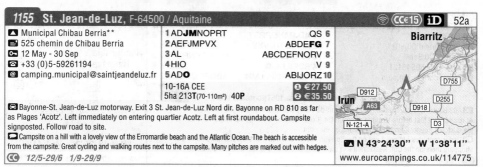

1155 St. Jean-de-Luz, F-64500 / Aquitaine

® CC€15 iD 52a

- ▲ Municipal Chibau Berria**
- ✉ 525 chemin de Chibau Berria
- ⌚ 12 May - 30 Sep
- ☎ +33 (0)5-59261194
- @ camping.municipal@saintjeandeluz.fr

1	ADJMNOPRT	QS 6
2	AEFJMPVX	ABDEFG 7
3	AL	ABCDEFNORV 8
4	HIO	V 9
5	ADO	ABIJORZ 10

10-16A CEE — ❶ €27.50
5ha 213T(70-110m²) 40P — ❷ €35.50

🚗 Bayonne-St. Jean-de-Luz motorway. Exit 3 St. Jean-de-Luz Nord dir. Bayonne on RD 810 as far as Plages 'Acotz'. Left immediately on entering quartier Acotz. Left at first roundabout. Campsite signposted. Follow road to site.

💬 Campsite on a hill with a lovely view of the Erromardie beach and the Atlantic Ocean. The beach is accessible from the campsite. Great cycling and walking routes next to the campsite. Many pitches are marked out with hedges.

CC 12/5-29/6 1/9-29/9

Biarritz

🏕 N 43°24'30" W 1°38'11"

www.eurocampings.co.uk/114775

1156 St. Jean-Pied-de-Port, F-64220 / Aquitaine

♿ ☏ CC€19 iD 24 B2

- ▲ Narbaïtz - Vacances Pyrénées Basques****
- ✉ route de Bayonne (Ascarat)
- ⌚ 5 May - 16 Sep
- ☎ +33 (0)5-59371013
- @ camping-narbaitz@wanadoo.fr

1	AJMNOPRST	ABFGN 6
2	CFPVXY	BDEFGH 7
3	ALQ	CDEFJKNQRSV 8
4	AEFILO	EJ 9
5	ABDEFHJKMNO	ABDGHIJPRW 10

10A — ❶ €40.80
A150 2,8ha 101T(80-140m²) 16P — ❷ €51.30

🚗 A63 exit 5 Bayonne-Sud. Then take the D932 via Ustaritz and Cambo-les-Bains to St. Jean-Pied-du-Port. The site is located on the right of a bend on the D918 2.5 km before the town of Ascarat.

💬 The campsite is on the route to St. Jean-Pied-de-Port, a well-known stop for pilgrims on their way to Santiago de Compostela. Hydrangea bushes are everywhere. The swimming pool is heated to 28°C the entire season. Cash-only payment when using CampingCard ACSI.

CC 5/5-7/7 25/8-15/9

🏕 N 43°10'39" W 1°15'34"

www.eurocampings.co.uk/110002

1157 St. Pée-sur-Nivelle, F-64310 / Aquitaine

♿ ☏ CC€15 iD 52a

- ▲ d'Ibarron***
- ✉ D918
- ⌚ 16 Apr - 1 Oct
- ☎ +33 (0)5-59541043
- @ camping.dibarron@wanadoo.fr

1	ADJMNOPRT	ABF 6
2	ACOPVWXY	ABDEFGH 7
3	BELQ	ABCDEFJKNOQRSV 8
4	FHIO	EV 9
5	ABDFGNO	ABFGHIJOPST 10

6-10A — ❶ €29.80
3ha 119T(80-130m²) 23P — ❷ €39.70

🚗 A63 exit 3 St. Jean-de-Luz Nord. Then D810 dir. St. Jean-de-Luz. Left just before the centre towards Ascain and St. Pée-sur-Nivelle. Site located 2 km before St. Pée by a roundabout and opposite Intermarché.

💬 Large, level, marked pitches at the foot of the Pyrenees. 8 km from the Spanish border and 10 km from the Atlantic coast at St. Jean-de-Luz. Beautiful heated swimming pool. Marked-out footpaths. Bus stop outside campsite.

CC 16/4-5/7 1/9-30/9

🏕 N 43°21'28" W 1°34'29"

www.eurocampings.co.uk/114779

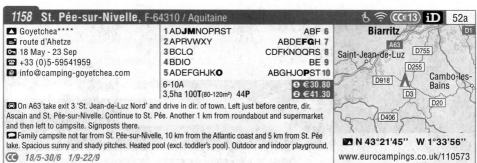

1158 St. Pée-sur-Nivelle, F-64310 / Aquitaine

♿ ☏ CC€13 iD 52a

- ▲ Goyetchea****
- ✉ route d'Ahetze
- ⌚ 18 May - 23 Sep
- ☎ +33 (0)5-59541959
- @ info@camping-goyetchea.com

1	ADJMNOPRST	ABF 6
2	APRVWXY	ABDEFGH 7
3	BCLQ	CDFKNOQRS 8
4	BDIO	BE 9
5	ADEFGHJKO	ABGHJOPST 10

6-10A — ❶ €30.80
3,5ha 100T(80-120m²) 44P — ❷ €41.30

🚗 On A63 take exit 3 'St. Jean-de-Luz Nord' and drive in dir. of town. Left just before centre, dir. Ascain and St. Pée-sur-Nivelle. Continue to St. Pée. Another 1 km from roundabout and supermarket and then left to campsite. Signposts show.

💬 Family campsite not far from St. Pée-sur-Nivelle, 10 km from the Atlantic coast and 5 km from St. Pée lake. Spacious sunny and shady pitches. Heated pool (excl. toddler's pool). Outdoor and indoor playground.

CC 18/5-30/6 1/9-22/9

Biarritz

🏕 N 43°21'45" W 1°33'56"

www.eurocampings.co.uk/110573

1159 Urrugne, F-64122 / Aquitaine   ♿ 🛜 CC€17 iD 52a

- ▲ Col d'Ibardin***
- 🏠 220 route d'Olhette
- 📅 1 Apr - 30 Sep
- ☎ +33 (0)5-59543121
- @ info@col-ibardin.com

1	ADJMNOPRST	ABF	6
2	AFPQRTUVXY	ABDEFGH	7
3	BDEKLQT	ABCDFKNRSTUV	8
4	BDEILNOQ	ABEJK	9
5	ACDEFGHJLMN	ABDFGIJNORWZ	10

6-10A   ❶ €43.00
A90   8ha 105T(80-100m²)   103P   ❷ €53.00

🚐 A63 Bayonne-St. Sébastian. Exit 2 St. Jean-de-Luz. D810 direction Urrugne/Hendaye.
At roundabout just before Urrugne direction D4 (Col D'Ibardin). Don't go up the hill, but turn left by
the customs house. Campsite 200 metres on the right.
💬 Under centuries-old oak trees on the Spanish border at the foot of the Col d'Ibardin. Bargain
shopping there on the Col. Restaurant and swimming pool with a splash pool for children.
CC 1/4-30/6   1/9-29/9

Hondarribia   Hendaye   A63   D918   D255   D3   N-121-A   D306   D4   D406

🏕 N 43°20'2'' W 1°41'5''
www.eurocampings.co.uk/103492

1160 Urrugne, F-64122 / Aquitaine   ♿ 🛜 CC€19 iD 52a

- 🌼 Flower camping de la Corniche****
- 🏠 chemin Antziola
- 📅 31 Mar - 30 Sep
- ☎ +33 (0)5-59200687
- @ contact@camping-corniche.com

1	ADEJMNOPRT	ABFGNOPQX	6
2	ABHJMOPTUVWXY	ABDEFGH	7
3	BEKLQS	ABCDEFGKNORS	8
4	BCDFHILNO	BE	9
5	ABDEFGHJLMNO	ABFGHIJORVZ	10

10A   ❶ €36.20
6ha 60T(80-120m²)   140P   ❷ €46.20

🚐 A63 Bordeaux to Spain exit 2, St. Jean-de-Luz Sud. Direction Socoa-Hendaye Plage on the D192.
At 3rd roundabout direction Hendaye Plage along the Corniche Basque. Campsite about 3 km on the
left in a small valley.
💬 A campsite on the Basque Corniche. Many marked-out and shaded pitches. Lovely views of the
Bay of Biscay in the Atlantic Ocean from the Corniche. Spain 6 km, San Sebastian 25 km.
CC 31/3-30/6   1/9-29/9   7=6, 14=12, 18=16, 21=18

Hendaye   A63   D912   D918   Irun   N-121-A   D406

🏕 N 43°22'37'' W 1°43'59''
www.eurocampings.co.uk/122728

1161 Urrugne, F-64122 / Aquitaine   ♿ 🛜 ✿ CC€17 iD 52a

- ▲ Larrouleta***
- 🏠 210 route de Socoa
- 📅 1 Jan - 31 Dec
- ☎ +33 (0)5-59473784
- @ info@larrouleta.com

1	ADEJMNOPRST	CDFLMNQ	6
2	ACDFGHOPRSVWXY	ABDEFGH	7
3	BDEKLMQST	ABCDFJKNQRSTUV	8
4	FIO	KLT	9
5	ACDEFHJLMNO	ABFGHIJNPR	10

Ad on this page   5-10A   ❶ €31.50
10ha 327T(80-120m²)   ❷ €45.00

🚐 From Bordeaux A63 dir. Bayonne-St.Sébastian exit 2 (St. Jean-de-Luz Sud). Then drive towards
the coast and the Corniche Basque. Take second on the left after the bridge then follow signs.
💬 The owner is a real, proud Basque. He can be proud of his campsite. The front part is less beautiful
than the back part. Here there are pleasant pitches by a small lake, with a quiet part for swimming,
sunbathing and fishing. There is also an indoor swimming pool!
CC 1/1-30/6   1/9-31/12

Hendaye   A63   Hondarribia   D918   D255   D3   N-121-A   D306   D4   D406

🏕 N 43°22'13'' W 1°41'10''
www.eurocampings.co.uk/103493

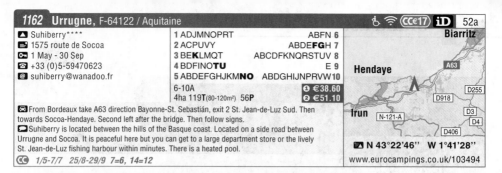

1162 Urrugne, F-64122 / Aquitaine ♿ 📶 (CC€17) iD 52a

▲ Suhiberry****
🏠 1575 route de Socoa
📅 1 May - 30 Sep
☎ +33 (0)5-59470623
@ suhiberry@wanadoo.fr

1 ADJMNOPRT	ABFN	6
2 ACPUVY	ABDE**FG**H	7
3 BE**K**LMQT	ABCDFKNQRSTUV	8
4 BDFINO**TU**	E	9
5 ABDEFGHJKM**NO**	ABDGHIJNPRVW	10

6-10A
4ha 119T(80-120m²) 56P

❸ €38.60
❷ €51.10

🗺 From Bordeaux take A63 direction Bayonne-St. Sebastián, exit 2 St. Jean-de-Luz Sud. Then towards Socoa-Hendaye. Second left after the bridge. Then follow signs.

🛏 Suhiberry is located between the hills of the Basque coast. Located on a side road between Urrugne and Socoa. It is peaceful here but you can get to a large department store or the lively St. Jean-de-Luz fishing harbour within minutes. There is a heated pool.

CC 1/5-7/7 25/8-29/9 7=6, 14=12

Biarritz
Hendaye A63
Irun N-121-A D918 D255 D3 D4
D406

📷 N 43°22'46'' W 1°41'28''
www.eurocampings.co.uk/103494

France

Rich land between the mountains

Comprising the regions Champagne-Ardenne, Lorraine and Alsace, Grand Est has a complicated history. The region borders Belgium, Luxembourg and Germany, with the Ardennes Mountains in the north and the Vosges Mountains in the southeast. There are still traces of past invaders, from the earliest farmers to the battlefields of World War II. See the famous Porte Mars arch in Reims that was built by the Romans, while the extensive military fortifications in Metz date from Classical Antiquity to the Maginot line in the 1930s.

History, culture, and adrenaline

Grand-Est has something for everyone: History buffs and culture vultures will adore historic towns such as Reims, Metz and Colmar, with soaring Gothic cathedrals, mediaeval castles and houses, and 20th-century battlefields, while adrenaline junkies will love the activities on offer in the region's many nature parks: complete with hiking, biking and horse-riding trails over mountain paths. Or try out the climbing tours, ziplines through the treetops and even parasailing and paragliding over the forests.

Fun for all the family

Grand-Est has so many places with activities guaranteed to keep the entire family happy: the Aqua Mundo waterpark at Hattigny; animals of the region at Musée Faune Lorraine in Xonrupt-Longemer; the fun side of science at Le Vaisseau Museum near Strasbourg; steam trains and locomotives at the Cite du Train in Mulhouse; toy trains and other toys at the Musée du Jouet en des petits train at Colmar; and tropical fish and other marine life at the Museum-Aquarium at Nancy.

A tradition of wine and food

When you think of Champagne in the Grand-Est region, you immediately think of bubbly wine. The Romans brought viticulture to this region and the soil and climate in the area are also perfect for the cultivation of Riesling, Sylvaner and Gewurztraminer grapes. Did you know that there is a vast network of tunnels and cellars under the city of Reims exclusively for champagne? Wine-tasting tours are offered in picturesque locations such as Mittelbergheim, Dambach and Riquewihr.

Local gastronomic specialities include Quiche Lorraine, the Macarons of Nancy, Alsace Flammekueche, choucroute paired with local pork sausages, the slow-cooked stew known as Baekeoffe, and of course the famous coq-au-vin – all of which are complimented by delicious local wines.

Our tips

1. *Parc Animalier de Sainte-Croix, Rhodes: wildlife park for families*
2. *The Museum of Beer in Stenay: everything about the craft of brewing*
3. *Musée de l'Outil et de la Pensée Ouvriere in Troyes*
4. *La Porte de la Craffe in Nancy, surrounded by cafés and shops*
5. *For art lovers: the Camille Claudel Museum in Nogent-sur-Seine*

1163 Buzancy, F-08240 / Champagne-Ardenne   ♿ 🛜 (CC€15) iD   15 B2

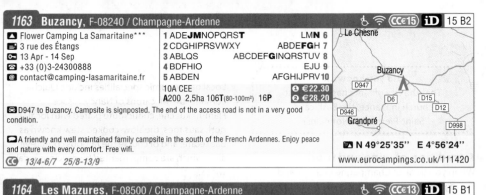

▲ Flower Camping La Samaritaine***
🏠 3 rue des Étangs
🕐 13 Apr - 14 Sep
☎ +33 (0)3-24300888
@ contact@camping-lasamaritaine.fr

1 ADE**JM**NOPQRS**T**	LM**N** 6	
2 CDG**H**IPRSVWXY	ABDE**FGH** 7	
3 ABLQS	ABCDEF**G**INQRSTUV 8	
4 BDFHIO	EJU 9	
5 ABDEN	AFGHIJPRV 10	
10A CEE	❶ €22.30	
A200 2,5ha 106T(80-100m²) 16P	❷ €28.20	

🚗 D947 to Buzancy. Campsite is signposted. The end of the access road is not in a very good condition.

💬 A friendly and well maintained family campsite in the south of the French Ardennes. Enjoy peace and nature with every comfort. Free wifi.

(CC) 13/4-6/7   25/8-13/9

Le Chesne

Buzancy

D947   D6   D15

D946   D12

Grandpré   D998

📷 N 49°25'35''   E 4°56'24''

www.eurocampings.co.uk/111420

1164 Les Mazures, F-08500 / Champagne-Ardenne   ♿ 🛜 (CC€13) iD   15 B1

▲ Du Lac des Vieilles Forges***
🕐 7 Apr - 16 Sep
☎ +33 (0)3-24401731
@ campinglesvieillesforges@
homair.com

1 AD**IL**NOPQRST	LMN**Q**SXY**Z** 6	
2 BDHRSTUVXY	BE**FG** 7	
3 BELMQ	BDFNR 8	
4 BCFILNO	ELU 9	
5 ADEJN	ABGHKO**P**RVZ 10	
10A CEE	❶ €20.10	
A300 12ha 200T(80-100m²) 76P	❷ €29.10	

🚗 Lac des Vieilles Forges is signposted on the D40 from Renwez to Les Mazures/Revin.

💬 A terraced campsite located in a wood and by a reservoir where you can go swimming, surfing, sailing and fishing. Spacious marked-out pitches on paved surfaces.

(CC) 7/4-7/7   2/9-15/9

N964   Revin

D877   D988   D1

N51   Bogny-sur-
D8043   Meuse

D985   N43   Nouzonville
D978   D2   D989

📷 N 49°52'21''   E 4°36'18''

www.eurocampings.co.uk/101171

1165 Arrigny, F-51290 / Champagne-Ardenne   🛜 (CC€15) iD   15 B2

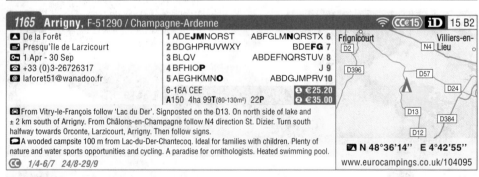

▲ De la Forêt
🏠 Presqu'île de Larzicourt
🕐 1 Apr - 30 Sep
☎ +33 (0)3-26726317
@ laforet51@wanadoo.fr

1 ADE**JM**NORST	ABFGLM**N**QRSTX 6	
2 BDG**H**PRUVWXY	BDE**FG** 7	
3 BLQV	ABDEFNQRSTUV 8	
4 BFHIO**P**	J 9	
5 AEGHKMN**O**	ABDGJMPRV 10	
6-16A CEE	❶ €25.20	
A150 4ha 99T(80-130m²) 22P	❷ €35.00	

🚗 From Vitry-le-François follow 'Lac du Der'. Signposted on the D13. On north side of lake and ± 2 km south of Arrigny. From Châlons-en-Champagne follow N4 direction St. Dizier. Turn south halfway towards Orconte, Larzicourt, Arrigny. Then follow signs.

💬 A wooded campsite 100 m from Lac-du-Der-Chantecoq. Ideal for families with children. Plenty of nature and water sports opportunities and cycling. A paradise for ornithologists. Heated swimming pool.

(CC) 1/4-6/7   24/8-29/9

Frignicourt   Villiers-en-
D2   N4 Lieu

D396   D57   D24

D13   D384

D12

📷 N 48°36'14''   E 4°42'55''

www.eurocampings.co.uk/104095

1166 Châlons-en-Champagne, F-51000 / Champagne-Ardenne   ♿ 🛜 (CC€15) iD   15 B2

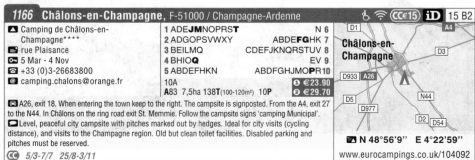

▲ Camping de Châlons-en-
Champagne****
🏠 rue Plaisance
🕐 5 Mar - 4 Nov
☎ +33 (0)3-26683800
@ camping.chalons@orange.fr

1 ADE**JM**NOPRS**T**	N 6	
2 ADGOPSVWXY	ABDE**FG**HK 7	
3 BEILMQ	CDEFJKNQRSTUV 8	
4 BHIO**Q**	EV 9	
5 ABDEFHKN	ABDFGHJMO**P**R 10	
10A	❶ €23.90	
A83 7,5ha 138T(100-120m²) 10P	❷ €29.70	

🚗 A26, exit 18. When entering the town keep to the right. The campsite is signposted. From the A4, exit 27 to the N44. In Châlons on the ring road exit St. Memmie. Follow the campsite signs 'camping Municipal'.

💬 Level, peaceful city campsite with pitches marked out by hedges. Ideal for city visits (cycling distance), and visits to the Champagne region. Old but clean toilet facilities. Disabled parking and pitches must be reserved.

(CC) 5/3-7/7   25/8-3/11

D1   A4

Châlons-en-
Champagne   D3

D933 A26

D5   N44

D977

D2   D54

📷 N 48°56'9''   E 4°22'59''

www.eurocampings.co.uk/104092

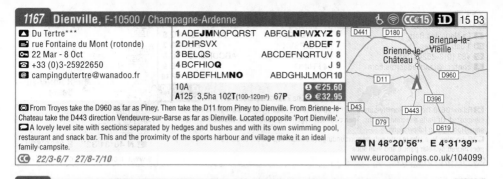

1167 Dienville, F-10500 / Champagne-Ardenne
♿ 🛜 CCe15 iD 15 B3

- 🏕 Du Tertre***
- ✉ rue Fontaine du Mont (rotonde)
- 📅 22 Mar - 8 Oct
- ☎ +33 (0)3-25922650
- @ campingdutertre@wanadoo.fr

1 ADE**JM**NOPQRST	ABFGL**N**PW**XYZ**	6
2 DHPSVX	ABDE**F**	7
3 BELQS	ABCDEFNQRTUV	8
4 BCFHIO**Q**	J	9
5 ABDEFHLM**NO**	ABDGHIJLMOR	10

10A · ❶ €25.60
A125 3,5ha 102T(100-120m²) 67P · ❷ €32.95

🚗 From Troyes take the D960 as far as Piney. Then take the D11 from Piney to Dienville. From Brienne-le-Chateau take the D443 direction Vendeuvre-sur-Barse as far as Dienville. Located opposite 'Port Dienville'.
💬 A lovely level site with sections separated by hedges and bushes and with its own swimming pool, restaurant and snack bar. This and the proximity of the sports harbour and village make it an ideal family campsite.
CC 22/3-6/7 27/8-7/10

📷 N 48°20'56'' E 4°31'39''
www.eurocampings.co.uk/104099

1168 Géraudot-Plage, F-10220 / Champagne-Ardenne
♿ 🛜 CCe15 ♟♟ iD 15 B3

- 🏕 Les Rives du Lac/L'Epine aux Moines**
- ✉ rue de Fort St. Georges, RD43
- 📅 2 Jan - 23 Dec
- ☎ +33 (0)3-25412436
- @ camping.lepineauxmoines@orange.fr

1 ADE**JM**NOPQRST	LMNQS**X**Y	6
2 DGHIPRSVWXY	ABDE**FG**	7
3 B**IKLMQT**	BDFJNORV	8
4 FH	EFPQRTUV	9
5 ABDEFGHJKM**NO**	ABDFGHJLM**P**QRV	10

10A · ❶ €27.20
3,5ha 156T(80-150m²) 18P · ❷ €36.60

🚗 From Troyes D960 dir. Piney. In or before Piney exit towards Geraudot. From the D619 Troyes - Bar-sur-Aube dir. north, take the D1 in Lusigny or the D79/D43 in Vendeuvre to Geraudot. Located on the north side of Lac d'Orient.
💬 Convivial family site with pitches more or less separated by the trees. Good toilet facilities. Separate section for teenagers. Close to a lovely (patrolled) beach, also suitable for small children. Cycling possible close by.
CC 2/1-5/7 23/8-22/12

📷 N 48°18'10'' E 4°20'15''
www.eurocampings.co.uk/100281

1169 Mesnil-St-Père, F-10140 / Champagne-Ardenne
♿ 🛜 CCe17 iD 15 B3

- 🏕 Camping Le Lac D'Orient****
- ✉ 17 rue du Lac
- 📅 7 Apr - 22 Sep
- ☎ +33 (0)3-25406185
- @ info@camping-lacdorient.com

1 ADE**JM**NOPQRST	ABEFGHLNQRST**XYZ**	6
2 DGHPRSVWXY	ABDE**FGH**	7
3 BELST	ABCDEFJKNQRSTUV	8
4 BDFHILO	EJ	9
5 ABDFGHJK**O**	ABDFGHIJMNO**PR**	10

10A CEE · ❶ €36.00
A165 4ha 160T(80-160m²) 38P · ❷ €49.00

🚗 From the D619 Troyes - Bar-sur-Aube, D43 dir. North (between La Villeneuve-au-Chêne and Lusigny-sur-Barce) to Mesnil-St-Père. Located on the south side of the Lac d'Orient, on the D43.
💬 Large, beautiful campsite on even grounds with parts marked out with hedges and bushes. Restaurant and indoor and outdoor pools. Close to a beautiful beach and little marina. Options and facilities for water freaks, outdoor enthusiasts, anglers and nature lovers.
CC 7/4-5/7 23/8-21/9 7=6

📷 N 48°15'48'' E 4°20'48''
www.eurocampings.co.uk/111772

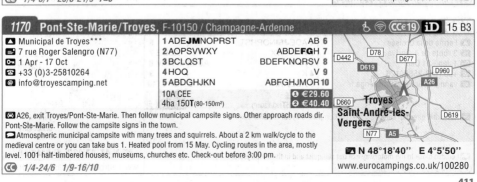

1170 Pont-Ste-Marie/Troyes, F-10150 / Champagne-Ardenne
♿ 🛜 CCe19 iD 15 B3

- 🏕 Municipal de Troyes***
- ✉ 7 rue Roger Salengro (N77)
- 📅 1 Apr - 17 Oct
- ☎ +33 (0)3-25810264
- @ info@troyescamping.net

1 ADE**JM**NOPRST	AB	6
2 AOPSVWXY	ABDE**FGH**	7
3 BCLQST	BDEFKNQRSV	8
4 HOQ	V	9
5 ABDGHJKN	ABFGHJMOR	10

10A CEE · ❶ €29.60
4ha 150T(80-150m²) · ❷ €40.40

🚗 A26, exit Troyes/Pont-Ste-Marie. Then follow municipal campsite signs. Other approach roads dir. Pont-Ste-Marie. Follow the campsite signs in the town.
💬 Atmospheric municipal campsite with many trees and squirrels. About a 2 km walk/cycle to the medieval centre or you can take bus 1. Heated pool from 15 May. Cycling routes in the area, mostly level. 1001 half-timbered houses, museums, churches etc. Check-out before 3:00 pm.
CC 1/4-24/6 1/9-16/10

📷 N 48°18'40'' E 4°5'50''
www.eurocampings.co.uk/100280

France

1171 St. Hilaire-sous-Romilly, F-10100 / Champagne-Ardenne   ♿ 📶 ✿ CC€17 iD 15 A2

La Noue des Rois****
1 Jan - 31 Dec
+33 (0)3-25244160
contact@lanouedesrois.com

1 ADILNOPRST	ABCDFGHNQ	6
2 DGIPSVX	ABDEFG	7
3 ABEILMQ	ABCDFIJNORTU	8
4 FHINO	E	9
5 ABDEH	ABFGHIJLOR	10
16A	❶ €32.00	
A73 30ha 70T(120-200m²) 180P	❷ €45.00	

Follow D619 Troyes - Romilly-sur-Seine. Follow St. Hilaire-sous-Romilly. Campsite is clearly signposted. Or Paris direction Provins. Then direction Nogent-sur-Seine. Then direction St. Hilaire-sous-Romilly and follow signs.

Relaxation by a lake in very natural surroundings (30 hectares). Indoor and outdoor swimming pool heated by solar panels and with slide

CC 1/1-1/7 31/8-31/12

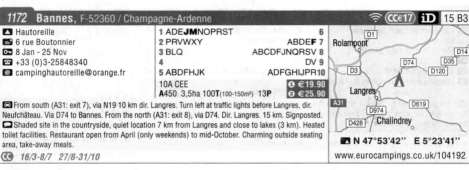

N 48°31'32'' E 3°39'53''

www.eurocampings.co.uk/117707

1172 Bannes, F-52360 / Champagne-Ardenne   📶 CC€17 iD 15 B3

Hautoreille
6 rue Boutonnier
8 Jan - 25 Nov
+33 (0)3-25848340
campinghautoreille@orange.fr

1 ADEJMNOPRST		6
2 PRVWXY	ABDEF	7
3 BLQ	ABCDFJNQRSV	8
4	DV	9
5 ABDFHJK	ADFGHIJPR	10
10A CEE	❶ €19.90	
A450 3,5ha 100T(100-150m²) 13P	❷ €25.90	

From south (A31: exit 7), via N19 10 km dir. Langres. Turn left at traffic lights before Langres, dir. Neufchâteau. Via D74 to Bannes. From the north (A31: exit 8), via D74. Dir. Langres. 15 km. Signposted.

Shaded site in the countryside, quiet location 7 km from Langres and close to lakes (3 km). Heated toilet facilities. Restaurant open from April (only weekends) to mid-October. Charming outside seating area, take-away meals.

CC 16/3-8/7 27/8-31/10

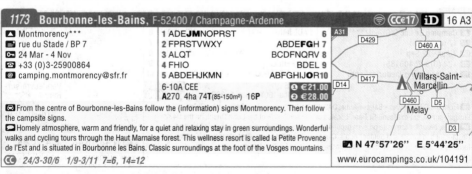

N 47°53'42'' E 5°23'41''

www.eurocampings.co.uk/104192

1173 Bourbonne-les-Bains, F-52400 / Champagne-Ardenne   📶 CC€17 iD 16 A3

Montmorency***
rue du Stade / BP 7
24 Mar - 4 Nov
+33 (0)3-25900864
camping.montmorency@sfr.fr

1 ADEJMNOPRST		6
2 FPRSTVWXY	ABDEFGH	7
3 ALQT	BCDFNQRV	8
4 FHIO	BDEL	9
5 ABDEHJKMN	ABFGHIJOR	10
6-10A CEE	❶ €21.00	
A270 4ha 74T(85-150m²) 16P	❷ €28.00	

From the centre of Bourbonne-les-Bains follow the (information) signs Montmorency. Then follow the campsite signs.

Homely atmosphere, warm and friendly, for a quiet and relaxing stay in green surroundings. Wonderful walks and cycling tours through the Haut Marnaise forest. This wellness resort is called la Petite Provence de l'Est and is situated in Bourbonne les Bains. Classic surroundings at the foot of the Vosges mountains.

CC 24/3-30/6 1/9-3/11 7=6, 14=12

N 47°57'26'' E 5°44'25''

www.eurocampings.co.uk/104191

1174 Flagey, F-52250 / Champagne-Ardenne   ♿ 📶 CC€15 iD 15 B3

Ferme de la Croisée
3 route de Auberive
1 Jan - 31 Dec
+33 (0)3-25880126
yannick.durenne52@orange.fr

1 ADEJMNOPRST		6
2 APSVWX	ABDE	7
3 AFQ	ABCDEFNRV	8
4 K		9
5 ADEHKN	ADFGHIJPST	10
10A CEE	❶ €17.00	
5ha 106T(90-130m²)	❷ €23.00	

A31 exit 6 direction Langres via D428. Campsite on your left after 1 km.

Located close to the motorway exit but still quiet and in the countryside.

CC 1/4-30/6 1/9-31/10

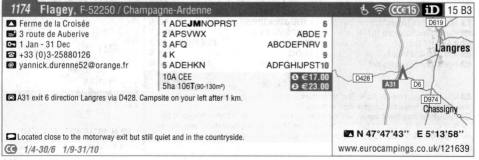

N 47°47'43'' E 5°13'58''

www.eurocampings.co.uk/121639

1175 Montigny-le-Roi, F-52140 / Champagne-Ardenne

♿ 🛜 (CC€17) **iD** 16 A3

- 🏕 Du Chateau***
- 📧 rue Hubert Collot
- 🗓 15 Apr - 30 Sep
- ☎ +33 (0)3-25873893
- @ camping@communevaldemeuse.fr

1 ADEJMNOPRST		6
2 AFPRTUVWXY	ABDE	7
3 BLMQ	ABCDFNQR	8
4 F		9
5 ABDE	AFGHIJPR	10

Ad on this page 6-10A CEE   ❶ €24.00
A400 6ha 75**T**(90-110m²)   ❷ €32.00

🅿 From the A31 exit 8, Montigny-le-Roi, direction centre. From there on, campsite is clearly signposted.

💬 This lovely well maintained campsite is an ideal stopover location on your way south and invites you to stay longer. Close to the motorway but still very quiet. Pitches are spacious and marked out, some with extensive panoramas. The village is close by within walking distance.

CC 15/4-30/6   20/8-29/9

Nogent — D33 — D74 — A31 — D429 — D1 — Val-de-Meuse — D14 — D417 — D35

🗺 **N 48°0'3" E 5°29'47"**

www.eurocampings.co.uk/101189

France

1176 Peigney, F-52200 / Champagne-Ardenne

♿ 🛜 ✿ (CC€19) **iD** 15 B3

- 🏕 Le Lac de la Liez*****
- 📧 rue des Voiliers
- 🗓 31 Mar - 30 Sep
- ☎ +33 (0)3-25902779
- @ contact@camping-liez.fr

1 ADE**JM**NOPRST	AEFHLM**N**QSWXY**Z**	6
2 DFGHIPSTUVWXY	ABDE**FG**H	7
3 BE**HLMQR**T	ABCDEFJK**L**NQRSTUV	8
4 BDFHILO**PQT**U	BCEJMOPQRTUV	9
5 ACDFGHLN	ABFGHIJ**NO**PR	10

Ad on this page 10A CEE   ❶ €37.00
6ha 157**T**(90-140m²) 30**P**   ❷ €47.00

🅿 From Langres N19 direction Vesoul. Or D74 direction Montigny. Follow campsite signs.

💬 These terraced grounds overlooking a lake are ideally located between Champagne and Burgundy. Direct access from the campsite to the sandy beach for swimming, sailing and pedalos. Indoor water complex with swimming pool, sauna, spa and waterslide. Bar, restaurant and tennis court. New toilet block with large comfort cabin.

CC 31/3-8/7   27/8-29/9

Rolampont — A5 — A31 — D3 — D74 — D35 — D120 — Langres — D619 — D428 — Chalindrey — D974 — D6

🗺 **N 47°52'19" E 5°22'50"**

www.eurocampings.co.uk/111971

1177 Saints-Geosmes/Langres, F-52200 / Champagne-Ardenne   ♿ 🛜 (CC €15) iD 15 B3

- 🏠 La Croix d'Arles***
- 🛣 route de Dijon
- 📅 15 Mar - 31 Oct
- ☎ +33 (0)3-25882402
- @ croix.arles@yahoo.fr

1 ADEJMNOPRST	AF	6
2 ABPRVWXY	ABDE**FG**	7
3 BLQ	ABCDEFJNRS	8
4 FH**T**	AEF	9
5 ABDFHJKMN	ADGHIJLORV	10
10A CEE	① €22.00	
A420 7ha 100**T**(85-100m²) 17**P**	② €28.00	

🚗 A31 exit 6 Langres-Sud, Direction Langres via D428, then to Dijon via D974. After 2 km the campsite is clearly signposted on your right.

💬 A busy stopover site with a friendly restaurant and swimming pool. The old fortified town of Langres is close by. You can cycle to Langres via the 'Voie Verte' (7 km). There are quiet pitches at the back of the campsite among the trees which are recommended for longer stays.

(CC) 15/3-30/6 31/8-30/10

📍 N 47°48'47'' E 5°19'16''

www.eurocampings.co.uk/104194

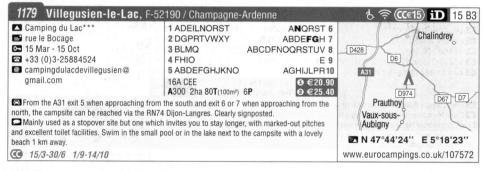

1178 Thonnance-les-Moulins, F-52230 / Champagne-Ardenne   ♿ 🛜 ✿ (CC €17) iD 15 B3

- 🏠 La Forge de Ste Marie*****
- 🛣 D427
- 📅 21 Apr - 7 Sep
- ☎ +33 (0)3-25944200
- @ info@laforgesaintemarie.com

1 ADE**JM**NOPRST	EFG**N**	6
2 BCGPSUVWXY	ABDE**FGH**	7
3 BE**H**LQRT	ABCDFIJKNQRSTUV	8
4 ABCDEFHIKLO**PQ**U	EIV	9
5 ABDEFGHLMN	ABDGHIJ**PR**V	10
6-10A CEE	① €37.60	
A250 11ha 144**T**(100-200m²) 55**P**	② €47.60	

🚗 From Joinville via the D60 to Thonnance-les-Joinville (2 km), then via the D427 through Poissons and Noncourt in the dir. of Thonnance-les-Moulins (10 km).

💬 Luxurious five-star campsite located in wooded surroundings in the heart of the Champagne region. Lovely and peaceful. Enjoy the jacuzzi and the heated indoor pool with its outside seating area. All facilities open during the opening period. Spacious pitches, trout fishing, 100% wifi coverage.

(CC) 21/4-7/7 26/8-6/9 7=6, 14=12

📍 N 48°24'23'' E 5°16'16''

www.eurocampings.co.uk/108792

1179 Villegusien-le-Lac, F-52190 / Champagne-Ardenne   ♿ 🛜 (CC €15) iD 15 B3

- 🏠 Camping du Lac***
- 🛣 rue le Bocage
- 📅 15 Mar - 15 Oct
- ☎ +33 (0)3-25884524
- @ campingdulacdevillegusien@gmail.com

1 ADEILNORST	A**N**QRST	6
2 DGPRTVWXY	ABDE**FGH**	7
3 BLMQ	ABCDFNOQRSTUV	8
4 FHIO	E	9
5 ABDEFGHJKNO	AGHIJLPR	10
16A CEE	① €20.90	
A300 2ha 80**T**(100m²) 6**P**	② €25.40	

🚗 From the A31 exit 5 when approaching from the south and exit 6 or 7 when approaching from the north, the campsite can be reached via the RN74 Dijon-Langres. Clearly signposted.

💬 Mainly used as a stopover site but one which invites you to stay longer, with marked-out pitches and excellent toilet facilities. Swim in the small pool or in the lake next to the campsite with a lovely beach 1 km away.

(CC) 15/3-30/6 1/9-14/10

📍 N 47°44'24'' E 5°18'23''

www.eurocampings.co.uk/107572

1180 Varennes-en-Argonne, F-55270 / Lorraine   🛜 iD 15 B2

- 🏠 Le Paquis**
- 🛣 rue Saint Jean
- 📅 8 Apr - 7 Oct
- ☎ +33 (0)3-29807101
- @ mairievarennesenargonne@wanadoo.fr

1 AE**JM**NOPRST	**N**	6
2 COPWXY	ABDE**F**	7
3 A	ABCDFNR	8
4	D	9
5 D	AIJOPR	10
6-16A	① €13.70	
A136 1,5ha 80**T**(80-150m²) 27**P**	② €17.50	

🚗 Follow the camping signs alongside the D946 in Varennes-en-Argonne. Large caravans and motorhomes need to ignore the no entry sign just before the campsite (right turn too tight).

💬 Beautifully located by the water, with well-mown fields and a friendly reception by the Belgian replacement manager. Various places of interest from WWI in the surrounding area.

📍 N 49°13'46'' E 5°2'4''

www.eurocampings.co.uk/104182

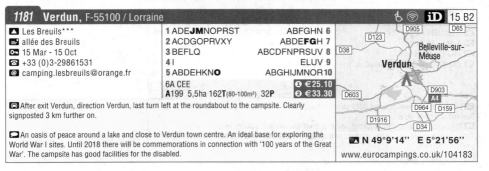

1181 Verdun, F-55100 / Lorraine
   🚲 🛜 **iD** 15 B2

- ▲ Les Breuils***
- 📧 allée des Breuils
- 🗓 15 Mar - 15 Oct
- ☎ +33 (0)3-29861531
- @ camping.lesbreuils@orange.fr

1 ADE**JM**NOPRST	ABFGHN	6
2 ACDGOPRVXY	ABDE**FGH**	7
3 BEFLQ	ABCDFNPRSUV	8
4 I	ELUV	9
5 ABDEHKN**O**	ABGHIJMNOR	10
6A CEE		❶ €25.10
A199 5,5ha 162**T**(80-100m²) 32**P**		❷ €33.30

🚗 After exit Verdun, direction Verdun, last turn left at the roundabout to the campsite. Clearly signposted 3 km further on.

💬 An oasis of peace around a lake and close to Verdun town centre. An ideal base for exploring the World War I sites. Until 2018 there will be commemorations in connection with '100 years of the Great War'. The campsite has good facilities for the disabled.

📌 N 49°9'14'' E 5°21'56''

www.eurocampings.co.uk/104183

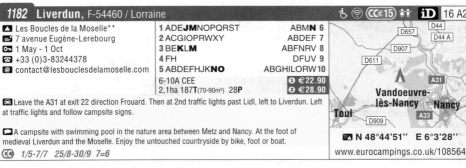

1182 Liverdun, F-54460 / Lorraine
   🚲 🛜 **CC€15** ⛄ **iD** 16 A2

- ▲ Les Boucles de la Moselle**
- 📧 7 avenue Eugène-Lerebourg
- 🗓 1 May - 1 Oct
- ☎ +33 (0)3-83244378
- @ contact@lesbouclesdelamoselle.com

1 ADE**JM**NOPQRST	ABM**N**	6
2 ACGIOPRWXY	ABDEF	7
3 BE**KLM**	ABFNRV	8
4 FH	DFUV	9
5 ABDEFHJK**NO**	ABGHILORW	10
6-10A CEE		❶ €22.90
2,1ha 187**T**(70-90m²) 28**P**		❷ €28.90

🚗 Leave the A31 at exit 22 direction Frouard. Then at 2nd traffic lights past Lidl, left to Liverdun. Left at traffic lights and follow campsite signs.

💬 A campsite with swimming pool in the nature area between Metz and Nancy. At the foot of medieval Liverdun and the Moselle. Enjoy the untouched countryside by bike, foot or boat.

🆑 1/5-7/7 25/8-30/9 7=6

📌 N 48°44'51'' E 6°3'28''

www.eurocampings.co.uk/108564

France

1183 Nancy/Villers-lès-Nancy, F-54600 / Lorraine
   🚲 🛜 **CC€15** ⛄ **iD** 16 A2

- ▲ Campéole Le Brabois***
- 📧 2301 avenue Paul Muller
- 🗓 30 Mar - 14 Oct
- ☎ +33 (0)3-83271828
- @ brabois@campeole.com

1 ADE**JM**NOPQRST		6
2 AOPRSVWXY	ABDE**FG**HIJ	7
3 BELQT	ABCDEFJNQRSV	8
4 IO	CE	9
5 ABDEFHK	ABDGHIJL**NOR**VZ	10
6-15A CEE		❶ €21.30
A370 4ha 182**T**(70-100m²) 18**P**		❷ €31.00

🚗 A33, exit 2B (Brabois). Keep on the left to turn left at the roundabout. Follow camp signs.
💬 Easily accessible from the A33 (exit 2B). Parkland setting with spacious, shaded pitches. Excellent bus connections to historic Nancy. Covered picnic area with cooking facilities, modern toilet facilities. Attractive snack bar (home-grown products) and outdoor seating area. Internet and wifi. Reductions for various sights from the reception.

🆑 30/3-6/7 25/8-13/10

📌 N 48°39'26'' E 6°8'25''

www.eurocampings.co.uk/104283

1184 Villey-le-Sec, F-54840 / Lorraine
   🚲 🛜 **CC€17** **iD** 16 A2

- ▲ Villey-le-Sec***
- 📧 34 rue de la Gare
- 🗓 31 Mar - 30 Sep
- ☎ +33 (0)3-83636428
- @ info@campingvilleylesec.com

1 ADE**JM**NOPRST	**N**X	6
2 ACPRVWX	ABDE**FG**	7
3 B**I**LQT	ABCDFJKNRSUV	8
4	EJLY	9
5 ACDEFHL	ABDHKL**O**RVWX	10
6-10A CEE		❶ €23.20
A213 3ha 90**T**(90-120m²) 7**P**		❷ €30.10

🚗 From Nancy: A31, exit 15. Take the 2nd road D909 direction Villey-le-Sec after 1 km at the roundabout near the Leclerc supermarket. Follow signs to 'Camping/Base de Loisirs' in the village 4 km further on.
💬 A pleasant campsite for overnight and longer stays in natural surroundings right on the Mosel. 8 km from the old town of Toul. Some noise from jet fighters. Lovely walking and cycling. Good catering. Ideal for fishing in the Mosel.

🆑 31/3-30/6 18/8-29/9

📌 N 48°39'10'' E 5°59'33''

www.eurocampings.co.uk/112527

1185 Baerenthal, F-57230 / Lorraine   ♿ 📶 CC€17 iD 16 B2

- 🏕 Ramstein Plage***
- 📅 1 Apr - 30 Sep
- ☎ +33 (0)3-87065073
- @ camping.ramstein@wanadoo.fr

1 ADE**JM**NOPRST	ABLM**N**	**6**
2 DGHPRVX	ABDE**FGH**	**7**
3 BEMQ	BDFJNRST	**8**
4 BEFHIO	FT	**9**
5 DEFGKLN	ABDGHIJPRVZ	**10**
6-16A CEE	❶ €22.90	
A250 12ha 100**T**(100m²) 317**P**	❷ €31.30	

🚗 From Sarreguemines take the D662 direction Haguenau. At Phillipsbourg turn right onto D36 to Baerenthal. Follow signs.

💬 The campsite has an idyllic location next to a small lake which is suitable for swimming. The surrounding area is heavily wooded and has been designated by UNESCO as a site of ecological world importance.

CC 1/4-30/6   1/9-29/9

📍 N 48°58'53''   E 7°30'53''

www.eurocampings.co.uk/104417

1186 Lutzelbourg, F-57820 / Lorraine   ♿ 📶 CC€17 iD 16 B2

- 🏕 Piscine du Plan Incliné***
- 🛣 D98
- 📅 1 Apr - 15 Oct
- ☎ +33 (0)3-87253013
- @ campingplanincline@orange.fr

1 ADE**JL**NOPRST	AFM**NX**	**6**
2 AFGOPX	ABD**FG**	**7**
3 AELQ	ABCDFJKNRT	**8**
4 FHI	DEL	**9**
5 ABDFHKLM	AFGH**OST**	**10**
Ad on this page 6-16A CEE	❶ €18.40	
A200 2ha 45**T**(100m²) 24**P**	❷ €24.40	

🚗 From Phalsbourg D38 to Lutzelbourg. Then the D98 direction Dabo. The campsite is located near the boat lift, 2 km outside Lutzelbourg, on the right.

💬 This campsite is located on the Marne-Rhine Canal in a beautiful, wooded area. Wifi for 1 Euro per day!

CC 1/4-6/7   25/8-14/10

📍 N 48°43'10''   E 7°13'35''

www.eurocampings.co.uk/109406

Camping Piscine Du Plan Incliné ★ ★ ★

Charming campsite by fishing grounds and next to the Marne/Rijnkanaal with its famous boat lift (open to visitors). Swimming pool and paddling pool (free), restaurant, bar. Mapped out trails and bicycle routes (for mountain bikes also).

Wi Fi™   €1.00 a day

D98, 57820 Lutzelbourg • Tel. 03-87253013
E-mail: campingplanincline@orange.fr
Internet: www.camping-planincline.com

Renovated bathroom facilities

1187 Vilsberg, F-57370 / Lorraine   ♿ 📶 CC€17 👫 iD 16 B2

- 🏕 Les Bouleaux***
- 🛣 5 rue des Trois Journaux
- 📅 1 Apr - 15 Oct
- ☎ +33 (0)3-87241872
- @ info@campinglesbouleaux.fr

1 ADE**JM**NOPRST	AB	**6**
2 APRX	ABDE**FGH**	**7**
3 AEILQS	ABCDFNRSV	**8**
4 FIO	DEJ	**9**
5 ADEHKMN	AHIJOST	**10**
Ad on page 417 6-10A	❶ €24.80	
A300 7ha 85**T**(100-200m²) 19**P**	❷ €27.80	

🚗 The campsite is 2 km outside Phalsbourg on the N61 to Sarreguemines. Don't turn at the 'Vilsberg' sign but at the next sign: 'Camping'.

💬 A peaceful family campsite, also suitable for longer stays. Lovely spacious pitches with plenty of grass. You will be welcomed by a Dutch-German couple. Free wifi.

CC 1/4-7/7   25/8-14/10   7=6, 14=12, 21=18

📍 N 48°47'0''   E 7°14'58''

www.eurocampings.co.uk/104418

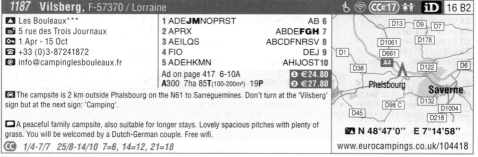

Les Bouleaux ★★★

The owner speaks English.
We are looking forward to welcoming you to our beautiful and quiet nature campsite with spacious pitches. There are two sanitary blocks, a bar, place to eat, crazy golf, table tennis and playground.

**5 rue des Trois Journaux
57370 Vilsberg
Tel. 03-87241872
E-mail: info@campinglesbouleaux.fr
Internet: www.campinglesbouleaux.fr**

1188 Bulgnéville, F-88140 / Lorraine

       🚗 📶 CC€17 iD 16 A3

- ⛺ Porte des Vosges***
- 🏕 ZA la Grande Tranchée
- 📅 30 Mar - 1 Nov
- ☎ +33 (0)3-29091200
- @ contact@
  camping-portedesvosges.com

1 ADEJMNORST	AB	**6**
2 ARTWXY	ABDE	**7**
3 AELQ	ABCDFJNQRST	**8**
4 FO	BEH	**9**
5 ADEFHN	AGHIJOR	**10**

10A CEE   ❶ €20.50
A355   3,5ha 100T(85m²)   7P   ❷ €25.70

🚗 A31 exit 9, through Bulgnéville via D164 direction Contrexéville. Follow campsite signs.

💬 Well maintained stopover campsite, located near the motorway exit. Restaurants and shops within walking distance. Heated pool. Snackbar also open in both low seasons. The well-known spa resorts Contrexéville and Vittel are only a few minutes' drive away.

CC 30/3-6/7   1/9-31/10

🧭 N 48°11'57''   E 5°50'41''
www.eurocampings.co.uk/104188

1189 Bussang, F-88540 / Lorraine

       ⛷ 🚗 📶 CC€17 iD 45a

- ⛺ Le Domaine de Champé*****
- 🏕 14 rue des Champs-Navets
- 📅 1 Jan - 31 Dec
- ☎ +33 (0)3-29616151
- @ info@domaine-de-champe.com

1 ADE**IL**NOPQRST	AB**EFGHI**N	**6**
2 CGOPVWXY	ABDE**FG**H	**7**
3 ABCDELMNQRSTV	BDFGHIJNPQRSTUV	**8**
4 ABDEFGHIKLNOR**TUVWXYZ**	EJUVWZ	**9**
5 ADEFGHLMN	ABDFGHIJP**RZ**10	

10A CEE   ❶ €34.00
A650   5,5ha 110T(90-110m²)   50P   ❷ €48.00

🚗 The campsite is signposted in Bussang from the RN66. At the church follow the campsite signs.

💬 A well maintained, sporty campsite, partly divided by hedges. Very relaxed ambiance. The 3.5 km long Old Moselle river flows through the campsite. Paragliding takes place on the hill above the campsite and you can take your maiden flight here.

CC 1/4-5/7   23/8-20/11   7=6, 14=12

🧭 N 47°53'20''   E 6°51'27''
www.eurocampings.co.uk/104300

1190 Celles-sur-Plaine, F-88110 / Lorraine

       🚗 📶 CC€17 iD 16 A2

- ⛺ Camping des Lacs***
- 🏕 6 Place de la Gare
- 📅 1 Apr - 30 Sep
- ☎ +33 (0)3-29412800
- @ camping@paysdeslacs.com

1 ADE**JM**NOPRST	AFGJLM**N**QSUVXY	**6**
2 CDGHPRVX	ABDE**FG**	**7**
3 ABEILMQ**RSTU**	BDFGJKNRSU	**8**
4 **A**BDFHILNO**PQ**	AFJQRT	**9**
5 ABDEFHJKN	ABHIJ**P**ST**10**	

10A   ❶ €25.00
A350   3ha 123T(75-140m²)   40P   ❷ €37.50

🚗 From Nancy, first the N4, then the N59. In Raon-l'Étape follow 'Lacs de Pierre Percée'. In Celles-sur-Plaine, the campsite is signposted.

💬 A lovely campsite with many activities for young and old. New heated toilet facilities, heated outdoor swimming pool. Wifi on the site. All watersports activities are a ten-minute walk from the campsite.

CC 1/4-6/7   1/9-29/9   7=6, 14=12

🧭 N 48°27'18''   E 6°56'52''
www.eurocampings.co.uk/108422

France

1191 Charmes, F-88130 / Lorraine ♿ 📶 (CC€13) iD 16 A3

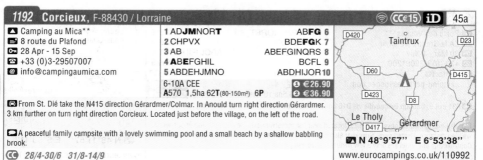

- ⛺ Les Îles***
- 🏠 20 rue de l'Écluse
- 📅 1 Apr - 30 Sep
- ☎ +33 (0)3-29388771
- @ violettefleurs@gmail.com

1 AJMNOPRT	JN 6	
2 ACPQX	ABDEF 7	
3 AEILQ	ABCDEFNRV 8	
4 FI	QRUV 9	
5 ABDEFJMNO	AGHIJLPRZ 10	
10A CEE	❶ €17.50	
A300 3,5ha 67T(100-200m²) 7P	❷ €23.60	

🚗 From Nancy take the N57 direction Epinal. At Charmes take exit Charmes/Mirecourt (D55) and follow the campsite signs in the village.

💬 Simple, quiet campsite situated between a tributary of the Moselle and the l'Est canal. Medium-sized trees on the corners of the pitches.

CC 1/4-6/7 25/8-29/9 7=6, 14=12

N 48°22'37'' E 6°17'23''

www.eurocampings.co.uk/100282

1192 Corcieux, F-88430 / Lorraine 📶 (CC€15) iD 45a

- ⛺ Camping au Mica**
- 🏠 8 route du Plafond
- 📅 28 Apr - 15 Sep
- ☎ +33 (0)3-29507007
- @ info@campingaumica.com

1 ADJMNORT	ABFG 6	
2 CHPVX	BDEFGK 7	
3 AB	ABEFGINQRS 8	
4 ABEFGHIL	BCFL 9	
5 ABDEHJMNO	ABDHIJOR 10	
6-10A CEE	❶ €26.90	
A570 1,5ha 62T(80-150m²) 6P	❷ €36.90	

🚗 From St. Dié take the N415 direction Gérardmer/Colmar. In Anould turn right direction Gérardmer. 3 km further on turn right direction Corcieux. Located just before the village, on the left of the road.

💬 A peaceful family campsite with a lovely swimming pool and a small beach by a shallow babbling brook.

CC 28/4-30/6 31/8-14/9

N 48°9'57'' E 6°53'38''

www.eurocampings.co.uk/110992

1193 Corcieux, F-88430 / Lorraine ♿ 📶 ❀ (CC€15) iD 45a

- ⛺ Sites & Paysages Au Clos de la Chaume***
- 🏠 21 rue d'Alsace
- 📅 21 Apr - 20 Sep
- ☎ +33 (0)3-29507676
- @ info@camping-closdelachaume.com

1 ADEJMNOPRST	CDN 6	
2 CGPRVXY	BEFGH 7	
3 BELQR	BDFIKNQRSTUV 8	
4 EFHILPQ	BEFJ 9	
5 ABDFJMNO	ABDFGHIJLOPR 10	
Ad on this page 6-10A	❶ €26.90	
A570 5ha 100T(80-150m²) 34P	❷ €37.20	

🚗 From St. Dié take the N415 in the directon of Gérardmer/Colmar. In Anould turn right direction Gérardmer. 3 km further on turn right direction Corcieux. Located just before the village on the right side of the road.

💬 Pascaline and Michael, an Anglo-French couple, welcome you to their quiet campsite with large pitches, swimming pool and new toilet facilities. Ideal for visiting the Vosges and Alsace. New: the pool is heated and covered.

CC 21/4-6/7 25/8-19/9 7=6, 14=12

N 48°10'5'' E 6°53'24''

www.eurocampings.co.uk/108802

1194 Épinal, F-88000 / Lorraine · 📶 CC€17 ♟♙ iD · 45a

- 🔺 Parc du Château**
- 📧 37 chemin du Petit Chaperon Rouge
- 📅 15 Feb - 15 Nov
- ☎ +33 (0)3-29344365
- @ camping.parcduchateau@gmail.com

1 ADEJMNOPQRST	AF	6
2 AOPSVWXY	ABDEFG	7
3 AQ	ABEFJNQRSV	8
4 FHO	BEJ	9
5 ADEFHJKLN	ADFGHIJNPST	10
Ad on this page 16A CEE	❶ €23.00	
A375 1,7ha 43T(60-200m²) 10P	❷ €31.00	

🔲 From Nancy or Besançon, dir. Épinal, take exit 'Razimont' or 'Parc des Expositions'. Drive towards centre. Signposted from here on. The campsite is located 500m from the exit, 1st road on the right.
📬 Pleasant, quiet, small campsite. No entertainment. Located in the grounds of a castle park with swimming pool and free wifi. Restaurant with varied and tasty dishes. You can stay on the campsite outside the opening period by reserving in advance.
CC 15/2-7/7 25/8-14/11 7=6, 14=12

Thaon-les-Vosges · Épinal 🔺

www.eurocampings.co.uk/112345

📍 N 48°10'47'' E 6°28'5''

France

1195 Gérardmer, F-88400 / Lorraine · ♿ 📶 CC€17 iD · 45a

- 🔺 Les Sapins**
- 📧 18 chemin de Sapois
- 📅 1 Apr - 15 Oct
- ☎ +33 (0)3-29631501
- @ les.sapins@camping-gerardmer.com

1 AJMNOPQRST	LN	6
2 DGIPVY	ABDE	7
3 BEL	ABCDFKNORSU	8
4 FHIO	E	9
5 ABDEHJNO	AHIJLNOR	10
6-10A	❶ €20.25	
A666 1,3ha 67T(80-120m²) 6P	❷ €27.05	

🔲 The campsite is located at the start of the southern section of the Gérardmer ring road (chemin du Tour du Lac D69).

📬 Pleasant, peaceful campsite within walking distance of the tourist town of Gérardmer. Spacious pitches with views of the wooded hills. Gérardmer Lake is 200 m away from the campsite.
CC 1/4-6/7 31/8-14/10 7=6, 14=12

Gérardmer 🔺 · Vagney · Cornimont

📍 N 48°3'48'' E 6°51'21''

www.eurocampings.co.uk/109405

1196 Granges-sur-Vologne, F-88640 / Lorraine · ♿ 📶 CC€13 iD · 45a

- 🔺 Flower Camping La Sténiole***
- 📧 1 le Haut Rain
- 📅 2 Apr - 16 Oct
- ☎ +33 (0)3-29514375
- @ steniole@wanadoo.fr

1 ADEJMNOPRT	CDN	6
2 CDGPRTUX	ABDEFGH	7
3 ABEFLQS	ABCDFGIJNOQRSV	8
4 BFHIO	AEHI	9
5 ABDEFGHJMN	ABGHJLPR	10
10A CEE	❶ €23.60	
A730 7ha 119T(80-200m²) 20P	❷ €30.60	

🔲 From Gérardmer take the D423 in the direction of Granges-sur-Vologne. Turn left just before Granges. Follow the signs.

📬 A friendly family campsite by a small lake. Large pitches. Campfires permitted on your pitch. New, heated pool with retractable roof.
CC 2/4-8/7 26/8-15/10 7=6, 14=12

Bruyères · Gérardmer 🔺 · Saint-Amé

📍 N 48°7'16'' E 6°49'43''

www.eurocampings.co.uk/108532

1197 Herpelmont, F-88600 / Lorraine ♿ 📶 (CC€17) iD 45a

- 🏕 Domaine des Messires****
- 🏘 rue des Messires
- 📅 13 Apr - 30 Sep
- ☎ +33 (0)3-29585629
- @ mail@domainedesmessires.com

1 ADE**JM**NOPRST	LNX **6**	
2 DHIPQRVXY	ABDE**FG 7**	
3 ALQ	CDFGHIKNQRSTV **8**	
4 BFHILO	EQU **9**	
5 ABDEJN	ABDHJOST**10**	
10A CEE		❶ €29.80
A450 12ha 115**T**(80-100m²) 22**P**		❷ €37.80

🚗 N57, exit N420 direction St. Dié. After 27 km D423 direction Bruyères/Gérardmer. Turn right after 4 km towards Herpelmont/Lac des Messires.

💬 Lovely four-star campsite on a small lake in unspoilt nature. Fishing is free. New toilet facilities. Walking and mountain-biking possible from the campsite.

(CC) 13/4-6/7 27/8-29/9 14=12

🗺 N 48°10'43'' E 6°44'34''

www.eurocampings.co.uk/104290

1198 La Bresse, F-88250 / Lorraine ⛷ ♿ 📶 ❀ iD 45a

- 🏕 Belle-Hutte****
- 🏘 1 bis Vouille de Belle Hutte
- 📅 1/1 - 1/11, 16/12 - 31/12
- ☎ +33 (0)3-29254975
- @ camping-belle-hutte@wanadoo.fr

1 ADE**JM**NOPR**T**	ABH**N 6**	
2 CFPRUVX	ABDE**FGH 7**	
3 ABLQST	ABCDFJKNQRSV **8**	
4 FHIO**P**	FIJ **9**	
5 ABDEHJM**N**	AGHIJPR**10**	
Ad on this page 2-10A		❶ €31.70
A900 3ha 99**T**(80-120m²) 33**P**		❷ €41.70

🚗 In La Bresse take the D34 in the direction of La Schlucht. The campsite is located after 9 km on the left side of the road.

💬 Quiet family campsite with swimming pool during the summer. During winter, ideal location near the ski slopes. Very well-kept toilet facilities. This campsite has the hallmark 'camping qualité'. Internet possibility.

🗺 N 48°2'6'' E 6°57'45''

www.eurocampings.co.uk/110669

Belle-Hutte ★ ★ ★ ★

CAMPING Qualité

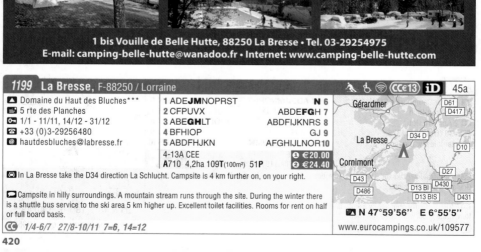

1 bis Vouille de Belle Hutte, 88250 La Bresse • Tel. 03-29254975
E-mail: camping-belle-hutte@wanadoo.fr • Internet: www.camping-belle-hutte.com

---

1199 La Bresse, F-88250 / Lorraine ⛷ ♿ 📶 (CC€13) iD 45a

- 🏕 Domaine du Haut des Bluches***
- 🏘 5 rte des Planches
- 📅 1/1 - 11/11, 14/12 - 31/12
- ☎ +33 (0)3-29256480
- @ hautdesbluches@labresse.fr

1 ADE**JM**NOPRST	**N 6**	
2 CFPUVX	ABDE**FGH 7**	
3 ABE**GH**LT	ABDFIJKNRS **8**	
4 BFHIOP	GJ **9**	
5 ABDFHJKN	AFGHIJLNOR**10**	
4-13A CEE		❶ €20.00
A710 4,2ha 109**T**(100m²) 51**P**		❷ €24.40

🚗 In La Bresse take the D34 direction La Schlucht. Campsite is 4 km further on, on your right.

💬 Campsite in hilly surroundings. A mountain stream runs through the site. During the winter there is a shuttle bus service to the ski area 5 km higher up. Excellent toilet facilities. Rooms for rent on half or full board basis.

(CC) 1/4-6/7 27/8-10/11 7=6, 14=12

🗺 N 47°59'56'' E 6°55'5''

www.eurocampings.co.uk/109577

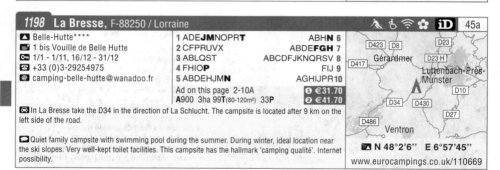

1200 Le Tholy, F-88530 / Lorraine ♿ 🛜 CC€17 iD 45a

- 🏕 JP Vacances - camping de Noirrupt****
- 🏠 15 chemin de l'Étang
- 📅 1 May - 30 Sep
- ☎ +33 (0)3-29618127
- @ info@jpvacances.com

1	ADE**JM**NOPRT	AB**N**	6
2	FPUVXY	BDE**FGH**	7
3	B**G**LMPQ	BDFNOQRSV	8
4	FHIO**T**	JL	9
5	ABDFGHJM**NO**	ABDGHIJ**PR**	10

2-10A CEE ❶ €29.10
A630 3ha 77T(90-200m²) 12**P** ❷ €40.00

🚗 From Gérardmer take D417 direction Remiremont. Turn right onto D11 at Le Tholy. Turn left 0.5 km after leaving Le Tholy. Follow arrows.

💬 An attractive campsite, peacefully located and surrounded by lovely big trees. Five minutes from Gérardmer. Panoramic views. Heated swimming pool.

CC 1/5-6/7 24/8-29/9 7=6, 14=12, 21=18

📍 N 48°5'20'' E 6°43'44''
www.eurocampings.co.uk/104293

1201 Sanchey, F-88390 / Lorraine ♿ 🛜 CC€19 ⚥ iD 45a

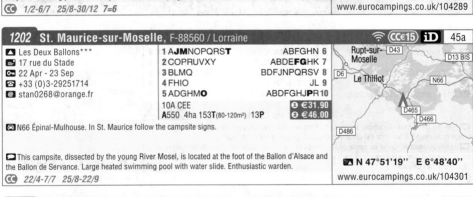

- 🏕 Club Lac de Bouzey****
- 🏠 19 rue du Lac
- 📅 1 Feb - 31 Dec
- ☎ +33 (0)3-29824941
- @ lacdebouzey@orange.fr

1	ADE**JM**NOPQRST	ABFGL**N**QRSTUVXY	6
2	ADGHOPRUVWXY	ABDE**FGH**	7
3	ABE**K**LM**P**QST**U**	BDFJKNORSTUV	8
4	**A**BCDEFHIJLMNOP**X**	ELMOTUVW	9
5	ACDEFGHJKLMNO	ABFGHIJORZ	10

10-16A ❶ €38.10
A380 3,5ha 155T(58-100m²) 30**P** ❷ €54.10

🚗 From Nancy take the N57/E23 in the direction of Épinal. Exit Chavelot direction Uxegney. In Uxegney take the D41 in the direction of Lac de Bouzey. Then follow the signs.

💬 A lovely family campsite located by a lake, suitable for a longer stay. Extensive recreational opportunities: tennis, carting, golf, rock climbing, kayaking, horse riding, Jorkyball. Lovely unusually shaped swimming pool. The campsite has the 'Camping Qualité' hallmark.

CC 1/2-6/7 25/8-30/12 7=6

📍 N 48°10'1'' E 6°21'35''
www.eurocampings.co.uk/104289

1202 St. Maurice-sur-Moselle, F-88560 / Lorraine 🛜 CC€15 iD 45a

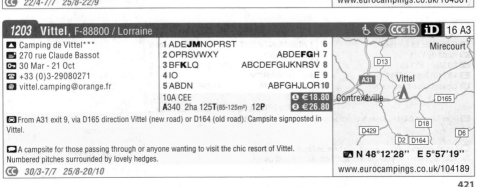

- 🏕 Les Deux Ballons***
- 🏠 17 rue du Stade
- 📅 22 Apr - 23 Sep
- ☎ +33 (0)3-29251714
- @ stan0268@orange.fr

1	**A**JMNOPQRS**T**	ABFGHN	6
2	COPRUVXY	ABDE**FG**HK	7
3	BLMQ	BDFJNPQRSV	8
4	FHIO	JL	9
5	ADGHM**O**	ABDFGHJ**PR**	10

10A CEE ❶ €31.90
A550 4ha 153T(80-120m²) 13**P** ❷ €46.00

🚗 N66 Épinal-Mulhouse. In St. Maurice follow the campsite signs.

💬 This campsite, dissected by the young River Mosel, is located at the foot of the Ballon d'Alsace and the Ballon de Servance. Large heated swimming pool with water slide. Enthusiastic warden.

CC 22/4-7/7 25/8-22/9

📍 N 47°51'19'' E 6°48'40''
www.eurocampings.co.uk/104301

1203 Vittel, F-88800 / Lorraine ♿ 🛜 CC€15 iD 16 A3

- 🏕 Camping de Vittel***
- 🏠 270 rue Claude Bassot
- 📅 30 Mar - 21 Oct
- ☎ +33 (0)3-29080271
- @ vittel.camping@orange.fr

1	ADE**JM**NOPRST		6
2	OPRSVWXY	ABDE**FGH**	7
3	BF**K**LQ	ABCDEFGIJKNRSV	8
4	IO	E	9
5	ABDN	ABFGHJLOR	10

10A CEE ❶ €18.80
A340 2ha 125T(85-125m²) 12**P** ❷ €26.80

🚗 From A31 exit 9, via D165 direction Vittel (new road) or D164 (old road). Campsite signposted in Vittel.

💬 A campsite for those passing through or anyone wanting to visit the chic resort of Vittel. Numbered pitches surrounded by lovely hedges.

CC 30/3-7/7 25/8-20/10

📍 N 48°12'28'' E 5°57'19''
www.eurocampings.co.uk/104189

1204 Xonrupt-Longemer, F-88400 / Lorraine ♿ ⚹ 🤟 (CC€17) ♀♂ iD 45a

- 🏕 Flower Camping Verte Vallée***
- 🏠 4092 route du Lac
- 📅 1/1 - 31/10, 15/12 - 31/12
- ☎ +33 (0)3-29632177
- @ contact@campingvertevallee.com

1 ADE**JM**NOPRS**T**	ABCFGG**N** 6
2 CRVWX	BE**FG**HK 7
3 ABELMSTV	ABCDEFJNQRSV 8
4 BD**E**FHILNO**PQ**	BDEFVW 9
5 ABDFHJN	ABDHIJLNPR 10

Ad on this page 4-10A
A742 3,5ha 82T(80-140m²) 50P
❶ €29.60
❷ €39.60

From Gérardmer take the D417 towards Colmar. Just past Xonrupt, at Hotel du Lac de Longemer turn right onto D67. Campsite at the end of the lake.

A beautiful campsite with a new, heated indoor pool with a sliding roof. The campsite is located 300 m from the lake.

🧭 N 48°3'45'' E 6°57'53''

CC 1/3-30/6 1/9-30/10 7=6, 14=12

www.eurocampings.co.uk/109822

1205 Xonrupt-Longemer, F-88400 / Lorraine ⚹ 🤟 (CC€13) iD 45a

- 🏕 Les Jonquilles***
- 🏠 2552 route du Lac
- 📅 21 Apr - 30 Sep
- ☎ +33 (0)3-29633401
- @ info@camping-jonquilles.com

1 ADE**JM**NOPRST	LNQSX 6
2 DFGKPRTVX	ABDE**FG**H 7
3 BELPQ	ABCDEFNORS 8
4 DFHIO**P**	9
5 ACDEFGJKMN	ABDFGHIJOR 10

6-10A
A740 4,5ha 228T(80-120m²)
❶ €20.70
❷ €27.70

Take the D417 from Gérardmer to Xonrupt-Longemer. Take the D67a in this village to the campsite, which is situated 2.5 km from the church in Xonrupt-Longemer left of the road.

Beautiful, pleasant family campsite on the shores of the lake of Longemer. Suitable for longer visits. Large pitches, which nearly all have a view over the lake. Many different walking (hiking) routes start from the campsite.

🧭 N 48°4'4'' E 6°56'53''

CC 21/4-6/7 25/8-29/9 7=6, 14=12, 21=18

www.eurocampings.co.uk/104298

1206 Bassemberg, F-67220 / Alsace ⚹ 🤟 (CC€15) ♀♂ iD 16 B3

- 🏕 Campéole Le Giessen****
- 🏠 route de Villé
- 📅 30 Mar - 30 Sep
- ☎ +33 (0)3-88589814
- @ giessen@campeole.com

1 ADE**JM**NOPRS**T**	ABEFGH**N** 6
2 CGPSWXY	ABDE**FG**HK 7
3 BEL**MQT**	ABCDEFGKNORSV 8
4 BCDFHINR**TV**	EJL 9
5 ADEFGH**J**N	ABDFGHIJ**P**STZ 10

10A CEE
A285 4ha 70T(80-110m²) 89P
❶ €31.50
❷ €42.50

From Sélestat D424 in westerly direction. After 12 km Villé, D39 to Bassemberg. Follow 'Campéole' signs.

A lovely campsite well endowed with trees and bushes and situated by a mountain stream. The adjacent swimming pool (indoors and outdoors) is free of charge.

🧭 N 48°20'11'' E 7°17'20''

CC 30/3-6/7 25/8-29/9

www.eurocampings.co.uk/110503

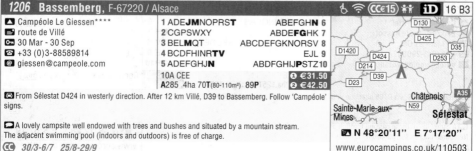

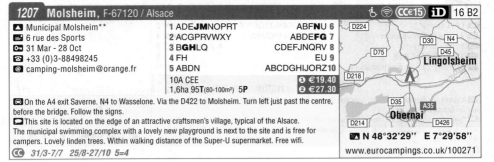

1207 Molsheim, F-67120 / Alsace
  ♿ 🛜 (CC€15) **iD**   16 B2

▲ Municipal Molsheim**
🏠 6 rue des Sports
📅 31 Mar - 28 Oct
☎ +33 (0)3-88498245
@ camping-molsheim@orange.fr

1 ADE**JM**NOPRT	ABF**NU** 6
2 ACGPRVWXY	ABDE**FG** 7
3 B**GH**LQ	CDEFJNQRV 8
4 FH	EU 9
5 ABDN	ABCDGHIJORZ 10

10A CEE   ❶ €19.40
1,6ha 95T(80-100m²) **5P**   ❷ €27.30

🚗 On the A4 exit Saverne. N4 to Wasselone. Via the D422 to Molsheim. Turn left just past the centre, before the bridge. Follow the signs.
💬 This site is located on the edge of an attractive craftsmen's village, typical of the Alsace. The municipal swimming complex with a lovely new playground is next to the site and is free for campers. Lovely linden trees. Within walking distance of the Super-U supermarket. Free wifi.
🆑 31/3-7/7   25/8-27/10   5=4

N 48°32'29''   **E 7°29'58''**
www.eurocampings.co.uk/100271

1208 Obernai, F-67210 / Alsace
  ♿ 🛜 ✿ (CC€17) **iD**   16 B2

▲ Mun. Le Vallon de l'Ehn***
🏠 1 rue de Berlin
📅 1/1 - 7/1, 16/3 - 31/12
☎ +33 (0)3-88953848
@ camping@obernai.fr

1 ADEF**JM**NOPRST	**N** 6
2 OPVWXY	ABDE**FG** 7
3 BFLQV	ABCDEFJNQRSUV 8
4 **AE**FGI	JKLV 9
5 ABDNO	ABFGHIJPRZ 10

16A CEE   ❶ €21.90
A200 3ha 142T(90-95m²) **4P**   ❷ €27.50

🚗 From Molsheim or Strasbourg take Obernai exit. Not to Centre Ville, but follow Le Mont-Ste-Odile at roundabouts. Right at end of ring road then immediate left. Campsite 100m on the left.
💬 A lovely campsite close to a tourist village. Level pitches with some shade. Good modern amenities.
🆑 1/1-6/1   16/3-30/6   1/9-31/12   11=10

N 48°27'53''   **E 7°28'3''**
www.eurocampings.co.uk/110663

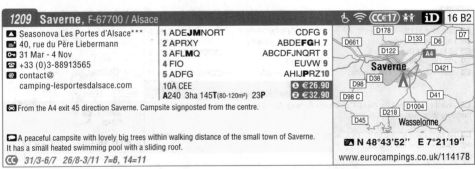

1209 Saverne, F-67700 / Alsace
  ♿ 🛜 (CC€17) 🚼 **iD**   16 B2

▲ Seasonova Les Portes d'Alsace***
🏠 40, rue du Père Liebermann
📅 31 Mar - 4 Nov
☎ +33 (0)3-88913565
@ contact@camping-lesportesdalsace.com

1 ADE**JM**NORT	CDFG 6
2 APRXY	ABDE**FGH** 7
3 AFL**M**Q	ABCDFJNQRT 8
4 FIO	EUVW 9
5 ADFG	AHIJ**PR**Z 10

10A CEE   ❶ €26.90
A240 3ha 145T(80-120m²) **23P**   ❷ €32.90

🚗 From the A4 exit 45 direction Saverne. Campsite signposted from the centre.
💬 A peaceful campsite with lovely big trees within walking distance of the small town of Saverne. It has a small heated swimming pool with a sliding roof.
🆑 31/3-6/7   26/8-3/11   7=6, 14=11

N 48°43'52''   **E 7°21'19''**
www.eurocampings.co.uk/114178

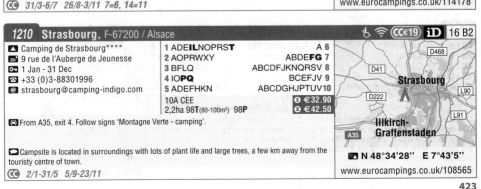

1210 Strasbourg, F-67200 / Alsace
  ♿ 🛜 (CC€19) **iD**   16 B2

▲ Camping de Strasbourg****
🏠 9 rue de l'Auberge de Jeunesse
📅 1 Jan - 31 Dec
☎ +33 (0)3-88301996
@ strasbourg@camping-indigo.com

1 ADE**IL**NOPRS**T**	A 6
2 AOPRWXY	ABDE**FG** 7
3 BFLQ	ABCDFJKNQRSV 8
4 IO**PQ**	BCEFJV 9
5 ADEFHKN	ABCDGHJPTUV 10

10A CEE   ❶ €32.90
2,2ha 98T(80-100m²) **98P**   ❷ €42.50

🚗 From A35, exit 4. Follow signs 'Montagne Verte - camping'.
💬 Campsite is located in surroundings with lots of plant life and large trees, a few km away from the touristy centre of town.
🆑 2/1-31/5   5/9-23/11

N 48°34'28''   **E 7°43'5''**
www.eurocampings.co.uk/108565

France

1211 Burnhaupt-le-Haut, F-68520 / Alsace

⊚ CC€17 †† iD 45a

- ▲ Les Castors***
- 🏠 4 route de Guewenheim
- 📅 1 Feb - 15 Nov
- ☎ +33 (0)3-89487858
- @ camping-castors@outlook.com

1 ADEJMNOPQRST	JLN	6
2 ACDGHJPQVWXY	ABDEFG	7
3 BL	ABCDEFHNPS	8
4 FHIO	EJ	9
5 ABDFKMNO	AGHIJO	10
10A CEE	❶ €18.30	
A320 4ha 120T(100-150m²) 33P	❷ €22.30	

🚗 A36 exit 15 'Burnhaupt-le-Haut' direction Cernay. First exit (D484). Then take direction Maseveaux at roundabout D466.

💬 Spacious campsite on the river, with lake for swimming and fishing. The restaurant is open the entire season. Many opportunities for young families, such as the swimming lake with beach and inflatable slide.

CC 1/2-6/7 25/8-14/11 7=6

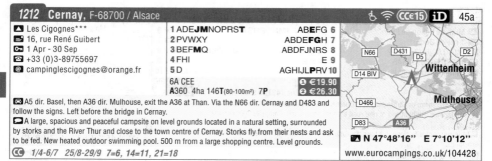

📍 N 47°44'49" E 7°7'28"

www.eurocampings.co.uk/114181

1212 Cernay, F-68700 / Alsace

♿ ⊚ CC€15 iD 45a

- ▲ Les Cigognes***
- 🏠 16, rue René Guibert
- 📅 1 Apr - 30 Sep
- ☎ +33 (0)3-89755697
- @ campinglescigognes@orange.fr

1 ADEJMNOPRST	ABEFG	6
2 PVWXY	ABDEFGH	7
3 BEFMQ	ABDFJNRS	8
4 FHI	E	9
5 D	AGHIJLPRV	10
6A CEE	❶ €19.90	
A360 4ha 146T(80-100m²) 7P	❷ €26.30	

🚗 A5 dir. Basel, then A36 dir. Mulhouse, exit the A36 at Than. Via the N66 dir. Cernay and D483 and follow the signs. Left before the bridge in Cernay.

💬 A large, spacious and peaceful campsite on level grounds located in a natural setting, surrounded by storks and the River Thur and close to the town centre of Cernay. Storks fly from their nests and ask to be fed. New heated outdoor swimming pool. 500 m from a large shopping centre. Level grounds.

CC 1/4-6/7 25/8-29/9 7=6, 14=11, 21=18

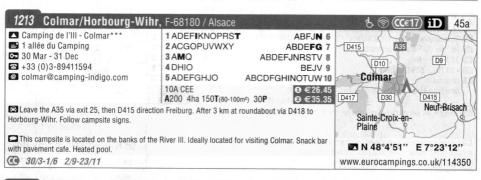

📍 N 47°48'16" E 7°10'12"

www.eurocampings.co.uk/104428

1213 Colmar/Horbourg-Wihr, F-68180 / Alsace

♿ ⊚ CC€17 iD 45a

- ▲ Camping de l'Ill - Colmar***
- 🏠 1 allée du Camping
- 📅 30 Mar - 31 Dec
- ☎ +33 (0)3-89411594
- @ colmar@camping-indigo.com

1 ADEFIKNOPRST	ABFJN	6
2 ACGOPUVWXY	ABDEFG	7
3 AMQ	ABDEFJNRSTV	8
4 DHIO	BEJV	9
5 ADEFGHJO	ABCDFGHINOTUW	10
10A CEE	❶ €26.45	
A200 4ha 150T(80-100m²) 30P	❷ €35.35	

🚗 Leave the A35 via exit 25, then D415 direction Freiburg. After 3 km at roundabout via D418 to Horbourg-Wihr. Follow campsite signs.

💬 This campsite is located on the banks of the River Ill. Ideally located for visiting Colmar. Snack bar with pavement cafe. Heated pool.

CC 30/3-1/6 2/9-23/11

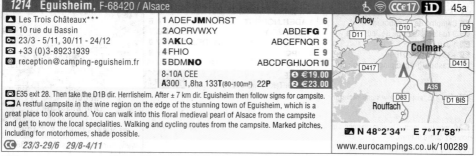

📍 N 48°4'51" E 7°23'12"

www.eurocampings.co.uk/114350

1214 Eguisheim, F-68420 / Alsace

♿ ⊚ CC€17 iD 45a

- ▲ Les Trois Châteaux***
- 🏠 10 rue du Bassin
- 📅 23/3 - 5/11, 30/11 - 24/12
- ☎ +33 (0)3-89231939
- @ reception@camping-eguisheim.fr

1 ADEFJMNORST		6
2 AOPRVWXY	ABDEFG	7
3 AKLQ	ABCEFNQR	8
4 FHIO	E	9
5 BDMNO	ABCDFGHIJOR	10
8-10A CEE	❶ €19.00	
A300 1,8ha 133T(80-100m²) 22P	❷ €23.00	

🚗 E35 exit 28. Then take the D1B dir. Herrlisheim. After ± 7 km dir. Eguisheim then follow signs for campsite.

💬 A restful campsite in the wine region on the edge of the stunning town of Eguisheim, which is a great place to look around. You can walk into this floral medieval pearl of Alsace from the campsite and get to know the local specialities. Walking and cycling routes from the campsite. Marked pitches, including for motorhomes, shade possible.

CC 23/3-29/6 29/8-4/11

📍 N 48°2'34" E 7°17'58"

www.eurocampings.co.uk/100289

1215 Masevaux, F-68290 / Alsace

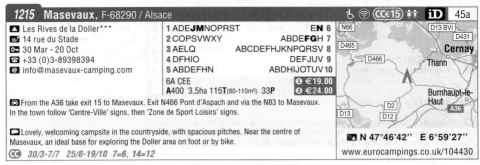

- ▲ Les Rives de la Doller***
- 🏠 14 rue du Stade
- 📅 30 Mar - 20 Oct
- ☎ +33 (0)3-89398394
- @ info@masevaux-camping.com

1 ADEJMNOPRST	EN	6
2 COPSVWXY	ABDEFGH	7
3 AELQ	ABCDEFHJKNPQRSV	8
4 DFHIO	DEFJUV	9
5 ABDEFHN	ABDHIJOTUV	10
6A CEE	❶ €19.00	
A400 3,5ha 115T(80-110m²) 33P	❷ €24.00	

🚗 From the A36 take exit 15 to Masevaux. Exit N466 Pont d'Aspach and via the N83 to Masevaux. In the town follow 'Centre-Ville' signs, then 'Zone de Sport Loisirs' signs.

💬 Lovely, welcoming campsite in the countryside, with spacious pitches. Near the centre of Masevaux, an ideal base for exploring the Doller area on foot or by bike.

CC 30/3-7/7 25/8-19/10 7=6, 14=12

▲ N 47°46'42" E 6°59'27"

www.eurocampings.co.uk/104430

45a

1216 Neuf-Brisach, F-68600 / Alsace

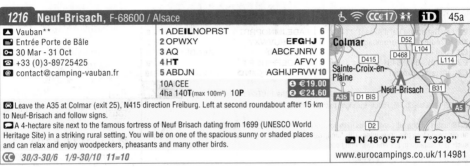

- ▲ Vauban**
- 🏠 Entrée Porte de Bâle
- 📅 30 Mar - 31 Oct
- ☎ +33 (0)3-89725425
- @ contact@camping-vauban.fr

1 ADEILNOPRST		6
2 OPWXY	EFGHJ	7
3 AQ	ABCFJNRV	8
4 HT	AFVY	9
5 ABDJN	AGHIJPRVW	10
10A CEE	❶ €19.00	
4ha 140T(max 100m²) 10P	❷ €24.60	

🚗 Leave the A35 at Colmar (exit 25), N415 direction Freiburg. Left at second roundabout after 15 km to Neuf-Brisach and follow signs.

💬 A 4-hectare site next to the famous fortress of Neuf Brisach dating from 1699 (UNESCO World Heritage Site) in a striking rural setting. You will be on one of the spacious sunny or shaded places and can relax and enjoy woodpeckers, pheasants and many other birds.

CC 30/3-30/6 1/9-30/10 11=10

▲ N 48°0'57" E 7°32'8"

www.eurocampings.co.uk/114981

45a

1217 Osenbach, F-68570 / Alsace

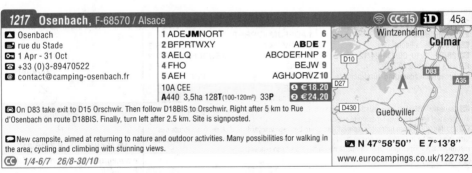

- ▲ Osenbach
- 🏠 rue du Stade
- 📅 1 Apr - 31 Oct
- ☎ +33 (0)3-89470522
- @ contact@camping-osenbach.fr

1 ADEJMNORT		6
2 BFPRTWXY	ABDE	7
3 AELQ	ABCDEFHNP	8
4 FHO	BEJW	9
5 AEH	AGHJORVZ	10
10A CEE	❶ €18.20	
A440 3,5ha 128T(100-120m²) 33P	❷ €24.20	

🚗 On D83 take exit to D15 Orschwir. Then follow D18BIS to Orschwir. Right after 5 km to Rue d'Osenbach on route D18BIS. Finally, turn left after 2.5 km. Site is signposted.

💬 New campsite, aimed at returning to nature and outdoor activities. Many possibilities for walking in the area, cycling and climbing with stunning views.

CC 1/4-6/7 26/8-30/10

▲ N 47°58'50" E 7°13'8"

www.eurocampings.co.uk/122732

45a

1218 Riquewihr, F-68340 / Alsace

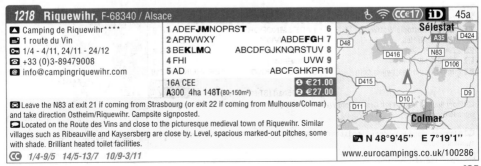

- ▲ Camping de Riquewihr****
- 🏠 1 route du Vin
- 📅 1/4 - 4/11, 24/11 - 24/12
- ☎ +33 (0)3-89479008
- @ info@campingriquewihr.com

1 ADEFJMNOPRST		6
2 APRVWXY	ABDEFGH	7
3 BEKLMQ	ABCDFGJKNQRSTUV	8
4 FHI	UVW	9
5 AD	ABCFGHKPR	10
16A CEE	❶ €21.00	
A300 4ha 148T(80-150m²)	❷ €27.00	

🚗 Leave the N83 at exit 21 if coming from Strasbourg (or exit 22 if coming from Mulhouse/Colmar) and take direction Ostheim/Riquewihr. Campsite signposted.

💬 Located on the Route des Vins and close to the picturesque medieval town of Riquewihr. Similar villages such as Ribeauville and Kaysersberg are close by. Level, spacious marked-out pitches, some with shade. Brilliant heated toilet facilities.

CC 1/4-9/5 14/5-13/7 10/9-3/11

▲ N 48°9'45" E 7°19'1"

www.eurocampings.co.uk/100286

45a

France

1219 Ste Croix-en-Plaine, F-68127 / Alsace

CC€17 iD 45a

- ClairVacances****
- route de Herrlisheim
- 20 Apr - 8 Oct
- +33 (0)3-89492728
- reception@clairvacances.com

1 ADEFHKNOPRT	ABFG	6
2 APRVWY	BEFGH	7
3 BFLQ	ABCDFJKNQRS	8
4 BHILP	J	9
5 ABDEFMN	ABCDFHIJPTU	10
16A CEE	❶ €34.60	
A185 4ha 135T(90-100m²) 12P	❷ €43.10	

Exit 27 on the A35 direction Herrlisheim. Then follow campsite signs.

ClairVacances is located near Colmar and tourist attractions, among greenery with a large variety of bushes and flowers. The site is known for its excellent amenities which are superbly maintained. Heated swimming pool from 1 May. ClairVacances will enchant you.

CC 20/4-29/6 29/8-7/10

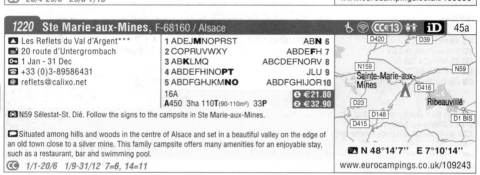

N 48°0'58'' E 7°21'1''

www.eurocampings.co.uk/109336

1220 Ste Marie-aux-Mines, F-68160 / Alsace

CC€13 iD 45a

- Les Reflets du Val d'Argent***
- 20 route d'Untergrombach
- 1 Jan - 31 Dec
- +33 (0)3-89586431
- reflets@calixo.net

1 ADEJMNOPRST	ABN	6
2 COPRUVWXY	ABDEFH	7
3 ABKLMQ	ABCDEFNORV	8
4 ABDEFHINOPT	JLU	9
5 ABDFGHJKMNO	ABDFGHIJOR	10
16A	❶ €21.80	
A450 3ha 110T(90-110m²) 33P	❷ €32.90	

N59 Sélestat-St. Dié. Follow the signs to the campsite in Ste Marie-aux-Mines.

Situated among hills and woods in the centre of Alsace and set in a beautiful valley on the edge of an old town close to a silver mine. This family campsite offers many amenities for an enjoyable stay, such as a restaurant, bar and swimming pool.

CC 1/1-20/6 1/9-31/12 7=6, 14=11

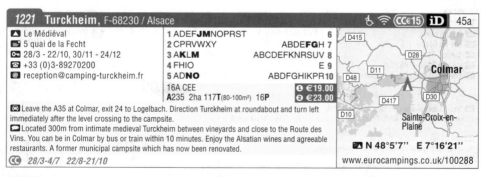

N 48°14'7'' E 7°10'14''

www.eurocampings.co.uk/109243

1221 Turckheim, F-68230 / Alsace

CC€15 iD 45a

- Le Médiéval
- 5 quai de la Fecht
- 28/3 - 22/10, 30/11 - 24/12
- +33 (0)3-89270200
- reception@camping-turckheim.fr

1 ADEFJMNOPRST		6
2 CPRVWXY	ABDEFGH	7
3 AKLM	ABCDEFKNRSUV	8
4 FHIO	E	9
5 ADNO	ABDFGHIKPR	10
16A CEE	❶ €19.00	
A235 2ha 117T(80-100m²) 16P	❷ €23.00	

Leave the A35 at Colmar, exit 24 to Logelbach. Direction Turckheim at roundabout and turn left immediately after the level crossing to the campsite.

Located 300m from intimate medieval Turckheim between vineyards and close to the Route des Vins. You can be in Colmar by bus or train within 10 minutes. Enjoy the Alsatian wines and agreeable restaurants. A former municipal campsite which has now been renovated.

CC 28/3-4/7 22/8-21/10

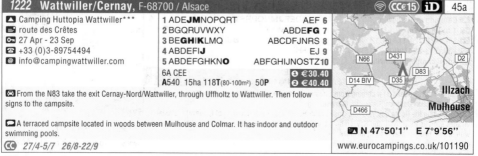

N 48°5'7'' E 7°16'21''

www.eurocampings.co.uk/100288

1222 Wattwiller/Cernay, F-68700 / Alsace

CC€15 iD 45a

- Camping Huttopia Wattwiller***
- route des Crêtes
- 27 Apr - 23 Sep
- +33 (0)3-89754494
- info@campingwattwiller.com

1 ADEJMNOPQRT	AEF	6
2 BGQRUVWXY	ABDEFG	7
3 BEGHIKLMQ	ABCDFJNRS	8
4 ABDEFIJ	EJ	9
5 ABDEFGHKNO	ABFGHIJNOSTZ	10
6A CEE	❶ €30.40	
A540 15ha 118T(80-100m²) 50P	❷ €40.40	

From the N83 take the exit Cernay-Nord/Wattwiller, through Uffholtz to Wattwiller. Then follow signs to the campsite.

A terraced campsite located in woods between Mulhouse and Colmar. It has indoor and outdoor swimming pools.

CC 27/4-5/7 26/8-22/9

N 47°50'1'' E 7°9'56''

www.eurocampings.co.uk/101190

France

Jewel of Eastern France

Bourgogne-Franche-Comté was created by merging regions Bourgogne and Franche-Comté. Located in eastern France, surrounded by Grand Est, Ile de France, Centre-Val de Loire, Auvergne-Rhone-Alpes, it borders Switzerland to the east. The landscape is arable with many farms, vineyards and dramatic mountains. Rivers, lakes and canals make this a great region to explore from water.

Influenced from south and east

Historically this region has been influenced by German migrants, and before that, Romans – the amphitheatre in Autun is a clear example. Early Stone Age settlements have been found near the Rock of Solutré near Mâcon, and you can walk along picturesque mediaeval streets and castles in towns like Autun, Dijon, Montbéliard and Vezelay. Chateau Ancy-le France is a beautiful example of Renaissance architecture.

So much to see and do!

The main city Dijon is also home to the palace of the Dukes of Burgundy and the Tower of Philip the Good. The owl is the city emblem of Dijon, get the kids to look out for it and follow the owl route! A relic from the time of German rule, the castle of the Duchy of Wurtemberg is located in Montbéliard near Belfort, and well worth checking out, as is the 16th-century market hall. You'll appreciate the steep uphill walk to the basilica on the hill at Vezelay, and you can also enjoy the views over the countryside from the city walls. Those of a creative bent will be fascinated by the construction of the Guedelon fortress near Saint-Sauveur-en-Puisaye, started in 1997, and using 13th-century techniques – a living museum.

Autun is also the gateway to Morvan National Park, a rather adventurous place: the northern part has trout in streams, and otters and deer, while the southern part has quite dangerous terrain with wild animals. Keep your camera

ready as there are wolves and lynxes in Jura National Park and Ballons des Vosges, a haven for horse-riders, mountain-bikers, hikers, and those who like flying model airplanes.

Laughing cows and mustard

You've heard of Dijon mustard, but did you know that The Laughing Cow cheese (La Vache Qui Rit) is also from here? Local dishes include Boeuf Bourguinon, civet de lievre (marinated hare stew), coq au vin, Morteau and Montebéliard sausage. And then there are the wines ...

Our tips

1. *Like modern music? Check out the Garcon al note and Catalpa music festivals in Auxerre*

2. *Visit the Musée de l'hotel-Dieu or Hospice of Baune*

3. *Explore the lakes in the heart of Vosges Nature Park*

4. *Visit the town of Besançon, with its Vauban citadel and three great museums*

5. *Petrolheads will like Sochaux, site of the Peugeot car manufacturer and Peugeot Museum*

1223 Belfort, F-90000 / Franche-Comté ♿ 📶 iD 45a

- ▲ L'Etang des Forges***
- 🏠 4 rue Béthouart
- 📅 1 Apr - 31 Oct
- ☎ +33 (0)3-84225492
- @ contact@camping-belfort.com

1 ADE**JM**NOPQRST	ABN**QS** 6
2 ADGPVWXY	ABDE**FGH** 7
3 AELQRU	CDFNOQRSV 8
4 BEFHILO	EFJUVW 9
5 ADEN	ABHIJ**PRZ**10
10A CEE	❶ €26.00
A260 3,5ha 110T(90-110m²) 19P	❷ €34.00

🚗 A36, exit 13 to Belfort (les Glacis du Château). First follow 'centre ville' signs, then follow campsite signs after about 1 km.

💬 A lovely, well-kept campsite. The lake is not directly accessible from the site. Spacious pitches, partly divided by hedges. Located in a natural area and within walking distance of the old town centre.

📷 N 47°39'12" E 6°51'54"
www.eurocampings.co.uk/110559

1224 Marnay, F-70150 / Franche-Comté ♿ 📶 (CC€15) ♜ iD 20 A1

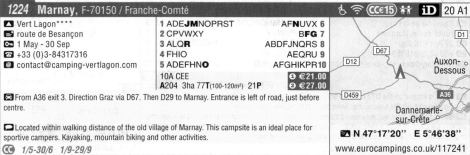

- ▲ Vert Lagon****
- 🏠 route de Besançon
- 📅 1 May - 30 Sep
- ☎ +33 (0)3-84317316
- @ contact@camping-vertlagon.com

1 ADE**JM**NOPRST	AF**N**UVX 6
2 CPVWXY	B**FG** 7
3 ALQ**R**	ABDFJNQRS 8
4 FHIO	AEQRU 9
5 ADEFHN**O**	AFGHIKPR10
10A CEE	❶ €21.00
A204 3ha 77T(100-120m²) 21P	❷ €27.00

🚗 From A36 exit 3. Direction Graz via D67. Then D29 to Marnay. Entrance is left of road, just before centre.

💬 Located within walking distance of the old village of Marnay. This campsite is an ideal place for sportive campers. Kayaking, mountain biking and other activities.

CC 1/5-30/6 1/9-29/9

📷 N 47°17'20" E 5°46'38"
www.eurocampings.co.uk/117241

1225 Vesoul, F-70000 / Franche-Comté ♿ 📶 iD 45a

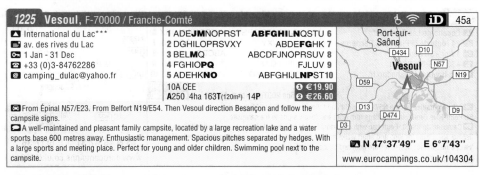

- ▲ International du Lac***
- 🏠 av. des rives du Lac
- 📅 1 Jan - 31 Dec
- ☎ +33 (0)3-84762286
- @ camping_dulac@yahoo.fr

1 ADE**JM**NOPRST	**ABFGHIL**NQSTU 6
2 DGHILOPRSVXY	ABDE**FGH**K 7
3 BEL**MQ**	ABCDFJNOPRSUV 8
4 FGHIO**PQ**	FJLUV 9
5 ADEHK**NO**	ABFGHIJL**NP**ST10
10A CEE	❶ €19.90
A250 4ha 163T(120m²) 14P	❷ €26.60

🚗 From Épinal N57/E23. From Belfort N19/E54. Then Vesoul direction Besançon and follow the campsite signs.

💬 A well-maintained and pleasant family campsite, located by a large recreation lake and a water sports base 600 metres away. Enthusiastic management. Spacious pitches separated by hedges. With a large sports and meeting place. Perfect for young and older children. Swimming pool next to the campsite.

📷 N 47°37'49" E 6°7'43"
www.eurocampings.co.uk/104304

1226 Chalezeule/Besançon, F-25220 / Franche-Comté 📶 (CC€17) iD 20 A1

- ▲ Camping de Besançon - La Plage***
- 🏠 12 route de Belfort
- 📅 15 Mar - 31 Oct
- ☎ +33 (0)3-81880426
- @ contact@campingdebesancon.com

1 ADE**JM**NOPRST	**N** 6
2 ACOPSWXY	ABDE**FGH** 7
3 AE**IK**LQ	ABCDEFHJKNOPQRSV 8
4 FHO	BE 9
5 ADE	ABDFGHIKNPR10
16A CEE	❶ €24.75
A345 2,5ha 99T(75-120m²) 10P	❷ €30.55

🚗 RD683, Belfort-Besançon. Campsite signposted from there.

💬 A campsite in a good location for visiting the World Heritage Site of Besançon. There are many opportunities for sports in and around the campsite. Fast connection to centre of Besançon with new tram.

CC 15/3-1/7 25/8-30/10 7=6

📷 N 47°15'57" E 6°4'18"
www.eurocampings.co.uk/114071

1227 Huanne-Montmartin, F-25680 / Franche-Comté
🛜 iD 20 A1

🏕 Du Bois de Reveuge****
🏠 route de Rougemont
📅 30 Apr - 21 Sep
☎ +33 (0)3-81843860
@ info@campingduboisdereveuge.com

1	ADE**JM**NOPRST	ABEFGHINU 6
2	ABDFGHIPRSTUVWXY	ABDE**FG**H 7
3	ABCDE**GHIK**LQR	ABDFNOQRSTUV 8
4	BDFHILNO**PR**	EFLPQRTUV 9
5	ABDEFGHM**N**	ABFGHIJ**NP**STVY 10

6-16A CEE ❶ €35.00
A325 24ha 168T(80-180m²) 152P ❷ €53.00

🚗 From A36 exit Baume-les-Dames, follow direction Villersexel. Follow signs 'camping Huanne'.

💬 A lovely rural 4-star campsite with an indoor swimming pool. You can go fishing, cycling, play crazy golf or visit towns (Belfort, Mont Beliard, Besançon), caves and castles.

📍 N 47°26'26'' E 6°20'36''
www.eurocampings.co.uk/101195

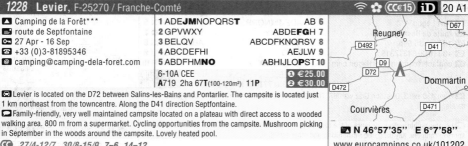

1228 Levier, F-25270 / Franche-Comté
🛜 ❀ CC€15 iD 20 A1

🏕 Camping de la Forêt***
🏠 route de Septfontaine
📅 27 Apr - 16 Sep
☎ +33 (0)3-81895346
@ camping@camping-dela-foret.com

1	ADE**JM**NOPQRS**T**	AB 6
2	GPVWXY	ABDE**FG**H 7
3	BELQV	ABCDFKNQRSV 8
4	ABCDEFHI	AEJLW 9
5	ABDFHM**NO**	ABHIJLO**P**ST 10

6-10A CEE ❶ €25.00
A719 2ha 67T(100-120m²) 11P ❷ €30.00

🚗 Levier is located on the D72 between Salins-les-Bains and Pontarlier. The campsite is located just 1 km northeast from the towncentre. Along the D41 direction Septfontaine.

💬 Family-friendly, very well maintained campsite located on a plateau with direct access to a wooded walking area. 800 m from a supermarket. Cycling opportunities from the campsite. Mushroom picking in September in the woods around the campsite. Lovely heated pool.

CC 27/4-12/7 30/8-15/9 7=6, 14=12

📍 N 46°57'35'' E 6°7'58''
www.eurocampings.co.uk/101202

1229 Malbuisson, F-25160 / Franche-Comté
♿ 🛜 CC€17 iD 20 A1

🏕 Locahome Les Fuvettes***
🏠 24 route de la Plage des Perrières
📅 1 Apr - 30 Sep
☎ +33 (0)3-81693150
@ les-fuvettes@wanadoo.fr

1	ADE**JM**NOPQRST	ABEFGHIL**N**QSX 6
2	DHKPVWXY	BDE**FG** 7
3	ABE**I**LQST	ABCDFKNQRSV 8
4	BCDFHIKLN	EJMPQRT 9
5	ACDEFGHKM**O**	ABDGHIJ**P**ST 10

6A CEE ❶ €27.90
A840 6ha 200T(80-140m²) 142P ❷ €36.30

🚗 After Pontarlier (on the N57) turn right and follow route D437 to Malbuisson direction Lac St. Point-Rive Droite. In the village turn right and follow signs to the campsite.

💬 Campsite on the St. Point Lac with opportunities for watersports recreation opportunities and fishing. Ideal base for long and short walks and for trips out in the ever-changing countryside of the 'Haut-Jura'. Indoor heated leisure pool and outdoor pool.

CC 1/4-30/6 1/9-29/9

📍 N 46°47'31'' E 6°17'36''
www.eurocampings.co.uk/104311

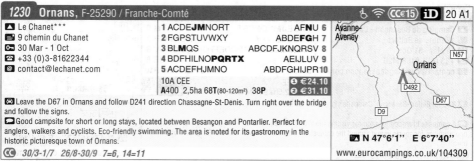

1230 Ornans, F-25290 / Franche-Comté
♿ 🛜 CC€15 iD 20 A1

🏕 Le Chanet***
🏠 9 chemin du Chanet
📅 30 Mar - 1 Oct
☎ +33 (0)3-81622344
@ contact@lechanet.com

1	ACDE**JM**NORT	AF**N**U 6
2	FGPSTUVWXY	ABDE**FG**H 7
3	BLM**Q**S	ABCDFJKNQRSV 8
4	BDFHILNO**PQRTX**	AEIJLUV 9
5	ACDEFHJMNO	ABDFGHIJPR 10

10A CEE ❶ €24.10
A400 2,5ha 68T(80-120m²) 38P ❷ €31.10

🚗 Leave the D67 in Ornans and follow D241 direction Chassagne-St-Denis. Turn right over the bridge and follow the signs.

💬 Good campsite for short or long stays, located between Besançon and Pontarlier. Perfect for anglers, walkers and cyclists. Eco-friendly swimming. The area is noted for its gastronomy in the historic picturesque town of Ornans.

CC 30/3-1/7 26/8-30/9 7=6, 14=11

📍 N 47°6'1'' E 6°7'40''
www.eurocampings.co.uk/104309

1231 Ornans, F-25290 / Franche-Comté

♿ 🛜 (CCE17) ⚥ **iD** 20 A1

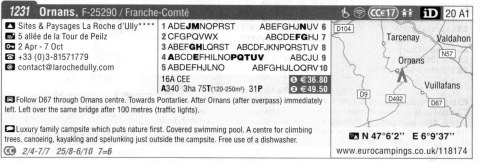

- 🔺 Sites & Paysages La Roche d'Ully★★★★
- 🏠 5 allée de la Tour de Peilz
- 📅 2 Apr - 7 Oct
- ☎ +33 (0)3-81571779
- @ contact@larochedully.com

1 ADE**JM**NOPRST	ABEFGHJ**N**UV	6
2 CFGPQVWX	ABCDE**FG**HJ	7
3 ABEF**GHL**QRST	ABCDFJKNPQRSTUV	8
4 **ABCD**EFHILNO**PQTUV**	ABCJU	9
5 ABDEFHJLNO	ABFGHIJLOQRV	10
16A CEE	❶ €36.80	
A340 3ha 75T(120-250m²) 31P	❷ €49.50	

🚗 Follow D67 through Ornans centre. Towards Pontarlier. After Ornans (after overpass) immediately left. Left over the same bridge after 100 metres (traffic lights).

💬 Luxury family campsite which puts nature first. Covered swimming pool. A centre for climbing trees, canoeing, kayaking and spelunking just outside the campsite. Free use of a dishwasher.
(CC) 2/4-7/7 25/8-6/10 7=6

📷 N 47°6'2" E 6°9'37"

www.eurocampings.co.uk/118174

1232 Bonlieu, F-39130 / Franche-Comté

♿ 🛜 (CCE15) **iD** 20 A2

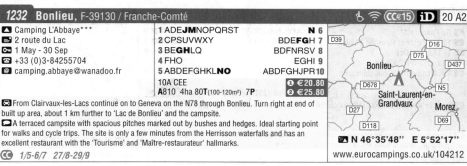

- 🔺 Camping L'Abbaye★★★
- 🏠 2 route du Lac
- 📅 1 May - 30 Sep
- ☎ +33 (0)3-84255704
- @ camping.abbaye@wanadoo.fr

1 ADE**JM**NOPQRST	N	6
2 CPSUVWXY	BDE**FG**H	7
3 BE**GH**LQ	BDFNRSV	8
4 FHO	EGHI	9
5 ABDEFGHKL**NO**	ABDFGHJPR	10
10A CEE	❶ €20.80	
A810 4ha 80T(100-120m²) 7P	❷ €25.80	

🚗 From Clairvaux-les-Lacs continue on to Geneva on the N78 through Bonlieu. Turn right at end of built up area, about 1 km further to 'Lac de Bonlieu' and the campsite.
💬 A terraced campsite with spacious pitches marked out by bushes and hedges. Ideal starting point for walks and cycle trips. The site is only a few minutes from the Herrisson waterfalls and has an excellent restaurant with the 'Tourisme' and 'Maître-restaurateur' hallmarks.
(CC) 1/5-6/7 27/8-29/9

📷 N 46°35'48" E 5°52'17"

www.eurocampings.co.uk/104212

1233 Champagnole, F-39300 / Franche-Comté

♿ 🛜 (CCE17) **iD** 20 A2

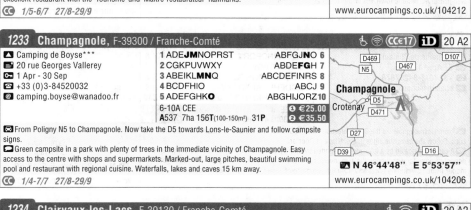

- 🔺 Camping de Boyse★★★
- 🏠 20 rue Georges Vallerey
- 📅 1 Apr - 30 Sep
- ☎ +33 (0)3-84520032
- @ camping.boyse@wanadoo.fr

1 ADE**JM**NOPRST	ABFGJ**N**O	6
2 CGKPUVWXY	ABDE**FG**H	7
3 ABEIKL**MN**Q	ABCDEFINRS	8
4 BCDFHIO	ABCJ	9
5 ADEFGHK**O**	ABGHIJORZ	10
6-10A CEE	❶ €25.00	
A537 7ha 156T(100-150m²) 31P	❷ €35.50	

🚗 From Poligny N5 to Champagnole. Now take the D5 towards Lons-le-Saunier and follow campsite signs.
💬 Green campsite in a park with plenty of trees in the immediate vicinity of Champagnole. Easy access to the centre with shops and supermarkets. Marked-out, large pitches, beautiful swimming pool and restaurant with regional cuisine. Waterfalls, lakes and caves 15 km away.
(CC) 1/4-7/7 27/8-29/9

📷 N 46°44'48" E 5°53'57"

www.eurocampings.co.uk/104206

1234 Clairvaux-les-Lacs, F-39130 / Franche-Comté

♿ 🛜 **iD** 20 A2

- 🔺 La Grisière et Europe Vacances★★★
- 🏠 chemin du Langard, BP 19
- 📅 1 May - 30 Sep
- ☎ +33 (0)3-84258048
- @ bailly@la-grisiere.com

1 ADE**JM**NOPQRST	LN**Q**SX	6
2 DHIPTVWXY	ABDE**FG**	7
3 ABELQT	BDFNORSV	8
4 FHO**P**	EQRT	9
5 ABDEFGHM**O**	AGHIJ**N**PR	10
10A	❶ €25.30	
A550 11ha 530T(100m²) 20P	❷ €29.90	

🚗 Enter Clairvaux-les-Lacs via D678. Follow D118 for a little while and then the sign 'campings'.

💬 A quiet family campsite with grass terrain that slightly slopes towards the lake. The campsite is located by the shore of the lake suitable for swimming and with a small beach.

📷 N 46°34'3" E 5°45'17"

www.eurocampings.co.uk/111314

France

1235 Clairvaux-les-Lacs, F-39130 / Franche-Comté

♿ 📶 (CC€11) iD 20 A2

- ⛺ Le Grand Lac***
- 🏕 chemin du Langard
- 🗓 19 May - 23 Sep
- ☎ +33 (0)3-84252214
- @ grandlac@odesia.eu

1 ADE**IL**NOPQRS**T**	ABFGLMM**N**QSX	6
2 DGHIPRUVWXY	ABD**EFG**	7
3 AEFLQT	ABCDFIKNORSV	8
4 ABDFHIL	BELT	9
5 ABDGN	ABDGHIJORV	10
10A CEE	❶ €29.00	
A560 6ha 147T(80-100m²) 61P	❷ €35.30	

🚗 Enter Clairvaux-les-Lacs via the D678. Follow the D118 then the campsite signs.
💬 A quiet family campsite with direct access to the lake and the public beach (patrolled in high season). Within walking distance of the centre. Gently sloping grounds with mostly shaded pitches. The grounds are fenced and access to the beach is via a gate with an entry code (safe for small children). There is a pool on the campsite.
CC 19/5-6/7 25/8-22/9

Perrigny
La Chaux-du-Dombief
Orgelet
📷 N 46°34'6'' E 5°45'19''
www.eurocampings.co.uk/112982

1236 Dole, F-39100 / Franche-Comté

♿ 📶 (CC€15) iD 20 A1

- ⛺ Du Pasquier***
- 🏕 18 ch. Victor et Georges Thévenot
- 🗓 15 Mar - 15 Oct
- ☎ +33 (0)3-84720261
- @ lola@camping-le-pasquier.com

1 ADE**JM**NORST	AB**N**	6
2 ACGKPVWXY	ACD**FG**	7
3 BLQST	ABDEFNQRS	8
4 N	BEKQUV	9
5 ABDEFHM	ABFGHIJPR	10
10A	❶ €22.10	
A220 2ha 120T(80-110m²) 13P	❷ €30.70	

🚗 From the A36 take the Dole exit. In Dole follow 'camping' or 'stade-camping' signs.

💬 A friendly and attractive campsite 15 minutes' walk from the town centre. The town of Dole is a well-preserved historic town, the birthplace of Louis Pasteur.
CC 15/3-6/7 25/8-14/10

Orchamps
Dole
Tavaux
📷 N 47°5'22'' E 5°30'11''
www.eurocampings.co.uk/104203

1237 Doucier, F-39130 / Franche-Comté

♿ 📶 (CC€17) iD 20 A2

- ⛺ Domaine de Chalain****
- 🗓 27 Apr - 17 Sep
- ☎ +33 (0)3-84257878
- @ chalain@chalain.com

1 ADE**JM**NOPQR**T**	AEFGHILM**N**QSUXY	6
2 DGHKPUVWXY	BE**FG**H	7
3 ABEF**IJLM**QRTV	BDFJKNRS	8
4 BCDFHIKLMO**TUVY**	EFJKLQRTU	9
5 ACDEFGHKM**NO**	ABDFGHIJ**N**PRYZ	10
10A CEE	❶ €43.00	
A474 30ha 417T(90-120m²) 231P	❷ €49.00	

🚗 From Champagnole via the D471 direction Lons-le-Saunier. Via the D27 direction Clairvaux-les-Lacs. Follow the campsite signs in the village of Doucier.
💬 A campsite located by a lake and surrounded by a richly wooded and hilly landscape. An excellent departure point for discovering the area: rivers, panoramas, waterfalls. Water park with 400 m² of indoor heated swimming pools and from the beginning of June 500 m² of outdoor pools.
CC 27/4-6/7 1/9-16/9

Champagnole
Saint-Laurent-en-Grandvaux
📷 N 46°39'51'' E 5°48'50''
www.eurocampings.co.uk/100362

1238 Doucier, F-39130 / Franche-Comté

♿ 📶 (CC€15) iD 20 A2

- ⛺ Les Merilles***
- 🏕 rue des 3 Lacs
- 🗓 15 Apr - 30 Sep
- ☎ +33 (0)3-84257306
- @ camping.lesmerilles@wanadoo.fr

1 ADE**JM**NOPRT	ABFG**N**U	6
2 CGPVWXY	ABDE**FG**H	7
3 BE**GH**LQS	ABCDEFIJKLNORSV	8
4 ABCDEFHINO**P**	DEJQRUW	9
5 ABDEFHM**NO**	ABDGHIJ**P**R	10
6-10A CEE	❶ €27.80	
A513 2ha 96T(80-140m²) 20P	❷ €34.80	

🚗 In Doucier via the D27 follow signs to Clairvaux-les-Lacs. Campsite located 150 metres from the outskirts of Doucier.
💬 A friendly campsite close to lakes and waterfalls. The village with various restaurants and shops is within walking distance. You can walk and cycle in beautiful and surprising countryside. You will find information about numerous trips out in the Jura at the reception.
CC 15/4-30/6 31/8-29/9

Champagnole
Saint-Laurent-en-Grandvaux
📷 N 46°39'6'' E 5°46'29''
www.eurocampings.co.uk/108845

France

1239 Ecrille, F-39270 / Franche-Comté

♿ 🛜 ⓒⓒ€15 **iD** 20 A2

▲ La Faz***
🏠 4 Pont de Vaux
🔓 1 May - 30 Sep
☎ +33 (0)3-84254027
@ campinglafaz@gmail.com

1 A**IL**NOPQRST	AB**N**X	6
2 CGPVXY	ABD**F**	7
3 BELQ	BCDFNRV	8
4 BCDFHIO**Q**	DEJL	9
5 ABDEFGHN**O**	ABGIJO**P**STV	10
6A CEE	💶 €22.50	
A402 6ha 99**T**(100-150m²) 16**P**	💶 €29.50	

🚗 From Lons-le-Saunier D52 direction Orgelet via the D678 and then D52e and D52 as far as Orgelet. Take the D470 and turn immediately right to Ecrille. Follow campsite signs.

💬 A campsite located in extensive grounds by a river and a stone's throw from Lake Vouglans. The area is perfect for peace, relaxation and nature walks. Pitches marked out by hedges. There is a snack bar and a swimming pool. No toilet facilities in April and October.

ⓒⓒ 1/5-6/7 27/8-29/9

🗺 N 46°30'35'' E 5°37'14''

www.eurocampings.co.uk/112453

1240 La Tour-du-Meix, F-39270 / Franche-Comté

🛜 ⓒⓒ€13 **iD** 20 A2

▲ Domaine du Surchauffant***
🏠 Le Pont de la Pyle
🔓 27 Apr - 17 Sep
☎ +33 (0)3-84254108
@ info@camping-surchauffant.fr

1 ADE**JM**NOPQRST	ABF**L**NQSWXY**Z**	6
2 DGHPUVWXY	ABDE**FG**	7
3 ABLQ	ABCDFKNRSTV	8
4 BCDFGHIO	EJKLU	9
5 ABDEFGHKL**N**	ABGHIJ**P**R**Z**10	
10A CEE	💶 €25.50	
A455 3ha 156**T**(80-110m²) 48**P**	💶 €33.50	

🚗 From Lons-le-Saunier take the N78 then the D52. In Orgelet take D470 direction St. Claude. Follow campsite signs.

💬 An extensive campsite sloping down to the lake. marked-out pitches, some with shade. Various watersports possibilities in the swimming pool and in the lake.

ⓒⓒ 27/4-6/7 1/9-16/9

🗺 N 46°31'24'' E 5°40'27''

www.eurocampings.co.uk/100364

France

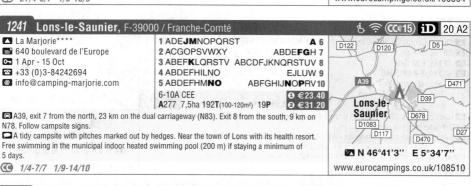

1241 Lons-le-Saunier, F-39000 / Franche-Comté

♿ 🛜 ⓒⓒ€15 **iD** 20 A2

▲ La Marjorie****
🏠 640 boulevard de l'Europe
🔓 1 Apr - 15 Oct
☎ +33 (0)3-84242694
@ info@camping-marjorie.com

1 ADE**JM**NOPQRST	A	6
2 ACGOPSVWXY	ABDE**FGH**	7
3 ABEF**K**LQRSTV ABCDFJKNQRSTUV		8
4 ABDEFHILNO	EJLUW	9
5 ABDEFHM**NO**	ABFGHIJ**N**OP RV	10
6-10A CEE	💶 €23.40	
A277 7,5ha 192**T**(100-120m²) 19**P**	💶 €31.20	

🚗 A39, exit 7 from the north, 23 km on the dual carriageway (N83). Exit 8 from the south, 9 km on N78. Follow campsite signs.

💬 A tidy campsite with pitches marked out by hedges. Near the town of Lons with its health resort. Free swimming in the municipal indoor heated swimming pool (200 m) if staying a minimum of 5 days.

ⓒⓒ 1/4-7/7 1/9-14/10

🗺 N 46°41'3'' E 5°34'7''

www.eurocampings.co.uk/108510

1242 Maisod, F-39260 / Franche-Comté

🛜 **iD** 20 A2

▲ Trélachaume***
🏠 50 route du Mont du Cerf
🔓 22 Apr - 9 Sep
☎ +33 (0)3-84420326
@ info@trelachaume.fr

1 ADE**JM**NOPRST	ABF**N**OQSWXY**Z**	6
2 FGHIPRUVWXY	ABDE**FG**H	7
3 BELQ	ABCDFNQR	8
4 BEFHIO	AEFJLOPQR	9
5 ABDEFGHK**N**	ABHIJ**O**R10	
5-10A CEE	💶 €26.80	
A530 3,5ha 180**T**(80-200m²) 36**P**	💶 €34.20	

🚗 From Lons-le-Saunier take the D52 to Orgelet, via the D470 direction St. Claude. After Pont de la Pyle follow signs to Maisod, then campsite signs. Caravans need to follow the N78 from Lons due to a steep slope (signposted).

💬 Beautiful, spacious, and with a view of the large Vouglans reservoir, this campsite is perfect for families with young children. The lake provides plenty of water sports options and the large beach is easily accessible by car. The campsite has various amenities for the disabled.

🗺 N 46°28'7'' E 5°41'19''

www.eurocampings.co.uk/104217

1243 Mesnois/Clairvaux-les-Lacs, F-39130 / Franche-Comté   ⬆ 🤸 (CC€17) iD 20 A2

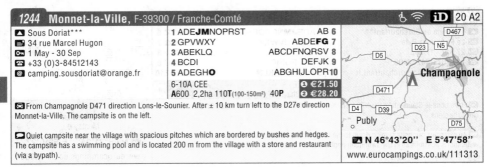

▲ Sites & Paysages Beauregard★★★★
🏠 2 Grande rue Mesnois
📅 29 Mar - 30 Sep
☎ +33 (0)3-84483251
@ reception@
   juracampingbeauregard.com

1 ADEJMNOPQRST	AEFGHIN 6
2 PVXY	BEFGH 7
3 BEILMQTV	BDFJKNORSUV 8
4 BFHITUVY	AE 9
5 ABDFGHKLNO	ABDFGHIJPST 10
6A	❶ €31.30
A460 6ha 195T(100-120m²) 49P	❷ €40.10

Lons-le-Saunier

🚗 From Lons-le-Saunier via the D52 direction Clairvaux-les-Lacs. Caravans go via the D678 (D52 prohibited for caravans). Follow the campsite signs.
💬 A well maintained, friendly family campsite with fitness apparatus, playground and bouncy castle in rustic surroundings. An ideal location for exploring this surprising region. Excellent restaurant! New indoor pool with water slide.

▦ N 46°35'59'' E 5°41'18''
www.eurocampings.co.uk/104211

CC 29/3-6/7 26/8-29/9

1244 Monnet-la-Ville, F-39300 / Franche-Comté   ⬆ 🤸 iD 20 A2

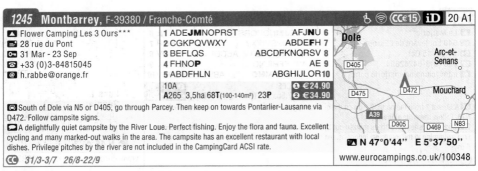

▲ Sous Doriat★★★
🏠 34 rue Marcel Hugon
📅 1 May - 30 Sep
☎ +33 (0)3-84512143
@ camping.sousdoriat@orange.fr

1 ADEJMNOPRST	AB 6
2 GPVWXY	ABDEFG 7
3 ABEKLQ	ABCDFNQRSV 8
4 BCDI	DEFJK 9
5 ADEGHO	ABGHIJLOPR 10
6-10A CEE	❶ €21.50
A600 2,2ha 110T(100-150m²) 40P	❷ €28.20

Champagnole
Publy

🚗 From Champagnole D471 direction Lons-le-Saunier. After ± 10 km turn left to the D27e direction Monnet-la-Ville. The campsite is on the left.

💬 Quiet campsite near the village with spacious pitches which are bordered by bushes and hedges. The campsite has a swimming pool and is located 200 m from the village with a store and restaurant (via a bypath).

▦ N 46°43'20'' E 5°47'58''
www.eurocampings.co.uk/111313

1245 Montbarrey, F-39380 / Franche-Comté   ⬆ 🤸 (CC€15) iD 20 A1

▲ Flower Camping Les 3 Ours★★★
🏠 28 rue du Pont
📅 31 Mar - 23 Sep
☎ +33 (0)3-84815045
@ h.rabbe@orange.fr

1 ADEJMNOPRST	AFJNU 6
2 CGKPQVWXY	ABDEFH 7
3 BEFLQS	ABCDFKNORSV 8
4 FHNOP	AE 9
5 ABDFHLN	ABGHIJLOR 10
10A	❶ €24.90
A265 3,5ha 68T(100-140m²) 23P	❷ €34.90

Dole
Arc-et-Senans
Mouchard

🚗 South of Dole via N5 or D405, go through Parcey. Then keep on towards Pontarlier-Lausanne via D472. Follow campsite signs.
💬 A delightfully quiet campsite by the River Loue. Perfect fishing. Enjoy the flora and fauna. Excellent cycling and many marked-out walks in the area. The campsite has an excellent restaurant with local dishes. Privilege pitches by the river are not included in the CampingCard ACSI rate.

▦ N 47°0'44'' E 5°37'50''
www.eurocampings.co.uk/100348

CC 31/3-3/7 26/8-22/9

1246 Ounans, F-39380 / Franche-Comté   ⬆ 🤸 (CC€17) iD 20 A1

▲ Huttopia La Plage Blanche★★★
🏠 2 rue de la Plage
📅 27 Apr - 23 Sep
☎ +33 (0)3-84376963
@ plageblanche@huttopia.com

1 ADEJMNOPRST	AEFJMNUV 6
2 CGIJPVWXY	ABDEFGH 7
3 ABELQ	ABCDEFJKNQRSV 8
4 BCDFHILOPQ	AELQRU 9
5 ABDEFGHN	ABDGHIJNOR 10
6-10A CEE	❶ €31.30
A220 17ha 180T(120-200m²) 40P	❷ €41.45

Dole
Arc-et-Senans
Arbois

🚗 N5 Dole-Poligny. After about 18 km from Dole at Mont-sous-Vaudrey take the D472 in the direction of Pontarlier. Then follow the campsite signs.
💬 An extensive grassy campsite along the river, partly shaded. Countless opportunities for walking and cycling in the wooded surroundings. The Jura with its waterfalls, lakes, villages and towns is not far away. Free wifi. CampingCard ACSI is not valid for pitches on the river.

▦ N 47°0'9'' E 5°39'49''
www.eurocampings.co.uk/100361

CC 27/4-5/7 26/8-22/9

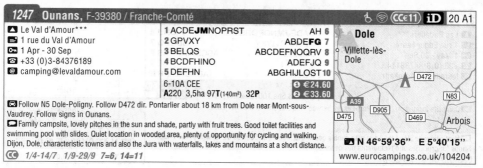

1247 Ounans, F-39380 / Franche-Comté

♿ 🛜 (CC€11) iD 20 A1

🏕 Le Val d'Amour***
✉ 1 rue du Val d'Amour
🗓 1 Apr - 30 Sep
☎ +33 (0)3-84376189
@ camping@levaldamour.com

1	ACDEJMNOPRST	AH	6
2	GPVXY	ABDEFG	7
3	BELQS	ABCDEFNOQRV	8
4	BCDFHINO	ADEFJQ	9
5	DEFHN	ABGHIJLOST	10
6-10A CEE		① €24.60	
A220 3,5ha 97T(140m²) 32P		② €33.60	

🚗 Follow N5 Dole-Poligny. Follow D472 dir. Pontarlier about 18 km from Dole near Mont-sous-Vaudrey. Follow signs in Ounans.
💬 Family campsite, lovely pitches in the sun and shade, partly with fruit trees. Good toilet facilities and swimming pool with slides. Quiet location in wooded area, plenty of opportunity for cycling and walking. Dijon, Dole, characteristic towns and also the Jura with waterfalls, lakes and mountains at a short distance.
Ⓒ 1/4-14/7 1/9-29/9 7=6, 14=11

Dole
Villette-lès-Dole
Arbois

🧭 N 46°59'36'' E 5°40'15''
www.eurocampings.co.uk/104204

1248 Parcey, F-39100 / Franche-Comté

♿ 🛜 (CC€15) iD 20 A1

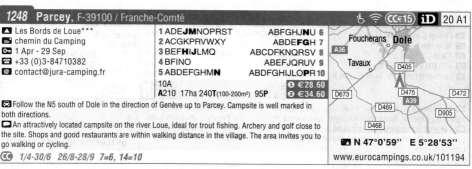

🏕 Les Bords de Loue***
✉ chemin du Camping
🗓 1 Apr - 29 Sep
☎ +33 (0)3-84710382
@ contact@jura-camping.fr

1	ADEJMNOPRST	ABFGHJNU	6
2	ACGKPRVWXY	ABDEFGH	7
3	BEFHIJLMQ	ABCDFKNQRSV	8
4	BFINO	ABEFJQRUV	9
5	ABDEFGHMN	ABDFGHIJLOPR	10
10A		① €28.60	
A210 17ha 240T(100-200m²) 95P		② €34.60	

🚗 Follow the N5 south of Dole in the direction of Genève up to Parcey. Campsite is well marked in both directions.
💬 An attractively located campsite on the river Loue, ideal for trout fishing. Archery and golf close to the site. Shops and good restaurants are within walking distance in the village. The area invites you to go walking or cycling.
Ⓒ 1/4-30/6 26/8-28/9 7=6, 14=10

Foucherans Dole
Tavaux

🧭 N 47°0'59'' E 5°28'53''
www.eurocampings.co.uk/101194

1249 Patornay, F-39130 / Franche-Comté

♿ 🛜 (CC€17) iD 20 A2

🏕 Le Moulin****
✉ chemin du Camping
🗓 27 Apr - 16 Sep
☎ +33 (0)3-84483121
@ contact@camping-moulin.com

1	ADEILNOPRT	ABCDFGHJNUX	6
2	CGKPVXY	ABDEFG	7
3	ABELQ	BDFKNQRSV	8
4	ABCDHILNOTUV	EFJL	9
5	ABDEFGHMNO	ABDGHIJNOPST	10
6A CEE		① €35.60	
A455 5ha 217T(80-100m²) 111P		② €45.60	

🚗 From Lons-le-Saunier via the D52 direction Clairvaux-les-Lacs. Caravans via the D678. D52 is prohibited for caravans. Follow campsite signs in Patornay.
💬 A campsite with plenty of greenery and shade. Outdoor swimming pool with slide and indoor pool with sauna thanks to a sliding roof. Located by a river with a beach and plenty of water sports opportunities.
Ⓒ 27/4-6/7 26/8-15/9 7=6

Lons-le-Saunier

🧭 N 46°35'14'' E 5°42'3''
www.eurocampings.co.uk/104213

1250 Pont-de-Poitte, F-39130 / Franche-Comté

♿ 🛜 iD 20 A2

🏕 Des Pêcheurs***
✉ 9 chemin de la Plage
🗓 15 Jun - 9 Sep
☎ +33 (0)3-84483133
@ contact@camping-pecheurs.com

1	ADEJMNOPRT	JNUX	6
2	CGPVWXY	ABDEFG	7
3	BELQT	ABCDEFNQRV	8
4	IO	CER	9
5	ADHMNO	ABHJPST	10
6A CEE		① €24.00	
A444 3,5ha 145T(80-150m²) 32P		② €30.00	

🚗 From Lons-le-Saunier via D52 direction Clairvaux-les-Lacs. Caravans should take the D678. D52 is forbidden for caravans. Follow the campsite signs in Pont-de-Poitte.

💬 A peaceful campsite with both sunny and shaded pitches by a river (the Ain) and within walking distance of the village centre. Perfect for fishing and exploring the Jura.

Lons-le-Saunier

🧭 N 46°35'13'' E 5°41'43''
www.eurocampings.co.uk/110380

France

1251 Port-Lesney, F-39600 / Franche-Comté   ♿ 🛜 (CC€15) 🚻 iD 20 A1

🏕 Les Radeliers***
📧 1 rue Edgar Faure
🗓 1 May - 30 Sep
☎ +33 (0)3-84738144
@ lesradeliers@woka.fr

1 ADE**JM**NOPQRS**T**		**J**NU 6
2 CJKPRVWXY		ABDE**FG** 7
3 BL**MQ**		ABCDFIKNPRS 8
4 DFHI		BE 9
5 DEH		ADFGHJLPR10
8A CEE		❶ €23.60
A300 3,5ha 100T(max 80m²) 11P		❷ €31.60

🗺 Campsite located on D48 in Port-Lesney between the church and the river Loue.

💬 Neat campsite along the Loue with pebble beach and located just beside the church in the village. Shops for groceries and restaurants beside the campsite.

(CC) 1/5-30/6 1/9-29/9

📍 N 47°0'12'' E 5°49'25''

www.eurocampings.co.uk/118671

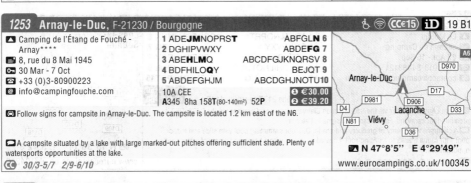

1252 Villard-Saint-Sauveur, F-39200 / Franche-Comté   ♿ 🛜 (CC€15) iD 20 A2

🏕 Flower Camping Le Martinet***
📧 12 le Martinet
🗓 1 Apr - 30 Sep
☎ +33 (0)3-84450040
@ contact@camping-saint-claude.fr

1 ADE**JM**NOPRST		ABFG**N** 6
2 CGPRSTUVWXY		ABDE**FG**H 7
3 A**KLMN**QS		ABCDFJKNQRSTUV 8
4 FHIO		ABFJLU 9
5 ABDEFGHKN		ABFGHJPRV10
10A CEE		❶ €20.90
A450 3ha 110T(50-100m²) 21P		❷ €28.40

🗺 On entering St. Claude from the west, cross the bridge over the Bienne via de D436. Immediately right at the cathedral. Follow campsite signs. Narrow entrance to campsite. Beware of oncoming traffic.
💬 A very large and completely renovated campsite on the River Tacon. It has a large swimming pool complex. St. Claude is a picturesque village in the south of the high Jura with views of the beautiful rock formations.

(CC) 1/4-7/7 1/9-29/9

📍 N 46°22'18'' E 5°52'21''

www.eurocampings.co.uk/104219

1253 Arnay-le-Duc, F-21230 / Bourgogne   ♿ 🛜 (CC€15) iD 19 B1

🏕 Camping de l'Étang de Fouché - Arnay****
📧 8, rue du 8 Mai 1945
🗓 30 Mar - 7 Oct
☎ +33 (0)3-80900223
@ info@campingfouche.com

1 ADE**JM**NOPRS**T**		ABFGL**N** 6
2 DGHIPVWXY		ABDE**FG** 7
3 ABE**HLMQ**		ABCDFGJKNQRSV 8
4 BDFHILO**QY**		BEJQT 9
5 ABDEFGHJM		ABCDGHJNOTU10
10A CEE		❶ €30.00
A345 8ha 158T(80-140m²) 52P		❷ €39.20

🗺 Follow signs for campsite in Arnay-le-Duc. The campsite is located 1.2 km east of the N6.

💬 A campsite situated by a lake with large marked-out pitches offering sufficient shade. Plenty of watersports opportunities at the lake.

(CC) 30/3-5/7 2/9-6/10

📍 N 47°8'5'' E 4°29'49''

www.eurocampings.co.uk/100345

1254 Athée, F-21130 / Bourgogne   🛜 (CC€17) iD 19 B1

🏕 De l'Arquebuse***
📧 D24
🗓 15 Jan - 23 Dec
☎ +33 (0)3-80310689
@ camping.arquebuse@wanadoo.fr

1 ADE**JM**NOPRST		**ABFN**WXYZ 6
2 ACGPRVWXY		ABDE**FG** 7
3 BLQST		ABCDFJNORTV 8
4 O**PQ**		BE 9
5 ABDFGHJLM		ABDHIJN**PR**10
10A CEE		❶ €21.80
A180 4,5ha 100T(100m²) 29P		❷ €28.00

🗺 From Dijon take the N5 in the dir. of Auxonne. Before Auxonne exit D24, direction Athée. The campsite is located on the right after about 500m.
💬 A peaceful campsite right next to the River Saône. Bar/restaurant with big-screen TV. Large open-air swimming pool next to the site and all sorts of watersports on the river. Restaurant closed Sunday and Monday in the low season. You can walk along the Saône to Auxonne with its various shops and restaurants.

(CC) 1/5-25/6 9/9-30/9

📍 N 47°11'56'' E 5°22'57''

www.eurocampings.co.uk/104201

France

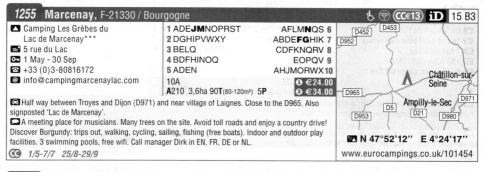

1255 Marcenay, F-21330 / Bourgogne   ♿ 🛜 (CC€13) iD 15 B3

▲ Camping Les Grèbes du
  Lac de Marcenay***
🏠 5 rue du Lac
🗓 1 May - 30 Sep
☎ +33 (0)3-80816172
@ info@campingmarcenaylac.com

1 ADE**JM**NOPRST	AFLMN**Q**S 6
2 DGHIPVWXY	ABDE**FG**HIK 7
3 BELQ	CDFKNQRV 8
4 BDFHINOQ	EOPQV 9
5 ADEN	AHJMORWX 10
10A	
A210 3,6ha 90**T**(80-120m²) 5**P**	❶ €24.00 ❷ €34.00

🚗 Half way between Troyes and Dijon (D971) and near village of Laignes. Close to the D965. Also signposted 'Lac de Marcenay'.
💬 A meeting place for musicians. Many trees on the site. Avoid toll roads and enjoy a country drive! Discover Burgundy: trips out, walking, cycling, sailing, fishing (free boats). Indoor and outdoor play facilities. 3 swimming pools, free wifi. Call manager Dirk in EN, FR, DE or NL.
CC 1/5-7/7 25/8-29/9

N 47°52'12'' E 4°24'17''
www.eurocampings.co.uk/101454

1256 Montbard, F-21500 / Bourgogne   ♿ 🛜 (CC€15) iD 15 B3

▲ Municipal de Montbard
  'Les Treilles'***
🏠 rue Michel Servet
🗓 1 Apr - 31 Oct
☎ +33 (0)3-80926950
@ camping.lestreilles@montbard.fr

1 ADE**JM**NOPRS**T**	ABEFG**H**N 6
2 FPSVWXY	ABDE**FG**HK 7
3 ABLMNQ	ABCDEFJNQRSTUV 8
4 BDEFHIOQ**TUV**Y	EJ 9
5 ADEHJN	ABDFGHJPRVZ 10
16A CEE	
2,5ha 78**T**(100-150m²) 21**P**	❶ €20.10 ❷ €27.30

🚗 Follow D980 around Montbard town. Turn off to the north at sharp bend between the Canal de Bourgogne and the D5 to Laignes. Signposted 'Camping/Piscine'.
💬 A campsite with large shaded pitches in a region that is rich in historical heritage and gastronomy. Located near a swimming pool complex (free entry for campers, closed till 18/4 and from 1/9 to 15/9) and the Canal de Bourgogne. Bakery service, bar, wifi, tennis, volleyball, billiards.
CC 1/4-6/7 24/8-30/10

N 47°37'52'' E 4°19'56''
www.eurocampings.co.uk/113283

France

1257 Pontailler-sur-Saône, F-21270 / Bourgogne   🛜 (CC€15) iD 19 B1

▲ La Chanoie***
🏠 46 rue de la Chanoie
🗓 15 Mar - 15 Oct
☎ +33 (0)3-80672198
@ camping.municipal1@orange.fr

1 ADE**JM**NOPRST	JN**X**YZ 6
2 CGHIPVWXY	ABDE**FG** 7
3 ABEQ	ABCDEFIKNOSUV 8
4 FHN	DEJ 9
5 ADFHJKMN	AHIJOR 10
10A	
A175 6ha 160**T**(80-120m²) 11**P**	❶ €16.50 ❷ €20.50

🚗 Coming from Dijon on D959, drive through Pontailler-sur-Saone and turn left before bridge. Follow campsite signs.
💬 Campsite located on the Saône, with a large lawn and a small sandy beach. There's a lovely view of the river from the restaurant's terrace. The surrounding area is great for water sports, walking, and cycling.
CC 15/3-6/7 24/8-14/10

N 47°18'31'' E 5°25'32''
www.eurocampings.co.uk/115208

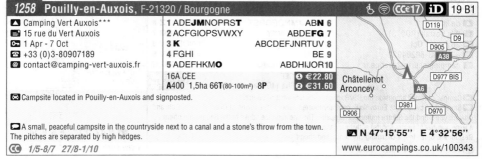

1258 Pouilly-en-Auxois, F-21320 / Bourgogne   ♿ 🛜 (CC€17) iD 19 B1

▲ Camping Vert Auxois***
🏠 15 rue du Vert Auxois
🗓 1 Apr - 7 Oct
☎ +33 (0)3-80907189
@ contact@camping-vert-auxois.fr

1 ADE**JM**NOPRS**T**	AB**N** 6
2 ACFGIOPSVWXY	ABDE**FG** 7
3 **K**	ABCDEFJNRTUV 8
4 FGHI	BE 9
5 ADEFHKM**O**	ABDHIJOR 10
16A CEE	
A400 1,5ha 66**T**(80-100m²) 8**P**	❶ €22.80 ❷ €31.60

🚗 Campsite located in Pouilly-en-Auxois and signposted.

💬 A small, peaceful campsite in the countryside next to a canal and a stone's throw from the town. The pitches are separated by high hedges.
CC 1/5-8/7 27/8-1/10

N 47°15'55'' E 4°32'56''
www.eurocampings.co.uk/100343

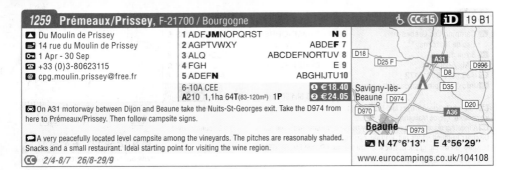

1259 Prémeaux/Prissey, F-21700 / Bourgogne   🚶 CC€15 iD 19 B1

- 🏕 Du Moulin de Prissey
- 🏠 14 rue du Moulin de Prissey
- 🗓 1 Apr - 30 Sep
- ☎ +33 (0)3-80623115
- @ cpg.moulin.prissey@free.fr

1 ADF**JM**NOPQRST	**N** 6	
2 AGPTVWXY	ABDE**F** 7	
3 ALQ	ABCDEFNORTUV 8	
4 FGH	E 9	
5 ADEF**N**	ABGHIJTU10	
6-10A CEE	❶ €18.40	
A210 1,1ha 64**T**(83-120m²) 1**P**	❷ €24.05	

🚗 On A31 motorway between Dijon and Beaune take the Nuits-St-Georges exit. Take the D974 from here to Prémeaux/Prissey. Then follow campsite signs.

🛈 A very peacefully located level campsite among the vineyards. The pitches are reasonably shaded. Snacks and a small restaurant. Ideal starting point for visiting the wine region.

CC 2/4-8/7 26/8-29/9

📍 N 47°6'13'' E 4°56'29''

www.eurocampings.co.uk/104108

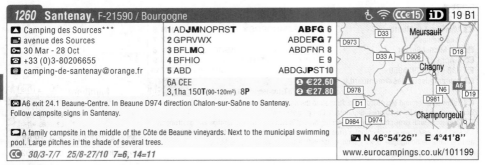

1260 Santenay, F-21590 / Bourgogne   🚶 📶 CC€15 iD 19 B1

- 🏕 Camping des Sources***
- 🏠 avenue des Sources
- 🗓 30 Mar - 28 Oct
- ☎ +33 (0)3-80206655
- @ camping-de-santenay@orange.fr

1 AD**JM**NOPRS**T**	**ABFG** 6	
2 GPRVWX	ABDE**FG** 7	
3 B**F**L**MQ**	ABDFNR 8	
4 B**F**HIO	E 9	
5 ABD	ABDGJ**P**ST10	
6A CEE	❶ €22.60	
3,1ha 150**T**(90-120m²) 8**P**	❷ €27.80	

🚗 A6 exit 24.1 Beaune-Centre. In Beaune D974 direction Chalon-sur-Saône to Santenay. Follow campsite signs in Santenay.

🛈 A family campsite in the middle of the Côte de Beaune vineyards. Next to the municipal swimming pool. Large pitches in the shade of several trees.

CC 30/3-7/7 25/8-27/10 7=6, 14=11

📍 N 46°54'26'' E 4°41'8''

www.eurocampings.co.uk/101199

1261 Saulieu, F-21210 / Bourgogne   🚶 📶 CC€15 iD 19 B1

- 🏕 Camping de Saulieu***
- 🏠 Le Perron
- 🗓 30 Mar - 28 Oct
- ☎ +33 (0)3-80641619
- @ camping.saulieu@wanadoo.fr

1 ADE**JM**NOPQRS**T**	AF**N** 6	
2 GPRVWXY	ABDE**FG**H 7	
3 BE**GH**ILMQ	ABCDFJNQRSTUV 8	
4 **ABCD**E**FHILOPQX**	EFJKLUV 9	
5 ABDEGHJN**O**	ABDGHIJO**P**R**W**10	
10A CEE	❶ €21.70	
A540 6ha 63**T**(100-110m²) 38**P**	❷ €27.70	

🚗 Campsite located near the north exit of the town on the N6.

🛈 A campsite located in the countryside with large, sunny camping pitches and a swimming pool. Countless recreational possibilities in the immediate vicinity.

CC 30/3-7/7 25/8-27/10 7=6, 14=11

📍 N 47°17'22'' E 4°13'26''

www.eurocampings.co.uk/104102

1262 Seurre/Pouilly-sur-Saône, F-21250 / Bourgogne   🚶 📶 CC€13 iD 19 B1

- 🏕 de la Plage**
- 🏠 3 le Portail (RD973)
- 🗓 28 Apr - 1 Oct
- ☎ +33 (0)3-80204922
- @ camping.seurre@orange.fr

1 A**JM**NOPQRST	**ABFHN**QSWXY**Z** 6	
2 ACGPWXY	BE**FG** 7	
3 BLQ	BFNORTUV 8	
4 H	EPQRTUV 9	
5 ADEFHKL**NO**	ABHIJORZ10	
6-10A CEE	❶ €17.00	
A180 6ha 110**T**(98-100m²) 2**P**	❷ €22.40	

🚗 Campsite located alongside the D973 towards Beaune west of Seurre.

🛈 Situated on cycle route Eurovélo 6, centrally located between the towns of Dijon, Beaune, Dole and Chalon, you'll find the Seurre municipal campsite. The site is on the banks of the Saone, and offers a large number of (water sports) activities: canoe rental, pedal boating, water skiing, and fishing. Restaurant. Close to the charming city centre and shops.

CC 28/4-15/6 30/6-6/7 25/8-30/9

📍 N 47°0'1'' E 5°8'14''

www.eurocampings.co.uk/100347

1263 Vandenesse-en-Auxois, F-21320 / Bourgogne

♿ 📶 (CC€17) ✛✛ **iD** 19 B1

🏕 Lac de Panthier****
📧 1 chemin du Lac
📅 30 Mar - 30 Sep
☎ +33 (0)3-80492194
@ info@lac-de-panthier.com

1	ADEJMNOPRST	AEFHLNQRSTXY	6
2	ADFGHLPRVWXY	ABDEFGK	7
3	ABDHKLQS	ABCDEFGJKNQRSTUV	8
4	BCDFGHILNOQRTX	BELOPQUV	9
5	ABDFGHKLMNO	ABCDFGHIJLNOPSTWZ	10
6A CEE		❶ €28.80	
A390 7ha 127T(110-150m²) 73P		❷ €39.80	

🚗 Leave motorway at A6 and A38 intersection near Pouilly-en-Auxois. Then follow Dijon, Créancey and campsite signs.

🏕 A campsite located between a lake and the edge of a wood. Pitches marked out by hedges with sufficient shade, some of which have a view of the lake. There is also an indoor swimming pool. The restaurant and pavement cafe have a panoramic view.

(CC) 30/3-6/7 26/8-29/9 7=6, 14=11

📍 N 47°14'13'' E 4°37'41''

www.eurocampings.co.uk/104103

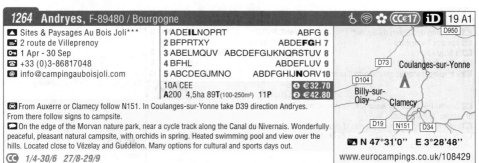

1264 Andryes, F-89480 / Bourgogne

♿ 📶 ✿ (CC€17) **iD** 19 A1

🏕 Sites & Paysages Au Bois Joli***
📧 2 route de Villeprenoy
📅 1 Apr - 30 Sep
☎ +33 (0)3-86817048
@ info@campingauboisjoli.com

1	ADEILNOPRT	ABFG	6
2	BFPRTXY	ABDEFGH	7
3	ABELMQUV	ABCDEFGIJKNQRSTUV	8
4	BFHL	ABDEFLUV	9
5	ABCDEGJMNO	ABDFGHIJNORV	10
10A CEE		❶ €32.70	
A200 4,5ha 89T(100-250m²) 11P		❷ €42.80	

🚗 From Auxerre or Clamecy follow N151. In Coulanges-sur-Yonne take D39 direction Andryes. From there follow signs to campsite.

🏕 On the edge of the Morvan nature park, near a cycle track along the Canal du Nivernais. Wonderfully peaceful, pleasant natural campsite, with orchids in spring. Heated swimming pool and view over the hills. Located close to Vézelay and Guédelon. Many options for cultural and sports days out.

(CC) 1/4-30/6 27/8-29/9

📍 N 47°31'0'' E 3°28'48''

www.eurocampings.co.uk/108429

1265 Charny, F-89120 / Bourgogne

♿ 📶 (CC€11) **iD** 15 A3

🏕 Les Platanes***
📧 41 route de la Mothe
📅 1 Apr - 31 Oct
☎ +33 (0)3-86918360
@ info@campinglesplatanes.fr

1	ADEJMNORST	ABN	6
2	COPVXY	ABDEFGH	7
3	ALMQRS	ABCDEFJNOQRTUV	8
4	BDFHILO	BEV	9
5	ABDHJ	ABFHIJPR	10
16A CEE		❶ €22.50	
A130 2ha 87T(100-120m²) 17P		❷ €34.50	

🚗 A6 exit 18. Follow the recommended route to the campsite.

🏕 Located between Auxerre, Sens and Montargis. Within walking distance of Charny. A campsite with plenty of plant life and flowers, with level pitches, partly partitioned camping pitches. Guests can use a heated pool. Wifi everywhere. A multilingual reception offers comfort and quality.

(CC) 1/4-7/7 25/8-30/10 7=6, 14=12

📍 N 47°53'29'' E 3°5'39''

www.eurocampings.co.uk/112502

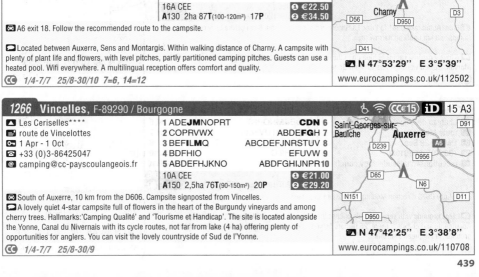

1266 Vincelles, F-89290 / Bourgogne

♿ 📶 (CC€15) **iD** 15 A3

🏕 Les Ceriselles****
📧 route de Vincelottes
📅 1 Apr - 1 Oct
☎ +33 (0)3-86425047
@ camping@cc-payscoulangeois.fr

1	ADEJMNOPRT	CDN	6
2	COPRVWX	ABDEFGH	7
3	BEFILMQ	ABCDEFJNRSTUV	8
4	BDFHIO	EFUVW	9
5	ABDEFHJKNO	ABDFGHIJNPR	10
10A CEE		❶ €21.00	
A150 2,5ha 76T(90-150m²) 20P		❷ €29.20	

🚗 South of Auxerre, 10 km from the D606. Campsite signposted from Vincelles.

🏕 A lovely quiet 4-star campsite full of flowers in the heart of the Burgundy vineyards and among cherry trees. Hallmarks:'Camping Qualité' and 'Tourisme et Handicap'. The site is located alongside the Yonne, Canal du Nivernais with its cycle routes, not far from lake (4 ha) offering plenty of opportunities for anglers. You can visit the lovely countryside of Sud de l'Yonne.

(CC) 1/4-7/7 25/8-30/9

📍 N 47°42'25'' E 3°38'8''

www.eurocampings.co.uk/110708

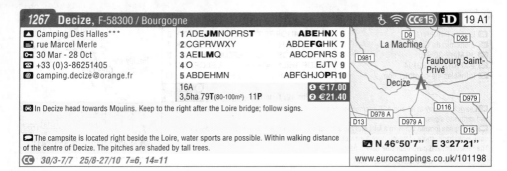

1267 Decize, F-58300 / Bourgogne

   ♿ 📶 (CC€15) iD 19 A1

- ▲ Camping Des Halles***
- ✉ rue Marcel Merle
- 📅 30 Mar - 28 Oct
- ☎ +33 (0)3-86251405
- @ camping.decize@orange.fr

1 ADEJMNOPRST	ABEHNX 6
2 CGPRVWXY	ABDEFGHIK 7
3 AEILMQ	ABCDFNRS 8
4 O	EJTV 9
5 ABDEHMN	ABFGHJOPR 10

16A | ❶ €17.00
3,5ha 79T(80-100m²) 11P | ❷ €21.40

🔜 In Decize head towards Moulins. Keep to the right after the Loire bridge; follow signs.

💬 The campsite is located right beside the Loire, water sports are possible. Within walking distance of the centre of Decize. The pitches are shaded by tall trees.

CC 30/3-7/7 25/8-27/10 7=6, 14=11

N 46°50'7'' E 3°27'21''

www.eurocampings.co.uk/101198

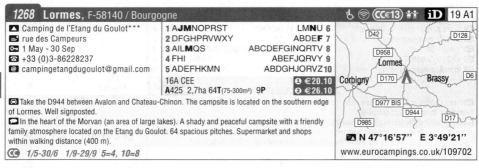

1268 Lormes, F-58140 / Bourgogne

   ♿ 📶 (CC€13) 👫 iD 19 A1

- ▲ Camping de l'Etang du Goulot***
- ✉ rue des Campeurs
- 📅 1 May - 30 Sep
- ☎ +33 (0)3-86228237
- @ campingetangdugoulot@gmail.com

1 AJMNOPRST	LMNU 6
2 DFGHPRVWXY	ABDEF 7
3 AILMQS	ABCDEFGINQRTV 8
4 FHI	ABEFJQRVY 9
5 ADEFHKMN	ABDGHJORVZ 10

16A CEE | ❶ €20.10
A425 2,7ha 64T(75-300m²) 9P | ❷ €26.10

🔜 Take the D944 between Avalon and Chateau-Chinon. The campsite is located on the southern edge of Lormes. Well signposted.

💬 In the heart of the Morvan (an area of large lakes). A shady and peaceful campsite with a friendly family atmosphere located on the Etang du Goulot. 64 spacious pitches. Supermarket and shops within walking distance (400 m).

CC 1/5-30/6 1/9-29/9 5=4, 10=8

N 47°16'57'' E 3°49'21''

www.eurocampings.co.uk/109702

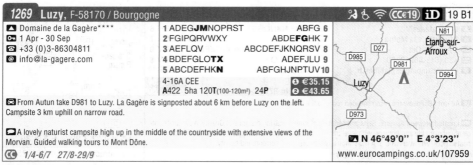

1269 Luzy, F-58170 / Bourgogne

   🚴 ♿ 📶 (CC€19) iD 19 B1

- ▲ Domaine de la Gagère****
- 📅 1 Apr - 30 Sep
- ☎ +33 (0)3-86304811
- @ info@la-gagere.com

1 ADEGJMNOPRST	ABFG 6
2 FGIPQRVWXY	ABDEFGHK 7
3 AEFLQV	ABCDEFJKNQRSV 8
4 BDEFGLOTX	ADEFJLU 9
5 ABCDEFHKN	ABFGHJNPTUV 10

4-16A CEE | ❶ €35.15
A422 5ha 120T(100-120m²) 24P | ❷ €43.65

🔜 From Autun take D981 to Luzy. La Gagère is signposted about 6 km before Luzy on the left. Campsite 3 km uphill on narrow road.

💬 A lovely naturist campsite high up in the middle of the countryside with extensive views of the Morvan. Guided walking tours to Mont Dône.

CC 1/4-6/7 27/8-29/9

N 46°49'0'' E 4°3'23''

www.eurocampings.co.uk/107959

1270 Luzy/Tazilly, F-58170 / Bourgogne

   ♿ 📶 (CC€17) iD 19 A1

- ▲ Château de Chigy****
- ✉ route Moulins
- 📅 1 May - 29 Sep
- ☎ +33 (0)3-86301080
- @ reception@chateaudechigy.com.fr

1 ADEJMNOPRT	ACN 6
2 DGPQRTUVWXY	ABDEFGH 7
3 AEILQ	CDEFJLNQRSV 8
4 BDFHILO	EFIJ 9
5 ABDEFHKN	ABDJOR 10

6A CEE | ❶ €31.00
10ha 100T(100-150m²) 46P | ❷ €39.00

🔜 In Luzy D973 direction Moulins. Campsite signposted.

💬 Large grounds with very spacious pitches, heated swimming pool, shaded by tall trees. Apartments and chalets for rent, 25 hectare fishing lake, indoor swimming pool in 70 hectares of grounds. Fresh bread available.

CC 1/5-6/7 25/8-28/9

N 46°45'28'' E 3°56'39''

www.eurocampings.co.uk/100355

1271 Montsauche-les-Settons, F-58230 / Bourgogne

⬛ Les Mésanges***
▥ Rive Gauche
📅 14 May - 15 Sep
☎ +33 (0)3-86845577
@ campinglesmesanges@orange.fr

1	ADE**JM**NOPQRST	LNQSWXY**Z**	6
2	DFGHIPRVWXY	ABDE**FG**HK	7
3	BELQ	CDFKNORSTUV	8
4	FH		9
5	ABDFG**N**	ABHIJOR	10

16A
A595 5ha 100**T**(100-200m²)
❶ €22.10
❷ €27.90

🚐 Take the D977 bis from Saulieu to Montsauche-les-Settons. In Montsauche follow the direction of Lac des Settons, then Rive Gauche. Then follow campsite signs.

💬 A peaceful campsite with large, fenced, well maintained pitches, opposite Lac des Settons in the heart of the Morvan. Plenty of walking and cycling routes in the rural surroundings. You will find relaxation here. Clean toilet facilities, large fishing lake.

CC 14/5-7/7 25/8-14/9 7=6

N 47°10'54'' E 4°3'10''

www.eurocampings.co.uk/104105

19 B1

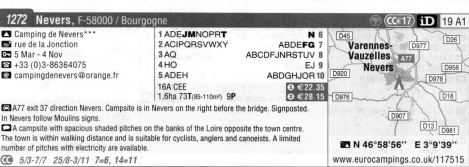

1272 Nevers, F-58000 / Bourgogne

⬛ Camping de Nevers***
▥ rue de la Jonction
📅 5 Mar - 4 Nov
☎ +33 (0)3-86364075
@ campingdenevers@orange.fr

1	ADE**JM**NOPR**T**	**N**	6
2	ACIPQRSVWXY	ABDE**FG**	7
3	AQ	ABCDFJNRSTUV	8
4	HO	EJ	9
5	ADEH	ABDGHJOR	10

16A CEE
1,6ha 73**T**(85-110m²) 9**P**
❶ €22.35
❷ €28.15

🚐 A77 exit 37 direction Nevers. Campsite is in Nevers on the right before the bridge. Signposted. In Nevers follow Moulins signs.

💬 A campsite with spacious shaded pitches on the banks of the Loire opposite the town centre. The town is within walking distance and is suitable for cyclists, anglers and canoeists. A limited number of pitches with electricity are available.

CC 5/3-7/7 25/8-3/11 7=6, 14=11

N 46°58'56'' E 3°9'39''

www.eurocampings.co.uk/117515

19 A1

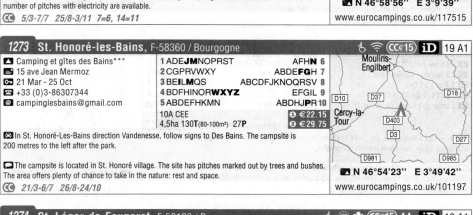

1273 St. Honoré-les-Bains, F-58360 / Bourgogne

⬛ Camping et gîtes des Bains***
▥ 15 ave Jean Mermoz
📅 21 Mar - 25 Oct
☎ +33 (0)3-86307344
@ campinglesbains@gmail.com

1	ADE**JM**NOPRST	AFH**N**	6
2	CGPRVWXY	ABDE**FGH**	7
3	BE**ILM**QS	ABCDFJKNOQRSV	8
4	BDFHINOR**WXYZ**	EFGIL	9
5	ABDEFHKMN	ABDHJ**P**R	10

10A CEE
4,5ha 130**T**(80-100m²) 27**P**
❶ €22.15
❷ €29.75

🚐 In St. Honoré-Les-Bains direction Vandenesse, follow signs to Des Bains. The campsite is 200 metres to the left after the park.

💬 The campsite is located in St. Honoré village. The site has pitches marked out by trees and bushes. The area offers plenty of chance to take in the nature: rest and space.

CC 21/3-6/7 26/8-24/10

N 46°54'23'' E 3°49'42''

www.eurocampings.co.uk/101197

19 A1

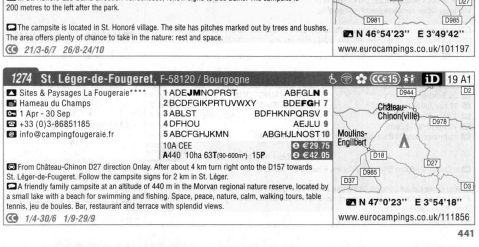

1274 St. Léger-de-Fougeret, F-58120 / Bourgogne

⬛ Sites & Paysages La Fougeraie****
▥ Hameau des Champs
📅 1 Apr - 30 Sep
☎ +33 (0)3-86851185
@ info@campingfougeraie.fr

1	ADE**JM**NOPRST	ABFGL**N**	6
2	BCDFGIKPRTUVWXY	BDE**FG**H	7
3	ABLST	BDFHKNPQRSV	8
4	DFHOU	AEJLU	9
5	ABCFGHJKMN	ABGHJLNOST	10

10A CEE
A440 10ha 63**T**(90-600m²) 15**P**
❶ €29.75
❷ €42.05

🚐 From Château-Chinon D27 direction Onlay. After about 4 km turn right onto the D157 towards St. Léger-de-Fougeret. Follow the campsite signs for 2 km in St. Léger.

💬 A friendly family campsite at an altitude of 440 m in the Morvan regional nature reserve, located by a small lake with a beach for swimming and fishing. Space, peace, nature, calm, walking tours, table tennis, jeu de boules. Bar, restaurant and terrace with splendid views.

CC 1/4-30/6 1/9-29/9

N 47°0'23'' E 3°54'18''

www.eurocampings.co.uk/111856

19 A1

France

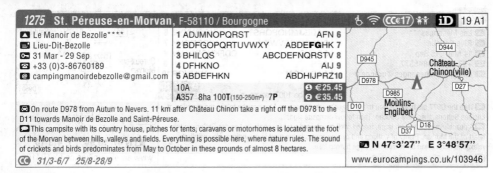

1275 St. Péreuse-en-Morvan, F-58110 / Bourgogne ♿ 🛜 (CC€17) ⚦ iD 19 A1

🏕 Le Manoir de Bezolle★★★★
🏠 Lieu-Dit-Bezolle
📅 31 Mar - 29 Sep
☎ +33 (0)3-86760189
@ campingmanoirdebezolle@gmail.com

1 ADJMNOPQRST	AFN 6
2 BDFGOPQRTUVWXY	ABDE**FG**HK 7
3 BHILQS	ABCDEFNQRSTV 8
4 DFHKNO	AIJ 9
5 ABDEFHKN	ABDHIJPRZ10

| 10A | ❶ €25.45 |
| A357 8ha 100T(150-250m²) 7P | ❷ €35.45 |

🚗 On route D978 from Autun to Nevers. 11 km after Château Chinon take a right off the D978 to the D11 towards Manoir de Bezolle and Saint-Péreuse.

💬 This campsite with its country house, pitches for tents, caravans or motorhomes is located at the foot of the Morvan between hills, valleys and fields. Everything is possible here, where nature rules. The sound of crickets and birds predominates from May to October in these grounds of almost 8 hectares.

CC 31/3-6/7 25/8-28/9

📍 N 47°3'27" E 3°48'57"

www.eurocampings.co.uk/103946

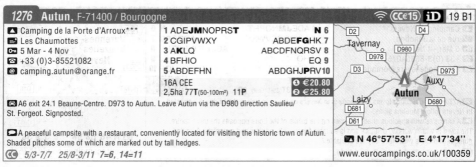

1276 Autun, F-71400 / Bourgogne 🛜 (CC€15) iD 19 B1

🏕 Camping de la Porte d'Arroux★★★
🏠 Les Chaumottes
📅 5 Mar - 4 Nov
☎ +33 (0)3-85521082
@ camping.autun@orange.fr

1 ADE**JM**NOPRS**T**	**N** 6
2 CGIPVWXY	ABDE**FG**HK 7
3 A**K**LQ	ABCDFNQRSV 8
4 BFHIO	EQ 9
5 ABDEFHN	ABDGHJP**R**V10

| 16A CEE | ❶ €20.80 |
| 2,5ha 77T(50-100m²) 11P | ❷ €25.80 |

🚗 A6 exit 24.1 Beaune-Centre. D973 to Autun. Leave Autun via the D980 direction Saulieu/St. Forgeot. Signposted.

💬 A peaceful campsite with a restaurant, conveniently located for visiting the historic town of Autun. Shaded pitches some of which are marked out by tall hedges.

CC 5/3-7/7 25/8-3/11 7=6, 14=11

📍 N 46°57'53" E 4°17'34"

www.eurocampings.co.uk/100359

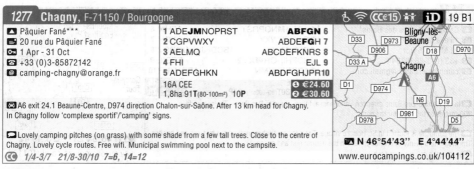

1277 Chagny, F-71150 / Bourgogne ♿ 🛜 (CC€15) ⚦ iD 19 B1

🏕 Pâquier Fané★★★
🏠 20 rue du Pâquier Fané
📅 1 Apr - 31 Oct
☎ +33 (0)3-85872142
@ camping-chagny@orange.fr

1 ADE**JM**NOPRST	**ABFGN** 6
2 CGPVWXY	ABDE**FG**H 7
3 AELMQ	ABCDEFKNRS 8
4 FHI	EJL 9
5 ADEFGHKN	ABDFGHJPR10

| 16A CEE | ❶ €24.60 |
| 1,8ha 91T(80-100m²) 10P | ❷ €30.60 |

🚗 A6 exit 24.1 Beaune-Centre, D974 direction Chalon-sur-Saône. After 13 km head for Chagny. In Chagny follow 'complexe sportif'/'camping' signs.

💬 Lovely camping pitches (on grass) with some shade from a few tall trees. Close to the centre of Chagny. Lovely cycle routes. Free wifi. Municipal swimming pool next to the campsite.

CC 1/4-3/7 21/8-30/10 7=6, 14=12

📍 N 46°54'43" E 4°44'44"

www.eurocampings.co.uk/104112

1278 Chalon-sur-Saône/St. Marcel, F-71380 / Bourgogne ♿ 🛜 (CC€17) ⚦ iD 19 B1

🏕 Du Pont de Bourgogne★★★
🏠 12 rue Julien Leneveu
📅 1 Apr - 30 Sep
☎ +33 (0)3-85482686
@ campingchalon71@wanadoo.fr

1 ADEF**JM**NOPQRST	**N**SWX 6
2 ACGPRSVWXY	ABDE**FG** 7
3 A**K**L	ABCDEFGKNQRSV 8
4 HO	BE 9
5 ABDEFGHMN	ABDGHKORZ10

| 10A CEE | ❶ €30.70 |
| 3ha 91T(50-100m²) 12P | ❷ €43.60 |

🚗 In Chalon-sur-Saône follow campsite and Roseraie St. Nicolas signs.

💬 A campsite located along the Saône with shaded pitches. Near exit 26 Chalon Sud on the A6. Within walking distance (15 min) of the centre of Chalon-sur-Saône. Starting point for cycling: Voie Verte. Modern toilet facilities.

CC 1/4-6/7 26/8-29/9 7=6, 14=12

📍 N 46°47'3" E 4°52'21"

www.eurocampings.co.uk/110165

1279 Chauffailles, F-71170 / Bourgogne   19 B2

- ▲ Mun. les Feuilles***
- ▣ 18 la Chatillon
- ▭ 1 May - 30 Sep
- ☎ +33 (0)3-85264812
- @ campingchauffailles@orange.fr

1 ADEJMNOPRST	ABFGN	6
2 GPQSTVWXY	ABDEFH	7
3 ABEILMQ	ABCDFNOQRTV	8
4 ADEFHIO	FJW	9
5 ADNO	ABHJLORV	10
10A		
4ha 60T(80-100m²) 17P	❶ €17.90	
	❷ €22.30	

🚗 In Chauffailles continue on the D985 direction Les Echarmeaux, then follow the campsite signs.

💬 This campsite is located near Chauffailles in the shade of various high trees and sloping downwards to a small brook. In walking distance of the town and with options for bike rides in the vicinity.

✈ N 46°11'59'' E 4°20'14''

www.eurocampings.co.uk/100380

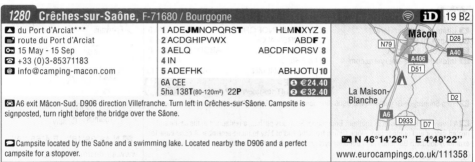

1280 Crêches-sur-Saône, F-71680 / Bourgogne   19 B2

- ▲ du Port d'Arciat***
- ▣ route du Port d'Arciat
- ▭ 15 May - 15 Sep
- ☎ +33 (0)3-85371183
- @ info@camping-macon.com

1 ADEJMNOPQRST	HLMNXYZ	6
2 ACDGHIPVWX	ABDF	7
3 AELQ	ABCDFNORSV	8
4 IN		9
5 ADEFHK	ABHJOTU	10
6A CEE	❶ €24.40	
5ha 138T(80-120m²) 22P	❷ €32.40	

🚗 A6 exit Mâcon-Sud. D906 direction Villefranche. Turn left in Crêches-sur-Saône. Campsite is signposted, turn right before the bridge over the Sâone.

💬 Campsite located by the Saône and a swimming lake. Located nearby the D906 and a perfect campsite for a stopover.

✈ N 46°14'26'' E 4°48'22''

www.eurocampings.co.uk/111358

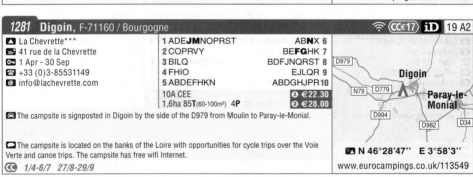

1281 Digoin, F-71160 / Bourgogne   19 A2

- ▲ La Chevrette***
- ▣ 41 rue de la Chevrette
- ▭ 1 Apr - 30 Sep
- ☎ +33 (0)3-85531149
- @ info@lachevrette.com

1 ADEJMNOPRST	ABNX	6
2 COPRVY	BEFGHK	7
3 BILQ	BDFJNQRST	8
4 FHIO	EJLQR	9
5 ABDEFHKN	ABDGHJPR	10
10A CEE	❶ €22.30	
1,6ha 85T(60-100m²) 4P	❷ €28.00	

🚗 The campsite is signposted in Digoin by the side of the D979 from Moulin to Paray-le-Monial.

💬 The campsite is located on the banks of the Loire with opportunities for cycle trips over the Voie Verte and canoe trips. The campsite has free wifi Internet.

✈ N 46°28'47'' E 3°58'3''

🅒🅒 1/4-6/7 27/8-29/9

www.eurocampings.co.uk/113549

1282 Dompierre-les-Ormes, F-71520 / Bourgogne   19 B2

- ▲ Le Village des Meuniers****
- ▣ 344 rue du Stade
- ▭ 1 Apr - 13 Oct
- ☎ +33 (0)3-85503660
- @ contact@villagedesmeuniers.com

1 ADEJMNOPRST	ABFGHN	6
2 FGIPTUVWXY	ABCDEFGH	7
3 ABEHILMQSV	ABCDEFGJKNQRSTUV	8
4 BDFHIKLNOPQ	ACEJUV	9
5 ABDEFGHLMN	ABDGJOPRV	10
10-16A CEE	❶ €30.70	
4ha 76T(80-300m²) 33P	❷ €41.70	

🚗 A6 Mâcon-Sud direction Charolles N79. Dompierre-les-Ormes is signposted via D41. Follow campsite signs in Dompierre.

💬 Friendly campsite with spacious pitches in the sun or shade. Heated pool. Walking and cycling trips through the area possible. Restaurant with extensive menu.

🅒🅒 1/4-6/7 27/8-12/10 14=12

✈ N 46°21'50'' E 4°28'29''

www.eurocampings.co.uk/101207

France

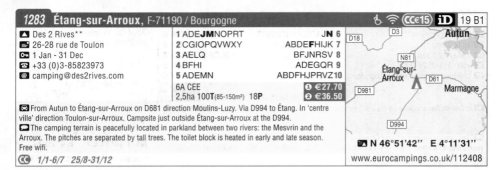

1283 Étang-sur-Arroux, F-71190 / Bourgogne

♿ 🛜 (CC€15) iD · 19 B1

- ▲ Des 2 Rives**
- 🍴 26-28 rue de Toulon
- 📅 1 Jan - 31 Dec
- ☎ +33 (0)3-85823973
- @ camping@des2rives.com

1 ADEJMNOPRT	JN	6
2 CGIOPQVWXY	ABDEFHIJK	7
3 AELQ	BFJNRSV	8
4 BFHI	ADEGQR	9
5 ADEMN	ABDFHJPRVZ	10
6A CEE	❶ €27.70	
2,5ha 100T(85-150m²) 18P	❷ €36.50	

🚗 From Autun to Étang-sur-Arroux on D681 direction Moulins-Luzy. Via D994 to Étang. In 'centre ville' direction Toulon-sur-Arroux. Campsite just outside Étang-sur-Arroux at the D994.
💬 The camping terrain is peacefully located in parkland between two rivers: the Mesvrin and the Arroux. The pitches are separated by tall trees. The toilet block is heated in early and late season. Free wifi.
(CC) 1/1-6/7 25/8-31/12

N 46°51'42" E 4°11'31"

www.eurocampings.co.uk/112408

1284 Gigny-sur-Saône, F-71240 / Bourgogne

♿ 🛜 (CC€19) iD · 19 B2

- ▲ Château de l'Epervière*****
- 📅 1 Apr - 30 Sep
- ☎ +33 (0)3-85941690
- @ info@domaine-eperviere.com

1 ADEJMNOPQRST	ABEFGN	6
2 GPRSVWX	ABDEFGH	7
3 ALQ	ABCDEFKNQRS	8
4 FHILOQ	ABEIV	9
5 ACDFGHLMN	ABFGHJORZ	10
10A CEE	❶ €41.70	
10ha 114T(100-130m²) 49P	❷ €54.70	

🚗 From Sennecey-le-Grand leave the D906 direction Gigny-sur-Saône (D18). Follow campsite signs.

💬 A lovely castle campsite in southern Bourgogne. Spacious pitches, a restaurant in the castle and heated indoor and outdoor pool. Wine tasting from the end of May to mid-September. A good base for exploring southern Burgundy, and good for cycling (15 km from Voie Bleue).
(CC) 1/4-30/6 2/9-29/9

N 46°39'16" E 4°56'39"

www.eurocampings.co.uk/101200

1285 Issy-l'Évêque, F-71760 / Bourgogne

🛜 iD · 19 A2

- ▲ Les Portes du Morvan****
- 🍴 route de Grury
- 📅 1 Jan - 31 Dec
- ☎ +33 (0)3-85249605
- @ contact@
  camping-portesdumorvan.com

1 ADEJMNOPRST	ABFLN	6
2 DFGHIPVWX	ABDEFGH	7
3 AEFILMQ	ABCDFJKNORSV	8
4 BFHIOR	EJUVW	9
5 ABDEHKN	ABFGHJPR	10
6-10A CEE	❶ €20.90	
4ha 70T(80-120m²) 8P	❷ €24.70	

🚗 The campsite is signposted on the D973 to Issy-l'Évêque.

💬 A lovely campsite with beautiful views of the surroundings, with a swimming pool and fishing facilities. The site has a part with sunny pitches and a part in the shade. Large marked pitches. Free wifi.

N 46°42'28" E 3°57'37"

www.eurocampings.co.uk/108841

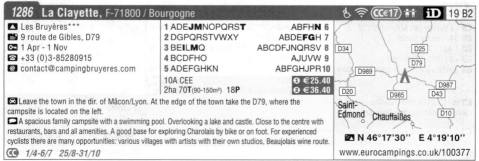

1286 La Clayette, F-71800 / Bourgogne

♿ 🛜 (CC€17) 👫 iD · 19 B2

- ▲ Les Bruyères***
- 🍴 9 route de Gibles, D79
- 📅 1 Apr - 1 Nov
- ☎ +33 (0)3-85280915
- @ contact@campingbruyeres.com

1 ADEJMNOPQRST	ABFHN	6
2 DGPQRSTVWXY	ABDEFGH	7
3 BEILMQ	ABCDFJNQRSV	8
4 BCDFHO	AJUVW	9
5 ADEFGHKN	ABFGHJPR	10
10A CEE	❶ €25.40	
2ha 70T(90-150m²) 18P	❷ €36.40	

🚗 Leave the town in the dir. of Mâcon/Lyon. At the edge of the town take the D79, where the campsite is located on the left.
💬 A spacious family campsite with a swimming pool. Overlooking a lake and castle. Close to the centre with restaurants, bars and all amenities. A good base for exploring Charolais by bike or on foot. For experienced cyclists there are many opportunities: various villages with artists with their own studios, Beaujolais wine route.
(CC) 1/4-6/7 25/8-31/10

N 46°17'30" E 4°19'10"

www.eurocampings.co.uk/100377

France

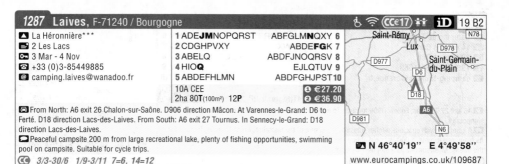

1287 Laives, F-71240 / Bourgogne
♿ 📶 CC€17 ♟ iD 19 B2

- ⛰ La Héronnière***
- 🏕 2 Les Lacs
- 🗓 3 Mar - 4 Nov
- ☎ +33 (0)3-85449885
- @ camping.laives@wanadoo.fr

1	ADE**JM**NOPQRST	ABFGLM**N**QXY	6
2	CDGHPVXY	ABDE**FG**K	7
3	ABELQ	ABDFJNOQRSV	8
4	HIO**Q**	EJLQTUV	9
5	ABDEFHLMN	ABDFGHJPST	10
10A CEE		❶ €27.20	
2ha 80**T**(100m²) 12**P**		❷ €36.90	

🚗 From North: A6 exit 26 Chalon-sur-Saône. D906 direction Mâcon. At Varennes-le-Grand: D6 to Ferté. D18 direction Lacs-des-Laives. From South: A6 exit 27 Tournus. In Sennecy-le-Grand: D18 direction Lacs-des-Laives.

💬 Peaceful campsite 200 m from large recreational lake, plenty of fishing opportunities, swimming pool on campsite. Suitable for cycle trips.

CC 3/3-30/6 1/9-3/11 7=6, 14=12

🧭 N 46°40'19'' E 4°49'58''

www.eurocampings.co.uk/109687

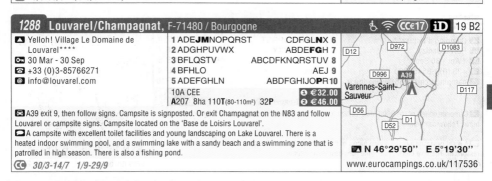

1288 Louvarel/Champagnat, F-71480 / Bourgogne
♿ 📶 CC€17 iD 19 B2

- ⛰ Yelloh! Village Le Domaine de Louvarel****
- 🗓 30 Mar - 30 Sep
- ☎ +33 (0)3-85766271
- @ info@louvarel.com

1	ADE**JM**NOPQRST	CDFGL**N**X	6
2	ADGHPUVWX	ABDE**FG**H	7
3	BFLQSTV	ABCDFKNQRSTUV	8
4	BFHLO	AEJ	9
5	ADEFGHLN	ABDFGHIJO**P**R	10
10A CEE		❶ €32.00	
A207 8ha 110**T**(80-110m²) 32**P**		❷ €46.00	

🚗 A39 exit 9, then follow signs. Campsite is signposted. Or exit Champagnat on the N83 and follow Louvarel or campsite signs. Campsite located on the 'Base de Loisirs Louvarel'.

💬 A campsite with excellent toilet facilities and young landscaping on Lake Louvarel. There is a heated indoor swimming pool, and a swimming lake with a sandy beach and a swimming zone that is patrolled in high season. There is also a fishing pond.

CC 30/3-14/7 1/9-29/9

🧭 N 46°29'50'' E 5°19'30''

www.eurocampings.co.uk/117536

France

1289 Matour, F-71520 / Bourgogne
♿ 📶 CC€15 iD 19 B2

- ⛰ Flower Camping Le Paluet***
- 🏕 2 rue de la Piscine
- 🗓 7 Apr - 30 Oct
- ☎ +33 (0)3-85597092
- @ lepaluet@matour.fr

1	ADE**JM**NOPQRST	ABFGH**N**	6
2	DGPRVWXY	ABDE**FG**H	7
3	ABEFLQ	CDEFNQRSV	8
4	BDFHILNOQTU	BJ	9
5	DEFHN	ABDGJO**P**RVZ	10
10A CEE		❶ €23.70	
3ha 61**T**(80-120m²) 22**P**		❷ €31.70	

🚗 Follow the campsite signs in the town.

💬 A family campsite with sunny and shaded places next to a free municipal swimming pool. Located in the beautiful area known as 'Little Switzerland'. Hiking trails in the area. Within walking distance of the centre and all shops. 30 minutes' free wifi close to the campsite reception. Free sauna.

CC 7/4-9/7 27/8-29/10 7=6, 14=10

🧭 N 46°18'16'' E 4°28'43''

www.eurocampings.co.uk/100378

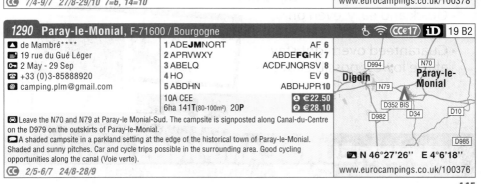

1290 Paray-le-Monial, F-71600 / Bourgogne
♿ 📶 CC€17 iD 19 B2

- ⛰ de Mambré****
- 🏕 19 rue du Gué Léger
- 🗓 2 May - 29 Sep
- ☎ +33 (0)3-85888920
- @ camping.plm@gmail.com

1	ADE**JM**NORT	AF	6
2	APRVWXY	ABDE**FG**HK	7
3	ABELQ	ACDFJNQRSV	8
4	HO	EV	9
5	ABDHN	ABDHJPR	10
10A CEE		❶ €22.50	
6ha 141**T**(80-100m²) 20**P**		❷ €28.10	

🚗 Leave the N70 and N79 at Paray le Monial-Sud. The campsite is signposted along Canal-du-Centre on the D979 on the outskirts of Paray-le-Monial.

💬 A shaded campsite in a parkland setting at the edge of the historical town of Paray-le-Monial. Shaded and sunny pitches. Car and cycle trips possible in the surrounding area. Good cycling opportunities along the canal (Voie verte).

CC 2/5-6/7 24/8-28/9

🧭 N 46°27'26'' E 4°6'18''

www.eurocampings.co.uk/100376

1291 Tournus, F-71700 / Bourgogne

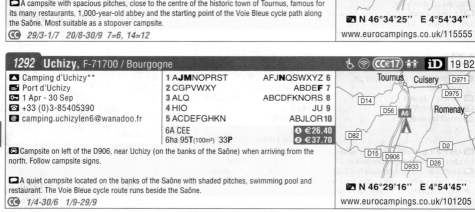

♿ 🛜 (CC€17) iD 19 B2

🏕 Camping de Tournus***
✉ 14 rue des Canes
📅 29 Mar - 1 Oct
☎ +33 (0)3-85511658
@ camping-tournus@orange.fr

1 ADEILNOPQRST	ABFGHN 6
2 ACPSVWX	ABDEFG 7
3 AL	ABCDEFNOQRSV 8
4 HO	JV 9
5 ADEFHN	ABDFGHJPTU 10

10A CEE
1,5ha 94T(80-100m²) 2P

❶ €28.00
❷ €37.60

Laives
A6
Tournus
Cuisery D971
D14
D906
D975
D56
D933

🅿 A6 exit 27 Tournus. Follow D906 towards Tournus. Turn off opposite the station. Campsite signposted.
💬 A campsite with spacious pitches, close to the centre of the historic town of Tournus, famous for its many restaurants, 1,000-year-old abbey and the starting point of the Voie Bleue cycle path along the Saône. Most suitable as a stopover campsite.

🅲🅲 29/3-1/7 20/8-30/9 7=6, 14=12

N 46°34'25'' E 4°54'34''
www.eurocampings.co.uk/115555

1292 Uchizy, F-71700 / Bourgogne

♿ 🛜 (CC€17) 🚻 iD 19 B2

🏕 Camping d'Uchizy**
✉ Port d'Uchizy
📅 1 Apr - 30 Sep
☎ +33 (0)3-85405390
@ camping.uchizylen6@wanadoo.fr

1 AJMNOPRST	AFJNQSWXYZ 6
2 CGPVWXY	ABDEF 7
3 ALQ	ABCDFKNORS 8
4 HIO	JU 9
5 ACDEFGHKN	ABJLOR 10

6A CEE
6ha 95T(100m²) 33P

❶ €26.40
❷ €37.70

Tournus Cuisery D971
D14 D975
D56 A6 Romenay
D82
D15 D906 D2
D933 D26

🅿 Campsite on left of the D906, near Uchizy (on the banks of the Saône) when arriving from the north. Follow campsite signs.
💬 A quiet campsite located on the banks of the Saône with shaded pitches, swimming pool and restaurant. The Voie Bleue cycle route runs beside the Saône.

🅲🅲 1/4-30/6 1/9-29/9

N 46°29'16'' E 4°54'45''
www.eurocampings.co.uk/101205

France

Auvergne-Rhône-Alpes

Wine, lavender and black rocks

As you wind your way through this largely rocky landscape, chances are you'll catch an elusive sweet scent on the wind – besides volcanoes, Auvergne-Rhône-Alpes is noted for lavender. Extending from central France to the border with Switzerland and Italy, you'll also come across relics from the Roman, Celtic and Visigoth eras, as well as fabulous mediaeval villages, perched on the mountains and in the valleys of this incredible landscape.

Sights and aromas

You also get a whiff of grapes – this is Beaujolais country. Capital Lyon is a base for winery tours, but you can also admire Notre Dame de Fourvier basilica, and the Roman amphitheatre, and go shopping in the historic old town. Look out for street art! Located between two Nature Parks,

Clermont-Ferrand has a rich history: admire the town's great mansions, and the black lava stones of the Gothic Cathedral Our Lady of Assumption, or go see the Black Madonna in the crypt of Notre-Dame-du-Port. Hop on the cable car to Grenoble's Fort de la Bastille for great views. Art lovers are enchanted with the Museum de Grenoble and Centre for Contemporary Art, afterwards head to St-André square for refreshment, and admire the former Dauphiné Palace.

Out in the country

Walkers, hikers, climbers and nature lovers are drawn to Vercors, La Vanoise and Écrins Nature Parks. Fire up your children's imagination and curiosity at Volcania in Auvergne Volcano Park. Swimmers cool down in Lake Aydat, and for sightseers there is Murol castle and the

Romanesque churches of Orcival and Saint-Nectaire. Puy de Dome Mountain, heart of the Massif Central, is a mecca for paragliders, hang gliders and diehard hikers. Prefer something a little more sedate? Charming 12th century village

Charroux is full of artisan workshops: including candle makers, a soap maker and a potter.

Bon appetite!

You probably already know Evian and Volvic water, but do you know Génépi liqueur? Auvergne-Rhone-Alpes produces an incredible variety of cheeses, and green lentils from Le Puy, but what about tartiflette, simple but delicious with bacon, potatoes, onion and cheese; or gratin Daupinois? Incidentally, lavender honey is used in Montélimar nougat, like you need an excuse to visit a factory ...

Our tips

1. Need a little pampering? Book a spa day at Vichy or Aix-les Bains
2. Up, up and away! Ride a hot-air balloon as part of the Festival of Montgolfière
3. See the distinctive black lava rock houses at Salers
4. Check out the Les Grandes Alpes walking route, at over 2000 metres
5. Learn about lavender at the Museum in Cabrieres-d'Avignon

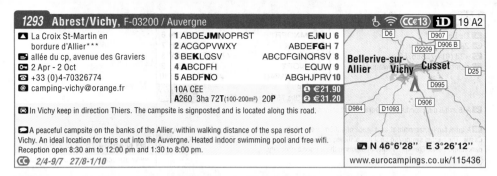

1293 Abrest/Vichy, F-03200 / Auvergne
♿ 📶 (CC€13) **iD** 19 A2

- 🏕 La Croix St-Martin en bordure d'Allier***
- 📧 allée du cp, avenue des Graviers
- 📅 2 Apr - 2 Oct
- ☎ +33 (0)4-70326774
- @ camping-vichy@orange.fr

1 ABDEJMNOPRST	EJNU 6
2 ACGOPVWXY	ABDEFGH 7
3 BEKLQSV	ABCDFGINQRSV 8
4 ABCDFH	EQUW 9
5 ABDFNO	ABGHJPRV 10

10A CEE — ❶ €21.90
A260 3ha 72T(100-200m²) 20P — ❷ €31.20

🚗 In Vichy keep in direction Thiers. The campsite is signposted and is located along this road.

💬 A peaceful campsite on the banks of the Allier, within walking distance of the spa resort of Vichy. An ideal location for trips out into the Auvergne. Heated indoor swimming pool and free wifi. Reception open 8:30 am to 12:00 pm and 1:30 to 8:00 pm.

CC 2/4-9/7 27/8-1/10

📷 N 46°6'28'' E 3°26'12''

www.eurocampings.co.uk/115436

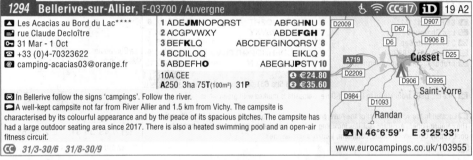

1294 Bellerive-sur-Allier, F-03700 / Auvergne
♿ 📶 (CC€17) **iD** 19 A2

- 🏕 Les Acacias au Bord du Lac****
- 📧 rue Claude Decloître
- 📅 31 Mar - 1 Oct
- ☎ +33 (0)4-70323622
- @ camping-acacias03@orange.fr

1 ADEJMNOPQRST	ABFGHNU 6
2 ACGPVWXY	ABDEFGH 7
3 BEFKLQ	ABCDEFGINOQRSV 8
4 BCDILOQ	EIKLQ 9
5 ABDEFHO	ABEGHJPSTV 10

10A CEE — ❶ €24.80
A250 3ha 75T(100m²) 31P — ❷ €35.60

🚗 In Bellerive follow the signs 'campings'. Follow the river.

💬 A well-kept campsite not far from River Allier and 1.5 km from Vichy. The campsite is characterised by its colourful appearance and by the peace of its spacious pitches. The campsite has had a large outdoor seating area since 2017. There is also a heated swimming pool and an open-air fitness circuit.

CC 31/3-30/6 31/8-30/9

📷 N 46°6'59'' E 3°25'33''

www.eurocampings.co.uk/103955

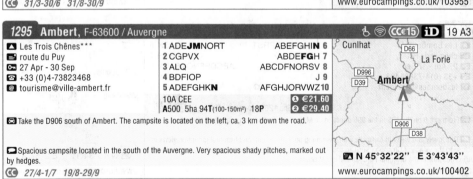

1295 Ambert, F-63600 / Auvergne
♿ 📶 (CC€15) **iD** 19 A3

- 🏕 Les Trois Chênes***
- 📧 route du Puy
- 📅 27 Apr - 30 Sep
- ☎ +33 (0)4-73823468
- @ tourisme@ville-ambert.fr

1 ADEJMNORT	ABEFGHIN 6
2 CGPVX	ABDEFGH 7
3 ALQ	ABCDFNORSV 8
4 BDFIOP	J 9
5 ADEFGHKN	AFGHJORVWZ 10

10A CEE — ❶ €21.60
A500 5ha 94T(100-150m²) 18P — ❷ €29.40

🚗 Take the D906 south of Ambert. The campsite is located on the left, ca. 3 km down the road.

💬 Spacious campsite located in the south of the Auvergne. Very spacious shady pitches, marked out by hedges.

CC 27/4-1/7 19/8-29/9

📷 N 45°32'22'' E 3°43'43''

www.eurocampings.co.uk/100402

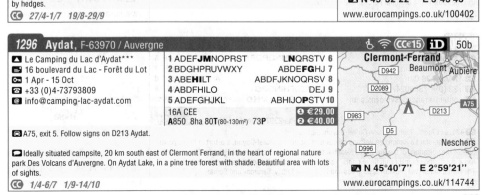

1296 Aydat, F-63970 / Auvergne
♿ 📶 (CC€15) **iD** 50b

- 🏕 Le Camping du Lac d'Aydat***
- 📧 16 boulevard du Lac - Forêt du Lot
- 📅 1 Apr - 15 Oct
- ☎ +33 (0)4-73793809
- @ info@camping-lac-aydat.com

1 ADEFJMNOPRST	LNQRSTV 6
2 BDGHPRUVWXY	ABDEFGHJ 7
3 ABEHILT	ABDFJKNOQRSV 8
4 ABDFHILO	DEJ 9
5 ADEFGHJKL	ABHIJOPSTV 10

16A CEE — ❶ €29.00
A850 8ha 80T(80-130m²) 73P — ❷ €40.00

🚗 A75, exit 5. Follow signs on D213 Aydat.

💬 Ideally situated campsite, 20 km south east of Clermont Ferrand, in the heart of regional nature park Des Volcans d'Auvergne. On Aydat Lake, in a pine tree forest with shade. Beautiful area with lots of sights.

CC 1/4-6/7 1/9-14/10

📷 N 45°40'7'' E 2°59'21''

www.eurocampings.co.uk/114744

France

1297 Chambon-sur-Lac, F-63790 / Auvergne ♿ 📶 ✿ CC€15 iD 50b

- ▲ De Serrette***
- ◉ 28 Apr - 16 Sep
- ☎ +33 (0)4-73886767
- @ camping.de.serrette@wanadoo.fr

1 AJMNOPRT	CDFGN 6
2 CFPUVX	ABDEFGH 7
3 ABLR	ABCDFIKNRSV 8
4 EFHIOPT	DEFL 9
5 ABDEFHMNO	ABDGHIJOST 10
10A CEE	❶ €27.90
A1000 3ha 75T(80-130m²) 18P	❷ €38.90

🚗 A75 exit 6 direction Le Mont Doré. Follow campsite signs past Murol.

💬 A quiet family campsite at an altitude of 1000m with wonderful views of Lac Chambon and Murol Castle. The heated swimming pool has a sliding roof and there is also a sauna. Restaurant with panoramic views. Free wifi. Plenty of sights in the immediate vicinity.

CC 28/4-1/7 27/8-15/9 14=12

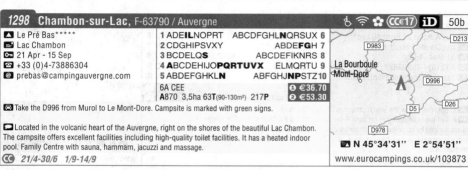

🏴 N 45°34'16" E 2°53'28"

www.eurocampings.co.uk/112548

1298 Chambon-sur-Lac, F-63790 / Auvergne ♿ 📶 ✿ CC€17 iD 50b

- ▲ Le Pré Bas*****
- 🏞 Lac Chambon
- ◉ 21 Apr - 15 Sep
- ☎ +33 (0)4-73886304
- @ prebas@campingauvergne.com

1 ADEILNOPRT	ABCDFGHLNQRSUX 6
2 CDGHIPSVXY	ABDEFGH 7
3 BCDELQS	ABCDEFIKNRS 8
4 ABCDEHIJOPQRTUVX	ELMQRTU 9
5 ABDEFGHKLN	ABFGHJNPSTZ 10
6A CEE	❶ €36.70
A870 3,5ha 63T(90-130m²) 217P	❷ €53.30

🚗 Take the D996 from Murol to Le Mont-Dore. Campsite is marked with green signs.

💬 Located in the volcanic heart of the Auvergne, right on the shores of the beautiful Lac Chambon. The campsite offers excellent facilities including high-quality toilet facilities. It has a heated indoor pool. Family Centre with sauna, hammam, jacuzzi and massage.

CC 21/4-30/6 1/9-14/9

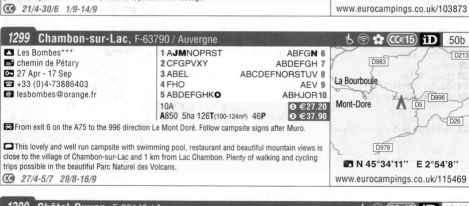

🏴 N 45°34'31" E 2°54'51"

www.eurocampings.co.uk/103873

1299 Chambon-sur-Lac, F-63790 / Auvergne ♿ 📶 ✿ CC€15 iD 50b

- ▲ Les Bombes***
- 🏞 chemin de Pétary
- ◉ 27 Apr - 17 Sep
- ☎ +33 (0)4-73886403
- @ lesbombes@orange.fr

1 AJMNOPRST	ABFGN 6
2 CFGPVXY	ABDEFGH 7
3 ABEL	ABCDEFNORSTUV 8
4 FHO	AEV 9
5 ABDEFGHKO	ABHJOR 10
10A	❶ €27.20
A850 5ha 126T(100-124m²) 46P	❷ €37.90

🚗 From exit 6 on the A75 to the 996 direction Le Mont Doré. Follow campsite signs after Muro.

💬 This lovely and well run campsite with swimming pool, restaurant and beautiful mountain views is close to the village of Chambon-sur-Lac and 1 km from Lac Chambon. Plenty of walking and cycling trips possible in the beautiful Parc Naturel des Volcans.

CC 27/4-5/7 29/8-16/9

🏴 N 45°34'11" E 2°54'8"

www.eurocampings.co.uk/115469

1300 Châtel-Guyon, F-63140 / Auvergne ♿ 📶 CC€15 iD 19 A2

- ▲ Le Ranch des Volcans***
- 🏞 route de la Piscine
- ◉ 17 Mar - 28 Oct
- ☎ +33 (0)4-73860247
- @ contact@ranchdesvolcans.com

1 ADEJMNOPQRST	AF 6
2 AOPQVXY	ABDEFGH 7
3 ABEGHILQRT	ABCDFJNORS 8
4 BCDFHINOPQ	ABEJ 9
5 ABDEFHKLMNO	ABDFGHJLORW 10
6A	❶ €28.70
A400 5ha 239T(80-200m²) 51P	❷ €35.70

🚗 A71, exit Riom. Then direction Châtel-Guyon. Signposted.

💬 The three-star Le Ranch des Volcans campsite is located in Châtel-Guyon, a resort in the regional park of the volcanoes of the Auvergne. Near the towns of Volvic and Clermont-Ferrand. The campsite has a swimming complex with three pools, a playground, mini-golf and other sports activities. The restaurant serves regional specialities and is open on Friday, Saturday and Sunday.

CC 17/3-6/7 25/8-27/10 7=6

🏴 N 45°54'54" E 3°4'38"

www.eurocampings.co.uk/103960

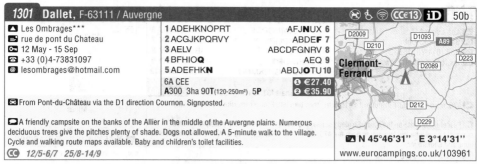

1301 Dallet, F-63111 / Auvergne

(icons) CC€13 iD 50b

- ▲ Les Ombrages***
- 🏠 rue de pont du Chateau
- ⏳ 12 May - 15 Sep
- ☎ +33 (0)4-73831097
- @ lesombrages@hotmail.com

1 ADEHKNOPRT	AFJNUX 6
2 ACGJKPQRVY	ABDEF 7
3 AELV	ABCDFGNRV 8
4 BFHIOQ	AEQ 9
5 ADEFHKN	ABDJOTU 10
6A CEE	€ 27.40
A300 3ha 90T(120-250m²) 5P	€ 35.90

From Pont-du-Château via the D1 direction Cournon. Signposted.

A friendly campsite on the banks of the Allier in the middle of the Auvergne plains. Numerous deciduous trees give the pitches plenty of shade. Dogs not allowed. A 5-minute walk to the village. Cycle and walking route maps available. Baby and children's toilet facilities.

CC 12/5-6/7 25/8-14/9

N 45°46'31'' E 3°14'31''

www.eurocampings.co.uk/103961

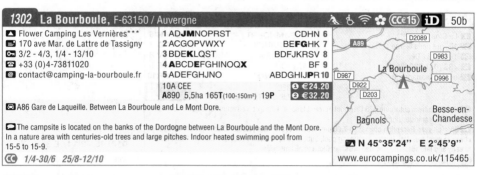

1302 La Bourboule, F-63150 / Auvergne

(icons) CC€15 iD 50b

- ▲ Flower Camping Les Vernières***
- 🏠 170 ave Mar. de Lattre de Tassigny
- ⏳ 3/2 - 4/3, 1/4 - 13/10
- ☎ +33 (0)4-73811020
- @ contact@camping-la-bourboule.fr

1 ADJMNOPRST	CDHN 6
2 ACGOPVWXY	BEFGHK 7
3 BDEKLQST	BDFJKRSV 8
4 ABCDEFGHINOQX	BF 9
5 ADEFGHJNO	ABDGHIJPR 10
10A CEE	€ 24.20
A890 5,5ha 165T(100-150m²) 19P	€ 32.20

A86 Gare de Laqueille. Between La Bourboule and Le Mont Dore.

The campsite is located on the banks of the Dordogne between La Bourboule and the Mont Dore. In a nature area with centuries-old trees and large pitches. Indoor heated swimming pool from 15-5 to 15-9.

CC 1/4-30/6 25/8-12/10

N 45°35'24'' E 2°45'9''

www.eurocampings.co.uk/115465

France

1303 Les Pradeaux/Issoire, F-63500 / Auvergne

(icons) CC€17 iD 50b

- ▲ Château de Grange Fort***
- 🏠 La Grange Fort
- ⏳ 5 Apr - 31 Oct
- ☎ +33 (0)4-73710243
- @ chateau@lagrangefort.eu

1 ADEJMNOPRT	AEFJNUX 6
2 ABCFGKPRTVWXY	ABDEFG 7
3 BEGHLMQRV	ADEFKNRSV 8
4 BDEFHILOPQT	ABEGIJQRU 9
5 ABDEFGHKMN	ABFGHJNOR 10
6A CEE	€ 34.00
A430 7ha 120T(80-120m²) 49P	€ 43.75

On A75 exit 13 dir. Parentignat. 1st turn to right at roundabout after 1.5 km, dir. St. Rémy-de-Chargnat via D999. Then right again at 2nd roundabout after 1.5 km, dir. Les Pradeaux (D34). Campsite 1 km on the right.

This castle campsite located in the heart of the Auvergne offers peace, ambiance and numerous leisure activities. You can enjoy the heated indoor swimming pool and a delicious meal in the castle in early and late seasons.

CC 5/4-7/7 25/8-30/10 14=12

N 45°30'31'' E 3°17'5''

www.eurocampings.co.uk/100400

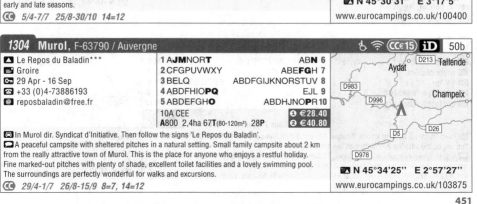

1304 Murol, F-63790 / Auvergne

(icons) CC€15 iD 50b

- ▲ Le Repos du Baladin***
- 🏠 Groire
- ⏳ 29 Apr - 16 Sep
- ☎ +33 (0)4-73886193
- @ reposbaladin@free.fr

1 AJMNORT	ABN 6
2 CFGPUVWXY	ABEFGH 7
3 BELQ	ABDFGIJKNORSTUV 8
4 ABDFHIOPQ	EJL 9
5 ABDEFGHO	ABDHJNOPR 10
10A CEE	€ 28.40
A800 2,4ha 67T(80-120m²) 28P	€ 40.80

In Murol dir. Syndicat d'Initiative. Then follow the signs 'Le Repos du Baladin'.

A peaceful campsite with sheltered pitches in a natural setting. Small family campsite about 2 km from the really attractive town of Murol. This is the place for anyone who enjoys a restful holiday. Fine marked-out pitches with plenty of shade, excellent toilet facilities and a lovely swimming pool. The surroundings are perfectly wonderful for walks and excursions.

CC 29/4-1/7 26/8-15/9 8=7, 14=12

N 45°34'25'' E 2°57'27''

www.eurocampings.co.uk/103875

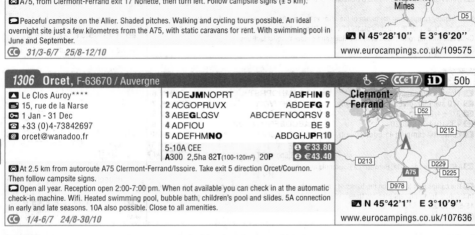

1305 Nonette, F-63340 / Auvergne — 📶 CC€15 iD 50b

- 🏕 Les Loges***
- 📅 31 Mar - 13 Oct
- ☎ +33 (0)4-73716582
- @ les.loges.nonette@wanadoo.fr

1 ADEIMNOPQRST	ABFGHJNU 6
2 ACJKPQRVXY	ABDEFGHIK 7
3 ABFLQT	ABDFNRSV 8
4 ABDIOPT	EQ 9
5 ABDEFGHJKMNO	ABDHIJOPS 10
6A CEE	❶ €19.00
A330 3ha 143T(80-130m²) 32P	❷ €27.00

🚗 A75, from Clermont-Ferrand exit 17 Nonette, then turn left. Follow campsite signs (± 5 km).

💬 Peaceful campsite on the Allier. Shaded pitches. Walking and cycling tours possible. An ideal overnight site just a few kilometres from the A75, with static caravans for rent. With swimming pool in June and September.

CC 31/3-6/7 25/8-12/10

Issoire — D26 — D996 — D214 — D999 — A75 — Brassac-les-Mines — D5

📍 N 45°28'10'' E 3°16'20''

www.eurocampings.co.uk/109575

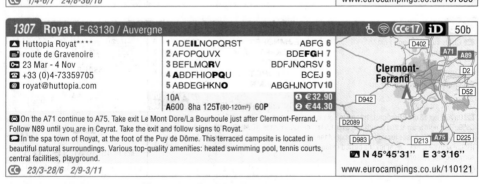

1306 Orcet, F-63670 / Auvergne — ♿ 📶 CC€17 iD 50b

- 🏕 Le Clos Auroy****
- 🏠 15, rue de la Narse
- 📅 1 Jan - 31 Dec
- ☎ +33 (0)4-73842697
- @ orcet@wanadoo.fr

1 ADEJMNOPRT	ABFHIN 6
2 ACGOPRUVX	ABDEFG 7
3 ABEGLQSV	ABCDEFNOQRSV 8
4 ADFIOU	BE 9
5 ADEFHMNO	ABDGHJPR 10
5-10A CEE	❶ €33.80
A300 2,5ha 82T(100-120m²) 20P	❷ €43.40

🚗 At 2.5 km from autoroute A75 Clermont-Ferrand/Issoire. Take exit 5 direction Orcet/Cournon. Then follow campsite signs.

💬 Open all year. Reception open 2:00-7:00 pm. When not available you can check in at the automatic check-in machine. Wifi. Heated swimming pool, bubble bath, children's pool and slides. 5A connection in early and late seasons. 10A also possible. Close to all amenities.

CC 1/4-6/7 24/8-30/10

Clermont-Ferrand — D52 — D212 — D213 — D229 — A75 — D225 — D978

📍 N 45°42'1'' E 3°10'9''

www.eurocampings.co.uk/107636

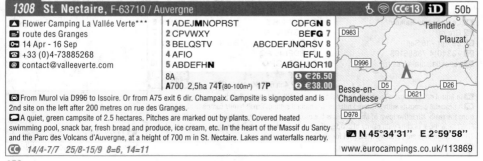

1307 Royat, F-63130 / Auvergne — ♿ 📶 CC€17 iD 50b

- 🏕 Huttopia Royat****
- 🏠 route de Gravenoire
- 📅 23 Mar - 4 Nov
- ☎ +33 (0)4-73359705
- @ royat@huttopia.com

1 ADEILNOPQRST	ABFG 6
2 AFOPQUVX	BDEFGH 7
3 BEFLMQRV	BDFJNQRSV 8
4 ABDFHIOPQU	BCEJ 9
5 ABDEGHKNO	ABGHJNOTV 10
10A	❶ €32.90
A600 8ha 125T(80-120m²) 60P	❷ €44.30

🚗 On the A71 continue to A75. Take exit Le Mont Dore/La Bourboule just after Clermont-Ferrand. Follow N89 until you are in Ceyrat. Take the exit and follow signs to Royat.

💬 In the spa town of Royat, at the foot of the Puy de Dôme. This terraced campsite is located in beautiful natural surroundings. Various top-quality amenities: heated swimming pool, tennis courts, central facilities, playground.

CC 23/3-28/6 2/9-3/11

D402 — A71 — A89 — Clermont-Ferrand — D2 — D52 — D942 — D2089 — D983 — D213 — A75 — D225

📍 N 45°45'31'' E 3°3'16''

www.eurocampings.co.uk/110121

1308 St. Nectaire, F-63710 / Auvergne — ♿ 📶 CC€13 iD 50b

- 🏕 Flower Camping La Vallée Verte***
- 🏠 route des Granges
- 📅 14 Apr - 16 Sep
- ☎ +33 (0)4-73885268
- @ contact@valleeverte.com

1 ADEJMNOPRST	CDFGN 6
2 CPVWXY	BEFG 7
3 BELQSTV	ABCDEFJNQRSV 8
4 AFIO	EFJL 9
5 ABDEFHN	ABGHJOR 10
8A	❶ €26.50
A700 2,5ha 74T(80-100m²) 17P	❷ €38.00

🚗 From Murol via D996 to Issoire. Or from A75 exit 6 dir. Champaix. Campsite is signposted and is 2nd site on the left after 200 metres on rue des Granges.

💬 A quiet, green campsite of 2.5 hectares. Pitches are marked out by plants. Covered heated swimming pool, snack bar, fresh bread and produce, ice cream, etc. In the heart of the Massif du Sancy and the Parc des Volcans d'Auvergne, at a height of 700 m in St. Nectaire. Lakes and waterfalls nearby.

CC 14/4-7/7 25/8-15/9 8=6, 14=11

Tallende — Plauzat — D983 — D996 — D5 — D26 — D621 — Besse-en-Chandesse — D978

📍 N 45°34'31'' E 2°59'58''

www.eurocampings.co.uk/113869

France

1309 St. Nectaire, F-63710 / Auvergne

🚹 🛜 (CC€15) **iD** 50b

- 🏕 Le Viginet***
- 📧 2 chemin du Manoir
- 📅 7 Apr - 30 Sep
- ☎ +33 (0)4-73885380
- @ info@camping-viginet.com

1 ADE**JM**NOPRST	ABFG	6
2 FGPSVWXY	ABDE**FG**HK	7
3 ABELQ	ABCDEFG**I**KNOQRSTUV	8
4 FIO	FJL	9
5 ABDEFGH**NO**	ABDFGHJLPTUV	10

10A CEE   € 24.70
A800   3,5ha 63T(90-140m²)   26P   € 33.90

🚗 A75 exit 6 to St. Nectaire. First road right in the village.

💬 Set in the beautiful Auvergne countryside, a true paradise for walkers and nature lovers. You can choose from the spacious marked-out pitches in this beautifully maintained parkland campsite. Snack bar, pizzeria, small shop, library, free wifi and freshly baked bread. Just 5 minutes' walk from St. Nectaire with its various restaurants and sights.

CC 7/4-8/7 26/8-29/9 7=6, 14=11, 21=16

📍 N 45°34'46'' E 3°0'10''

www.eurocampings.co.uk/110629

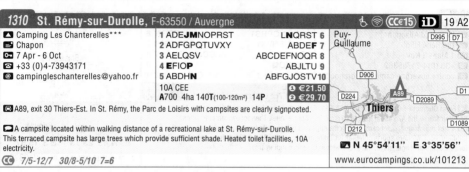

1310 St. Rémy-sur-Durolle, F-63550 / Auvergne

🚹 🛜 (CC€15) **iD** 19 A2

- 🏕 Camping Les Chanterelles***
- 📧 Chapon
- 📅 7 Apr - 6 Oct
- ☎ +33 (0)4-73943171
- @ campingleschanterelles@yahoo.fr

1 ADE**JM**NOPRST	LNQRST	6
2 ADFGPQTUVXY	ABDE**F**	7
3 AELQSV	ABCDEFNOQR	8
4 **EF**IO**P**	ABJLTU	9
5 ABDH**N**	ABFGJOSTV	10

10A CEE   € 21.50
A700   4ha 140T(100-120m²)   14P   € 29.70

🚗 A89, exit 30 Thiers-Est. In St. Rémy, the Parc de Loisirs with campsites are clearly signposted.

💬 A campsite located within walking distance of a recreational lake at St. Rémy-sur-Durolle. This terraced campsite has large trees which provide sufficient shade. Heated toilet facilities, 10A electricity.

CC 7/5-12/7 30/8-5/10 7=6

📍 N 45°54'11'' E 3°35'56''

www.eurocampings.co.uk/101213

France

1311 Tauves, F-63690 / Auvergne

🚹 🛜 ✿ (CC€15) **iD** 50b

- 🏕 Les Aurandeix***
- 📅 30 Mar - 30 Sep
- ☎ +33 (0)3-86379583
- @ camping.lesaurandeix@gmail.com

1 AD**JM**NOPRS**T**	ABFG	6
2 AGPVXY	ABDE**FG**HIK	7
3 BELMQ	ABCDFIJNOQRSV	8
4 AFI	EJ	9
5 ABDM**NO**	ABFGHIJLOV	10

10A CEE   € 19.50
A850   2,5ha 75T(45-110m²)   22P   € 27.30

🚗 From the A71 to the A89. Exit 25 on the D922 to Tauves. Follow campsite signs.

💬 A well maintained campsite at the foot of the Massif du Sancy and near the Parc des Volcans. Own field for football, basketball and volleyball. Heated swimming pool. Close to the village of Tauves.

CC 30/3-7/7 25/8-29/9 7=6, 14=11

📍 N 45°33'40'' E 2°37'29''

www.eurocampings.co.uk/115477

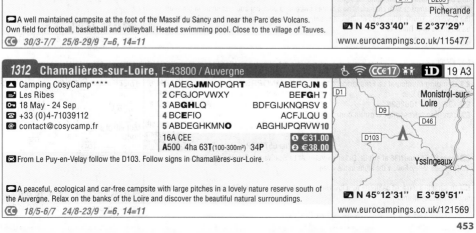

1312 Chamalières-sur-Loire, F-43800 / Auvergne

🚹 🛜 (CC€17) ✚✚ **iD** 19 A3

- 🏕 Camping CosyCamp****
- 📧 Les Ribes
- 📅 18 May - 24 Sep
- ☎ +33 (0)4-71039112
- @ contact@cosycamp.fr

1 ADEG**JM**NOPQR**T**	ABEFG**J**N	6
2 CFGJOPVWXY	BE**FG**H	7
3 AB**GHL**Q	BDFGIJKNQRSV	8
4 BC**E**FIO	ACFJLQU	9
5 ABDEGHKMN**O**	ABGHIJPQRVW	10

16A CEE   € 31.00
A500   4ha 63T(100-300m²)   34P   € 38.00

🚗 From Le Puy-en-Velay follow the D103. Follow signs in Chamalières-sur-Loire.

💬 A peaceful, ecological and car-free campsite with large pitches in a lovely nature reserve south of the Auvergne. Relax on the banks of the Loire and discover the beautiful natural surroundings.

CC 18/5-6/7 24/8-23/9 7=6, 14=11

📍 N 45°12'31'' E 3°59'51''

www.eurocampings.co.uk/121569

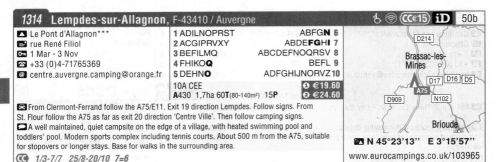

1313 Le Puy-en-Velay, F-43000 / Auvergne ♿ 🛜 (CC€15) iD 19 A3

- ▲ de Bouthezard***
- 🏠 chemin de Bouthezard Aiguilhe
- 📅 30 Mar - 28 Oct
- ☎ +33 (0)4-71095509
- @ camping.puyenvelay@orange.fr

1 A**JM**NOPRS**T**	N	6
2 COPQRX	ABDE**FG**	7
3 **LM**	ABCDFNRSV	8
4 FO		9
5 ABDNO	ABFGHIKOR	10
6A CEE	**❶ €15.20**	
A630 1,5ha 72T(50-100m²)	**❷ €18.40**	

🗺 Signposted in Le Puy-en-Velay. Campsite located on the foot of the high rock church on the N88.

💬 Welcoming, small, town campsite with plenty of shade at the foot of one of Le Puy's most famous volcanic cones. Suitable base for visiting the town.

CC 30/3-7/7 25/8-27/10 7=6, 14=11

www.eurocampings.co.uk/103968

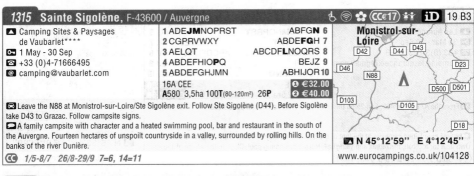

1314 Lempdes-sur-Allagnon, F-43410 / Auvergne ♿ 🛜 (CC€15) iD 50b

- ▲ Le Pont d'Allagnon***
- 🏠 rue René Filiol
- 📅 1 Mar - 3 Nov
- ☎ +33 (0)4-71765369
- @ centre.auvergne.camping@orange.fr

1 ADILNOPRST	ABFGN	6
2 ACGIPRVXY	ABDE**FGHI**	7
3 BEFILMQ	ABCDEFNOQRSV	8
4 FHIKO**Q**	BEFL	9
5 DEHN**O**	ADFGHIJNORVZ	10
10A CEE	**❶ €19.60**	
A430 1,7ha 60T(80-140m²) 15P	**❷ €24.60**	

🗺 From Clermont-Ferrand follow the A75/E11. Exit 19 direction Lempdes. Follow signs. From St. Flour follow the A75 as far as exit 20 direction 'Centre Ville'. Then follow camping signs.

💬 A well maintained, quiet campsite on the edge of a village, with heated swimming pool and toddlers' pool. Modern sports complex including tennis courts. About 500 m from the A75, suitable for stopovers or longer stays. Base for walks in the surrounding area.

CC 1/3-7/7 25/8-20/10 7=6

www.eurocampings.co.uk/103965

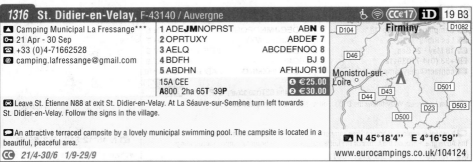

1315 Sainte Sigolène, F-43600 / Auvergne ♿ 🛜 ✿ (CC€17) 👥 iD 19 B3

- ▲ Camping Sites & Paysages de Vaubarlet****
- 📅 1 May - 30 Sep
- ☎ +33 (0)4-71666495
- @ camping@vaubarlet.com

1 ADE**JM**NOPRST	ABFGN	6
2 CGPRVWXY	ABDE**FG**H	7
3 AELQT	ABCDF**L**NOQRS	8
4 ABDEFHIO**PQ**	BEJZ	9
5 ABDEFGHJMN	ABHIJOR	10
16A CEE	**❶ €32.00**	
A580 3,5ha 100T(80-120m²) 26P	**❷ €40.00**	

🗺 Leave the N88 at Monistrol-sur-Loire/Ste Sigolène exit. Follow Ste Sigolène (D44). Before Sigolène take D43 to Grazac. Follow campsite signs.

💬 A family campsite with character and a heated swimming pool, bar and restaurant in the south of the Auvergne. Fourteen hectares of unspoilt countryside in a valley, surrounded by rolling hills. On the banks of the river Dunière.

CC 1/5-8/7 26/8-29/9 7=6, 14=11

www.eurocampings.co.uk/104128

1316 St. Didier-en-Velay, F-43140 / Auvergne ♿ 🛜 (CC€17) iD 19 B3

- ▲ Camping Municipal La Fressange***
- 📅 21 Apr - 30 Sep
- ☎ +33 (0)4-71662528
- @ camping.lafressange@gmail.com

1 ADE**JM**NOPRST	AB**N**	6
2 OPRTUXY	ABDEF	7
3 AELQ	ABCDEFNOQ	8
4 BDFH	BJ	9
5 ABDHN	AFHIJOR	10
15A CEE	**❶ €25.00**	
A800 2ha 65T 39P	**❷ €30.00**	

🗺 Leave St. Étienne N88 at exit St. Didier-en-Velay. At La Séauve-sur-Semène turn left towards St. Didier-en-Velay. Follow the signs in the village.

💬 An attractive terraced campsite by a lovely municipal swimming pool. The campsite is located in a beautiful, peaceful area.

CC 21/4-30/6 1/9-29/9

📍 N 45°18'4'' E 4°16'59''

www.eurocampings.co.uk/104124

1317 St. Paulien, F-43350 / Auvergne

♿ 🛜 ⓒⒸ€17 ⚤ iD 19 A3

- ⛺ Flower Camping La Rochelambert★★★★
- 🚩 route de Lanthenas
- 📅 1 Apr - 30 Sep
- ☎ +33 (0)4-71005402
- @ infos@camping-rochelambert.com

1 ADE**JM**NOPRST	ABF**G**N	6
2 CGIPRTUVWX	ABDE**FGH**	7
3 BEFLMQT	ABCDFJKNQRSTUV	8
4 BFHILNO**PT**	BFJ	9
5 ABDEFGHKN	ABDGHIJORZ	10

16A CEE ❶ €23.80
A700 4ha 80T(80-120m²) 32P ❷ €32.80

🚗 The campsite is signposted from the N102 Le Puy - Clermont-Ferrand in the direction of St. Paulien. Follow campsite signs (3 km) from St. Paulien centre (D906).
💬 Well maintained, quiet campsite with an informal ambiance in the undiscovered east of the Auvergne, 15 km from Le Puy. Starting point for walks. The site is located by a river in natural surroundings with a heated pool and toddlers' pool. Own tennis court.

ⓒ 1/4-7/7 27/8-29/9

N102 D13 D103 D590 D906 **Le Puy-en-Velay**

📌 N 45°7'13'' E 3°47'38''

www.eurocampings.co.uk/110940

1318 Lanobre, F-15270 / Auvergne

♿ 🛜 ⓒⒸ€17 iD 50b

- ⛺ Le Lac de la Siauve★★★
- 🚩 La Siauve
- 📅 8 Apr - 17 Sep
- ☎ +33 (0)4-71403185
- @ campinglelacdelasiauve@orange.fr

1 ADJMNORST	ABFGL**NQSWXYZ**	6
2 DFGHJKPQTUVXY	ABDE**FGH**	7
3 ABDELQ	ABCDEFKNOQRSUV	8
4 BCDFILNO**PQ**	EFJUV	9
5 ABDEFGH**NO**	ABCFGHIJO**P**RV	10

6-16A CEE ❶ €23.30
A592 17ha 171T(80-120m²) 71P ❷ €32.30

🚗 From Clermont-Ferrand exit Bordeaux, then the N89 in Laqueraille. Then take the D922 direction Bort-les-Orgues. The campsite is signposted beyond Lanobre.
💬 Large, fun, terraced campsite in very green surroundings with a beautiful view of the Lac des Bort-les-Orgues. Indoor heated pool. Direct access to the lake and also to the pontoon/ramp for boats. Luxurious toilet block.

ⓒ 8/4-6/7 1/9-15/9

Bagnols D47 D979 **Bort-les-Orgues** D922 D679 Ydes D3

📌 N 45°25'50'' E 2°30'14''

www.eurocampings.co.uk/108844

France

1319 Mauriac, F-15200 / Auvergne

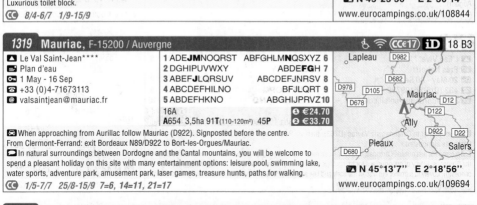

♿ 🛜 ⓒⒸ€17 iD 18 B3

- ⛺ Le Val Saint-Jean★★★★
- 🚩 Plan d'eau
- 📅 1 May - 16 Sep
- ☎ +33 (0)4-71673113
- @ valsaintjean@mauriac.fr

1 ADE**JM**NOQRST	ABFGHLM**N**QSXYZ	6
2 DGHIPUVWXY	ABDE**FGH**	7
3 ABEF**J**LQRSUV	ABCDEFJNRSV	8
4 ABCDEFHILNO	BFJLQRT	9
5 ABDEFHKNO	ABGHIJPRVZ	10

16A ❶ €24.70
A654 3,5ha 91T(110-120m²) 45P ❷ €33.70

🚗 When approaching from Aurillac follow Mauriac (D922). Signposted before the centre. From Clermont-Ferrand: exit Bordeaux N89/D922 to Bort-les-Orgues/Mauriac.
💬 In natural surroundings between Dordogne and the Cantal mountains, you will be welcome to spend a pleasant holiday on this site with many entertainment options: leisure pool, swimming lake, water sports, adventure park, amusement park, laser games, treasure hunts, paths for walking.

ⓒ 1/5-7/7 25/8-15/9 7=6, 14=11, 21=17

Lapleau D982 D682 D978 D105 **Mauriac** D12 D678 D122 Ally D922 D22 Pleaux D680 Salers

📌 N 45°13'7'' E 2°18'56''

www.eurocampings.co.uk/109694

1320 Neuvéglise, F-15260 / Auvergne

♿ 🛜 ⓒⒸ€15 iD 19 A3

- ⛺ Flower Camping Le Belvédère★★★★
- 🚩 Lanau
- 📅 30 Mar - 22 Sep
- ☎ +33 (0)4-71235050
- @ belvedere.cantal@orange.fr

1 ADE**JM**NORST	CDF**N**U	6
2 FPRUVX	ABDE**FG**HK	7
3 ABELQ	ABCDEFNPQRSUV	8
4 BD**E**FILNO**QRT**	BEJL	9
5 ABDEFGHJKM**NO**	ABDGHIJOST	10

6-15A ❶ €31.00
A700 3,5ha 80T(80-100m²) 79P ❷ €41.50

🚗 On D921 take exit St. Flour/Chaudes-Aigues. Pass Neuvéglise on right. Direction Lanau, 1st right when you have reached the dam (signposted).
💬 This terraced campsite is located on a south-facing slope with beautiful views of the valley, some pitches have a view of Lanau Lake. Snacks available, indoor and heated pool. Sportive as well as cultural outings are possible. The health spa Chaudes-Aigues is 5 km away with a hot water spring of 82 °C.

ⓒ 30/3-6/7 29/8-21/9

D990 **Neuvéglise** Pierrefort **Chaudes-Aigues** D921 D13 D989

📌 N 44°53'42'' E 3°0'5''

www.eurocampings.co.uk/101232

1321 Ruynes-en-Margeride, F-15320 / Auvergne ⚒ 🚲 (CC€17) iD 19 A3

■ Le Petit Bois***
🔲 14 Apr - 29 Sep
☎ +33 (0)4-71234226
@ contact@revea-vacances.com

1 ADEJMNOPRST	ABFG	6
2 ABFGIPRTVWXY	ABDEFH	7
3 ALMQ	ABCDEFKNQRV	8
4 BFHINO	JKU	9
5 ABDN	AGHIJRV	10
10A CEE	❶ €21.80	
A920 7ha 90T(100-150m²) 20P	❷ €28.00	

🚗 Leave the A75 at exit 30 after St. Flour. Via the D4 towards Ruynes-en-Margeride, then follow campsite signs.
💬 Lightly undulating meadow on the edge of a wood with a wide view over the hills of Auvergne with some pitches that are marked out and some that are not. Swimming pool. There are also many pitches in the pine forest. 15% discount for a stay from 7 nights (not in July and August).
CC 14/4-7/7 25/8-28/9

📍 N 44°59'56'' E 3°13'8''

www.eurocampings.co.uk/103971

1322 St. Flour, F-15100 / Auvergne 🛜 (CC€15) iD 19 A3

■ International Roche Murat***
🚐 N9
🔲 8 Apr - 4 Nov
☎ +33 (0)4-71604363
@ courrier@camping-saint-flour.com

1 ADJMNOPRST		6
2 APRUVWX	ABDEFGHK	7
3 BQ	ABCDFJNRSTUV	8
4 IO	J	9
5 ABD	ABGHIJOR	10
16A CEE	❶ €17.00	
A930 3ha 120T(50-100m²) 11P	❷ €20.70	

🚗 The campsite is located on the A75 just north of St. Flour. Take exit 28. Follow the signs at the roundabout.
💬 Terraced campsite close to entrance and exit of the A75. Excellent stopover campsite. A good base for visiting the historic town of St. Flour. 15% discount for a stay from 7 nights (not in July and August).
CC 8/4-7/7 25/8-3/11

📍 N 45°3'2'' E 3°6'28''

www.eurocampings.co.uk/103970

1323 Carennac, F-46110 / Midi-Pyrénées ⚒ 🛜 (CC€15) ✸ iD 18 B3

■ L'Eau Vive****
🚐 Prés Nabots
🔲 20 May - 30 Sep
☎ +33 (0)5-65109739
@ info@dordogne-soleil.com

1 AJMNOPRST	AFJNU	6
2 CPVWXY	ABDEFGH	7
3 BEFIKLQ	ABCDEFNRSV	8
4 BDFHIOPQ	AELQR	9
5 ABDEFGHNO	ABGHIJOSTV	10
6A CEE	❶ €25.60	
A160 3ha 100T(80-120m²) 38P	❷ €38.50	

🚗 From Martel to Carennac via Vayrac (D703), then via Bétaille and via the D20 to Carennac. Campsite signposted.
💬 A campsite just outside Carennac, one of France's most beautiful villages, in the middle of the countryside in the Dordogne. Plenty of opportunities for tourist trips such: culture (villages, caves) and nature (walking, cycling, canoeing). Lovely in summer but also in the early and late seasons. Pitches with sun or shade. Family atmosphere.
CC 20/5-7/7 31/8-29/9 7=6, 14=11

📍 N 44°54'36'' E 1°44'27''

www.eurocampings.co.uk/111263

1324 Creysse, F-46600 / Midi-Pyrénées ⚒ 🛜 (CC€15) iD 50a

■ Du Port***
🔲 21 Apr - 30 Sep
☎ +33 (0)5-65322082
@ contact@campingduport.com

1 ADEJMNOPRT	AJNUVXY	6
2 CGJPVWXY	ABDEFH	7
3 ABFLQ	ABCDEFKNRSV	8
4 BDFHIOP	CEQRUV	9
5 ABCDEFHMN	ABHJOSTV	10
10A CEE	❶ €18.10	
A110 5ha 86T(100-300m²) 14P	❷ €26.10	

🚗 A20 exit Rocamadour/Martel. Via the N140 as far as Martel. In Martel via the D23 towards Creysse. Then follow the campsite signs.
💬 Direct access to the Dordogne. Close to the historic village of Creysse. The restaurant/brasserie is open during the CampingCard ACSI validity period. You can book canoeing, climbing and potholing trips at the campsite. Beautiful pool. Free wifi.
CC 21/4-30/6 26/8-29/9 10=8

📍 N 44°53'7'' E 1°35'58''

www.eurocampings.co.uk/114019

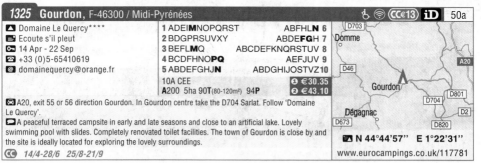

1325 Gourdon, F-46300 / Midi-Pyrénées ♿ 🅰 (CC€13) iD 50a

- ▲ Domaine Le Quercy★★★★
- 🏠 Ecoute s'il pleut
- ☷ 14 Apr - 22 Sep
- ☎ +33 (0)5-65410619
- @ domainequercy@orange.fr

1 ADEI**M**NOPQRST	ABFHL**N**	6
2 BDGPRSUVXY	ABDE**FGH**	7
3 BEF**LMQ**	ABCDEFKNQRSTUV	8
4 BCDFHNO**PQ**	AEFJUV	9
5 ABDEFGHJ**N**	ABDGHIJOSTVZ	10

10A CEE
A200 5ha 90**T**(80-120m²) 94**P**

❶ €30.35
❷ €43.10

🚗 A20, exit 55 or 56 direction Gourdon. In Gourdon centre take the D704 Sarlat. Follow 'Domaine Le Quercy'.

💬 A peaceful terraced campsite in early and late seasons and close to an artificial lake. Lovely swimming pool with slides. Completely renovated toilet facilities. The town of Gourdon is close by and the site is ideally located for exploring the lovely surroundings.

CC 14/4-28/6 25/8-21/9

N 44°44'57'' E 1°22'31''

www.eurocampings.co.uk/117781

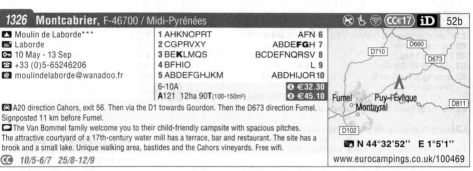

1326 Montcabrier, F-46700 / Midi-Pyrénées ⊗ ♿ 🅰 (CC€17) iD 52b

- ▲ Moulin de Laborde★★★
- 🏠 Laborde
- ☷ 10 May - 13 Sep
- ☎ +33 (0)5-65246206
- @ moulindelaborde@wanadoo.fr

1 AHKNOPRT	AFN	6
2 CGPRVXY	ABDE**FGH**	7
3 BE**K**LMQS	BCDEFNQRSV	8
4 BFHIO	L	9
5 ABDEFGHJKM	ABDHIJOR	10

6-10A
A121 12ha 90**T**(100-150m²)

❶ €32.30
❷ €45.10

🚗 A20 direction Cahors, exit 56. Then via the D1 towards Gourdon. Then the D673 direction Fumel. Signposted 11 km before Fumel.

💬 The Van Bommel family welcome you to their child-friendly campsite with spacious pitches. The attractive courtyard of a 17th-century water mill has a terrace, bar and restaurant. The site has a brook and a small lake. Unique walking area, bastides and the Cahors vineyards. Free wifi.

CC 10/5-6/7 25/8-12/9

N 44°32'52'' E 1°5'1''

www.eurocampings.co.uk/100469

France

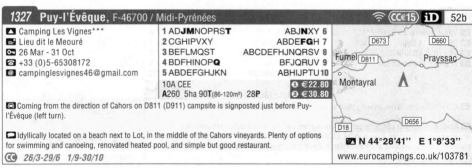

1327 Puy-l'Évêque, F-46700 / Midi-Pyrénées 🅰 (CC€15) iD 52b

- ▲ Camping Les Vignes★★★
- 🏠 Lieu dit le Meouré
- ☷ 26 Mar - 31 Oct
- ☎ +33 (0)5-65308172
- @ campinglesvignes46@gmail.com

1 AD**JM**NOPRS**T**	ABJ**N**XY	6
2 CGHIPVXY	ABDE**FGH**	7
3 BEFLMQST	ABCDEFHJNQRSV	8
4 BDFHINOP**Q**	BFJQRUV	9
5 ABDEFGHJKN	ABHIJPTU	10

10A CEE
A260 5ha 90**T**(86-120m²) 28**P**

❶ €22.80
❷ €30.80

🚗 Coming from the direction of Cahors on D811 (D911) campsite is signposted just before Puy-l'Évêque (left turn).

💬 Idyllically located on a beach next to Lot, in the middle of the Cahors vineyards. Plenty of options for swimming and canoeing, renovated heated pool, and simple but good restaurant.

CC 26/3-29/6 1/9-30/10

N 44°28'41'' E 1°8'33''

www.eurocampings.co.uk/103781

1328 Souillac, F-46200 / Midi-Pyrénées ♿ 🅰 (CC€17) ⚥ iD 50a

- ▲ Castels Domaine de la Paille Basse★★★★★
- ☷ 7 Apr - 15 Sep
- ☎ +33 (0)5-65378548
- @ info@lapaillebasse.com

1 ABDE**JM**NOPRST	ABFGHU	6
2 AFPRSUVXY	BE**FGH**	7
3 BEF**K**LMQT	BDFNQRS	8
4 A**E**FHILO**P**	AEK	9
5 ABCDEFHKLM	ABHIJLM**O**RZ	10

Ad on page 458 16A
12ha 120**T**(100-110m²) 84**P**

❶ €41.20
❷ €58.20

🚗 Don't use SatNav. Take exit 55 on A20. At 2nd roundabout direction Salignac. Follow signs 'La Paille Basse'. Site is 8 km from Souillac.

💬 A medieval village (3 farmhouses) restored and reconstructed into an 80-hectare campsite, all of this without losing its authenticity. Positioned on a hill with lovely views and romantic sunsets. This, with all the facilities you would expect, means this Castels campsite deserves its five stars.

CC 7/4-7/7 25/8-14/9 7=6, 14=12, 21=18

N 44°56'44'' E 1°26'29''

www.eurocampings.co.uk/109092

DORDOGNE - LOT

DOMAINE DE LA Paille Basse ★★★★★

www.lapaillebasse.com +33 5 65 37 85 48 LES CASTELS

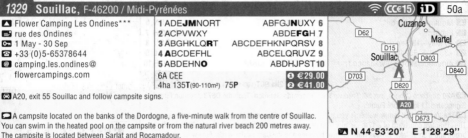

1329 Souillac, F-46200 / Midi-Pyrénées
📶 (CC€15) iD 50a

🏕 Flower Camping Les Ondines***
📧 rue des Ondines
🗓 1 May - 30 Sep
☎ +33 (0)5-65378644
@ camping.les.ondines@
flowercampings.com

1	ADE**JM**NORT	ABFGJ**N**UXY	6
2	ACPVWXY	ABDE**FG**H	7
3	ABGHKLQ**RT**	ABCDEFHKNPQRSV	8
4	**A**BCDEFHL	ABCELQRUVZ	9
5	ABDEHN**O**	ABDHJPST	10

6A CEE ❶ €29.00
4ha 135T(90-110m²) 75P ❷ €41.00

🚗 A20, exit 55 Souillac and follow campsite signs.

💬 A campsite located on the banks of the Dordogne, a five-minute walk from the centre of Souillac. You can swim in the heated pool on the campsite or from the natural river beach 200 metres away. The campsite is located between Sarlat and Rocamadour.

CC 1/5-6/7 25/8-29/9 7=6

N 44°53'20'' E 1°28'29''
www.eurocampings.co.uk/113258

Map: Cuzance, D62, D15, Martel, Souillac, D803, D840, D703, D820, A20, D673

1330 Souillac, F-46200 / Midi-Pyrénées
♿ 📶 ✿ (CC€15) iD 50a

🏕 Vakantiepark 'La Draille'****
🗓 28 Apr - 15 Sep
☎ +33 (0)5-65326501
@ la.draille@wanadoo.fr

1	ADE**IL**NORT	ABFHNUV	6
2	ACGHPRUVY	ABDE**FG**H	7
3	BE**GHIKL**MQRS	ABCDEFNRSV	8
4	**A**EFHIJLO	AEJLQRUV	9
5	ACDEFGHKM**N**	ABHIJLMO**P**QSTZ	10

10A CEE ❶ €39.10
A150 35ha 146T(100-120m²) 83P ❷ €52.10

🚗 A20 exit Soulliac. When entering Soulliac turn right onto the D15 and then the D62.

💬 A beautiful four-star campsite: perfectly maintained pitches, toilet facilities and amenities. Set among the hills on the River Borrèze. Ideal as stopover campsite and/or starting point for many places of interest. Beautiful woodland walks in the 35-hectare park. Limited services on Sundays.

CC 28/4-6/7 25/8-14/9

N 44°56'9'' E 1°26'14''
www.eurocampings.co.uk/100467

Map: Cressensac, D60, D62, A20, D820, Martel, D803, Souillac, D703

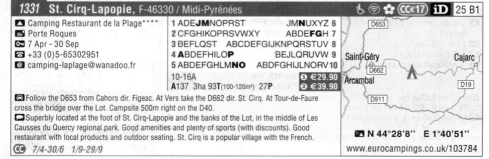

1331 St. Cirq-Lapopie, F-46330 / Midi-Pyrénées
♿ 📶 ✿ (CC€17) iD 25 B1

🏕 Camping Restaurant de la Plage****
📧 Porte Roques
🗓 7 Apr - 30 Sep
☎ +33 (0)5-65302951
@ camping-laplage@wanadoo.fr

1	ADE**JM**NOPRST	**JMN**UXYZ	6
2	CFGHIKOPRSVWXY	ABDE**FG**H	7
3	BEFLQST	ABCDEFGIJKNPQRSTUV	8
4	**A**BDEFHILO**P**	BEJLQRUVW	9
5	ABDEFGHLM**NO**	ABDFGHIJLNORV	10

10-16A ❶ €29.90
A137 3ha 93T(100-120m²) 27P ❷ €39.90

🚗 Follow the D653 from Cahors dir. Figeac. At Vers take the D662 dir. St. Cirq. At Tour-de-Faure cross the bridge over the Lot. Campsite 500m right on the D40.

💬 Superbly located at the foot of St. Cirq-Lapopie and the banks of the Lot, in the middle of Les Causses du Quercy regional park. Good amenities and plenty of sports (with discounts). Good restaurant with local products and outdoor seating. St. Cirq is a popular village with the French.

CC 7/4-30/6 1/9-29/9

N 44°28'8'' E 1°40'51''
www.eurocampings.co.uk/103784

Map: D653, Saint-Géry, D662, Cajarc, Arcambal, D19, D911

France

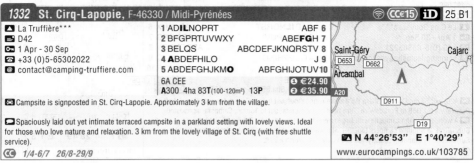

1332 St. Cirq-Lapopie, F-46330 / Midi-Pyrénées
📶 (CC€15) iD 25 B1

- ▲ La Truffière***
- ▤ D42
- ☛ 1 Apr - 30 Sep
- ☎ +33 (0)5-65302022
- @ contact@camping-truffiere.com

1 AD**IL**NOPRT	ABF	**6**
2 BFGPRTUVWXY	ABE**FG**H	**7**
3 BELQS	ABCDEFJKNQRSTV	**8**
4 **A**BDEFHILO	J	**9**
5 ABDEFGHJKM**O**	ABFGHIJOTUV	**10**
6A CEE		❶ €24.90
A300 4ha 83T(100-120m²) 13P		❷ €35.90

Campsite is signposted in St. Cirq-Lapopie. Approximately 3 km from the village.

Spaciously laid out yet intimate terraced campsite in a parkland setting with lovely views. Ideal for those who love nature and relaxation. 3 km from the lovely village of St. Cirq (with free shuttle service).

CC 1/4-6/7   26/8-29/9

Saint-Géry · Cajarc · Arcambal
D653 · D662 · D911 · D19 · A20

📍 N 44°26'53''   E 1°40'29''
www.eurocampings.co.uk/103785

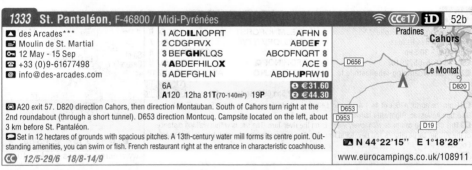

1333 St. Pantaléon, F-46800 / Midi-Pyrénées
📶 (CC€17) iD 52b

- ▲ des Arcades***
- ▤ Moulin de St. Martial
- ☛ 12 May - 15 Sep
- ☎ +33 (0)9-61677498
- @ info@des-arcades.com

1 ACD**IL**NOPRT	AFHN	**6**
2 CDGPRVX	ABDE**F**	**7**
3 BEF**GH**KLQS	ABCDFNQRT	**8**
4 **A**BDEFHILO**X**	ACE	**9**
5 ADEFGHLN	ABDHJ**P**RW	**10**
6A		❶ €31.60
A120 12ha 81T(70-140m²) 19P		❷ €44.30

A20 exit 57. D820 direction Cahors, then direction Montauban. South of Cahors turn right at the 2nd roundabout (through a short tunnel). D653 direction Montcuq. Campsite located on the left, about 3 km before St. Pantaléon.

Set in 12 hectares of grounds with spacious pitches. A 13th-century water mill forms its centre point. Outstanding amenities, you can swim or fish. French restaurant right at the entrance in characteristic coachhouse.

CC 12/5-29/6   18/8-14/9

Pradines · Cahors · Le Montat
D656 · D820 · D653 · D953 · D19

📍 N 44°22'15''   E 1°18'28''
www.eurocampings.co.uk/108911

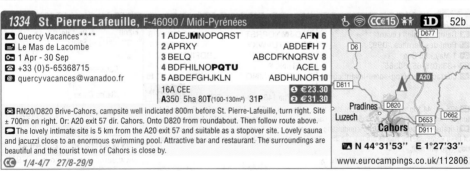

1334 St. Pierre-Lafeuille, F-46090 / Midi-Pyrénées
♿ 📶 (CC€15) ♙♙ iD 52b

- ▲ Quercy Vacances****
- ▤ Le Mas de Lacombe
- ☛ 1 Apr - 30 Sep
- ☎ +33 (0)5-65368715
- @ quercyvacances@wanadoo.fr

1 ADE**JM**NOPQRST	AF**N**	**6**
2 APRXY	ABDE**F**H	**7**
3 BELQ	ABCDFKNQRSV	**8**
4 BDFHILNO**PQTU**	ACEL	**9**
5 ABDEFGHJKLN	ABDHIJNOR	**10**
16A CEE		❶ €23.30
A350 5ha 80T(100-130m²) 31P		❷ €31.30

RN20/D820 Brive-Cahors, campsite well indicated 800m before St. Pierre-Lafeuille, turn right. Site ± 700m on right. Or: A20 exit 57 dir. Cahors. Onto D820 from roundabout. Then follow route above.

The lovely intimate site is 5 km from the A20 exit 57 and suitable as a stopover site. Lovely sauna and jacuzzi close to an enormous swimming pool. Attractive bar and restaurant. The surroundings are beautiful and the tourist town of Cahors is close by.

CC 1/4-4/7   27/8-29/9

D677 · D6 · A20 · D811 · Pradines · D820 · Luzech · Cahors · D653 · D662 · D911

📍 N 44°31'53''   E 1°27'33''
www.eurocampings.co.uk/112806

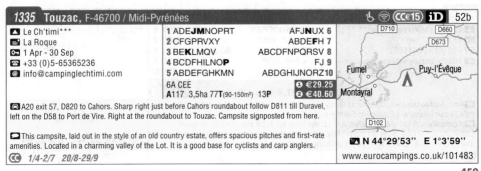

1335 Touzac, F-46700 / Midi-Pyrénées
♿ 📶 (CC€15) iD 52b

- ▲ Le Ch'timi***
- ▤ La Roque
- ☛ 1 Apr - 30 Sep
- ☎ +33 (0)5-65365236
- @ info@campinglechtimi.com

1 ADE**JM**NOPRT	AFJ**N**UX	**6**
2 CFGPRVXY	ABDE**F**H	**7**
3 BE**K**LMQV	ABCDFNPQRSV	**8**
4 BCDFHILNO**P**	FJ	**9**
5 ABDEFGHKMN	ABDGHIJNORZ	**10**
6A CEE		❶ €29.25
A117 3,5ha 77T(90-150m²) 13P		❷ €40.60

A20 exit 57, D820 to Cahors. Sharp right just before Cahors roundabout follow D811 till Duravel, left on the D58 to Port de Vire. Right at the roundabout to Touzac. Campsite signposted from here.

This campsite, laid out in the style of an old country estate, offers spacious pitches and first-rate amenities. Located in a charming valley of the Lot. It is a good base for cyclists and carp anglers.

CC 1/4-2/7   20/8-29/9

D710 · D660 · D673 · Fumel · Puy-l'Évêque · Montayral · D102

📍 N 44°29'53''   E 1°3'59''
www.eurocampings.co.uk/101483

459

France

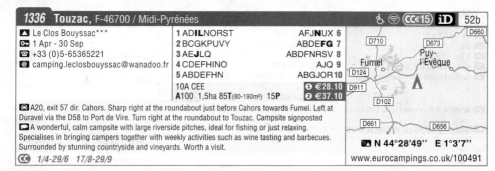

1336 Touzac, F-46700 / Midi-Pyrénées
♿ ⊚ (CC€15) iD 52b

🏕 Le Clos Bouyssac***
📅 1 Apr - 30 Sep
☎ +33 (0)5-65365221
@ camping.leclosbouyssac@wanadoo.fr

1 AD**IL**NORST	AFJNUX	6
2 BCGKPUVY	ABDE**FG**	7
3 AEJLQ	ABDFNRSV	8
4 CDEFHINO	AJQ	9
5 ABDEFHN	ABGJOR	10

10A CEE ❶ €28.10
A100 1,5ha 85T(80-190m²) 15P ❷ €37.10

🅰 A20, exit 57 dir. Cahors. Sharp right at the roundabout just before Cahors towards Fumel. Left at Duravel via the D58 to Port de Vire. Turn right at the roundabout to Touzac. Campsite signposted
💬 A wonderful, calm campsite with large riverside pitches, ideal for fishing or just relaxing. Specialises in bringing campers together with weekly activities such as wine tasting and barbecues. Surrounded by stunning countryside and vineyards. Worth a visit.
🆑 1/4-29/6 17/8-29/9

📍 N 44°28'49'' E 1°3'7''
www.eurocampings.co.uk/100491

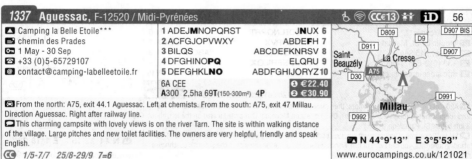

1337 Aguessac, F-12520 / Midi-Pyrénées
♿ ⊚ (CC€13) ⚎ iD 56

🏕 Camping la Belle Etoile***
🚏 chemin des Prades
📅 1 May - 30 Sep
☎ +33 (0)5-65729107
@ contact@camping-labelleetoile.fr

1 ADEJ**M**NOPQRST	JNUX	6
2 ACFGJOPVWXY	ABDE**F**H	7
3 BILQS	ABCDEFKNRSV	8
4 DFGHINO**PQ**	ELQRU	9
5 DEFGHKL**NO**	ABDFGHIJORYZ	10

6A CEE ❶ €22.40
A300 2,5ha 69T(150-300m²) 4P ❷ €30.90

🅰 From the north: A75, exit 44.1 Aguessac. Left at chemists. From the south: A75, exit 47 Millau. Direction Aguessac. Right after railway line.
💬 This charming campsite with lovely views is on the river Tarn. The site is within walking distance of the village. Large pitches and new toilet facilities. The owners are very helpful, friendly and speak English.
🆑 1/5-7/7 25/8-29/9 7=6

📍 N 44°9'13'' E 3°5'53''
www.eurocampings.co.uk/121021

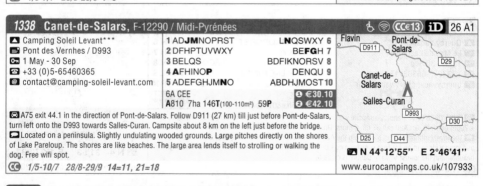

1338 Canet-de-Salars, F-12290 / Midi-Pyrénées
♿ ⊚ (CC€13) iD 26 A1

🏕 Camping Soleil Levant***
🚏 Pont des Vernhes / D993
📅 1 May - 30 Sep
☎ +33 (0)5-65460365
@ contact@camping-soleil-levant.com

1 ADJ**M**NOPRST	LNQSWXY	6
2 DFHPTUVWXY	BE**FG**H	7
3 BELQS	BDFIKNORSV	8
4 **A**FHINO**P**	DENQU	9
5 ADEFGHJM**N**O	ABDHJMOST	10

6A CEE ❶ €30.10
A810 7ha 146T(100-110m²) 59P ❷ €42.10

🅰 A75 exit 44.1 in the direction of Pont-de-Salars. Follow D911 (27 km) till just before Pont-de-Salars, turn left onto the D993 towards Salles-Curan. Campsite about 8 km on the left just before the bridge.
💬 Located on a peninsula. Slightly undulating wooded grounds. Large pitches directly on the shores of Lake Pareloup. The shores are like beaches. The large area lends itself to strolling or walking the dog. Free wifi spot.
🆑 1/5-10/7 28/8-29/9 14=11, 21=18

📍 N 44°12'55'' E 2°46'41''
www.eurocampings.co.uk/107933

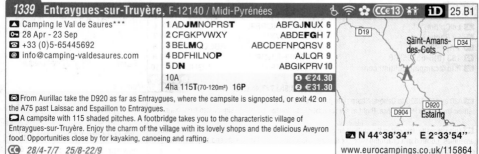

1339 Entraygues-sur-Truyère, F-12140 / Midi-Pyrénées
♿ ⊚ ✿ (CC€13) ⚎ iD 25 B1

🏕 Camping le Val de Saures***
📅 28 Apr - 23 Sep
☎ +33 (0)5-65445692
@ info@camping-valdesaures.com

1 ADJ**M**NOPRS**T**	ABFGJNUX	6
2 CFGKPVWXY	ABDE**FG**H	7
3 BEL**MQ**	ABCDEFNPQRSV	8
4 BDFHILNO**P**	AJLQR	9
5 D**N**	ABGIKPRV	10

10A ❶ €24.30
4ha 115T(70-120m²) 16P ❷ €31.30

🅰 From Aurillac take the D920 as far as Entraygues, where the campsite is signposted, or exit 42 on the A75 past Laissac and Espaillon to Entraygues.
💬 A campsite with 115 shaded pitches. A footbridge takes you to the characteristic village of Entraygues-sur-Truyère. Enjoy the charm of the village with its lovely shops and the delicious Aveyron food. Opportunities close by for kayaking, canoeing and rafting.
🆑 28/4-7/7 25/8-22/9

📍 N 44°38'34'' E 2°33'54''
www.eurocampings.co.uk/115864

1340 Flagnac, F-12300 / Midi-Pyrénées

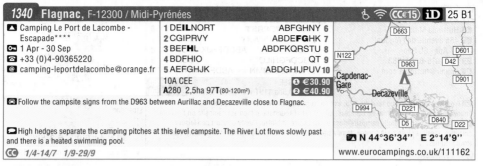

25 B1

🏕 Camping Le Port de Lacombe - Escapade****
📅 1 Apr - 30 Sep
☎ +33 (0)4-90365220
@ camping-leportdelacombe@orange.fr

1	DE**IL**NORT	ABFGHNY	6
2	CGIPRVY	ABDE**FG**HK	7
3	BEF**HL**	ABDFKQRSTU	8
4	BDFHIO	QT	9
5	AEFGHJK	ABDGHIJPUV	10

10A CEE
A280 2,5ha 97**T**(80-120m²)

❶ €30.90
❷ €40.90

Follow the campsite signs from the D963 between Aurillac and Decazeville close to Flagnac.

High hedges separate the camping pitches at this level campsite. The River Lot flows slowly past and there is a heated swimming pool.

CC 1/4-14/7 1/9-29/9

N 44°36'34'' E 2°14'9''

www.eurocampings.co.uk/111162

1341 Martiel, F-12200 / Midi-Pyrénées

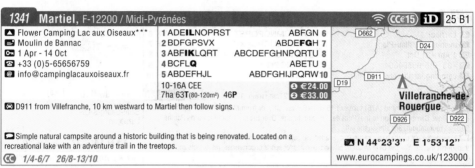

25 B1

🏕 Flower Camping Lac aux Oiseaux***
🏠 Moulin de Bannac
📅 1 Apr - 14 Oct
☎ +33 (0)5-65656759
@ info@campinglacauxoiseaux.fr

1	ADE**IL**NOPRST	ABFGN	6
2	BDFGPSVX	ABDE**FGH**	7
3	ABF**IK**LQRT	ABCDEFGHNPQRTU	8
4	BCFL**Q**	ABETU	9
5	ABDEFHJL	ABDFGHIJPQRW	10

10-16A CEE
7ha 63**T**(80-120m²) 46**P**

❶ €24.00
❷ €33.00

D911 from Villefranche, 10 km westward to Martiel then follow signs.

Simple natural campsite around a historic building that is being renovated. Located on a recreational lake with an adventure trail in the treetops.

CC 1/4-6/7 26/8-13/10

N 44°23'3'' E 1°53'12''

www.eurocampings.co.uk/123000

1342 Millau, F-12100 / Midi-Pyrénées

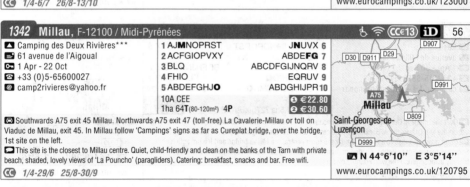

56

🏕 Camping des Deux Rivières***
🏠 61 avenue de l'Aigoual
📅 1 Apr - 22 Oct
☎ +33 (0)5-65600027
@ camp2rivieres@yahoo.fr

1	A**J**MNOPRST	JNUVX	6
2	ACFGIOPVXY	ABDE**FG**	7
3	BLQ	ABCDFGIJNQRV	8
4	FHIO	EQRUV	9
5	ABDEFGHJ**O**	ABDGHIJPR	10

10A CEE
1ha 64**T**(80-120m²) 4**P**

❶ €22.80
❷ €30.60

Southwards A75 exit 45 Millau. Northwards A75 exit 47 (toll-free) La Cavalerie-Millau or toll on Viaduc de Millau, exit 45. In Millau follow 'Campings' signs as far as Cureplat bridge, over the bridge, 1st site on the left.

This site is the closest to Millau centre. Quiet, child-friendly and clean on the banks of the Tarn with private beach, shaded, lovely views of 'La Pouncho' (paragliders). Catering: breakfast, snacks and bar. Free wifi.

CC 1/4-29/6 25/8-30/9

N 44°6'10'' E 3°5'14''

www.eurocampings.co.uk/120795

1343 Millau, F-12100 / Midi-Pyrénées

56

🏕 Du Viaduc****
🏠 121 avenue de Millau-Plage
📅 14 Apr - 30 Sep
☎ +33 (0)5-65601575
@ info@camping-du-viaduc.com

1	ADE**IL**NOPQRST	ABFGHIJ**N**PUVX	6
2	ABCFGHKOPQVWXY	ABDE**FGH**	7
3	BELQSTV	ABCDEFGHIJKNPQRSTUV	8
4	BCDFGHILNO**PQ**RY	AEQRUVW	9
5	ACDEFGHJKLM**O**	ABGHIJ**P**R	10

6A CEE
A358 5ha 185**T**(80-130m²) 50**P**

❶ €38.70
❷ €52.50

From Clermont-Ferrand A75, exit 45 (turn off SatNav). From Montpellier A75, exit 47. Then follow camping signs as far as 'Pont de Cureplat', towards Paulhe D187 at the roundabout, 1st campsite on the left.

500m from the centre of Millau. Spacious pitches in natural surroundings. Private beach with sun loungers on the River Tarn. Heated, modern toilet facilities. Unlimited wifi for 1.50 euro per day per device. Heated leisure pool from 1 May.

CC 14/4-7/7 27/8-29/9

N 44°6'18'' E 3°5'18''

www.eurocampings.co.uk/101064

France

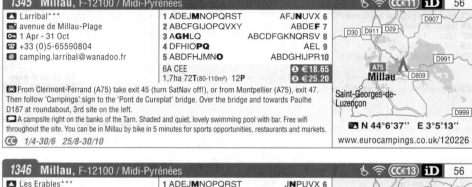
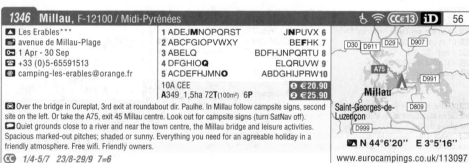

1344 Millau, F-12100 / Midi-Pyrénées ⅋ ⬡ (CC€15) iD 56

🏕 Huttopia Millau***
✉ 455 avenue de l'Aigoual
📅 27 Apr - 30 Sep
☎ +33 (0)5-65611883
@ millau@huttopia.com

1 ADE**IL**NOPRS**T**	ABFJ**N**UVX 6
2 ACFGIJOPVWXY	ABDE**FGH** 7
3 BLQV	ABCDFHJKNOQRSTV 8
4 BCDFGHILO	BCDEUV 9
5 ABDEFGHJMN	ABDFGHIJNOTUW 10

6-10A CEE ❶ €32.80
A365 3,5ha 119T(100-190m²) 46P ❷ €43.50

🚗 From Clermont-Ferrand take the A75, exit 45 (turn off SatNav.). From Montpellier A75, exit 47. Follow camping signs to 'Pont de Cureplat', take D991 at roundabout then 1st campsite on the right.
💬 A peaceful, natural family campsite close to the centre of Millau. Plenty of sport and leisure activities possible close by. A friendly family site. Spacious pitches, both shaded and sunny. Heated toilet facilities.

(CC) 27/4-28/6 2/9-29/9

Millau

N 44°6'9'' E 3°5'27''
www.eurocampings.co.uk/103986

1345 Millau, F-12100 / Midi-Pyrénées ⅋ ⬡ (CC€11) iD 56

🏕 Larribal***
✉ avenue de Millau-Plage
📅 1 Apr - 31 Oct
☎ +33 (0)5-65590804
@ camping.larribal@wanadoo.fr

1 ADE**JM**NOPQRST	AFJ**N**UVX 6
2 ABCFGIJOPQVXY	ABDE**F** 7
3 A**GH**LQ	ABCDFGKNQRSV 8
4 DFHIO**PQ**	AEL 9
5 ABDFHJMN**O**	ABDGHIJPR 10

6A CEE ❶ €18.65
1,7ha 72T(80-110m²) 12P ❷ €25.20

🚗 From Clermont-Ferrand (A75) take exit 45 (turn SatNav off!), or from Montpellier (A75), exit 47. Then follow 'Campings' sign to the 'Pont de Cureplat' bridge. Over the bridge and towards Paulhe D187 at roundabout, 3rd site on the left.
💬 A campsite right on the banks of the Tarn. Shaded and quiet, lovely swimming pool with bar. Free wifi throughout the site. You can be in Millau by bike in 5 minutes for sports opportunities, restaurants and markets.

(CC) 1/4-30/6 25/8-30/10

Millau

N 44°6'37'' E 3°5'13''
www.eurocampings.co.uk/120226

1346 Millau, F-12100 / Midi-Pyrénées ⅋ ⬡ (CC€13) iD 56

🏕 Les Erables***
✉ avenue de Millau-Plage
📅 1 Apr - 30 Sep
☎ +33 (0)5-65591513
@ camping-les-erables@orange.fr

1 ADE**JM**NOPQRST	J**N**PUVX 6
2 ABCFGIOPVWXY	BE**F**HK 7
3 ABELQ	BDFHJNPQRTU 8
4 DFGHIO**Q**	ELQRUVW 9
5 ACDEFHJMN**O**	ABDGHIJPRW 10

10A CEE ❶ €20.90
A349 1,5ha 72T(100m²) 6P ❷ €25.90

🚗 Over the bridge in Cureplat, 3rd exit at roundabout dir. Paulhe. In Millau follow campsite signs, second site on the left. Or take the A75, exit 45 Millau centre. Look out for campsite signs (turn SatNav off).
💬 Quiet grounds close to a river and near the town centre, the Millau bridge and leisure activities. Spacious marked-out pitches; shaded or sunny. Everything you need for an agreeable holiday in a friendly atmosphere. Free wifi. Friendly owners.

(CC) 1/4-5/7 23/8-29/9 7=6

Millau

N 44°6'20'' E 3°5'16''
www.eurocampings.co.uk/113097

1347 Millau, F-12100 / Midi-Pyrénées ⅋ ⬡ (CC€15) iD 56

🏕 Les Rivages****
✉ 860 avenue de l'Aigoual
📅 7 Apr - 30 Sep
☎ +33 (0)5-65610107
@ info@campinglesrivages.com

1 ADE**JM**NOPQRST	ABFGIJ**N**UVX 6
2 ACFGIJPVWXY	ABDE**FGH** 7
3 BCEF**GHILMO**QSV	ABCDFGHIJKNPRSTUV 8
4 **A**BCD**E**FGHILNO**PQR**U	AEHQRUV 9
5 ACDEFGHJLMN	ABDFGHIJLO**P**RV 10

10A CEE ❶ €38.50
A363 7,5ha 277T(100-160m²) 45P ❷ €49.20

🚗 A75 from north, exit 45 Millau. Exit 47 from south (SatNav off!). Follow 'campsites' signs up to Cureplat bridge. 1st exit D991 on roundabout after bridge. Campsite 800m further at next small roundabout.
💬 Enormous pitches, indoor tennis/squash hall, magnificent restaurant, heated pools, private beach on the river Dourbie. Only campsite in Millau with a view of the famous viaduct. The site is really peaceful, you cannot hear any noise from traffic.

(CC) 7/4-5/7 23/8-29/9 7=6, 14=12

Millau

N 44°6'3'' E 3°5'45''
www.eurocampings.co.uk/100496

1348 Millau, F-12100 / Midi-Pyrénées

♿ 📶 (CC€13) iD 56

- ▲ St. Lambert***
- ✉ 2050 avenue de l'Aigoual
- ⊙ 27 Apr - 30 Sep
- ☎ +33 (0)5-65600048
- @ contact@campingsaintlambert.fr

1 ADEJMNOPRST	AJNUX 6
2 ABCFGHIJKPQVWXY	ABDEFG 7
3 BEFILQ	ABCDFGHIKNPRSV 8
4 BCDFHILOPQ	ABELUV 9
5 ACDEFGHJKMNO	ABDFGHIJLOPSTWX 10

| 6A | ❶ €22.40 |
| A365 3,5ha 107T(80-160m²) 26P | ❷ €29.50 |

🚗 A75 exit 44.1 Millau and follow campsite signs. Take D991 direction La Roque-Sainte-Marguerite. Turn right after the bridge in Cureplat and follow campsite signs again.

💬 A campsite quietly located at the entrance to the Gorges du Tarn, between the Grands Causses and the Cévennes, 2.5 km from the centre of Millau. It has a lovely big private pebble beach on the River Dourbie. Friendly atmosphere.

CC 27/4-6/7 27/8-29/9 7=6, 14=12

🅿 N 44°5'59'' E 3°6'42''

www.eurocampings.co.uk/103987

1349 Nant, F-12230 / Midi-Pyrénées

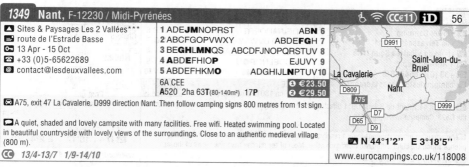

♿ 📶 (CC€11) iD 56

- ▲ Sites & Paysages Les 2 Vallées***
- ✉ route de l'Estrade Basse
- ⊙ 13 Apr - 15 Oct
- ☎ +33 (0)5-65622689
- @ contact@lesdeuxvallees.com

1 ADEJMNOPRST	ABN 6
2 ABCFGOPVWXY	ABDEFGH 7
3 BEGHLMNQS	ABCDFJNOPQRSTUV 8
4 ABDEFHIOP	EJUVY 9
5 ABDEFHKMO	ADGHIJLNPTUV 10

| 6A CEE | ❶ €23.50 |
| A520 2ha 63T(80-140m²) 17P | ❷ €29.50 |

🚗 A75, exit 47 La Cavalerie. D999 direction Nant. Then follow camping signs 800 metres from 1st sign.

💬 A quiet, shaded and lovely campsite with many facilities. Free wifi. Heated swimming pool. Located in beautiful countryside with lovely views of the surroundings. Close to an authentic medieval village (800 m).

CC 13/4-13/7 1/9-14/10

🅿 N 44°1'2'' E 3°18'5''

www.eurocampings.co.uk/118008

France

1350 Nant-d'Aveyron, F-12230 / Midi-Pyrénées

♿ 📶 (CC€17) iD 56

- ▲ Camping RCN Val de Cantobre****
- ⊙ 20 Apr - 24 Sep
- ☎ +31 034-3745090
- @ reserveringen@rcn.nl

1 ADEJLNOPQRST	ABFGHIJN 6
2 ABCFGJPRSTUVWXY	ABDEFGH 7
3 BEILMQS	ABCDEFGHIKNPQRSTV 8
4 ABCDEFHILNOPQUX	ABEJLU 9
5 ACDEFGHJLMN	ABCDGHIJPSTZ 10

| Ad on this page 6A CEE | ❶ €48.50 |
| A450 6,5ha 139T(60-150m²) 84P | ❷ €62.50 |

🚗 After Clermont-Ferrand take the A75 over the Millau Bridge (toll) exit 47 direction Nant/La Cavalerie. Through La Cavalerie towards Nant. Campsite signposted in Nant. Turn left immediately to D991.

💬 A terraced, luxury campsite with stunning views of the beautiful Vale of Dourbie. Lovely touring pitches. Good catering facilities. Service and customer focus are strong assets!

CC 20/4-2/7 25/8-23/9

🅿 N 44°2'44'' E 3°18'8''

www.eurocampings.co.uk/101485

1351 Naucelle, F-12800 / Midi-Pyrénées ♿ 🛜 CC€17 iD 25 B1

▲ Flower Camping
du Lac de Bonnefon***
📧 route de Bonnefon
📅 1 Apr - 30 Sep
☎ +33 (0)5-65693320
@ info@
camping-du-lac-de-bonnefon.com

1 ADEILNOPRT	ABFGN 6
2 DPTUVWXY	ABDEFGH 7
3 BDFILQST	ACDFGKNOQRTUV 8
4 ABCDEFHILNOPU	AEFJLU 9
5 ADEFGHNO	ABFGHJOPST 10
10A CEE	❶ €28.90
A500 4,5ha 67T(80-165m²) 45P	❷ €38.40

🚗 N88 Rodez-Albi, exit Naucelle/Sauveterre-de-Rouergue. Then follow Naucelle. Then follow campsite signs.
💬 Open from 1 April to 30 September. Close to a lake abundant with fish (free fishing) in peaceful, richly planted surroundings. Campsite with swimming pool and jacuzzi. 1,200 m from the town of Naucelle.
CC 1/4-6/7 25/8-29/9 7=6

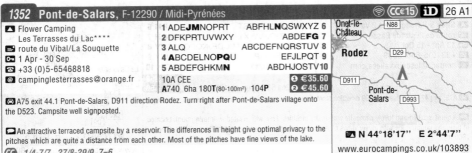

🗺 N 44°11'17" E 2°20'54"
www.eurocampings.co.uk/103896

1352 Pont-de-Salars, F-12290 / Midi-Pyrénées 🛜 CC€15 iD 26 A1

▲ Flower Camping
Les Terrasses du Lac****
📧 route du Vibal/La Souquette
📅 1 Apr - 30 Sep
☎ +33 (0)5-65468818
@ campinglesterrasses@orange.fr

1 ADEJMNOPRT	ABFHLNQSWXYZ 6
2 DFKPRTUVWXY	ABDEFG 7
3 ALQ	ABCDEFNQRSTUV 8
4 ABCDELNOPQU	EFJLPQT 9
5 ABDEFGHKMN	ABDHJOSTV 10
10A CEE	❶ €35.60
A740 6ha 180T(80-100m²) 104P	❷ €45.60

🚗 A75 exit 44.1 Pont-de-Salars. D911 direction Rodez. Turn right after Pont-de-Salars village onto the D523. Campsite well signposted.
💬 An attractive terraced campsite by a reservoir. The differences in height give optimal privacy to the pitches which are quite a distance from each other. Most of the pitches have fine views of the lake.
CC 1/4-7/7 27/8-29/9 7=6

🗺 N 44°18'17" E 2°44'7"
www.eurocampings.co.uk/103893

1353 Rivière-sur-Tarn, F-12640 / Midi-Pyrénées ♿ 🛜 CC€17 iD 56

▲ Flower Camping Le Peyrelade****
📧 rte des Gorges du Tarn
📅 9 May - 15 Sep
☎ +33 (0)5-65626254
@ contact@campingpeyrelade.com

1 ADEJMNOPRST	ABFGIJNUXY 6
2 ABCFGHJPUVXY	ABDEFGH 7
3 BDILMQR	ABCDEFGHIKNPQRSV 8
4 ABCDFGHILNOPQUWY	BEQRUVW 9
5 ACDEFGHJLMNO	ABCDGHIJMOPR 10
10A CEE	❶ €43.90
A382 4ha 137T(90-130m²) 53P	❷ €57.90

🚗 A75 exit 44.1.Turn left in Aguessac to get on the D907. The first campsite after the village Rivière-sur-Tarn. The campsite is situated exactly at the entrance of the Gorges du Tarn.
💬 A beautiful site in every way: nature, toilet facilities, beach, entertainment! And the longest pebble beach on the Tarn. Leisure pool including a Balnéo room and children's play area. Relaxation on holiday with all facilities imaginable: restaurant, supermarket, etc.
CC 9/5-6/7 25/8-14/9 7=6, 14=12, 21=18

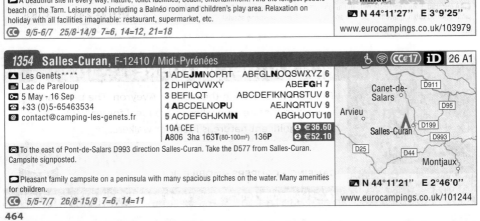

🗺 N 44°11'27" E 3°9'25"
www.eurocampings.co.uk/103979

1354 Salles-Curan, F-12410 / Midi-Pyrénées ♿ 🛜 CC€17 iD 26 A1

▲ Les Genêts****
📧 Lac de Pareloup
📅 5 May - 16 Sep
☎ +33 (0)5-65463534
@ contact@camping-les-genets.fr

1 ADEJMNOPRT	ABFGLNOQSWXYZ 6
2 DHIPQVWXY	ABEFGH 7
3 BEFILQT	ABCDEFIKNQRSTUV 8
4 ABCDELNOPU	AEJNQRTUV 9
5 ACDEFGHJKMN	ABGHJOTU 10
10A CEE	❶ €36.60
A806 3ha 163T(80-100m²) 136P	❷ €52.10

🚗 To the east of Pont-de-Salars D993 direction Salles-Curan. Take the D577 from Salles-Curan. Campsite signposted.
💬 Pleasant family campsite on a peninsula with many spacious pitches on the water. Many amenities for children.
CC 5/5-7/7 26/8-15/9 7=6, 14=11

🗺 N 44°11'21" E 2°46'0"
www.eurocampings.co.uk/101244

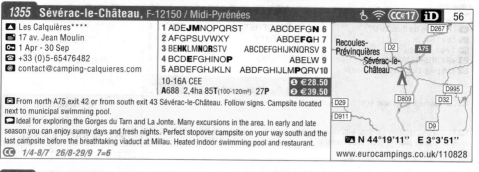

1355 Sévérac-le-Château, F-12150 / Midi-Pyrénées

🚶 🛜 (CC€17) **iD** 56

- ⛺ Les Calquières****
- ✉ 17 av. Jean Moulin
- 🕐 1 Apr - 30 Sep
- ☎ +33 (0)5-65476482
- @ contact@camping-calquieres.com

1 ADE**JM**NOPQRST	ABCDEFG**N**	6
2 AFGPSUVWXY	ABDE**FGH**	7
3 BE**HK**LM**NQR**STV	ABCDEFGHIJKNQRSV	8
4 BCD**E**FGHINO**P**	ABELW	9
5 ABDEFGHJKLN	ABDFGHIJLM**P**QRV	10
10-16A CEE		❶ €28.50
A688 2,4ha 85T(100-120m²) 27P		❷ €39.50

🚌 From north A75 exit 42 or from south exit 43 Sévérac-le-Château. Follow signs. Campsite located next to municipal swimming pool.

💬 Ideal for exploring the Gorges du Tarn and La Jonte. Many excursions in the area. In early and late season you can enjoy sunny days and fresh nights. Perfect stopover campsite on your way south and the last campsite before the breathtaking viaduct at Millau. Heated indoor swimming pool and restaurant.

© 1/4-8/7 26/8-29/9 7=6

📍 N 44°19'11'' E 3°3'51''

www.eurocampings.co.uk/110828

1356 St. Jean-du-Bruel, F-12230 / Midi-Pyrénées

🚶 🛜 (CC€13) **iD** 56

- ⛺ La Dourbie****
- ✉ route de Nant
- 🕐 13 Apr - 30 Sep
- ☎ +33 (0)5-65460640
- @ campingladourbie@orange.fr

1 ADE**J**MNOPQRST	AFJ**N**	6
2 CFGJKPVWX	ABDE**FGH**	7
3 BLQST	ABCDEFJKNPQRS	8
4 AFHIOUY	EFL	9
5 ABDEFGHLN	ABDFGHIJ**P**TUVW	10
10A CEE		❶ €25.00
A530 2,3ha 60T(100-163m²) 20P		❷ €35.00

🚌 A75, exit 47 La Cavalerie. Site between Nant and St. Jean-du-Bruel. 1 km before St. Jean-du-Bruel, well signposted along the route de Nant.

💬 This modernly equipped campsite with a heated swimming pool, bar, à la carte restaurant and all amenities for motorhomes is located between the Gorges du Tarn and the Cévennes. Located on the River Dourbie (trout) with beautiful views. You will be warmly received. Restaurant open at weekends in the low season.

© 13/4-7/7 25/8-29/9 7=6, 14=12

📍 N 44°1'11'' E 3°20'46''

www.eurocampings.co.uk/118541

France

1357 St. Rome-de-Tarn, F-12490 / Midi-Pyrénées

🛜 (CC€15) **iD** 26 A1

- ⛺ de la Cascade****
- 🕐 1 Jan - 31 Dec
- ☎ +33 (0)5-65625659
- @ contact@
  camping-cascade-aveyron.com

1 AD**IL**NOPRT	AFJ**N**UW**X**YZ	6
2 CFG**I**NPRTUVWXY	ABDE**FGH**	7
3 BELMQT	ABCDEFGJKNQRSV	8
4 BCDEFHJNO**PQ**	AEFJKLNPQRTUVW	9
5 ABDEFGHKM**N**	ABFGHJ**P**ST	10
6A CEE		❶ €35.40
A360 4ha 99T(80-120m²) 97P		❷ €44.40

🚌 In Millau take the D992 direction Albi. In St. Georges-de-Luzençan take the D73 direction St. Rome-de-Tarn. Well signposted in the village.

💬 An attractive campsite with terraces and excellent facilities situated right on the Tarn. You can ask for help when positioning your caravan.

© 1/4-8/7 26/8-15/10

📍 N 44°3'11'' E 2°53'59''

www.eurocampings.co.uk/101484

1358 Villefranche-de-Rouergue, F-12200 / Midi-Pyrénées

🚶 🛜 (CC€13) **iD** 25 B1

- ⛺ Le Rouergue***
- ✉ 35 avenue de Fondies
- 🕐 14 Apr - 30 Sep
- ☎ +33 (0)5-65451624
- @ campingrouergue@wanadoo.fr

1 ADEF**JM**NOPRS**T**	A	6
2 CPSVWXY	ABDE**FHJ**	7
3 A**K**LQRS	ABCDEFNOPQRSTUV	8
4 CD**E**FIOU	ADEL	9
5 ABDEH**NO**	ABDGHIJMORZ	10
16A CEE		❶ €19.80
A250 2ha 93T(100-175m²) 30P		❷ €25.60

🚌 The campsite is located 2 km from the centre of Villefranche-de-Rouergue. Follow 'Stade' signs towards Monteils-Najac.

💬 Camping du Rouergue is situated close to the Villefranche-de-Rouergue royal fortified town with its lovely market square. The site offers you peace and comfort in shady natural surroundings. This campsite has spacious pitches with water and electricity (grand comfort), the toilet facilities meet modern expectations completely.

© 14/4-7/7 25/8-29/9

📍 N 44°20'33'' E 2°1'35''

www.eurocampings.co.uk/115867

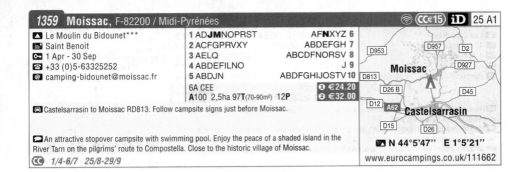

1359 Moissac, F-82200 / Midi-Pyrénées ☞ (CC€15) iD 25 A1

- ⛺ Le Moulin du Bidounet***
- 🏠 Saint Benoit
- 📅 1 Apr - 30 Sep
- ☎ +33 (0)5-63325252
- @ camping-bidounet@moissac.fr

1 ADJMNOPRST	AFNXYZ	6
2 ACFGPRVXY	ABDEFGH	7
3 AELQ	ABCDFNORSV	8
4 ABDEFILNO	J	9
5 ABDJN	ABDFGHIJOSTV	10
6A CEE	❶ €24.20	
A100 2,5ha 97T(70-90m²) 12P	❷ €32.00	

🚗 Castelsarrasin to Moissac RD813. Follow campsite signs just before Moissac.

💬 An attractive stopover campsite with swimming pool. Enjoy the peace of a shaded island in the River Tarn on the pilgrims' route to Compostella. Close to the historic village of Moissac.

CC 1/4-6/7 25/8-29/9

📍 N 44°5'47'' E 1°5'21''

www.eurocampings.co.uk/111662

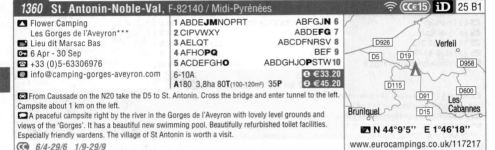

1360 St. Antonin-Noble-Val, F-82140 / Midi-Pyrénées ☞ (CC€15) iD 25 B1

- ⛺ Flower Camping
  Les Gorges de l'Aveyron***
- 🏠 Lieu dit Marsac Bas
- 📅 6 Apr - 30 Sep
- ☎ +33 (0)5-63306976
- @ info@camping-gorges-aveyron.com

1 ABDEJMNOPRT	ABFGJN	6
2 CIPVWXY	ABDEFG	7
3 AELQT	ABCDFNRSV	8
4 AFHOPQ	BEF	9
5 ACDEFGHO	ABDGHJOPSTW	10
6-10A	❶ €33.20	
A180 3,8ha 80T(100-120m²) 35P	❷ €45.20	

🚗 From Caussade on the N20 take the D5 to St. Antonin. Cross the bridge and enter tunnel to the left. Campsite about 1 km on the left.

💬 A peaceful campsite right by the river in the Gorges de l'Aveyron with lovely level grounds and views of the 'Gorges'. It has a beautiful new swimming pool. Beautifully refurbished toilet facilities. Especially friendly wardens. The village of St Antonin is worth a visit.

CC 6/4-29/6 1/9-29/9

📍 N 44°9'5'' E 1°46'18''

www.eurocampings.co.uk/117217

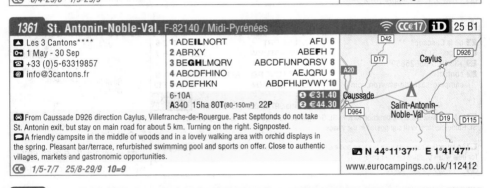

1361 St. Antonin-Noble-Val, F-82140 / Midi-Pyrénées ☞ (CC€17) iD 25 B1

- ⛺ Les 3 Cantons****
- 📅 1 May - 30 Sep
- ☎ +33 (0)5-63319857
- @ info@3cantons.fr

1 ADEILNORT	AFU	6
2 ABRXY	ABEFH	7
3 BEGHLMQRV	ABCDFIJNPQRSV	8
4 ABCDFHINO	AEJQRU	9
5 ADEFHKN	ABDFHIJPVWY	10
6-10A	❶ €31.40	
A340 15ha 80T(80-150m²) 22P	❷ €44.30	

🚗 From Caussade D926 direction Caylus, Villefranche-de-Rouergue. Past Septfonds do not take St. Antonin exit, but stay on main road for about 5 km. Turning on the right. Signposted.

💬 A friendly campsite in the middle of woods and in a lovely walking area with orchid displays in the spring. Pleasant bar/terrace, refurbished swimming pool and sports on offer. Close to authentic villages, markets and gastronomic opportunities.

CC 1/5-7/7 25/8-29/9 10=9

📍 N 44°11'37'' E 1°41'47''

www.eurocampings.co.uk/112412

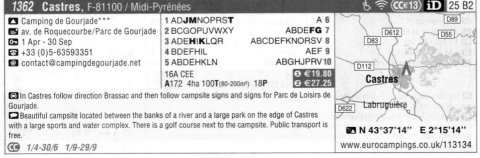

1362 Castres, F-81100 / Midi-Pyrénées ♿ ☞ (CC€13) iD 25 B2

- ⛺ Camping de Gourjade***
- 🏠 av. de Roquecourbe/Parc de Gourjade
- 📅 1 Apr - 30 Sep
- ☎ +33 (0)5-63593351
- @ contact@campingdegourjade.net

1 ADJMNOPRST	A	6
2 BCGOPUVWXY	ABDEFG	7
3 ADEHIKLQR	ABCDEFKNORSV	8
4 BDEFHIL	AEF	9
5 ABDEHKLN	ABGHJPRV	10
16A CEE	❶ €19.80	
A172 4ha 100T(80-200m²) 18P	❷ €27.25	

🚗 In Castres follow direction Brassac and then follow campsite signs and signs for Parc de Loisirs de Gourjade.

💬 Beautiful campsite located between the banks of a river and a large park on the edge of Castres with a large sports and water complex. There is a golf course next to the campsite. Public transport is free.

CC 1/4-30/6 1/9-29/9

📍 N 43°37'14'' E 2°15'14''

www.eurocampings.co.uk/113134

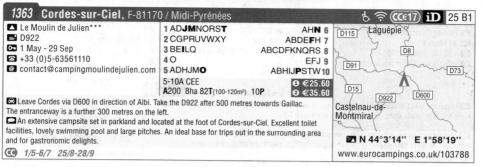

1363 Cordes-sur-Ciel, F-81170 / Midi-Pyrénées
♿ 📶 (CC€17) iD 25 B1

- Le Moulin de Julien***
- D922
- 1 May - 29 Sep
- +33 (0)5-63561110
- contact@campingmoulindejulien.com

1 ADJMNORST	AHN 6
2 CGPRUVWXY	ABDEFH 7
3 BEILQ	ABCDFKNQRS 8
4 O	EFJ 9
5 ADHJMO	ABHIJPSTW 10

5-10A CEE
A200 8ha 82T(100-120m²) 10P
❶ €25.60
❷ €35.60

Leave Cordes via D600 in direction of Albi. Take the D922 after 500 metres towards Gaillac. The entranceway is a further 300 metres on the left.

An extensive campsite set in parkland and located at the foot of Cordes-sur-Ciel. Excellent toilet facilities, lovely swimming pool and large pitches. An ideal base for trips out in the surrounding area and for gastronomic delights.

CC 1/5-6/7 25/8-28/9

N 44°3'14'' E 1°58'19''

www.eurocampings.co.uk/103788

1364 Lamontélarié, F-81260 / Midi-Pyrénées
♿ 📶 (CC€15) iD 25 B2

- Le Rouquié du Lac
- Rouquié
- 1 May - 31 Oct
- +33 (0)5-63709806
- contact@campingrouquie.fr

1 ADEJMNOPRST	ABLNQSWXY 6
2 DFGHIPUVWXY	ABDEFGH 7
3 ABL	ABEFNQRSV 8
4 BCDFHILNOP	EFLMOPQRT 9
5 ABDEFHMNO	ABHIJNORV 10

6A CEE
A690 3ha 82T(85-148m²) 29P
❶ €26.95
❷ €36.50

Clermont-Ferrand-Millau from Millau towards St. Afrique on the D992. Then follow D32 to Lacaune. Then follow D607/D52 to Lamontélarié.

Family-run campsite in the heart of the regional park Haut Languedoc. Campsite overlooks the Lac de La Raviège. Plenty of (water) sports and recreational activities.

CC 1/5-8/7 26/8-30/10

N 43°35'49'' E 2°36'28''

www.eurocampings.co.uk/115949

France

1365 La Romieu, F-32480 / Midi-Pyrénées
♿ 📶 (CC€17) iD 25 A1

- Le Camp de Florence****
- Au Camp
- 27 Apr - 24 Sep
- +33 (0)5-62281558
- info@lecampdeflorence.com

1 ABDEJMNOPQRST	ABFG 6
2 BGPSVWXY	ABDEFGH 7
3 BEFLMQST	ABCDEFIJKNQRSTUV 8
4 BCDEFHIKLNOQRU	AEJUVW 9
5 ADEFHLN	ABFGHIJNOPRYZ 10

10A CEE
A191 15ha 95T(100-250m²) 86P
❶ €36.60
❷ €47.70

From Agen D931 to Condom. D36 at Ligarde then D166 direction Collegiale de la Romieu. Left in village and follow signs.

A gently undulating campsite near a 19th-century farmhouse. 500 metres from the fortified village of La Romieu with its magnificent collegiate church, cloister and tower. Armagnac, Floc, Madiran and local wines are in close proximity and there are plenty of opportunities for walking.

CC 27/4-7/6 1/9-23/9

N 43°59'0'' E 0°30'7''

www.eurocampings.co.uk/100517

1366 Lelin-Lapujolle, F-32400 / Midi-Pyrénées
♿ 📶 (CC€15) iD 24 B2

- La Solanilla***
- Lieu-dit Lahount
- 1 Jan - 31 Dec
- +33 (0)5-62696409
- info@campinglasolanilla.com

1 ADEJMNOPQRST	AFN 6
2 PUVWXY	BDEFGHK 7
3 ALQ	BCDEFJKNOQRSV 8
4 ADFIKNOPQ	DEJ 9
5 ABDEGHKMNO	ABDFGHIJOTUV 10

10A CEE
A116 3ha 86T 31P
❶ €20.80
❷ €30.80

From A65, exit 6 direction Tarbes. In Saint-Germé direction Lelin-Lapujolle. Then follow signs.

Welcoming campsite in a rural area with many amenities such as: croissants, a little shop, snack bar and bar. Wine tasting sessions in the vicinity and all through the year. Free wifi.

CC 1/1-29/6 25/8-31/12 7=6, 14=12, 21=18

N 43°41'49'' W 0°8'17''

www.eurocampings.co.uk/115872

1367 Marciac, F-32230 / Midi-Pyrénées   ⚬ 🛜 CC€15 iD 25 A2

- 🏕 Flower Camping Du Lac***
- 📅 24 Mar - 6 Oct
- ☎ +33 (0)5-62082119
- @ info@camping-marciac.com

1 ADEJMNOPRST	ABXZ	6
2 GPSTUVWXY	BDEFH	7
3 BEKLMQ	ABCDEFHJNOPQRSTV	8
4 FHI	BEJ	9
5 ABDEHMNO	ABFGHJPR	10

10A CEE   ❶ €19.10
A160 4,5ha 72T(100-120m²) 23P   ❷ €24.10

🚗 Follow the D943 in Marciac direction Bassoues, after about 300 metres over the bridge turn left. From the lake; follow signs. From Plaisance; turn left on D3.

💬 Located by a lake suitable for water recreation, 800 metres from a 'bastide' fortified town with a jazz museum. With the exception of the annual jazz festival, peace and quiet are the order of the day.

CC 24/3-7/7 25/8-5/10 7=6

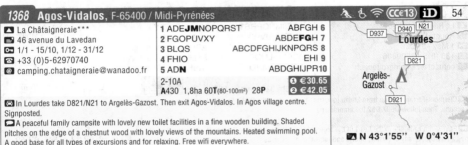

📍 N 43°31'56'' E 0°10'0''
www.eurocampings.co.uk/108791

1368 Agos-Vidalos, F-65400 / Midi-Pyrénées   🎿 ⚬ 🛜 CC€13 iD 54

- 🏕 La Châtaigneraie***
- 🏠 46 avenue du Lavedan
- 📅 1/1 - 15/10, 1/12 - 31/12
- ☎ +33 (0)5-62970740
- @ camping.chataigneraie@wanadoo.fr

1 ADEJMNOPQRST	ABFGH	6
2 FGOPUVXY	ABDEFGH	7
3 BLQS	ABCDFGHIJKNPQRS	8
4 FHIO	EHI	9
5 ADN	ABDGHIJPR	10

2-10A   ❶ €30.65
A430 1,8ha 60T(80-100m²) 28P   ❷ €42.05

🚗 In Lourdes take D821/N21 to Argelès-Gazost. Then exit Agos-Vidalos. In Agos village centre. Signposted.

💬 A peaceful family campsite with lovely new toilet facilities in a fine wooden building. Shaded pitches on the edge of a chestnut wood with lovely views of the mountains. Heated swimming pool. A good base for all types of excursions and for relaxing. Free wifi everywhere.

CC 1/4-10/7 28/8-14/10 7=6, 14=13, 21=19, 30=27

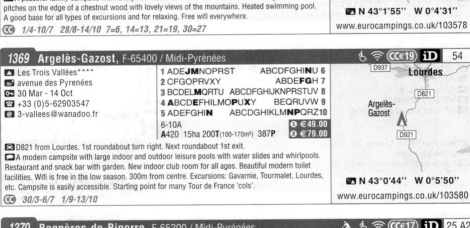

📍 N 43°1'55'' W 0°4'31''
www.eurocampings.co.uk/103578

1369 Argelès-Gazost, F-65400 / Midi-Pyrénées   ⚬ 🛜 CC€19 iD 54

- 🏕 Les Trois Vallées****
- 🏠 avenue des Pyrénées
- 📅 30 Mar - 14 Oct
- ☎ +33 (0)5-62903547
- @ 3-vallees@wanadoo.fr

1 ADEJMNOPRST	ABCDFGHINU	6
2 CFGOPRVXY	ABDEFGH	7
3 BCDELMQRTU	ABCDFGHIJKNPRSTUV	8
4 ABCDEFHILMOPUXY	BEQRUVW	9
5 ADEFGHIN	ABCDGHIKLMNPQRZ	10

6-10A   ❶ €49.00
A420 15ha 200T(100-170m²) 387P   ❷ €79.00

🚗 D821 from Lourdes. 1st roundabout turn right. Next roundabout 1st exit.

💬 A modern campsite with large indoor and outdoor leisure pools with water slides and whirlpools. Restaurant and snack bar with garden. New indoor club room for all ages. Beautiful modern toilet facilities. Wifi is free in the low season. 300m from centre. Excursions: Gavarnie, Tourmalet, Lourdes, etc. Campsite is easily accessible. Starting point for many Tour de France 'cols'.

CC 30/3-6/7 1/9-13/10

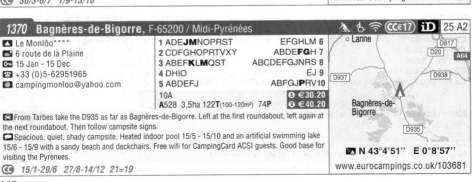

📍 N 43°0'44'' W 0°5'50''
www.eurocampings.co.uk/103580

1370 Bagnères-de-Bigorre, F-65200 / Midi-Pyrénées   🎿 ⚬ 🛜 CC€17 iD 25 A2

- 🏕 Le Monlôo****
- 🏠 6 route de la Plaine
- 📅 15 Jan - 15 Dec
- ☎ +33 (0)5-62951965
- @ campingmonloo@yahoo.com

1 ADEJMNOPRST	EFGHLM	6
2 CDFGHOPRTVXY	ABDEFGH	7
3 ABEFKLMQST	ABCDEFGJNRS	8
4 DHIO	EJ	9
5 ABDEFJ	ABFGJPRV	10

10A   ❶ €30.20
A528 3,5ha 122T(100-120m²) 74P   ❷ €40.20

🚗 From Tarbes take the D935 as far as Bagnères-de-Bigorre. Left at the first roundabout, left again at the next roundabout. Then follow campsite signs.

💬 Spacious, quiet, shady campsite. Heated indoor pool 15/5 - 15/10 and an artificial swimming lake 15/6 - 15/9 with a sandy beach and deckchairs. Free wifi for CampingCard ACSI guests. Good base for visiting the Pyrenees.

CC 15/1-29/6 27/8-14/12 21=19

📍 N 43°4'51'' E 0°8'57''
www.eurocampings.co.uk/103681

1371 Boô-Silhen, F-65400 / Midi-Pyrénées

A 🚲 🛜 (CC€13) iD 54

- ▲ Deth-Potz**
- 🏠 40 route de Silhen
- 🕐 1/1 - 10/10, 10/12 - 31/12
- ☎ +33 (0)5-62903723
- @ contact@deth-potz.fr

1 ADE**JM**NORT	AF	6
2 FPRTUVWXY	ABDF**H**	7
3 AEILQT	ABCEFGHJKNOPRS	8
4 BDFHIO	E	9
5 ABDM**NO**	ABCDGIJOR	10
10A		
A480 4ha 74T(85-110m²) 26P	❶ €18.95	
	❷ €25.45	

🔄 From Lourdes towards Luz-St-Sauveur, Gavarnie. Last exit at 2nd roundabout, over bridge, immediate left. Campsite 1500 metres on the left.

💬 This campsite is located in an oasis of greenery and relaxation at the foot of a 16th-century chapel, two kilometres from Argelès-Gazost in the heart of the Pyrenees. Modern toilet facilities, motorhome service point, playing field. Ideally located for countless sports activities and exploring the countryside.

(CC) 1/1-30/6 1/9-9/10 10/12-31/12

📍 N 43°0'40'' W 0°4'39''

www.eurocampings.co.uk/117124

1372 Capvern, F-65130 / Midi-Pyrénées

🚲 🛜 (CC€15) iD 25 A2

- ▲ Les Craouès***
- 🏠 682 rue du 8 Mai 1945
- 🕐 1 Apr - 30 Oct
- ☎ +33 (0)5-62390254
- @ camping-les-craoues@orange.fr

1 ADE**JM**NOPRST	AF	6
2 AOPSVWXY	ABDE**FG**H	7
3 A**K**LQS	ABCDEFKNOS	8
4 O	AF	9
5 AD	ABFGHKL**P**RV	10
8A CEE		
A597 1,5ha 66T(85-150m²) 21P	❶ €19.25	
	❷ €26.75	

🔄 Campsite is on the 1st roundabout on D817 1 km after the exit from A64.

💬 Quiet, shady campsite located on the roundabout, ideal for those stopping over before heading through the Bielsa Tunnel. Good base for visiting the pretty region Les Baronnies. Cycling enthusiasts can take a ride up the Col d'Aspin from here.

(CC) 1/4-14/7 1/9-29/10

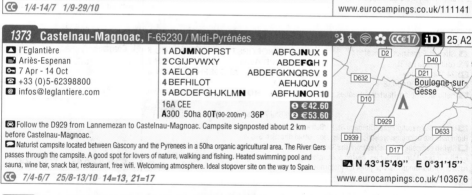

📍 N 43°6'20'' E 0°19'24''

www.eurocampings.co.uk/111141

1373 Castelnau-Magnoac, F-65230 / Midi-Pyrénées

🛝 🚲 🛜 🌸 (CC€17) iD 25 A2

- ▲ l'Eglantière
- 🏠 Ariès-Espenan
- 🕐 7 Apr - 14 Oct
- ☎ +33 (0)5-62398800
- @ infos@leglantiere.com

1 ADJMNOPRST	ABFGJN**U**X	6
2 CGIJPVWXY	ABDE**FG**H	7
3 AELQR	ABCDEFGKNQRSV	8
4 BEFHILOT	AEHJQUV	9
5 ABCDEFGHJKLM**N**	ABFHJ**N**OR	10
16A CEE		
A300 50ha 80T(90-200m²) 36P	❶ €42.60	
	❷ €53.60	

🔄 Follow the D929 from Lannemezan to Castelnau-Magnoac. Campsite signposted about 2 km before Castelnau-Magnoac.

💬 Naturist campsite located between Gascony and the Pyrenees in a 50ha organic agricultural area. The River Gers passes through the campsite. A good spot for lovers of nature, walking and fishing. Heated swimming pool and sauna, wine bar, snack bar, restaurant, free wifi. Welcoming atmosphere. Ideal stopover site on the way to Spain.

(CC) 7/4-6/7 25/8-13/10 14=13, 21=17

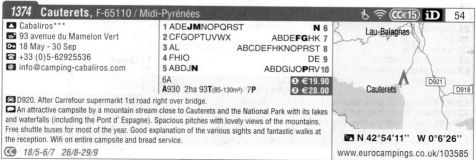

📍 N 43°15'49'' E 0°31'15''

www.eurocampings.co.uk/103676

1374 Cauterets, F-65110 / Midi-Pyrénées

🚲 🛜 (CC€15) iD 54

- ▲ Cabaliros***
- 🏠 93 avenue du Mamelon Vert
- 🕐 18 May - 30 Sep
- ☎ +33 (0)5-62925536
- @ info@camping-cabaliros.com

1 ADE**JM**NOPQRST	**N**	6
2 CFGOPTUVWX	ABDE**FG**HK	7
3 AL	ABCDEFHKNOPRST	8
4 FHIO	DE	9
5 ABDJ**N**	ABDGIJO**P**RV	10
6A		
A930 2ha 93T(85-130m²) 7P	❶ €19.90	
	❷ €28.00	

🔄 D920. After Carrefour supermarkt 1st road right over bridge.

💬 An attractive campsite by a mountain stream close to Cauterets and the National Park with its lakes and waterfalls (including the Pont d' Espagne). Spacious pitches with lovely views of the mountains. Free shuttle buses for most of the year. Good explanation of the various sights and fantastic walks at the reception. Wifi on entire campsite and bread service.

(CC) 18/5-6/7 26/8-29/9

📍 N 42°54'11'' W 0°6'26''

www.eurocampings.co.uk/103585

1375 Loudenvielle, F-65510 / Midi-Pyrénées ▲ ♿ 🛜 (CC€15) iD 25 A2

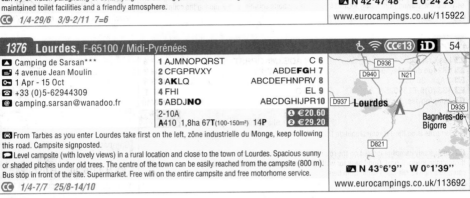

▲ La Vacance Pène Blanche**
🗓 1 Apr - 3 Nov
☎ +33 (0)5-62996885
@ info@peneblanche.com

1	ADE**JM**NOPRS**T**	6
2	CFGPSUWX	ABDEF**GH** 7
3	BL	ABCDFJNQRV 8
4	**A**BDFH	BEUW 9
5	AD	ABDHJOR 10
10A CEE		
A980 3,5ha 76T(80-120m²) 48P		➊ €28.30 ➋ €38.80

Follow the D929 as far as Arreau then continue left on the D618. At the junction with the D25 continue to Loudenvielle. Campsite 50 metres before the town on the right.
A lovely well maintained terraced campsite in an open and sunny valley by a large lake where you can try or watch paragliding or delta flying. The starting point for 30 walking and mountain tours. Well maintained toilet facilities and a friendly atmosphere.

(CC) 1/4-29/6 3/9-2/11 7=6

Bourg-d'Oueil
Saint-Lary-Soulan

N 42°47'48" E 0°24'23"
www.eurocampings.co.uk/115922

1376 Lourdes, F-65100 / Midi-Pyrénées ♿ 🛜 (CC€13) iD 54

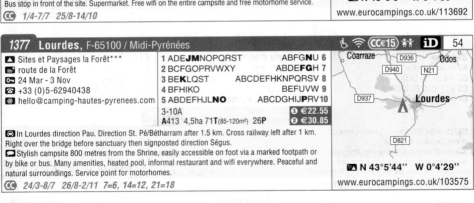

▲ Camping de Sarsan***
🗺 4 avenue Jean Moulin
🗓 1 Apr - 15 Oct
☎ +33 (0)5-62944309
@ camping.sarsan@wanadoo.fr

1	AJMNOPQRST	C 6
2	CFGPRVXY	ABDEF**GH** 7
3	A**KL**Q	ABCDEFHNPRV 8
4	FHI	EL 9
5	ABDJ**NO**	ABCDGHIJPR 10
2-10A		
A410 1,8ha 67T(100-150m²) 14P		➊ €20.60 ➋ €29.20

From Tarbes as you enter Lourdes take first on the left, zône industrielle du Monge, keep following this road. Campsite signposted.
Level campsite (with lovely views) in a rural location and close to the town of Lourdes. Spacious sunny or shaded pitches under old trees. The centre of the town can be easily reached from the campsite (800 m). Bus stop in front of the site. Supermarket. Free wifi on the entire campsite and free motorhome service.

(CC) 1/4-7/7 25/8-14/10

Lourdes
Bagnères-de-Bigorre

N 43°6'9" W 0°1'39"
www.eurocampings.co.uk/113692

1377 Lourdes, F-65100 / Midi-Pyrénées ♿ 🛜 (CC€15) 🚻 iD 54

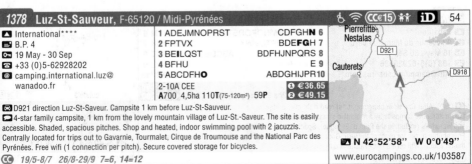

▲ Sites et Paysages la Forêt***
🗺 route de la Forêt
🗓 24 Mar - 3 Nov
☎ +33 (0)5-62940438
@ hello@camping-hautes-pyrenees.com

1	ADE**JM**NOPQRST	ABFG**N**U 6
2	BCFGOPRVWXY	ABDEF**GH** 7
3	BE**K**LQST	ABCDEFHKNPQRSV 8
4	BFHIKO	BEFUVW 9
5	ABDEFHJL**NO**	ABCDGHIJ**P**RV 10
3-10A		
A413 4,5ha 71T(85-120m²) 26P		➊ €22.55 ➋ €30.85

In Lourdes direction Pau. Direction St. Pé/Bétharram after 1.5 km. Cross railway left after 1 km. Right over the bridge before sanctuary then signposted direction Ségus.
Stylish campsite 800 metres from the Shrine, easily accessible on foot via a marked footpath or by bike or bus. Many amenities, heated pool, informal restaurant and wifi everywhere. Peaceful and natural surroundings. Service point for motorhomes.

(CC) 24/3-8/7 26/8-2/11 7=6, 14=12, 21=18

Coarraze
Odos
Lourdes

N 43°5'44" W 0°4'29"
www.eurocampings.co.uk/103575

1378 Luz-St-Sauveur, F-65120 / Midi-Pyrénées ♿ 🛜 (CC€15) 🚻 iD 54

▲ International****
🗺 B.P. 4
🗓 19 May - 30 Sep
☎ +33 (0)5-62928202
@ camping.international.luz@wanadoo.fr

1	ADEJMNOPRST	CDFGH**N** 6
2	FPTVX	BDEF**GH** 7
3	BE**I**LQST	BDFHJNPQRS 8
4	BFHU	E 9
5	ABCDFH**O**	ABDGHIJPR 10
2-10A CEE		
A700 4,5ha 110T(75-120m²) 59P		➊ €36.65 ➋ €49.15

D921 direction Luz-St-Sauveur. Campsite 1 km before Luz-St-Sauveur.
4-star family campsite, 1 km from the lovely mountain village of Luz-St.-Sauveur. The site is easily accessible. Shaded, spacious pitches. Shop and heated, indoor swimming pool with 2 jacuzzis. Centrally located for trips out to Gavarnie, Tourmalet, Cirque de Troumouse and the National Parc des Pyrénées. Free wifi (1 connection per pitch). Secure covered storage for bicycles.

(CC) 19/5-8/7 26/8-29/9 7=6, 14=12

Pierrefitte-Nestalas
Cauterets

N 42°52'58" W 0°0'49"
www.eurocampings.co.uk/103587

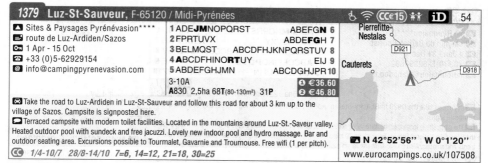

1379 Luz-St-Sauveur, F-65120 / Midi-Pyrénées 🕭 📶 (CC€15) ♨♨ iD 54

- ▲ Sites & Paysages Pyrénévasion****
- 🛣 route de Luz-Ardiden/Sazos
- 🗓 1 Apr - 15 Oct
- ☎ +33 (0)5-62929154
- @ info@campingpyrenevasion.com

1 ADE**JM**NOPQRST	ABEFG**N**	6
2 FPRTUVX	ABDE**FG**H	7
3 BELMQST	ABCDFHJKNPQRSTUV	8
4 **A**BCDFHINOR**RT**UY	EIJ	9
5 ABDEFGHJMN	ABCDGHJPR	10

3-10A
A830 2,5ha 68T(80-130m²) 31P

❶ €36.60
❷ €46.80

Pierrefitte-Nestalas — D921 — Cauterets — D918

🛣 Take the road to Luz-Ardiden in Luz-St-Sauveur and follow this road for about 3 km up to the village of Sazos. Campsite is signposted here.

🏕 Terraced campsite with modern toilet facilities. Located in the mountains around Luz-St.-Saveur valley. Heated outdoor pool with sundeck and free jacuzzi. Lovely new indoor pool and hydro massage. Bar and outdoor seating area. Excursions possible to Tourmalet, Gavarnie and Troumouse. Free wifi (1 per pitch).

◉ N 42°52'56'' W 0°1'20''

CC 1/4-10/7 28/8-14/10 7=6, 14=12, 21=18, 30=25

www.eurocampings.co.uk/107508

1380 Luz-St-Sauveur/Esquièze-Sère, F-65120 / Midi-Pyrénées 🕭 📶 (CC€15) iD 54

- ▲ Airotel Pyrénées*****
- 🛣 46 avenue du Barège
- 🗓 1 May - 24 Sep
- ☎ +33 (0)5-62928918
- @ airotel.pyrenees@wanadoo.fr

1 ADE**JM**NOPQRT	ABEFH	6
2 FGPTUVX	ABDE**FG**H	7
3 BELQTU	BDFHJKNOPQRS	8
4 BCDFHINOR**TUV**	EIJL	9
5 ABDFM**N**	ABDGHJPR	10

3-10A
A700 2,8ha 66T(80-100m²) 69P

❶ €36.65
❷ €50.15

Pierrefitte-Nestalas — Beaucens — D921 — D918

🛣 D921 to Luz-St-Sauveur. Located ca. 1 km before Luz-St-Sauveur left of the D921. Clearly signposted.

🏕 A challenging campsite. Plenty of fitness equipment, a sauna, indoor and outdoor swimming pools on site. Rafting and cycling. Sports ground for multi-sports. Wifi on entire campsite.

◉ N 42°52'49'' W 0°0'40''

CC 1/5-1/7 27/8-23/9

www.eurocampings.co.uk/103588

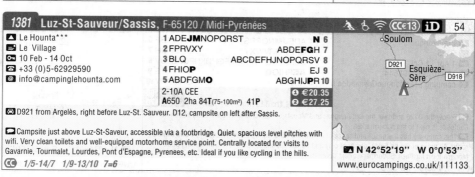

1381 Luz-St-Sauveur/Sassis, F-65120 / Midi-Pyrénées ⛷ 🕭 📶 (CC€13) iD 54

- ▲ Le Hounta***
- 🏠 Le Village
- 🗓 10 Feb - 14 Oct
- ☎ +33 (0)5-62929590
- @ info@campinglehounta.com

1 ADE**JM**NOPQRST	**N**	6
2 FPRVXY	ABDE**FG**H	7
3 BLQ	ABCDEFHJNOPQRSV	8
4 FHIO**P**	EJ	9
5 ABDFGM**O**	ABGHIJ**P**R	10

2-10A CEE
A650 2ha 84T(75-100m²) 41P

❶ €20.35
❷ €27.25

Soulom — D921 — Esquièze-Sère — D918

🛣 D921 from Argelès, right before Luz-St. Sauveur. D12, campsite on left after Sassis.

🏕 Campsite just above Luz-St-Saveur, accessible via a footbridge. Quiet, spacious level pitches with wifi. Very clean toilets and well-equipped motorhome service point. Centrally located for visits to Gavarnie, Tourmalet, Lourdes, Pont d'Espagne, Pyrenees, etc. Ideal if you like cycling in the hills.

◉ N 42°52'19'' W 0°0'53''

CC 1/5-14/7 1/9-13/10 7=6

www.eurocampings.co.uk/111133

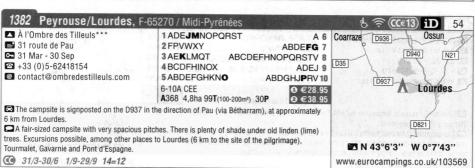

1382 Peyrouse/Lourdes, F-65270 / Midi-Pyrénées 🕭 📶 (CC€13) iD 54

- ▲ À l'Ombre des Tilleuls***
- 🏠 31 route de Pau
- 🗓 31 Mar - 30 Sep
- ☎ +33 (0)5-62418154
- @ contact@ombredestilleuls.com

1 ADE**JM**NOPQRST	A	6
2 FPVWXY	ABDE**FG**	7
3 AE**K**LMQT	ABCDEFHNOPQRSTV	8
4 BCDFHINOX	ADEJ	9
5 ABDEFGHKN**O**	ABDGHJ**P**RV	10

6-10A CEE
A368 4,8ha 99T(100-200m²) 30P

❶ €28.95
❷ €38.95

Coarraze — D936 — Ossun — D940 — N21 — D35 — D937 — Lourdes — D821

🛣 The campsite is signposted on the D937 in the direction of Pau (via Bétharram), at approximately 6 km from Lourdes.

🏕 A fair-sized campsite with very spacious pitches. There is plenty of shade under old linden (lime) trees. Excursions possible, among other places to Lourdes (6 km to the site of the pilgrimage), Tourmalet, Gavarnie and Pont d'Espagne.

◉ N 43°6'3'' W 0°7'43''

CC 31/3-30/6 1/9-29/9 14=12

www.eurocampings.co.uk/103569

France

1383 St. Lary-Soulan, F-65170 / Midi-Pyrénées — CC€15 iD 25 A2

- Le Rioumajou****
- chemin du Bernet/Bourisp
- 1 Jan - 31 Dec
- ☎ +33 (0)5-62394832
- @ lerioumajou@wanadoo.fr

1	ADEJMNOPRST	ABFNU 6
2	CGPRSVXY	ABDEFGH 7
3	ABELQ	ABCDEFJKNQRSV 8
4	ABCDEFINOPQTU	AE 9
5	ABDEFGHJMN	ABGHJNORVZ10
2-10A		❶ €27.40
A800	5ha 122T(100-130m²) 74P	❷ €33.80

In Arreau take the D929 to St. Lary-Soulan. About 1.5 km past the bridge at Bazus-Aure follow campsite signs.

The campsite is located in the Aure valley on the river, close to the mountain village of St. Lary. You can explore the Néouvielle National Nature Park with its 70 lakes and, while making lovely trips, you can discover many rare plants and animals. Also an excellent site for an overnight stop on your journey to Spain (via the Bielsa tunnel).

CC 1/1-30/6 1/9-31/12

N 42°50'19'' E 0°20'20''
www.eurocampings.co.uk/103687

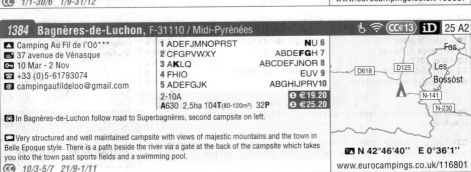

1384 Bagnères-de-Luchon, F-31110 / Midi-Pyrénées — CC€13 iD 25 A2

- Camping Au Fil de l'Oô***
- 37 avenue de Vénasque
- 10 Mar - 2 Nov
- ☎ +33 (0)5-61793074
- @ campingaufildeloo@gmail.com

1	ADEFJMNOPRST	NU 6
2	CFGPVWXY	ABDEFGH 7
3	AKLQ	ABCDEFJNOR 8
4	FHIO	EUV 9
5	ADEFGJK	ABGHIJPRV10
2-10A		❶ €19.20
A630	2,5ha 104T(80-120m²) 32P	❷ €25.20

In Bagnères-de-Luchon follow road to Superbagnères, second campsite on left.

Very structured and well maintained campsite with views of majestic mountains and the town in Belle Epoque style. There is a path beside the river via a gate at the back of the campsite which takes you into the town past sports fields and a swimming pool.

CC 10/3-5/7 21/9-1/11

N 42°46'40'' E 0°36'1''
www.eurocampings.co.uk/116801

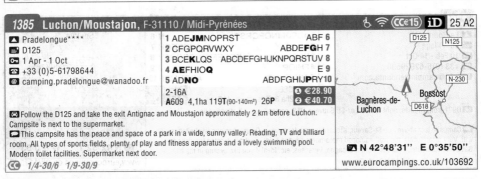

1385 Luchon/Moustajon, F-31110 / Midi-Pyrénées — CC€15 iD 25 A2

- Pradelongue****
- D125
- 1 Apr - 1 Oct
- ☎ +33 (0)5-61798644
- @ camping.pradelongue@wanadoo.fr

1	ADEJMNOPRST	ABF 6
2	CFGPQRVWXY	ABDEFGH 7
3	BCEKLQS	ABCDEFGHIJKNPQRSTUV 8
4	AEFHIOQ	E 9
5	ADNO	ABDFGHIJPRY10
2-16A		❶ €28.90
A609	4,1ha 119T(90-140m²) 26P	❷ €40.70

Follow the D125 and take the exit Antignac and Moustajon approximately 2 km before Luchon. Campsite is next to the supermarket.

This campsite has the peace and space of a park in a wide, sunny valley. Reading, TV and billiard room. All types of sports fields, plenty of play and fitness apparatus and a lovely swimming pool. Modern toilet facilities. Supermarket next door.

CC 1/4-30/6 1/9-30/9

N 42°48'31'' E 0°35'50''
www.eurocampings.co.uk/103692

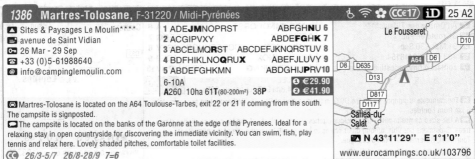

1386 Martres-Tolosane, F-31220 / Midi-Pyrénées — CC€17 iD 25 A2

- Sites & Paysages Le Moulin****
- avenue de Saint Vidian
- 26 Mar - 29 Sep
- ☎ +33 (0)5-61988640
- @ info@campinglemoulin.com

1	ADEJMNOPRST	ABFGHNU 6
2	ACGIPVXY	ABDEFGHK 7
3	ABCELMQRST	ABCDEFJKNQRSTUV 8
4	BDFHIKLNOQRUX	ABEFJLUVY 9
5	ABDEFGHKMN	ABDGHIJPRV10
6-10A		❶ €29.90
A260	10ha 61T(80-200m²) 38P	❷ €41.90

Martres-Tolosane is located on the A64 Toulouse-Tarbes, exit 22 or 21 if coming from the south. The campsite is signposted.

The campsite is located on the banks of the Garonne at the edge of the Pyrenees. Ideal for a relaxing stay in open countryside for discovering the immediate vicinity. You can swim, fish, play tennis and relax here. Lovely shaded pitches, comfortable toilet facilities.

CC 26/3-5/7 26/8-28/9 7=6

N 43°11'29'' E 1°1'0''
www.eurocampings.co.uk/103796

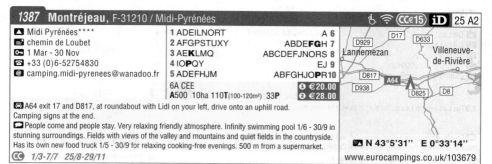

1387 Montréjeau, F-31210 / Midi-Pyrénées
♿ 🤟 (CC€15) iD 25 A2

- 🏕 Midi Pyrénées****
- 📧 chemin de Loubet
- 📅 1 Mar - 30 Nov
- ☎ +33 (0)6-52754830
- @ camping.midi-pyrenees@wanadoo.fr

1	ADEILNORT	A 6
2	AFGPSTUXY	ABDE**FGH** 7
3	AE**K**LMQ	ABCDEFJNORS 8
4	IO**PQ**Y	EJ 9
5	ADEFHJM	ABFGHJO**PR**10
6A CEE		🔌 €20.00
A500 10ha 110**T**(100-120m²) 33**P**		🔌 €28.00

🚗 A64 exit 17 and D817, at roundabout with Lidl on your left, drive onto an uphill road. Camping signs at the end.

💬 People come and people stay. Very relaxing friendly atmosphere. Infinity swimming pool 1/6 - 30/9 in stunning surroundings. Fields with views of the valley and mountains and quiet fields in the countryside. Has its own new food truck 1/5 - 30/9 for relaxing cooking-free evenings. 500 m from a supermarket.

(CC) 1/3-7/7 25/8-29/11

📍 N 43°5'31" E 0°33'14"

www.eurocampings.co.uk/103679

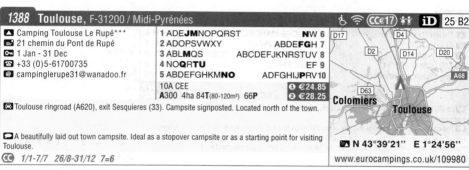

1388 Toulouse, F-31200 / Midi-Pyrénées
♿ 🤟 (CC€17) 🚻 iD 25 B2

- 🏕 Camping Toulouse Le Rupé***
- 📧 21 chemin du Pont de Rupé
- 📅 1 Jan - 31 Dec
- ☎ +33 (0)5-61700735
- @ campinglerupe31@wanadoo.fr

1	ADE**JM**NOPQRST	**NW** 6
2	ADOPSVWXY	ABDE**FGH** 7
3	ABL**MQS**	ABCDEFJKNRSTUV 8
4	NO**QR**T**U**	EF 9
5	ABDEFGHKM**NO**	ADFGHIJ**PR**V10
10A CEE		🔌 €24.85
A300 4ha 84**T**(80-120m²) 66**P**		🔌 €28.25

🚗 Toulouse ringroad (A620), exit Sesquieres (33). Campsite signposted. Located north of the town.

💬 A beautifully laid out town campsite. Ideal as a stopover campsite or as a starting point for visiting Toulouse.

(CC) 1/1-7/7 26/8-31/12 7=6

📍 N 43°39'21" E 1°24'56"

www.eurocampings.co.uk/109980

1389 Alliat/Niaux, F-09400 / Midi-Pyrénées
♿ 🤟 (CC€15) iD 25 B2

- 🏕 Des Grottes****
- 📅 1 Mar - 15 Oct
- ☎ +33 (0)5-61058821
- @ info@campingdesgrottes.com

1	AD**J**LNOPQRST	ABFHIN 6
2	CFGPVX	ABDE**FGH** 7
3	BE**G**LQ	ABDEFHJKNPQRSV 8
4	BDFHILNO**PQ**RTU	F 9
5	ACDEFGHKM**N**	ABDGHJ**PR**10
16A CEE		🔌 €29.10
A600 7ha 120**T**(90-110m²) 80**P**		🔌 €40.10

🚗 From Foix N20 direction Andorra. Turn right just past Tarascon towards Niaux/Vicdessos. Campsite 2 km on the right.

💬 A lovely campsite with plenty of atmosphere. Attractive separated pitches in avenues. Now with a heated toilet block. Good starting point for cultural trips and mountain hiking. Good views of the Niaux cave.

(CC) 1/3-3/7 21/8-14/10 7=6, 14=11, 21=14

📍 N 42°48'47" E 1°35'21"

www.eurocampings.co.uk/103810

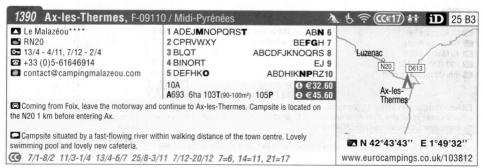

1390 Ax-les-Thermes, F-09110 / Midi-Pyrénées
♿ ♿ 🤟 (CC€17) 🚻 iD 25 B3

- 🏕 Le Malazéou****
- 📧 RN20
- 📅 13/4 - 4/11, 7/12 - 2/4
- ☎ +33 (0)5-61646914
- @ contact@campingmalazeou.com

1	ADE**J**MNOPQRS**T**	AB**N** 6
2	CPRVWXY	BE**FGH** 7
3	BLQT	ABCDFJKNOQRS 8
4	BINORT	EJ 9
5	DEFHK**O**	ABDHIK**NPR**Z10
10A		🔌 €32.60
A693 6ha 103**T**(90-100m²) 105**P**		🔌 €45.60

🚗 Coming from Foix, leave the motorway and continue to Ax-les-Thermes. Campsite is located on the N20 1 km before entering Ax.

💬 Campsite situated by a fast-flowing river within walking distance of the town centre. Lovely swimming pool and lovely new cafeteria.

(CC) 7/1-8/2 11/3-1/4 13/4-6/7 25/8-3/11 7/12-20/12 7=6, 14=11, 21=17

📍 N 42°43'43" E 1°49'32"

www.eurocampings.co.uk/103812

France

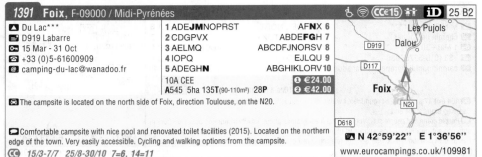

1391 Foix, F-09000 / Midi-Pyrénées   ♿ 📶 (CC€15) ♚♛ iD 25 B2

- 🏕 Du Lac***
- 🛏 D919 Labarre
- 📅 15 Mar - 31 Oct
- ☎ +33 (0)5-61600909
- @ camping-du-lac@wanadoo.fr

1 ADE**JM**NOPRST	AF**N**X	6
2 CDGPVX	ABDE**FG**H	7
3 AELMQ	ABCDFJNORSV	8
4 IOPQ	EJLQU	9
5 ADEGH**N**	ABGHIKLORV	10
10A CEE	❶ €24.00	
A545 5ha 135T(90-110m²) 28P	❷ €42.00	

🗺 The campsite is located on the north side of Foix, direction Toulouse, on the N20.

💬 Comfortable campsite with nice pool and renovated toilet facilities (2015). Located on the northern edge of the town. Very easily accessible. Cycling and walking options from the campsite.

CC 15/3-7/7 25/8-30/10 7=6, 14=11

N 42°59'22'' E 1°36'56''
www.eurocampings.co.uk/109981

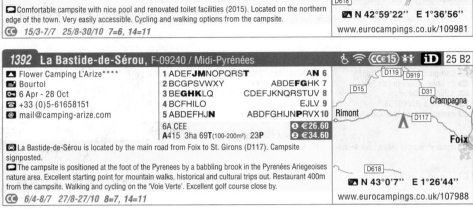

1392 La Bastide-de-Sérou, F-09240 / Midi-Pyrénées   ♿ 📶 (CC€15) ♚♛ iD 25 B2

- 🏕 Flower Camping L'Arize****
- 🛏 Bourtol
- 📅 6 Apr - 28 Oct
- ☎ +33 (0)5-61658151
- @ mail@camping-arize.com

1 ADEF**JM**NOPQRS**T**	A**N**	6
2 BCGPSVWXY	ABDE**FG**HK	7
3 BE**GHK**LQ	CDEFJKNQRSTUV	8
4 BCFHILO	EJLV	9
5 ABDEFHJ**N**	ABDFGHIJN**P**RVX	10
6A CEE	❶ €26.60	
A415 3ha 69T(100-200m²) 23P	❷ €34.60	

🗺 La Bastide-de-Sérou is located by the main road from Foix to St. Girons (D117). Campsite signposted.

💬 The campsite is positioned at the foot of the Pyrenees by a babbling brook in the Pyrénées Ariegeoises nature area. Excellent starting point for mountain walks, historical and cultural trips out. Restaurant 400m from the campsite. Walking and cycling on the 'Voie Verte'. Excellent golf course close by.

CC 6/4-8/7 27/8-27/10 8=7, 14=11

N 43°0'7'' E 1°26'44''
www.eurocampings.co.uk/107988

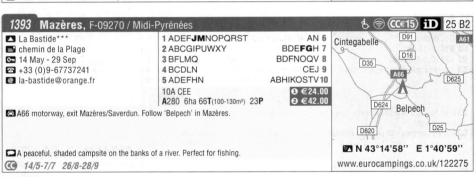

1393 Mazères, F-09270 / Midi-Pyrénées   ♿ 📶 (CC€15) iD 25 B2

- 🏕 La Bastide***
- 🛏 chemin de la Plage
- 📅 14 May - 29 Sep
- ☎ +33 (0)9-67737241
- @ la-bastide@orange.fr

1 ADEF**JM**NOPQRST	A**N**	6
2 ABCGIPUWXY	BDEF**FG**H	7
3 BFLMQ	BDFNOQV	8
4 BCDLN	CEJ	9
5 ADEFHN	ABHIKOSTV	10
10A CEE	❶ €24.00	
A280 6ha 66T(100-130m²) 23P	❷ €42.00	

🗺 A66 motorway, exit Mazères/Saverdun. Follow 'Belpech' in Mazères.

💬 A peaceful, shaded campsite on the banks of a river. Perfect for fishing.

CC 14/5-7/7 26/8-28/9

N 43°14'58'' E 1°40'59''
www.eurocampings.co.uk/122275

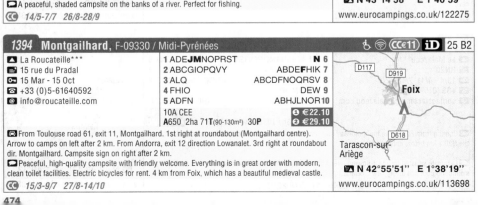

1394 Montgailhard, F-09330 / Midi-Pyrénées   ♿ 📶 (CC€11) iD 25 B2

- 🏕 La Roucateille***
- 🛏 15 rue du Pradal
- 📅 15 Mar - 15 Oct
- ☎ +33 (0)5-61640592
- @ info@roucateille.com

1 ADE**JM**NOPRST	**N**	6
2 ABCGIOPQVY	ABDE**F**HIK	7
3 ALQ	ABCDFNOQRSV	8
4 FHIO	DEW	9
5 ADFN	ABHJLNOR	10
10A CEE	❶ €22.10	
A650 2ha 71T(90-130m²) 30P	❷ €29.10	

🗺 From Toulouse road 61, exit 11, Montgailhard. 1st right at roundabout (Montgailhard centre). Arrow to camps on left after 2 km. From Andorra, exit 12 direction Lowanalet. 3rd right at roundabout dir. Montgailhard. Campsite sign on right after 2 km.

💬 Peaceful, high-quality campsite with friendly welcome. Everything is in great order with modern, clean toilet facilities. Electric bicycles for rent. 4 km from Foix, which has a beautiful medieval castle.

CC 15/3-9/7 27/8-14/10

N 42°55'51'' E 1°38'19''
www.eurocampings.co.uk/113698

Occitania

Where the mountains come down to the sea

Comprising the former departments of Languedoc-Roussillon and Midi-Pyrénées, Occitanie also borders Spain, Catalonia and Andorra. You'll be amazed at the variety in this landscape; mountains with river basins and gorges, forests, heathlands, farms and vineyards – all before you reach the Mediterranean coast.

Historic cities and towns

In Toulouse, see the largest Romanesque church in Europe and the Daurade Basilica, originally a Roman temple. Take the kids to Jardin des Plantes Park for fun games. Artistic? Check out the harbour town of Collioure, which locals refer to as the town of painters. Luminaries like Picasso, Matisse, Derain, and Chagall worked here, if only the walls of this town could talk! Be wowed by

the Roman monuments in Nîmes: the Pont du Gard aqueduct and Tour Magne are spectacular, and the Roman arena is the venue for the annual Great Roman Games, with re-enactments and workshops, bring your camera! The kids will also be enthralled at the Summer Festival at Carcassone, with music, dancing, art, and knights' tournaments in Europe's largest mediaeval fortified town. Magnifique!

Activities in the countryside

The mountains, forests and rivers attract nature lovers to Occitanie in droves. In addition to pretty villages, Haut-Languedoc Nature Park has super trails for hikers, climbers and mountain bikers, while the rivers and lakes are ideal for canyoning and kayaking. Cevennes Nature Park is as marvellous below the ground as above: check out the stalagmites and the caves, and you also see Stone Age menhirs and dolmens. Marvel at the peculiar river basins at Navacelles and Gavarnie created by river bends in the gorges, and look out for Iberian ibex in the Pyrenees Nature park. At maritime park Golfe du Lion, take

Our tips

1. Visit Albi, birthplace of artist Toulouse-Lautrec and cradle of mediaeval Catharism
2. Enjoy the landscape at a slower pace: travel by boat along the Canal du Midi
3. Take in the panorama of the Pyrenees at Midi de Bigorre
4. See the Palace of Kings of Majorca in Perpignan, upgraded by military engineer Vauban
5. Take a break from sightseeing for some shopping in Montpellier

the underwater path to see the seafloor, coral formations, fish and bottlenose dolphins.

Eat like a king

You'll find the produce rich too: try gateau à la broche (pin cake); sip some local wine with Lacaune meats or Roquefort cheese, or fill up with Aligot (with rich, garlicky potato), cassoulet Toulousain (stew of pork and beans) or garbure (cabbage soup with poultry). Locals love ratatouille with Saucisse de Toulouse. If you still have room, have some fresh cherries.

1395 Balbigny, F-42510 / Rhône-Alpes — 🖙 🤚 CC€15 ⚐⚐ iD 19 B2

- 🏕 La Route Bleue***
- 🏠 Pralery, D56
- 📅 15 Mar - 31 Oct
- ☎ +33 (0)4-77272497
- @ camping.balbigny@wanadoo.fr

1 ADEJMNOPRST	AF**N**	6
2 ACGPRVWXY	ABDE**FG**H	7
3 Q	ABCDEFNOQRV	8
4 HIO	E	9
5 ADEFGHJMNO	ABGHIJPR	10
10A	❶ €21.80	
A320 2ha 100T(100m²) 2P	❷ €29.80	

🗺 On the north side of Balbigny. From the N82 take the D56. Campsite signposted.

💬 A peaceful campsite with a friendly atmosphere. Direct access to the Loire shores. Easy access. Tourist region. Ideal for a holiday in the open air. You can go fishing and walking here. The site has a bar, snack bar, take away meals. Swimming pool and toddlers' pool.

CC 15/3-2/7 20/8-30/10

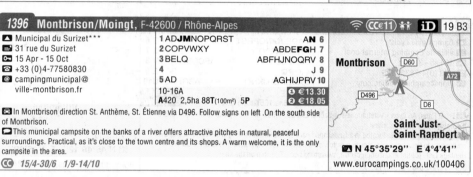

📷 N 45°49'45'' E 4°9'39''

www.eurocampings.co.uk/107557

1396 Montbrison/Moingt, F-42600 / Rhône-Alpes — 🤚 CC€11 ⚐⚐ iD 19 B3

- 🏕 Municipal du Surizet***
- 🏠 31 rue du Surizet
- 📅 15 Apr - 15 Oct
- ☎ +33 (0)4-77580830
- @ campingmunicipal@
  ville-montbrison.fr

1 AD**JM**NOPQRST	A**N**	6
2 COPVWXY	ABDE**FG**H	7
3 BELQ	ABFHJNOQRV	8
4	J	9
5 AD	AGHIJPRV	10
10-16A	❶ €13.30	
A420 2,5ha 88T(100m²) 5P	❷ €18.05	

🗺 In Montbrison direction St. Anthème, St. Étienne via D496. Follow signs on left .On the south side of Montbrison.

💬 This municipal campsite on the banks of a river offers attractive pitches in natural, peaceful surroundings. Practical, as it's close to the town centre and its shops. A warm welcome, it is the only campsite in the area.

CC 15/4-30/6 1/9-14/10

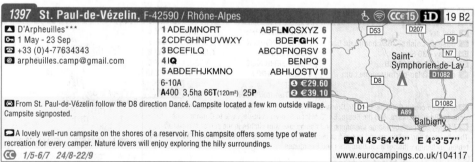

📷 N 45°35'29'' E 4°4'41''

www.eurocampings.co.uk/100406

1397 St. Paul-de-Vézelin, F-42590 / Rhône-Alpes — 🖙 🤚 CC€15 iD 19 B2

- 🏕 D'Arpheuilles***
- 📅 1 May - 23 Sep
- ☎ +33 (0)4-77634343
- @ arpheuilles.camp@gmail.com

1 ADEJMNORT	ABFL**N**QSXYZ	6
2 CDFGHNPUVWXY	BDE**FG**HK	7
3 BCEFILQ	ABCDFNORSV	8
4 I**Q**	BENPQ	9
5 ABDEFHJKMNO	ABHIJOSTV	10
6-10A	❶ €29.60	
A400 3,5ha 66T(120m²) 25P	❷ €39.10	

🗺 From St. Paul-de-Vézelin follow the D8 direction Dancé. Campsite located a few km outside village. Campsite signposted.

💬 A lovely well-run campsite on the shores of a reservoir. This campsite offers some type of water recreation for every camper. Nature lovers will enjoy exploring the hilly surroundings.

CC 1/5-6/7 24/8-22/9

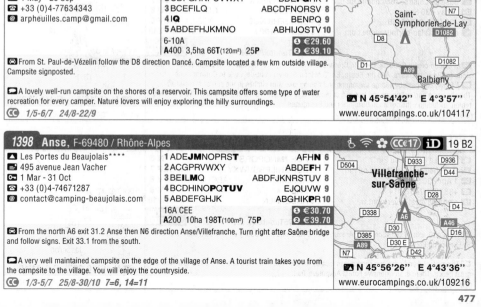

📷 N 45°54'42'' E 4°3'57''

www.eurocampings.co.uk/104117

1398 Anse, F-69480 / Rhône-Alpes — 🖙 🤚 ✿ CC€17 iD 19 B2

- 🏕 Les Portes du Beaujolais****
- 🏠 495 avenue Jean Vacher
- 📅 1 Mar - 31 Oct
- ☎ +33 (0)4-74671287
- @ contact@camping-beaujolais.com

1 ADE**JM**NOPRS**T**	AFH**N**	6
2 ACGPRVWXY	ABDE**F**H	7
3 BE**IL**MQ	ABDFJKNRSTUV	8
4 BCDHINO**PQT**UV	EJQUVW	9
5 ABDEFGHJK	ABGHIK**P**R	10
16A CEE	❶ €30.70	
A200 10ha 198T(100m²) 75P	❷ €39.70	

🗺 From the north A6 exit 31.2 Anse then N6 direction Anse/Villefranche. Turn right after Saône bridge and follow signs. Exit 33.1 from the south.

💬 A very well maintained campsite on the edge of the village of Anse. A tourist train takes you from the campsite to the village. You will enjoy the countryside.

CC 1/3-5/7 25/8-30/10 7=6, 14=11

📷 N 45°56'26'' E 4°43'36''

www.eurocampings.co.uk/109216

France

1399 Cublize/Amplepuis, F-69550 / Rhône-Alpes ♿ 🛜 CC€17 ♀♂ iD 19 B2

🔺 Campéole Le Lac des Sapins****
✉ rue du Stade
🗓 30 Mar - 23 Sep
☎ +33 (0)4-74895283
@ lacdessapins@campeole.com

1 ADE**JM**NOPRS**T**	ALM**N**QRSTX	6
2 CDGHIPRSVWXY	ABDE**FG**	7
3 BE**GHI**LM**QR**	ABCDEFKNORSTUV	8
4 DFHL	CEJMOPQRTU	9
5 ABDEH	ABDGHJ**O**STZ	10

16A CEE	❶ €27.30
A450 8ha 79T(50-100m²) 100P	❷ €35.50

🚗 Follow the camping signs in the village. Drive past the village campsite. The entrance to the campsite 'Du Lac des Sapins' is located after about 600 metres.

💬 Family campsite located close to the lake with plenty of water sports. It has a bar and restaurant at the lake.

CC 30/3-6/7 25/8-22/9

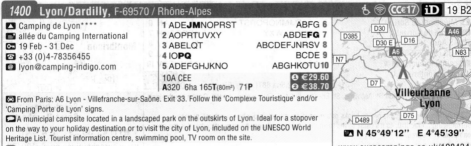

🧭 N 46°0'47'' E 4°22'54''

www.eurocampings.co.uk/100384

1400 Lyon/Dardilly, F-69570 / Rhône-Alpes ♿ 🛜 CC€17 iD 19 B2

🔺 Camping de Lyon****
✉ allée du Camping International
🗓 19 Feb - 31 Dec
☎ +33 (0)4-78356455
@ lyon@camping-indigo.com

1 ADE**JM**NOPRST	ABFG	6
2 AOPRTUVXY	ABDE**FG**	7
3 ABELQT	ABCDEFJNRSV	8
4 IO**PQ**	BCDE	9
5 ADEFGHJKNO	ABGHKOTU	10

10A CEE	❶ €29.60
A320 6ha 165T(80m²) 71P	❷ €38.70

🚗 From Paris: A6 Lyon - Villefranche-sur-Saône. Exit 33. Follow the 'Complexe Touristique' and/or 'Camping Porte de Lyon' signs.

💬 A municipal campsite located in a landscaped park on the outskirts of Lyon. Ideal for a stopover on the way to your holiday destination or to visit the city of Lyon, included on the UNESCO World Heritage List. Tourist information centre, swimming pool, TV room on the site.

CC 19/2-28/6 3/9-1/12

🧭 N 45°49'12'' E 4°45'39''

www.eurocampings.co.uk/108434

1401 Cormoranche-sur-Saône, F-01290 / Rhône-Alpes ♿ 🛜 CC€15 ♀♂ iD 19 B2

🔺 du Lac****
✉ Base de Loisirs, 365 chemin du Lac
🗓 1 May - 30 Sep
☎ +33 (0)3-85239710
@ contact@lac-cormoranche.com

1 ADE**JM**NOPRST	LMN**Q**STXY	6
2 ADGHIPQVWX	ABDE**FG**H	7
3 BEF**K**LQRT	CDFKNQRSTU	8
4 BCDEFHILNO**P**	ABEJLQRTUV	9
5 ABDEFGHKN	ABDGHIKLNO**P**RVZ	10

10A CEE	❶ €22.50
4ha 90T(80-100m²) 56P	❷ €28.50

🚗 In Mâcon-centre D906 dir. Lyon. In Crêches turn left (D51) over the Saône. In Cormorane follow signs for Base de Loisirs. A40 dir. Bourg. Exit 3 Mâcon-Sud via Pont-de-Veyle to Cormoranche.

💬 A family campsite by a large swimming and fishing lake with pitches in the sun or in the shade. The site has a bar/restaurant and free wifi at reception. 5 minutes from a supermarket. A very touristy region, including wine cellars in Beaujolais and Bourgogne.

CC 1/5-14/7 1/9-29/9 7=6, 14=12

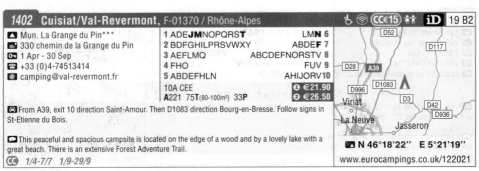

🧭 N 46°15'5'' E 4°49'33''

www.eurocampings.co.uk/100379

1402 Cuisiat/Val-Revermont, F-01370 / Rhône-Alpes ♿ 🛜 CC€15 ♀♂ iD 19 B2

🔺 Mun. La Grange du Pin***
✉ 330 chemin de la Grange du Pin
🗓 1 Apr - 30 Sep
☎ +33 (0)4-74513414
@ camping@val-revermont.fr

1 ADE**JM**NOPQRS**T**	LM**N**	6
2 BDFGHILPRSVWXY	ABDE**F**	7
3 AEFLMQ	ABCDEFNORSTV	8
4 FHO	FUV	9
5 ABDEFHLN	AHIJORV	10

10A CEE	❶ €21.90
A221 75T(80-100m²) 33P	❷ €26.50

🚗 From A39, exit 10 direction Saint-Amour. Then D1083 direction Bourg-en-Bresse. Follow signs in St-Etienne du Bois.

💬 This peaceful and spacious campsite is located on the edge of a wood and by a lovely lake with a great beach. There is an extensive Forest Adventure Trail.

CC 1/4-7/7 1/9-29/9

🧭 N 46°18'22'' E 5°21'19''

www.eurocampings.co.uk/122021

France

Register and win!

Visit www.EUROCAMPINGS.co.uk/extravaganza

A relaxed start to your holiday,
by being sure you have your pitch already booked

- Book directly with the campsite
- Quick and easy, even on the road
- Camping pitches and holiday rentals

For more information please visit:
www.EUROCAMPINGS.co.uk/bookonline

1403 Divonne-les-Bains, F-01220 / Rhône-Alpes

♿ 📶 (C€17) iD 20 A2

🏠 Huttopia Divonne-les-Bains***
📧 Quart. Villard, 2465 Vie de l'Etraz
🔓 27 Apr - 30 Sep
☎ +33 (0)4-50200195
@ divonne@huttopia.com

1	ADEJMNOPRT	ABFN	6
2	ACFPTUVWXY	ABDEFGH	7
3	BEKLMQ	ABCDEFJNQRS	8
4	ABCDEFHIO	ABCEFJU	9
5	ABDEFGHKN	ABGHIJNPTU	10
10A CEE		❶ €32.15	
A600 8ha 175T(80-150m²)	101P	❷ €43.45	

🚗 From Gex D984 direction Divonne. Take the road to St. Gixet before Divonne and follow the campsite signs.
🏕 A lovely wooded campsite laid out in terraces. Pitches delightfully set among trees. A large swimming pool, plenty of amenities for children, fun activities. Switzerland, Geneva and Lake Geneva are close by.

CC 27/4-5/7 26/8-29/9

📷 N 46°22'29'' E 6°7'16''

www.eurocampings.co.uk/108896

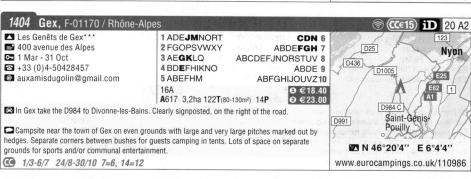

1404 Gex, F-01170 / Rhône-Alpes

📶 (C€15) iD 20 A2

🏠 Les Genêts de Gex***
📧 400 avenue des Alpes
🔓 1 Mar - 31 Oct
☎ +33 (0)4-50428457
@ auxamisdugolin@gmail.com

1	ADEJMNORT	CDN	6
2	FGOPSVWXY	ABDEFGH	7
3	AEGKLQ	ABCDEFJNORSTUV	8
4	BDEFHIKNO	ABDE	9
5	ABEFHM	ABFGHIJOUVZ	10
16A		❶ €18.40	
A617 3,2ha 122T(80-130m²)	14P	❷ €23.00	

🚗 In Gex take the D984 to Divonne-les-Bains. Clearly signposted, on the right of the road.

🏕 Campsite near the town of Gex on even grounds with large and very large pitches marked out by hedges. Separate corners between bushes for guests camping in tents. Lots of space on separate grounds for sports and/or communal entertainment.

CC 1/3-6/7 24/8-30/10 7=6, 14=12

📷 N 46°20'4'' E 6°4'4''

www.eurocampings.co.uk/110986

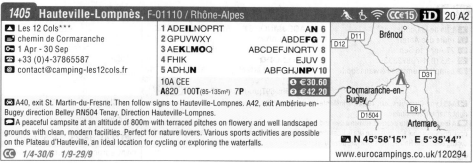

France

1405 Hauteville-Lompnès, F-01110 / Rhône-Alpes

⛷ ♿ 📶 (C€15) iD 20 A2

🏠 Les 12 Cols***
📧 chemin de Cormaranche
🔓 1 Apr - 30 Sep
☎ +33 (0)4-37865587
@ contact@camping-les12cols.fr

1	ADEILNOPRT	AN	6
2	GPUVWXY	ABDEFG	7
3	AEKLMOQ	ABCDEFJNQRTV	8
4	FHIK	EJUV	9
5	ADHJN	ABFGHJNPV	10
10A CEE		❶ €30.60	
A820 100T(85-135m²)	7P	❷ €42.20	

🚗 A40, exit St. Martin-du-Fresne. Then follow signs to Hauteville-Lompnes. A42, exit Ambérieu-en-Bugey direction Belley RN504 Tenay. Direction Hauteville-Lompnes.
🏕 A peaceful campsite at an altitude of 800m with terraced pitches on flowery and well landscaped grounds with clean, modern facilities. Perfect for nature lovers. Various sports activities are possible on the Plateau d'Hauteville, an ideal location for cycling or exploring the waterfalls.

CC 1/4-30/6 1/9-29/9

📷 N 45°58'15'' E 5°35'44''

www.eurocampings.co.uk/120294

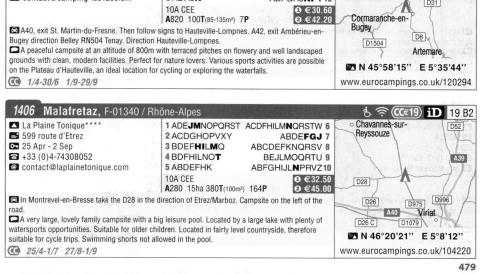

1406 Malafretaz, F-01340 / Rhône-Alpes

♿ 📶 (C€19) iD 19 B2

🏠 La Plaine Tonique****
📧 599 route d'Etrez
🔓 25 Apr - 2 Sep
☎ +33 (0)4-74308052
@ contact@laplainetonique.com

1	ADEJMNOPQRST	ACDFHILMNQRSTW	6
2	ACDGHOPVXY	ABDEFGJ	7
3	BDEFHILMQ	ABCDEFKNQRSV	8
4	BDFHILNOT	BEJLMOQRTU	9
5	ABDEFHK	ABFGHIJLNPRVZ	10
10A CEE		❶ €32.50	
A280 15ha 380T(100m²)	164P	❷ €45.00	

🚗 In Montrevel-en-Bresse take the D28 in the direction of Etrez/Marboz. Campsite on the left of the road.
🏕 A very large, lovely family campsite with a big leisure pool. Located by a large lake with plenty of watersports opportunities. Suitable for older children. Located in fairly level countryside, therefore suitable for cycle trips. Swimming shorts not allowed in the pool.

CC 25/4-1/7 27/8-1/9

📷 N 46°20'21'' E 5°8'12''

www.eurocampings.co.uk/104220

1407 Massignieu-de-Rives, F-01300 / Rhône-Alpes ⚒ 🛜 (CC€17) iD 20 A2

- ◣ Lac du Lit du Roi****
- ▣ La Tuillière
- ☷ 31 Mar - 23 Sep
- ☎ +33 (0)4-79421203
- @ info@camping-savoie.com

1 ADEJMNORST	AFLMNQSXYZ	6
2 DGIPRUVWXY	ABDEFGH	7
3 ADFLMQT	ABCDFNOQRSTUV	8
4 BDFHILNOQ	EFJUV	9
5 ABDFGHJKMN	ABHJOS	10

10A — ❶ €28.60
A235 2,5ha 84T(80-120m²) 48P — ❷ €38.20

🛣 A40 direction Genève. Exit 11 Eloise. RN508 direction Frangy. D992 direction Culoz. Continue on D992 for a further 12 km past Culoz. Over the bridge to Massignieu-de-Rives. Well signposted.
💬 Extensive grounds with three toilet blocks. Almost all pitches have views of the lake that is connected to the Rhône. There is also a small swimming pool. 300 metres from a small harbour with a slipway.
(CC) 31/3-6/7 24/8-22/9 7=6, 14=11

🧭 N 45°46'7'' E 5°46'11''
www.eurocampings.co.uk/100409

D904 — D1504 — D921 — D991 — D914 — A41 — Belley — D992 — D48 — D10 — D1516 — Aix-les-Bains

1408 Matafelon-Granges, F-01580 / Rhône-Alpes 🛜 (CC€17) iD 20 A2

- ◣ Les Gorges de l'Oignin***
- ▣ 724 rue du Lac
- ☷ 15 Apr - 29 Sep
- ☎ +33 (0)4-74768097
- @ camping.lesgorgesdeloignin@orange.fr

1 ADEJMNOPQRT	ABFLNQXZ	6
2 DFGIPRSUVWXY	ABDEFG	7
3 ABEKLQ	ABCDEFJNRSTV	8
4 BFIKLOP	EJT	9
5 ABDEFGHKMN	ABDHIJOR	10

10A CEE — ❶ €30.50
A400 2,6ha 128T 24P — ❷ €40.10

🛣 From Bourg-en-Bresse in the direction of Nantua, turn left at roundabout and take D18 as far as Matafelon, follow the signs. Matafelon is not signposted coming from Oyonax.
💬 A lovely modern and spacious terraced campsite with heated swimming pools by a small reservoir. The campsite has wonderful views. The Gorges de l'Ain are close by. For a day out, Geneva or Lyon, the Jura or the bird park at Villars-les-Dombes.
(CC) 15/4-6/7 25/8-28/9 7=6, 14=12

🧭 N 46°15'19'' E 5°33'26''
www.eurocampings.co.uk/110730

D109 E1 — D436 — D117 — D31 — D109 — Oyonnax — D936 — D13 — D18 — A404 — D42 — Montréal-la-Cluse — A40

1409 Murs-et-Gélignieux, F-01300 / Rhône-Alpes ⚒ 🛜 (CC€17) iD 20 A2

- ◣ L'Île de la Comtesse****
- ▣ route des Abrets
- ☷ 27 Apr - 16 Sep
- ☎ +33 (0)4-79872333
- @ camping.comtesse@wanadoo.fr

1 ADEJMNORST	ABFGHNQSWXYZ	6
2 ACDPQVWX	BDEFGH	7
3 ADEFLQST	BCFNQRSTV	8
4 EHILNOPQ	AEFJV	9
5 ACDEFGHJKMN	ABGHJNPST	10

6A CEE — ❶ €32.55
A210 3ha 69T(100-120m²) 41P — ❷ €45.65

🛣 A43 Lyon-Chambéry, exit 10 Chimilin/Aoste, then on the D592 dir. Belley. Campsite located on the right after the 2nd bridge.
💬 A friendly campsite located between a lake and mountain, close to Chambéry and Lyon. It has a swimming pool, children's pool and slide. The site is located on the unique 'Via Rhôna' cycle route. Many kilometres of cycling beside the Rhône. The snack bar, pizzeria and restaurant are only open at weekends in the low season.
(CC) 27/4-6/7 25/8-15/9

🧭 N 45°38'23'' E 5°38'56''
www.eurocampings.co.uk/104229

D992 — Yenne — D33 — D10 — D1075 — D1516 — D921 — D916 — Chimilin — Fitilieu — A43

1410 Pont-de-Vaux, F-01190 / Rhône-Alpes ⚒ 🛜 (CC€17) 🚻 iD 19 B2

- ◣ Aux Rives du Soleil***
- ▣ D933A
- ☷ 13 Apr - 15 Oct
- ☎ +33 (0)3-85303365
- @ info@rivesdusoleil.com

1 ADEJMNOPQRST	AFJNQSWXYZ	6
2 ACGIPRVWXY	ABDFGH	7
3 AEKLQST	ABCDFKNQRSV	8
4 BDFHIKLO	AEPQRVWY	9
5 ABDEGHLMN	ABDGHJOR	10

6A — ❶ €31.50
7ha 160T(100m²) 33P — ❷ €45.50

🛣 From the north: A6, exit 27 Tournus. From the south: A6, exit Mâcon. Mâcon-Nord. Then the D906 direction Pont-de-Vaux. At roundabout Fleurville over the Saône. Campsite located on the Saône.

💬 Spacious natural campsite on the banks of the Saône, suitable for cycling, walking and fishing. Separate overnight terrain.
(CC) 13/4-2/7 1/9-14/10

🧭 N 46°26'49'' E 4°53'56''
www.eurocampings.co.uk/101206

D14 — N6 — D56 — D933 — D975 — D82 — A6 — D15 — D2 — Saint-Martin-Belle-Roche — Hurigny — D26

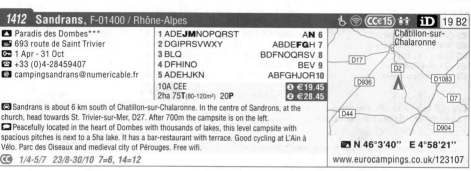

1411 Pont-de-Vaux, F-01190 / Rhône-Alpes

🦽 📶 (CC€15) ♦♦ **iD** 19 B2

- 🔺 Champ d'Été****
- 🏕 Base de Loisirs
- 📅 24 Mar - 13 Oct
- ☎ +33 (0)3-85239610
- @ info@camping-champ-dete.com

1	ADE**JM**NOPRS**T**	ABEFGHI**N** 6
2	DGIOPSVXY	ABDE**FG**H 7
3	AEHLQ	DFKNQRSTUV 8
4	BDFHIO**RTUV**	BEJUVW 9
5	ABDEHN	ABDFGHJNO**P**R 10

| 10A CEE | ❶ €25.65 |
| **A**200 3,5ha 108**T**(80-100m²) 36**P** | ❷ €34.65 |

📧 At Fleurville (D906) over the Saône to Pont-de-Vaux (D933). In Pont-de-Vaux follow Base-de-Loisirs and campsite signs. Use GPS coordinates.

💬 This quiet campsite is located in park-like surroundings, within walking distance of the vibrant village of Pont-de-Vaux, on a large fishing lake, beside the municipal pool (free entrance). The campsite is not far from the A6.

🎫 24/3-6/7 24/8-12/10

📍 N 46°25'46'' E 4°56'0''

www.eurocampings.co.uk/112645

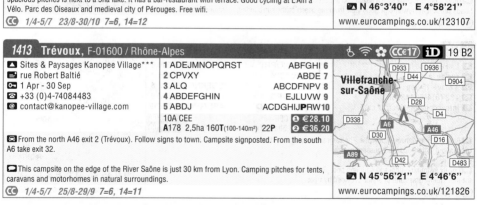

1412 Sandrans, F-01400 / Rhône-Alpes

🦽 📶 (CC€15) ♦♦ **iD** 19 B2

- 🔺 Paradis des Dombes***
- 🏕 693 route de Saint Trivier
- 📅 1 Apr - 31 Oct
- ☎ +33 (0)4-28459407
- @ campingsandrans@numericable.fr

1	ADE**JM**NOPQRST	A**N** 6
2	DGIPRSVWXY	ABDE**FG**H 7
3	BLQ	BDFNOQRSV 8
4	DFHINO	BEV 9
5	ADEHJKN	ABFGHJOR 10

| 10A CEE | ❶ €19.45 |
| 2ha 75**T**(80-120m²) 20**P** | ❷ €28.45 |

📧 Sandrans is about 6 km south of Chatillon-sur-Chalaronne. In the centre of Sandrons, at the church, head towards St. Trivier-sur-Mer, D27. After 700m the campsite is on the left.

💬 Peacefully located in the heart of Dombes with thousands of lakes, this level campsite with spacious pitches is next to a 5ha lake. It has a bar-restaurant with terrace. Good cycling at L'Ain à Vélo. Parc des Oiseaux and medieval city of Pérouges. Free wifi.

🎫 1/4-5/7 23/8-30/10 7=6, 14=12

📍 N 46°3'40'' E 4°58'21''

www.eurocampings.co.uk/123107

France

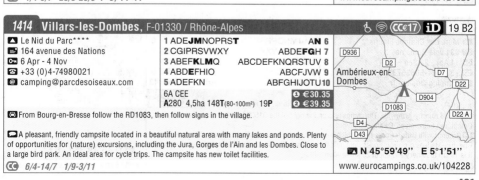

1413 Trévoux, F-01600 / Rhône-Alpes

🦽 📶 ♻ (CC€17) **iD** 19 B2

- 🔺 Sites & Paysages Kanopee Village***
- 🏕 rue Robert Baltié
- 📅 1 Apr - 30 Sep
- ☎ +33 (0)4-74084483
- @ contact@kanopee-village.com

1	ADEJMNOPQRST	ABFGHI 6
2	CPVXY	ABDE 7
3	ALQ	ABCDFNPV 8
4	ABDEFGHIN	EJLUVW 9
5	ABDJ	ACDGHIJ**P**RW 10

| 10A CEE | ❶ €28.10 |
| **A**178 2,5ha 160**T**(100-140m²) 22**P** | ❷ €36.20 |

📧 From the north A46 exit 2 (Trévoux). Follow signs to town. Campsite signposted. From the south A6 take exit 32.

💬 This campsite on the edge of the River Saône is just 30 km from Lyon. Camping pitches for tents, caravans and motorhomes in natural surroundings.

🎫 1/4-5/7 25/8-29/9 7=6, 14=11

📍 N 45°56'21'' E 4°46'6''

www.eurocampings.co.uk/121826

1414 Villars-les-Dombes, F-01330 / Rhône-Alpes

🦽 📶 (CC€17) **iD** 19 B2

- 🔺 Le Nid du Parc****
- 🏕 164 avenue des Nations
- 📅 6 Apr - 4 Nov
- ☎ +33 (0)4-74980021
- @ camping@parcdesoiseaux.com

1	ADE**JM**NOPRS**T**	A**N** 6
2	CGIPRSVWXY	ABDE**FG**H 7
3	ABEF**KLM**Q	ABCDEFKNQRSTUV 8
4	ABD**E**FHIO	ABCFJVW 9
5	ADEFKN	ABFGHIJOTU 10

| 6A CEE | ❶ €30.35 |
| **A**280 4,5ha 148**T**(80-100m²) 19**P** | ❷ €39.35 |

📧 From Bourg-en-Bresse follow the RD1083, then follow signs in the village.

💬 A pleasant, friendly campsite located in a beautiful natural area with many lakes and ponds. Plenty of opportunities for (nature) excursions, including the Jura, Gorges de l'Ain and les Dombes. Close to a large bird park. An ideal area for cycle trips. The campsite has new toilet facilities.

🎫 6/4-14/7 1/9-3/11

📍 N 45°59'49'' E 5°1'51''

www.eurocampings.co.uk/104228

1415 Vonnas, F-01540 / Rhône-Alpes

CC€15 iD 19 B2

- Le Renom***
- 240 avenue des Sports
- 31 Mar - 30 Sep
- +33 (0)4-74500275
- @ campingvonnas@wanadoo.fr

1 ADE**JM**NOPQRST	ABFGH**N** 6
2 CPVWX	ABDE**FGH** 7
3 AEL**MQ**	ABCDFNRSV 8
4 DHINO	EFV 9
5 ADEHKN	ABFGHJPR 10

16A CEE ❶ €24.70
2,6ha 82**T**(80-100m²) 20**P** ❷ €33.30

Campsite is signposted in the town of Vonnas.

The campsite is located 300 metres from the centre of Vonnas with many amenities in the Bresse region, which is known for its good food. The site is located beside two rivers, has spacious pitches marked out by hedges which are about 2 metres high and is filled with flowers. Free wifi.

CC 31/3-29/6 17/8-29/9

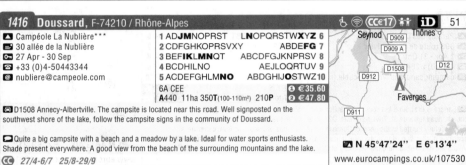

Mâcon
Saint-Didier-sur-Chalaronne

N 46°13'15'' E 4°59'15''
www.eurocampings.co.uk/121612

1416 Doussard, F-74210 / Rhône-Alpes

CC€17 iD 51

- Campéole La Nublière***
- 30 allée de la Nublière
- 27 Apr - 30 Sep
- +33 (0)4-50443344
- @ nubliere@campeole.com

1 AD**JM**NOPRST	L**N**OPQRSTW**XYZ** 6
2 CDFGHKOPRSVXY	ABDE**FG** 7
3 BEF**IKLMN**QT	ABCDFGJKNPRSV 8
4 BCDHILNO	AEJLOQRTUV 9
5 ACDEFGHLM**NO**	ABDGHIJ**O**STWZ 10

6A CEE ❶ €35.60
A440 11ha 350**T**(100-110m²) 210**P** ❷ €47.80

D1508 Annecy-Albertville. The campsite is located near this road. Well signposted on the southwest shore of the lake, follow the campsite signs in the community of Doussard.

Quite a big campsite with a beach and a meadow by a lake. Ideal for water sports enthusiasts. Shade present everywhere. A good view from the beach of the surrounding mountains and the lake.

CC 27/4-6/7 25/8-29/9

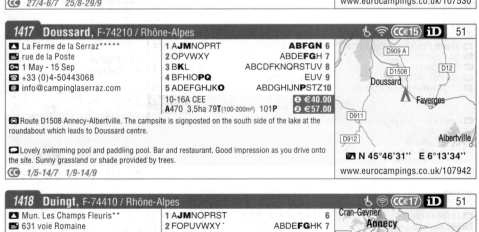

Seynod Thônes
Faverges

N 45°47'24'' E 6°13'4''
www.eurocampings.co.uk/107530

1417 Doussard, F-74210 / Rhône-Alpes

CC€15 iD 51

- La Ferme de la Serraz*****
- rue de la Poste
- 1 May - 15 Sep
- +33 (0)4-50443068
- @ info@campinglaserraz.com

1 A**JM**NOPRT	**ABFGN** 6
2 OPVWXY	ABDE**FGH** 7
3 B**KL**	ABCDFKNQRSTUV 8
4 BFHIO**PQ**	EUV 9
5 ADEFGHJK**O**	ABDGHIJN**P**STZ 10

10-16A CEE ❶ €40.00
A470 3,5ha 79**T**(100-200m²) 101**P** ❷ €57.00

Route D1508 Annecy-Albertville. The campsite is signposted on the south side of the lake at the roundabout which leads to Doussard centre.

Lovely swimming pool and paddling pool. Bar and restaurant. Good impression as you drive onto the site. Sunny grassland or shade provided by trees.

CC 1/5-14/7 1/9-14/9

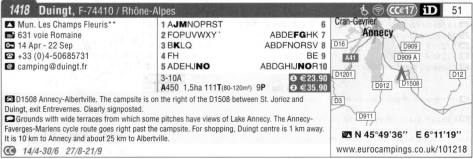

Doussard
Faverges
Albertville

N 45°46'31'' E 6°13'34''
www.eurocampings.co.uk/107942

1418 Duingt, F-74410 / Rhône-Alpes

CC€17 iD 51

- Mun. Les Champs Fleuris**
- 631 voie Romaine
- 14 Apr - 22 Sep
- +33 (0)4-50685731
- @ camping@duingt.fr

1 A**JM**NOPRST	6
2 FOPUVWXY '	ABDE**FG**HK 7
3 B**KL**Q	ABDFNORSV 8
4 FH	BE 9
5 ADEHJ**NO**	ABDGHIJ**NO**R 10

3-10A ❶ €23.90
A450 1,5ha 111**T**(80-120m²) 9**P** ❷ €35.90

D1508 Annecy-Albertville. The campsite is on the right of the D1508 between St. Jorioz and Duingt, exit Entrevernes. Clearly signposted.

Grounds with wide terraces from which some pitches have views of Lake Annecy. The Annecy-Faverges-Marlens cycle route goes right past the campsite. For shopping, Duingt centre is 1 km away. It is 10 km to Annecy and about 25 km to Albertville.

CC 14/4-30/6 27/8-21/9

Cran-Gevrier
Annecy

N 45°49'36'' E 6°11'19''
www.eurocampings.co.uk/101218

1419 Excenevex-Plage, F-74140 / Rhône-Alpes

♿ 📶 CC€17 🚻 iD 20 A2

- 🏕 Campéole La Pinède***
- ✉ 10 avenue de la Pinède
- 📅 27 Apr - 30 Sep
- ☎ +33 (0)4-50728505
- @ pinede@campeole.com

1 ADEILNOPRST	ABCDFGLMNOQSW**XY**Z	6
2 BDGHIOPQVXY	ABDE**FG**H	7
3 BE**GILM**QT	ABCDFNORS	8
4 BCDEFILNO**TUXYZ**	EJMOTV	9
5 ACD	ABGHIJ**PR**Z	10
16A CEE		❶ €36.60
A380 12ha 246T 386P		❷ €48.80

🚗 N5 Genève direction Thonon-les-Bains. Before Bonnatrait turn left to Yvoire/Excenevex. The campsite is 500 metres to the right after the roundabout.
💬 A large family campsite set in a wood right next to Lake Geneva with its sandy beaches. Quite secluded but with all amenities next to the entrance. Pitches spread out among the permanent camp facilities.
CC 27/4-6/7 25/8-29/9

📍 N 46°20'45'' E 6°21'29''
www.eurocampings.co.uk/101465

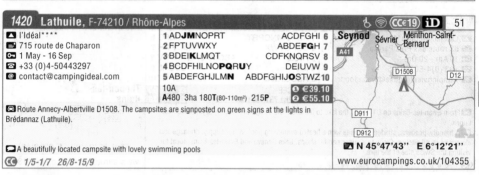

1420 Lathuile, F-74210 / Rhône-Alpes

♿ 📶 CC€19 iD 51

- 🏕 l'Idéal****
- ✉ 715 route de Chaparon
- 📅 1 May - 16 Sep
- ☎ +33 (0)4-50443297
- @ contact@campingideal.com

1 AD**JM**NOPRT	ACDFGHI	6
2 FPTUVWXY	ABDE**FG**H	7
3 BDEI**K**LMQT	CDFKNQRSV	8
4 BCDFHILNO**PQRU**Y	DEIUVW	9
5 ABDEFGHJLM**N**	ABDFGHIJ**O**STWZ	10
10A		❶ €39.10
A480 3ha 180T(80-110m²) 215P		❷ €55.10

🚗 Route Annecy-Albertville D1508. The campsites are signposted on green signs at the lights in Brédannaz (Lathuile).

💬 A beautifully located campsite with lovely swimming pools
CC 1/5-1/7 26/8-15/9

📍 N 45°47'43'' E 6°12'21''
www.eurocampings.co.uk/104355

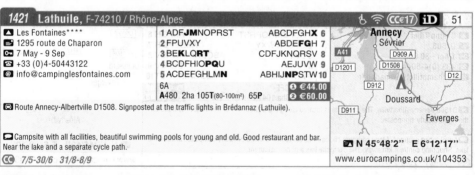

1421 Lathuile, F-74210 / Rhône-Alpes

♿ 📶 CC€17 iD 51

- 🏕 Les Fontaines****
- ✉ 1295 route de Chaparon
- 📅 7 May - 9 Sep
- ☎ +33 (0)4-50443122
- @ info@campinglesfontaines.com

1 ADF**JM**NOPRST	ABCDFGH**X**	6
2 FPUVXY	ABDE**FG**H	7
3 BE**K**LQR**T**	CDFJKNQRSV	8
4 BCDFHIO**PQU**	AEJUVW	9
5 ACDEFGHLM**N**	ABHIJ**NP**STW	10
6A		❶ €44.00
A480 2ha 105T(80-100m²) 65P		❷ €60.00

🚗 Route Annecy-Albertville D1508. Signposted at the traffic lights in Brédannaz (Lathuile).

💬 Campsite with all facilities, beautiful swimming pools for young and old. Good restaurant and bar. Near the lake and a separate cycle path.
CC 7/5-30/6 31/8-8/9

📍 N 45°48'2'' E 6°12'17''
www.eurocampings.co.uk/104353

1422 Le Grand-Bornand, F-74450 / Rhône-Alpes

⛷ ♿ 📶 CC€19 iD 20 A2

- 🏕 l'Escale***
- ✉ 33 chemin du Plein Air
- 📅 18/5 - 23/9, 21/12 - 8/4
- ☎ +33 (0)4-50022069
- @ contact@campinglescale.com

1 AD**JM**NOPQRST	ABEFG**N**	6
2 CFOPRUVWX	ABDE**FG**H	7
3 B**I**KLMQ**RS**	CDEFIJKNQRSTUV	8
4 FHI**J**LOP**QU**	EGHIJUVW	9
5 ADFHJLM**O**	ABDFGHIJLNORVXZ	10
2-10A CEE		❶ €34.10
A900 3,2ha 142T(80-100m²) 63P		❷ €48.30

🚗 A41 exit Annecy-Nord, then direction Thônes. In Thônes head for St. Jean-de-Sixt. Go towards Le Grand-Bornand at the roundabout. Turn right before the centre towards 'Vallée du Bouchet'. Campsite 1 km on the right.
💬 Campsite 150 metres from the centre of Le Grand-Bornand. Combined 240 m² indoor and outdoor swimming pool. Restaurant is located in an old farmhouse in traditional Savoy style. New toilet facilities and free wifi.
CC 28/3-7/4 18/5-6/7 31/8-22/9

📍 N 45°56'26'' E 6°25'40''
www.eurocampings.co.uk/104340

France

1423 Les Contamines-Montjoie, F-74170 / Rhône-Alpes
⛷ ⚲ 📶 (CC€17) iD 20 A2

- ⛰ Le Pontet***
- 🏠 2485 rte de Notre Dame de la Gorge
- 📅 1/1 - 23/9, 22/12 - 31/12
- ☎ +33 (0)4-50470404
- @ campinglepontet74@orange.fr

1 ADJMNOPQRST	LMN 6
2 CDFGHIOPRVWXY	ABDEFGH 7
3 AEGHILMNQRSTU	ABCDFJNOQRSV 8
4 FIO	J 9
5 ABDEGJKMNO	ABGHIJOR10

2-10A   ❶ €22.60
A1200 2,8ha 150T(90-120m²) 13P   ❷ €30.40

🛣 A40 exit St. Gervais, direction St. Gervais-centre. Another 9 km past the centre to Les Contamines. Site is located 3 km beyond the centre on the left of the D902, the Route de Notre Dame de la Gorge.

💬 A campsite for winter and summer. You can go for mountain walks as early as April. Ideal base for touring Mont Blanc.

CC 1/4-9/7   27/8-22/9

📍 N 45°48'9''   E 6°43'19''

www.eurocampings.co.uk/104339

1424 Lugrin, F-74500 / Rhône-Alpes
⚲ 📶 (CC€17) iD 20 A2

- ⛰ La Vieille-Eglise***
- 🏠 53 route des Prés Parrau
- 📅 10 Apr - 20 Oct
- ☎ +33 (0)4-50760195
- @ campingvieilleeglise@wanadoo.fr

1 ADEJMNOPRT	ABFG 6
2 FGPUVWX	ABDFGH 7
3 AILQ	ABCDFIJNQRSTUV 8
4 IOP	BDEHL 9
5 ABDGHNO	ABDHIJPRZ10

4-10A CEE   ❶ €27.90
A437 2ha 73T(100-120m²) 32P   ❷ €39.10

🛣 From Evian-les-Bains on D1005 by the lake to the east. The campsite is clearly signposted near Lugrin.

💬 A friendly, peaceful, shaded campsite with a heated swimming pool. Water supply, drainage and electricity on all pitches. Close to a supermarket, shops, Lake Geneva and Evian-les-Bains. Ideal for visiting the Swiss side of the lake.

CC 10/4-8/7   26/8-19/10   7=6, 14=12, 21=18

📍 N 46°24'2''   E 6°38'48''

www.eurocampings.co.uk/111349

1425 Marlens, F-74210 / Rhône-Alpes
⚲ 📶 (CC€17) iD 20 A2

- ⛰ Champ Tillet***
- 🏠 D1508
- 📅 1 Apr - 30 Oct
- ☎ +33 (0)4-50443374
- @ duchamptillet@wanadoo.fr

1 ADFJMNOPRST	ABFGH 6
2 OPQRVWXY	ABDEFGH 7
3 BKLQS	ABCDFJKNQRSV 8
4 HNO	BEJUV 9
5 ADFGHLN	ABDGHIKNOST10

6-10A CEE   ❶ €37.40
A470 3ha 104T(80-110m²) 29P   ❷ €50.40

🛣 D1508 Annecy-Albertville. The campsite is located along the D1508, about 4 km past Faverges on the right. Clearly signposted.

💬 Level, open grounds. Many campers choose this campsite to avoid the busy campsites around the lake. Shopping centre 4 km away. The campsite has a good restaurant.

CC 1/4-6/7   25/8-29/10

📍 N 45°45'43''   E 6°20'12''

www.eurocampings.co.uk/104356

1426 Neydens, F-74160 / Rhône-Alpes
⚲ 📶 ✿ (CC€19) iD 20 A2

- ⛰ Sites & Paysages La Colombière****
- 🏠 166 chemin Neuf
- 📅 28 Mar - 31 Oct
- ☎ +33 (0)4-50351314
- @ la.colombiere@wanadoo.fr

1 ADEJMNOPRST	ABEF 6
2 AFOPSVWX	ABDEFGHK 7
3 ABCELQRT	ABCDEFJKLNQRSTUV 8
4 ABDEFGHILNOQTUVX	EJKLVWZ 9
5 ABDFGHJLMN	ABDFGHIJPRVXZ10

10-16A   ❶ €39.70
A560 2,3ha 113T(80-120m²) 83P   ❷ €47.70

🛣 From Lausanne follow signs to France. From Macon the A40. Exit St. Julien. Follow the green signs to Annecy, D1201 to the village Neydens/campsite.

💬 Pitches marked out by overgrowth. Peaceful location but close to Geneva. The warden organises guided visits to Geneva, including in the low season (min. 6 participants). Indoor pool and excellent restaurant (open all year). Heated outdoor pool with children's section and jacuzzi, also sauna and hammam.

CC 28/3-6/7   24/8-30/10

📍 N 46°7'11''   E 6°6'19''

www.eurocampings.co.uk/104326

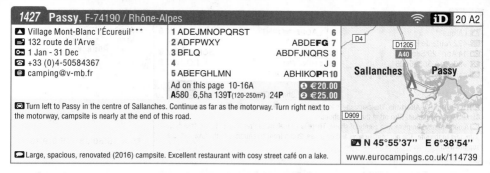

1427 Passy, F-74190 / Rhône-Alpes

🛰 iD 20 A2

- 🏔 Village Mont-Blanc l'Écureuil★★★
- 🚏 132 route de l'Arve
- 🔓 1 Jan - 31 Dec
- ☎ +33 (0)4-50584367
- @ camping@v-mb.fr

1 ADEJMNOPQRST		6
2 ADFPWXY	ABDEFG	7
3 BFLQ	ABDFJNQRS	8
4	J	9
5 ABEFGHLMN	ABHIKOPR	10

Ad on this page 10-16A   ❶ €20.00
A580 6,5ha 139T(120-250m²) 24P   ❷ €25.00

🔄 Turn left to Passy in the centre of Sallanches. Continue as far as the motorway. Turn right next to the motorway, campsite is nearly at the end of this road.

🏕 Large, spacious, renovated (2016) campsite. Excellent restaurant with cosy street café on a lake.

Sallanches   **Passy**

D4   D1205   A40   D909

🗺 N 45°55'37''   E 6°38'54''
www.eurocampings.co.uk/114739

Village Mont-Blanc l'Écureuil ★★★
Pays du Mont Blanc

The campsite "Village Mont-Blanc l'Ecureuil" is located in the heart of the Mont-Blanc area, facing the massif, offering one of the most beautiful panoramas. Open all year, it is ideally located 600m from the lake of Passy, 2 km from the town center of Sallanches and its shops.

132 route de l'Arve, 74190 Passy
Tel. 04-50584367
E-mail: camping@v-mb.fr
Internet: www.vacances-mont-blanc.com

France

1428 Samoëns, F-74340 / Rhône-Alpes

🎿 ♿ 🛰 CCe17 iD 20 A2

- 🏔 Camping Caravaneige Le Giffre★★★
- 🚏 1064 route du Lac aux Dames
- 🔓 1 Jan - 31 Dec
- ☎ +33 (0)4-50344192
- @ camping.samoens@wanadoo.fr

1 ADEJMNOPRST	ABHNU	6
2 CDFGOPRVWXY	ABDEFG	7
3 BCEGLMQR	ABCDEFJNOQRSTUV	8
4 HP	AEJ	9
5 DGKN	ABDFGHIKLNPRVZ	10

6-10A CEE   ❶ €26.35
A765 6,9ha 212T(80-110m²) 43P   ❷ €32.55

🔄 Towards Samoëns via D907. Then follow campsite signs.
🏕 A beautiful site on level ground beside a river. Marked-out pitches. Separate area for small tents. Several trees. Municipal swimming pool and tennis courts right beside the site (free for campsite guests). Small lake near the site with all types of sports facilities. Ice rink in winter also free. Village of Samoëns with its alpine garden within walking distance. Very suitable for winter sports.

CC 6/1-2/2 28/4-29/6 25/8-14/12

D902   Taninges   Cluses   Magland   A40

🗺 N 46°4'38''   E 6°43'7''
www.eurocampings.co.uk/101467

1429 Sévrier, F-74320 / Rhône-Alpes

♿ 🛰 CCe17 iD 51

- 🏔 Au Coeur du Lac★★★
- 🚏 3233 route d'Albertville
- 🔓 29 Mar - 30 Sep
- ☎ +33 (0)4-50524645
- @ info@aucoeurdulac.com

1 ADJKNOPRST	LNQSWX	6
2 ADFGOPTUVWXY	ABDEFGH	7
3 AFILMNPQT	ABCDEFJNORSTUV	8
4 DEFHIO	ERUV	9
5 ABDFGJNO	ABFGHIOSTW	10

5-16A CEE   ❶ €30.50
A465 1,7ha 73T(70-100m²) 10P   ❷ €41.00

🔄 Route Annecy-Albertville. From Annecy; when leaving Sévrier left of the D1508, 500 metres past McDonalds.
🏕 Located right by the lake 4 km from Annecy in the small village of Sevrier, 40 km from Geneva. Camping pitches on terraces. Some have views of the lake and the mountains. The campsite has direct access to a 24 km paved, traffic-free cycle path. This is also the best way to get to Annecy without traffic tailbacks (approx. 15 minutes by bike).

CC 29/3-7/7 25/8-29/9

Cran-Gevrier   **Annecy**   D909
D16   A41   D1508
D1201   D912   D909 A
D3

🗺 N 45°51'17''   E 6°8'39''
www.eurocampings.co.uk/100414

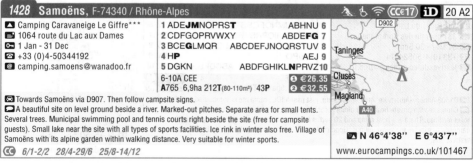
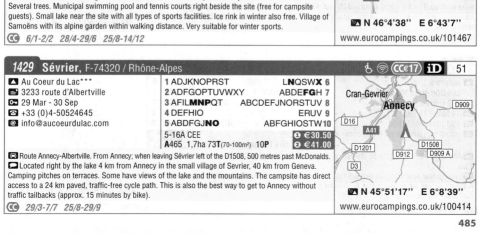

1430 Sévrier, F-74320 / Rhône-Alpes ♿ ⓦ (CC€17) iD 51

- ▲ l'Aloua**
- ⛺ 492 route de Piron
- 📅 14 Apr - 29 Sep
- ☎ +33 (0)4-50526006
- @ camping-de-l-aloua@orange.fr

1 ADF**I**KNOPRT	X 6
2 AOPRVWXY	ABD**FGH** 7
3 A**K**LQ	BDFNQRSV 8
4 HINO**PQ**	EQUVW 9
5 ADEFGHJN**O**	ABGHIKOSTW 10

| 6-10A | ❶ €25.20 |
| A465 2,3ha 173**T**(90-130m²) 11**P** | ❷ €39.10 |

🅿 D1508 Annecy-Albertville. The campsite is located between Sévrier and St. Jorioz, behind the Carrefour supermarket. Turn off at the roundabout.
💬 A quiet family campsite with plenty of shade. There is a small nature reserve and a car-free cycle path next to the site. The pitches are level and on grass. 200m from an entrance to the lake and to a supermarket.

© 14/4-7/7 26/8-28/9

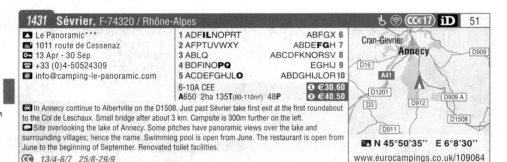

N 45°50'38'' E 6°9'13''

www.eurocampings.co.uk/104345

1431 Sévrier, F-74320 / Rhône-Alpes ♿ ⓦ (CC€17) iD 51

- ▲ Le Panoramic***
- ⛺ 1011 route de Cessenaz
- 📅 13 Apr - 30 Sep
- ☎ +33 (0)4-50524309
- @ info@camping-le-panoramic.com

1 ADF**IL**NOPRT	ABFGX 6
2 AFPTUVWXY	ABDE**FGH** 7
3 A**B**LQ	ABCDFKNORSV 8
4 BDFINO**PQ**	EGHIJ 9
5 ACDEFGHJL**O**	ABDGHIJLOR 10

| 6-10A CEE | ❶ €30.60 |
| A650 2ha 135**T**(80-110m²) 48**P** | ❷ €40.50 |

🅿 In Annecy continue to Albertville on the D1508. Just past Sévrier take first exit at the first roundabout to the Col de Leschaux. Small bridge after about 3 km. Campsite is 300m further on the left.
💬 Site overlooking the lake of Annecy. Some pitches have panoramic views over the lake and surrounding villages; hence the name. Swimming pool is open from June. The restaurant is open from June to the beginning of September. Renovated toilet facilities.

© 13/4-6/7 25/8-29/9

N 45°50'35'' E 6°8'30''

www.eurocampings.co.uk/109064

1432 Sévrier, F-74320 / Rhône-Alpes ♿ ⓦ (CC€19) iD 51

- ▲ Les Rives du Lac***
- ⛺ 331 chemin des Communaux
- 📅 31 Mar - 30 Sep
- ☎ +33 (0)4-50524014
- @ lesrivesdulac-annecy@ffcc.fr

1 ADEJMNOPQRST	LMNQSW**X**YZ 6
2 ADFGHIOPRSVWX	ABDE**FGH** 7
3 BF**GH**LQT	ABCDEFGIJKNQRSTV 8
4 HIPQ	BEV 9
5 A**N**	ABCDFGHIJPTUVZ 10

| 10A CEE | ❶ €30.00 |
| A470 1,5ha 100**T**(80-100m²) 25**P** | ❷ €41.40 |

🅿 D1508 Annecy-Albertville. After about 5 km, just past 'LIDL', campsite is signposted on left.
💬 Campsite with private beach and direct access to Annecy lake. Very modern and well maintained toilet facilities. There is a boat ramp and 20 berths for boat owners. You can rent bicycles at the campsite to explore the surroundings. Good cycle paths from the campsite. All kinds of options for watersports.

© 31/3-29/6 3/9-29/9

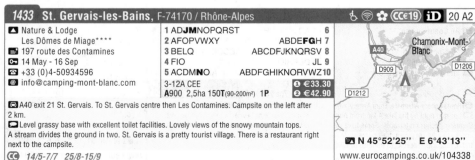

N 45°50'55'' E 6°9'4''

www.eurocampings.co.uk/121753

1433 St. Gervais-les-Bains, F-74170 / Rhône-Alpes ♿ ⓦ ✿ (CC€19) iD 20 A2

- ▲ Nature & Lodge
  Les Dômes de Miage****
- ⛺ 197 route des Contamines
- 📅 14 May - 16 Sep
- ☎ +33 (0)4-50934596
- @ info@camping-mont-blanc.com

1 AD**J**MNOPQRST	6
2 AFOPVWXY	ABDE**FGH** 7
3 BELQ	ABCDFJKNQRSV 8
4 FIO	JL 9
5 ACDM**N**O	ABDFGHIKNORVWZ 10

| 3-12A CEE | ❶ €33.30 |
| A900 2,5ha 150**T**(90-200m²) 1**P** | ❷ €42.90 |

🅿 A40 exit 21 St. Gervais. To St. Gervais centre then Les Contamines. Campsite on the left after 2 km.
💬 Level grassy base with excellent toilet facilities. Lovely views of the snowy mountain tops.
A stream divides the ground in two. St. Gervais is a pretty tourist village. There is a restaurant right next to the campsite.

© 14/5-7/7 25/8-15/9

N 45°52'25'' E 6°43'13''

www.eurocampings.co.uk/104338

1434 St. Jorioz, F-74410 / Rhône-Alpes ♿ 🛜 (CC€17) iD 51

- ⛺ Europa****
- 🏠 1444 route d'Albertville
- 📅 28 Apr - 14 Sep
- ☎ +33 (0)4-50685101
- @ info@camping-europa.com

1 ADILNOPRT	ABFGHIX	6
2 AFOPVXY	ABDEFGH	7
3 BDEKLQR	ABDFKNQRSTUV	8
4 BFHILNOUY	EJUV	9
5 ADGHL	ABDHILPT	10

Ad on this page 6A CEE
A450 3,2ha 141T(80-100m²) 59P

❶ €45.80
❷ €62.80

🚗 D1508 Annecy-Albertville. The campsite is located along this road, just past St. Jorioz it is the second site on the right hand side.

💬 An excellent site 400m from the lake, 9 km from Annecy. The lovely leisure pool has 3 open-air pools with additional facilities (deckchairs with water massage), slides and child-friendly water games. Excellent restaurant. Direct access to a cycle path beside the lake. Comfort pitches for an extra fee.

CC 30/4-6/7 27/8-13/9

Cran-Gevrier
Annecy
D16 · D909 · A41 · D909 A · D1201 · D912 · D1508 · D12 · D3 · D911

📍 N 45°49'48'' E 6°10'54''

www.eurocampings.co.uk/104349

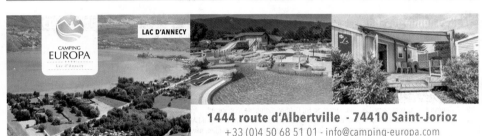

LAC D'ANNECY

CAMPING EUROPA
Lac d'Annecy

1444 route d'Albertville - 74410 Saint-Jorioz
+33 (0)4 50 68 51 01 - info@camping-europa.com

www.camping-europa.com f

1435 St. Jorioz, F-74410 / Rhône-Alpes ♿ 🛜 (CC€19) iD 51

- ⛺ International du Lac d'Annecy****
- 🏠 1184 route d'Albertville (D1508)
- 📅 14 Apr - 15 Sep
- ☎ +33 (0)4-50686793
- @ contact@camping-lac-annecy.com

1 ADJMNOPRT	ABFGHI	6
2 AFOPVWXY	ABDFGH	7
3 AEKLQS	ABCDFKNQRSTUV	8
4 BCDHILNO	BEJLUV	9
5 ADEFGHK	ABDHIPT	10

6-10A CEE
A450 2,5ha 110T(85-110m²) 49P

❶ €43.80
❷ €60.80

🚗 D1508 Annecy-Albertville. Campsite located on this road, just past the centre of St. Jorioz.

💬 Campsite with excellent toilet facilities in an attractively lit building. Shaded pitches 400m from Lake Annecy and 1 km from the beach. Heated, child-friendly and tropical leisure pool with slide. Direct access to a secure cycle path.

CC 14/4-5/7 27/8-14/9

Cran-Gevrier
Annecy
D16 · D909 · A41 · D909 A · D1201 · D912 · D1508 · D12 · D3 · D911

📍 N 45°49'51'' E 6°10'42''

www.eurocampings.co.uk/104348

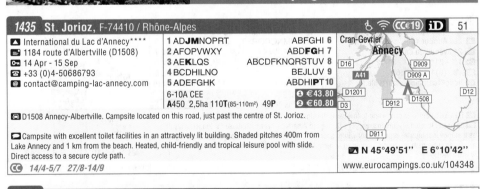

1436 St. Jorioz, F-74410 / Rhône-Alpes ♿ 🛜 (CC€17) iD 51

- ⛺ Le Crêtoux***
- 🏠 1059 route d'Entredozon
- 📅 1 Apr - 15 Nov
- ☎ +33 (0)4-50686194
- @ info@campinglecretoux.com

1 ADJMNORT	N	6
2 FPTUVWXY	ABDEFGH	7
3 BKL	ABCDFJKNORSV	8
4 IO	DEFIJ	9
5 ADO	ABDFGHJNOST	10

3-10A
A575 6ha 75T(100-120m²) 15P

❶ €25.80
❷ €34.05

🚗 D1508 Annecy-Albertville. At traffic lights in St. Jorioz D10a direction St. Eustache. Signposted (about 2 km). Short, steep access road.

💬 A basic campsite in natural surroundings on a hill just outside the centre of St. Jorioz. Views over Annecy Lake from certain pitches. The site is recommended for anyone who appreciates peace and nature. The fairly steep access road is short, but not a problem.

CC 1/4-7/7 25/8-14/11

Meythet · Annecy · D16 · D909
Seynod
D1201 · A41 · D909 A · D3 · D912 · D1508 · D911

📍 N 45°49'4'' E 6°8'49''

www.eurocampings.co.uk/104350

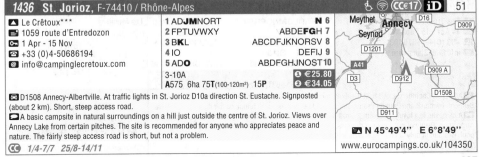

1437 St. Jorioz, F-74410 / Rhône-Alpes

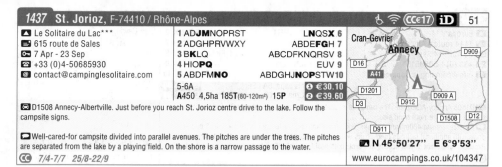

♿ 📶 (CC€17) iD 51

- 🏕 Le Solitaire du Lac***
- 📮 615 route de Sales
- 🗓 7 Apr - 23 Sep
- ☎ +33 (0)4-50685930
- @ contact@campinglesolitaire.com

1 ADJMNOPRST	LNQSX 6
2 ADGHPRVWXY	ABDEFGH 7
3 BKLQ	ABCDFKNQRSV 8
4 HIOPQ	EUV 9
5 ABDFMNO	ABDGHJNOPSTW10
5-6A	❶ €30.10
A450 4,5ha 185T(80-120m²) 15P	❷ €39.60

🚗 D1508 Annecy-Albertville. Just before you reach St. Jorioz centre drive to the lake. Follow the campsite signs.

💬 Well-cared-for campsite divided into parallel avenues. The pitches are under the trees. The pitches are separated from the lake by a playing field. On the shore is a narrow passage to the water.
CC 7/4-7/7 25/8-22/9

📍 N 45°50'27'' E 6°9'53''
www.eurocampings.co.uk/104347

1438 Thonon-les-Bains, F-74200 / Rhône-Alpes

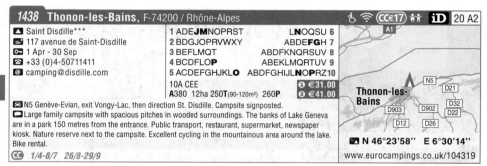

♿ 📶 (CC€17) 👫 iD 20 A2

- 🏕 Saint Disdille***
- 📮 117 avenue de Saint-Disdille
- 🗓 1 Apr - 30 Sep
- ☎ +33 (0)4-50711411
- @ camping@disdille.com

1 ADEJMNOPRST	LNOQSU 6
2 BDGJOPRVWXY	ABDEFGH 7
3 BEFLMQT	ABDFKNQRSUV 8
4 BCDFLOP	ABEKLMQRTUV 9
5 ACDEFGHJKLO	ABDFGHIJLNOPRZ10
10A CEE	❶ €31.00
A380 12ha 250T(90-120m²) 260P	❷ €41.00

🚗 N5 Genève-Evian, exit Vongy-Lac, then direction St. Disdille. Campsite signposted.
💬 Large family campsite with spacious pitches in wooded surroundings. The banks of Lake Geneva are in a park 150 metres from the entrance. Public transport, restaurant, supermarket, newspaper kiosk. Nature reserve next to the campsite. Excellent cycling in the mountainous area around the lake. Bike rental.
CC 1/4-8/7 26/8-29/9

📍 N 46°23'58'' E 6°30'14''
www.eurocampings.co.uk/104319

1439 Albertville, F-73200 / Rhône-Alpes

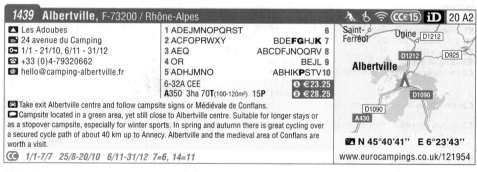

⛷ ♿ 📶 (CC€15) iD 20 A2

- 🏕 Les Adoubes
- 📮 24 avenue du Camping
- 🗓 1/1 - 21/10, 6/11 - 31/12
- ☎ +33 (0)4-79320662
- @ hello@camping-albertville.fr

1 ADEJMNOPQRST	6
2 ACFOPRWXY	BDEFGHJK 7
3 AEQ	ABCDFJNOQRV 8
4 OR	BEJL 9
5 ADHJMNO	ABHIKPSTV10
6-32A CEE	❶ €23.25
A350 3ha 70T(100-120m²) 15P	❷ €28.25

🚗 Take exit Albertville centre and follow campsite signs or Médiévale de Conflans.
💬 Campsite located in a green area, yet still close to Albertville centre. Suitable for longer stays or as a stopover campsite, especially for winter holidays. In spring and autumn there is great cycling over a secured cycle path of about 40 km up to Annecy. Albertville and the medieval area of Conflans are worth a visit.
CC 1/1-7/7 25/8-20/10 6/11-31/12 7=6, 14=11

📍 N 45°40'41'' E 6°23'43''
www.eurocampings.co.uk/121954

1440 Belmont-Tramonet, F-73330 / Rhône-Alpes

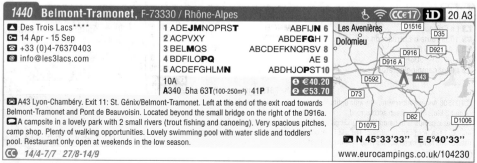

♿ 📶 (CC€17) iD 20 A3

- 🏕 Des Trois Lacs****
- 🗓 14 Apr - 15 Sep
- ☎ +33 (0)4-76370403
- @ info@les3lacs.com

1 ADEJMNOPRST	ABFIJN 6
2 ACPVXY	ABDEFGH 7
3 BELMQS	ABCDEFKNQRSV 8
4 BDFILOPQ	AE 9
5 ACDEFGHLMN	ABDHJOPST10
10A	❶ €40.20
A340 5ha 63T(100-250m²) 41P	❷ €53.70

🚗 A43 Lyon-Chambéry. Exit 11: St. Génix/Belmont-Tramonet. Left at the end of the exit road towards Belmont-Tramonet and Pont de Beauvoisin. Located beyond the small bridge on the right of the D916a.
💬 A campsite in a lovely park with 2 small rivers (trout fishing and canoeing). Very spacious pitches, camp shop. Plenty of walking opportunities. Lovely swimming pool with water slide and toddlers' pool. Restaurant only open at weekends in the low season.
CC 14/4-7/7 27/8-14/9

📍 N 45°33'33'' E 5°40'33''
www.eurocampings.co.uk/104230

1441 Bourg-St-Maurice, F-73700 / Rhône-Alpes

▲ Huttopia Bourg-St-Maurice***
🛏 route des Arcs
📅 25 May - 21 Oct
☎ +33 (0)4-79070345
@ bourgsaintmaurice@huttopia.com

1 ADJMNOPQRST	ABFNUV 6
2 CFPSVWX	ABDEFGH 7
3 BEFLMNQ	ABCDFGJKQRSV 8
4 BDEFIO	BCEJ 9
5 ADFGNO	ABFGHIKLNOTUV 10

10A CEE
A840 5ha 153T(50-200m²) 45P
❶ €27.30
❷ €37.90

🚗 From Albertville via Moutiers to Bourg-St-Maurice. Turn right at the station direction Les Arcs. Then continue for about 300 metres.

💬 Within walking distance of the centre and a supermarket. Level grounds shaded by several trees. Fully refurbished toilet facilities, also geared up to winter sports. New swimming pool and playground.
CC 25/5-6/7 2/9-20/10

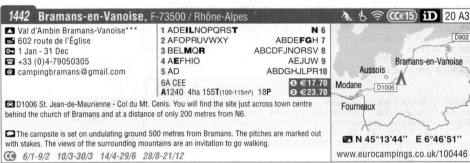

20 A3
N 45°37'21'' E 6°47'6''
www.eurocampings.co.uk/104359

1442 Bramans-en-Vanoise, F-73500 / Rhône-Alpes

▲ Val d'Ambin Bramans-Vanoise***
🛏 602 route de l'Église
📅 1 Jan - 31 Dec
☎ +33 (0)4-79050305
@ campingbramans@gmail.com

1 ADEILNOPQRST	N 6
2 AFOPRUVWXY	ABDEFGH 7
3 BELMQR	ABCDFJNORSV 8
4 AEFHIO	AEJUW 9
5 AD	ABDGHJLPR 10

6A CEE
A1240 4ha 155T(100-115m²) 18P
❶ €17.70
❷ €23.70

🚗 D1006 St. Jean-de-Maurienne - Col du Mt. Cenis. You will find the site just across town centre behind the church of Bramans and at a distance of only 200 metres from N6.

💬 The campsite is set on undulating ground 500 metres from Bramans. The pitches are marked out with stakes. The views of the surrounding mountains are an invitation to go walking.
CC 6/1-9/2 10/3-30/3 14/4-29/6 28/8-21/12

20 A3
N 45°13'44'' E 6°46'51''
www.eurocampings.co.uk/100446

1443 Challes-les-Eaux, F-73190 / Rhône-Alpes

▲ Municipal Le Savoy***
🛏 av. du Parc
📅 1 Apr - 30 Sep
☎ +33 (0)4-79729731
@ contact@
   camping-challesleseaux.com

1 ADEJMNORST	MN 6
2 ADJOPSVWX	ABDEFG 7
3 ALMNQ	ABCDEFJNQRSTUV 8
4 FHIO	EJ 9
5 ADEFHMNO	ABFGHIJPTUV 10

6-10A CEE
A287 2,8ha 66T(80-150m²) 12P
❶ €20.55
❷ €24.35

🚗 A43 Lyon-Chambéry. In Chambéry dir. Grenoble as far as Challes-les-Eaux exit. Then D1006 Albertville-Grenoble. Campsite located just before the centre on the left of the road.
💬 A quiet, well maintained campsite with spacious, partly marked-out pitches and paved roads. Heated toilet facilities by the entrance. Walking, cycling, swimming and fishing close by. Close to Chambéry. Snack bar is only open at weekends in the low season.
CC 1/4-7/7 2/9-29/9

20 A3
N 45°33'5'' E 5°59'3''
www.eurocampings.co.uk/100412

1444 Lanslevillard, F-73480 / Rhône-Alpes

▲ Camping Caravaneige de Val Cenis***
📅 26/5 - 30/9, 19/12 - 30/4
☎ +33 (0)4-79059052
@ campoland@orange.fr

1 ADEFILNOPQRST	6
2 CFOPRVW	ABDEFG 7
3 AELMQ	ABCDEFGJKNRSV 8
4 EFHIOT	9
5 ADEFGHKMNO	ABDGHJPR 10

10A CEE
A1450 2,5ha 86T(100-140m²) 30P
❶ €19.20
❷ €26.20

🚗 A43 exit Modané. Then D1006 direction Mont-Cenis. Campsite located on the left of the village.

💬 A spacious level campsite with 360° panorama views of the mountain range and village. All pitches are marked out. 200 metres from the ski lifts.
CC 8/1-9/2 12/3-19/4 26/5-13/7 31/8-29/9

20 B3
N 45°17'28'' E 6°54'32''
www.eurocampings.co.uk/113722

1445 Lépin-le-Lac, F-73610 / Rhône-Alpes

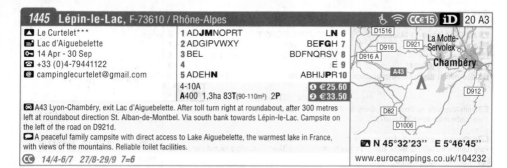

&♿ 🛜 (CC€15) iD 20 A3

- 🔺 Le Curtelet***
- 🏞 Lac d'Aiguebelette
- 🗓 14 Apr - 30 Sep
- ☎ +33 (0)4-79441122
- @ campinglecurtelet@gmail.com

1 ADJMNOPRT	L**N**	6
2 ADGIPVWXY	BE**FG**H	7
3 BEL	BDFNQRSV	8
4	E	9
5 ADEH**N**	ABHIJ**PR**	10
4-10A	❶ €25.60	
A400 1,3ha 83T(90-110m²) 2P	❷ €33.50	

🚗 A43 Lyon-Chambéry, exit Lac d'Aiguebelette. After toll turn right at roundabout, after 300 metres left at roundabout direction St. Alban-de-Montbel. Via south bank towards Lépin-le-Lac. Campsite on the left of the road on D921d.

💬 A peaceful family campsite with direct access to Lake Aiguebelette, the warmest lake in France, with views of the mountains. Reliable toilet facilities.

CC 14/4-6/7 27/8-29/9 7=6

🗺 N 45°32'23" E 5°46'45"

www.eurocampings.co.uk/104232

1446 Lépin-le-Lac, F-73610 / Rhône-Alpes

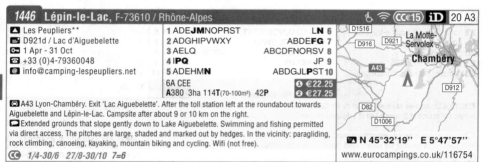

&♿ 🛜 (CC€15) iD 20 A3

- 🔺 Les Peupliers**
- 🏞 D921d / Lac d'Aiguebelette
- 🗓 1 Apr - 31 Oct
- ☎ +33 (0)4-79360048
- @ info@camping-lespeupliers.net

1 ADE**JM**NOPRST	L**N**	6
2 ADGHIPVWXY	ABDE**FG**	7
3 AELQ	ABCDFNORSV	8
4 I**PQ**	JP	9
5 ADEH**MN**	ABDGJL**P**ST	10
6A CEE	❶ €22.25	
A380 3ha 114T(70-100m²) 42P	❷ €27.25	

🚗 A43 Lyon-Chambéry. Exit 'Lac Aiguebelette'. After the toll station left at the roundabout towards Aiguebelette and Lépin-le-Lac. Campsite after about 9 or 10 km on the right.

💬 Extended grounds that slope gently down to Lake Aiguebelette. Swimming and fishing permitted via direct access. The pitches are large, shaded and marked out by hedges. In the vicinity: paragliding, rock climbing, canoeing, kayaking, mountain biking and cycling. Wifi (not free).

CC 1/4-30/6 27/8-30/10 7=6

🗺 N 45°32'19" E 5°47'57"

www.eurocampings.co.uk/116754

1447 Les Marches/Montmélian, F-73800 / Rhône-Alpes

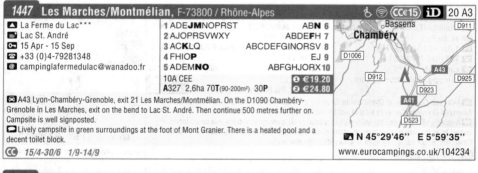

&♿ 🛜 (CC€15) iD 20 A3

- 🔺 La Ferme du Lac***
- 🏞 Lac St. André
- 🗓 15 Apr - 15 Sep
- ☎ +33 (0)4-79281348
- @ campinglafermedulac@wanadoo.fr

1 ADE**JM**NOPRST	AB**N**	6
2 AJOPRSVWXY	ABDE**F**H	7
3 AC**K**LQ	ABCDEFGINORSV	8
4 FHIO**P**	EJ	9
5 ADEM**NO**	ABFGHJORX	10
10A CEE	❶ €19.20	
A327 2,6ha 70T(90-200m²) 30P	❷ €24.80	

🚗 A43 Lyon-Chambéry-Grenoble, exit 21 Les Marches/Montmélian. On the D1090 Chambéry-Grenoble in Les Marches, exit on the bend to Lac St. André. Then continue 500 metres further on. Campsite is well signposted.

💬 Lively campsite in green surroundings at the foot of Mont Granier. There is a heated pool and a decent toilet block.

CC 15/4-30/6 1/9-14/9

🗺 N 45°29'46" E 5°59'35"

www.eurocampings.co.uk/104234

1448 St. Alban-de-Montbel, F-73610 / Rhône-Alpes

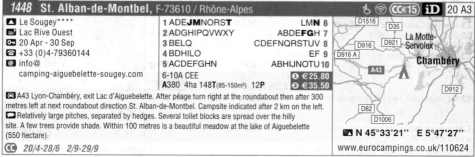

&♿ 🛜 (CC€15) iD 20 A3

- 🔺 Le Sougey****
- 🏞 Lac Rive Ouest
- 🗓 20 Apr - 30 Sep
- ☎ +33 (0)4-79360144
- @ info@ camping-aiguebelette-sougey.com

1 ADE**JM**NORS**T**	LM**N**	6
2 ADGHIPQVWXY	ABDE**FG**H	7
3 BELQ	CDEFNQRSTUV	8
4 BDHILO	EF	9
5 ACDEFGHN	ABHIJNOTU	10
6-10A CEE	❶ €25.80	
A380 4ha 148T(85-150m²) 12P	❷ €35.50	

🚗 A43 Lyon-Chambéry, exit Lac d'Aiguebelette. After péage turn right at the roundabout then after 300 metres left at next roundabout direction St. Alban-de-Montbel. Campsite indicated after 2 km on the left.

💬 Relatively large pitches, separated by hedges. Several toilet blocks are spread over the hilly site. A few trees provide shade. Within 100 metres is a beautiful meadow at the lake of Aiguebelette (550 hectare).

CC 20/4-28/6 2/9-29/9

🗺 N 45°33'21" E 5°47'27"

www.eurocampings.co.uk/110624

1449 St. Jean-de-Chevelu, F-73170 / Rhône-Alpes

& 🛜 CC€15 iD 20 A2

🏕 Camping des Lacs***
📅 28 Apr - 16 Sep
☎ +33 (0)6-59498394
@ campingdeslacs73@gmail.com

1 ADE**JM**NOPRS**T**	JLMN**Q**U 6
2 ACDFGHIOPVWXY	ABDE**FGH** 7
3 ALQ	ABCDEFIKNQRSV 8
4 **A**CEFHILO	AEF 9
5 ADEFHM**N**	BFGHJOR 10

16A CEE
A350 4ha 95**T**(100-150m²) 20**P**

❶ €26.70
❷ €36.70

🚗 A41 as far as Chambéry exit 13, N504 direction Aix-les-Bains tunnel direction Yenne, then D210 direction St. Jean-de-Chevelu; campsite signposted from there.

💬 A comfortable family campsite on the Saint-Jean-de-Chevelu lake, with large, shady pitches, patrolled beach, playground.

CC 28/4-6/7 25/8-15/9

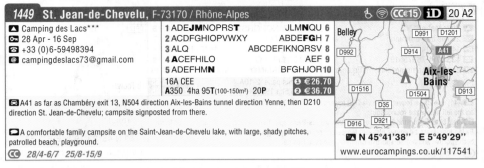

⬛ N 45°41'38'' E 5°49'29''

www.eurocampings.co.uk/117541

1450 St. Jean-de-Maurienne, F-73300 / Rhône-Alpes

& 🛜 CC€17 iD 20 A3

🏕 Des Grands Cols***
📧 422 ave du Mont-Cenis
📅 10 May - 22 Sep
☎ +33 (0)9-52174655
@ info@campingdesgrandscols.com

1 ADEF**JM**NOPQRST	6
2 AFOPRSVWXY	ABD**FG** 7
3 BELQ	ABCDEFKNORSTUV 8
4 FHIOR	EW 9
5 ABDEHJM**NO**	ABDFGHJL**OR** 10

16A CEE
A565 2ha 92**T**(80-100m²) 7**P**

❶ €24.00
❷ €36.00

🚗 D1006 Chambéry - St. Jean-de-Maurienne. In St. Jean direction centre, then follow 'Toutes directions' and 'camping' signs.

💬 Located in the heart of the Maurienne valley at the foot of prestigious 'cols' such as the Glandon, Croix de Fer and Madeleine. The warden will be pleased to help you plan your bike rides, walks or cultural trips out. Cycle shop and free cycle storage available. Easy to reach via the D1006. 500 m from town centre.

CC 10/5-30/6 25/8-21/9

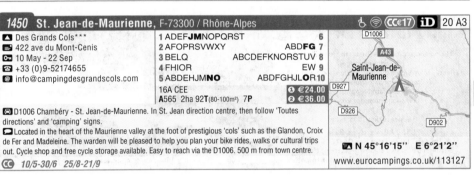

⬛ N 45°16'15'' E 6°21'2''

www.eurocampings.co.uk/113127

1451 St. Pierre-d'Albigny, F-73250 / Rhône-Alpes

& 🛜 CC€17 iD 20 A3

🏕 Lac de Carouge***
📧 Base de Loisirs
📅 28 Apr - 15 Sep
☎ +33 (0)6-25913831
@ contact@lacdecarouge.com

1 AD**JM**NOPRS**T**	LMN 6
2 ADFHIJPVWXY	ABDE**FGH** 7
3 BE**H**LQ	ABCDEFGKNQRSV 8
4 BDFILNO	AETV 9
5 ABDEFGHJM**NO**	ABDGHIORVW 10

10A CEE
A400 1,9ha 64**T**(100-150m²) 24**P**

❶ €28.45
❷ €36.45

🚗 From Chambéry A43, exit 23 St. Pierre-d'Albigny which is well signposted 3.5 km from the campsite. From Albertville A43, exit 24 drive to St. Pierre-d'Albigny then follow the campsite signs.

💬 Campsite is at a lake. The camping pitches are a minimum of 100 m² and nearly all of them are marked out by hedges. Swimming in the lake is permitted in the patrolled area. The Arbin vineyards and Miolans castle are in the neighbourhood. Good toilet facilities.

CC 28/4-6/7 25/8-14/9 7=6, 14=12, 21=18

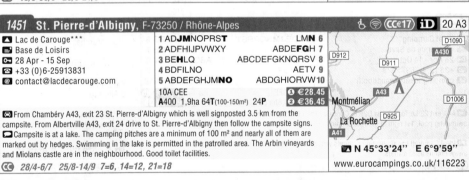

⬛ N 45°33'24'' E 6°9'59''

www.eurocampings.co.uk/116223

1452 Allemont, F-38114 / Rhône-Alpes

& 🛜 CC€13 iD 20 A3

🏕 Le Grand Calme
📅 1 May - 30 Sep
☎ +33 (0)6-84302175
@ info@campinglegrandcalme.com

1 ADE**JM**NOPQRST	6
2 CFOPVWXY	ABDE**F** 7
3 AQV	ABCDE**FG**KNQRSV 8
4 FH	EJ 9
5 DGMN	ABCGJLORV 10

10A
A694 3ha 114**T**(100-110m²) 21**P**

❶ €16.45
❷ €22.85

🚗 D1091 towards Briançon. In Rochetaillée D526 towards Allemont/Col du Glandon. Campsite is in the middle of the village on the right of the road. Well signposted.

💬 Le Grand Calme is situated in the centre of Allemont, the last village before the Glandon and Croix de Fer cols. Views of the surrounding mountains from the spacious pitches.

CC 1/5-1/6 10/6-30/6 18/8-29/9

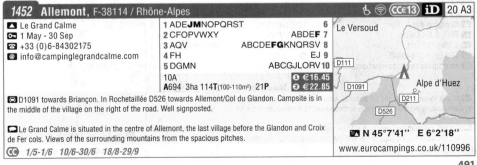

⬛ N 45°7'41'' E 6°2'18''

www.eurocampings.co.uk/110996

1453 Allevard-les-Bains, F-38580 / Rhône-Alpes   ♿ 📶 (CC€15) iD 20 A3

- ⛺ Clair Matin***
- 🏤 20 rue de Pommiers
- 📅 14 Apr - 14 Oct
- ☎ +33 (0)4-76975519
- @ contact@camping-clair-matin.com

1 ADE**J**MNOPQRS**T**		AF 6
2 BFOPUVXY		ABDE**FG**H 7
3 BELQ		ABCDFINORSV 8
4 ABCD**E**FHILO		EJL 9
5 ADE**F**HJKM**NO**		ABCDFGHJ**P**RVX10
Ad on this page 2-10A		❶ €25.65
A512 5,5ha 195T(100-110m²) 151P		❷ €32.45

La Rochette
Allevard
Le Touvet

🚗 A41, exit 23 Le Touvet. Then via D29 towards Goncelin. Then D525 direction Allevard. Campsite is on the left before the roundabout.

⛺ Clair Matin is located 500m from the Allevard-les-Bains spa. Thanks to its sheltered location in the Belledonne-Massif it enjoys pleasant temperatures, even in spring and autumn. Recommended for both sportive and not-so-sportive campers. Camping Qualité.

(CC) 14/4-7/7 25/8-13/10

📍 N 45°23'19'' E 6°3'53''

www.eurocampings.co.uk/110356

1454 Allevard-les-Bains, F-38580 / Rhône-Alpes   ♿ 📶 (CC€15) iD 20 A3

- ⛺ Idéal Camping***
- 🏤 67 avenue de Savoie
- 📅 28 Apr - 14 Oct
- ☎ +33 (0)4-76975023
- @ camping.ideal@wanadoo.fr

1 ADE**J**MNOPRS**T**		ABFG 6
2 CFOPVXY		ABDE**FG**H 7
3 AELQ		ABCDEFKRSV 8
4 FHIOP		EIJ 9
5 AEFGMN**O**		ABGHKN**P**RV 10
4-10A CEE		❶ €21.90
A504 1,8ha 62T(80-120m²) 19P		❷ €28.30

Les Marches
Saint-Pierre-d'Allevard
Lumbin

🚗 A41 exit 23 Le Touvet. Via D29 to Concelin. Then D525 to Allevard. Campsite opposite the swimming pool, 1st right at the roundabout.

⛺ Idéal Camping has undulating grounds with plenty of shade. The centre and the spas are 700m away. Enthusiastic owners.

(CC) 28/4-8/7 26/8-13/10

📍 N 45°24'3'' E 6°4'51''

www.eurocampings.co.uk/121836

1455 Auberives-sur-Varèze, F-38550 / Rhône-Alpes   ♿ 📶 (CC€17) iD 19 B3

- ⛺ Camping des Nations***
- 🏤 RN7, 8 Bis Louze
- 📅 1 Mar - 31 Oct
- ☎ +33 (0)4-74849513
- @ contact@campingdesnations.com

1 ADEJMNOPQRST		A 6
2 AOPSVWXY		ABDEFGH 7
3 ALQ		ABCDEFJNRSV 8
4 IO		E 9
5 ADFHJK		AHIJOTU 10
8-10A		❶ €26.00
A200 1,5ha 63T(100m²) 11P		❷ €38.00

Salaise-sur-Sanne
Jarcieu

🚗 A7 exit Vienne, follow the N7 as far as Auberives-s-V. Campsite on the right, south of the village. You are advised to take exit 11 from north and exit 12 from south of the A7.

⛺ A small, pleasant stopover campsite on the RN7 between Vienne and Chanas. Shaded, marked-out pitches. Suitable for day trips to the Ardèche and the Vercors. Friendly, helpful reception. Free wifi.

(CC) 1/3-30/6 1/9-30/10

📍 N 45°24'46'' E 4°48'48''

www.eurocampings.co.uk/109525

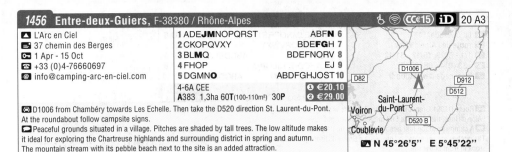

1456 Entre-deux-Guiers, F-38380 / Rhône-Alpes ♿ 🛜 (CC€15) iD 20 A3

- ▲ L'Arc en Ciel
- 🏠 37 chemin des Berges
- ☀ 1 Apr - 15 Oct
- ☎ +33 (0)4-76660697
- @ info@camping-arc-en-ciel.com

1 ADE**JM**NOPQRST	ABF**N**	**6**
2 CKOPQVXY	BDE**FG**H	**7**
3 BL**MQ**	BDEFNORV	**8**
4 FHOP	EJ	**9**
5 DGMN**O**	ABDFGHJOST	**10**

4-6A CEE	❶ €20.10
A383 1,3ha 60**T**(100-110m²) 30**P**	❷ €29.00

🚗 D1006 from Chambéry towards Les Echelle. Then take the D520 direction St. Laurent-du-Pont. At the roundabout follow campsite signs.
💬 Peaceful grounds situated in a village. Pitches are shaded by tall trees. The low altitude makes it ideal for exploring the Chartreuse highlands and surrounding district in spring and autumn. The mountain stream with its pebble beach next to the site is an added attraction.

CC 1/4-6/7 27/8-14/10

🧭 N 45°26'5'' E 5°45'22''
www.eurocampings.co.uk/111549

1457 Gresse-en-Vercors, F-38650 / Rhône-Alpes ⛷ 🛜 (CC€17) iD 60

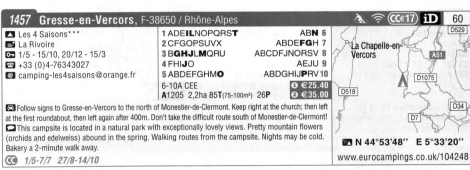

- ▲ Les 4 Saisons***
- 🏠 La Rivoire
- ☀ 1/5 - 15/10, 20/12 - 15/3
- ☎ +33 (0)4-76343027
- @ camping-les4saisons@orange.fr

1 ADE**IL**NOPQRS**T**	AB**N**	**6**
2 CFGOPSUVX	ABDE**FG**H	**7**
3 B**GHJLMQ**RU	ABCDFJNORSV	**8**
4 FH**IJ**O	AEJU	**9**
5 ABDEFGH**MO**	ABDGHIJP**RV**	**10**

6-10A CEE	❶ €25.40
A1205 2,2ha 85**T**(75-100m²) 26**P**	❷ €35.00

🚗 Follow signs to Gresse-en-Vercors to the north of Monestier-de-Clermont. Keep right at the church; then left at the first roundabout, then left again after 400m. Don't take the difficult route south of Monestier-de-Clermont!
💬 This campsite is located in a natural park with exceptionally lovely views. Pretty mountain flowers (orchids and edelweiss) abound in the spring. Walking routes from the campsite. Nights may be cold. Bakery a 2-minute walk away.

CC 1/5-7/7 27/8-14/10

🧭 N 44°53'48'' E 5°33'20''
www.eurocampings.co.uk/104248

1458 Le Bourg-d'Oisans, F-38520 / Rhône-Alpes ♿ 🛜 (CC€15) iD 20 A3

- ▲ Camping RCN Belledonne****
- 🏠 Rochetailleé
- ☀ 11 May - 2 Oct
- ☎ +31 034-3745090
- @ reserveringen@rcn.fr

1 ADE**IL**NOPRST	ABFG	**6**
2 OPQVXY	ABDE**FG**H	**7**
3 BEL**MQ**T	ABCDEFIKNOPQRSV	**8**
4 ABCEFHILNO**TV**	BEU	**9**
5 ABDEFGHJKMN	ABCDHJ**NOP**RVWZ	**10**

Ad on this page 10A	❶ €41.60
A730 4ha 175**T**(80-140m²) 26**P**	❷ €51.60

🚗 D1091 Grenoble-Briançon. In Rochetaillée turn right towards Allemont (D526). Campsite is on the right after 500 metres and is signposted.
💬 A spacious campsite with extensive facilities. Lovely views from the marked-out pitches. The site is located in a mountainous landscape. Thanks to its location at the start of a valley (l'Eau d'Olle), the park-like grounds are level and easy accessible. A large number of trees provide plenty of shaded areas.

CC 11/5-5/6 8/6-6/7 25/8-1/10

🧭 N 45°6'53'' E 6°0'32''
www.eurocampings.co.uk/112112

France

493

1459 Le Bourg-d'Oisans, F-38520 / Rhône-Alpes

🏃 ♿ 📶 CC€17 iD 60

- 🔼 La Cascade★★★★
- 🏕 route de l'Alpe d'Huez
- 🗓 1/1 - 30/9, 15/12 - 31/12
- ☎ +33 (0)4-76800242
- @ lacascade@wanadoo.fr

1 ADEJMNOPRST	ABFG**NU** 6
2 CFOPQRVWXY	ABDE**FG**H 7
3 BEFLQ	ABCDEFJNOQRSV 8
4 **ABCD**E**FHILOPQ**	J 9
5 ADEGHM**NO**	ABCDHIJLNPRVX 10

16A   ❶ €35.70
A739 2,5ha 128T(90-100m²) 33P   ❷ €52.70

🗺 Route D1091 Grenoble-Briançon. Turn left as you leave Le Bourg-d'Oisans via ring road direction l'Alpe d'Huez, the campsite 500 metres on the right.
💬 A campsite on the first bend of the climb up l'Alpe d'Huez, well known from the Tour de France. The pitches are separated by hedges. Le Bourg d'Oisans just a stroll away. The l'Alpe d'Huez ski bus stops in front of the site.
CC 1/1-30/5   10/6-28/6   22/8-29/9

D111   Allemond
D1091
Le Bourg-d'Oisans
D526

🗺 N 45°3'51''   E 6°2'21''
www.eurocampings.co.uk/104364

1460 Les Abrets, F-38490 / Rhône-Alpes

♿ 📶 CC€17 iD 20 A3

- 🔼 Le Coin Tranquille★★★★
- 🏕 6 chemin des Vignes (Le Véroud)
- 🗓 31 Mar - 1 Nov
- ☎ +33 (0)4-76321348
- @ contact@coin-tranquille.com

1 ADE**JM**NOPRST	ABF 6
2 AFPVWXY	ABDE**FG**H 7
3 BELRT	ABCDEFJNQRSV 8
4 BDFHILNO	EJV 9
5 ACDEFGHJKLM**N**	ABGHIJOSTW 10

Ad on this page 6-10A   ❶ €39.00
A398 10ha 176T(100-120m²) 16P   ❷ €52.00

🗺 A43 Lyon-Chambéry. Exit 10 Les Abrets. Left on roundabout to centre. Then direction Pont-de-Beauvoisin (N6). After 1.5 km campsite is indicated on left. Cross miniature train tracks and stay on road for another 1 km.
💬 Welcoming family campsite with flowers and green fields all around. There is a heated swimming pool, a good restaurant and modern and well maintained toilet facilities.
CC 31/3-7/7   25/8-31/10   7=6

D16   D1516
Saint-Jean-de-Soudain   D916
A43   D916 A
D73   D203
D1075   D1006

🗺 N 45°32'29''   E 5°36'29''
www.eurocampings.co.uk/104233

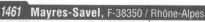

Le Coin Tranquille ★ ★ ★ ★

This friendly campsite is located in an area with wonderful flowers and fields. With a heated swimming pool, a good restaurant and modern, well-maintained toilet facilities.

6 chemin des Vignes (Le Véroud), 38490 Les Abrets
Tel. 0033 (0)4-76321348
E-mail: contact@coin-tranquille.com
Internet: www.coin-tranquille.com

1461 Mayres-Savel, F-38350 / Rhône-Alpes

📶 CC€13 iD 60

- 🔼 Camping de Savel★★
- 🏕 D116
- 🗓 1 Apr - 31 Oct
- ☎ +33 (0)4-76811479
- @ contact@camping-savel.com

1 ADE**JM**NOPRST	AL**N**QRSUWXY**Z** 6
2 DFGIJKPRUVWXY	ABDE**FG**H 7
3 ABELQ	ABCDFKNRSTV 8
4 BCDFHINO**PQRTV**	CEFJMNQ 9
5 ABEFGHJKM**NO**	ABDFGHIJLN**P**TUWZ 10

12A CEE   ❶ €28.40
A480 7ha 100T(100-120m²) 72P   ❷ €41.80

🗺 Grenoble N85 dir. Vizille-La Mure. In La Mure, at the roundabout signs for Mayres-Savel and 'Camping de Savel', then another 15 km to the campsite.
💬 The campsite is located right by a lake. Swimming pool. Ample trees which give necessary shade. Large restaurant with spacious terrace with views of the mountains and lake. 3 km from the campsite is one of Europe's most beautiful footpaths, La Passerelle du Drac with a footbridge over the lake.
CC 1/4-30/6   1/9-30/10

A51   D529
Monestier-de-Clermont   La Mure   D26
D26 A
D34
D7   D526   Mens
D1075
D66

🗺 N 44°52'56''   E 5°41'16''
www.eurocampings.co.uk/109680

1462 Mens, F-38710 / Rhône-Alpes 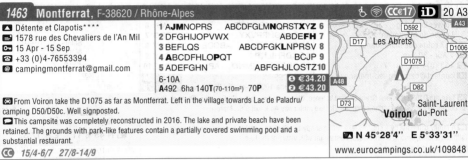 📶 CC€15 iD 60

▲ Le Pré Rolland***
🏕 rue de la Piscine
📅 21 Apr - 30 Sep
☎ +33 (0)4-76346580
@ contact@prerolland.fr

1	ADEJMNOPRST	ABFGHN 6
2	FGOPRVWXY	ABDEFGHJK 7
3	AEGHLMQ	ABCDFNOQRSV 8
4	BEFHIO	EJUV 9
5	ADEFHN	ABDGHIJPTUV 10
10A CEE		❶ €27.05
A755 2,5ha 90T(100-200m²) 15P		❷ €36.70

🛣 N75 Grenoble-Sisteron. At Clelles take D526 towards Mens. In Mens follow signs.

💬 A very peaceful campsite within walking distance of a village in rural, mountainous surroundings. Spacious pitches separated by low trees and bushes.

CC 21/4-30/6 1/9-29/9

📍 N 44°48'54'' E 5°44'56''
www.eurocampings.co.uk/109976

1463 Montferrat, F-38620 / Rhône-Alpes ♿ 📶 CC€17 iD 20 A3

▲ Détente et Clapotis****
🏕 1578 rue des Chevaliers de l'An Mil
📅 15 Apr - 15 Sep
☎ +33 (0)4-76553394
@ campingmontferrat@gmail.com

1	AJMNOPRS	ABCDFGLMNQRSTXYZ 6
2	DFGHIJOPVWX	ABDEFH 7
3	BEFLQS	ABCDFGKLNPRSV 8
4	ABCDFHLOPQT	BCJP 9
5	ADEFGHN	ABFGHJLOSTZ 10
6-10A		❶ €34.20
A492 6ha 140T(70-110m²) 70P		❷ €43.20

🛣 From Voiron take the D1075 as far as Montferrat. Left in the village towards Lac de Paladru/camping D50/D50c. Well signposted.

💬 This campsite was completely reconstructed in 2016. The lake and private beach have been retained. The grounds with park-like features contain a partially covered swimming pool and a substantial restaurant.

CC 15/4-6/7 27/8-14/9

📍 N 45°28'4'' E 5°33'31''
www.eurocampings.co.uk/109848

1464 Petichet/St. Théoffrey, F-38119 / Rhône-Alpes ♿ 📶 CC€17 iD 60

▲ Ser Sirant***
🏕 Lac de Laffrey
📅 29 Apr - 30 Sep
☎ +33 (0)4-76839197
@ info@campingsersirant.com

1	ADJMNOPRST	LNOQRSTUVXYZ 6
2	DFGHIJPUVWXY	ABDEFGH 7
3	ABEGHLQRS	ABCDFGJKNQRSV 8
4	ABCEFHILO	EJMPQRU 9
5	ABDEFGHKLN	ABDGHIJLNOPR 10
10A		❶ €29.00
A910 2ha 87T(90-110m²) 13P		❷ €38.40

🛣 N85 direction Napoléon, 30 km south of Grenoble towards Gap. Turn left at traffic lights in village of Petichet. Follow signs.

💬 A campsite right by a large lake where you can go rowing, surfing and sailing. It has the French quality hallmark 'Camping Qualité'. An active family campsite: activities during the day and relaxation in the evening. A wonderful area for (mountain) hiking, cycling and mountain biking.

CC 29/4-6/7 25/8-29/9

📍 N 45°0'0'' E 5°46'39''
www.eurocampings.co.uk/110871

1465 Roybon, F-38940 / Rhône-Alpes ♿ 📶 CC€13 iD 19 B3

▲ Camping de Roybon***
🏕 D20
📅 15 Apr - 30 Sep
☎ +33 (0)4-76362367
@ campingroybon38@gmail.com

1	ADEJMNOPRST	ABLMNQR 6
2	CDGJOPVWXY	BDFH 7
3	AEFGLQ	ACDFNORSV 8
4	FHIO	EPT 9
5	ADEFHKMN	ABDGHIJLOSTVWX 10
6-10A CEE		❶ €18.30
A525 2,5ha 85T(80-110m²) 16P		❷ €22.30

🛣 A7/E15 exit 12, D519 direction Voiron. Turn right D71 Bressieux/Roybon. Campsite located 1 km out of the village and is indicated.

💬 A peaceful campsite with a homely atmosphere on the shore of the lake and 800 metres from Roybon. The area has a Tuscan feel to it. Enjoy the heated swimming pool and the restaurant with delicious regional dishes.

CC 15/4-14/7 1/9-29/9 6=5, 12=10

📍 N 45°14'49'' E 5°14'53''
www.eurocampings.co.uk/100440

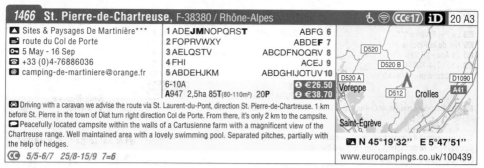

1466 St. Pierre-de-Chartreuse, F-38380 / Rhône-Alpes   ♿ 🛜 (CC€17) iD 20 A3

🏕 Sites & Paysages De Martinière***
🛏 route du Col de Porte
📅 5 May - 16 Sep
☎ +33 (0)4-76886036
@ camping-de-martiniere@orange.fr

1 ADE**JM**NOPQRS**T**	ABFG	6
2 FOPRVWXY	ABDE**F**	7
3 AELQSTV	ABCDFNOQRV	8
4 FHI	ACEJ	9
5 ABDEHJKM	ABDGHIJOTUV	10

6-10A   ❶ €26.50
A947 2,5ha 85T(80-110m²) 20P   ❷ €38.70

🚗 Driving with a caravan we advise the route via St. Laurent-du-Pont, direction St. Pierre-de-Chartreuse. 1 km before St. Pierre in the town of Diat turn right direction Col de Porte. From there, it's only 2 km to the campsite.
📄 Peacefully located campsite within the walls of a Cartusienne farm with a magnificent view of the Chartreuse range. Well maintained area with a lovely swimming pool. Separated pitches, partially with the help of hedges.
ⒸⒸ 5/5-6/7   25/8-15/9   7=6

📷 N 45°19'32''   E 5°47'51''
www.eurocampings.co.uk/100439

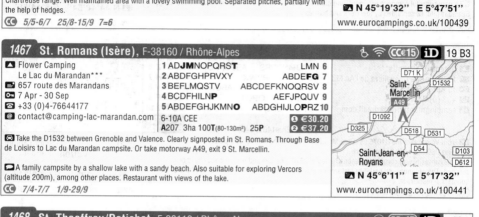

1467 St. Romans (Isère), F-38160 / Rhône-Alpes   ♿ 🛜 (CC€15) iD 19 B3

🏕 Flower Camping
    Le Lac du Marandan***
🛏 657 route des Marandans
📅 7 Apr - 30 Sep
☎ +33 (0)4-76644177
@ contact@camping-lac-marandan.com

1 AD**JM**NOPQRS**T**	LMN	6
2 ABDFGHPRVXY	ABDE**FG**	7
3 BEFLMQSTV	ABCDEFKNOQRSV	8
4 BCDFHILN**P**	AEFJPQUV	9
5 ABDEFGHJKMN**O**	ABDGHIJLO**P**RZ	10

6-10A CEE   ❶ €30.20
A207 3ha 100T(80-130m²) 25P   ❷ €37.20

🚗 Take the D1532 between Grenoble and Valence. Clearly signposted in St. Romans. Through Base de Loisirs to Lac du Marandan campsite. Or take motorway A49, exit 9 St. Marcellin.

📄 A family campsite by a shallow lake with a sandy beach. Also suitable for exploring Vercors (altitude 200m), among other places. Restaurant with views of the lake.
ⒸⒸ 7/4-7/7   1/9-29/9

📷 N 45°6'11''   E 5°17'32''
www.eurocampings.co.uk/100441

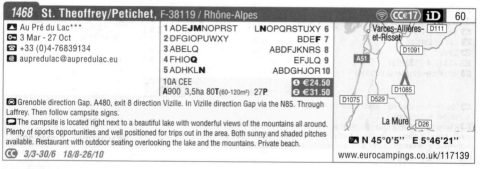

1468 St. Theoffrey/Petichet, F-38119 / Rhône-Alpes   🛜 (CC€17) iD 60

🏕 Au Pré du Lac***
📅 3 Mar - 27 Oct
☎ +33 (0)4-76839134
@ aupredulac@aupredulac.eu

1 ADE**JM**NOPRST	L**N**OPQRSTUXY	6
2 DFGIOPUWXY	BDE**F**	7
3 ABELQ	ABDFJKNRS	8
4 FHIO**Q**	EFJLQ	9
5 ADHKL**N**	ABDGHJOR	10

10A CEE   ❶ €24.50
A900 3,5ha 80T(60-120m²) 27P   ❷ €31.50

🚗 Grenoble direction Gap. A480, exit 8 direction Vizille. In Vizille direction Gap via the N85. Through Laffrey. Then follow campsite signs.
📄 The campsite is located right next to a beautiful lake with wonderful views of the mountains all around. Plenty of sports opportunities and well positioned for trips out in the area. Both sunny and shaded pitches available. Restaurant with outdoor seating overlooking the lake and the mountains. Private beach.
ⒸⒸ 3/3-30/6   18/8-26/10

📷 N 45°0'5''   E 5°46'21''
www.eurocampings.co.uk/117139

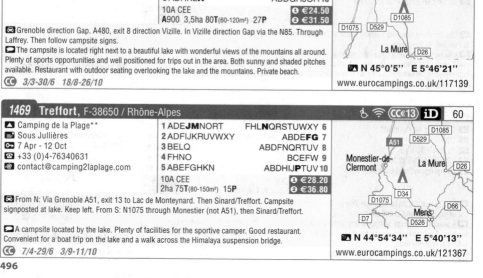

1469 Treffort, F-38650 / Rhône-Alpes   ♿ 🛜 (CC€13) iD 60

🏕 Camping de la Plage**
🛏 Sous Jullières
📅 7 Apr - 12 Oct
☎ +33 (0)4-76340631
@ contact@camping2laplage.com

1 ADE**JM**NORT	FHL**N**QRSTUVWXY	6
2 ADFIJKRUVWXY	ABDE**FG**	7
3 BELQ	ABDFNQRTUV	8
4 FHNO	BCEFW	9
5 ABEFGHKN	ABDHIJ**P**TUV	10

10A CEE   ❶ €28.20
2ha 75T(80-150m²) 15P   ❷ €36.80

🚗 From N: Via Grenoble A51, exit 13 to Lac de Monteynard. Then Sinard/Treffort. Campsite signposted at lake. Keep left. From S: N1075 through Monestier (not A51), then Sinard/Treffort.

📄 A campsite located by the lake. Plenty of facilities for the sportive camper. Good restaurant. Convenient for a boat trip on the lake and a walk across the Himalaya suspension bridge.
ⒸⒸ 7/4-29/6   3/9-11/10

📷 N 44°54'34''   E 5°40'13''
www.eurocampings.co.uk/121367

1470 Trept, F-38460 / Rhône-Alpes

♿ 📶 (CC€15) 🆔 19 B2

🔺 Les 3 Lacs du Soleil★★★★
📧 La Plaine de Serrières
📅 28 Apr - 9 Sep
☎ +33 (0)4-74929206
@ les3lacsdusoleil@hotmail.fr

1 ADE**JM**NORS**T**	AFHLM**N** 6
2 DGHIKOPVWXY	ABDE**FG**HK 7
3 BEFILMQRS	ABCDEFNQRSV 8
4 BCDFHILO**PQR**U	AEFJTUVW 9
5 ABDEGHKM	ABHJLN**P**STWZ 10

6A   ❶ €36.50
A270 26ha 160**T**(100-120m²) 67**P**   ❷ €46.50

🚗 Bourg-en-Bresse direction Lyon. Exit Ambérieu. N75 direction Lagnieu. Then direction Lancin. Follow D522 and D517 towards Trept and Crémieu. Campsite located 3 km before Trept. Well signposted.
💬 A family campsite with a swimming pool and toddlers' pool located in grounds with three lakes, one of which has a water slide. Lovely area for walking and cycling. Spacious level pitches and a restaurant in the grounds.
CC 28/4-6/7   27/8-8/9   7=6, 14=11

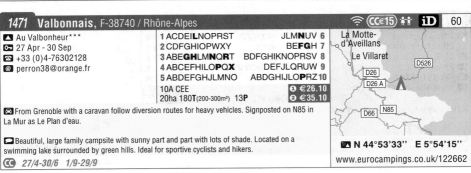

📍 N 45°41'21''   E 5°21'6''
www.eurocampings.co.uk/101216

1471 Valbonnais, F-38740 / Rhône-Alpes

📶 (CC€15) ✚† 🆔 60

🔺 Au Valbonheur★★★
📅 27 Apr - 30 Sep
☎ +33 (0)4-76302128
@ perron38@orange.fr

1 ACDEI**L**NOPRST	JLM**N**UV 6
2 CDFGHIOPWXY	BE**FG**H 7
3 ABE**GH**LM**NQRT**	BDFGHIKNOPRSV 8
4 ABCEFHILO**PQX**	DEFJLQRUW 9
5 ABDEFGHJLMNO	ABDGHIJLO**P**RZ 10

10A CEE   ❶ €26.10
20ha 180**T**(200-300m²) 13**P**   ❷ €35.10

🚗 From Grenoble with a caravan follow diversion routes for heavy vehicles. Signposted on N85 in La Mur as Le Plan d'eau.
💬 Beautiful, large family campsite with sunny part and part with lots of shade. Located on a swimming lake surrounded by green hills. Ideal for sportive cyclists and hikers.
CC 27/4-30/6   1/9-29/9

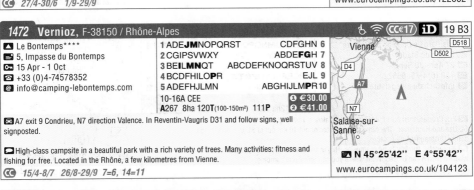

📍 N 44°53'33''   E 5°54'15''
www.eurocampings.co.uk/122662

1472 Vernioz, F-38150 / Rhône-Alpes

♿ 📶 (CC€17) 🆔 19 B3

🔺 Le Bontemps★★★★
📧 5, Impasse du Bontemps
📅 15 Apr - 1 Oct
☎ +33 (0)4-74578352
@ info@camping-lebontemps.com

1 ADE**JM**NOPQRST	CDFGHN 6
2 CGIPSVWXY	ABDE**FG**H 7
3 BEIL**MN**QT	ABCDEFKNOQRSTUV 8
4 BCDFHILO**PR**	EJL 9
5 ADEFHJLMN	ABGHIJLM**P**R 10

10-16A CEE   ❶ €30.00
A267 8ha 120**T**(100-150m²) 111**P**   ❷ €41.00

🚗 A7 exit 9 Condrieu, N7 direction Valence. In Reventin-Vaugris D31 and follow signs, well signposted.
💬 High-class campsite in a beautiful park with a rich variety of trees. Many activities: fitness and fishing for free. Located in the Rhône, a few kilometres from Vienne.
CC 15/4-8/7   26/8-29/9   7=6, 14=11

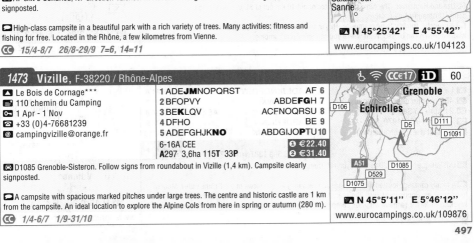

📍 N 45°25'42''   E 4°55'42''
www.eurocampings.co.uk/104123

1473 Vizille, F-38220 / Rhône-Alpes

♿ 📶 (CC€17) 🆔 60

🔺 Le Bois de Cornage★★★
📧 110 chemin du Camping
📅 1 Apr - 1 Nov
☎ +33 (0)4-76681239
@ campingvizille@orange.fr

1 ADE**JM**NOPQRST	AF 6
2 BFOPVY	ABDE**FG**H 7
3 BE**K**LQV	ACFNOQRSU 8
4 DFHO	BE 9
5 ADEFGHJK**NO**	ABDGIJO**P**TU 10

6-16A CEE   ❶ €22.40
A297 3,6ha 115**T** 33**P**   ❷ €31.40

🚗 D1085 Grenoble-Sisteron. Follow signs from roundabout in Vizille (1,4 km). Campsite clearly signposted.
💬 A campsite with spacious marked pitches under large trees. The centre and historic castle are 1 km from the campsite. An ideal location to explore the Alpine Cols from here in spring or autumn (280 m).
CC 1/4-6/7   1/9-31/10

📍 N 45°5'11''   E 5°46'12''
www.eurocampings.co.uk/109876

1474 Barbières, F-26300 / Rhône-Alpes   CC€17 iD 59

- Le Gallo-Romain****
- 1090 route du Col de Tourniol
- 23 Apr - 15 Sep
- +33 (0)4-75474407
- info@legalloromain.net

1	ADE**JM**NOPRST	AFUV 6
2	ACFGPRUVXY	ABE**FGH** 7
3	ABE**GHK**LQT	ABCDEFIJKNQRSTV 8
4	BDEFHILNO**PQX**	EL 9
5	ABDEFGHJLN	ABDHIJ**N**OTUX 10

6A CEE	❶ €33.00
A450 3ha 75T(80-100m²) 14P	❷ €44.60

From Lyon A7 exit 14, A49 dir. Grenoble. Then exit 5 towards Alixan. In Alixan D101 to Barbières, via Besayes and follow the campsite signs. You will find the campsite beyond Barbières on the right.

A beautiful campsite, proclaimed to be one of the loveliest in France, located close to the Vercours, which can be explored on foot, by bike or by car. Orchid season from the beginning of May to mid-June, with more than 20 varieties near the site.

CC *23/4-6/7 24/8-14/9 7=6, 14=12*

Romans-sur-Isère

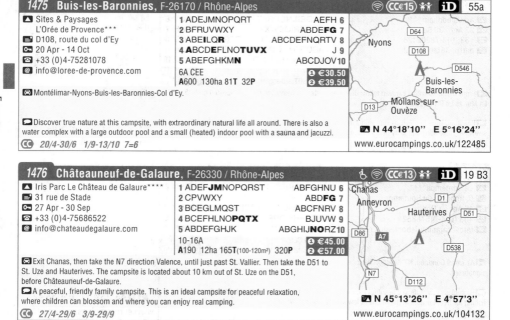

N 44°56'40" E 5°9'4"

www.eurocampings.co.uk/104244

1475 Buis-les-Baronnies, F-26170 / Rhône-Alpes   CC€15 iD 55a

- Sites & Paysages L'Orée de Provence***
- D108, route du col d'Ey
- 20 Apr - 14 Oct
- +33 (0)4-75281078
- info@loree-de-provence.com

1	ADEJMNOPQRT	AEFH 6
2	BFRUVWXY	ABDE**FG** 7
3	ABE**I**LQ**R**	ABCDEFNQRTV 8
4	**ABCD**E**FL**NO**TUVX**	J 9
5	ABEFGHKM**N**	ABCDJOV 10

6A CEE	❶ €30.50
A600 130ha 81T 32P	❷ €39.50

Montélimar-Nyons-Buis-les-Baronnies-Col d'Ey.

Discover true nature at this campsite, with extraordinary natural life all around. There is also a water complex with a large outdoor pool and a small (heated) indoor pool with a sauna and jacuzzi.

CC *20/4-30/6 1/9-13/10 7=6*

Nyons

Buis-les-Baronnies

Mollans-sur-Ouvèze

N 44°18'10" E 5°16'24"

www.eurocampings.co.uk/122485

1476 Châteauneuf-de-Galaure, F-26330 / Rhône-Alpes   CC€13 iD 19 B3

- Iris Parc Le Château de Galaure****
- 31 rue de Stade
- 27 Apr - 30 Sep
- +33 (0)4-75686522
- info@chateaudegalaure.com

1	ADEF**JM**NOPQRST	ABFGHNU 6
2	CPVWXY	ABD**FG** 7
3	BCEGLMQST	ABCFNRV 8
4	BCEFHLNO**PQTX**	BJUVW 9
5	ABDEFGHJK	ABGHIJ**N**O**R**Z 10

10-16A	❶ €45.00
A190 12ha 165T(100-120m²) 320P	❷ €57.00

Exit Chanas, then take the N7 direction Valence, until just past St. Vallier. Then take the D51 to St. Uze and Hauterives. The campsite is located about 10 km out of St. Uze on the D51, before Châteauneuf-de-Galaure.

A peaceful, friendly family campsite. This is an ideal campsite for peaceful relaxation, where children can blossom and where you can enjoy real camping.

CC *27/4-29/6 3/9-29/9*

Chanas
Anneyron
Hauterives

N 45°13'26" E 4°57'3"

www.eurocampings.co.uk/104132

1477 Châteauneuf-sur-Isère, F-26300 / Rhône-Alpes   CC€19 iD 59

- Le Soleil Fruité****
- 480 chemin des Communaux
- 21 Apr - 15 Sep
- +33 (0)4-75841970
- contact@lesoleilfruite.com

1	ADE**I**KNOPRS**T**	ACDFGH 6
2	AFPRVWX	BDE**FG**H 7
3	BF**KL**QST	ABCDEFGKNSV 8
4	ABDFHILNO	EV 9
5	ABDEFGHJK	ABGHIJNOTU 10

10A CEE	❶ €37.40
A100 3,5ha 138T(140m²) 34P	❷ €49.80

Exit Valence North A7. Direction Lyon N7. Direction Pont d'Isère. Follow campsite signs.

A family campsite located in an orchard and with magnificent views of the Drôme valley. Modern toilet facilities. Sports lovers will find everything to their satisfaction. Cycle trips and canoeing/kayaking make the range of activities complete. The campsite has an indoor heated swimming pool.

CC *21/4-8/7 26/8-14/9*

Romans-sur-Isère
Valence

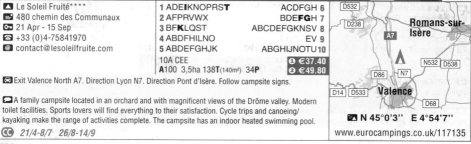

N 45°0'3" E 4°54'7"

www.eurocampings.co.uk/117135

France

1478 Châtillon-en-Diois, F-26410 / Rhône-Alpes
⌖ ⌃ (CC€17) ⚤ iD 59

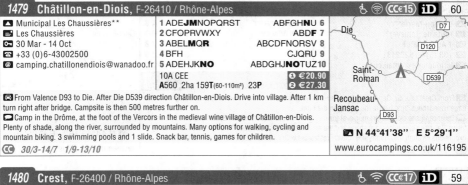

- 🏔 Le Lac Bleu***
- 🏠 Quartier la Touche
- 📅 14 Apr - 22 Sep
- ☎ +33 (0)4-75218530
- @ info@lacbleu-diois.com

1	ADE**JM**NOPRST	CDFGJL**N**XZ 6
2	CDFGHIPRVWXY	ABDE**F** 7
3	ABFLQT	ABCDEFKNQSV 8
4	BCDFHILNO**PQ**	BEQUV 9
5	ABDEFGHJKM**O**	ABDHIJNOTU 10

6A CEE
A550 6,5ha 75T(100-130m²) 157P
❶ €30.00
❷ €39.00

🚗 From Loriol dir. Die; then D539 dir. Châtillon-en-Diois. Right 1 km beyond St. Roman. The campsite is well signposted.

💬 Located on the shores of a lake where swimming is possible from early in the season. Wonderful views of the lake and the surrounding mountains from the terrace. The valley is wide and flat. An excellent location for making lovely trips out. Restaurant and shop are open for the whole season. Lovely indoor pool with jacuzzi.

CC 14/4-30/6 1/9-21/9

🧭 N 44°40'59'' E 5°26'56''

www.eurocampings.co.uk/112481

1479 Châtillon-en-Diois, F-26410 / Rhône-Alpes
⌖ ⌃ (CC€15) iD 60

- 🏔 Municipal Les Chaussières**
- 🏠 Les Chaussières
- 📅 30 Mar - 14 Oct
- ☎ +33 (0)6-43002500
- @ camping.chatillonendiois@wanadoo.fr

1	ADE**JM**NOPQRST	ABFGH**NU** 6
2	CFOPRVWXY	ABD**F** 7
3	ABEL**MQR**	ABCDFNORSV 8
4	BFH	CJQRU 9
5	ADEHJK**NO**	ABDGHJ**NO**TUZ 10

10A CEE
A560 2ha 159T(60-110m²) 23P
❶ €20.90
❷ €27.30

🚗 From Valence D93 to Die. After Die D539 direction Châtillon-en-Diois. Drive into village. After 1 km turn right after bridge. Campsite is then 500 metres further on.

💬 Camp in the Drôme, at the foot of the Vercors in the medieval wine village of Châtillon-en-Diois. Plenty of shade, along the river, surrounded by mountains. Many options for walking, cycling and mountain biking. 3 swimming pools and 1 slide. Snack bar, tennis, games for children.

CC 30/3-14/7 1/9-13/10

🧭 N 44°41'38'' E 5°29'1''

www.eurocampings.co.uk/116195

1480 Crest, F-26400 / Rhône-Alpes
⌖ ⌃ (CC€17) iD 59

- 🏔 Les Clorinthes***
- 🏠 Quai Soubeyran
- 📅 29 Apr - 16 Sep
- ☎ +33 (0)4-75250528
- @ clorinthes@wanadoo.fr

1	AD**JM**NOPRS**T**	AFJNU 6
2	CGKPRVWXY	ABDE**FGH** 7
3	AB**GHKLMQ**	ABCDFNRSV 8
4	BCFHILNO**P**	AEJQRUVY 9
5	ADEFGHJ**O**	ABDGHIJLPTU 10

6A CEE
A198 4ha 154T(90-120m²) 32P
❶ €33.30
❷ €41.60

🚗 Leave the A7 at Loriol. D104 dir. Crest. Left at 2nd traffic lights towards centre. Over railway line. Turn right at large roundabout with monument. Continue for 600m beside the river to campsite.

💬 Lovely park with shade-giving trees. Modern toilet facilities. Swimming in swimming pool or in the Drôme, the river that flows past the campsite. Good start for cycling, walking or car trips. Medieval Crest within walking distance.

CC 29/4-5/7 23/8-15/9

🧭 N 44°43'27'' E 5°1'40''

www.eurocampings.co.uk/104251

1481 Die, F-26150 / Rhône-Alpes
⌖ ⌃ (CC€13) iD 59

- 🏔 Chamarges**
- 🏠 route de Valence
- 📅 24 Mar - 6 Oct
- ☎ +33 (0)4-75221413
- @ campingchamarges@orange.fr

1	ADE**IL**NOPRS**T**	AJ**N**UX 6
2	CFGJKPWXY	ABDE 7
3	AELQ	ABCDEFNOQRV 8
4	BFHO	DJQRU 9
5	ADEFGHJKLNO	ABIJPTU 10

3-6A CEE
A410 3,5ha 150T(80-110m²) 9P
❶ €19.20
❷ €27.40

🚗 From Valence take the D93. Campsite just before Die. Take campsite exit at roundabout. Campsite sign on the right.

💬 Level, sunny and shaded grounds. Beautiful views. Canoeing and kayaking on the Drôme right from the campsite. Swimming pool. Good restaurant with pleasant outdoor seating area. Lovely trips into the beautiful countryside and picturesque villages. Free wifi.

CC 24/3-1/7 19/8-5/10

🧭 N 44°45'44'' E 5°20'47''

www.eurocampings.co.uk/104250

1482 Die, F-26150 / Rhône-Alpes   ♿ 📶 (CC€13) iD 59

- 🔺 Le Glandasse***
- 📧 550 route de Gap
- 📅 10 Apr - 30 Sep
- ☎ +33 (0)4-75220250
- @ camping-glandasse@wanadoo.fr

1 ADE**JM**NOPQRT	ABFG**J**N**U** 6
2 BCFGJKPQRVWXY	ABD**FGH** 7
3 ABE**I**LQ	ABCDEFKNRSV 8
4 BCDFHILNOPU	ELQRU 9
5 ABDEFGHJKM**NO**	ABHIJPTU 10
10A CEE	❶ €28.60
A418 3,5ha 120**T**(80-120m²) 34**P**	❷ €40.60

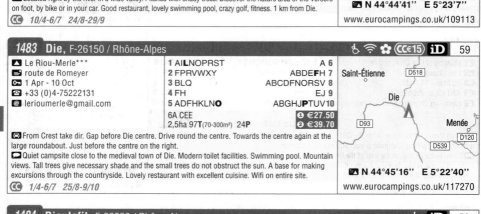

Saint-Étienne   D518
Die
D93   Menée
D120
D539

🅿 N 44°44'41''   E 5°23'7''

🛣 Exit Valence, then dir. Crest/Die. After centre of Die, 1 km south of town continue towards Gap. Campsite clearly signposted. You reach campsite via tunnel (max. height 2.80m). Not accessible for high motorhomes or extra-wide caravans.
🛏 Located right by the river in a wide valley. Pitches with shady trees. Discover the nature area of the Vercors on foot, by bike or in your car. Good restaurant, lovely swimming pool, crazy golf, fitness. 1 km from Die.
CC 10/4-6/7 24/8-29/9

www.eurocampings.co.uk/109113

1483 Die, F-26150 / Rhône-Alpes   ♿ 📶 ✿ (CC€15) iD 59

- 🔺 Le Riou-Merle***
- 📧 route de Romeyer
- 📅 1 Apr - 10 Oct
- ☎ +33 (0)4-75222131
- @ lerioumerle@gmail.com

1 AI**L**NOPRST	A 6
2 FPRVWXY	ABDE**F**H 7
3 B**L**Q	ABCDFNORSV 8
4 FH	E**J** 9
5 ADFHKLN**O**	ABGHJ**P**TUV 10
6A CEE	❶ €27.50
2,5ha 97**T**(70-300m²) 24**P**	❷ €39.70

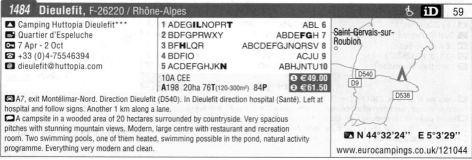

Saint-Étienne   D518
Die
D93   Menée
D120
D539

🅿 N 44°45'16''   E 5°22'40''

🛣 From Crest take dir. Gap before Die centre. Drive round the centre. Towards the centre again at the large roundabout. Just before the centre on the right.
🛏 Quiet campsite close to the medieval town of Die. Modern toilet facilities. Swimming pool. Mountain views. Tall trees give necessary shade and the small trees do not obstruct the sun. A base for making excursions through the countryside. Lovely restaurant with excellent cuisine. Wifi on entire site.
CC 1/4-6/7 25/8-9/10

www.eurocampings.co.uk/117270

1484 Dieulefit, F-26220 / Rhône-Alpes   ♿ iD 59

- 🔺 Camping Huttopia Dieulefit***
- 📧 Quartier d'Espeluche
- 📅 7 Apr - 2 Oct
- ☎ +33 (0)4-75546394
- @ dieulefit@huttopia.com

1 ADEG**IL**NOPR**T**	ABL 6
2 BDFGPRWXY	ABDE**FGH** 7
3 BF**HL**QR	ABCDEFGJNQRSV 8
4 BDFIO	ACJU 9
5 ACDEFGHJK**N**	ABHJNTU 10
10A CEE	❶ €49.00
A198 20ha 76**T**(120-300m²) 84**P**	❷ €61.50

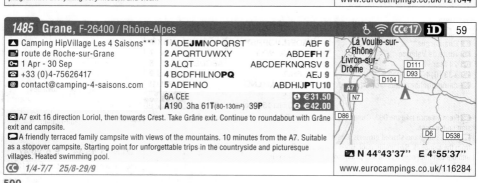

Saint-Gervais-sur-Roubion
D540
D9
D538

🅿 N 44°32'24''   E 5°3'29''

🛣 A7, exit Montélimar-Nord. Direction Dieulefit (D540). In Dieulefit direction hospital (Santé). Left at hospital and follow signs. Another 1 km along a lane.
🛏 A campsite in a wooded area of 20 hectares surrounded by countryside. Very spacious pitches with stunning mountain views. Modern, large centre with restaurant and recreation room. Two swimming pools, one of them heated, swimming possible in the pond, natural activity programme. Everything very modern and clean.

www.eurocampings.co.uk/121044

1485 Grane, F-26400 / Rhône-Alpes   ♿ 📶 (CC€17) iD 59

- 🔺 Camping HipVillage Les 4 Saisons***
- 📧 route de Roche-sur-Grane
- 📅 1 Apr - 30 Sep
- ☎ +33 (0)4-75626417
- @ contact@camping-4-saisons.com

1 ADE**JM**NOPQRST	ABF 6
2 APQRTUVWXY	ABDE**F**H 7
3 ALQT	ABCDEFKNQRSV 8
4 BCDFHILNO**PQ**	AEJ 9
5 ADEHNO	ABDHIJ**P**TU 10
6A CEE	❶ €31.50
A190 3ha 61**T**(80-130m²) 39**P**	❷ €42.00

La Voulte-sur-Rhône
Livron-sur-Drôme
D111
D104   D93
A7
N7
D86
D6   D538

🅿 N 44°43'37''   E 4°55'37''

🛣 A7 exit 16 direction Loriol, then towards Crest. Take Grâne exit. Continue to roundabout with Grâne exit and campsite.
🛏 A friendly terraced family campsite with views of the mountains. 10 minutes from the A7. Suitable as a stopover campsite. Starting point for unforgettable trips in the countryside and picturesque villages. Heated swimming pool.
CC 1/4-7/7 25/8-29/9

www.eurocampings.co.uk/116284

1486 Hauterives, F-26390 / Rhône-Alpes

 🚴 📶 (CC€15) ♟ **iD** 19 B3

- 🏕 Flower Camping Le Château★★★
- ✉ 5 route de Romans (D538)
- 📅 1 Mar - 23 Sep
- ☎ +33 (0)4-75688019
- @ contact@camping-hauterives.com

1 ADE**JM**NOPRST	ABFG**N** 6
2 COPRSVWXY	ABDE**FG**H 7
3 BE**GH**LQSV ABCDEFGIKNOQRSV 8	
4 **A**BCDEFHILO**P**	ACEJUV 9
5 DEFGHJKMN	ABDFGIJ**NOP**TV 10
10A CEE	❶ €29.00
A302 4ha 73T(80-120m²) 75P	❷ €38.00

🚗 A7, exit 12. Via D519 and D538 towards Hauterives. Well signposted.

💬 A campsite with marked-out pitches, mostly in the shade. The town of Hauterives and its Palais Ideal, which is a World Heritage Site, is just 200 metres away. Plenty of culture and nature to be discovered in the immediate surroundings.

CC 1/3-7/7 26/8-22/9 7=6

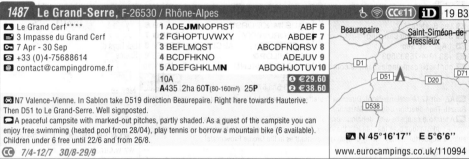

⬛ N 45°15'10'' E 5°1'37''

www.eurocampings.co.uk/118432

1487 Le Grand-Serre, F-26530 / Rhône-Alpes

 🚴 📶 (CC€11) **iD** 19 B3

- 🏕 Le Grand Cerf★★★★
- ✉ 3 Impasse du Grand Cerf
- 📅 7 Apr - 30 Sep
- ☎ +33 (0)4-75688614
- @ contact@campingdrome.fr

1 ADE**JM**NOPRST	ABF 6
2 FGHOPTUVWXY	ABDE**F** 7
3 BEFLMQST	ABCDFNQRSV 8
4 BCDFHKNO	ADEJUV 9
5 ADEFGHKLM**N**	ABDGHJOTUV 10
10A	❶ €29.60
A435 2ha 60T(80-160m²) 25P	❷ €38.60

🚗 N7 Valence-Vienne. In Sablon take D519 direction Beaurepaire. Right here towards Hauterive. Then D51 to Le Grand-Serre. Well signposted.

💬 A peaceful campsite with marked-out pitches, partly shaded. As a guest of the campsite you can enjoy free swimming (heated pool from 28/04), play tennis or borrow a mountain bike (6 available). Children under 6 free until 22/6 and from 26/8.

CC 7/4-12/7 30/8-29/9

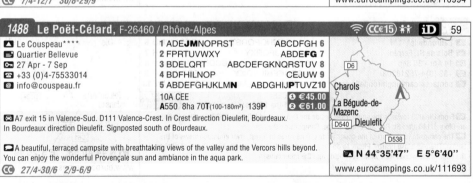

⬛ N 45°16'17'' E 5°6'6''

www.eurocampings.co.uk/110994

1488 Le Poët-Célard, F-26460 / Rhône-Alpes

 📶 (CC€15) ♟ **iD** 59

- 🏕 Le Couspeau★★★★
- ✉ Quartier Bellevue
- 📅 27 Apr - 7 Sep
- ☎ +33 (0)4-75533014
- @ info@couspeau.fr

1 ADE**JM**NOPRST	ABCDFGH 6
2 FPRTUVWXY	ABDE**FG** 7
3 BDELQRT ABCDEFGKNQRSTUV 8	
4 BDFHILNOP	CEJUW 9
5 ABDEFGHJKLM**N** ABDGHIJ**P**TUVZ 10	
10A CEE	❶ €45.00
A550 8ha 70T(100-180m²) 139P	❷ €61.00

🚗 A7 exit 15 in Valence-Sud. D111 Valence-Crest. In Crest direction Dieulefit, Bourdeaux. In Bourdeaux direction Dieulefit. Signposted south of Bourdeaux.

💬 A beautiful, terraced campsite with breathtaking views of the valley and the Vercors hills beyond. You can enjoy the wonderful Provençale sun and ambiance in the aqua park.

CC 27/4-30/6 2/9-6/9

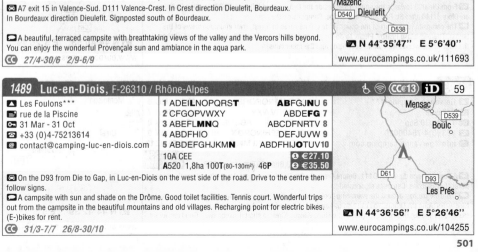

⬛ N 44°35'47'' E 5°6'40''

www.eurocampings.co.uk/111693

1489 Luc-en-Diois, F-26310 / Rhône-Alpes

 🚴 📶 (CC€13) **iD** 59

- 🏕 Les Foulons★★★
- ✉ rue de la Piscine
- 📅 31 Mar - 31 Oct
- ☎ +33 (0)4-75213614
- @ contact@camping-luc-en-diois.com

1 ADEILNOPQRS**T**	**AB**FGJN**U** 6
2 CFGOPVWXY	ABDE**FG** 7
3 ABEFL**MN**Q	ABCDFNRTV 8
4 ABDFHIO	DEFJUVW 9
5 ABDEFGHJKM**N**	ABDFHIJ**O**TUV 10
10A CEE	❶ €27.10
A520 1,8ha 100T(80-130m²) 46P	❷ €35.50

🚗 On the D93 from Die to Gap, in Luc-en-Diois on the west side of the road. Drive to the centre then follow signs.

💬 A campsite with sun and shade on the Drôme. Good toilet facilities. Tennis court. Wonderful trips out from the campsite in the beautiful mountains and old villages. Recharging point for electric bikes. (E-)bikes for rent.

CC 31/3-7/7 26/8-30/10

⬛ N 44°36'56'' E 5°26'46''

www.eurocampings.co.uk/104255

France

1490 Lus-la-Croix-Haute, F-26620 / Rhône-Alpes

CC€15 iD 60

- Champ la Chèvre***
- Le Village
- 7 Apr - 7 Oct
- +33 (0)4-92585014
- champlachevre@orange.fr

1	ABDE**JM**NOPRS**T**	ABCDFG**N** 6
2	FGPTUXY	ABE**F** 7
3	ABLQTV	ABDEFGIJKNQRSV 8
4	**A**BDEFHIOU	BEFJ 9
5	ADEFGHKLMN	ABFGIJN**P**ST 10

6A CEE
3,7ha 85T(80-150m^2) 37P
① €28.80
② €37.40

From Grenoble N75 dir. Sisteron. Past Col de la Croix-Haute, enter the town of Lus-la-Croix-Haute, then follow the signs. Not the first campsite. Drive on to the village.

Beautiful peaceful campsite, with spacious feel. All around are mountains, shopping 200m from the campsite. Lovely restaurant. Perfect resting place for campers on their way south or returning home. 500m from the N1075 but you don't hear it. Also very suitable for longer stays.

CC *7/4-7/7 25/8-6/10*

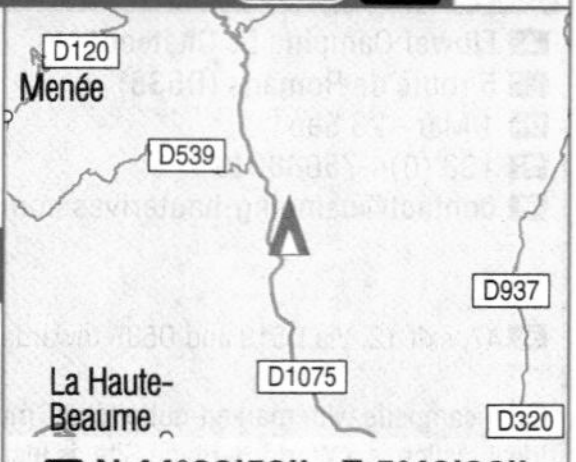

N 44°39'52'' E 5°42'26''
www.eurocampings.co.uk/113142

1491 Marsanne, F-26740 / Rhône-Alpes

CC€17 iD 59

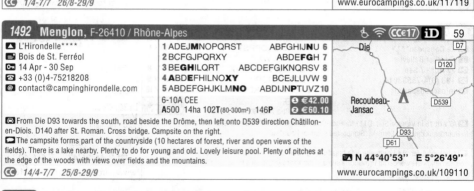

- Les Bastets****
- 335 chemin du Camping
- 1 Apr - 30 Sep
- +33 (0)4-75903503
- contact@campinglesbastets.com

1	ADEJ**M**NOPQRS**T**	AB 6
2	AFPQRUVWXY	ABDE**FG** 7
3	ABE**IK**LQST	ABCDEFJKNQRSTV 8
4	BDFHILO**PQ**	AEJ 9
5	ABDEFGHJKLN**O**	ABDGHJO**P**V 10

10A CEE
A250 3,5ha 67T(80-120m^2) 27P
① €36.50
② €46.50

A7, exit 17 Montélimar-Nord. Direction Tourette then towards La Coucourde. Left in centre towards Sauzet. Then direction Condillac/Marsanne.

A terraced campsite with stunning views of the Plaine de la Valdaine. A unique swimming pool where you can look over the side into the valley. The new owners will do all they can to ensure you enjoy a wonderful holiday. Plenty of cycling opportunities in the Drôme Provençale!

CC *1/4-7/7 26/8-29/9*

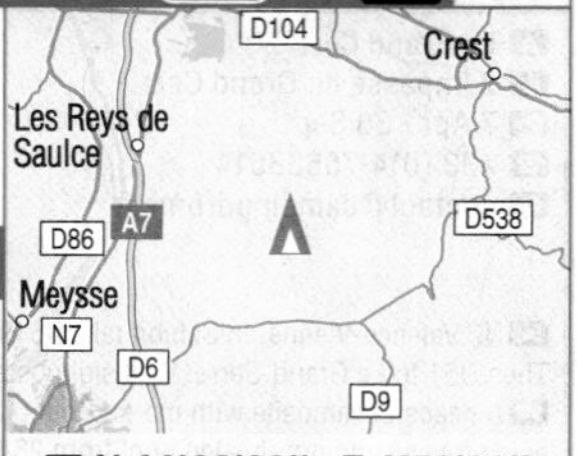

N 44°39'29'' E 4°53'28''
www.eurocampings.co.uk/117119

1492 Menglon, F-26410 / Rhône-Alpes

CC€17 iD 59

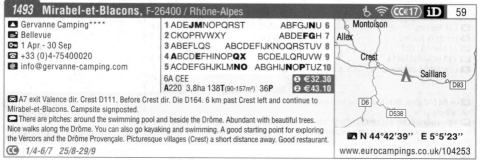

- L'Hirondelle****
- Bois de St. Ferréol
- 14 Apr - 30 Sep
- +33 (0)4-75218208
- contact@campinghirondelle.com

1	ADEJ**M**NOPQRST	ABFGHIJ**N**U 6
2	BCFGJPQRXY	ABDE**FG**H 7
3	BE**GH**ILQRT	ABCDEFGIKNQRSV 8
4	**A**BD**E**FHILNO**XY**	BCEJLUVW 9
5	ABDEFGHJKLM**NO**	ABDIJN**P**TUVZ 10

6-10A CEE
A500 14ha 102T(80-300m^2) 146P
① €42.00
② €60.10

From Die D93 towards the south, road beside the Drôme, then left onto D539 direction Châtillon-en-Diois. D140 after St. Roman. Cross bridge. Campsite on the right.

The campsite forms part of the countryside (10 hectares of forest, river and open views of the fields). There is a lake nearby. Plenty to do for young and old. Lovely leisure pool. Plenty of pitches at the edge of the woods with views over fields and the mountains.

CC *14/4-7/7 25/8-29/9*

N 44°40'53'' E 5°26'49''
www.eurocampings.co.uk/109110

1493 Mirabel-et-Blacons, F-26400 / Rhône-Alpes

CC€17 iD 59

- Gervanne Camping****
- Bellevue
- 1 Apr - 30 Sep
- +33 (0)4-75400020
- info@gervanne-camping.com

1	ADE**JM**NOPQRST	ABFGJ**N**U 6
2	CKOPRVWXY	ABDE**FG**H 7
3	ABEFLQS	ABCDEFIJKNOQRSTUV 8
4	**A**BCD**E**FHINOP**QX**	BCDEJLQRUVW 9
5	ACDEFGHJKLM**NO**	ABGHIJ**NO**PTUZ 10

6A CEE
A220 3,8ha 138T(90-157m^2) 36P
① €32.30
② €43.10

A7 exit Valence dir. Crest D111. Before Crest dir. Die D164. 6 km past Crest left and continue to Mirabel-et-Blacons. Campsite signposted.

There are pitches: around the swimming pool and beside the Drôme. Abundant with beautiful trees. Nice walks along the Drôme. You can also go kayaking and swimming. A good starting point for exploring the Vercors and the Drôme Provençale. Picturesque villages (Crest) a short distance away. Good restaurant.

CC *1/4-6/7 25/8-29/9*

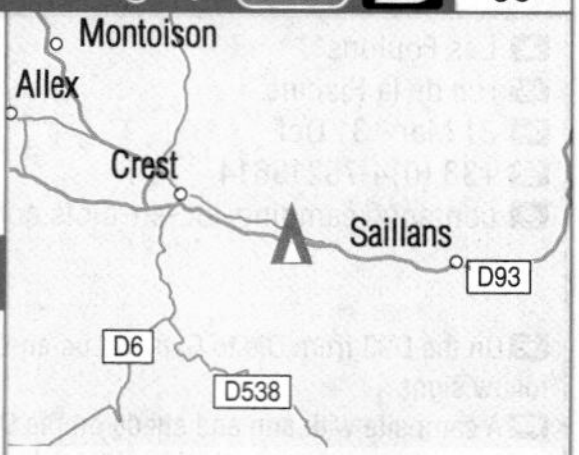

N 44°42'39'' E 5°5'23''
www.eurocampings.co.uk/104253

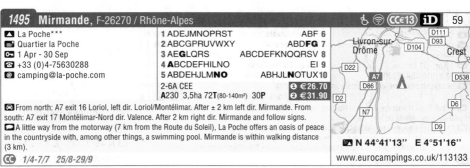

1494 Mirabel-et-Blacons, F-26400 / Rhône-Alpes
♢ 🛜 (CC€19) ✠ iD 59

- ⛰ Val Drôme Soleil
- 🏠 830 chemin Sans Souci
- 📅 1 Apr - 27 Oct
- ☎ +33 (0)4-75400157
- @ camping@valdromesoleil.com

1	**AI**LNOPRST	AEF 6
2	**B**FGRSUVWXY	ABDE**FG** 7
3	ABFLQS	ABEFIJNQRSV 8
4	ABCDEFHINOR**T**	DFI 9
5	ABDEFGHJKL**N**	ABHJ**N**PTUZ 10
6-10A CEE		❶ €33.90
A327 11ha 120**T**(40-150m²) 58**P**		❷ €45.90

🚗 A1 exit Valence D111 towards Crest. After Crest D93 towards Die. After Mirabel-et-Blacons turn left onto D617 to Charsac-Montclair.

💬 A naturist campsite hidden in the mountains with fields of lavender and the vineyards of the Drôme. The pitches on these sloping grounds have sun or shade and often wonderful views. The daily grind is far away from this site, which has a swimming pool, restaurant, sauna and walks. The sun shines in early and late season.

(CC) 1/4-2/6 1/9-26/10

📍 N 44°42'25'' E 5°8'0''

www.eurocampings.co.uk/111876

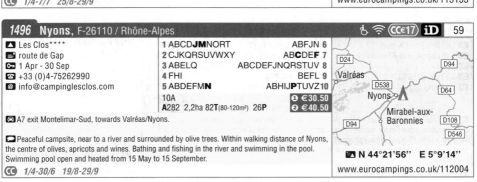

1495 Mirmande, F-26270 / Rhône-Alpes
♿ 🛜 (CC€13) iD 59

- ⛰ La Poche***
- 🏠 Quartier la Poche
- 📅 1 Apr - 30 Sep
- ☎ +33 (0)4-75630288
- @ camping@la-poche.com

1	ADEJMNOPRST	ABF 6
2	ABCGPRUVWXY	ABD**FG** 7
3	AE**G**LQRS	ABCDEFKNOQRSV 8
4	**A**BCDEFHILNO	EI 9
5	ABDEHJLM**NO**	ABHJL**N**OTUX 10
2-6A CEE		❶ €26.70
A230 3,5ha 72**T**(80-140m²) 30**P**		❷ €31.90

🚗 From north: A7 exit 16 Loriol, left dir. Loriol/Montélimar. After ± 2 km left dir. Mirmande. From south: A7 exit 17 Montélimar-Nord dir. Valence. After 2 km right dir. Mirmande and follow signs.

💬 A little way from the motorway (7 km from the Route du Soleil), La Poche offers an oasis of peace in the countryside with, among other things, a swimming pool. Mirmande is within walking distance (3 km).

(CC) 1/4-7/7 25/8-29/9

📍 N 44°41'13'' E 4°51'16''

www.eurocampings.co.uk/113133

France

1496 Nyons, F-26110 / Rhône-Alpes
♿ 🛜 (CC€17) iD 59

- ⛰ Les Clos****
- 🏠 route de Gap
- 📅 1 Apr - 30 Sep
- ☎ +33 (0)4-75262990
- @ info@campinglesclos.com

1	ABCD**JM**NORT	ABFJN 6
2	CJKQRSUVWXY	ABCDE**F** 7
3	ABELQ	ABCDEFJNQRSTUV 8
4	FHI	BEFL 9
5	ABDEFM**N**	ABHIJ**P**TUVZ 10
10A		❶ €30.50
A282 2,2ha 82**T**(80-120m²) 26**P**		❷ €40.50

🚗 A7 exit Montelimar-Sud, towards Valréas/Nyons.

💬 Peaceful campsite, near to a river and surrounded by olive trees. Within walking distance of Nyons, the centre of olives, apricots and wines. Bathing and fishing in the river and swimming in the pool. Swimming pool open and heated from 15 May to 15 September.

(CC) 1/4-30/6 19/8-29/9

📍 N 44°21'56'' E 5°9'14''

www.eurocampings.co.uk/112004

1497 Nyons/Venterol/Novézan, F-26110 / Rhône-Alpes
♿ 🛜 (CC€15) iD 59

- ⛰ Les Terrasses Provençales****
- 🏠 450 route de Rousset
- 📅 31 Mar - 30 Sep
- ☎ +33 (0)4-75279236
- @ lesterrassesprovencales@gmail.com

1	AD**JM**NOPRT	AB 6
2	FPRSUVWXY	ABDE**F**GHK 7
3	BFLQ	ABCDFJNQRSV 8
4	FHIO**PQ**	EUVW 9
5	ABDEFGHKM**NO**	ABGHIJNOTU 10
10A CEE		❶ €28.50
A 2,5ha 69**T**(80-100m²) 20**P**		❷ €38.90

🚗 Campsite located between Valréas and Nyons D538. From Valréas 3 km before Venterol.

💬 A terraced campsite with beautiful views of the mountains, vineyards, apricot and olive trees. The toilet facilities and swimming pool, with outdoor seating and bar, are heated. Close to Mont Ventoux, Nyons, Vaison la Romaine and Orange.

(CC) 31/3-7/7 25/8-29/9

📍 N 44°24'30'' E 5°4'48''

www.eurocampings.co.uk/116196

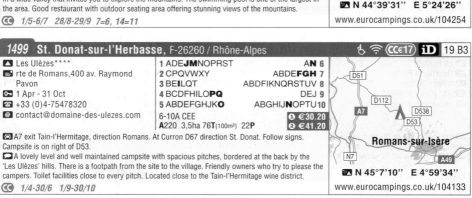

1498 Recoubeau-Jansac, F-26310 / Rhône-Alpes

🚹 📶 (CC€15) **iD** 59

- 🏕 Domaine du Couriou****
- 📧 D93
- 📅 1 May - 30 Sep
- ☎ +33 (0)4-85880138
- @ contact@lecouriou.fr

1 ADE**JM**NOPRST	ABFHI**N**U	6
2 FPRUVWXY	ABDE**FGH**	7
3 BE**GH**LQT	ABCDFNQRSV	8
4 BCDFHILNO**PQX**	EJLU	9
5 ABDEFGHJKLMNO	ABHIJN**O**TUV	10
10A CEE		❶ €33.00
A500 7ha 90T(80-150m²) 92P		❷ €44.50

🚗 Exit Valence-Sud direction Gap/Crest/Die. After Die direction Gap. Campsite on the right before Recoubeau.
💬 Camping Le Couriou is a lovely terraced campsite with panoramic views. The campsite is located in a wide valley that invites you to explore the mountains. The swimming pool is one of the largest in the area. Good restaurant with outdoor seating area offering stunning views of the mountains.
(CC) 1/5-6/7 28/8-29/9 7=6, 14=11

▲ N 44°39'31" E 5°24'26"
www.eurocampings.co.uk/104254

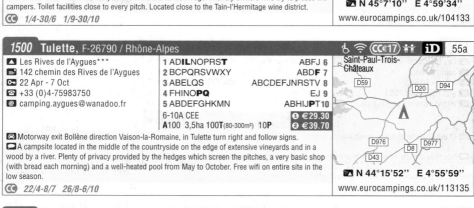

1499 St. Donat-sur-l'Herbasse, F-26260 / Rhône-Alpes

🚹 📶 (CC€17) **iD** 19 B3

- 🏕 Les Ulèzes****
- 📧 rte de Romans,400 av. Raymond Pavon
- 📅 1 Apr - 31 Oct
- ☎ +33 (0)4-75478320
- @ contact@domaine-des-ulezes.com

1 ADE**JM**NOPRST	AN	6
2 CPQVWXY	ABDE**FGH**	7
3 BEILQT	ABDFIKNQRSTUV	8
4 BCDFHILO**PQ**	DEJ	9
5 ABDEFGHJK**O**	ABGHIJ**N**OPTU	10
6-10A CEE		❶ €30.20
A220 3,5ha 76T(100m²) 22P		❷ €41.20

🚗 A7 exit Tain-l'Hermitage, direction Romans. At Curron D67 direction St. Donat. Follow signs. Campsite is on right of D53.
💬 A lovely level and well maintained campsite with spacious pitches, bordered at the back by the 'Les Ulèzes' hills. There is a footpath from the site to the village. Friendly owners who try to please the campers. Toilet facilities close to every pitch. Located close to the Tain-l'Hermitage wine district.
(CC) 1/4-30/6 1/9-30/10

▲ N 45°7'10" E 4°59'34"
www.eurocampings.co.uk/104133

1500 Tulette, F-26790 / Rhône-Alpes

🚹 📶 (CC€17) 🚻 **iD** 55a

- 🏕 Les Rives de l'Aygues***
- 📧 142 chemin des Rives de l'Aygues
- 📅 22 Apr - 7 Oct
- ☎ +33 (0)4-75983750
- @ camping.aygues@wanadoo.fr

1 AD**IL**NOPRS**T**	ABFJ	6
2 BCPQRSVWXY	ABD**F**	7
3 ABELQS	ABCDEFJNRSTV	8
4 FHINO**PQ**	EJ	9
5 ABDEFGHKMN	ABHIJ**PT**10	10
6-10A CEE		❶ €29.30
A100 3,5ha 100T(80-300m²) 10P		❷ €39.70

🚗 Motorway exit Bollène direction Vaison-la-Romaine, in Tulette turn right and follow signs.
💬 A campsite located in the middle of the countryside on the edge of extensive vineyards and in a wood by a river. Plenty of privacy provided by the hedges which screen the pitches, a very basic shop (with bread each morning) and a well-heated pool from May to October. Free wifi on entire site in the low season.
(CC) 22/4-8/7 26/8-6/10

▲ N 44°15'52" E 4°55'59"
www.eurocampings.co.uk/113135

1501 Vercheny, F-26340 / Rhône-Alpes

🚹 📶 (CC€15) **iD** 59

- 🏕 Les Acacias***
- 📧 Les Tours
- 📅 1 Apr - 15 Sep
- ☎ +33 (0)4-75217251
- @ infos@campinglesacacias.com

1 ADE**JM**NOPRT	JNUV	6
2 BCFJRVXY	ABDE**FJ**	7
3 BLQST	ABCDEFNOQRV	8
4 BCDFHILO	BCEQR	9
5 ABDEFHJKMN**O**	ABDHIJLPTU	10
6A CEE		❶ €28.10
3,6ha 90T(80-120m²) 28P		❷ €37.70

🚗 A7 exit Valence, dir. Crest (D111). After Crest dir. Die (D93). Campsite located between Crest and Die on the D93, 2 km before Vercheny on the south side of the road.
💬 Well shaded campsite on the Drôme, ideal as a starting point for exploring the beautiful surroundings by bike or by car. Basic but good and inexpensive restaurant. You can hire canoes and kayaks for sailing on the Drôme. Free wifi.
(CC) 1/4-5/7 24/8-14/9

▲ N 44°41'44" E 5°14'29"
www.eurocampings.co.uk/112776

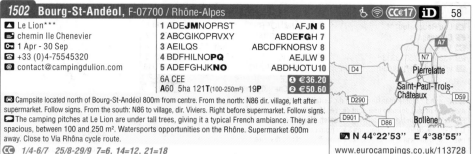

1502 Bourg-St-Andéol, F-07700 / Rhône-Alpes   CC€17 | iD | 58

- ▲ Le Lion***
- ☰ chemin Ile Chenevier
- ☐ 1 Apr - 30 Sep
- ☎ +33 (0)4-75545320
- @ contact@campingdulion.com

1	ADEJMNOPRST	AFJN 6
2	ABCGIKOPRVXY	ABDEFGH 7
3	AEILQS	ABCDFKNORSV 8
4	BDFHILNOPQ	AEJLW 9
5	ADEFGHJKNO	ABDHJOTU 10
6A CEE		❶ €36.20
A60 5ha 121T(100-250m²) 19P		❷ €50.60

🚘 Campsite located north of Bourg-St-Andéol 800m from centre. From the north: N86 dir. village, left after supermarket. Follow signs. From the south: N86 to village, dir. Viviers. Right before supermarket. Follow signs.
💬 The camping pitches at Le Lion are under tall trees, giving it a typical French ambiance. They are spacious, between 100 and 250 m². Watersports opportunities on the Rhône. Supermarket 600m away. Close to Via Rhôna cycle route.

CC 1/4-6/7 25/8-29/9 7=6, 14=12, 21=18

📷 N 44°22'53''   E 4°38'55''

www.eurocampings.co.uk/113728

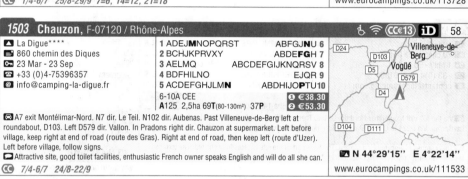

1503 Chauzon, F-07120 / Rhône-Alpes   CC€13 | iD | 58

- ▲ La Digue****
- ☰ 860 chemin des Diques
- ☐ 23 Mar - 23 Sep
- ☎ +33 (0)4-75396357
- @ info@camping-la-digue.fr

1	ADEJMNOPQRST	ABFGJNU 6
2	BCHJKPRVXY	ABDEFGH 7
3	AELMQ	ABCDEFGIJKNQRSV 8
4	BDFHILNO	EJQR 9
5	ACDEFGHJLMN	ABDHIJOPTU 10
6-10A CEE		❶ €38.30
A125 2,5ha 69T(80-130m²) 37P		❷ €53.30

🚘 A7 exit Montélimar-Nord. N7 dir. Le Teil. N102 dir. Aubenas. Past Villeneuve-de-Berg left at roundabout, D103. Left D579 dir. Vallon. In Pradons right dir. Chauzon at supermarket. Left before village, keep right at end of road (route des Gras). Right at end of road, then keep left (route d'Uzer). Left before village, follow signs.
💬 Attractive site, good toilet facilities, enthusiastic French owner speaks English and will do all she can.

CC 7/4-6/7 24/8-22/9

📷 N 44°29'15''   E 4°22'14''

www.eurocampings.co.uk/111533

France

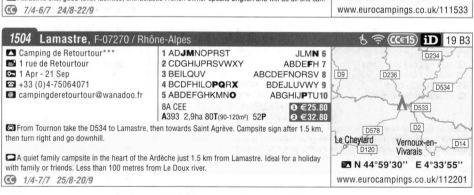

1504 Lamastre, F-07270 / Rhône-Alpes   CC€15 | iD | 19 B3

- ▲ Camping de Retourtour***
- ☰ 1 rue de Retourtour
- ☐ 1 Apr - 21 Sep
- ☎ +33 (0)4-75064071
- @ campingderetourtour@wanadoo.fr

1	ADJMNOPRST	JLMN 6
2	CDGHIJPRSVWXY	ABDEFH 7
3	BEILQUV	ABCDEFNORSV 8
4	BCDFHILOPQRX	BDEJLUVWY 9
5	ABDEFGHKMNO	ABGHIJPTU 10
8A CEE		❶ €25.80
A393 2,9ha 80T(90-120m²) 52P		❷ €32.80

🚘 From Tournon take the D534 to Lamastre, then towards Saint Agrève. Campsite sign after 1.5 km, then turn right and go downhill.
💬 A quiet family campsite in the heart of the Ardèche just 1.5 km from Lamastre. Ideal for a holiday with family or friends. Less than 100 metres from Le Doux river.

CC 1/4-7/7 25/8-20/9

📷 N 44°59'30''   E 4°33'55''

www.eurocampings.co.uk/112201

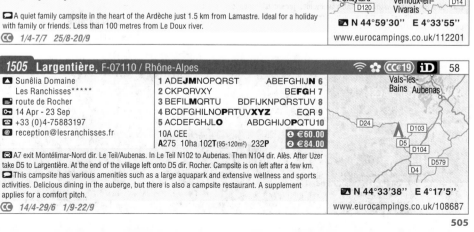

1505 Largentière, F-07110 / Rhône-Alpes   CC€19 | iD | 58

- ▲ Sunêlia Domaine
  Les Ranchisses*****
- ☰ route de Rocher
- ☐ 14 Apr - 23 Sep
- ☎ +33 (0)4-75883197
- @ reception@lesranchisses.fr

1	ADEJMNOPQRST	ABEFGHIJN 6
2	CKPQRVXY	BEFGH 7
3	BEFILMQRTU	BDFIJKNPQRSTUV 8
4	BCDFGHILNOPRTUVXYZ	EQR 9
5	ACDEFGHJLO	ABDGHIJOPQTU 10
10A CEE		❶ €60.00
A275 10ha 102T(95-120m²) 232P		❷ €84.00

🚘 A7 exit Montélimar-Nord dir. Le Teil/Aubenas. In Le Teil N102 to Aubenas. Then N104 dir. Alès. After Uzer take D5 to Largentière. At the end of the village left onto D5 dir. Rocher. Campsite is on left after a few km.
💬 This campsite has various amenities such as a large aquapark and extensive wellness and sports activities. Delicious dining in the auberge, but there is also a campsite restaurant. A supplement applies for a comfort pitch.

CC 14/4-29/6 1/9-22/9

📷 N 44°33'38''   E 4°17'5''

www.eurocampings.co.uk/108687

1506 Les Vans, F-07140 / Rhône-Alpes ♿ 🛜 CCe17 iD 58

- ▲ Lou Rouchetou***
- 🏠 Chassagnes
- 🗓 1 Apr - 30 Sep
- ☎ +33 (0)4-75373313
- @ info@rouchetou.com

1 AJMNOPRST	AFJN 6
2 CHJKPRVXY	ABDEFH 7
3 AELQT	ABCDEFGJKNRSV 8
4 DFINO	AELW 9
5 ABDFGHLMO	ABDFGHIJPTU 10
10A CEE	❶ €33.20
A150 5ha 98T(80-100m²) 22P	❷ €43.70

🚗 A7, exit 17 Montélimar-Nord. Then dir. Le Teil/Aubenas. In Le Teil Nioz dir. Aubenas. Then N104 dir. Alès. ± 3 km past Joyeuse turn right dir. Les Vans/Chambonas, D104A. Then D295 dir. Chassagnes. Follow road and in big bend turn right then left. Use SatNav coordinates.

🏕 A site in attractive surroundings 3 km from Les Vans. Plenty of space in the grounds and by the river. Swim and sail in the Chassezac. Swimming pool and restaurant open all season.

CC 1/4-6/7 25/8-29/9

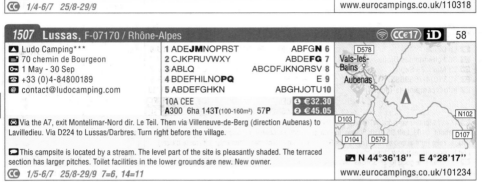

N 44°24'38'' E 4°10'16''

www.eurocampings.co.uk/110318

1507 Lussas, F-07170 / Rhône-Alpes 🛜 CCe17 iD 58

- ▲ Ludo Camping***
- 🏠 70 chemin de Bourgeon
- 🗓 1 May - 30 Sep
- ☎ +33 (0)4-84800189
- @ contact@ludocamping.com

1 ADEJMNOPRST	ABFGN 6
2 CJKPRUVWXY	ABDEFG 7
3 ABLQ	ABCDFJKNQRSV 8
4 BDEFHILNOPQ	E 9
5 ABDEFGHKN	ABGHJOTU 10
10A CEE	❶ €32.30
A300 6ha 143T(100-160m²) 57P	❷ €45.05

🚗 Via the A7, exit Montelimar-Nord dir. Le Teil. Then via Villeneuve-de-Berg (direction Aubenas) to Lavilledieu. Via D224 to Lussas/Darbres. Turn right before the village.

🏕 This campsite is located by a stream. The level part of the site is pleasantly shaded. The terraced section has larger pitches. Toilet facilities in the lower grounds are new. New owner.

CC 1/5-6/7 25/8-29/9 7=6, 14=11

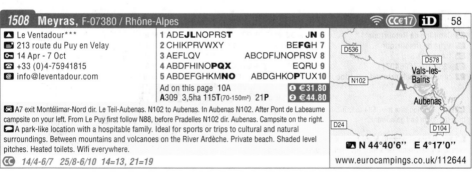

N 44°36'18'' E 4°28'17''

www.eurocampings.co.uk/101234

1508 Meyras, F-07380 / Rhône-Alpes 🛜 CCe17 iD 58

- ▲ Le Ventadour***
- 🏠 213 route du Puy en Velay
- 🗓 14 Apr - 7 Oct
- ☎ +33 (0)4-75941815
- @ info@leventadour.com

1 ADEJLNOPRST	JN 6
2 CHIKPRVWXY	BEFGH 7
3 AEFLQV	ABCDFIJNOPRSV 8
4 ABDFHINOPQX	EQRU 9
5 ABDEFGHKMNO	ABDGHKOPTUX 10
Ad on this page 10A	❶ €31.80
A309 3,5ha 115T(70-150m²) 21P	❷ €44.80

🚗 A7 exit Montélimar-Nord dir. Le Teil-Aubenas. N102 to Aubenas. In Aubenas N102. After Pont de Labeaume campsite on your left. From Le Puy first follow N88, before Pradelles N102 dir. Aubenas. Campsite on the right.

🏕 A park-like location with a hospitable family. Ideal for sports or trips to cultural and natural surroundings. Between mountains and volcanoes on the River Ardèche. Private beach. Shaded level pitches. Heated toilets. Wifi everywhere.

CC 14/4-6/7 25/8-6/10 14=13, 21=19

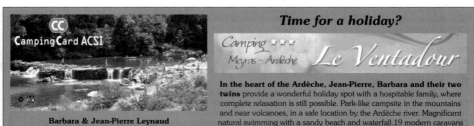

N 44°40'6'' E 4°17'0''

www.eurocampings.co.uk/112644

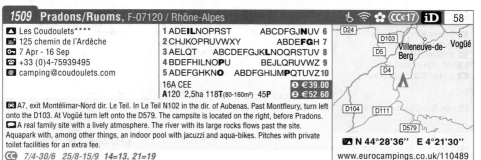

1509 Pradons/Ruoms, F-07120 / Rhône-Alpes

                                                           iD   58

- Les Coudoulets****
- 125 chemin de l'Ardèche
- 7 Apr - 16 Sep
- +33 (0)4-75939495
- camping@coudoulets.com

1	ADEILNOPRST	ABCDFGJNUV 6
2	CHJKOPRUVWXY	ABDEFGH 7
3	AELQT	ABCDEFGJKLNOQRSTUV 8
4	BDEFHILNOPU	BEJLQRUVWVZ 9
5	ADEFGHKNO	ABDFGHIJMPQTUVZ 10

16A CEE € €39.00
A120 2,5ha 118T(80-160m²) 45P € €52.60

A7, exit Montélimar-Nord dir. Le Teil. In Le Teil N102 in the dir. of Aubenas. Past Montfleury, turn left onto the D103. At Vogüé turn left onto the D579. The campsite is located on the right, before Pradons.
A real family site with a lively atmosphere. The river with its large rocks flows past the site. Aquapark with, among other things, an indoor pool with jacuzzi and aqua-bikes. Pitches with private toilet facilities for an extra fee.

7/4-30/6 25/8-15/9 14=13, 21=19

N 44°28'36'' E 4°21'30''

www.eurocampings.co.uk/110489

1510 Privas, F-07000 / Rhône-Alpes

iD   58

- Ardèche Camping****
- chemin du Camping
- 14 Apr - 28 Sep
- +33 (0)4-75640580
- ardechecamping07@gmail.com

1	ADEJLNOPQRST	ABCDFGHMN 6
2	CGKPUVXY	BEFH 7
3	BELQST	ABCDFGHKNQRSV 8
4	BCDEFILNO	AEFJVW 9
5	ADEFGHL	ABDGHJMOPTUV 10

10A CEE € €36.20
A400 5,5ha 111T(100-150m²) 55P € €48.20

A7, exit 16 Loriol. Dir. Le Pouzin. Then dir. Aubenas N304 (former D104). In Privas D2 dir. Montélimar. On 1st roundabout take dir. Villeneuve de Berg. Campsite left, next to Espace Ouvèze.
Shaded campsite on the edge of Privas. Plenty of foliage in the grounds. Fishing in the river, swimming in the heated outdoor pool or the covered pool. Lovely market and many shops in Privas. The restaurant is open in the afternoon and evening.

14/4-6/7 24/8-27/9 7=6

N 44°43'34'' E 4°35'53''

www.eurocampings.co.uk/112425

1511 Rosières, F-07260 / Rhône-Alpes

iD   58

- Domaine Arleblanc Camping****
- Domaine Arleblanc
- 30 Mar - 28 Oct
- +33 (0)4-75395311
- info@arleblanc.com

1	ADEJMNOPQRST	ABFJNU 6
2	CHJPRVWXY	ABDEFGH 7
3	AEILMQR	ABCDFGJKNRSTUV 8
4	BCDEFHILNOPQ	EILQRUVW 9
5	ACDEFGHLMNO	ABDGHIJNPTUVZ 10

6-10A CEE € €37.20
A120 7ha 127T(100-150m²) 45P € €42.20

A7, exit 17, 2nd right on roundabout, follow route N7 to Le Teil. Take the N102 to Aubenas, then the D104 towards Alès. Left before Rosières at the supermarket. Site on the right.
Domaine Arleblanc has an excellent restaurant in a historic building. Excellent toilet facilities, heated in the low season. The site has a typical French ambiance. It has extended grounds along the River Beaume with its lovely cliffs. There is free wifi on the grounds.

30/3-1/7 25/8-27/10 14=12, 21=18

N 44°27'51'' E 4°16'22''

www.eurocampings.co.uk/109088

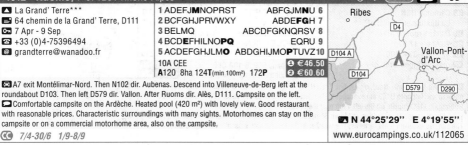

1512 Ruoms, F-07120 / Rhône-Alpes

iD   58

- La Grand' Terre***
- 64 chemin de la Grand' Terre, D111
- 7 Apr - 9 Sep
- +33 (0)4-75396494
- grandterre@wanadoo.fr

1	ADEFJMNOPRST	ABFGJMNU 6
2	BCFGHJPRVWXY	ABDEFGH 7
3	BELMQ	ABCDFGKNQRSV 8
4	BCDEFHILNOPQ	EQRU 9
5	ACDEFGHJLMO	ABDGHIJMOPTUVZ 10

10A CEE € €46.50
A120 8ha 124T(min 100m²) 172P € €60.60

A7 exit Montélimar-Nord. Then N102 dir. Aubenas. Descend into Villeneuve-de-Berg left at the roundabout D103. Then left D579 dir. Vallon. After Ruoms dir. Alès, D111. Campsite on the left.
Comfortable campsite on the Ardèche. Heated pool (420 m²) with lovely view. Good restaurant with reasonable prices. Characteristic surroundings with many sights. Motorhomes can stay on the campsite or on a commercial motorhome area, also on the campsite.

7/4-30/6 1/9-8/9

N 44°25'29'' E 4°19'55''

www.eurocampings.co.uk/112065

1513 Ruoms, F-07120 / Rhône-Alpes ♿ 📶 ❄ (CC€19) iD 58

- ⛺ Sunêlia Aluna Vacances*****
- 🏠 route de Lagorce
- 📅 30 Mar - 5 Nov
- ☎ +33 (0)4-75939315
- @ contact@alunavacances.fr

1 ADE**IL**NOPRST	ABEFGHIU	6
2 BQRUVXY	ABDE**FGH**	7
3 ADEFGHL**MNQ**	ABEFGJKNQRSV	8
4 **ABCDE**FILNO**PQUVXYZ**	AEQR	9
5 ACDEFGHJLM**O**	ABDGHIJO**P**QUVZ	10
10A CEE		❶ €57.45
A140 15ha 60**T**(120m²) 262**P**		❷ €80.85

🚗 From Ruoms take the D559 direction Lagorce. After 2 km you'll find the campsite on the right.

💬 Campsite set in woodland with many naturally laid out pitches on a somewhat rugged terrain. Many sports opportunities. An Oriental style covered and heated 1,000 m² leisure pool.

CC 30/3-29/6 1/9-3/11

Largentière

📍 N 44°26'49'' E 4°21'55''

www.eurocampings.co.uk/104143

1514 Sampzon, F-07120 / Rhône-Alpes ♿ 📶 (CC€17) 🏃 iD 58

- ⛺ Flower Camping Le Rivièra****
- 🏠 3319 route du Rocher, D161
- 📅 20 Apr - 16 Sep
- ☎ +33 (0)4-75396757
- @ leriviera@wanadoo.fr

1 ADE**JM**NOPRST	ABFGJ**NU**	6
2 CHKOPQRVWXY	ABDE**FG**H	7
3 AELQ	ABCDEFGJKNQRSV	8
4 ABCDEFHILNO**PQ**	AELQRU	9
5 ABDEFGHJL**O**	ABDHIKMPTZ	10
10A		❶ €50.70
A188 6,5ha 116**T**(85-100m²) 60**P**		❷ €67.50

🚗 A7, exit Montélimar-Nord direction Le Teil. In Le Teil N102 direction Aubenas. Go down into Villeneuve-de-Berg and left at the roundabout, D103. At Vogüé left D579 towards Vallon. About 3 km past Ruoms right over the bridge.

💬 Site on the Ardèche river with private sandy beach. Pitches under acacia trees. Excellent toilet facilities with a great deal of comfort. Close to the Pont d'Arc and La Caverne du Pont d'Arc (Grotte Chauvet).

CC 20/4-30/6 25/8-15/9 21=18

Saint-Alban-Auriolles

📍 N 44°25'45'' E 4°21'19''

www.eurocampings.co.uk/101489

1515 Sampzon, F-07120 / Rhône-Alpes ♿ 📶 (CC€13) iD 58

- ⛺ Le Chassezac***
- 🏠 RD111
- 📅 6 Apr - 9 Sep
- ☎ +33 (0)4-75396071
- @ campinglechassezac@wanadoo.fr

1 ADE**IL**NOPQRST	ABJ**NU**	6
2 CJPRVXY	ABDE**FG**H	7
3 ALQ	ABCDEFGJKNQRSV	8
4 BCDEFHINO**PXZ**	AEJLQR	9
5 ABDEFGHJKN**O**	ABDFGHIJ**P**TU	10
10A CEE		❶ €40.40
A100 4,3ha 118**T**(80-100m²) 22**P**		❷ €54.20

🚗 A7 exit Montélimar-Nord, direction Le Teil/Aubenas. In Le Teil N102 direction Aubenas. Descend into Villeneuve-de-Berg, left at roundabout D103. Then left D579 direction Vallon. After Ruoms direction Alès D111. Campsite on right.

💬 Situated in peace and quiet on the banks of the Chassezac. Thanks to a spring, there's always water in the river. Great for swimming, fishing or canoeing. The famous Pont d'Arc is about a 15-km drive away.

CC 6/4-7/7 25/8-8/9 14=13

Vallon-Pont-d'Arc

Saint-Paul-le-Jeune

📍 N 44°25'27'' E 4°18'49''

www.eurocampings.co.uk/116451

1516 Sampzon/Ruoms, F-07120 / Rhône-Alpes ♿ 📶 (CC€17) iD 58

- ⛺ Camping RCN
  La Bastide en Ardèche****
- 🏠 D111, 1 route d'Alès
- 📅 23 Mar - 17 Sep
- ☎ +31 034-3745090
- @ reserveringen@rcn.nl

1 ADE**IL**NOPRT	ABFGHIJ**NU**	6
2 CHJPRVWXY	ABDE**FG**H	7
3 AE**GH**LQT	ABCDEFGIJKNPQRSTUV	8
4 **A**BCDEFHILNO**QRX**	AELQRUVW	9
5 ACDEFGHLN	ABDGHIKPQTUZ	10
Ad on page 509 6-10A CEE		❶ €57.20
A80 7,8ha 212**T**(100-140m²) 88**P**		❷ €71.20

🚗 A7, exit Montélimar-Nord, dir. Le Teil. Then N102 direction Aubenas. Downhill at Villeneuve-de-Berg and left onto D103 at roundabout. Then left on D579 direction Vallon. Direction Alès after Ruoms, D111. Campsite on the left 1 km past the bridge.

💬 A family campsite with views of Mount Sampzon. Many activities make it great for young and old. The site has excellent toilet facilities. The weather in the low season is usually very agreeable.

CC 23/3-31/3 3/4-7/7 25/8-16/9

Ruoms

Saint-Alban-Auriolles

📍 N 44°25'23'' E 4°19'18''

www.eurocampings.co.uk/101486

RCN LA BASTIDE EN ARDÈCHE

The camping is located at the bank of the river Ardèche. A visit to Chateau de Sampzon, canoeing and Pont d'Arc are some must do's in the nearby surroundings.

CAMPING – MOBILE HOME – RESTAURANT/SNACK BAR

RCN HOLIDAY PARKS

📞 +31 85 0400 700   🌐 www.rcn.fr

1517 St. Alban-Auriolles/Ruoms, F-07120 / Rhône-Alpes   ♿ 📶 ✿ (CC€19) iD 58

- 🏕 Sunêlia Le Ranc Davaine*****
- 📧 500 chemin du Ranc Davaine
- 📅 6 Apr - 16 Sep
- ☎ +33 (0)4-75396055
- @ contact@rancdavaine.fr

1 ADE**IL**NOPRST	ACDFGHIJ**N**U	6
2 CJPRVXY	ABDE**FG**H	7
3 BDE**GHLMN**Q	ABCDEFGIJKNQRSV	8
4 **ABCD**EFILNO**PQTUVXYZ**	AELQR	9
5 ACDEFGHJLM**NO**	ABDGHIJO**P**QUVZ	10
10A CEE	❶ €56.45	
A120 13ha 93T(80-150m²) 291P	❷ €79.25	

🚗 From Ruoms on the D579 turn onto the D111 towards Alès. Right after 5 km onto the D246 (at Grospierres). Left at end of road towards Chandolas. Campsite on your left.
🏕 A large campsite. The small river is not very deep. Plenty of entertainment, but still set peacefully under oak trees. There is a lovely leisure pool with an indoor pool for those who like swimming. Wellness facilities.

CC 6/4-29/6 1/9-15/9

Saint-Alban-Auriolles
Les Vans
D104 D901 D4
Saint-Paul-le-Jeune D290
D579
D979

📍 N 44°24'49" E 4°16'18"

www.eurocampings.co.uk/104142

France

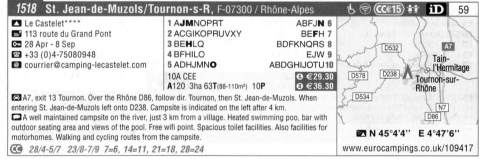

1518 St. Jean-de-Muzols/Tournon-s-R, F-07300 / Rhône-Alpes   ♿ 📶 (CC€15) 👫 iD 59

- 🏕 Le Castelet****
- 📧 113 route du Grand Pont
- 📅 28 Apr - 8 Sep
- ☎ +33 (0)4-75080948
- @ courrier@camping-lecastelet.com

1 A**JM**NOPRT	ABF**JN**	6
2 ACGIKOPRUVXY	BEFH	7
3 BE**HL**Q	BDFKNQRS	8
4 BFHILO	EJW	9
5 ADHJMN**O**	ABDGHIJOTU	10
10A CEE	❶ €29.30	
A120 3ha 63T(88-110m²) 10P	❷ €36.30	

🚗 A7, exit 13 Tournon. Over the Rhône D86, follow dir. Tournon, then St. Jean-de-Muzols. When entering St. Jean-de-Muzols left onto D238. Campsite is indicated on the left after 4 km.
🏕 A well maintained campsite on the river, just 3 km from a village. Heated swimming poo, bar with outdoor seating area and views of the pool. Free wifi point. Spacious toilet facilities. Also facilities for motorhomes. Walking and cycling routes from the campsite.

CC 28/4-5/7 23/8-7/9 7=6, 14=11, 21=18, 28=24

D532 A7
Tain-l'Hermitage
D578 D238
Tournon-sur-Rhône
D534
N7
D86

📍 N 45°4'4" E 4°47'6"

www.eurocampings.co.uk/109417

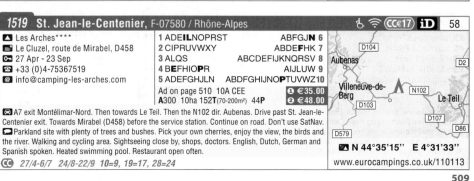

1519 St. Jean-le-Centenier, F-07580 / Rhône-Alpes   ♿ 📶 (CC€17) iD 58

- 🏕 Les Arches****
- 📧 Le Cluzel, route de Mirabel, D458
- 📅 27 Apr - 23 Sep
- ☎ +33 (0)4-75367519
- @ info@camping-les-arches.com

1 ADE**IL**NOPRST	ABFG**J**N	6
2 CIPRUVWXY	ABDE**F**HK	7
3 ALQS	ABCDEFIJKNQRSV	8
4 B**E**FHIO**PR**	AIJLUW	9
5 ADEFGHJLN	ABDFGHIJNO**P**TUVWZ	10
Ad on page 510 10A CEE	❶ €35.00	
A300 10ha 152T(70-200m²) 44P	❷ €48.00	

🚗 A7 exit Montélimar-Nord. Then towards Le Teil. Then the N102 dir. Aubenas. Drive past St. Jean-le-Centenier exit. Towards Mirabel (D458) before the service station. Continue on road. Don't use SatNav.
🏕 Parkland site with plenty of trees and bushes. Pick your own cherries, enjoy the view, the birds and the river. Walking and cycling area. Sightseeing close by, shops, doctors. English, Dutch, German and Spanish spoken. Heated swimming pool. Restaurant open often.

CC 27/4-6/7 24/8-22/9 10=9, 19=17, 28=24

D104 D2
Aubenas
Villeneuve-de-Berg N102
D103 Le Teil
D107
D579 D86

📍 N 44°35'15" E 4°31'33"

www.eurocampings.co.uk/110113

1520 St. Julien-en-St-Alban, F-07000 / Rhône-Alpes

⊚ CC€17 iD 59

▲ L'Albanou***
280 chemin de Pampelonne
13 Apr - 31 Oct
+33 (0)4-75660097
@ campingalbanou@orange.fr

1 ADE**JM**NOPQRS**T**	ABFJ**N** 6
2 ACGKOPRVWXY	ABDE**FG** 7
3 AELQS	ABCDEFHNRV 8
4 BFHILU	E 9
5 ABDEFGHJN**O**	ABDFGHJOTU 10
10A CEE	❶ €30.10
A107 2ha 84**T**(100-110m²) 3**P**	❷ €40.10

A7 exit 16 Loriol, then towards Le Pouzin. Then dir. Aubenas via D104. Site is signposted on left before village (at small industrial site). Then left again and 2nd site on right.
Ideal springboard to your holiday destination, but also suitable for longer stays. Swimming pool with jacuzzi. Heated toilet facilities. Free wifi point. Nearly all pitches are marked out by hedges. Easily reached from the A7 autoroute.
CC 13/4-3/7 21/8-30/10 8=7, 14=12, 21=18, 28=24

N 44°45'26'' E 4°42'46''
www.eurocampings.co.uk/104138

1521 St. Laurent-du-Pape, F-07800 / Rhône-Alpes

♿ ⊚ CC€19 ♦♦ iD 59

▲ Camping La Garenne***
383 Montée de la Garenne
1 Apr - 30 Sep
+33 (0)4-75622462
@ info@campinglagarenne-ardeche.fr

1 A**JM**NOPRT	AF 6
2 OPQRUVWXY	ABDE**FG** 7
3 BDLQ	ABCDEFIKNQRSV 8
4 BDEFHILO	AEU 9
5 ABDEFGHLMN	ABDHJP 10
6-10A CEE	❶ €37.70
A120 6ha 117**T**(80-125m²) 19**P**	❷ €49.70

A7, exit 16 (Loriol). D104 to Privas. After Rhônebrug right D86 to La Voulte s/Rhône. Roundabout in La Voulte, direction St. Laurent-du-Pape. After La Voulte left D120 to St. Laurent. Cross bridge and left. Right after 200m (before La Poste).
On the edge of a wood, close to the village centre. Friendly atmosphere. Plenty of walking and cycling opportunities. A wide range of daily menus. Jeu de boules. Dutch, French, English and German spoken.
CC 1/4-7/7 25/8-29/9

N 44°49'34'' E 4°45'44''
www.eurocampings.co.uk/100475

1522 St. Martin-d'Ardèche, F-07700 / Rhône-Alpes

⊚ CC€15 ♦♦ iD 55a

▲ Camping Le Pontet***
quartier Le Pontet
6 Apr - 24 Sep
+33 (0)4-75046307
@ contact@campinglepontet.com

1 ADE**JM**NOPRT	AFU 6
2 BORVXY	ABDEF 7
3 AELQS	ABCDFKNORSV 8
4 ABCDFHILNO**P**	EQR 9
5 ABDEFGHJLN	ABFGHJ**P**R 10
16A CEE	❶ €27.40
A50 2,5ha 81**T**(80-120m²) 18**P**	❷ €34.00

A7, exit Bollène, direction Pont St. Esprit. Then N86 as far as St. Just. Then follow St. Martin d'Ardèche. Then Sauze landing stage. Campsite on the left.
Nice, smaller campsite with young, enthusiastic owners. The swimming pool and the play and sports facilities are on separate grounds. The famous Route des Gorges de L'Ardeche begins in St. Martin d'Ardeche (1 km). Free wifi in the low season.
CC 6/4-6/7 24/8-22/9 7=6

N 44°18'14'' E 4°35'4''
www.eurocampings.co.uk/112734

France

1523 St. Martin-d'Ardèche, F-07700 / Rhône-Alpes ♿ 🛜 CC€17 iD 58

- ⛺ Des Gorges****
- 🛒 Sauze
- 📅 27 Apr - 16 Sep
- ☎ +33 (0)4-75046109
- @ info@camping-des-gorges.com

1 ADEJ**M**NOPRST	ABFGJM**N**U 6
2 CHKPRUVWXY	ABDE**FG**H 7
3 AELQRT	ABCDEFGJKNOQRSV 8
4 BCDFILNO**Q**U	ELQR 9
5 ACDEFGHJL**O**	ABDGHIJ**P**TU10

10A CEE ❶ €44.20
A60 3,5ha 114**T**(80-120m²) 26**P** ❷ €60.20

🅿 Route A7, exit Bollène direction Pont-St-Esprit. Then N86 to St. Just. Then follow St. Martin-d'Ardèche and Sauze débarcadère. Campsite on left.

💬 Des Gorges has a lovely pool with a bubble wall. Lovely views from the terraces. Pitches under tall trees and the Ardèche flows past the grounds. St. Martin d'Ardèche is a lovely tourist village. Toilet facilities partially renovated. Family shower. Free wifi in the low season throughout the grounds.

CC 27/4-30/6 1/9-15/9

📍 N 44°18'40'' E 4°33'22''

www.eurocampings.co.uk/104150

1524 St. Martin-d'Ardèche, F-07700 / Rhône-Alpes 🛜 CC€17 iD 55a

- ⛺ Huttopia Le Moulin***
- 🛒 Le Moulin
- 📅 20 Apr - 30 Sep
- ☎ +33 (0)4-75046620
- @ lemoulin@huttopia.com

1 ADE**IL**NOPRST	ABFJ**N**U 6
2 CFGJKPRVWXY	ABDE**FG** 7
3 BELQR	ABCDEFGINQRSV 8
4 BCDFIO**PQ**	ADEJ 9
5 ABDEFGHJKN	ABDGHJNOTU10

10A CEE ❶ €37.20
A50 7ha 111**T**(100-200m²) 89**P** ❷ €50.90

🅿 A7 exit Bollène. From there towards Pont Saint Esprit. Then follow 'Gorges de l'Ardeche' signs as far as Saint Martin-d'Ardèche.

💬 The campsite is located near the Gorges de l'Ardèche in natural surroundings. An ideal location for taking trips out. Located at the end of the famous descent of the Ardèche by canoe. Lovely pitches on the banks of the river. 300 metres from the village.

CC 20/4-28/6 2/9-29/9

📍 N 44°18'2'' E 4°34'17''

www.eurocampings.co.uk/116253

France

1525 St. Privat, F-07200 / Rhône-Alpes ♿ 🛜 CC€15 iD 58

- ⛺ Flower Camping Le Plan d'Eau***
- 🛒 route de Lussas
- 📅 28 Apr - 22 Sep
- ☎ +33 (0)4-75354498
- @ info@campingleplandeau.fr

1 ADE**JM**NOPQRS**T**	ABFGJ**N** 6
2 CGHKPRVXY	ABDE**FH** 7
3 AEFLQS	ABCDEFJKNRSV 8
4 BCDFGHILNO**Q**	AJ 9
5 ABDEFGHJLMN**O**	ABDGHIJO**P**TVZ10

Ad on this page 8A CEE ❶ €38.15
A204 3ha 75**T**(80-150m²) 27**P** ❷ €48.55

🅿 A7 exit Montélimar-Nord, direction Le Teil/Aubenas. Right onto D304 towards St. Privat/Privas before Aubenas. After bridge direction Lussas at roundabout. Campsite on the right. Do not use SatNav!

💬 A campsite with direct access to the River Ardèche. Sandy beach with deckchairs. Lovely views of the surrounding rock formations. Not far from Aubenas. Pitches often surrounded by hedges. You pay extra for XL pitches.

CC 28/4-6/7 25/8-21/9 27=24

📍 N 44°37'8'' E 4°25'56''

www.eurocampings.co.uk/110115

1526 St. Sauveur-de-Montagut, F-07190 / Rhône-Alpes ⚑ 🛜 (CC€19) iD 58

- ⛺ l'Ardéchois*****
- 🏠 Le Chambon Gluiras, D102
- 📅 19 May - 22 Sep
- ☎ +33 (0)4-75666187
- @ ardechois.camping@wanadoo.fr

1 ADE**JM**NOPQRST	ABFGJ**N** 6
2 CFGHIKPRUVWXY	ABDE**FG**H 7
3 AELQ	ABCDEFGIJKNQRSV 8
4 BCD**EF**HILO**PQ**	EJU 9
5 ABDEFHLMN	ABDGHJMN**P**TU 10
10A CEE	❶ €37.35
A420 6,5ha 78**T**(90-160m²) 56**P**	❷ €52.55

🚗 A7 exit 15 Valence-Sud. Dir. Le Puy-en-Velay. N7 Montélimar. Right on D111a to Carmes-sur-Rhone. D86 to Privas. In Beauchastel D21. D120 dir. Le Cheylard to St. Sauveur. Then D102 to Mezilhac. Campsite on right after 8 km.

💬 This site is located in the middle of the Ardèche. The ideal site if you are seeking rest, space, luxury and friendliness. A site where you are not just a number but where a family atmosphere and a personal approach are important.

(CC) 19/5-6/7 1/9-21/9

www.eurocampings.co.uk/100474

N 44°49'44'' E 4°31'23''

1527 St. Thomé, F-07220 / Rhône-Alpes 🛜 (CC€13) iD 58

- ⛺ Le Médiéval***
- 🏠 120 Impasse du Médiéval
- 📅 27 Apr - 30 Sep
- ☎ +33 (0)4-75526876
- @ contact@campinglemedievalardeche.fr

1 ADEJMNOPRST	ABFG**N** 6
2 ACKOPRVXY	ABDE**FG**H 7
3 ALQT	ABCDEFGJNQRSV 8
4 BDEFHILNO**PQ**	AEIQR 9
5 ABDEFGHJKMN	ABDHJ**P**TU 10
Ad on this page 10-16A CEE	❶ €31.90
A80 4ha 84**T**(90-120m²) 38**P**	❷ €46.75

🚗 A7 exit Montélimar-Sud/Viviers. After 1 km on N7 dir. Montélimar take D126/D73 to Viviers, then N86 dir. Le Teil. After 6 km take D107 to St. Thomé. Site on the left. From North: continue to 1st roundabout St. Thomé, then turn back to D107, campsite on left.

💬 Genuine French ambiance. Views from the terrace over the pool or authentic reception building. Some pitches under old tall trees. New toilet facilities. Wifi on nearly the entire grounds.

(CC) 27/4-6/7 1/9-29/9 7=6, 14=11

www.eurocampings.co.uk/108783

N 44°30'25'' E 4°37'9''

1528 Vallon-Pont-d'Arc, F-07150 / Rhône-Alpes ⚑ 🛜 (CC€17) iD 58

- ⛺ Beau Rivage****
- 🏠 quartier les Mazes
- 📅 28 Apr - 8 Sep
- ☎ +33 (0)4-75880354
- @ campingbeaurivage@wanadoo.fr

1 ADE**JM**NOPRST	ABFGJM**N**UV 6
2 CHPRVXY	ABDE**F**H 7
3 BEFLQT	ABCDEFJKNOQRSV 8
4 BDEILNO**PQ**	ELQR 9
5 ABDEFGHJL**NO**	ABDFHIJOTU 10
Ad on page 513 10A CEE	❶ €42.20
A100 2,2ha 86**T**(100-110m²) 14**P**	❷ €56.20

🚗 From Ruoms take D579 dir. Vallon-Pont-d'Arc. Turn right at Les Mazes, left at end of road, campsite on right. Don't use SatNav but rather these route instructions.

💬 This campsite is located among the vineyards by the river. It has a wide beach and there is enough water in the Ardèche for swimming and sailing. The heated swimming pool has a bubble wall. Plenty of shaded pitches. Heated toilet facilities. The owners are very friendly and hospitable.

(CC) 28/4-6/7 24/8-7/9 14=13, 21=19

www.eurocampings.co.uk/104146

N 44°24'23'' E 4°21'51''

Beau Rivage ★ ★ ★ ★

Very quiet campsite in a magnificent area by the Ardèche river. The wide campsite beach along the river is 100m long. Friendly management. Excellent and clean toilet facilities. Heated swimming pool and paddling pool.

07150 Vallon-Pont-d'Arc
Tel. 04-75880354
E-mail: campingbeaurivage@wanadoo.fr
Internet: www.beaurivage-camping.fr

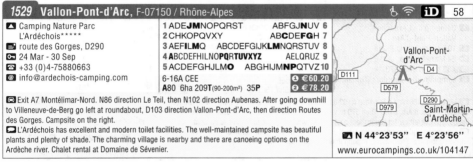

1529 Vallon-Pont-d'Arc, F-07150 / Rhône-Alpes ♿ 🛜 iD 58

- ⛰ Camping Nature Parc L'Ardéchois*****
- 🛏 route des Gorges, D290
- 🕐 24 Mar - 30 Sep
- ☎ +33 (0)4-75880663
- @ info@ardechois-camping.com

1 ADEJMNOPQRST	ABFGJNUV 6	
2 CHKOPQVXY	ABCDEFGH 7	
3 AEFILMQ ABCDEFGIJKLMNQRSTUV 8		
4 ABCDEFHILNOPQRTUVXYZ	AELQRUZ 9	
5 ACDEFGHJLMO ABGHIJMNPQTVZ 10		
6-16A CEE	❶ €60.20	
A80 6ha 209T(90-200m²) 35P	❷ €78.20	

🚗 Exit A7 Montélimar-Nord. N86 direction Le Teil, then N102 direction Aubenas. After going downhill to Villeneuve-de-Berg go left at roundabout, D103 direction Vallon-Pont-d'Arc, then direction Routes des Gorges. Campsite on the right.

💬 L'Ardéchois has excellent and modern toilet facilities. The well-maintained campsite has beautiful plants and plenty of shade. The charming village is nearby and there are canoeing options on the Ardèche river. Chalet rental at Domaine de Sévenier.

⛰ N 44°23'53" E 4°23'56"

www.eurocampings.co.uk/104147

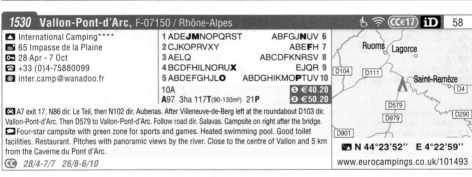

1530 Vallon-Pont-d'Arc, F-07150 / Rhône-Alpes ♿ 🛜 (CC€17) iD 58

- ⛰ International Camping****
- 🛏 65 Impasse de la Plaine
- 🕐 28 Apr - 7 Oct
- ☎ +33 (0)4-75880099
- @ inter.camp@wanadoo.fr

1 ADEJMNOPQRST	ABFGJNUV 6	
2 CJKOPRVXY	ABEFH 7	
3 AELQ	ABCDFKNRSV 8	
4 BCDFHILNORUX	EJQR 9	
5 ABDEFGHJLO ABDGHIKMOPTUV 10		
10A	❶ €40.20	
A97 3ha 117T(90-130m²) 21P	❷ €50.20	

🚗 A7 exit 17. N86 dir. Le Teil, then N102 dir. Aubenas. After Villeneuve-de-Berg left at the roundabout D103 dir. Vallon-Pont-d'Arc. Then D579 to Vallon-Pont-d'Arc. Follow road dir. Salavas. Campsite on right after the bridge.

💬 Four-star campsite with green zone for sports and games. Heated swimming pool. Good toilet facilities. Restaurant. Pitches with panoramic views by the river. Close to the centre of Vallon and 5 km from the Caverne du Pont d'Arc.

🆑 28/4-7/7 26/8-6/10

⛰ N 44°23'52" E 4°22'59"

www.eurocampings.co.uk/101493

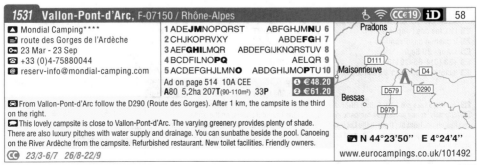

1531 Vallon-Pont-d'Arc, F-07150 / Rhône-Alpes ♿ 🛜 (CC€19) iD 58

- ⛰ Mondial Camping****
- 🛏 route des Gorges de l'Ardèche
- 🕐 23 Mar - 23 Sep
- ☎ +33 (0)4-75880044
- @ reserv-info@mondial-camping.com

1 ADEJMNOPQRST	ABFGHJMNU 6	
2 CHJOKPRVXY	ABDEFGH 7	
3 AEFGHILMQR ABDEFGIJKNQRSTUV 8		
4 BCDFILNOPQ	AELQR 9	
5 ACDEFGHJLMNO ABDGHIJMOPTU 10		
Ad on page 514 10A CEE	❶ €48.20	
A80 5,2ha 207T(90-110m²) 33P	❷ €61.20	

🚗 From Vallon-Pont-d'Arc follow the D290 (Route des Gorges). After 1 km, the campsite is the third on the right.

💬 This lovely campsite is close to Vallon-Pont-d'Arc. The varying greenery provides plenty of shade. There are also luxury pitches with water supply and drainage. You can sunbathe beside the pool. Canoeing on the River Ardèche from the campsite. Refurbished restaurant. New toilet facilities. Friendly owners.

🆑 23/3-6/7 26/8-22/9

⛰ N 44°23'50" E 4°24'4"

www.eurocampings.co.uk/101492

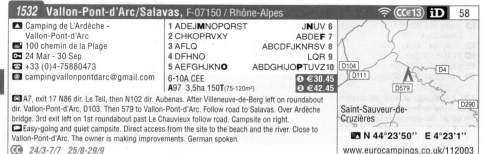

Three kilometres from the famous Pont-d'Arc and in a wonderfully sunny Mediterranean climate with direct access to the river. It has a heated swimming paradise, canoe rental and many wonderful and cultural activities, such as riding, hiking and bicycle routes and the interesting prehistoric Chauvet cave. With a daily entertainment program for all ages in the high season, including a mini club, sports tournaments and evening entertainment.

MONDIAL Camping ☆ ☆ ☆ ☆

Mondial Camping is located in an exceptionally lovely area in the heart of the 'Gorges de l'Ardèche'

Route des Gorges de l'Ardèche
07150 Vallon-Pont-d'Arc
Tel. 04-75880044 • Fax 04-75371373
E-mail: reserv-info@mondial-camping.com
Internet: www.mondial-camping.com

1532 Vallon-Pont-d'Arc/Salavas, F-07150 / Rhône-Alpes 🛜 (CC€13) iD 58

⛺ Camping de L'Ardèche - Vallon-Pont-d'Arc	1 ADEJ**M**NOPQRST	J**N**UV 6
🏠 100 chemin de la Plage	2 CHKOPRVXY	ABDE**F** 7
🕐 24 Mar - 30 Sep	3 AFLQ	ABCDFJKNRSV 8
☎ +33 (0)4-75880473	4 DFHNO	LQR 9
@ campingvallonpontdarc@gmail.com	5 AEFGHJKN**O**	ABDGHIJO**P**TUVZ10
	6-10A CEE	❶ €30.45
	A97 3,5ha 150**T**(75-120m²)	❷ €42.45

🚗 A7, exit 17 N86 dir. Le Teil, then N102 dir. Aubenas. After Villeneuve-de-Berg left on roundabout dir. Vallon-Pont-d'Arc, D103. Then 579 to Vallon-Pont-d'Arc. Follow road to Salavas. Over Ardèche bridge. 3rd exit left on 1st roundabout past Le Chauvieux follow road. Campsite on right.
💬 Easy-going and quiet campsite. Direct access from the site to the beach and the river. Close to Vallon-Pont-d'Arc. The owner is making improvements. German spoken.
(CC) 24/3-7/7 25/8-29/9

Saint-Sauveur-de-Cruzières

🏕 N 44°23'50" E 4°23'1"

www.eurocampings.co.uk/112003

1533 Villeneuve-de-Berg, F-07170 / Rhône-Alpes 🛜 (CC€19) iD 58

⛺ Domaine le Pommier*****	1 ADEI**L**NOPRS**T**	ABFGHI 6
🏠 Quartier Forcemâle, RN102	2 CFJKOPRUVWXY	ABDE**FG**H 7
🕐 13 Apr - 12 Sep	3 BE**I**L**M**Q	ABCDEFGIJKNQRSV 8
☎ +33 (0)4-75948281	4 **A**BCD**E**FHILNO**P**U	AEJW 9
@ lepommier@cielavillage.com	5 ACDEFGHIJL**MN**	ABDFGHIJM**P**QTUXZ10
	6-10A CEE	❶ €53.70
	A337 40ha 171**T**(80-120m²) 595**P**	❷ €74.70

🚗 A7 exit Montélimar-Nord direction Le Teil/Aubenas. In Le Teil take the N102 to Villeneuve-de-Berg. Just before the village and the roundabout you'll find the campsite on the right hand side.
💬 This place is ideal for those who like to have lots of fun. There is always something fun to do. There is a level part and there are terraces with wonderful views of Mirabel. Various restaurants. Lovely swimming pools. New management.
(CC) 13/4-22/6 1/9-11/9

Aubenas

Villeneuve-de-Berg

🏕 N 44°34'21" E 4°30'40"

www.eurocampings.co.uk/108689

1534 Barjac, F-48000 / Languedoc-Roussillon ♿ 🛜 (CC€15) iD 26 A1

⛺ Le Clos des Peupliers**	1 ADE**JM**NORT	ABFG**J**N 6
🏠 2 chemin des Peupliers	2 CFOPRVWXY	ABDE**FG**HK 7
🕐 1 Apr - 30 Sep	3 ALQ	ABCDEFJNOQRSTU 8
☎ +33 (0)4-66470116	4 DFHIN**PQ**	BEI 9
@ leclosdespeupliers@wanadoo.fr	5 ADEFGHJ**NO**	ABGHIJOV10
	10A CEE	❶ €20.50
	A654 3,2ha 61**T**(90-240m²) 39**P**	❷ €28.50

🚗 From A75 take exit 39.1. Follow RN88 direction Mende until Barjac. Campsite is indicated.
💬 A homely, sunny and shady campsite in the heart of the beautiful Lozère, on the banks of the Lot. The heated pool and the trout in the Lot await you. The village is not far away and the surrounding hills offer a beautiful panoramic view. A good base for exploring the Tarn and a number of typical French, active villages.
(CC) 1/4-7/7 25/8-29/9

Marvejols

Mende

🏕 N 44°30'3" E 3°24'26"

www.eurocampings.co.uk/121637

France

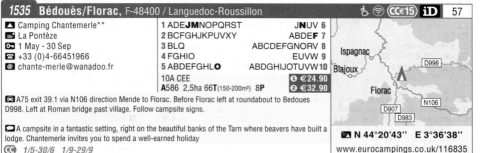

1535 Bédouès/Florac, F-48400 / Languedoc-Roussillon   🚻 🛜 (CC€15) iD   57

- 🏕 Camping Chantemerle**
- 📧 La Pontèze
- 📅 1 May - 30 Sep
- ☎ +33 (0)4-66451966
- @ chante-merle@wanadoo.fr

1 ADE**JM**NOPQRST	JNUV 6
2 BCFGHJKPUVXY	ABDE**F** 7
3 BLQ	ABCDEFGNORV 8
4 FGHIO	EUVW 9
5 ABDEFGHL**O**	ABDGHIJOTUVW 10
10A CEE	❶ €24.90
A586 2,5ha 66**T**(150-200m²) 8**P**	❷ €32.90

🚗 A75 exit 39.1 via N106 direction Mende to Florac. Before Florac left at roundabout to Bedoues D998. Left at Roman bridge past village. Follow campsite signs.

💬 A campsite in a fantastic setting, right on the beautiful banks of the Tarn where beavers have built a lodge. Chantemerle invites you to spend a well-earned holiday

CC 1/5-30/6 1/9-29/9

📍 N 44°20'43'' E 3°36'38''

www.eurocampings.co.uk/116835

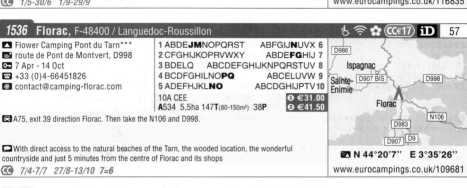

1536 Florac, F-48400 / Languedoc-Roussillon   🚻 🛜 🌸 (CC€17) iD   57

- 🏕 Flower Camping Pont du Tarn***
- 📧 route de Pont de Montvert, D998
- 📅 7 Apr - 14 Oct
- ☎ +33 (0)4-66451826
- @ contact@camping-florac.com

1 ABDE**JM**NOPQRST	ABFGIJ**N**UVX 6
2 CFGHIJKOPRVWXY	ABDE**FG**HIJ 7
3 BDELQ	ABCDEFGHIJKNPQRSTUV 8
4 BCDFGHILNO**PQ**	ABCELUVW 9
5 ADEFHJKL**NO**	ABCDGHIJPTV 10
10A CEE	❶ €31.00
A534 5,5ha 147**T**(80-150m²) 38**P**	❷ €41.50

🚗 A75, exit 39 direction Florac. Then take the N106 and D998.

💬 With direct access to the natural beaches of the Tarn, the wooded location, the wonderful countryside and just 5 minutes from the centre of Florac and its shops

CC 7/4-7/7 27/8-13/10 7=6

📍 N 44°20'7'' E 3°35'26''

www.eurocampings.co.uk/109681

France

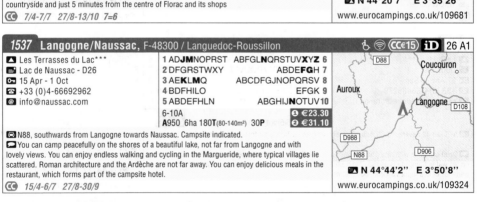

1537 Langogne/Naussac, F-48300 / Languedoc-Roussillon   🚻 🛜 (CC€15) iD   26 A1

- 🏕 Les Terrasses du Lac***
- 📧 Lac de Naussac - D26
- 📅 15 Apr - 1 Oct
- ☎ +33 (0)4-66692962
- @ info@naussac.com

1 AD**JM**NOPRST	ABFGL**N**QRSTUV**XYZ** 6
2 DFGRSTWXY	ABDE**FG**H 7
3 AE**KLMQ**	ABCDFGJNOPQRSV 8
4 BDFHILO	EFGK 9
5 ABDEFHLN	ABGHIJ**N**OTUV 10
6-10A	❶ €23.30
A950 6ha 180**T**(80-140m²) 30**P**	❷ €31.10

🚗 N88, southwards from Langogne towards Naussac. Campsite indicated.
💬 You can camp peacefully on the shores of a beautiful lake, not far from Langogne and with lovely views. You can enjoy endless walking and cycling in the Margueride, where typical villages lie scattered. Roman architecture and the Ardèche are not far away. You can enjoy delicious meals in the restaurant, which forms part of the campsite hotel.

CC 15/4-6/7 27/8-30/9

📍 N 44°44'2'' E 3°50'8''

www.eurocampings.co.uk/109324

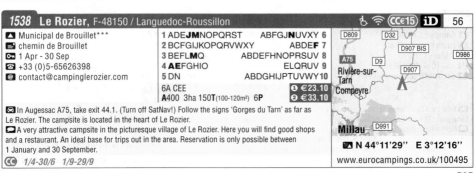

1538 Le Rozier, F-48150 / Languedoc-Roussillon   🚻 🛜 (CC€15) iD   56

- 🏕 Municipal de Brouillet***
- 📧 chemin de Brouillet
- 📅 1 Apr - 30 Sep
- ☎ +33 (0)5-65626398
- @ contact@campinglerozier.com

1 ADE**JM**NOPQRST	ABFG**J**N**UVX 6
2 BCFGIJKOPQRVWXY	ABDE**F** 7
3 BEF**LMQ**	ABDEFHNOPRSUV 8
4 **AE**FGHIO	ELQRUV 9
5 DN	ABDGHIJPTUVWY 10
6A CEE	❶ €23.10
A400 3ha 150**T**(100-120m²) 6**P**	❷ €33.10

🚗 In Augessac A75, take exit 44.1. (Turn off SatNav!) Follow the signs 'Gorges du Tarn' as far as Le Rozier. The campsite is located in the heart of Le Rozier.
💬 A very attractive campsite in the picturesque village of Le Rozier. Here you will find good shops and a restaurant. An ideal base for trips out in the area. Reservation is only possible between 1 January and 30 September.

CC 1/4-30/6 1/9-29/9

📍 N 44°11'29'' E 3°12'16''

www.eurocampings.co.uk/100495

1539 Le Rozier/Peyreleau, F-12720 / Languedoc-Roussillon   ♿ 🛜 (CC€15) iD   56

- 🏕 Les Prades****
- 🚏 D187
- 📅 1 May - 15 Sep
- ☎ +33 (0)5-65626209
- @ lesprades@orange.fr

1	ADEJMNOPQRST	ABFGHIJMNUXY	6
2	ACFGJKPQVWXY	ABDEFGH	7
3	BDELMQRS	ABCDEFGHIJKNOPQRSTUV	8
4	**ABDE**FGHI**J**LO**PQ**TUY	BEGQR	9
5	ACDEFGHJLMNO	ABDFGHIJNOSTVW	10

6A CEE   ① €37.90
A384 5ha 178T(100-120m²) 37P   ② €54.90

🚗 A75, exit 44.1 (navigation off!). N9 as far as Aguessac. Left onto the D907 Gorges du Tarn. Direction La Cresse. In La Cresse turn left D187. Campsite on the left after 4 km.
💬 A lovely campsite on the River Tarn. Clean toilet facilities, sauna, jacuzzi, bubble bath, the largest heated leisure pool in the area. Free tennis and 1 hour's free use of canoe per family for use near campsite. The à la carte restaurant is open all season.
CC 1/5-7/7   25/8-14/9

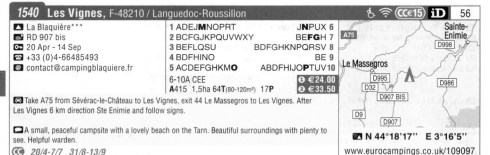

🏔 N 44°11'59''   E 3°10'24''
www.eurocampings.co.uk/103985

1540 Les Vignes, F-48210 / Languedoc-Roussillon   ♿ 🛜 (CC€15) iD   56

- 🏕 La Blaquière***
- 🚏 RD 907 bis
- 📅 20 Apr - 14 Sep
- ☎ +33 (0)4-66485493
- @ contact@campingblaquiere.fr

1	ADEJMNOPRT	JNPUX	6
2	BCFGJKPQUVWXY	BEFGH	7
3	BEFLQSU	BDFGHKNPQRSV	8
4	BDFHINO	BE	9
5	ACDEFGHKMO	ABDFHIJOPTUV	10

6-10A CEE   ① €24.00
A415 1,5ha 64T(80-120m²) 17P   ② €33.50

🚗 Take A75 from Sévérac-le-Château to Les Vignes, exit 44 Le Massegros to Les Vignes. After Les Vignes 6 km direction Ste Enimie and follow signs.
💬 A small, peaceful campsite with a lovely beach on the Tarn. Beautiful surroundings with plenty to see. Helpful warden.
CC 20/4-7/7   31/8-13/9

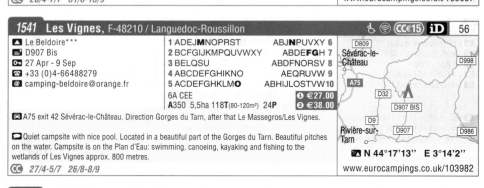

🏔 N 44°18'17''   E 3°16'5''
www.eurocampings.co.uk/109097

1541 Les Vignes, F-48210 / Languedoc-Roussillon   ♿ 🛜 (CC€15) iD   56

- 🏕 Le Beldoire***
- 🚏 D907 Bis
- 📅 27 Apr - 9 Sep
- ☎ +33 (0)4-66488279
- @ camping-beldoire@orange.fr

1	ADEJMNOPRST	ABJNPUVXY	6
2	BCFGIJKMPQUVWXY	ABDEFGH	7
3	BELQSU	ABDFNORSV	8
4	ABCDEFGHIKNO	AEQRUVW	9
5	ACDEFGHKLMO	ABHIJLOSTVW	10

6A CEE   ① €27.00
A350 5,5ha 118T(80-120m²) 24P   ② €38.00

🚗 A75 exit 42 Sévérac-le-Château. Direction Gorges du Tarn, after that Le Massegros/Les Vignes.
💬 Quiet campsite with nice pool. Located in a beautiful part of the Gorges du Tarn. Beautiful pitches on the water. Campsite is on the Plan d'Eau: swimming, canoeing, kayaking and fishing to the wetlands of Les Vignes approx. 800 metres.
CC 27/4-5/7   26/8-8/9

🏔 N 44°17'13''   E 3°14'2''
www.eurocampings.co.uk/103982

1542 St. Alban-sur-Limagnole, F-48120 / Languedoc-Roussillon   ♿ 🛜 (CC€15) iD   26 A1

- 🏕 Camping Le Galier**
- 🚏 route de Saint Chély
- 📅 1 Mar - 1 Oct
- ☎ +33 (0)4-66315880
- @ accueil@campinglegalier.fr

1	ABDJMNOPRST	CDFGJN	6
2	BCGPWXY	ABDEFH	7
3	ALMQ	ABEFNOPRV	8
4	BEFI	E	9
5	ADEGHMNO	ABHIJLOTV	10

6A   ① €19.70
A950 4ha 66T(100-200m²) 24P   ② €26.30

🚗 Take the A75 as far as St. Alban, exit 34, then take the N106 in the direction of St. Alban-sur-Limagnole. The campsite is located about 800 metres before the village, on the D987.
💬 Not far from the A75 in the Margeride region at the foot of a typical French village. Spacious pitches on the edge of a wood and on both banks of the Limagnole, wonderfully healthy. Free bikes for children. Fishing in the Limagnole. Walks with a locally available guide.
CC 1/3-8/7   26/8-30/9

🏔 N 44°46'31''   E 3°22'20''
www.eurocampings.co.uk/103973

1543 Anduze, F-30140 / Languedoc-Roussillon   ♿ 📶 CC€17 iD   57

🏕 Cévennes-Provence***
📧 Corbès-Thoiras
📅 20 Mar - 1 Oct
☎ +33 (0)4-66617310
@ info@campingcp.com

1 ADE**JM**NOPRT	JNP	6
2 BCFGHIJKOPQUVWXY	ABDE**FGH**	7
3 BEF**HILMQ**RUV	ABCDEFGHIJKNOPRSV	8
4 **ABDEFHIJOPQXZ**	JL	9
5 ACDEFGHKLM**NO**	ABDGHIJMNOTUVZ	10

10A CEE   ❶ €34.70
A125 30ha 226T(80-200m²) 16P   ❷ €45.10

🚗 Leave the A7 at Bollène. At Alès drive in dir. of Montpellier. In Anduze take the D907 dir. St. Jean-du-Gard. 3 km after Anduze turn right at bus stop (D284 Rte de Corbes).
💬 Lovely, natural campsite between two branches of the river Gardon. Direct access to a private beach. Swimming in the clear river water. Its micro-climate supports more than 120 types of trees and many different plants. New toilet block in 2017. Run by the same family for 60 years.
CC 20/3-30/6   1/9-30/9

📷 N 44°4'41''   E 3°57'53''
www.eurocampings.co.uk/103991

1544 Anduze, F-30140 / Languedoc-Roussillon   ♿ 📶 CC€17 iD   57

🏕 Le Castel Rose****
📧 610 chemin Recoulin
📅 7 Apr - 16 Sep
☎ +33 (0)4-66618015
@ castelrose@wanadoo.fr

1 A**JM**NOPRST	ABFGHIJ**N**PX	6
2 BCFGHIJKOPQVWXY	ABDE**FGH**	7
3 BDE**HK**LQRTV	ABCDEFGHIJKNOPQRSTU	8
4 ABCDFGHILNO**PQR**TUVX	CELQ	9
5 ACDEFGHJKLM**NO**	ABCDGHIJNO**P**TU	10

10A CEE   ❶ €44.20
A130 7ha 182T(100-260m²) 88P   ❷ €60.20

🚗 From Anduze the D907 dir. St. Jean-du-Gard. Turn right after the bend and continue to the end of the road.
💬 Family site on the banks of the Gardon with private beaches and views of the bamboo plantation. Large shaded pitches, level grounds with heated 1,800 m² water park. Wellness area, petanque, trampoline and playgrounds. Bar, snack bar, supermarket and restaurant. Free wifi. Pitches by the river and larger than 130 m²: 1 Euro per day extra.
CC 7/4-1/7   27/8-15/9

📷 N 44°3'52''   E 3°58'37''
www.eurocampings.co.uk/103992

1545 Anduze, F-30140 / Languedoc-Roussillon   ♿ 📶 CC€17 iD   57

🏕 Le Pradal****
📧 rte de Générargues
📅 1 Apr - 30 Sep
☎ +33 (0)4-66617981
@ camping-le-pradal@orange.fr

1 ADE**JM**NOPQRST	AFJM**N**O	6
2 BCFGHJKOPQVWXY	ABDE**FGH**	7
3 BF**HLMQ**RST	ABCDEFGJKNRSTUV	8
4 DFGHINO**PQXZ**	ABE	9
5 ACDEFGHJKM**O**	ABDGHIJMO**P**TUW	10

10A CEE   ❶ €34.20
A150 3,5ha 106T(90-400m²) 35P   ❷ €45.20

🚗 A7 Bollène. Then take Bagnols-Alès-Anduze road, turn right before the bridge, follow signs (500m).
💬 A ten-minute walk from Anduze and the bamboo garden. A pleasant site with a private beach on the River Gardon, large swimming pool. Peaceful, agreeable atmosphere. Large, level shaded pitches. Bar, restaurant with outdoor seating area, fresh bread, newspapers. Free tennis, jeu de boules, table tennis, playground. Free wifi.
CC 1/4-14/7   1/9-29/9

📷 N 44°3'44''   E 3°58'58''
www.eurocampings.co.uk/110491

1546 Anduze, F-30140 / Languedoc-Roussillon   ♿ 📶 CC€15 iD   57

🏕 Les Fauvettes***
📧 rte de St. Jean-du-Gard
📅 21 Apr - 30 Sep
☎ +33 (0)4-66617223
@ camping-les-fauvettes@wanadoo.fr

1 ADE**JM**NOPQRST	ABFHM**N**	6
2 BFGOPUVXY	ABDE**F**H	7
3 BE**HK**LQT	ABCDEFGINOQRSV	8
4 BCDFGILNO**PQ**U	AEJUV	9
5 ADEFGHJK**N**	ABGHIJOT	10

10A CEE   ❶ €29.70
A130 4ha 102T(90-140m²) 42P   ❷ €40.70

🚗 Campsite on the D907 Anduze - St. Jean-du-Gard. Signposted.

💬 A 10-minute walk from the centre. 500 metres to the river by a private footpath and the amenities are close by. Friendly campsite, marked-out pitches with shade, heated swimming pool, toddlers' pool, water slides, jeu de boules, table tennis. Free wifi.
CC 21/4-3/7   21/8-29/9

📷 N 44°3'37''   E 3°58'26''
www.eurocampings.co.uk/103990

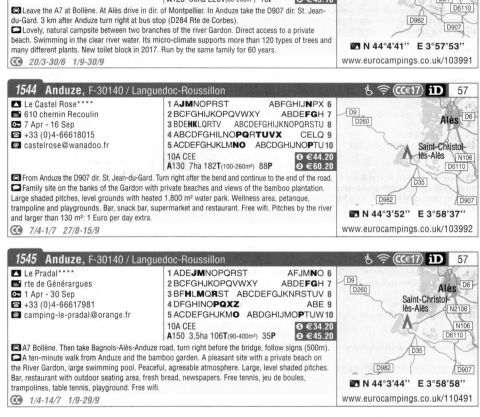

1547 Attuech/Anduze, F-30140 / Languedoc-Roussillon   ♿ 🛜 (CC€15) ♦♦ iD 57

- 🏕 Le Fief d'Anduze***
- 🏠 195 chemin du Plan d'Eau
- 🗓 1 Apr - 30 Sep
- ☎ +33 (0)4-66618171
- @ campingdufief@free.fr

1 ADEJMNOPRST	ABFJNP	6
2 BCDFHJKPRVWXY	ABDEFH	7
3 AEGHKLQST	ACDFKNOQRSV	8
4 BDFHINOTUVX	DE	9
5 ABDEFGHLN	ABDHIJNPT	10

6-10A CEE	❶ €27.50
6ha 90T(80-100m²) 22P	❷ €35.90

🚗 Exit Bollène direction Alès, then to Montpellier. In St. Christol-les-Alès direction Anduze. Past Intermarché left to Lézan. After Gardon bridge to Anduze at roundabout. 2nd campsite on right.
💬 You will enjoy your stay here close to a lake and a river at the start of the Cévennes and a 5-minute drive from Anduze. Plenty of opportunities for visiting beautiful towns, cultural and sports activities. Free wifi on entire campsite. Two swimming pools.

(CC) 1/4-6/7 26/8-29/9 7=6, 14=12

N 44°1'37'' E 4°1'40''

www.eurocampings.co.uk/110891

1548 Bagnols-sur-Cèze, F-30200 / Languedoc-Roussillon   ♿ 🛜 (CC€19) iD 55a

- 🏕 Les Genêts d'Or****
- 🏠 1840 chemin de Carmignan
- 🗓 20 Apr - 20 Sep
- ☎ +33 (0)4-66895867
- @ info@camping-genets-dor.com

1 ADEIKNOPRT	ABFJNU	6
2 CJKPRVWXY	ABDEFGH	7
3 ABEFLQ	ABCDEFJKNRSV	8
4 AFHIOPQ	E	9
5 ABDEFGHLMN	ABDGHIJPTUZ	10

6-10A	❶ €35.75
8ha 120T(90-100m²) 8P	❷ €47.75

🚗 A7 exit Bollène. D994 dir. Pont-St-Esprit. There N86 dir. Bagnols-sur-Cèze. About 500 metres past the city limits sign, just before service station turn left. Follow signs.
💬 On the banks of the river Cèze, you'll find this ambient family campsite surrounded by vineyards. Excellent service. Bridge games on Monday and Thursday from mid-May to mid-June. Located between Provence, Cévennes and Ardèche. Very suitable for seniors and families. Free wifi.

(CC) 20/4-8/7 26/8-19/9

N 44°10'25'' E 4°38'13''

www.eurocampings.co.uk/104149

1549 Barjac, F-30430 / Languedoc-Roussillon   🚭♿☺✿ (CC€17) iD 26 B1

- 🏕 Domaine de la Sablière****
- 🏠 St. Privat-de-Champclos
- 🗓 31 Mar - 30 Sep
- ☎ +33 (0)4-66245116
- @ contact@villagesabliere.com

1 ADEGJMNOPQRST	ABCDFJNU	6
2 BCFHJKPQRTUVWXY	ABDEFGHK	7
3 ABEFILMQR	ABCDEFKNQRSTUV	8
4 AEFHILNOPQRTVZ	AEJKL	9
5 ACDEFGHKLMO	ABGHIJOTUWZ	10

10A CEE	❶ €46.50
A235 62ha 204T(100-120m²) 305P	❷ €54.70

🚗 From Pont-Saint-Esprit take the D901, then the D266 on the left. Follow signs.

💬 This naturist site on the wooded slopes of the Cèze gorge includes: 2 swimming pools, 1 of which is covered, 2 saunas, a beauty centre, sports and other activities and a mini club. Shop, bar and restaurant (partly open, partly sheltered) contribute to your comfort in this dream paradise.

(CC) 31/3-30/6 1/9-29/9

N 44°16'1'' E 4°21'7''

www.eurocampings.co.uk/101246

1550 Boisset-Gaujac/Anduze, F-30140 / Languedoc-Roussillon   ♿☺ (CC€17) ♦♦ iD 57

- 🏕 Domaine de Gaujac***
- 🏠 2406 chemin de la Madeleine
- 🗓 1 May - 2 Sep
- ☎ +33 (0)4-66616757
- @ contact@domaine-de-gaujac.com

1 ADEJMNOPQRST	ABFGHIJN	6
2 BCJKPQUVY	ABDEFGH	7
3 BIKLMQST	ABCDEFJKNOPRSTV	8
4 BCDFHILNOPQUY	EJL	9
5 ABCDEFGHMNO	ABFGHIJNOTUVWZ	10

4-10A CEE	❶ €33.00
A130 10ha 145T(80-110m²) 205P	❷ €49.00

🚗 A7 exit Alès/Bollène. Before Alès direction Montpellier/St. Christol/Anduze. 5 km before Anduze turn left in Bagard towards Boisset and Gaujac.

💬 A large, green campsite, located just outside Anduze, 100 metres from River Gardon. Plenty of shade.

(CC) 1/5-3/7 21/8-1/9

N 44°2'9'' E 4°1'26''

www.eurocampings.co.uk/103993

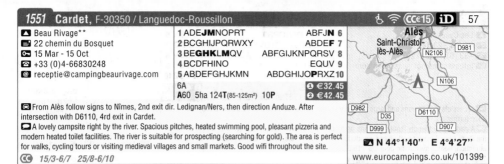

1551 Cardet, F-30350 / Languedoc-Roussillon iD 57

- ▲ Beau Rivage**
- 🏠 22 chemin du Bosquet
- 📅 15 Mar - 15 Oct
- ☎ +33 (0)4-66830248
- @ receptie@campingbeaurivage.com

1 ADE**JM**NOPRT	AB**FJ**N	6
2 BCGHIJPQRWXY	ABDE**F**	7
3 BE**GHKLM**QV	ABFGIJKNPQRSV	8
4 BCDFHINO	EQUV	9
5 ABDEFGHJKMN	ABDGHIJO**P**RXZ	10
6A		❶ €32.45
A60 5ha 124**T**(85-125m²) 10**P**		❷ €42.45

🚗 From Alès follow signs to Nîmes, 2nd exit dir. Ledignan/Ners, then direction Anduze. After intersection with D6110, 4rd exit in Cardet.

💬 A lovely campsite right by the river. Spacious pitches, heated swimming pool, pleasant pizzeria and modern heated toilet facilities. The river is suitable for prospecting (searching for gold). The area is perfect for walks, cycling tours or visiting medieval villages and small markets. Good wifi throughout the site.

CC 15/3-6/7 25/8-6/10

Alès
Saint-Christol-lès-Alès

N 44°1'40'' E 4°4'27''

www.eurocampings.co.uk/101399

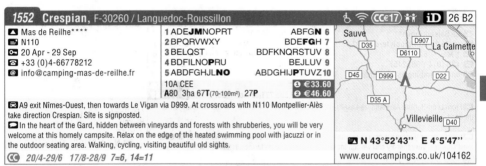

1552 Crespian, F-30260 / Languedoc-Roussillon iD 26 B2

- ▲ Mas de Reilhe****
- 🏠 N110
- 📅 20 Apr - 29 Sep
- ☎ +33 (0)4-66778212
- @ info@camping-mas-de-reilhe.fr

1 ADE**JM**NOPRT	ABF**G**N	6
2 BPQRVWXY	BDE**FG**H	7
3 BELQST	BDFKNQRSTUV	8
4 BDFILNO**P**RU	BEJLUV	9
5 ABDFGHJL**NO**	ABDGHIJ**P**TUVZ	10
10A CEE		❶ €33.60
A80 3ha 67**T**(70-100m²) 27**P**		❷ €46.60

🚗 A9 exit Nîmes-Ouest, then towards Le Vigan via D999. At crossroads with N110 Montpellier-Alès take direction Crespian. Site is signposted.

💬 In the heart of the Gard, hidden between vineyards and forests with shrubberies, you will be very welcome at this homely campsite. Relax on the edge of the heated swimming pool with jacuzzi or in the outdoor seating area. Walking, cycling, visiting beautiful old sights.

CC 20/4-29/6 17/8-28/9 7=6, 14=11

Sauve
La Calmette
Villevieille

N 43°52'43'' E 4°5'47''

www.eurocampings.co.uk/104162

France

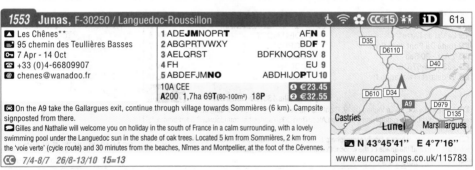

1553 Junas, F-30250 / Languedoc-Roussillon iD 61a

- ▲ Les Chênes**
- 🏠 95 chemin des Teullières Basses
- 📅 7 Apr - 14 Oct
- ☎ +33 (0)4-66809907
- @ chenes@wanadoo.fr

1 ADE**JM**NOPR**T**	AF**N**	6
2 ABGPRTVWXY	BD**F**	7
3 AELQRST	BDFKNOQRSV	8
4 FH	EU	9
5 ABDEFJM**NO**	ABDHIJO**P**TU	10
10A CEE		❶ €23.45
A200 1,7ha 69**T**(80-100m²) 18**P**		❷ €32.55

🚗 On the A9 take the Gallargues exit, continue through village towards Sommières (6 km). Campsite signposted from there.

💬 Gilles and Nathalie will welcome you on holiday in the south of France in a calm surrounding, with a lovely swimming pool under the Languedoc sun in the shade of oak trees. Located 5 km from Sommières, 2 km from the 'voie verte' (cycle route) and 30 minutes from the beaches, Nîmes and Montpellier, at the foot of the Cévennes.

CC 7/4-8/7 26/8-13/10 15=13

Castries
Lunel Marsillargues

N 43°45'41'' E 4°7'16''

www.eurocampings.co.uk/115783

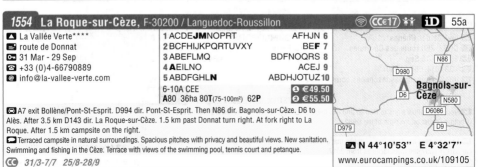

1554 La Roque-sur-Cèze, F-30200 / Languedoc-Roussillon iD 55a

- ▲ La Vallée Verte****
- 🏠 route de Donnat
- 📅 31 Mar - 29 Sep
- ☎ +33 (0)4-66790889
- @ info@la-vallee-verte.com

1 ACDE**JM**NOPRT	AFHJN	6
2 BCFHIJKPQRTUVXY	BE**F**	7
3 ABEFLMQ	BDFNOQRS	8
4 **A**EILNO	ACEJ	9
5 ABDFGHL**N**	ABDHJOTUZ	10
6-10A CEE		❶ €49.50
A80 36ha 80**T**(75-100m²) 62**P**		❷ €55.50

🚗 A7 exit Bollène/Pont-St-Esprit. D994 dir. Pont-St-Esprit. Then N86 dir. Bagnols-sur-Cèze. D6 to Alès. After 3.5 km D143 dir. La Roque-sur-Cèze. 1.5 km past Donnat turn right. At fork right to La Roque. After 1.5 km campsite on the right.

💬 Terraced campsite in natural surroundings. Spacious pitches with privacy and beautiful views. New sanitation. Swimming and fishing in the Cèze. Terrace with views of the swimming pool, tennis court and petanque.

CC 31/3-7/7 25/8-28/9

Bagnols-sur-Cèze

N 44°10'53'' E 4°32'7''

www.eurocampings.co.uk/109105

1555 La Roque-sur-Cèze, F-30200 / Languedoc-Roussillon   ♿ 🛜 (CC€17) ♨ iD 55a

- 🏕 Les Cascades****
- 🗓 20 Apr - 23 Sep
- ☎ +33 (0)4-66827297
- @ infos@campinglescascades.com

1 ADE**JM**NOPR**T**	ABFJLN	6
2 BCDGJMPRTUVXY	ABDE**FG**	7
3 AELQT	ABCDEFKNQRSUV	8
4 BDFLNO	ELU	9
5 ACDEFGHL**N**	ABFHIJ**NP**TUZ	10
10A CEE	❶ €43.70	
A85 6ha 76T(90-120m²) 57P	❷ €54.40	

🚗 Accessible for caravans and large cars only via the D6 Bagnols-Alès, exit Donnat (D143). Then 3 km further.

💬 A particularly friendly family campsite on predominantly level and shaded grounds on the banks of the River Cèze. Lovely beaches and wonderful swimming waters. The lovely waterfalls are an added attraction. Heated swimming pool 1/5 - 15/9.

CC 20/4-6/7 25/8-22/9 7=6, 14=11

▨ N 44°11'19'' E 4°31'31''

www.eurocampings.co.uk/111690

1556 Lasalle/Anduze, F-30460 / Languedoc-Roussillon   ♿ 🛜 (CC€17) iD 57

- 🏕 La Salendrinque***
- 🚩 route de St. Hippolyte-du-Fort
- 🗓 1 May - 15 Sep
- ☎ +33 (0)4-66852457
- @ info@campinglasalendrinque.fr

1 ADE**JM**NOPR**T**	ABFGJ**N**	6
2 BCFGIJKPTUVWXY	ABDE**FH**	7
3 BLQS	ABCDEFGHJKNPRSTU	8
4 FHIOPQ	BEFJL	9
5 ADEFGHM**NO**	ABDGHIJOTUVW	10
10A CEE	❶ €29.00	
A280 2,5ha 77T(80-140m²) 20P	❷ €39.50	

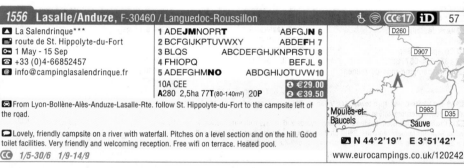

🚗 From Lyon-Bollène-Alès-Anduze-Lasalle-Rte. follow St. Hippolyte-du-Fort to the campsite left of the road.

💬 Lovely, friendly campsite on a river with waterfall. Pitches on a level section and on the hill. Good toilet facilities. Very friendly and welcoming reception. Free wifi on terrace. Heated pool.

CC 1/5-30/6 1/9-14/9

▨ N 44°2'19'' E 3°51'42''

www.eurocampings.co.uk/120242

1557 Le Vigan, F-30120 / Languedoc-Roussillon   ♿ 🛜 (CC€15) iD 57

- 🏕 Le Val de l'Arre****
- 🚩 route Du Pont de la Croix
- 🗓 1 Apr - 30 Sep
- ☎ +33 (0)4-67810277
- @ valdelarre@wanadoo.fr

1 ADE**IL**NORT	ABFJ**NX**	6
2 CGPRVXY	ABDE**FGH**	7
3 BE**GH**LQ	BDFNOQRSV	8
4 BCDFHIO	EILQRUW	9
5 ACDEFHKM**O**	ABDGHIJ**P**TU	10
10-16A	❶ €28.50	
A216 8ha 133T(80-120m²) 38P	❷ €41.00	

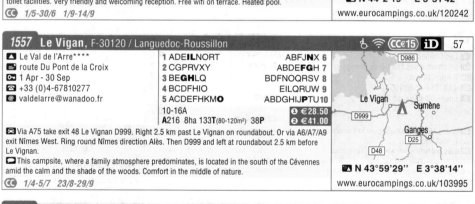

🚗 Via A75 take exit 48 Le Vignan D999. Right 2.5 km past Le Vignan on roundabout. Or via A6/A7/A9 exit Nîmes West. Ring round Nîmes direction Alès. Then D999 and left at roundabout 2.5 km before Le Vignan.

💬 This campsite, where a family atmosphere predominates, is located in the south of the Cévennes amid the calm and the shade of the woods. Comfort in the middle of nature.

CC 1/4-5/7 23/8-29/9

▨ N 43°59'29'' E 3°38'14''

www.eurocampings.co.uk/103995

1558 Lézan, F-30350 / Languedoc-Roussillon   ♿ 🛜 (CC€15) ♨ iD 57

- 🏕 Le Mas des Chênes***
- 🚩 D982, 760 route des Cévennes
- 🗓 1 May - 15 Sep
- ☎ +33 (0)4-66544830
- @ info@campingmasdeschenes.com

1 ADEG**JM**NOPQRS**T**	AFN	6
2 CGJPVWXY	ABDE**FGH**	7
3 A**K**LQ	ABCDFGKNRSV	8
4 FHIO	BEFU	9
5 ABDHJK	AGHJOTUV	10
10A CEE	❶ €26.90	
11ha 173T(100-120m²) 20P	❷ €37.90	

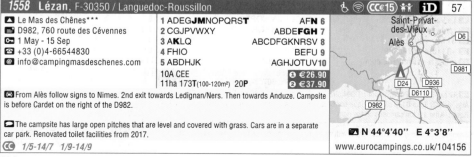

🚗 From Alès follow signs to Nimes. 2nd exit towards Ledignan/Ners. Then towards Anduze. Campsite is before Cardet on the right of the D982.

💬 The campsite has large open pitches that are level and covered with grass. Cars are in a separate car park. Renovated toilet facilities from 2017.

CC 1/5-14/7 1/9-14/9

▨ N 44°4'40'' E 4°3'8''

www.eurocampings.co.uk/104156

1559 Méjannes-le-Clap, F-30430 / Languedoc-Roussillon

🏕 La Genèse***
🛣 route de la Genèse
📅 31 Mar - 29 Sep
☎ +33 (0)5-33092092
@ reservations@tohapi-naturiste.fr

1	ABDJ**M**NOPR**T**	ABFHJNPU 6
2	BCFJKPQRUVXY	ABD**FG**K 7
3	ABDEILMQRSTU	ABEFGIKNOQRV 8
4	ABCDEFGILNOT	AEJKQ 9
5	ACDEFGHKLM**NO**	ABDHIJL**NO**TUVZ10

6-10A CEE ❶ €31.80
A310 50ha 458**T**(90-130m²) 135**P** ❷ €39.20

🚗 From the A7 exit Bollène, D994 direction Pont-St-Esprit. From there N86 direction Bagnols-sur-Cèze, then D6 direction Alès. Turn off to Lussan (D979) after 23.5 km. Follow signs in Méjannes.

💬 Located in the Gorges de la Cèze this family naturist campsite extends over 26 hectares of lush and rugged countryside. The river at the campsite offers opportunities for swimming and canoeing.

CC 31/3-6/7 25/8-28/9

N 44°16'3'' E 4°22'13''

www.eurocampings.co.uk/100500

1560 Mialet, F-30140 / Languedoc-Roussillon

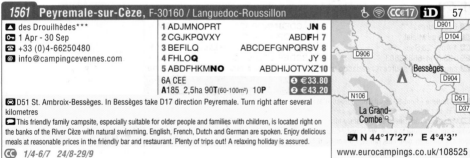

🏕 Les Plans****
🛣 D50
📅 13 Apr - 9 Sep
☎ +33 (0)4-66850246
@ info@camping-les-plans.fr

1	ADE**JM**NOPRST	ABFHIJ**M**NUV 6
2	BCFGJKOPQRSVWXY	ABDE**FK** 7
3	BDEF**H**ILQST	ABCDEFGKNRSTV 8
4	ABCDEFHILNO**PQ**R	EGJ 9
5	ACDEFGHJKLMNO	ABDFGHIJO**P**TU10

3-10A CEE ❶ €30.20
A185 6,5ha 133**T**(100-120m²) 150**P** ❷ €44.20

🚗 Route du Soleil, Bollène, Pont Saint Esprit-Bagnols, Alès, Anduze, Generargues, Mialet. Follow signs. The campsite is on the left.

💬 Campsite on the edge of Parc National des Cévennes, in Mialet, in the Gard. Ideal location on a river, with a private beach. Leisure pool, sports grounds, kids club, crazy golf, many activities and entertainment. 'La Bambouseraie de Prafrance' and the Trabuc caves can be reached by steam train. 9 km from Anduze.

CC 13/4-30/6 27/8-8/9 7=6, 14=12

N 44°7'30'' E 3°55'7''

www.eurocampings.co.uk/109692

1561 Peyremale-sur-Cèze, F-30160 / Languedoc-Roussillon

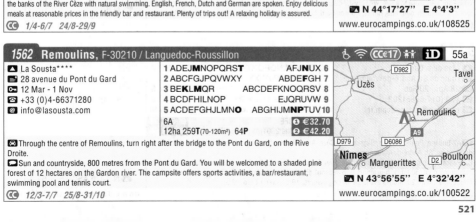

🏕 des Drouilhèdes***
📅 1 Apr - 30 Sep
☎ +33 (0)4-66250480
@ info@campingcevennes.com

1	ADJMNOPRT	JN 6
2	CGJKPQVXY	ABD**FH** 7
3	BEFILQ	ABCDEFGNPQRSV 8
4	FHLO**Q**	JY 9
5	ABDFHKM**NO**	ABDHIJOTVXZ10

6A CEE ❶ €33.80
A185 2,5ha 90**T**(60-100m²) 10**P** ❷ €43.20

🚗 D51 St. Ambroix-Bessèges. In Bessèges take D17 direction Peyremale. Turn right after several kilometres

💬 This friendly family campsite, especially suitable for older people and families with children, is located right on the banks of the River Cèze with natural swimming. English, French, Dutch and German are spoken. Enjoy delicious meals at reasonable prices in the friendly bar and restaurant. Plenty of trips out! A relaxing holiday is assured.

CC 1/4-6/7 24/8-29/9

N 44°17'27'' E 4°4'3''

www.eurocampings.co.uk/108525

1562 Remoulins, F-30210 / Languedoc-Roussillon

🏕 La Sousta****
🛣 28 avenue du Pont du Gard
📅 12 Mar - 1 Nov
☎ +33 (0)4-66371280
@ info@lasousta.com

1	ADE**JM**NOPQRS**T**	AFJ**N**UX 6
2	ABCFGJPQVWXY	ABDE**FG**H 7
3	BE**KLM**QR	ABCDEFKNOQRSV 8
4	BCDFHILNOP	EJQRUVW 9
5	ACDEFGHJLMN**O**	ABGHIJM**NP**TUV10

6A ❶ €32.70
12ha 259**T**(70-120m²) 64**P** ❷ €42.20

🚗 Through the centre of Remoulins, turn right after the bridge to the Pont du Gard, on the Rive Droite.

💬 Sun and countryside, 800 metres from the Pont du Gard. You will be welcomed to a shaded pine forest of 12 hectares on the Gardon river. The campsite offers sports activities, a bar/restaurant, swimming pool and tennis court.

CC 12/3-7/7 25/8-31/10

N 43°56'55'' E 4°32'42''

www.eurocampings.co.uk/100522

France

1563 Sommières, F-30250 / Languedoc-Roussillon ♿ 🛜 ✿ (CC€19) iD 61a

🔼 Domaine de Massereau*****
🏠 1990 route d'Aubais
📅 7 Apr - 30 Sep
☎ +33 (0)4-66531120
@ camping@massereau.com

1	ADE**JM**NOPQRS**T**	ABCDFGH**N** 6
2	ABGQVWXY	ABCD**F**GH 7
3	ABEF**GHILMN**QSV	CDEFGHIJK**LMN**QRSTU 8
4	ABCD**E**FHILO**PTUVX**	EJLQUVY 9
5	ACDEFGHJLNO	ABDFGHIJO**P**QTYZ 10

Ad on this page 16A CEE ❶ €50.40
A50 8ha 90T(100-200m²) 61P ❷ €75.10

🚗 A9, exit 26 direction Gallargues, then direction Sommières, in Sommières direction Aubais, is indicated.
💬 Located in the heart of a wine domain between the Cevennes and the Mediterranean. Quiet and child-friendly. Pitches with plenty of comfort. Heated pool, recreational swimming pool with slide, restaurant, pizzeria, bar, food, adventure park. Private beach, SUP (stand up paddle). Perfect for cycling and walking.
(CC) 7/4-2/6 | 1/9-29/9

D999 D35 A D6110 D40 D34 D610 A9 N113
Lunel
Valergues Vauvert
📍 **N 43°45'58'' E 4°5'50''**
www.eurocampings.co.uk/117264

1564 St. Jean-du-Gard, F-30270 / Languedoc-Roussillon ♿ 🛜 ✿ (CC€13) iD 57

🔼 Les Sources***
🏠 route de Mialet
📅 1 Apr - 23 Sep
☎ +33 (0)4-66853803
@ camping-des-sources@wanadoo.fr

1	ACDE**JM**NOPRS**T**	ABFGM 6
2	BFGOPQUVWXY	ABDE**FG**HK 7
3	BFLQR	ABCDEFJKLMNOQRSTUV 8
4	BCD**E**FGHILNO**PQ**	BDEIJ 9
5	ACDEFGHJKLM**NO**	ABDFGHIJ**N**OTU 10

6-10A CEE ❶ €32.20
A202 2,4ha 68T(80-120m²) 25P ❷ €42.60

🚗 A7 Bollène - Pont-St-Esprit - Bagnols-sur-Cèze - Alès - Anduze - St. Jean-du-Gard. After traffic lights right 1.3 km.
💬 Magnificent campsite, quiet and family-friendly, in the heart of the southern Cévennes. 1300 m from the village and very close to a river with crystal-clear water. In the surroundings there are a well-known bamboo forest, steam train to Anduze, Nimes, Pont du Gard, Uzès. Heated swimming pool and heated toilet facilities.
(CC) 1/4-30/6 1/9-22/9 10=7

La Grand-Combe
L'Habitarelle
D9 D260
D907
📍 **N 44°6'48'' E 3°53'31''**
www.eurocampings.co.uk/109094

1565 St. Jean-du-Gard, F-30270 / Languedoc-Roussillon ♿ 🛜 ✿ (CC€17) 👫 iD 57

🔼 Mas de la Cam****
🏠 route de St. André-de-Valborgne
📅 28 Apr - 20 Sep
☎ +33 (0)4-66851202
@ camping@masdelacam.fr

1	ADE**IL**NOPQRT	ABFG**IJN**P 6
2	BCFG**IJ**PVWXY	ABDE**FG**H 7
3	BDE**HL**MQ	ABCDEFKNOPQRSTV 8
4	ABCDFGHINO**PQ**Y	I 9
5	ACDEFGHJKLM**O**	ABDHIJOTUW 10

6-10A CEE ❶ €44.70
A206 8ha 200T(80-140m²) 9P ❷ €61.60

🚗 A7 Bollène, Pont-St-Esprit, Bagnols-sur-Cèze, Alès, dir. Montpellier, St. Christol, Anduze, St. Jean-du-Gard dir. St. André-de-Valbogne.
💬 Peaceful floral campsite located on the river. Beautiful views of the Cevennes mountains. Heated swimming pool (500 m²), free tennis (low season). Plenty of entertainment in spring: pétanque and bridge. Maximum 20 pitches available for dog owners. 10A power 1 Euro extra.
(CC) 28/4-5/7 24/8-19/9

La Grand-Combe
D9 D260
D907
Anduze
D982
📍 **N 44°6'45'' E 3°51'16''**
www.eurocampings.co.uk/107464

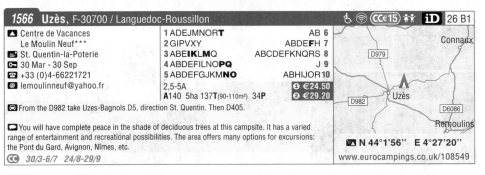

1566 Uzès, F-30700 / Languedoc-Roussillon

🚲 📶 (CC€15) ⚭ **iD** 26 B1

- 🏕 Centre de Vacances
  Le Moulin Neuf***
- 📧 St. Quentin-la-Poterie
- 📅 30 Mar - 30 Sep
- ☎ +33 (0)4-66221721
- @ lemoulinneuf@yahoo.fr

1 ADEJMNOR**T**	AB **6**
2 GIPVXY	ABDE**F**H **7**
3 ABE**IKLM**Q	ABCDEFKNQRS **8**
4 ABDEFILNO**PQ**	J **9**
5 ABDEFGJKM**NO**	ABHIJOR **10**
2,5-5A	❶ €24.50
A140 5ha 137**T**(90-110m²) 34**P**	❷ €29.20

🚗 From the D982 take Uzes-Bagnols D5, direction St. Quentin. Then D405.

💬 You will have complete peace in the shade of deciduous trees at this campsite. It has a varied range of entertainment and recreational possibilities. The area offers many options for excursions: the Pont du Gard, Avignon, Nîmes, etc.

CC 30/3-6/7 24/8-29/9

🗺 N 44°1'56'' E 4°27'20''

www.eurocampings.co.uk/108549

1567 Vallabrègues/Beaucaire/Tarasc., F-30300 / Languedoc-Roussillon

📶 (CC€17) ⚭ **iD** 55a

- 🏕 Lou Vincen***
- 📅 1 Apr - 1 Nov
- ☎ +33 (0)4-66592129
- @ contact@campinglouvincen.fr

1 ADEF**JM**NOPRT	A**N**V **6**
2 CDOPQRVXY	ABDE**F**H **7**
3 AELMQ	ABCDFNORTU **8**
4 FH	EUVW **9**
5 ABDEHM**NO**	ABDHIJ**P**TUZ **10**
6-8A	❶ €27.55
1,4ha 69**T**(max 100m²) 10**P**	❷ €40.60

🚗 From Beaucaire-Tarascon to Vallabrègues. The campsite is signposted in the village next to the Rhône.

💬 A basic, clean, shaded and attractively planted campsite. Wonderful for walking and cycling. Located by the Rhône between Beaucaire, Avignon, St. Rémy and the Camargue.

CC 1/4-30/6 20/8-31/10 7=6, 14=12, 21=18

🗺 N 43°51'18'' E 4°37'32''

www.eurocampings.co.uk/108459

1568 Villeneuve-lez-Avignon/Avignon, F-30400 / Languedoc-Roussillon

🚲 📶 (CC€17) ⚭ **iD** 55a

- 🏕 Campéole L'Île des Papes****
- 📧 1497 RD 780
- 📅 30 Mar - 4 Nov
- ☎ +33 (0)4-90151590
- @ ile-des-papes@campeole.com

1 ADE**JM**NOPQRS**T**	A**F**IN **6**
2 ACFGOPQRVWXY	ABE**FG** **7**
3 BE**IK**LQT	ABCDFKNQRSV **8**
4 BCDFHILNO**PQ**	AEFLQRV **9**
5 ABDEFGHL**NO**	ABDFGHIJ**O**TUVZ **10**
6-10A CEE	❶ €38.40
20ha 183**T**(100m²) 210**P**	❷ €47.70

🚗 A9, exit Roquemaure, direction Roquemaure-centre, then direction Sauveterre, and Barrage-de-Villeneuve. Campsite signposted.

💬 Spaciously appointed, luxurious campsite with very many amenities, located on an island in the Rhône. 6 km from Avignon.

CC 30/3-6/7 25/8-3/11

🗺 N 43°59'37'' E 4°49'4''

www.eurocampings.co.uk/108461

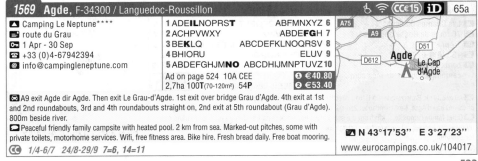

1569 Agde, F-34300 / Languedoc-Roussillon

🚲 📶 (CC€15) **iD** 65a

- 🏕 Camping Le Neptune****
- 📧 route du Grau
- 📅 1 Apr - 30 Sep
- ☎ +33 (0)4-67942394
- @ info@campingleneptune.com

1 ADE**IL**NOPRS**T**	ABF**MN**XYZ **6**
2 ACHP**V**WXY	ABDE**FG**H **7**
3 BE**K**LQ	ABCDEFKLNOQRSV **8**
4 B**HI**ORU	ELUV **9**
5 ABDEFGHJM**NO**	ABCDHIJMNPTUVZ **10**
Ad on page 524 10A CEE	❶ €40.80
2,7ha 100**T**(70-120m²) 54**P**	❷ €53.40

🚗 A9 exit Agde dir Agde. Then exit Le Grau-d'Agde. 1st exit over bridge Grau d'Agde. 4th exit at 1st and 2nd roundabouts, 3rd and 4th roundabouts straight on, 2nd exit at 5th roundabout (Grau d'Agde). 800m beside river.

💬 Peaceful friendly family campsite with heated pool. 2 km from sea. Marked-out pitches, some with private toilets, motorhome services. Wifi, free fitness area. Bike hire. Fresh bread daily. Free boat mooring.

CC 1/4-6/7 24/8-29/9 7=6, 14=11

🗺 N 43°17'53'' E 3°27'23''

www.eurocampings.co.uk/104017

France

Camping Le Neptune ★ ★ ★

A cycle path in front of the campsite

Beach at 2 kms

FISH FOR FREE

To rent

Near the river

Heated pool

Swimming pool near the bar

Wi Fi FREE

1570 Agde, F-34300 / Languedoc-Roussillon

♿ 🛜 CC€17 iD | 65a

🏕 L'Escale***
📧 route de la Tamarissière
🗓 25 Mar - 30 Sep
☎ +33 (0)4-67212109
@ camping.lescale.agde@gmail.com

1 ADE**JM**NOPRST	AFNQSWXY**Z** 6
2 ACHPVXY	BE**FGH** 7
3 BE**GK**LQ	BDFNORSV 8
4 BDIL**P**	EUVW 9
5 ABDEFGHJKLM	ABDHIJNPTUVZ 10

Ad on this page 10A
2,5ha 50**T**(80-90m²) 181**P**

❶ €40.00
❷ €48.00

🗺 A9 exit Agde. At the roundabout N312, direction Agde exit Tamarissière. Campsite about 3 km on the right.

💬 Attractive, shaded family campsite located on the Hérault. River or sea fishing. Wonderful cycling to Cap d'Agde or inland. Bridge competitions for enthusiasts on the campsite. Free wifi.

CC 25/3-6/7 25/8-29/9

📌 N 43°17'49'' E 3°26'57''
www.eurocampings.co.uk/104016

1571 Agde, F-34300 / Languedoc-Roussillon

♿ 🛜 CC€17 iD | 65a

🏕 Les Champs Blancs****
📧 76 route de Rochelongue
🗓 1 Apr - 15 Oct
☎ +33 (0)4-67942342
@ contact@
campingleschampsblancs.com

1 ADE**JM**NOPQRST	ABFGHIM**N** 6
2 AHOPRVWXY	BE**FGH** 7
3 BDEK**L**MQ	BCDEFLMNQRTUV 8
4 BCDHILNO**PQ**U	EUV 9
5 ACDEFGHJL**NO**	ACDGHIJMNPTUZ 10

10A CEE
6,5ha 160**T**(80-130m²) 158**P**

❶ €63.60
❷ €74.90

🗺 A9 exit 34 dir. Bezierz/Agde. On D1612 direction Grau d'Agde-Rochelongue. At roundabout (with statue) left direction Grau d'Agde. Next roundabout 2nd exit right. Next roundabout 1st exit right. After bridge 1st right.
💬 Quiet family campsite, 2 km from the sea. Large, heated aquapark and large pitches, marked out by oleander hedges, a few even have private toilet facilities. Wifi on the grounds and many activities for everybody.

CC 1/4-6/7 24/8-14/10 7=6, 14=11

📌 N 43°17'47'' E 3°28'37''
www.eurocampings.co.uk/104014

1572 Agde, F-34300 / Languedoc-Roussillon ♿ 🛜 (CC€15) ♟♀ iD 65a

- ⛺ Les Romarins****
- 🏕 6 route du Grau
- 📅 31 Mar - 6 Oct
- ☎ +33 (0)4-67941859
- @ contact@romarins.com

1 ADE**JM**NOPQRST	ABN**XZ** 6	
2 ACHOPVWXY	BDE**FG**H 7	
3 BE**KL**Q	ABCDFKNRSV 8	
4 BDHILNO	DEHJLUV 9	
5 ABDEFGHJK**O**	ABCDHIJ**N**O**P**TU 10	

10-13A CEE	❶ €39.60
2,5ha 120**T**(80-115m²) 59**P**	❷ €52.70

🚗 A9 exit Agde. Direction Agde. At Agde exit Le Grau d'Agde. Turn left after about 3 km.
💬 A friendly campsite on the River Hérault 900 m from the sea. A friendly couple who will do anything they can to help you. A good base for trips out, including by bike. Multifunctional sports field and some fitness apparatus. Heated swimming pool and free wifi on the terrace. Fishing at the campsite.
CC 31/3-6/7 26/8-5/10 7=6, 14=12, 21=18, 28=24

🏔 N 43°17'40'' E 3°27'0''
www.eurocampings.co.uk/111659

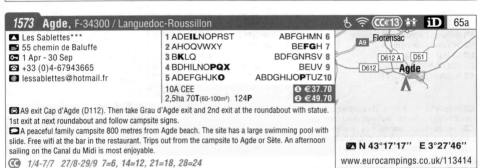

1573 Agde, F-34300 / Languedoc-Roussillon ♿ 🛜 (CC€13) ♟♀ iD 65a

- ⛺ Les Sablettes***
- 🏕 55 chemin de Baluffe
- 📅 1 Apr - 30 Sep
- ☎ +33 (0)4-67943665
- @ lessablettes@hotmail.fr

1 ADE**IL**NOPRST	ABFGHMN 6	
2 AHOQVWXY	BE**FG**H 7	
3 B**KL**Q	BDFGNRSV 8	
4 BDHILNO**PQX**	BEUV 9	
5 ADEFGHJK**O**	ABDGHIJO**P**TUZ 10	

10A CEE	❶ €37.70
2,5ha 70**T**(60-100m²) 124**P**	❷ €49.70

🚗 A9 exit Cap d'Agde (D112). Then take Grau d'Agde exit and 2nd exit at the roundabout with statue. 1st exit at next roundabout and follow campsite signs.
💬 A peaceful family campsite 800 metres from Agde beach. The site has a large swimming pool with slide. Free wifi at the bar in the restaurant. Trips out from the campsite to Agde or Sète. An afternoon sailing on the Canal du Midi is most enjoyable.
CC 1/4-7/7 27/8-29/9 7=6, 14=12, 21=18, 28=24

🏔 N 43°17'17'' E 3°27'46''
www.eurocampings.co.uk/113414

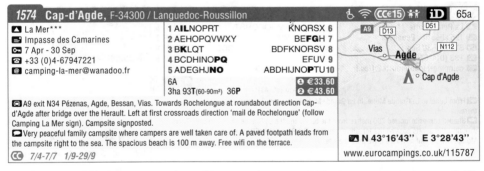

1574 Cap-d'Agde, F-34300 / Languedoc-Roussillon ♿ 🛜 (CC€15) ♟♀ iD 65a

- ⛺ La Mer***
- 🏕 Impasse des Camarines
- 📅 7 Apr - 30 Sep
- ☎ +33 (0)4-67947221
- @ camping-la-mer@wanadoo.fr

1 A**IL**NOPRT	KNQRSX 6	
2 AEHOPQVWXY	BE**FG**H 7	
3 B**KL**QT	BDFKNORSV 8	
4 BCDHINO**PQ**	EFUV 9	
5 ADEGHJ**NO**	ABDHIJNO**P**TU 10	

6A	❶ €33.60
3ha 93**T**(60-90m²) 36**P**	❷ €43.60

🚗 A9 exit N34 Pézenas, Agde, Bessan, Vias. Towards Rochelongue at roundabout direction Cap-d'Agde after bridge over the Herault. Left at first crossroads direction 'mail de Rochelongue' (follow Camping La Mer sign). Campsite signposted.
💬 Very peaceful family campsite where campers are well taken care of. A paved footpath leads from the campsite right to the sea. The spacious beach is 100 m away. Free wifi on the terrace.
CC 7/4-7/7 1/9-29/9

🏔 N 43°16'43'' E 3°28'43''
www.eurocampings.co.uk/115787

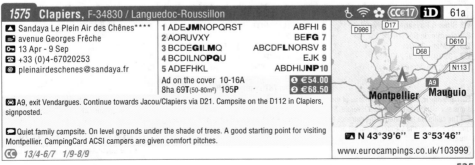

1575 Clapiers, F-34830 / Languedoc-Roussillon ♿ 🛜 ❁ (CC€17) iD 61a

- ⛺ Sandaya Le Plein Air des Chênes****
- 🏕 avenue Georges Frêche
- 📅 13 Apr - 9 Sep
- ☎ +33 (0)4-67020253
- @ pleinairdeschenes@sandaya.fr

1 ADE**JM**NOPQRST	ABFHI 6	
2 AORUVXY	BE**FG** 7	
3 BCDE**GILM**Q	ABCDF**L**NORSV 8	
4 BCDILNO**PQ**U	EJK 9	
5 ADEFHKL	ABDHIJ**NP** 10	

Ad on the cover 10-16A	❶ €54.00
8ha 69**T**(50-80m²) 195**P**	❷ €68.50

🚗 A9, exit Vendargues. Continue towards Jacou/Clapiers via D21. Campsite on the D112 in Clapiers, signposted.

💬 Quiet family campsite. On level grounds under the shade of trees. A good starting point for visiting Montpellier. CampingCard ACSI campers are given comfort pitches.
CC 13/4-6/7 1/9-8/9

🏔 N 43°39'6'' E 3°53'46''
www.eurocampings.co.uk/103999

France

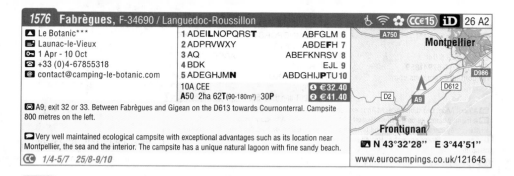

1576 Fabrègues, F-34690 / Languedoc-Roussillon

♿ 🛜 ✿ (CC€15) **iD** 26 A2

▲ Le Botanic***
🏕 Launac-le-Vieux
🗓 1 Apr - 10 Oct
☎ +33 (0)4-67855318
@ contact@camping-le-botanic.com

1 ADEI**L**NOPQRS**T**	ABFGLM 6
2 ADPRVWXY	ABDE**F**H 7
3 AQ	ABEFKNRSV 8
4 BDK	EJL 9
5 ADEGHJM**N**	ABDGHIJ**P**TU 10
10A CEE	❶ €32.40
A50 2ha 62**T**(90-180m²) 30**P**	❷ €41.40

🚗 A9, exit 32 or 33. Between Fabrègues and Gigean on the D613 towards Cournonterral. Campsite 800 metres on the left.

📋 Very well maintained ecological campsite with exceptional advantages such as its location near Montpellier, the sea and the interior. The campsite has a unique natural lagoon with fine sandy beach.

(CC) 1/4-5/7 25/8-9/10

N 43°32'28'' E 3°44'51''

www.eurocampings.co.uk/121645

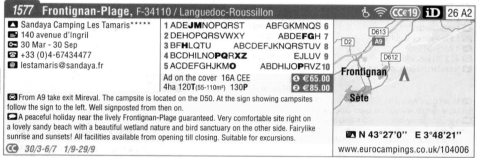

1577 Frontignan-Plage, F-34110 / Languedoc-Roussillon

♿ 🛜 (CC€19) **iD** 26 A2

▲ Sandaya Camping Les Tamaris*****
🏕 140 avenue d'Ingril
🗓 30 Mar - 30 Sep
☎ +33 (0)4-67434477
@ lestamaris@sandaya.fr

1 ADE**JM**NOPQRST	ABFGKMNQS 6
2 DEHOPQRSVWXY	ABDE**FG**H 7
3 BF**H**LQTU	ABCDEFJKNQRSTUV 8
4 BCDHILNO**PQR**X**Z**	EJLUV 9
5 ACDEFGHJKM**O**	ABDHIJO**P**RVZ 10
Ad on the cover 16A CEE	❶ €65.00
4ha 120**T**(55-110m²) 130**P**	❷ €85.00

🚗 From A9 take exit Mireval. The campsite is located on the D50. At the sign showing campsites follow the sign to the left. Well signposted from then on.

📋 A peaceful holiday near the lively Frontignan-Plage guaranteed. Very comfortable site right on a lovely sandy beach with a beautiful wetland nature and bird sanctuary on the other side. Fairylike sunrise and sunsets! All facilities available from opening till closing. Suitable for excursions.

(CC) 30/3-6/7 1/9-29/9

N 43°27'0'' E 3°48'21''

www.eurocampings.co.uk/104006

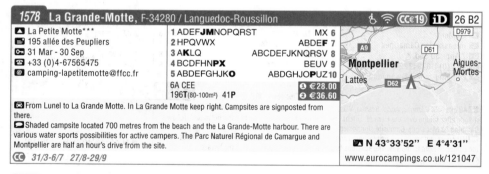

1578 La Grande-Motte, F-34280 / Languedoc-Roussillon

♿ 🛜 (CC€19) **iD** 26 B2

▲ La Petite Motte***
🏕 195 allée des Peupliers
🗓 31 Mar - 30 Sep
☎ +33 (0)4-67565475
@ camping-lapetitemotte@ffcc.fr

1 ADEF**JM**NOPQRST	MX 6
2 HPQVWX	ABDE**F** 7
3 A**K**LQ	ABCDEFJKNQRSV 8
4 BCDFHN**PX**	BEUV 9
5 ABDEFGHJK**O**	ABDGHJO**P**UZ 10
6A CEE	❶ €28.00
196**T**(80-100m²) 41**P**	❷ €36.60

🚗 From Lunel to La Grande Motte. In La Grande Motte keep right. Campsites are signposted from there.

📋 Shaded campsite located 700 metres from the beach and the La Grande-Motte harbour. There are various water sports possibilities for active campers. The Parc Naturel Régional de Camargue and Montpellier are half an hour's drive from the site.

(CC) 31/3-6/7 27/8-29/9

N 43°33'52'' E 4°4'31''

www.eurocampings.co.uk/121047

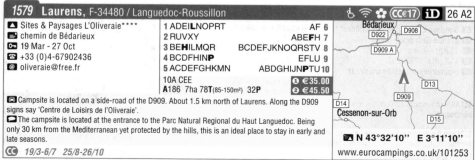

1579 Laurens, F-34480 / Languedoc-Roussillon

♿ 🛜 ✿ (CC€17) **iD** 26 A2

▲ Sites & Paysages L'Oliveraie****
🏕 chemin de Bédarieux
🗓 19 Mar - 27 Oct
☎ +33 (0)4-67902436
@ oliveraie@free.fr

1 ADEI**L**NOPRT	AF 6
2 RUVXY	ABE**F**H 7
3 BE**H**ILMQR	BCDEFJKNOQRSTV 8
4 BCDFHIN**P**	EFLU 9
5 ACDEFGHKMN	ABDGHIJN**P**TU 10
10A CEE	❶ €35.00
A186 7ha 78**T**(85-150m²) 32**P**	❷ €45.50

🚗 Campsite is located on a side-road of the D909. About 1.5 km north of Laurens. Along the D909 signs say 'Centre de Loisirs de l'Oliveraie'.

📋 The campsite is located at the entrance to the Parc Natural Regional du Haut Languedoc. Being only 30 km from the Mediterranean yet protected by the hills, this is an ideal place to stay in early and late seasons.

(CC) 19/3-6/7 25/8-26/10

N 43°32'10'' E 3°11'10''

www.eurocampings.co.uk/101253

France

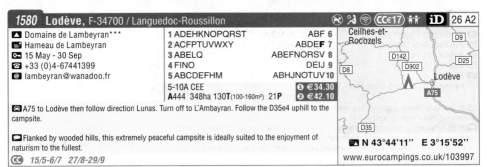

1580 Lodève, F-34700 / Languedoc-Roussillon
26 A2

- ▲ Domaine de Lambeyran***
- 🏠 Hameau de Lambeyran
- 📅 15 May - 30 Sep
- ☎ +33 (0)4-67441399
- @ lambeyran@wanadoo.fr

1 ADEHKNOPQRST	ABF	6
2 ACFPTUVWXY	ABDEF	7
3 ABELQ	ABEFNORSV	8
4 FINO	DEIJ	9
5 ABCDEFHM	ABHJNOTUV	10

5-10A CEE ❶ €34.30
A444 348ha 130T(100-160m²) 21P ❷ €42.10

🚗 A75 to Lodève then follow direction Lunas. Turn off to L'Ambayran. Follow the D35e4 uphill to the campsite.

💬 Flanked by wooded hills, this extremely peaceful campsite is ideally suited to the enjoyment of naturism to the fullest.

ⓒ 15/5-6/7 27/8-29/9

Ceilhes-et-Rocozels / Lodève

N 43°44'11'' E 3°15'52''
www.eurocampings.co.uk/103997

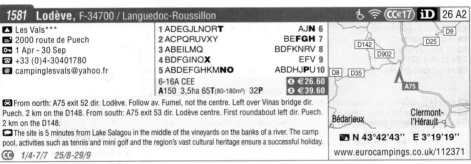

1581 Lodève, F-34700 / Languedoc-Roussillon
26 A2

- ▲ Les Vals***
- 🏠 2000 route de Puech
- 📅 1 Apr - 30 Sep
- ☎ +33 (0)4-30401780
- @ campinglesvals@yahoo.fr

1 ADEGJLNORT	AJN	6
2 ACPQRUVXY	BEFGH	7
3 ABEILMQ	BDFKNRV	8
4 BDFGINOX	EFV	9
5 ABDEFGHKMNO	ABDHJPU	10

6-16A CEE ❶ €26.60
A150 3,5ha 65T(80-180m²) 32P ❷ €39.60

🚗 From north: A75 exit 52 dir. Lodève. Follow av. Fumel, not the centre. Left over Vinas bridge dir. Puech. 2 km on the D148. From south: A75 exit 53 dir. Lodève centre. First roundabout left dir. Puech. 2 km on the D148.

💬 The site is 5 minutes from Lake Salagou in the middle of the vineyards on the banks of a river. The camp pool, activities such as tennis and mini golf and the region's vast cultural heritage ensure a successful holiday.

ⓒ 1/4-7/7 25/8-29/9

Bédarieux / Clermont-l'Hérault

N 43°42'43'' E 3°19'19''
www.eurocampings.co.uk/112371

France

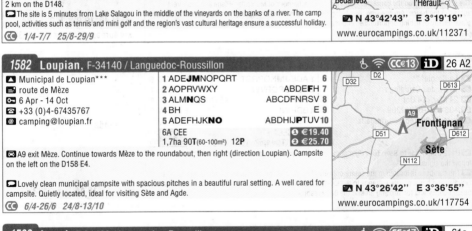

1582 Loupian, F-34140 / Languedoc-Roussillon
26 A2

- ▲ Municipal de Loupian***
- 🏠 route de Mèze
- 📅 6 Apr - 14 Oct
- ☎ +33 (0)4-67435767
- @ camping@loupian.fr

1 ADEJMNOPQRT		6
2 AOPRVWXY	ABDEFH	7
3 ALMNQS	ABCDFNRSV	8
4 BH	E	9
5 ADEFHJKNO	ABDHIJPTUV	10

6A CEE ❶ €19.40
1,7ha 90T(60-100m²) 12P ❷ €25.70

🚗 A9 exit Mèze. Continue towards Mèze to the roundabout, then right (direction Loupian). Campsite on the left on the D158 E4.

💬 Lovely clean municipal campsite with spacious pitches in a beautiful rural setting. A well cared for campsite. Quietly located, ideal for visiting Sète and Agde.

ⓒ 6/4-26/6 24/8-13/10

Frontignan / Sète

N 43°26'42'' E 3°36'55''
www.eurocampings.co.uk/117754

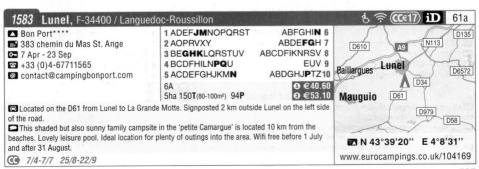

1583 Lunel, F-34400 / Languedoc-Roussillon
61a

- ▲ Bon Port****
- 🏠 383 chemin du Mas St. Ange
- 📅 7 Apr - 23 Sep
- ☎ +33 (0)4-67711565
- @ contact@campingbonport.com

1 ADEFJMNOPQRST	ABFGHIN	6
2 AOPRVXY	ABDEFGH	7
3 BEGHKLQRSTUV	ABCDFIKNRSV	8
4 BCDFHILNPQU	EUV	9
5 ACDEFGHJKMN	ABDGHJPTZ	10

6A ❶ €40.60
5ha 150T(80-100m²) 94P ❷ €53.10

🚗 Located on the D61 from Lunel to La Grande Motte. Signposted 2 km outside Lunel on the left side of the road.

💬 This shaded but also sunny family campsite in the 'petite Camargue' is located 10 km from the beaches. Lovely leisure pool. Ideal location for plenty of outings into the area. Wifi free before 1 July and after 31 August.

ⓒ 7/4-7/7 25/8-22/9

Baillargues / Lunel / Mauguio

N 43°39'20'' E 4°8'31''
www.eurocampings.co.uk/104169

1584 Marseillan-Plage, F-34340 / Languedoc-Roussillon   🚿 📶 (CC€17) iD   65a

- 🔺 Beauregard Plage***
- ⛺ 250 chemin de l'Airette
- 🕑 30 Mar - 15 Oct
- ☎ +33 (0)4-67771545
- @ reception@
  camping-beauregard-plage.com

1	ADE**J**KNOPRST	KMNQSTX	6
2	EHOPQVWXY	ABDE**F**	7
3	AB**K**LQ	BDEFNPRSV	8
4	HIO		9
5	ADEFHJK	ABCDGHIJ**P**TUX	10
6A CEE		❶ €49.00
3,3ha 200**T**(80-155m²)		❷ €65.00

🚗 A9 exit Agde. Continue towards Sète and take D612 direction Marseillan-Plage. Right at 2nd roundabout, follow signs to campsite.
💬 An authentic and lovely campsite with direct beach access, where respect for nature is tangible. There are only tents, caravans and motorhomes. Genuine campers will feel at home. Restaurant and bar overlooking the sea and beach. The shops and cafes on Marseillan-Plage are around the corner.
CC 30/3-30/6 1/9-14/10

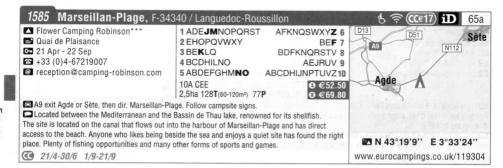

📧 N 43°18'54'' E 3°32'56''
www.eurocampings.co.uk/104011

1585 Marseillan-Plage, F-34340 / Languedoc-Roussillon   🚿 📶 (CC€17) iD   65a

- 🔺 Flower Camping Robinson***
- ⛺ Quai de Plaisance
- 🕑 21 Apr - 22 Sep
- ☎ +33 (0)4-67219007
- @ reception@camping-robinson.com

1	ADE**JM**NOPQRST	AFKNQSWXY**Z**	6
2	EHOPQVWXY	BE**F**	7
3	BE**K**LQ	BDFKNQRSTV	8
4	BCDHILNO	AEJRUV	9
5	ABDEFGHM**NO**	ABCDHIJNPTUVZ	10
10A CEE		❶ €52.50
2,5ha 128**T**(60-120m²) 77**P**		❷ €69.80

🚗 A9 exit Agde or Sète, then dir. Marseillan-Plage. Follow campsite signs.
💬 Located between the Mediterranean and the Bassin de Thau lake, renowned for its shellfish. The site is located on the canal that flows out into the harbour of Marseillan-Plage and has direct access to the beach. Anyone who likes being beside the sea and enjoys a quiet site has found the right place. Plenty of fishing opportunities and many other forms of sports and games.
CC 21/4-30/6 1/9-21/9

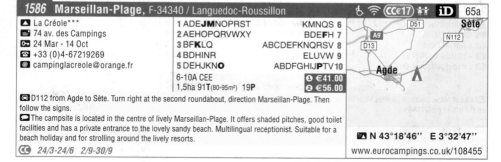

📧 N 43°19'9'' E 3°33'24''
www.eurocampings.co.uk/119304

1586 Marseillan-Plage, F-34340 / Languedoc-Roussillon   🚿 📶 (CC€17) 🚹 iD   65a

- 🔺 La Créole***
- ⛺ 74 av. des Campings
- 🕑 24 Mar - 14 Oct
- ☎ +33 (0)4-67219269
- @ campinglacreole@orange.fr

1	ADE**JM**NOPRST	KMNQS	6
2	AEHOPQRVWXY	BDEFH	7
3	BF**K**LQ	ABCDEFKNQRSV	8
4	BDHINR	ELUVW	9
5	DEHJKN**O**	ABDFGHIJ**P**TV	10
6-10A CEE		❶ €41.00
1,5ha 91**T**(80-95m²) 19**P**		❷ €56.00

🚗 D112 from Agde to Sète. Turn right at the second roundabout, direction Marseillan-Plage. Then follow the signs.
💬 The campsite is located in the centre of lively Marseillan-Plage. It offers shaded pitches, good toilet facilities and has a private entrance to the lovely sandy beach. Multilingual receptionist. Suitable for a beach holiday and for strolling around the lively resorts.
CC 24/3-24/6 2/9-30/9

📧 N 43°18'46'' E 3°32'47''
www.eurocampings.co.uk/108455

1587 Marseillan-Plage, F-34340 / Languedoc-Roussillon   🚿 📶 (CC€17) 🚹 iD   65a

- 🔺 Le Galet***
- ⛺ 233 avenue des Campings
- 🕑 1 Apr - 30 Sep
- ☎ +33 (0)4-67219561
- @ reception@camping-galet.com

1	ADE**JM**NORT	ABFGHKNQST	6
2	EHNOQVWXY	ABDE**FG**H	7
3	BEKLT	ABCDEFNRSV	8
4	HI	EL	9
5	ADHJO	ABDGHIJO**P**TUZ	10
10A		❶ €47.00
2,9ha 136**T**(50-80m²) 126**P**		❷ €62.00

🚗 A9 exit Agde, from here towards Sète. Right at first roundabout (Ranch la Camargue) then left at second roundabout. Follow signs.
💬 A quiet campsite with a heated swimming pool with slides and a children's pool. 150m from the beach. Well maintained toilet facilities. A site in the centre of Marseillan-Plage with good shopping. A large supermarket, greengrocer and various places to eat are next to the site. 1 hour's free wifi by the swimming pool.
CC 1/4-4/7 27/8-29/9

📧 N 43°18'41'' E 3°32'40''
www.eurocampings.co.uk/112083

1588 Marseillan-Plage, F-34340 / Languedoc-Roussillon 🚿 📶 (CC€19) ♦♦ **iD** 65a

- 🏕 Les Méditerranées - Beach Garden*****
- 🚌 avenue des Campings
- 🗓 7 Apr - 1 Oct
- ☎ +33 (0)4-67219283
- @ info@beach-garden-camping.com

1 ADE**JM**NOPQRST	ABEFGHIKNQRSX	6
2 AEHOPQRSVWXY	BE**FGH**	7
3 BDEF**K**LQT	BCDEFKNQRS	8
4 BCDHILNO**PQT**U**VXZ**	ELUV	9
5 ACDEFGHJLM**O**	ABDGHIJO**P**TUZ	10

6-10A CEE ❶ €63.20
15ha 370**T**(80-100m²) 516**P** ❷ €83.20

🚗 A9 exit Agde and via the D112 to the roundabout, turn right here (Plage de Rieu). Turn right at junction with the main road of Marseillan-Plage. Site is located at the end of the street (dead end road).
💬 Shaded campsite by a nature reserve and the Mediterranean. Marseillan-Plage is within walking distance. Spacious touring pitches, two restaurants, supermarket and good toilets. Swimming pool with 1,000 m² of fun in the water! Free wifi at the bar.
(CC) 7/4-30/6 2/9-30/9

📌 N 43°18'21'' E 3°32'16''
www.eurocampings.co.uk/108454

1589 Marseillan-Plage, F-34340 / Languedoc-Roussillon 🚿 📶 (CC€19) ♦♦ **iD** 65a

- 🏕 Les Méditerranées - Charlemagne*****
- 🚌 avenue des Campings
- 🗓 7 Apr - 1 Oct
- ☎ +33 (0)4-67219249
- @ info@charlemagne-camping.com

1 ADE**JM**NOPRST	ABEFGHIKMNSWX	6
2 AEHOPQVWXY	ABDE**FGH**	7
3 BF**K**L	ABCDEFKNOQRSTUV	8
4 H**Q**UY	EL	9
5 ACDEFGHJLM**O**	ABDHIJ**P**TUYZ	10

10A CEE ❶ €63.20
7ha 170**T**(70-100m²) 228**P** ❷ €83.20

🚗 From Agde via D112, right at first roundabout, Plage de Rieu. Campsite on right after last roundabout in Marseillan-Plage.
💬 A comfortable campsite with spacious and well maintained pitches. Lovely flowers and plants. Connected directly to Camping Nouvelle Floride, through which you can get to the sandy beach. All facilities at both campsites are available to campers, from the day it opens to the day it closes!
(CC) 7/4-7/7 2/9-30/9

📌 N 43°18'37'' E 3°32'36''
www.eurocampings.co.uk/101505

France

1590 Mèze, F-34140 / Languedoc-Roussillon 🚿 📶 (CC€17) ♦♦ **iD** 26 A2

- 🏕 Beau Rivage****
- 🚌 RD613
- 🗓 14 Apr - 15 Sep
- ☎ +33 (0)4-67438148
- @ reception@camping-beaurivage.fr

1 ADE**IL**NOPR**T**	AFNQRST	6
2 ADHOPVWX	ABDE**FH**	7
3 BELQ	ABCDEFKLMNRSTV	8
4 BCDHILN**PQ**R	E	9
5 DEFHK	ABGHJO**P**TV	10

6A ❶ €47.20
3,5ha 92**T**(80-95m²) 109**P** ❷ €63.20

🚗 Exit Mèze on A9 motorway. Campsite signposted on the RD163.
💬 At the entrance to the village, the campsite is on the edge of the beautiful Bassin de Thau. Walking, cycling, local market, supermarkets, shops, harbours, beaches, tourist attractions and Mediterranean cuisine. Warm, family-friendly atmosphere. Sunny and shady pitches. Swimming pool, free wifi at the bar/restaurant.
(CC) 14/4-6/7 25/8-14/9 14=13, 21=19

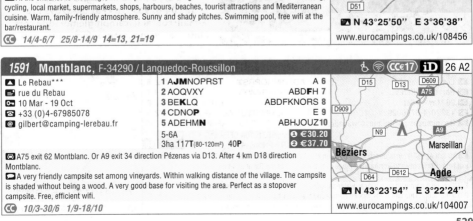

📌 N 43°25'50'' E 3°36'38''
www.eurocampings.co.uk/108456

1591 Montblanc, F-34290 / Languedoc-Roussillon 🚿 📶 (CC€17) **iD** 26 A2

- 🏕 Le Rebau***
- 🚌 rue du Rebau
- 🗓 10 Mar - 19 Oct
- ☎ +33 (0)4-67985078
- @ gilbert@camping-lerebau.fr

1 A**JM**NOPRST	A	6
2 AOQVXY	ABD**F**H	7
3 BE**K**LQ	ABDFKNORS	8
4 CDNO**P**	E	9
5 ADEHM**N**	ABHJOUZ	10

5-6A ❶ €30.20
3ha 117**T**(80-120m²) 40**P** ❷ €37.70

🚗 A75 exit 62 Montblanc. Or A9 exit 34 direction Pézenas via D13. After 4 km D18 direction Montblanc.
💬 A very friendly campsite set among vineyards. Within walking distance of the village. The campsite is shaded without being a wood. A very good base for visiting the area. Perfect as a stopover campsite. Free, efficient wifi.
(CC) 10/3-30/6 1/9-18/10

📌 N 43°23'54'' E 3°22'24''
www.eurocampings.co.uk/104007

1592 Palavas-les-Flots, F-34250 / Languedoc-Roussillon   ♿ 🛜 (CC€17) iD   26 A2

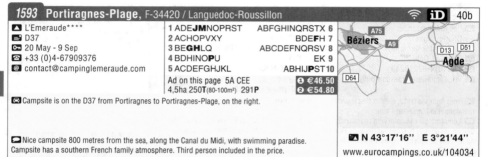

🔺 Montpellier Plage***
🛏 95 av. Saint Maurice
🗓 7 Apr - 23 Sep
☎ +33 (0)4-67680091
@ camping.montpellier.plage@ wanadoo.fr

1 ADEILNOPQRST	AF**N**X	6
2 AEHOPQVWXY	ABDE**FG**	7
3 ABEQ	ABCDFGKNRS	8
4 BCDIO	ELVW	9
5 ABDEFGHKKM**NO**	ABDFHIJO**P**TUZ	10
10A CEE	❶ €40.50	
10ha 500T(70-120m²) 150**P**	❷ €51.50	

🚗 Motorway A9 exit 29 Montpellier Est. Direction Les Plages and Palavas-les-Flots. In Palavas-les-Flots direction Rive Gauche. Campsite signposted on avenue St. Maurice.

💬 Excellent base for Montpellier and the cultural towns in Languedoc. 50 metres from a huge sandy beach. Within walking distance of the centre of Palavas-les-Flots.
(CC) 7/4-7/7 25/8-22/9

Montpellier

📍 N 43°32'4'' E 3°56'56''

www.eurocampings.co.uk/112093

1593 Portiragnes-Plage, F-34420 / Languedoc-Roussillon   🛜 iD   40b

🔺 L'Emeraude****
🛏 D37
🗓 20 May - 9 Sep
☎ +33 (0)4-67909376
@ contact@campinglemeraude.com

1 ADE**JM**NOPRST	ABFGHINQRSTX	6
2 ACHOPVXY	BDE**F**H	7
3 BE**GH**LQ	ABCDEFNQRSV	8
4 BDHINO**PU**	EK	9
5 ACDEFGHJKL	ABHIJ**P**ST	10
Ad on this page 5A CEE	❶ €46.50	
4,5ha 250T(80-100m²) 291**P**	❷ €54.80	

🚗 Campsite is on the D37 from Portiragnes to Portiragnes-Plage, on the right.

💬 Nice campsite 800 metres from the sea, along the Canal du Midi, with swimming paradise. Campsite has a southern French family atmosphere. Third person included in the price.

Béziers **Agde**

📍 N 43°17'16'' E 3°21'44''

www.eurocampings.co.uk/104034

1594 Portiragnes-Plage, F-34420 / Languedoc-Roussillon   ♿ 🛜 iD   40b

🔺 Les Mimosas*****
🛏 Port Cassafières
🗓 26 May - 8 Sep
☎ +33 (0)4-67909292
@ les.mimosas.portiragnes@wanadoo.fr

1 ADE**JM**NOPRS**T**	ABFGHI**N**XZ	6
2 ACGHOPRVWXY	BE**FG**H	7
3 BE**GH**KLQ	BDFIK**L**MNQRSV	8
4 ABDHILN**PQRTUXYZ**	AEJKLNUVWXZ	9
5 ACDEFGHJKLMN	ABGHIJ**NP**TUVYZ	10
Ad on page 531 10A CEE	❶ €50.80	
7ha 200T(80-100m²) 416**P**	❷ €73.80	

🚗 A9 exit Agde/Pézenas direction Agde. Then N112 direction Béziers. On the D37, turn left at 2nd exit from Portiragnes to Portiragnes-Plage over the bridge of the Canal du Midi.

💬 Nice, neat campsite with a large water park with wave pool, slides, jet stream, space hole and since 2016 the 'loop'. One half is for mobile homes and the other half is for touring caravans. A wonderful atmosphere. New in 2017: sunset bar with panoramic view and free shuttle bus to the beach.

Béziers **Agde**

📍 N 43°17'27'' E 3°22'22''

www.eurocampings.co.uk/104033

France

1595 Portiragnes-Plage, F-34420 / Languedoc-Roussillon   ♿ 🛜 (CC€19) ♟♟ iD | 40b

- ⛰ Les Sablons*****
- 🏕 av. des Muriers/Plage Est
- 📅 23 Mar - 30 Sep
- ☎ +33 (0)4-67909055
- @ contact@les-sablons.com

1	ADEJMNOPRST	ABCDFGHIKMNQSTWXY	6
2	ADEHOPQRVXY	ABDEFGHK	7
3	BCDEFGHKLMQR	ABCDFIJKNQRSUV	8
4	ABCDEFHILMNOPQRUXYZ	CEJLOQRTUVWY	9
5	ACDEFGHIJKLM	ABDGHINOPSTYZ	10

Ad on page 532 10A CEE
15ha 223T(85-120m²) 936P
❸ €62.00
❷ €86.00

🚗 A9 exit Béziers-Est, dir. Valras-Plage. At the roundabout left dir. Portiragnes. Then direction Portiragnes-Plage. Left past the roundabout.

💬 Large friendly campsite by the sea with swimming pools heated to 26°C from the opening date. Large 200m² indoor swimming pool from 2017. Plenty of entertainment for young and old. There is a lovely sandy beach. Free wifi for ½ hour every 6 hours. The spa is accessible from the age of 18 and open from 1 May.

CC 23/3-30/6 1/9-29/9

Béziers   A9 | D13
D612   Agde
D64

◤ N 43°16'48''   E 3°21'51''

www.eurocampings.co.uk/100544

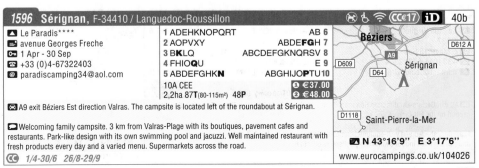

1596 Sérignan, F-34410 / Languedoc-Roussillon   ⊗ 🛜 (CC€17) iD | 40b

- ⛰ Le Paradis****
- 🏕 avenue Georges Freche
- 📅 1 Apr - 30 Sep
- ☎ +33 (0)4-67322403
- @ paradiscamping34@aol.com

1	ADEHKNOPQRT	AB	6
2	AOPVXY	ABDEFGH	7
3	BKLQ	ABCDEFGKNQRSV	8
4	FHIOQU	E	9
5	ABDEFGHKN	ABGHIJOPTU	10

10A CEE
2,2ha 87T(80-115m²) 48P
❸ €37.00
❷ €48.00

🚗 A9 exit Béziers Est direction Valras. The campsite is located left of the roundabout at Sérignan.

💬 Welcoming family campsite. 3 km from Valras-Plage with its boutiques, pavement cafes and restaurants. Park-like design with its own swimming pool and jacuzzi. Well maintained restaurant with fresh products every day and a varied menu. Supermarkets across the road.

CC 1/4-30/6 26/8-29/9

Béziers   D612 A
A9
D609   Sérignan
D64

D1118   Saint-Pierre-la-Mer

◤ N 43°16'9''   E 3°17'6''

www.eurocampings.co.uk/104026

France

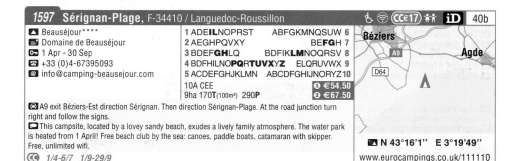

1597 Sérignan-Plage, F-34410 / Languedoc-Roussillon ♿ 🛜 (CC€17) ⛺ iD 40b

- ⛺ Beauséjour****
- 🏢 Domaine de Beauséjour
- 🗓 1 Apr - 30 Sep
- ☎ +33 (0)4-67395093
- @ info@camping-beausejour.com

1 ADE**IL**NOPRST	ABFGKMNQSUW	6
2 AEGHPQVXY	BE**FG**H	7
3 BDEF**GH**LQ	BDFIK**LM**NOQRSV	8
4 BDFHILNO**PQRTUVX**YZ	ELQRUVWX	9
5 ACDEFGHJKLMN	ABCDFGHIJNORYZ	10
10A CEE		❶ €54.50
9ha 170**T**(100m²) 290**P**		❷ €67.50

🚗 A9 exit Béziers-Est direction Sérignan. Then direction Sérignan-Plage. At the road junction turn right and follow the signs.

💬 This campsite, located by a lovey sandy beach, exudes a lively family atmosphere. The water park is heated from 1 April! Free beach club by the sea: canoes, paddle boats, catamaran with skipper. Free, unlimited wifi.

CC 1/4-6/7 1/9-29/9

Béziers · A9 · Agde · D64

⛺ N 43°16'1'' E 3°19'49''
www.eurocampings.co.uk/111110

1598 Sérignan-Plage, F-34410 / Languedoc-Roussillon ♿ 🛜 (CC€17) iD 40b

- ⛺ Le Clos Virgile****
- 🏢 CD37
- 🗓 5 May - 16 Sep
- ☎ +33 (0)4-67322064
- @ contact@leclosvirgile.fr

1 ADE**JM**NORT	AEFHKNQS	6
2 AEHPRVY	BDE**FG**H	7
3 ABE**GHI**LQ	ABCDFKNOQRSV	8
4 BDILNOUY	EJLUV	9
5 ACDEFGHJKLM**N**	ABDGHIJ**P**TUVY	10
10A		❶ €45.20
5ha 300**T**(80-90m²) 98**P**		❷ €61.20

🚗 A9 exit Béziers-Est direction Sérignan. Then take the D37e to Sérignan-Plage. The campsite is the second on the left.

💬 A fine, shaded and well-equipped campsite. The campsite is located 400 metres from the beach and has a heated indoor swimming pool and two jacuzzis.

CC 5/5-29/6 1/9-15/9

Béziers · D13 · A9 · D612 · Agde · D64

⛺ N 43°16'12'' E 3°19'52''
www.eurocampings.co.uk/104029

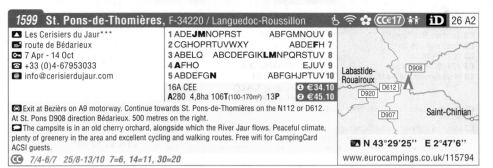

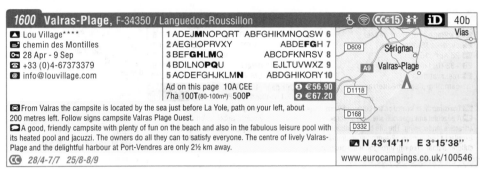

1599 St. Pons-de-Thomières, F-34220 / Languedoc-Roussillon   ♿ 🛜 ✿ (CC€17) ♦♦ iD | 26 A2

- ▲ Les Cerisiers du Jaur***
- 🚌 route de Bédarieux
- 📅 7 Apr - 14 Oct
- ☎ +33 (0)4-67953033
- @ info@cerisierdujaur.com

1 ADE**JM**NOPRST	ABFGMNOUV 6
2 CGHOPRTUVWXY	ABDE**F**H 7
3 ABELQ ABCDEFGIK**LM**NPQRSTUV 8	
4 **A**FHO	EJUV 9
5 ABDEFG**N**	ABFGHJPTUV 10

16A CEE   ❶ € 34.10
A280 4,8ha 106**T**(100-170m²) 13**P**   ❷ € 45.10

🚗 Exit at Bezièrs on A9 motorway. Continue towards St. Pons-de-Thomières on the N112 or D612. At St. Pons D908 direction Bédarieux. 500 metres on the right.
💬 The campsite is in an old cherry orchard, alongside which the River Jaur flows. Peaceful climate, plenty of greenery in the area and excellent cycling and walking routes. Free wifi for CampingCard ACSI guests.

CC 7/4-6/7 25/8-13/10 7=6, 14=11, 30=20

N 43°29'25'' E 2°47'6''

www.eurocampings.co.uk/115794

1600 Valras-Plage, F-34350 / Languedoc-Roussillon   ♿ 🛜 (CC€15) ♦♦ iD | 40b Vias

- ▲ Lou Village****
- 🚌 chemin des Montilles
- 📅 28 Apr - 9 Sep
- ☎ +33 (0)4-67373379
- @ info@louvillage.com

1 ADE**J M**NOPQRT ABFGHIKMNOQSW 6	
2 AEGHOPRVXY	ABDE**FG**H 7
3 BEF**GHL**MQ	ABCDFKNRSV 8
4 BDILNO**PQ**U	EJLTUVWXZ 9
5 ACDEFGHJKLM**N**	ABDGHIKORY 10

Ad on this page 10A CEE   ❶ € 56.90
7ha 100**T**(80-100m²) 500**P**   ❷ € 67.20

🚗 From Valras the campsite is located by the sea just before La Yole, path on your left, about 200 metres left. Follow signs campsite Valras Plage Ouest.
💬 A good, friendly campsite with plenty of fun on the beach and also in the fabulous leisure pool with its heated pool and jacuzzi. The owners do all they can to satisfy everyone. The centre of lively Valras-Plage and the delightful harbour at Port-Vendres are only 2½ km away.

CC 28/4-7/7 25/8-8/9

N 43°14'1'' E 3°15'38''

www.eurocampings.co.uk/100546

France

533

1601 Valras-Plage, F-34350 / Languedoc-Roussillon ⚡ 🤵 ♿ 🛜 (CC€17) iD 40b

- 🏕 Sandaya Blue Bayou*****
- 🏖 Vendres Plage Ouest
- 📅 20 Apr - 16 Sep
- ☎ +33 (0)4-67374197
- @ bluebayou@sandaya.fr

1 ADJMNOPRST	ABFGHIKNOPQRSTW 6
2 AEHOPQVWXY	ABDEFGH 7
3 BDEGHMQT	ABCDFJKLMNRSV 8
4 BCDILNOPQRXZ	EJLUV 9
5 ACDEFGHKLM	ABDHIJPTUV 10

Ad on the cover 10A CEE
6ha 350T(80-100m²) 360P
❶ €67.00
❷ €83.00

🗺 Campsite located on the Valras-Plage Ouest-Vendres-Plage (D37E9). Campsite south west of Vendre-Plage.

💬 A large campsite with pitches for touring guests. Some have private toilet facilities. Refurbished leisure pool with water playpark for small children. Lovely swimming pool. 300 metres from a sandy beach in a beautiful nature reserve. Attractive location, close to the sea and 5 km from the centre of Valras-Plage.

CC 20/4-6/7 1/9-15/9

🔼 N 43°13'38" E 3°14'38"

www.eurocampings.co.uk/100547

1602 Vendres, F-34350 / Languedoc-Roussillon ⊗ ♿ 🛜 (CC€17) 🚻 iD 40b

- 🏕 La Plage et du Bord de Mer
- 🏖 av. de la Mediterranee
- 📅 28 Apr - 16 Sep
- ☎ +33 (0)4-67373438
- @ reservation@
  camping-plage-mediterranee.com

1 ADEHKNOPQRST	ABFHIKMNQRST 6
2 AEGHOPQVWXY	ABDEFGH 7
3 ABEILMQ	ABCDEFKNORSV 8
4 BCDEFILNOPQU	BELUVY 9
5 ACDEFGHKLMN	ABEFGHIJPTU 10

Ad on this page 10A CEE
13ha 466T(80-100m²) 155P
❶ €53.00
❷ €63.00

🗺 The campsite is located on the boulevard Valras-Plage Ouest. Follow the signs when entering Valras-Plage.

💬 A peaceful and spacious site with direct access to a lovely sandy beach. Spacious pitches with attractive landscaping. The site has an attractive aquapark with swimming pools and a large slide. Excellent toilet facilities. Playground equipment throughout the campsite, including in the lovely children's pool. Free wifi throughout the grounds.

CC 28/4-23/6 25/8-15/9 14=13

🔼 N 43°14'7" E 3°16'8"

www.eurocampings.co.uk/108477

1603 Vendres-Plage/Valras-Plage, F-34350 / Languedoc-Roussillon

    CC€17 iD 40b Vias

- ▲ Sandaya Les Vagues****
- 🏠 chemin de Montilles
- 🗓 6 Apr - 16 Sep
- ☎ +33 (0)4-67373312
- @ t.hannier@sandaya.fr

1 ADE**IL**NOPQRST	ABFGHIKNQSW 6	
2 AEGHOQRVXY	ABDE**FGH** 7	
3 ABE**GH**ILQT	ABCDEFKNRSTUV 8	
4 BCDILMNO**PQ**RU**XZ**	BEFLUVX 9	
5 ACDEFGHLM	ABDGHIJMO**P**Y 10	

Ad on the cover 6A
❶ €64.00
8ha 107**T**(85-100m²) 338**P**   ❷ €78.00

🚗 From Valras follow Valras-Plage Ouest signs. Then follow camping signs.

💬 Located 500 metres from the Languedoc beaches. The shaded campsite comprises three separate sections. Lovely heated swimming pool with wave pool and slide. Many sights, activities and watersports opportunities in the area.

CC 6/4-6/7 1/9-15/9

📍 N 43°13'51" E 3°15'13"
www.eurocampings.co.uk/104036

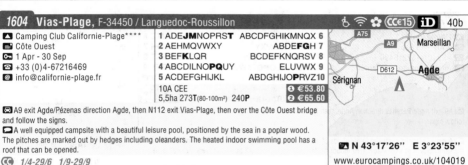

1604 Vias-Plage, F-34450 / Languedoc-Roussillon

    CC€15 iD 40b

- ▲ Camping Club Californie-Plage****
- 🏠 Côte Ouest
- 🗓 1 Apr - 30 Sep
- ☎ +33 (0)4-67216469
- @ info@californie-plage.fr

1 ADE**JM**NOPRS**T**	ABCDFGHIKMNQX 6
2 AEHMQVWXY	ABDE**FGH** 7
3 BEF**K**LQR	BCDEFKNQRSV 8
4 ABCDILNO**PQ**UY	ELUVWX 9
5 ACDEFGHIJKL	ABDGHIJO**P**RVZ 10

10A CEE
❶ €53.80
5,5ha 273**T**(80-100m²) 240**P**   ❷ €65.60

🚗 A9 exit Agde/Pézenas direction Agde, then N112 exit Vias-Plage, then over the Côte Ouest bridge and follow the signs.

💬 A well equipped campsite with a beautiful leisure pool, positioned by the sea in a poplar wood. The pitches are marked out by hedges including oleanders. The heated indoor swimming pool has a roof that can be opened.

CC 1/4-29/6 1/9-29/9

📍 N 43°17'26" E 3°23'55"
www.eurocampings.co.uk/104019

France

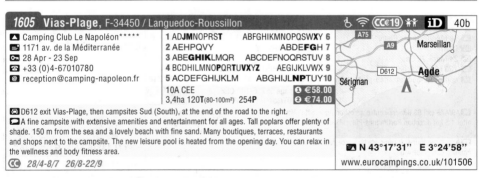

1605 Vias-Plage, F-34450 / Languedoc-Roussillon

    CC€19 ⛹ iD 40b

- ▲ Camping Club Le Napoléon*****
- 🏠 1171 av. de la Méditerranée
- 🗓 28 Apr - 23 Sep
- ☎ +33 (0)4-67010780
- @ reception@camping-napoleon.fr

1 ADJ**M**NOPRST	ABFGHIKMNOPQSW**X**Y 6
2 AEHPQVY	ABDE**FGH** 7
3 ABE**GHIK**LMQR	ABCDEFNOQRSTUV 8
4 BCDHILMNO**PQRT**U**VX**YZ	AEGIJKLVWX 9
5 ACDEFGHIJKLM	ABGHIJL**NP**TUY 10

10A CEE
❶ €58.00
3,4ha 120**T**(80-100m²) 254**P**   ❷ €74.00

🚗 D612 exit Vias-Plage, then campsites Sud (South), at the end of the road to the right.

💬 A fine campsite with extensive amenities and entertainment for all ages. Tall poplars offer plenty of shade. 150 m from the sea and a lovely beach with fine sand. Many boutiques, terraces, restaurants and shops next to the campsite. The new leisure pool is heated from the opening day. You can relax in the wellness and body fitness area.

CC 28/4-8/7 26/8-22/9

📍 N 43°17'31" E 3°24'58"
www.eurocampings.co.uk/101506

1606 Vias-Plage, F-34450 / Languedoc-Roussillon

    CC€15 iD 40b

- ▲ Helios****
- 🏠 avenue des Pêcheurs
- 🗓 21 Apr - 30 Sep
- ☎ +33 (0)4-67216366
- @ contact@camping-helios.com

1 ADE**JM**NOPRST	ABCDFGHKNXY 6
2 ACEHQVY	ABDE**F**H 7
3 BELQ	ABDEFLNORSV 8
4 DINO**PTUVX**Y**Z**	EF 9
5 ACDEFHJKMN	ABDHIJ**P**TZ 10

Ad on page 536 4-6A CEE
❶ €47.60
3ha 108**T**(80-90m²) 139**P**   ❷ €59.60

🚗 A9 exit Agde/Pézenas. D612 direction Agde; exit Vias-Plage. Then 'campings Sud' and follow the signs at the roundabout.

💬 A quiet, natural campsite with a homely ambiance. 200 m from the beach on the small River Libron and within walking distance of the lively centre of Vias-Plage. The toilet facilities have been renovated and there is a new wellness centre. Beautiful new (2015) heated leisure pool, partly covered.

CC 21/4-6/7 25/8-29/9

📍 N 43°17'33" E 3°24'26"
www.eurocampings.co.uk/108548

France

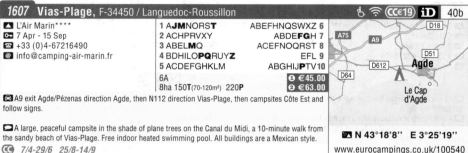

1607 Vias-Plage, F-34450 / Languedoc-Roussillon   ♿ 🛜 CC€19 iD 40b

- ⛺ L'Air Marin★★★★
- 🗓 7 Apr - 15 Sep
- ☎ +33 (0)4-67216490
- @ info@camping-air-marin.fr

1 A**JM**NORS**T**	ABEFHNQSWXZ	6
2 ACHPRVXY	ABDE**FG**H	7
3 ABEL**MQ**	ACEFNOQRST	8
4 BDHILO**PQ**RUY**Z**	EFL	9
5 ACDEFGHKLM	ABGHIJ**P**TV	10
6A		
8ha 150**T**(70-120m²) 220**P**	❶ €45.00	
	❷ €63.00	

🚗 A9 exit Agde/Pézenas direction Agde, then N112 direction Vias-Plage, then campsites Côte Est and follow signs.

💬 A large, peaceful campsite in the shade of plane trees on the Canal du Midi, a 10-minute walk from the sandy beach of Vias-Plage. Free indoor heated swimming pool. All buildings are a Mexican style.

CC 7/4-29/6 25/8-14/9

📍 N 43°18'8'' E 3°25'19''
www.eurocampings.co.uk/100540

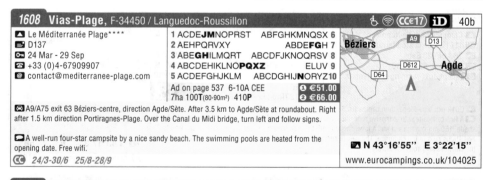

1608 Vias-Plage, F-34450 / Languedoc-Roussillon   ♿ 🛜 CC€17 iD 40b

- ⛺ Le Méditerranée Plage★★★★
- 🚏 D137
- 🗓 24 Mar - 29 Sep
- ☎ +33 (0)4-67909907
- @ contact@mediterranee-plage.com

1 ACDE**JM**NOPRST	ABFGHKMNQSX	6
2 AEHPQRVXY	ABDE**FG**H	7
3 ABE**GH**ILMQRT	ABCDFJKNOQRSV	8
4 ABCDEHIKLNO**PQXZ**	ELUV	9
5 ACDEFGHJKLM	ABCDGHIJ**N**ORYZ	10
Ad on page 537 6-10A CEE	❶ €51.00	
7ha 100**T**(80-90m²) 410**P**	❷ €66.00	

🚗 A9/A75 exit 63 Béziers-centre, direction Agde/Sète. After 3.5 km to Agde/Sète at roundabout. Right after 1.5 km direction Portiragnes-Plage. Over the Canal du Midi bridge, turn left and follow signs.

💬 A well-run four-star campsite by a nice sandy beach. The swimming pools are heated from the opening date. Free wifi.

CC 24/3-30/6 25/8-28/9

📍 N 43°16'55'' E 3°22'15''
www.eurocampings.co.uk/104025

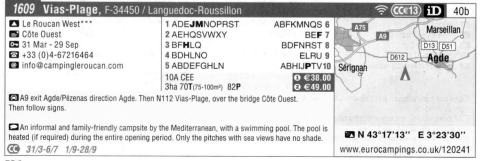

1609 Vias-Plage, F-34450 / Languedoc-Roussillon   🛜 CC€13 iD 40b

- ⛺ Le Roucan West★★★
- 🚏 Côte Ouest
- 🗓 31 Mar - 29 Sep
- ☎ +33 (0)4-67216464
- @ info@campingleroucan.com

1 ADE**JM**NOPRST	ABFKMNQS	6
2 AEHQSVWXY	BE**F**	7
3 BF**HLQ**	BDFNRST	8
4 BDHLNO	ELRU	9
5 ABDEFGHLN	ABHIJ**P**TV	10
10A CEE	❶ €38.00	
3ha 70**T**(75-100m²) 82**P**	❷ €49.00	

🚗 A9 exit Agde/Pézenas direction Agde. Then N112 Vias-Plage, over the bridge Côte Ouest. Then follow signs.

💬 An informal and family-friendly campsite by the Mediterranean, with a swimming pool. The pool is heated (if required) during the entire opening period. Only the pitches with sea views have no shade.

CC 31/3-6/7 1/9-28/9

📍 N 43°17'13'' E 3°23'30''
www.eurocampings.co.uk/120241

Méditerranée plage

CAMPING VILLAGE ★★★★

Open from March 24rd - September 29th 2018

34450 Vias-Plage
Languedoc - Southern France
Tel. +33 (0)4 67 90 99 07
www.mediterranee-plage.com
contact@mediterranee-plage.com

France

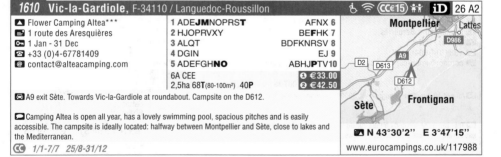

1610 Vic-la-Gardiole, F-34110 / Languedoc-Roussillon   ♿ 🛜 CC€15 ✶✶ iD 26 A2

- 🏕 Flower Camping Altea***
- 📧 1 route des Aresquières
- 🗓 1 Jan - 31 Dec
- ☎ +33 (0)4-67781409
- @ contact@alteacamping.com

1 ADE**JM**NOPRS**T**	AFNX	6
2 HJOPRVXY	BE**F**HK	7
3 ALQT	BDFKNRSV	8
4 DGIN	EJ	9
5 ADEFGH**NO**	ABHJ**P**TV	10
6A CEE	❶ €33.00	
2,5ha 68T(80-100m²) 40P	❷ €42.50	

🚗 A9 exit Sète. Towards Vic-la-Gardiole at roundabout. Campsite on the D612.

💬 Camping Altea is open all year, has a lovely swimming pool, spacious pitches and is easily accessible. The campsite is ideally located: halfway between Montpellier and Sète, close to lakes and the Mediterranean.

CC 1/1-7/7 25/8-31/12

Montpellier — Lattes
D986 D2 D613 A9 D612
Sète — Frontignan

📷 N 43°30'2'' E 3°47'15''

www.eurocampings.co.uk/117988

1611 Villeneuve-lès-Béziers, F-34420 / Languedoc-Roussillon   ♿ 🛜 CC€17 ✶✶ 40b

- 🏕 Les Berges du Canal***
- 📧 promenade des Vernets
- 🗓 10 Mar - 20 Oct
- ☎ +33 (0)4-67393609
- @ contact@campinglbdc.com

1 BDE**JM**NOPRS**T**	AFN**XZ**	6
2 ACOPRVY	ABE**FG**H	7
3 ABCELQ	BDFIJKLNOQRSV	8
4 ABDHIO**PQTX**	ELNUVW	9
5 ADEFGHJKLMN	ABFGHIJL**PQ**TU	10
Ad on page 538 16A CEE	❶ €31.20	
1,5ha 30T(80-90m²) 86P	❷ €43.20	

🚗 The campsite is located in the village on the Canal du Midi. When approaching from Béziers: before the bridge to the left.

💬 A quiet, well located, friendly family campsite next to the Canal du Midi. Just a few minutes' walk from Villeneuve-lès-Béziers. Ideally suited as a base for exploring the region. Good place for starting cycle tours. 7 km from the beach. Good, well maintained toilet facilities.

CC 10/3-6/7 25/8-19/10 7=6, 14=12, 21=18

D909 A75 D13
Béziers A9 Vias
D609 Sérignan

📷 N 43°19'0'' E 3°17'4''

www.eurocampings.co.uk/107555

1612 Camurac, F-11340 / Languedoc-Roussillon — 25 B2

🏂 ♿ 🛜 (CC€13) iD

- 🏕 Les Sapins**
- 1/1 - 1/11, 15/12 - 31/12
- ☎ +33 (0)4-68203811
- @ info@lessapins-camurac.com

1	AG**JM**NOPQR**T**	AFNUV 6
2	FGPVWXY	AB**FG** 7
3	AE**GHI**LQSV	ABCDFGIJNRSV 8
4	BCD**E**FGHIO	AEJ 9
5	ABDEFGHKM**N**	ABJLOTU 10
10A CEE		➊ €25.90
A1280 3,5ha 72**T**(80-100m²) 29**P**		➋ €35.90

🚗 From Quillan follow Ax-Les-Thermes and Belcaire. Via Ax-Les-Thermes from dir. Quillan in Camurac follow 'Piste de ski' signs. Right after 1 km. Route for large vehicles via Foix-Lavelanet (D117). Then D117 dir. Belesta and D16/D29 and D613 until the 'Piste de ski' signs.

💬 Welcoming campsite in countryside with lovely views. The Cathar Ruin of Montaillou is visible. Various walks through flower meadows and villages. Nearby skiing area (altitude 1625m).

CC 1/4-7/7 27/8-31/10

Fougax-et-Barrineuf

N20 D613

Ax-les-Thermes

📷 N 42°47'30'' E 1°55'30''

www.eurocampings.co.uk/113708

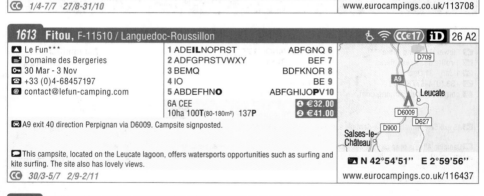

1613 Fitou, F-11510 / Languedoc-Roussillon — 26 A2

♿ 🛜 (CC€17) iD

- 🏕 Le Fun***
- 🏠 Domaine des Bergeries
- 30 Mar - 3 Nov
- ☎ +33 (0)4-68457197
- @ contact@lefun-camping.com

1	ADE**IL**NOPRST	ABFGNQ 6
2	ADFGPRSTVWXY	BEF 7
3	BEMQ	BDFKNOR 8
4	IO	BE 9
5	ABDEFHN**O**	ABFGHIJO**PV** 10
6A CEE		➊ €32.00
10ha 100**T**(80-180m²) 137**P**		➋ €41.00

🚗 A9 exit 40 direction Perpignan via D6009. Campsite signposted.

💬 This campsite, located on the Leucate lagoon, offers watersports opportunities such as surfing and kite surfing. The site also has lovely views.

CC 30/3-5/7 2/9-2/11

D709

A9 Leucate

D6009

D900 D627

Salses-le-Château

📷 N 42°54'51'' E 2°59'56''

www.eurocampings.co.uk/116437

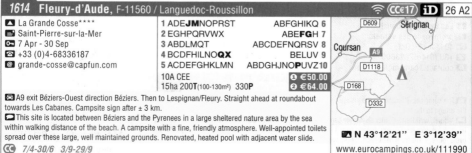

1614 Fleury-d'Aude, F-11560 / Languedoc-Roussillon — 26 A2

🛜 (CC€17) iD

- 🏕 La Grande Cosse****
- 🏠 Saint-Pierre-sur-la-Mer
- 7 Apr - 30 Sep
- ☎ +33 (0)4-68336187
- @ grande-cosse@capfun.com

1	ADE**JM**NOPRST	ABFGHIKQ 6
2	EGHPQRVWX	ABE**FG**H 7
3	ABDLMQT	ABCDEFNQRSV 8
4	BCDFHILNO**QX**	BELUV 9
5	ACDEFGHKLMN	ABDGHJNOP**UV**Z 10
10A CEE		➊ €50.00
15ha 200**T**(100-130m²) 330**P**		➋ €64.00

🚗 A9 exit Béziers-Ouest direction Béziers. Then to Lespignan/Fleury. Straight ahead at roundabout towards Les Cabanes. Campsite sign after ± 3 km.

💬 This site is located between Béziers and the Pyrenees in a large sheltered nature area by the sea within walking distance of the beach. A campsite with a fine, friendly atmosphere. Well-appointed toilets spread over these large, well maintained grounds. Renovated, heated pool with adjacent water slide.

CC 7/4-30/6 3/9-29/9

D609 Sérignan

Coursan A9

D1118

D168

D332

📷 N 43°12'21'' E 3°12'39''

www.eurocampings.co.uk/111990

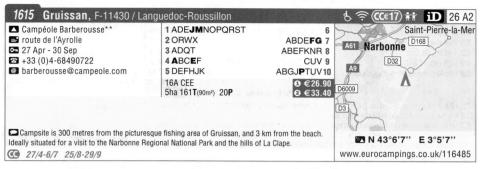

1615 Gruissan, F-11430 / Languedoc-Roussillon

 ♿ 🛜 (CC€17) ♀♂ iD 26 A2

- 🏕 Campéole Barberousse**
- 🛣 route de l'Ayrolle
- 📅 27 Apr - 30 Sep
- ☎ +33 (0)4-68490722
- @ barberousse@campeole.com

1 ADE**JM**NOPQRST		6
2 ORWX	ABDE**FG**	7
3 ADQT	ABEFKNR	8
4 **ABC**EF	CUV	9
5 DEFHJK	ABGJ**P**TUV	10
16A CEE	❶ €26.90	
5ha 161T(90m²) 20P	❷ €33.40	

Saint-Pierre-la-Mer
Narbonne

💻 Campsite is 300 metres from the picturesque fishing area of Gruissan, and 3 km from the beach. Ideally situated for a visit to the Narbonne Regional National Park and the hills of La Clape.

CC 27/4-6/7 25/8-29/9

📍 N 43°6'7'' E 3°5'7''
www.eurocampings.co.uk/116485

1616 La Franqui/Leucate, F-11370 / Languedoc-Roussillon

 ♿ (CC€13) iD 26 A2

- 🏕 La Franqui**
- 🛣 chemin des Coussoules
- 📅 13 Apr - 16 Sep
- ☎ +33 (0)4-68457493
- @ franqui@originalcamping.com

1 ADE**JM**NOPQRST	KMNQR	6
2 AEHQRVWX	ABDE**F**	7
3 A	ABEFNRSV	8
4		9
5 ABDF**O**	ABDHIJTU	10
6A CEE	❶ €24.60	
3,5ha 256T(60-80m²)	❷ €34.60	

Port-la-Nouvelle

🚗 A9 direction Perpignan, exit 40 Leucate. Stay on D627 to La Franqui exit. Follow campsite signs at La Franqui.

💻 La Fraqui is an unpretentious but attractive campsite with direct access to the wide flat beach and the sea. Beach surfing is a fun activity on the flat beach. The pitches are not all that big, but reasonably well shaded and marked out by beautiful planting.

CC 13/4-6/7 27/8-15/9

📍 N 42°56'37'' E 3°1'50''
www.eurocampings.co.uk/121416

France

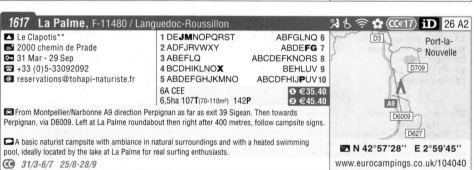

1617 La Palme, F-11480 / Languedoc-Roussillon

 🏹♿ 🛜 ✿ (CC€17) iD 26 A2

- 🏕 Le Clapotis**
- 🛣 2000 chemin de Prade
- 📅 31 Mar - 29 Sep
- ☎ +33 (0)5-33092092
- @ reservations@tohapi-naturiste.fr

1 DE**JM**NOPQRST	ABFGLNQ	6
2 ADFJRVWXY	ABDE**FG**	7
3 ABEFLQ	ABCDEFKNORS	8
4 BCDHIKLNO**X**	BEHLUV	9
5 ABDEFGHJKMNO	ABCDFHIJ**P**UV	10
6A CEE	❶ €35.40	
6,5ha 107T(70-110m²) 142P	❷ €45.40	

Port-la-Nouvelle

🚗 From Montpellier/Narbonne A9 direction Perpignan as far as exit 39 Sigean. Then towards Perpignan, via D6009. Left at La Palme roundabout then right after 400 metres, follow campsite signs.

💻 A basic naturist campsite with ambiance in natural surroundings and with a heated swimming pool, ideally located by the lake at La Palme for real surfing enthusiasts.

CC 31/3-6/7 25/8-28/9

📍 N 42°57'28'' E 2°59'45''
www.eurocampings.co.uk/104040

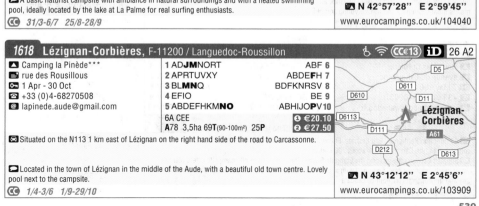

1618 Lézignan-Corbières, F-11200 / Languedoc-Roussillon

 ♿ 🛜 (CC€13) iD 26 A2

- 🏕 Camping la Pinède***
- 🛣 rue des Rousillous
- 📅 1 Apr - 30 Sep
- ☎ +33 (0)4-68270508
- @ lapinede.aude@gmail.com

1 AD**JM**NORT	ABF	6
2 APRTUVXY	ABDEFH	7
3 B**LMN**Q	BDFKNRSV	8
4 EFIO	BE	9
5 ABDEFHKM**NO**	ABHIJOP**V**	10
6A CEE	❶ €20.10	
A78 3,5ha 69T(90-100m²) 25P	❷ €27.50	

Lézignan-Corbières

🚗 Situated on the N113 1 km east of Lézignan on the right hand side of the road to Carcassonne.

💻 Located in the town of Lézignan in the middle of the Aude, with a beautiful old town centre. Lovely pool next to the campsite.

CC 1/4-3/6 1/9-29/10

📍 N 43°12'12'' E 2°45'6''
www.eurocampings.co.uk/103909

1619 Narbonne, F-11100 / Languedoc-Roussillon   👌 📶 (CC€19) ⚤ iD 26 A2

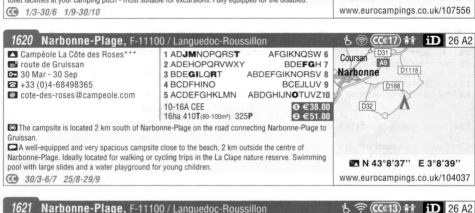

- 🏕 Camping La Nautique****
- ✉ 254 avenue des Etangs
- 📅 1 Mar - 31 Oct
- ☎ +33 (0)4-68904819
- @ info@campinglanautique.com

1 ADE**JM**NOPRST	ABFGHNQRSTXY	6
2 ADFGPRTVWXY	ABDE**FG**H	7
3 ABE**FILMQ**R**T	LQRTUV	8
4 ABCDEFGHILNO**PQ**	ELMOQTUV	9
5 ACDEFGHLN	ABDGHIJPUZ	10

10A   ➊ €47.70
16ha 250**T**(130-140m²) 230**P**   ➋ €63.10

🚗 A9 exit 38 Narbonne-Sud. At the roundabout turn left, follow the signs La Nautique. After about 2.5 km the campsite is on the right hand side.

💬 Exceptional location on the beautiful Bages bay - lovely panoramic views - and just a few kilometres from the beaches and the historic centre of Narbonne - a friendly welcome, heated swimming pool, private toilet facilities at your camping pitch - most suitable for excursions. Fully equipped for the disabled.

CC 1/3-30/6   1/9-30/10

📍 N 43°8'50''   E 3°0'14''
www.eurocampings.co.uk/107556

1620 Narbonne-Plage, F-11100 / Languedoc-Roussillon   👌 📶 (CC€17) ⚤ iD 26 A2

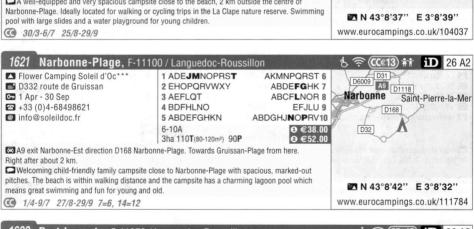

- 🏕 Campéole La Côte des Roses***
- ✉ route de Gruissan
- 📅 30 Mar - 30 Sep
- ☎ +33 (0)4-68498365
- @ cote-des-roses@campeole.com

1 AD**JM**NOPQRS**T**	AFGIKNQSW	6
2 ADEHOPQRVWXY	BDE**FG**H	7
3 BDE**GIL**Q**R**T	ABDEFGIKNORSV	8
4 BCDFHINO	BCEJLUV	9
5 ACDEFGHKLMN	ABDGHIJN**O**TUVZ	10

10-16A CEE   ➊ €38.00
16ha 410**T**(80-100m²) 325**P**   ➋ €51.00

🚗 The campsite is located 2 km south of Narbonne-Plage on the road connecting Narbonne-Plage to Gruissan.

💬 A well-equipped and very spacious campsite close to the beach, 2 km outside the centre of Narbonne-Plage. Ideally located for walking or cycling trips in the La Clape nature reserve. Swimming pool with large slides and a water playground for young children.

CC 30/3-6/7   25/8-29/9

📍 N 43°8'37''   E 3°8'39''
www.eurocampings.co.uk/104037

1621 Narbonne-Plage, F-11100 / Languedoc-Roussillon   👌 📶 (CC€13) ⚤ iD 26 A2

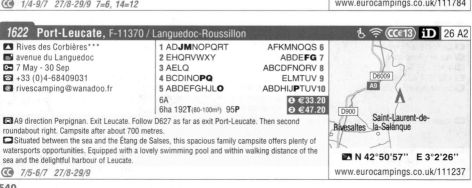

- 🏕 Flower Camping Soleil d'Oc***
- ✉ D332 route de Gruissan
- 📅 1 Apr - 30 Sep
- ☎ +33 (0)4-68498621
- @ info@soleildoc.fr

1 ADE**JM**NOPRS**T**	AKMNPQRST	6
2 EHOPQRVWXY	ABDE**FG**HK	7
3 AEFLQT	ABCF**L**NOR	8
4 BDFHLNO	EFJLU	9
5 ABDEFGHKN	ABDGHJ**N**OPRV	10

6-10A   ➊ €38.00
3ha 110**T**(80-120m²) 90**P**   ➋ €52.00

🚗 A9 exit Narbonne-Est direction D168 Narbonne-Plage. Towards Gruissan-Plage from here. Right after about 2 km.

💬 Welcoming child-friendly family campsite close to Narbonne-Plage with spacious, marked-out pitches. The beach is within walking distance and the campsite has a charming lagoon pool which means great swimming and fun for young and old.

CC 1/4-9/7   27/8-29/9 7=6, 14=12

📍 N 43°8'42''   E 3°8'32''
www.eurocampings.co.uk/111784

1622 Port-Leucate, F-11370 / Languedoc-Roussillon   👌 📶 (CC€13) iD 26 A2

- 🏕 Rives des Corbières***
- ✉ avenue du Languedoc
- 📅 7 May - 30 Sep
- ☎ +33 (0)4-68409031
- @ rivescamping@wanadoo.fr

1 AD**JM**NOPQRT	AFKMNOQS	6
2 EHQRVWXY	ABDE**FG**	7
3 AELQ	ABCDFNORV	8
4 BCDINO**PQ**	ELMTUV	9
5 ABDEFGHJL**O**	ABDHIJ**P**TUV	10

6A   ➊ €33.20
6ha 192**T**(80-100m²) 95**P**   ➋ €47.20

🚗 A9 direction Perpignan. Exit Leucate. Follow D627 as far as exit Port-Leucate. Then second roundabout right. Campsite after about 700 metres.

💬 Situated between the sea and the Étang de Salses, this spacious family campsite offers plenty of watersports opportunities. Equipped with a lovely swimming pool and within walking distance of the sea and the delightful harbour of Leucate.

CC 7/5-6/7   27/8-29/9

📍 N 42°50'57''   E 3°2'26''
www.eurocampings.co.uk/111237

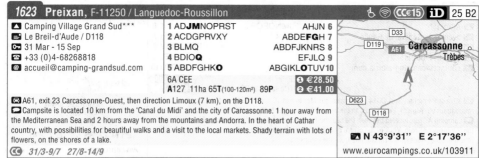

1623 Preixan, F-11250 / Languedoc-Roussillon
   📶 CC€15 iD 25 B2

- 🏕 Camping Village Grand Sud***
- 🛣 Le Breil-d'Aude / D118
- 📅 31 Mar - 15 Sep
- ☎ +33 (0)4-68268818
- @ accueil@camping-grandsud.com

1	ADJMNOPRST	AHJN 6
2	ACDGPRVXY	ABDEFGH 7
3	BLMQ	ABDFJKNRS 8
4	BDIOQ	EFJLQ 9
5	ABDFGHKO	ABGIKLOTUV10

6A CEE   ❶ €28.50
A127 11ha 65T(100-120m²) 89P   ❷ €41.00

🚗 A61, exit 23 Carcassonne-Ouest, then direction Limoux (7 km), on the D118.
🛏 Campsite is located 10 km from the 'Canal du Midi' and the city of Carcassonne. 1 hour away from the Mediterranean Sea and 2 hours away from the mountains and Andorra. In the heart of Cathar country, with possibilities for beautiful walks and a visit to the local markets. Shady terrain with lots of flowers, on the shores of a lake.
CC 31/3-9/7 27/8-14/9

📍 N 43°9'31'' E 2°17'36''
www.eurocampings.co.uk/103911

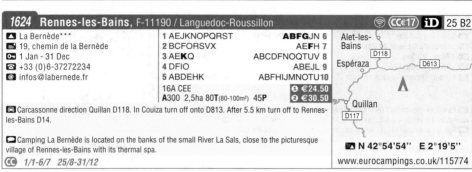

1624 Rennes-les-Bains, F-11190 / Languedoc-Roussillon
   📶 CC€17 iD 25 B2

- 🏕 La Bernède***
- 🛣 19, chemin de la Bernède
- 📅 1 Jan - 31 Dec
- ☎ +33 (0)6-37272234
- @ infos@labernede.fr

1	AEJKNOPQRST	ABFGJN 6
2	BCFORSVX	AEFH 7
3	AEKQ	ABCDFNOQTUV 8
4	DFIO	ABEJL 9
5	ABDEHK	ABFHIJMNOTU10

16A CEE   ❶ €24.50
A300 2,5ha 80T(80-100m²) 45P   ❷ €30.50

🚗 Carcassonne direction Quillan D118. In Couiza turn off onto D813. After 5.5 km turn off to Rennes-les-Bains D14.

🛏 Camping La Bernède is located on the banks of the small River La Sals, close to the picturesque village of Rennes-les-Bains with its thermal spa.
CC 1/1-6/7 25/8-31/12

📍 N 42°54'54'' E 2°19'5''
www.eurocampings.co.uk/115774

France

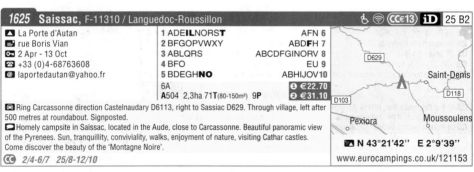

1625 Saissac, F-11310 / Languedoc-Roussillon
   📶 CC€13 iD 25 B2

- 🏕 La Porte d'Autan
- 🏠 rue Boris Vian
- 📅 2 Apr - 13 Oct
- ☎ +33 (0)4-68763608
- @ laportedautan@yahoo.fr

1	ADEILNORST	AFN 6
2	BFGOPVWXY	ABDFH 7
3	ABLQRS	ABCDFGINORV 8
4	BFO	EU 9
5	BDEGHNO	ABHIJOV10

6A   ❶ €22.70
A504 2,3ha 71T(80-150m²) 9P   ❷ €31.10

🚗 Ring Carcassonne direction Castelnaudary D6113, right to Sassiac D629. Through village, left after 500 metres at roundabout. Signposted.
🛏 Homely campsite in Saissac, located in the Aude, close to Carcassonne. Beautiful panoramic view of the Pyrenees. Sun, tranquillity, conviviality, walks, enjoyment of nature, visiting Cathar castles. Come discover the beauty of the 'Montagne Noire'.
CC 2/4-6/7 25/8-12/10

📍 N 43°21'42'' E 2°9'39''
www.eurocampings.co.uk/121153

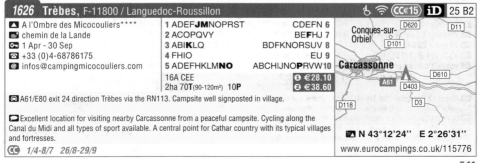

1626 Trèbes, F-11800 / Languedoc-Roussillon
   📶 CC€15 iD 25 B2

- 🏕 A l'Ombre des Micocouliers****
- 🏠 chemin de la Lande
- 📅 1 Apr - 30 Sep
- ☎ +33 (0)4-68786175
- @ infos@campingmicocouliers.com

1	ADEFJMNOPRST	CDEFN 6
2	ACOPQVY	BEFHJ 7
3	ABIKLQ	BDFKNORSUV 8
4	FHIO	EU 9
5	ADEFHKLMNO	ABCHIJNOPRVW10

16A CEE   ❶ €28.10
2ha 70T(90-120m²) 10P   ❷ €38.60

🚗 A61/E80 exit 24 direction Trèbes via the RN113. Campsite well signposted in village.

🛏 Excellent location for visiting nearby Carcassonne from a peaceful campsite. Cycling along the Canal du Midi and all types of sport available. A central point for Cathar country with its typical villages and fortresses.
CC 1/4-8/7 26/8-29/9

📍 N 43°12'24'' E 2°26'31''
www.eurocampings.co.uk/115776

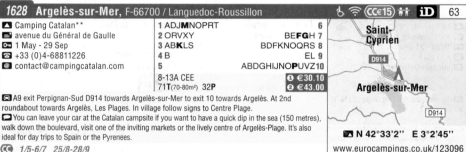

1627 Argelès-sur-Mer, F-66701 / Languedoc-Roussillon   ♿ 📶 (CC€15) ⚑⚑ iD | 63

- ⛺ Albizia***
- 🏠 avenue du Général de Gaulle
- 📅 7 Apr - 30 Sep
- ☎ +33 (0)4-68811562
- @ contact@camping-albizia.com

1 ADFJ**M**NOPQRT		K 6
2 EOPRVX	BE**FG**H	7
3 AE**K**L	ABCDEFNORSV	8
4 I		EL 9
5 D	ABDGHIOTU	10

10A CEE   ❶ €35.00
1ha 70**T**(70-90m²) 20**P**   ❷ €51.00

🚗 A9, exit Perpignan-Sud, D914 dir. Argelès-sur-Mer to exit 10, dir. Argelès. At the second roundabout dir. Argelès, Les Plages. In the village, follow signs to 'Centre Plage'.

💬 Camping Albizia, located between the sea and the mountains, is an ideal starting point for trips to the Pyrenees or Spain. Walk to the centre of Argelès-Plage, the lovely beach, the lively promenade, the little bars, the shops or the restaurants from the campsite.

📍 N 42°33'5''   E 3°2'40''

CC 7/4-7/7 25/8-29/9 7=6   www.eurocampings.co.uk/111786

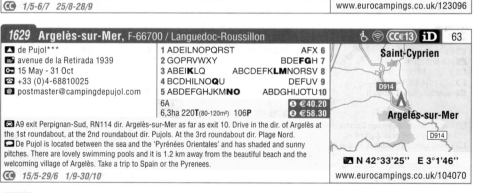

1628 Argelès-sur-Mer, F-66700 / Languedoc-Roussillon   ♿ 📶 (CC€15) ⚑⚑ iD | 63

- ⛺ Camping Catalan**
- 🏠 avenue du Général de Gaulle
- 📅 1 May - 29 Sep
- ☎ +33 (0)4-68811226
- @ contact@campingcatalan.com

1 ADJ**M**NOPRT		6
2 ORVXY	BE**FG**H	7
3 AB**K**LS	BDFKNOQRS	8
4 B		EL 9
5	ABDGHIJNOP**U**VZ	10

8-13A CEE   ❶ €30.10
71**T**(70-80m²) 32**P**   ❷ €43.00

🚗 A9 exit Perpignan-Sud D914 towards Argelès-sur-Mer to exit 10 towards Argelès. At 2nd roundabout towards Argelès, Les Plages. In village follow signs to Centre Plage.

💬 You can leave your car at the Catalan campsite if you want to have a quick dip in the sea (150 metres), walk down the boulevard, visit one of the inviting markets or the lively centre of Argelès-Plage. It's also ideal for day trips to Spain or the Pyrenees.

📍 N 42°33'2''   E 3°2'45''

CC 1/5-6/7 25/8-28/9   www.eurocampings.co.uk/123096

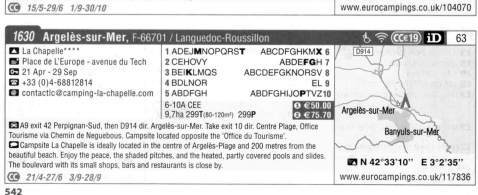

1629 Argelès-sur-Mer, F-66700 / Languedoc-Roussillon   ♿ 📶 (CC€13) iD | 63

- ⛺ de Pujol***
- 🏠 avenue de la Retirada 1939
- 📅 15 May - 31 Oct
- ☎ +33 (0)4-68810025
- @ postmaster@campingdepujol.com

1 ADEILNOPQRST		AFX 6
2 GOPRVWXY	BDE**FG**H	7
3 ABEI**K**LQ	ABCDEFK**LM**NORSV	8
4 BCDHILNO**QU**	DEFUV	9
5 ABDEFGHJKM**NO**	ABDGHIJOTU	10

6A   ❶ €40.20
6,3ha 220**T**(80-120m²) 106**P**   ❷ €58.30

🚗 A9 exit Perpignan-Sud, RN114 dir. Argelès-sur-Mer as far as exit 10. Drive in the dir. of Argelès at the 1st roundabout, at the 2nd roundabout dir. Pujols. At the 3rd roundabout dir. Plage Nord.

💬 De Pujol is located between the sea and the 'Pyrénées Orientales' and has shaded and sunny pitches. There are lovely swimming pools and it is 1.2 km away from the beautiful beach and the welcoming village of Argelès. Take a trip to Spain or the Pyrenees.

📍 N 42°33'25''   E 3°1'46''

CC 15/5-29/6 1/9-30/10   www.eurocampings.co.uk/104070

1630 Argelès-sur-Mer, F-66701 / Languedoc-Roussillon   ♿ 📶 (CC€19) iD | 63

- ⛺ La Chapelle****
- 🏠 Place de L'Europe - avenue du Tech
- 📅 21 Apr - 29 Sep
- ☎ +33 (0)4-68812814
- @ contactlc@camping-la-chapelle.com

1 ADEJ**M**NOPQRS**T**	ABCDFGHKM**X**	6
2 CEHOVY	ABDE**FG**H	7
3 BEI**K**LMQS	ABCDEFGKNORSV	8
4 BDLNOR		EL 9
5 ABDFGH	ABDFGHIJO**P**TVZ	10

6-10A CEE   ❶ €50.00
9,7ha 299**T**(80-120m²) 299**P**   ❷ €75.70

🚗 A9 exit 42 Perpignan-Sud, then D914 dir. Argelès-sur-Mer. Take exit 10 dir. Centre Plage, Office Tourisme via Chemin de Neguebous. Campsite located opposite the 'Office du Tourisme'.

💬 Campsite La Chapelle is ideally located in the centre of Argelès-Plage and 200 metres from the beautiful beach. Enjoy the peace, the shaded pitches, and the heated, partly covered pools and slides. The boulevard with its small shops, bars and restaurants is close by.

📍 N 42°33'10''   E 3°2'35''

CC 21/4-27/6 3/9-28/9   www.eurocampings.co.uk/117836

France

1631 Argelès-sur-Mer, F-66702 / Languedoc-Roussillon 🔌 📶 ✿ CC€17 ♙♙ iD 63

- ▲ La Marende****
- 🏠 avenue du Littoral
- 📅 27 Apr - 22 Sep
- ☎ +33 (0)4-68811209
- @ info@marende.com

1	ADJMNOPRST	ABFGKMNOQRX	6
2	EHOPVXY	ABDEFGH	7
3	BEKLQR	ABCDEFGHIJKNOPQRSTUV	8
4	BDFILNOPUXYZ	ELUV	9
5	ACDEFGHJKMNO	ABDGHINOTUV	10

6-10A CEE · ❶ €44.30
2,5ha 133T(90-120m²) 75P · ❷ €64.30

🚗 A9, exit Perpignan-Sud, D914 direction Argelès-sur-Mer, as far as exit 10 direction Taxo-d'Avall. Left at the 2nd roundabout direction Plage Nord and continue on this road until the campsite is signposted.
💬 The friendly La Marende campsite with its lovely heated swimming pool, restaurant and new luxurious heated toilet facilities is just 100 m from the beach. Close to Spain and the Pyrenees. An ideal starting point for many day trip possibilities.

CC 27/4-29/6 · 1/9-21/9

📍 N 42°34'20'' E 3°2'28''
www.eurocampings.co.uk/109339

1632 Argelès-sur-Mer, F-66701 / Languedoc-Roussillon 🔌 📶 CC€19 ♙♙ iD 63

- ▲ Le Dauphin*****
- 🏠 route de Taxo à la Mer
- 📅 14 Apr - 23 Sep
- ☎ +33 (0)4-68811754
- @ info@campingledauphin.com

1	ADJMNOPQRT	ABFGHIX	6
2	GOPRVX	ABDEFGH	7
3	BEFKLMQT	ABCDEFJLNQRSTUV	8
4	BCDILNOPQUXY	CEUV	9
5	ACDEFGHJK	ABDHIJNOPTU	10

10A · ❶ €51.30
7,5ha 144T(100-120m²) 202P · ❷ €67.30

🚗 A9 exit Perpignan-Sud, D914 dir. Argelès-sur-Mer as far as exit 10 Taxo-d'Avall. Left at 2nd roundabout dir. Taxo-d'Avall, Plage Nord. Follow signs.
💬 Campsite with spacious, marked-out pitches. 7,000 m² aqua park with heated swimming pools and a toddlers' pool. Bar/restaurant, supermarket and entertainment from April to September. For a small extra fee you can enjoy a pitch with private toilet facilities: shower, toilet and washing basin.

CC 14/4-29/6 · 1/9-22/9

📍 N 42°34'21'' E 3°1'18''
www.eurocampings.co.uk/104064

France

1633 Argelès-sur-Mer, F-66702 / Languedoc-Roussillon 🔌 📶 CC€19 ♙♙ iD 63

- ▲ Le Soleil*****
- 🏠 route du Littoral
- 📅 5 May - 22 Sep
- ☎ +33 (0)4-68811448
- @ contact@camping-le-soleil.fr

1	ADEJMNOPRT	ABFGHIKMNOQSX	6
2	CEHOPQVXY	ABDEFGH	7
3	BEFKLQSTU	ABCDEFJNQRSTUV	8
4	BCDIMNOPQUY	ELMOUV	9
5	ACDEFGHJKLMO	ABDGHIJMNPTUYZ	10

Ad on this page 6-10A CEE · ❶ €52.10
12ha 428T(90-120m²) 406P · ❷ €79.30

🚗 A9 exit Perpignan-Sud, D914 direction Argelès-sur-Mer as far as exit 10 direction Taxo-d'Avall. Turn left at the 2nd roundabout in the direction of Plage Nord, continue on this road and follow the campsite signs.
💬 All luxury amenities and activities are at your disposal for the entire season. Heated toilet facilities, heated pools and several direct access points to the sea. An ideal base for outings to the Pyrenees or Spain.

CC 5/5-6/7 · 25/8-21/9

📍 N 42°34'33'' E 3°2'33''
www.eurocampings.co.uk/104068

1634 Argelès-sur-Mer, F-66701 / Languedoc-Roussillon ♿ 🛜 (CC€19) iD | 63

- ▲ Les Criques de Porteils*****
- 🛏 RD114 - Corniche de Collioure
- 🗓 24 Mar - 27 Oct
- ☎ +33 (0)4-68811273
- @ contactcdp@lescriques.com

1 ADE**JM**NOPR**T**	ABFGHKMOPQS**X** 6	
2 EFJKMPQRTUVXY	ABDE**FG**H 7	
3 ABELMQ	ABCDFJKNOQRS 8	
4 AEFLOUY	AEL 9	
5 ACDFGHJK**O**	ABDFGHIJNO**P**T10	
10A CEE	❶ €58.50	
5ha 179**T**(80-100m²) 69**P**	❷ €87.20	

🚗 A9 direction Perpignan. Exit 42 Perpignan-Sud direction Argelès-sur-Mer. D914 towards Collioure, take exit 13. 'Collioure par la Corniche' till l'Hotel du Golfe, turn right in direction of campsite.
🛏 Beautiful terraced campsite close to Collioure in an exceptional area with endless views of the sea and the mountains of Roussillon. Private access to the sublime little creeks on the Mediterranean sea and all kinds of options for trips out.
CC 24/3-27/4 13/5-27/5 3/6-27/6 2/9-6/9 16/9-26/10

Argelès-sur-Mer
Collioure
D914
🧭 N 42°32'2'' E 3°4'4''
www.eurocampings.co.uk/110123

1635 Argelès-sur-Mer, F-66702 / Languedoc-Roussillon ♿ 🛜 (CC€17) iD | 63

- ▲ Les Marsouins****
- 🛏 avenue de la Retirada
- 🗓 13 Apr - 1 Oct
- ☎ +33 (0)4-68811481
- @ lesmarsouins@cielavillage.com

1 ADJ**M**NOPQRST	ABFGH 6	
2 GOPVXY	ABDE**FG**H 7	
3 BEF**GHK**LQTU	CDEFJKNQRSTUV 8	
4 **A**BCDILMNO**P**	ELNUV 9	
5 ACDEFGHJKLM**NO**	ABDFGHIJPTZ10	
Ad on this page 5A CEE	❶ €50.30	
12ha 337**T**(90-120m²) 251**P**	❷ €62.30	

🚗 A9, exit Perpignan-Sud, D914 direction Argelès-sur-Mer as far as exit 10. First roundabout direction Argelès, second roundabout direction Pujols. At the third roundabout direction Plage Nord.
🛏 Welcoming campsite with a beautiful heated pool, spacious pitches and paved motorhome pitches. All amenities are available throughout the season. Located 800 metres from the sea and close to the Pyrenees and Spain.
CC 13/4-29/6 1/9-30/9

D81 A
Saint-Cyprien
D914
D914
🧭 N 42°33'49'' E 3°2'5''
www.eurocampings.co.uk/100562

1636 Argelès-sur-Mer, F-66702 / Languedoc-Roussillon ♿ 🛜 (CC€17) iD | 63

- ▲ Les Pins****
- 🛏 avenue du Tech
- 🗓 7 Apr - 7 Oct
- ☎ +33 (0)4-68811046
- @ camping@les-pins.com

1 AD**JL**NOPQRT	ABFGHKMNX 6	
2 EHMOPVY	ABDE**FG**H 7	
3 ABE**K**LQ	ABCDEFJKNQRSV 8	
4 **A**BDINO**PRXZ**	CEL 9	
5 ADEFGHJK	ABDHIJO**P**TUZ10	
Ad on page 545 6A CEE	❶ €53.30	
4ha 173**T**(85-95m²) 175**P**	❷ €68.30	

🚗 A9, exit Perpignan-Sud, D914 direction Argelès-sur-Mer as far as exit 10 direction Argelès. At the second roundabout direction Argelès, les Plages. In the village follow the signs 'Centre Plage' and 'Plage des Pins'.
🛏 A peaceful and shaded campsite close to the centre of Argelès-Plage. Enjoy the walks along the magnificent beaches and a dive in the heated swimming pool. The Pyrenees and Spain are close by and invite you for a stunning day trip.
CC 7/4-3/7 24/8-6/10

D914
Argelès-sur-Mer
Banyuls-sur-Mer
🧭 N 42°33'21'' E 3°2'32''
www.eurocampings.co.uk/104071

France

Les Pins ★ ★ ★ ★

Quiet and shaded. Enjoy the magnificent beach 5 minutes from the Argelès-Plage centre (200m). Footpaths by the sea leading to the harbour. A swimming pool in total harmony with the environs. A perfect operating base for excursions to the Pyrenees and Spain.

Avenue du Tech
66702 Argelès-sur-Mer
Tel. 04-68811046 • Fax 04-68813506
E-mail: camping@les-pins.com
Internet: www.les-pins.com

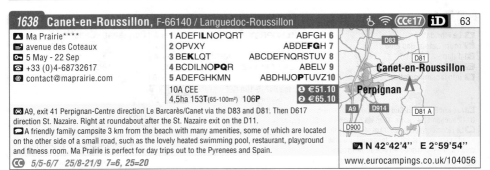

1637 Arles-sur-Tech, F-66150 / Languedoc-Roussillon ⊙ (CC€15) iD 25 B3

- ▲ Du Riuferrer**
- ☷ 1 Mar - 1 Nov
- ☎ +33 (0)4-68391106
- @ campingriuferrer@libertysurf.fr

1 ADILNORST	J 6
2 CPRVY	ABDE**F** 7
3 **GHQ**	ACDEFNORS 8
4 EI	E 9
5 DEFGHM	ABHIJ**OV**10
10A CEE	❶ €22.60
A310 4ha 150T(75-120m²) 12P	❷ €32.60

🚗 Campsite is 1 km from Arles-sur-Tech. Indicated with arrows along D115. New entrance to campsite.
💬 Campsite is now more easily accessible for motorhomes and caravans because of its new entrance. The site is located next to the authentic little town of Arles-sur-Tech, and is surrounded by unspoiled countryside. This area has the lowest humidity in Europe, often lower than 20%, due to its micro-climate.
CC 1/3-6/7 25/8-31/10

◪ N 42°27'26'' E 2°37'33''
www.eurocampings.co.uk/103919

1638 Canet-en-Roussillon, F-66140 / Languedoc-Roussillon ♿ ⊙ (CC€17) iD 63

- ▲ Ma Prairie****
- 🏠 avenue des Coteaux
- ☷ 5 May - 22 Sep
- ☎ +33 (0)4-68732617
- @ contact@maprairie.com

1 ADEFI**L**NOPQRT	ABFGH 6
2 OPVXY	ABDE**FG**H 7
3 BE**K**LQT	ABCDEFNQRSTUV 8
4 BCDILNO**PQ**R	ABELV 9
5 ADEFGHKMN	ABDHIJO**P**TUVZ10
10A CEE	❶ €51.10
4,5ha 153T(65-100m²) 106P	❷ €65.10

🚗 A9, exit 41 Perpignan-Centre direction Le Barcarès/Canet via the D83 and D81. Then D617 direction St. Nazaire. Right at roundabout after the St. Nazaire exit on the D11.
💬 A friendly family campsite 3 km from the beach with many amenities, some of which are located on the other side of a small road, close to the lovely heated swimming pool, restaurant, playground and fitness room. Ma Prairie is perfect for day trips out to the Pyrenees and Spain.
CC 5/5-6/7 25/8-21/9 7=6, 25=20

◪ N 42°42'4'' E 2°59'54''
www.eurocampings.co.uk/104056

1639 Canet-en-Roussillon, F-66140 / Languedoc-Roussillon ♿ ⊙ (CC€17) iD 63

- ▲ Mar Estang****
- 🏠 Voie des Flamants Roses
- ☷ 14 Apr - 16 Sep
- ☎ +33 (0)4-68803553
- @ contactme@marestang.com

1 ADEJ**M**NOPQRST	ABEFGHIKMOPQS**X** 6
2 ADEHOPQSVX	ABDE**FG**H 7
3 ABEF**K**LMQ	ABCDEFKNRS 8
4 BCDILMNO**P**RU**XZ**	AELUV 9
5 ACDEFGHJKL	ABDFGHIJLO**P**TVZ10
6-10A CEE	❶ €51.10
13ha 150T(60-100m²) 450P	❷ €77.10

🚗 A9, exit 41 direction Le Barcarès and Canet-en-Roussillon. Continue towards St. Cyprien or Plage Sud from Canet. Campsite located south of Canet on the right.
💬 Large campsite located between the Canet-en-Roussillon nature reserve and a beautiful beach, accessible via a tunnel (100 metres) directly from the campsite. Ample amenities including lovely heated swimming pools. Close to the centre of Canet and close to the Pyrenees and Spain.
CC 14/4-6/7 25/8-15/9

◪ N 42°40'31'' E 3°1'52''
www.eurocampings.co.uk/111785

France

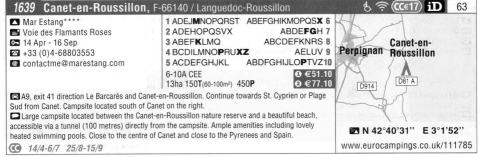

1640 Canet-en-Roussillon, F-66141 / Languedoc-Roussillon ♿ 📶 iD | 63

- ▲ Yelloh! Village le Brasilia*****
- 🏠 avenue des Anneaux du Roussillon
- 📅 14 Apr - 6 Oct
- ☎ +33 (0)4-68802382
- @ info@lebrasilia.fr

1	ADE**JM**NOPQRST	ABFGHIKMNQSX 6
2	CEHOPQVXY	BDE**FGH** 7
3	BEFH**KLMN**QRT	ABCDEFJKNQRSTUV 8
4	**A**BCDHILMNO**PQ**RU**VXZ**	EFLTUV 9
5	ACDEFGHJKLM**N**	ABGHIJM**NOP**TUYZ 10

6-10A CEE — ❶ €62.10
15ha 416**T**(80-120m²) 287**P** — ❷ €78.10

🚗 A9 exit 41 Perpignan-Centre. Direction Le Barcarès/Canet via the D83 and D81. In Canet 1st roundabout direction Ste Marie, then immediately right direction 'zone Artisanale las Bigues' and follow campsite signs.

🛏 Large 5-star campsite in a 15-ha pine forest, with a heated swimming pool and direct access to the sandy beach.

📍 N 42°42'30'' E 3°2'8''
www.eurocampings.co.uk/100560

1641 Canet-Plage, F-66140 / Languedoc-Roussillon ♿ 📶 (CC€15) ⚥ iD | 63

- ▲ Le Bosquet***
- 🏠 av. des Anneaux du Roussillon
- 📅 31 Mar - 5 Oct
- ☎ +33 (0)4-68802380
- @ contact@campinglebosquet.com

1	ADJ**JM**NOPQRT	AFKN 6
2	CEOPQRVWXY	BE**FGH**K 7
3	ABE**K**LQ	ABCDFJKNOQRS 8
4	BCDILNO**PUXZ**	ELUV 9
5	ABDEFGH**NO**	ABDGHIJO**P**TU 10

10A — ❶ €49.10
1,5ha 71**T**(70-100m²) 46**P** — ❷ €65.10

🚗 A9 exit 41 Perpignan-Centre dir. Barcarès/Canet via D83 and D81. In Canet dir. Ste Marie at first roundabout then immediately right dir. 'Zone Artisanale las Bigues' and follow camping signs.

🛏 A small, modest, intimate site with sunny and shaded pitches, with a snack bar and a lovely swimming pool. 400m to the beach via an entrance directly from the campsite. A 5-minute walk to the pleasure boat harbour and a little train to the centre of Canet-Plage.

CC 31/3-6/7 1/9-4/10 7=6

📍 N 42°42'33'' E 3°1'59''
www.eurocampings.co.uk/104058

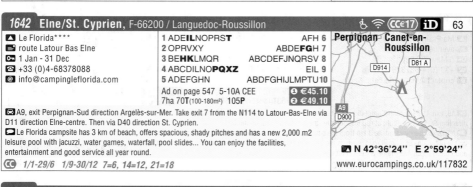

1642 Elne/St. Cyprien, F-66200 / Languedoc-Roussillon ♿ 📶 (CC€17) iD | 63

- ▲ Le Florida****
- 🏠 route Latour Bas Elne
- 📅 1 Jan - 31 Dec
- ☎ +33 (0)4-68378088
- @ info@campingleflorida.com

1	ADE**IL**NOPRS**T**	AFH 6
2	OPRVXY	ABDE**FG**H 7
3	BE**HK**LMQR	ABCDEFJNQRSV 8
4	ABCDILNO**PQXZ**	EIL 9
5	ADEFGHN	ABDFGHIJLMPTU 10

Ad on page 547 5-10A CEE — ❶ €45.10
7ha 70**T**(100-180m²) 105**P** — ❷ €49.10

🚗 A9, exit Perpignan-Sud direction Argelès-sur-Mer. Take exit 7 from the N114 to Latour-Bas-Elne via D11 direction Elne-centre. Then via D40 direction St. Cyprien.

🛏 Le Florida campsite has 3 km of beach, offers spacious, shady pitches and has a new 2,000 m2 leisure pool with jacuzzi, water games, waterfall, pool slides... You can enjoy the facilities, entertainment and good service all year round.

CC 1/1-29/6 1/9-30/12 7=6, 14=12, 21=18

📍 N 42°36'24'' E 2°59'24''
www.eurocampings.co.uk/117832

1643 Espira-de-Conflent, F-66320 / Languedoc-Roussillon ♿ 📶 (CC€15) iD | 25 B3

- ▲ Le Canigou***
- 📅 31 Mar - 31 Oct
- ☎ +33 (0)4-68058540
- @ canigou@yahoo.com

1	ADE**J**LNOPQRST	JNU 6
2	CKPRTVXY	ABD**FG** 7
3	AELQRV	ABCDEFNPR 8
4	**A**BCEFGHIO**PQ**	DJU 9
5	ABDEFGHKM	ABGHJOQT 10

10A — ❶ €33.30
A290 4ha 115**T**(100m²) 17**P** — ❷ €49.30

🚗 At Perpignan N116 direction Prades. Turn left about 2.5 km after Vinça. Espira-de-Conflent is signposted.

🛏 The campsite is set in an area where a whole new landscape opens up beyond every mountain, offering numerous walking routes. Adventurous excursions to Canigou Peak, visit the Gorges du Llech in a 4x4 Jeep.

CC 31/3-6/7 25/8-30/10

📍 N 42°37'0'' E 2°30'5''
www.eurocampings.co.uk/109121

Open all year

swimming pool of 2000 m²

le florida
CAMPING
★ ★ ★ ★

Spacious pitches
Stable subsoil
Water outlet
2 minutes from Saint-Cyprien • Route de Latour Bas Elne • 66200 Elne
TÉL. 04 68 37 80 88 / 04 68 37 80 76 • WWW.CAMPINGLEFLORIDA.COM

Wi Fi   ancv   QUALITÉ TOURISME   qualité

France

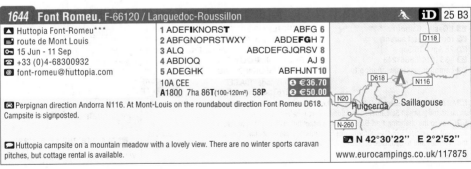

1644 Font Romeu, F-66120 / Languedoc-Roussillon   iD 25 B3

- ⛺ Huttopia Font-Romeu***
- 🚏 route de Mont Louis
- 📅 15 Jun - 11 Sep
- 📠 +33 (0)4-68300932
- @ font-romeu@huttopia.com

1 ADEFIKNORS**T**	ABFG **6**
2 ABFGNOPRSTWXY	ABDE**FG**H **7**
3 ALQ	ABCDEFGJQRSV **8**
4 ABDIOQ	AJ **9**
5 ADEGHK	ABFHJNT**10**

10A CEE
A1800 7ha 86**T**(100-120m²) 58**P**

❶ €36.70
❷ €50.00

🅿 Perpignan direction Andorra N116. At Mont-Louis on the roundabout direction Font Romeu D618. Campsite is signposted.

💬 Huttopia campsite on a mountain meadow with a lovely view. There are no winter sports caravan pitches, but cottage rental is available.

N 42°30'22'' E 2°2'52''

www.eurocampings.co.uk/117875

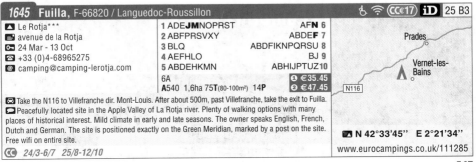

1645 Fuilla, F-66820 / Languedoc-Roussillon   ♿ 📶 (CC€17) iD 25 B3

- ⛺ Le Rotja***
- 🚏 avenue de la Rotja
- 📅 24 Mar - 13 Oct
- 📠 +33 (0)4-68965275
- @ camping@camping-lerotja.com

1 ADE**JM**NOPRST	AF**N 6**
2 ABFPRSVXY	ABDE**F 7**
3 BLQ	ABDFIKNPQRSU **8**
4 AEFHLO	BJ **9**
5 ABDEHKMN	ABHIJPTUZ**10**

6A
A540 1,6ha 75**T**(80-100m²) 14**P**

❶ €35.45
❷ €47.45

🅿 Take the N116 to Villefranche dir. Mont-Louis. After about 500m, past Villefranche, take the exit to Fuilla.
💬 Peacefully located site in the Apple Valley of La Rotja river. Plenty of walking options with many places of historical interest. Mild climate in early and late seasons. The owner speaks English, French, Dutch and German. The site is positioned exactly on the Green Meridian, marked by a post on the site. Free wifi on entire site.

CC 24/3-6/7 25/8-12/10

N 42°33'45'' E 2°21'34''

www.eurocampings.co.uk/111285

1646 Laroque-des-Albères, F-66740 / Languedoc-Roussillon 〈✕〉 ⚫ 🛜 (CC€17) iD 63

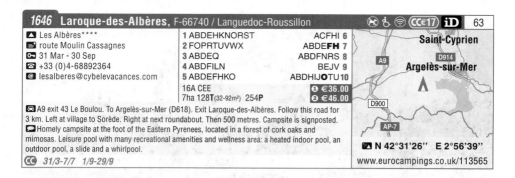

- ▲ Les Albères****
- 🏠 route Moulin Cassagnes
- 🗓 31 Mar - 30 Sep
- ☎ +33 (0)4-68892364
- @ lesalberes@cybelevacances.com

1 ABDEHKNORST	ACFHI	6
2 FOPRTUVWX	ABDE**FH**	7
3 ABDEQ	ABDFNRS	8
4 ABDFILN	BEJV	9
5 ABDEFHKO	ABDHIJ**O**TU	10
16A CEE	❶ €36.00	
7ha 128**T**(32-92m²) 254**P**	❷ €46.00	

🚗 A9 exit 43 Le Boulou. To Argelès-sur-Mer (D618). Exit Laroque-des-Albères. Follow this road for 3 km. Left at village to Sorède. Right at next roundabout. Then 500 metres. Campsite is signposted.
📷 Homely campsite at the foot of the Eastern Pyrenees, located in a forest of cork oaks and mimosas. Leisure pool with many recreational amenities and wellness area: a heated indoor pool, an outdoor pool, a slide and a whirlpool.
CC *31/3-7/7 1/9-29/9*

Saint-Cyprien
Argelès-sur-Mer

🧭 N 42°31'26'' E 2°56'39''
www.eurocampings.co.uk/113565

1647 Latour-de-France, F-66720 / Languedoc-Roussillon ⚫ 🛜 (CC€15) iD 25 B3

- ▲ La Tour de France***
- 🏠 ave du Général de Gaulle
- 🗓 1 Apr - 14 Oct
- ☎ +33 (0)6-15142346
- @ contact@camping-latourdefrance.fr

1 AB**IL**NORST	A	6
2 CPRVXY	BD**F**	7
3 ABLMQ	ABFINRSV	8
4 HI**Q**	BEF	9
5 ABDEGHI	ABFHIJMOVZ	10
6A CEE	❶ €22.50	
A107 1,5ha 70**T**(50-120m²) 27**P**	❷ €33.50	

🚗 Millas direction Estnagel. In Estnagel direction Latour-de-France. Campsite signposted on the D17.

📷 The campsite is located in the Catalan hinterland between the Mediterranean and the Pyrenees. Centrally located for trips out to the many Cathar sites and the wide beaches on the coast, including 'Le Barcarès'. And the rocky coast towards Spain with beautiful Collioure is not far away.
CC *1/4-6/7 25/8-13/10*

Ille-sur-Têt   Le Soler   Baho

🧭 N 42°45'57'' E 2°39'56''
www.eurocampings.co.uk/113089

1648 Le Barcarès, F-66420 / Languedoc-Roussillon ♿ 🛜 ✿ (CC€13) iD 63

- ▲ L'Oasis - California****
- 🏠 route de St. Laurent
- 🗓 28 Apr - 16 Sep
- ☎ +33 (0)4-68861243
- @ camping.loasis@wanadoo.fr

1 ADEF**IL**NOPQRST	ABFGH	6
2 AGOPQRVWXY	ABDE**FG**H	7
3 ABEL**M**QST	ABCDFKNOQRSV	8
4 BCDHILNOP**Q**UY	EJLUV	9
5 ABDEFGHJK**NO**	ABDGHIN**OP**TUVZ	10
Ad on this page 10A CEE	❶ €47.70	
9,7ha 278**T**(80-100m²) 470**P**	❷ €62.40	

🚗 A9 exit Perpignan-Centre. D83 direction Le Barcarès as far as exit 9. Take the D81 direction Canet as far as the first exit St. Laurent, direction Le Barcarès-Village.
📷 Close to the charming Port-Barcarès and a beautiful Mediterranean beach, with a heated pool and excellent amenities. L'Oasis-California offers its guests a pleasant stay. From here, great excursions to the Pyrenees and to Spain are possible.
CC *28/4-8/7 1/9-15/9*

Perpignan   Canet-Plage

🧭 N 42°46'35'' E 3°1'29''
www.eurocampings.co.uk/100559

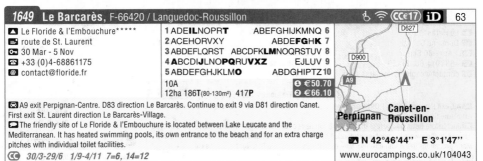

1649 Le Barcarès, F-66420 / Languedoc-Roussillon

♿ 📶 (CC€17) **iD** 63

- ⛰ Le Floride & l'Embouchure*****
- 🏠 route de St. Laurent
- 📅 30 Mar - 5 Nov
- ☎ +33 (0)4-68861175
- @ contact@floride.fr

1	ADE**IL**NOPR**T**	ABEFGHIJKMNQ	6
2	ACEHORVXY	ABDE**FG**H**K**	7
3	ABDEFLQRST	ABCDFK**LM**NOQRSTUV	8
4	**A**BCDIJLNO**PQ**RU**VXZ**	EJLUV	9
5	ABDEFGHJKLM**O**	ABDGHIPTZ	10
	10A	① €50.70	
	12ha 186**T**(80-130m²) 417**P**	② €66.10	

🚗 A9 exit Perpignan-Centre. D83 direction Le Barcarès. Continue to exit 9 via D81 direction Canet. First exit St. Laurent direction Le Barcarès-Village.
🛏 The friendly site of Le Floride & l'Embouchure is located between Lake Leucate and the Mediterranean. It has heated swimming pools, its own entrance to the beach and for an extra charge pitches with individual toilet facilities.
(CC) 30/3-29/6 1/9-4/11 7=6, 14=12

📍 N 42°46'44'' E 3°1'47''
www.eurocampings.co.uk/104043

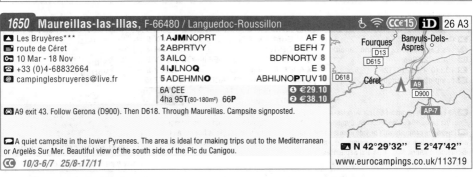

1650 Maureillas-las-Illas, F-66480 / Languedoc-Roussillon

♿ 📶 (CC€15) **iD** 26 A3

- ⛰ Les Bruyères***
- 🏠 route de Céret
- 📅 10 Mar - 18 Nov
- ☎ +33 (0)4-68832664
- @ campinglesbruyeres@live.fr

1	A**JM**NOPRT	AF	6
2	ABPRTVY	BEFH	7
3	AILQ	BDFNORTV	8
4	**I**JLNO**Q**	E	9
5	ADEHMN**O**	ABHIJNO**P**TUV	10
	6A CEE	① €29.10	
	4ha 95**T**(80-180m²) 66**P**	② €38.10	

🚗 A9 exit 43. Follow Gerona (D900). Then D618. Through Maureillas. Campsite signposted.

🛏 A quiet campsite in the lower Pyrenees. The area is ideal for making trips out to the Mediterranean or Argelès Sur Mer. Beautiful view of the south side of the Pic du Canigou.
(CC) 10/3-6/7 25/8-17/11

📍 N 42°29'32'' E 2°47'42''
www.eurocampings.co.uk/113719

1651 Maureillas-las-Illas, F-66480 / Languedoc-Roussillon

♿ 📶 (CC€17) **iD** 26 A3

- ⛰ Val Roma Park***
- 🏠 RD900
- 📅 5 May - 21 Sep
- ☎ +33 (0)4-68398813
- @ valromapark@wanadoo.fr

1	AF**JM**NOPQRT	AF	6
2	ABCOPVXY	ABDE**F**H	7
3	AEFLRT	ABCDFNQSV	8
4	DINO	E	9
5	ABDEFHK	ABCDHIJO**P**TV	10
	6A CEE	① €25.00	
	2,5ha 65**T**(80-100m²) 20**P**	② €34.30	

🚗 Follow A9 motorway from Perpignan as far as exit 43 direction Le Boulou. Follow RD900 towards Le Perthus, Les Thermes du Boulou. Campsite 500 metres after Les Thermes.
🛏 It's great to be a guest at the basic, but welcoming campsite Val Roma Park, located in a wood and by a little river. 100 metres from the Le Boulou spas, close to the Spanish border, the sea and the Pyrenees. Many outings are possible.
(CC) 5/5-14/7 1/9-20/9

📍 N 42°30'23'' E 2°49'22''
www.eurocampings.co.uk/118542

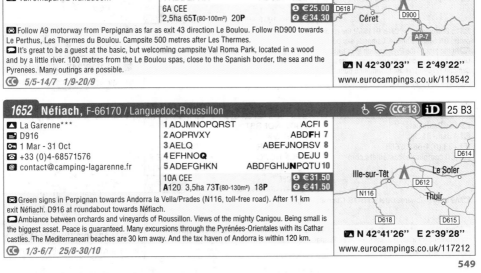

1652 Néfiach, F-66170 / Languedoc-Roussillon

♿ 📶 (CC€13) **iD** 25 B3

- ⛰ La Garenne***
- 🏠 D916
- 📅 1 Mar - 31 Oct
- ☎ +33 (0)4-68571576
- @ contact@camping-lagarenne.fr

1	ADJMNOPQRST	ACFI	6
2	AOPRVXY	ABD**F**H	7
3	AELQ	ABEFJNORSV	8
4	EFHNO**Q**	DEJU	9
5	ADEFGHKN	ABDFGHIJ**N**PQTU	10
	10A CEE	① €31.50	
	A120 3,5ha 73**T**(80-130m²) 18**P**	② €41.50	

🚗 Green signs in Perpignan towards Andorra la Vella/Prades (N116, toll-free road). After 11 km exit Néfiach. D916 at roundabout towards Néfiach.
🛏 Ambiance between orchards and vineyards of Roussillon. Views of the mighty Canigou. Being small is the biggest asset. Peace is guaranteed. Many excursions through the Pyrénées-Orientales with its Cathar castles. The Mediterranean beaches are 30 km away. And the tax haven of Andorra is within 120 km.
(CC) 1/3-6/7 25/8-30/10

📍 N 42°41'26'' E 2°39'28''
www.eurocampings.co.uk/117212

France

1653 Palau-del-Vidre, F-66690 / Languedoc-Roussillon   🚵 📶 (CC€17) iD   63

🏕 Le Haras***
📧 Domaine St. Galdric
📅 1 Apr - 30 Sep
☎ +33 (0)4-68221450
@ contact@camping-le-haras.com

1 ADILNOPQRT	A	6
2 OPRVXY	ABDEFGH	7
3 BELQS	ABEFNQRV	8
4 BCDIKOQ	BE	9
5 ADEFHJKN	ABDGIJPTUV	10
10A CEE	❶ €41.00	
4ha 99T(80-100m²) 32P	❷ €52.50	

🚗 A9, exit Perpignan-Sud, RD914 direction Argelès-sur-Mer. Exit 9 Palau-del-Vidre. Campsite on the left before the village.
💬 Just before Palau del Vidre is the park-like campsite of Le Haras with its varied flora. The attractive bar next to the swimming pool is surrounded by greenery and the beaches of Argeles are 7 km away. Many excursions in the immediate vicinity or to the Pyrenees and Barcelona are possible.

(CC) 1/4-3/7 28/8-29/9 25=20

🗺 N 42°34'33" E 2°57'53"

www.eurocampings.co.uk/104060

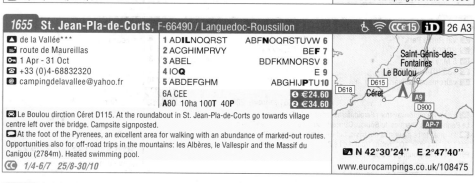

1654 St. Cyprien-Plage, F-66750 / Languedoc-Roussillon   🚵 📶 (CC€19) ⚲ iD   63

🏕 Cala Gogo*****
📧 Les Capellans, av. Armand Lanoux
📅 7 Apr - 29 Sep
☎ +33 (0)4-68210712
@ camping@calagogo66.fr

1 ADEJMNOPRST	ABFGKMNOX	6
2 EHOPRVX	ABDEFGH	7
3 BEFKLMQRTU ABCDEFJKNOQRSTUV		8
4 ABCDILMNOPQXZ	ELUV	9
5 ACDEFGHJKLMO ABDGHIJNPTUYZ		10
Ad on page 551 10A CEE	❶ €49.20	
12ha 407T(80-125m²) 217P	❷ €72.60	

🚗 A9 exit 42 Perpignan-Sud, dir. Argelès-sur-Mer. Follow D914 as far as exit 7 dir. St. Cyprien and Elne. Via Latour-Bas-Elne follow St. Cyprien-Plage. Then follow 'Grand Stade' and campsite signs.
💬 Luxurious campsite with private access to the beach. One of the toilet blocks is heated. All the amenities, including the heated swimming pool, are available throughout the season. Free coach excursions in April, May, June and September.

(CC) 7/4-6/7 25/8-28/9

🗺 N 42°35'58" E 3°2'18"

www.eurocampings.co.uk/104059

1655 St. Jean-Pla-de-Corts, F-66490 / Languedoc-Roussillon   🚵 📶 (CC€15) iD   26 A3

🏕 de la Vallée***
📧 route de Maureillas
📅 1 Apr - 31 Oct
☎ +33 (0)4-68832320
@ campingdelavallee@yahoo.fr

1 ADILNOQRST	ABFNOQRSTUVW	6
2 ACGHIMPRVY	BEF	7
3 ABEL	BDFKMNORSV	8
4 IOQ	E	9
5 ABDEFGHM	ABGHIJPTU	10
6A CEE	❶ €24.60	
A80 10ha 100T 40P	❷ €34.60	

🚗 Le Boulou dirction Céret D115. At the roundabout in St. Jean-Pla-de-Corts go towards village centre left over the bridge. Campsite signposted.
💬 At the foot of the Pyrenees, an excellent area for walking with an abundance of marked-out routes. Opportunities also for off-road trips in the mountains: les Albères, le Vallespir and the Massif du Canigou (2784m). Heated swimming pool.

(CC) 1/4-6/7 25/8-30/10

🗺 N 42°30'24" E 2°47'40"

www.eurocampings.co.uk/108475

1656 St. Jean-Pla-de-Corts, F-66490 / Languedoc-Roussillon   🚵 📶 (CC€13) iD   26 A3

🏕 Les Casteillets***
📅 1 Jan - 31 Dec
☎ +33 (0)4-68832683
@ jc@campinglescasteillets.com

1 ABDILNOPRST	ABF	6
2 AFGPRVX	ABDEFH	7
3 ABEILMNQR	BDFKNQR	8
4 ABCMNOPQ	AE	9
5 ABDFGHKLMN	ABGHIJPTUV	10
10-6A CEE	❶ €27.80	
5ha 134T(95-100m²) 109P	❷ €39.40	

🚗 A9 exit 43. Towards Céret via D115. Campsite is signposted.

💬 Campsite situated close to mountains and the sea. Ideal spot for relaxation. The area offers many opportunities for a day out, such as Céret, Perpignan and Spain.

(CC) 1/1-6/7 25/8-31/12

🗺 N 42°30'37" E 2°47'0"

www.eurocampings.co.uk/110227

France

1657 Ste Marie-la-Mer, F-66470 / Languedoc-Roussillon 📶 (CC€17) iD 63

- 🏕 Le Palais de la Mer****
- 📧 av. de Las-Illes
- 🔑 12 May - 29 Sep
- ☎ +33 (0)4-68730794
- @ contact@palaisdelamer.com

1 ADF**JM**NOPQRST	ABFGHKMNQS 6
2 EHPRVY	ABDE**FG**H 7
3 BEFILMQT	ABCDEFKNOQRSTV 8
4 BCDHIKLNO**PQ**RUV	EL 9
5 ACDEFGHJKLM**NO**	ABDHIJO**P**TU 10

10A
3ha 122T(80-100m²) 59P
❶ €48.30
❷ €62.30

🚗 On coastal road D81 take exit Ste Marie-Plage. Then drive straight at the roundabout and turn left at the third intersection. Signposted.

💬 You can discover the charms of the Catalan coastline from Le Palais de la Mer and visit the picturesque hinterland. Among the things to enjoy on the campsite are the swimming pool and slide near the lively restaurant or the various sports options. The site has its own entrance to a lovely beach.

CC 12/5-29/6 1/9-28/9

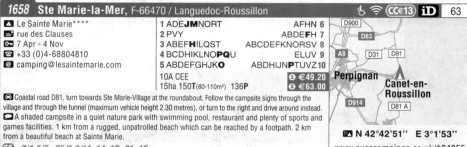

N 42°44'26'' E 3°2'1''
www.eurocampings.co.uk/104054

1658 Ste Marie-la-Mer, F-66470 / Languedoc-Roussillon ♿ 📶 (CC€13) iD 63

- 🏕 Le Sainte Marie****
- 📧 rue des Clauses
- 🔑 7 Apr - 4 Nov
- ☎ +33 (0)4-68804810
- @ camping@lesaintemarie.com

1 ADE**JM**NORT	AFHN 6
2 PVY	ABDE**F**H 7
3 ABEF**H**ILQST	ABCDEFKNORSV 8
4 BCDHIKLNO**PQ**U	ELUV 9
5 ABDEFGHJK**O**	ABDHIJN**P**TUVZ 10

10A CEE
15ha 150T(80-110m²) 136P
❶ €49.20
❷ €63.00

🚗 Coastal road D81, turn towards Ste Marie-Village at the roundabout. Follow the campsite signs through the village and through the tunnel (maximum vehicle height 2.30 metres), or turn to the right and drive around instead.

💬 A shaded campsite in a quiet nature park with swimming pool, restaurant and plenty of sports and games facilities. 1 km from a rugged, unpatrolled beach which can be reached by a footpath. 2 km from a beautiful beach at Sainte Marie.

CC 7/4-6/7 25/8-3/11 14=12, 21=16

N 42°42'51'' E 3°1'53''
www.eurocampings.co.uk/104055

1659 Ste Marie-Plage, F-66470 / Languedoc-Roussillon ♿ 📶 (CC€15) ⚹⚹ iD 63

- 🏕 De la Plage***
- 📧 av. de las-Illas
- 🔑 10 Mar - 27 Oct
- ☎ +33 (0)4-68806859
- @ contact@
  camping-municipal-de-la-plage.com

1 ADE**JM**NOPQRST	ABFGHKMNQRST 6
2 EHOPRVXY	ABDE**FG** 7
3 BEIL**MQ**R	ABCDFJNRSV 8
4 BCDHILNO**PQRTUVXZ**	EMPQRT 9
5 ACDEFGHJKLM**N**	ABDGHIJ**NP**TUZ 10

Ad on this page 6A CEE
7ha 275T(90-100m²) 99P
❶ €40.90
❷ €58.90

🚗 On the coastal road D81 take exit Ste Marie-Plage. Drive straight over the roundabout and turn left at the third road. Follow the campsite signs.

💬 Spacious, friendly campsite with floral landscaping, lovely big swimming pool and extensive sports facilities. Heated toilet facilities in early and late seasons. Right on the sea with its own access to the supervised sandy beach. Naturist beach in the area.

CC 10/3-29/6 25/8-26/10

N 42°44'22'' E 3°2'2''
www.eurocampings.co.uk/108476

1660 Torreilles-Plage, F-66440 / Languedoc-Roussillon ♿ 📶 ❀ (CC€17) 👫 **iD** 63

🔺 Les Tropiques★★★★
✉ boulevard de la Plage
📅 1 May - 15 Sep
☎ +33 (0)4-68280509
@ contact@lestropiques.fr

1 ADJMNOPQRST   ABFGHKMNQX 6
2 AEHOPRVWXY   ABDEFGH 7
3 ABELMQRT   ABCDFKNQRSV 8
4 BCDIMNOPQRUVXYZ   BCEJLUV 9
5 ACDEFGHJKLNO ABDGHIJOPTUYZ10
10A CEE
8ha 88T(100-115m²) 353P

❶ €59.00
❷ €73.00

🚗 A9 exit Perpignan-Centre. Direction Le Barcarès via the D83, then direction Canet/St. Cyprien as far as the exit Torreilles-Plage.
💬 This friendly family campsite is located 400 m from the lovely Torreilles Plage beach, where you can enjoy the heated swimming pool, the various wellness facilities or a delicious meal in the restaurant. The campsite is also a perfect starting point for many day trips possible along the coast to the Pyrenees and Spain.
(CC) 1/5-7/7 27/8-13/9 7=6

📍 N 42°46'3'' E 3°1'47''

www.eurocampings.co.uk/104051

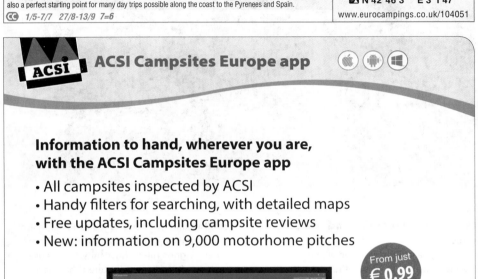

France

Mountains, lavender and the blue coast

Bordering Italy to the east, and with the Mediterranean to the south, the heat is the first thing you notice about Provence-Alpes-Cotes d'Azur. It's cooler in the mountains and forests, and you can always go for a refreshing dip in the rivers or lakes or any of the beaches. Or you can simply relax and admire the countryside – with its vineyards, lavender fields, and vivid colours, this is the landscape that inspired painters Cezanne, Van Gogh, Matisse, Gaugin and Picasso.

Well-known towns and cities

Look up: the Neo-Byzantine cathedral Notre Dame de la Gard overlooks the Old Port of Marseilles today. Explore Old Marseilles and visit the Museum of Contemporary Art. Avignon is a town with its own song: Sur le pont d'Avignon is about the city's famous bridge. History buffs can stroll around Avignon's ramparts, Papal Palace and Romanesque cathedral which date from when Avignon ruled Christianity. Chartreuse du Val de Benediction cloistered abbey is a nice surprise for the kids: with treasure hunts, geocaching and other games. Prefer more secular locations? Try Les Halles for food shopping and Place Pie for cafés. On the Cote d'Azur, stroll along the Promenade des Anglais in Nice, or walk up Castle Hill for panoramic views. Definitely take in the squares: Massena Square is used for public events like the colourful Carnival of Nice; while Rosetti Square and du Palais Square are lively night spots. Other historic places are Aix-en-Provence, nicknamed the city of a thousand fountains; and Arles, full of Roman monuments and associated with Van Gogh, who painted several of his best-known works here, including The Night Café.

Typical of the region

You'll notice the farmhouses as you go through the countryside: typical basic Mas farmhouses with barns for animals, and larger and more ornate Bastide stone houses. By contrast, Cabanons are simple huts. You'll also see Bories stone houses with rounded contours.

It goes without saying that good food is also typical of the region – locals refer to truffles as black gold, and lemons are celebrated at the festival in Menton. Try lavender honey, nougat, tasty bouillabaisse, tarte tropézienne – delicious! – salade Niçoise, olives, anchoïade (anchovy paste), local fruit and wines, and pastis. And don't forget the fruits de mer.

Other activities and day trips

Check out Montmajour Abbey, a fortified abbey with panoramic views beside Aphilles Nature Park. Want a challenge? Bring the kids zip-lining at Indian Forest near Aix-en-Provence, or go horse-back riding in the Camargue. Enjoy the scent of pine and cedar in the forests of Mont Ventoux or Le Mercantour Nature parks. Mountain climbers appreciate Les Ecrins National Park; and with hang-gliding, mountain-biking and white-water rafting on offer, Verdon Nature Park is a haven for thrill-seekers.

Our tips

1. Spend a couple of days at the hilltop city of Gordes, one of the region's best-kept secrets
2. Love a bargain? Get up early for the Saturday markets in Apt
3. Explore the harbour at Toulon, and see the French Naval vessels up close
4. Art lovers should visit Musée Matisse and Musée Chagall, both in Nice
5. How about a bird's eye view? Go up in a hot-air balloon!

1661 Baratier, F-05200 / Provence-Alpes-Côte d'Azur ♿ 📶 ✿ (CC€15) iD 55b

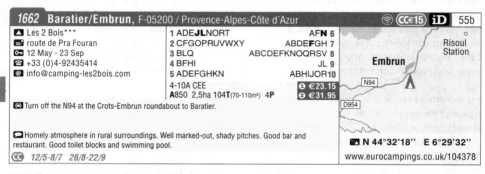

- ▲ Sites & Paysages Le Petit Liou***
- 🗺 ancienne route de Baratier
- 📅 1 May - 22 Sep
- ☎ +33 (0)4-92431910
- @ info@camping-lepetitliou.com

1 ADE**IL**NOPRST	ABFG	6
2 BFOPRVWXY	ABDE**FH**	7
3 BLQ	ABCDEFHKNOQRSV	8
4 ABFHILNO	BCEFJW	9
5 ABDEFGHJK**NO**	ABDGHJNO**P**R	10
3-10A CEE		❶ €22.10
A800 4,5ha 280T(100-120m²) 48P		❷ €33.70

🚗 On the N94 from Gap to Briançon, right at the first roundabout just before Embrun. First left after 150 metres then first right. Clearly signposted.

💬 A family campsite in rural surroundings and with spacious shaded pitches. Located between Embrun and Barratier.

🅒🅒 1/5-8/7 26/8-21/9

▪ N 44°32'50'' E 6°29'31''

www.eurocampings.co.uk/108692

1662 Baratier/Embrun, F-05200 / Provence-Alpes-Côte d'Azur 📶 (CC€15) iD 55b

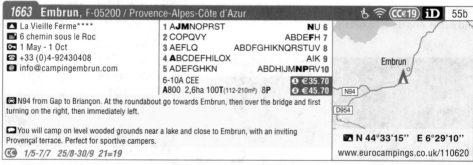

- ▲ Les 2 Bois***
- 🗺 route de Pra Fouran
- 📅 12 May - 23 Sep
- ☎ +33 (0)4-92435414
- @ info@camping-les2bois.com

1 ADE**JL**NORT	AF**N**	6
2 CFGOPRUVWXY	ABDE**FGH**	7
3 BLQ	ABCDEFKNOQRSV	8
4 BFHI	JL	9
5 ADEFGHKN	ABHIJOR	10
4-10A CEE		❶ €23.15
A850 2,5ha 104T(70-110m²) 4P		❷ €31.95

🚗 Turn off the N94 at the Crots-Embrun roundabout to Baratier.

💬 Homely atmosphere in rural surroundings. Well marked-out, shady pitches. Good bar and restaurant. Good toilet blocks and swimming pool.

🅒🅒 12/5-8/7 26/8-22/9

▪ N 44°32'18'' E 6°29'32''

www.eurocampings.co.uk/104378

1663 Embrun, F-05200 / Provence-Alpes-Côte d'Azur ♿ 📶 (CC€19) iD 55b

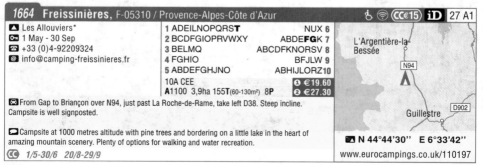

- ▲ La Vieille Ferme****
- 🗺 6 chemin sous le Roc
- 📅 1 May - 1 Oct
- ☎ +33 (0)4-92430408
- @ info@campingembrun.com

1 A**JM**NOPRST	**N**U	6
2 COPQVY	ABDE**FH**	7
3 AEFLQ	ABDFGHIKNQRSTUV	8
4 **A**BCDEFHILOX	AIK	9
5 ADEFGHKN	ABDHIJM**NP**RV	10
6-10A CEE		❶ €35.70
A800 2,6ha 100T(112-210m²) 8P		❷ €45.70

🚗 N94 from Gap to Briançon. At the roundabout go towards Embrun, then over the bridge and first turning on the right, then immediately left.

💬 You will camp on level wooded grounds near a lake and close to Embrun, with an inviting Provençal terrace. Perfect for sportive campers.

🅒🅒 1/5-7/7 25/8-30/9 21=19

▪ N 44°33'15'' E 6°29'10''

www.eurocampings.co.uk/110620

1664 Freissinières, F-05310 / Provence-Alpes-Côte d'Azur ♿ 📶 (CC€15) iD 27 A1

- ▲ Les Allouviers*
- 📅 1 May - 30 Sep
- ☎ +33 (0)4-92209324
- @ info@camping-freissinieres.fr

1 ADEILNOPQRS**T**	NU**X**	6
2 BCDFGIOPRVWXY	ABDE**FGK**	7
3 BELMQ	ABCDFKNORSV	8
4 FGHIO	BFJLW	9
5 ABDEFGHJNO	ABHIJLORZ	10
10A CEE		❶ €19.60
A1100 3,9ha 155T(60-130m²) 8P		❷ €27.30

🚗 From Gap to Briançon over N94, just past La Roche-de-Rame, take left D38. Steep incline. Campsite is well signposted.

💬 Campsite at 1000 metres altitude with pine trees and bordering on a little lake in the heart of amazing mountain scenery. Plenty of options for walking and water recreation.

🅒🅒 1/5-30/6 20/8-29/9

L'Argentière-la-Bessée
N94
Guillestre
D902

▪ N 44°44'30'' E 6°33'42''

www.eurocampings.co.uk/110197

1665 Gap, F-05000 / Provence-Alpes-Côte d'Azur

♿ 🛜 CCε17 iD 60

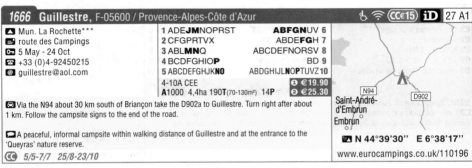

- △ Alpes Dauphiné★★★★
- 🛏 route Napoléon / N85
- 🕐 15 Apr - 20 Oct
- ☎ +33 (0)4-92512995
- @ info@alpesdauphine.com

1	ACDEJMNOPRST	ABF**H** 6
2	BFOPTUVWXY	ABDE**FGH** 7
3	ABEF**K**LQ	ABCDEFGJKNRSV 8
4	BEFHILOU	EFJL 9
5	ABDEFGHJKLM**N**	ABDFGHIJOR 10
6A CEE		❸ €27.70
A900 10ha 150**T**(70-120m²) 72**P**		❷ €38.90

🗺 Located 3 km north of Gap on 'Route Napoléon', direction Grenoble. Clearly signposted.

💬 Right next to the 'Route Napoléon' on the N85. Shaded pitches. Good restaurant. Heated swimming pool with waterslide from 1/6 to 16/9. Panoramic views.

CC 15/4-4/7 26/8-14/10

📍 N 44°34'49'' E 6°4'57''
www.eurocampings.co.uk/104374

1666 Guillestre, F-05600 / Provence-Alpes-Côte d'Azur

♿ 🛜 CCε15 iD 27 A1

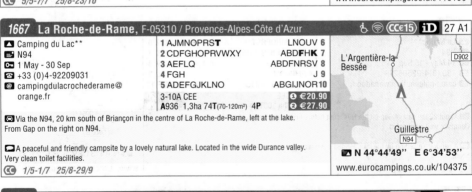

- △ Mun. La Rochette★★★
- 🛏 route des Campings
- 🕐 5 May - 24 Oct
- ☎ +33 (0)4-92450215
- @ guillestre@aol.com

1	ADE**JM**NOPRST	**ABFGN**UV 6
2	CFGPRTVX	ABDE**FGH** 7
3	ABL**MNQ**	ABCDEFNORSV 8
4	BCDFGHIO**P**	BD 9
5	ABCDEFGHJK**NO**	ABDGHIJL**NOP**TUVZ 10
4-10A CEE		❸ €19.90
A1000 4,4ha 190**T**(70-130m²) 14**P**		❷ €25.30

🗺 Via the N94 about 30 km south of Briançon take the D902a to Guillestre. Turn right after about 1 km. Follow the campsite signs to the end of the road.

💬 A peaceful, informal campsite within walking distance of Guillestre and at the entrance to the 'Queyras' nature reserve.

CC 5/5-7/7 25/8-23/10

📍 N 44°39'30'' E 6°38'17''
www.eurocampings.co.uk/110196

1667 La Roche-de-Rame, F-05310 / Provence-Alpes-Côte d'Azur

♿ 🛜 CCε15 iD 27 A1

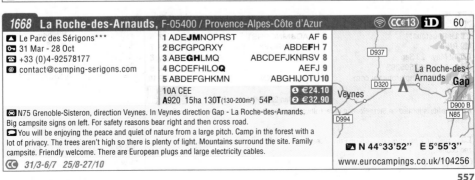

- △ Camping du Lac★★
- 🛏 N94
- 🕐 1 May - 30 Sep
- ☎ +33 (0)4-92209031
- @ campingdulacrochederame@
  orange.fr

1	AJMNOPRS**T**	LNOUV 6
2	CDFGHOPRVWXY	ABD**FH**K 7
3	AEFLQ	ABDFNRSV 8
4	FGH	J 9
5	ADEFGJKLNO	ABGIJNOR 10
3-10A CEE		❸ €20.90
A936 1,3ha 74**T**(70-120m²) 4**P**		❷ €27.90

🗺 Via the N94, 20 km south of Briançon in the centre of La Roche-de-Rame, left at the lake. From Gap on the right on N94.

💬 A peaceful and friendly campsite by a lovely natural lake. Located in the wide Durance valley. Very clean toilet facilities.

CC 1/5-1/7 25/8-29/9

📍 N 44°44'49'' E 6°34'53''
www.eurocampings.co.uk/104375

1668 La Roche-des-Arnauds, F-05400 / Provence-Alpes-Côte d'Azur

🛜 CCε13 iD 60

- △ Le Parc des Sérigons★★★
- 🕐 31 Mar - 28 Oct
- ☎ +33 (0)4-92578177
- @ contact@camping-serigons.com

1	ADE**JM**NOPRST	AF 6
2	BCFGPQRXY	ABD**EFH** 7
3	ABE**GH**LMQ	ABCDEFJKNRSV 8
4	BCDEFHILO**Q**	AEFJ 9
5	ABDEFGHKMN	ABGHIJOTU 10
10A CEE		❸ €24.10
A920 15ha 130**T**(130-200m²) 54**P**		❷ €32.90

🗺 N75 Grenoble-Sisteron, direction Veynes. In Veynes direction Gap - La Roche-des-Arnands. Big campsite signs on left. For safety reasons bear right and then cross road.
💬 You will be enjoying the peace and quiet of nature from a large pitch. Camp in the forest with a lot of privacy. The trees aren't light as there is plenty of light. Mountains surround the site. Family campsite. Friendly welcome. There are European plugs and large electricity cables.

CC 31/3-6/7 25/8-27/10

📍 N 44°33'52'' E 5°55'3''
www.eurocampings.co.uk/104256

France

1669 Les Vigneaux, F-05120 / Provence-Alpes-Côte d'Azur   ♿ 🛜 (CC€15) ♨ iD   20 A3

- ⛺ Campéole Le Courounba***
- 🏠 Le Pont Du Rif
- 🗓 11 May - 16 Sep
- ☎ +33 (0)4-92230209
- @ courounba@campeole.com

1	ABDE**JL**NOPRS**T**	ABFGH**NU** 6
2	BCFGIPRVWXY	ABDE**FGH** 7
3	ABEFLMQT	ABCDEFIJKNRSV 8
4	BFHLO**TU**	EL 9
5	ABDEFGHKN**O**	ABDGHIJO**P**SZ 10
6-10A CEE		❶ €34.50
A1130 12ha 250**T**(70-130m²) 90**P**		❷ €47.00

🗺 In L'Argentière-la-Bessée N94 follow the signs to Les Vigneaux, then turn right over the bridge.

💬 A peaceful family campsite in the countryside, at the foot of Mont Brison. Spacious shaded pitches. A completely refurbished ecological swimming pool with a slide and toddlers' pool, BMX area, sauna, jacuzzi, multisports field, tennis.

CC 11/5-6/7 25/8-15/9

🧭 N 44°49'30" E 6°31'33"

www.eurocampings.co.uk/104370

1670 Orpierre, F-05700 / Provence-Alpes-Côte d'Azur   🛜 (CC€19) iD   60

- ⛺ Les Princes d'Orange****
- 🏠 Flonsaine
- 🗓 30 Mar - 4 Nov
- ☎ +33 (0)4-92662253
- @ campingorpierre@wanadoo.fr

1	A**JM**NOPRS**T**	ABFGH**N** 6
2	DFPRUVXY	ABDE**FG**H 7
3	BEILQU	ABCDFKNQRS 8
4	**A**BCDEILO**P**	BCE 9
5	ADEFGHK	ABDHIJL**P**TU 10
10A CEE		❶ €45.40
A712 20ha 89**T**(80-110m²) 49**P**		❷ €57.40

🗺 N75 Serres-Sisteron. Turn off at Eyquians. Campsite in the town of Orpierre.

💬 A very hospitable and personal welcome awaits you at this smart family campsite with stunning views of the charming village of Orpierre. Lovely swimming pool. Renovated toilet facilities and playground. Plenty of activities in the mountains including climbing and walking. Indoor climbing wall at the campsite.

CC 30/3-4/6 17/6-7/7 25/8-3/11

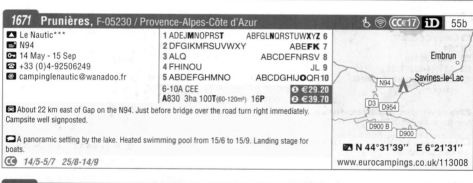

🧭 N 44°18'39" E 5°41'41"

www.eurocampings.co.uk/104262

1671 Prunières, F-05230 / Provence-Alpes-Côte d'Azur   ♿ 🛜 (CC€17) iD   55b

- ⛺ Le Nautic***
- 🏠 N94
- 🗓 14 May - 15 Sep
- ☎ +33 (0)4-92506249
- @ campinglenautic@wanadoo.fr

1	ADEJMNOPRS**T**	ABFGLNQRSTUW**XYZ** 6
2	DFGIKMRSUVWXY	ABE**FK** 7
3	ALQ	ABCDEFNRSV 8
4	FHINOU	JL 9
5	ABDEFGHMNO	ABCDGHIJO**QR** 10
6-10A CEE		❶ €29.20
A830 3ha 100**T**(60-120m²) 16**P**		❷ €39.70

🗺 About 22 km east of Gap on the N94. Just before bridge over the road turn right immediately. Campsite well signposted.

💬 A panoramic setting by the lake. Heated swimming pool from 15/6 to 15/9. Landing stage for boats.

CC 14/5-5/7 25/8-14/9

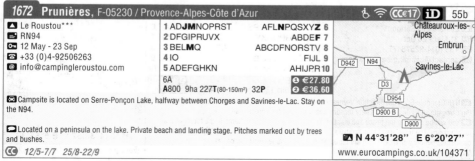

🧭 N 44°31'39" E 6°21'31"

www.eurocampings.co.uk/113008

1672 Prunières, F-05230 / Provence-Alpes-Côte d'Azur   ♿ 🛜 (CC€17) iD   55b

- ⛺ Le Roustou***
- 🏠 RN94
- 🗓 12 May - 23 Sep
- ☎ +33 (0)4-92506263
- @ info@campingleroustou.com

1	AD**JM**NOPRST	AFL**N**PQSXY**Z** 6
2	DFGIPRUVX	ABDE**F** 7
3	BEL**M**Q	ABCDFNORST**V** 8
4	**I**O	FIJL 9
5	ADEFGHKN	AHIJPR 10
6A		❶ €27.80
A800 9ha 227**T**(80-150m²) 32**P**		❷ €36.60

🗺 Campsite is located on Serre-Ponçon Lake, halfway between Chorges and Savines-le-Lac. Stay on the N94.

💬 Located on a peninsula on the lake. Private beach and landing stage. Pitches marked out by trees and bushes.

CC 12/5-7/7 25/8-22/9

🧭 N 44°31'28" E 6°20'27"

www.eurocampings.co.uk/104371

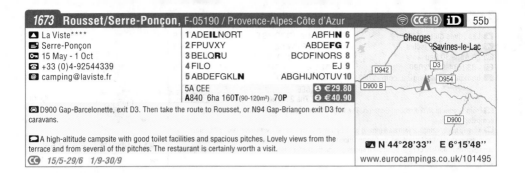

1673 Rousset/Serre-Ponçon, F-05190 / Provence-Alpes-Côte d'Azur ⓐ ⒸⒸ€19 iD 55b

- ▲ La Viste****
- ▣ Serre-Ponçon
- ⊙ 15 May - 1 Oct
- ☎ +33 (0)4-92544339
- @ camping@laviste.fr

1 ADE**IL**NORT	ABFH**N** 6
2 FPUVXY	ABDE**FG** 7
3 BELQ**R**U	BCDFINORS 8
4 FILO	EJ 9
5 ABDEFGKL**N**	ABGHIJNOTUV 10

5A CEE ❶ €29.80
A840 6ha 160T(90-120m²) 70P ❷ €40.90

🚐 D900 Gap-Barcelonette, exit D3. Then take the route to Rousset, or N94 Gap-Briançon exit D3 for caravans.

💬 A high-altitude campsite with good toilet facilities and spacious pitches. Lovely views from the terrace and from several of the pitches. The restaurant is certainly worth a visit.
Ⓒ 15/5-29/6 | 1/9-30/9

www.eurocampings.co.uk/101495

Chorges
Savines-le-Lac
D942 D3
D900 B D954
D900

N 44°28'33'' E 6°15'48''

1674 St. Crépin, F-05600 / Provence-Alpes-Côte d'Azur ♿ ⓐ ⒸⒸ€15 iD 27 A1

- ▲ Camping de L'Ile***
- ⊙ 1 May - 1 Oct
- ☎ +33 (0)9-67496790
- @ camping@saintcrepin.com

1 ADE**JM**NOPQRS**T**	ABFG**MN**UV 6
2 CDFGOPRVWXY	ABDE**FH** 7
3 ABFILMQ	ABCDEFNOQRV 8
4 DFGHO	DEJU 9
5 ADEFHJN	ABHJNOTUVZ 10

10A CEE ❶ €22.50
A900 5ha 94T(100-200m²) 7P ❷ €28.70

🚐 Campsite is on N94 and well signposted. Between Briançon and Guillestre on N94. At St. Crepin follow signs to Aerodrome. Cross railway tracks. Campsite is directly left.
💬 Campsite situated on the banks of a river with activities including wild-water rafting. Also ideally located for those who enjoy gliding, with the possibility of gliding in the Écrins National Park with its beautiful panorama.
Ⓒ 1/5-6/7 | 27/8-30/9

www.eurocampings.co.uk/122232

L'argentière-la-Bessée
N94
D902

N 44°42'18'' E 6°36'9''

France

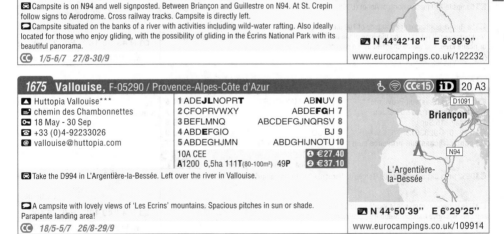

1675 Vallouise, F-05290 / Provence-Alpes-Côte d'Azur ♿ ⓐ ⒸⒸ€15 iD 20 A3

- ▲ Huttopia Vallouise***
- ▣ chemin des Chambonnettes
- ⊙ 18 May - 30 Sep
- ☎ +33 (0)4-92233026
- @ vallouise@huttopia.com

1 ADE**JL**NOPR**T**	AB**N**UV 6
2 CFOPRVWXY	ABDE**FG**H 7
3 BEFLMNQ	ABCDEFGJNQRSV 8
4 ABD**E**FGIO	BJ 9
5 ABDEGHJMN	ABDGHIJNOTU 10

10A CEE ❶ €27.40
A1200 6,5ha 111T(80-100m²) 49P ❷ €37.10

🚐 Take the D994 in L'Argentière-la-Bessée. Left over the river in Vallouise.

💬 A campsite with lovely views of 'Les Ecrins' mountains. Spacious pitches in sun or shade. Parapente landing area!
Ⓒ 18/5-5/7 | 26/8-29/9

www.eurocampings.co.uk/109914

D1091
Briançon
N94
L'Argentière-la-Bessée

N 44°50'39'' E 6°29'25''

1676 Veynes, F-05400 / Provence-Alpes-Côte d'Azur ♿ ⓐ ⒸⒸ€17 iD 60

- ▲ Camping Solaire****
- ▣ Quartier des Iscles
- ⊙ 1 Jan - 31 Dec
- ☎ +33 (0)4-92581234
- @ info@camping-solaire.com

1 AD**IL**NOPRST	AF**N**U 6
2 FGPVWXY	ABDE**FG**H 7
3 BE**GHIL**Q	ABCDEFJKNOQRSV 8
4 BCFGHILNOP**QU**	EJKUVW 9
5 ABDEFGHKM**NO**	ABHIJL**NP**QTUZ 10

6A CEE ❶ €31.10
6,5ha 158T(150-200m²) 94P ❷ €44.20

🚐 From Grenoble N75 direction Sisteron. Then D994 towards Veynes. Follow Plan d'Eau and campsite signs.
💬 A family campsite with a swimming pool, restaurant with terrace and views of the mountains. It has a shaded section but you can also choose a sunny pitch. Pitches of 150 m² or even more. Well maintained grass.
Ⓒ 1/4-1/7 | 19/8-30/9 8=7

www.eurocampings.co.uk/112722

D937
La Roche-des-Arnauds
Veynes
D993
D993 B
D994 Sigoyer
D1075

N 44°31'14'' E 5°48'15''

1677 Veynes, F-05400 / Provence-Alpes-Côte d'Azur ⅍ 훈 ✿ (CC€15) iD 60

- ▲ Les Rives du Lac★★★
- 🏕 Plan d'eau Les Iscles
- 🗓 28 Apr - 30 Sep
- ☎ +33 (0)4-92572090
- @ booking@camping-lac.com

1 ADE**JM**NOPQRST	CDFJLM**N**QU	6
2 CDFIJPVWXY	ABDE**F**H	7
3 ABCEF**GHI**LQSV	ABCDFGIJKNRSTUV	8
4 **A**BD**E**FGHILOU	BEFJQTUVW	9
5 ACDEFGHK**O**	ABDHIJNO**P**TU	10

10-16A CEE
A830 2,7ha 224T(80-190m²) 37P

- ❶ €29.00
- ❷ €45.00

🚗 From Grenoble N75 direction Sisteron. Then D994 direction Veynes. Follow Plan d'Eau and campsite signs.

💬 A lovely family campsite with a swimming pool, by a lake where you can swim from May to September. Countless opportunities for walking, cycling and mountain biking from the site up into the surrounding mountains. Fishing in the lake or river. Sports and sports ground for children. Restaurant with outdoor seating area.

CC 28/4-7/7 25/8-29/9 14=12

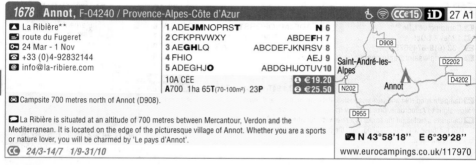

📍 N 44°31'8'' E 5°47'56''

www.eurocampings.co.uk/111480

1678 Annot, F-04240 / Provence-Alpes-Côte d'Azur ⅍ 훈 (CC€15) iD 27 A1

- ▲ La Ribière★★
- 🏕 route du Fugeret
- 🗓 24 Mar - 1 Nov
- ☎ +33 (0)4-92832144
- @ info@la-ribiere.com

1 ADE**JM**NOPRS**T**	**N**	6
2 CFKPRVWXY	ABDE**F**H	7
3 AE**GH**LQ	ABCDEFJKNRSV	8
4 FHIO	AEJ	9
5 ADEGHJ**O**	ABDGHIJOTUV	10

10A CEE
A700 1ha 65T(70-100m²) 23P

- ❶ €19.20
- ❷ €25.50

🚗 Campsite 700 metres north of Annot (D908).

💬 La Ribière is situated at an altitude of 700 metres between Mercantour, Verdon and the Mediterranean. It is located on the edge of the picturesque village of Annot. Whether you are a sports or nature lover, you will be charmed by 'Le pays d'Annot'.

CC 24/3-14/7 1/9-31/10

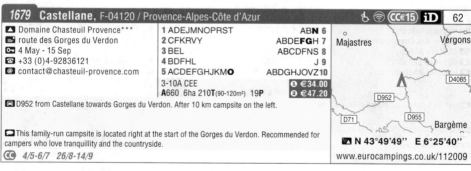

📍 N 43°58'18'' E 6°39'28''

www.eurocampings.co.uk/117970

1679 Castellane, F-04120 / Provence-Alpes-Côte d'Azur ⅍ 훈 (CC€15) iD 62

- ▲ Domaine Chasteuil Provence★★★
- 🏕 route des Gorges du Verdon
- 🗓 4 May - 15 Sep
- ☎ +33 (0)4-92836121
- @ contact@chasteuil-provence.com

1 ADEJMNOPRST	AB**N**	6
2 CFKRVY	ABDE**FGH**	7
3 BEL	ABCDFNS	8
4 BDFHL	J	9
5 ACDEFGHJKM**O**	ABDGHJOVZ	10

3-10A CEE
A660 6ha 210T(90-120m²) 19P

- ❶ €34.00
- ❷ €47.20

🚗 D952 from Castellane towards Gorges du Verdon. After 10 km campsite on the left.

💬 This family-run campsite is located right at the start of the Gorges du Verdon. Recommended for campers who love tranquillity and the countryside.

CC 4/5-6/7 26/8-14/9

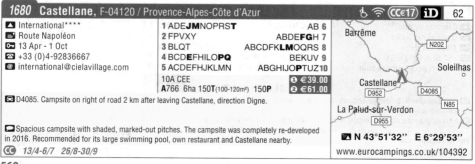

📍 N 43°49'49'' E 6°25'40''

www.eurocampings.co.uk/112009

1680 Castellane, F-04120 / Provence-Alpes-Côte d'Azur ⅍ 훈 (CC€17) iD 62

- ▲ International★★★★
- 🏕 Route Napoléon
- 🗓 13 Apr - 1 Oct
- ☎ +33 (0)4-92836667
- @ international@cielavillage.com

1 ADE**JM**NOPRS**T**	AB	6
2 FPVXY	ABDE**FGH**	7
3 BLQT	ABCDFK**LM**OQRS	8
4 BCD**E**FHILO**PQ**	BEKUV	9
5 ACDEFHJKLMN	ABGHIJO**P**TUZ	10

10A CEE
A766 6ha 150T(100-120m²) 150P

- ❶ €39.00
- ❷ €61.00

🚗 D4085. Campsite on right of road 2 km after leaving Castellane, direction Digne.

💬 Spacious campsite with shaded, marked-out pitches. The campsite was completely re-developed in 2016. Recommended for its large swimming pool, own restaurant and Castellane nearby.

CC 13/4-6/7 26/8-30/9

📍 N 43°51'32'' E 6°29'53''

www.eurocampings.co.uk/104392

France

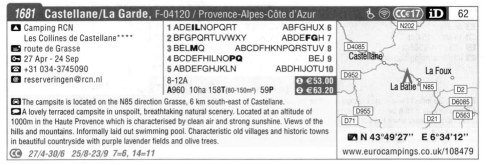

1681 Castellane/La Garde, F-04120 / Provence-Alpes-Côte d'Azur
⚿ 📶 (CC€17) iD 62

- ⛺ Camping RCN
  Les Collines de Castellane****
- 🚐 route de Grasse
- 📅 27 Apr - 24 Sep
- ☎ +31 034-3745090
- @ reserveringen@rcn.nl

1	ADEILNOPQRT	ABFGHUX	6
2	BFGPQRTUVWXY	ABDEFGH	7
3	BELMQ	ABCDFHKNPQRSTUV	8
4	BCDEFHILNOPQ	BEJ	9
5	ABDEFGHJKLN	ABDHIJOTU	10

8-12A   ❶ €53.00
A960 10ha 158T(80-150m²) 59P   ❷ €63.20

🚗 The campsite is located on the N85 direction Grasse, 6 km south-east of Castellane.
💬 A lovely terraced campsite in unspoilt, breathtaking natural scenery. Located at an altitude of 1000m in the Haute Provence which is characterised by clean air and strong sunshine. Views of the hills and mountains. Informally laid out swimming pool. Characteristic old villages and historic towns in beautiful countryside with purple lavender fields and olive trees.

CC 27/4-30/6   25/8-23/9   7=6, 14=11

🏕 N 43°49'27''   E 6°34'12''

www.eurocampings.co.uk/108479

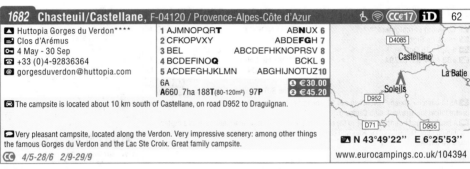

1682 Chasteuil/Castellane, F-04120 / Provence-Alpes-Côte d'Azur
⚿ 📶 (CC€17) iD 62

- ⛺ Huttopia Gorges du Verdon****
- 🚐 Clos d'Arémus
- 📅 4 May - 30 Sep
- ☎ +33 (0)4-92836364
- @ gorgesduverdon@huttopia.com

1	AJMNOPQRT	ABNUX	6
2	CFKOPVXY	ABDEFGH	7
3	BEL	ABCDEFHKNOPRSV	8
4	BCDEFINOQ	BCKL	9
5	ACDEFGHJKLMN	ABGHIJNOTUZ	10

6A   ❶ €30.00
A660 7ha 188T(80-120m²) 97P   ❷ €45.20

🚗 The campsite is located about 10 km south of Castellane, on road D952 to Draguignan.

💬 Very pleasant campsite, located along the Verdon. Very impressive scenery: among other things the famous Gorges du Verdon and the Lac Ste Croix. Great family campsite.

CC 4/5-28/6   2/9-29/9

🏕 N 43°49'22''   E 6°25'53''

www.eurocampings.co.uk/104394

France

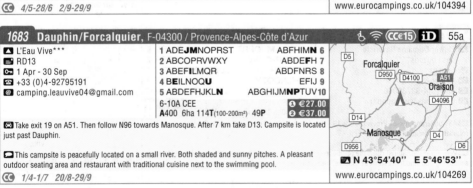

1683 Dauphin/Forcalquier, F-04300 / Provence-Alpes-Côte d'Azur
⚿ 📶 (CC€15) iD 55a

- ⛺ L'Eau Vive***
- 🚐 RD13
- 📅 1 Apr - 30 Sep
- ☎ +33 (0)4-92795191
- @ camping.leauvive04@gmail.com

1	ADEJMNOPRST	ABFHIMN	6
2	ABCOPRVWXY	ABDEFH	7
3	ABEFILMQR	ABDFNRS	8
4	BEILNOQU	EFIJ	9
5	ABDEFHJKLN	ABGHIJMNPTUV	10

6-10A CEE   ❶ €27.00
A400 6ha 114T(100-200m²) 49P   ❷ €37.00

🚗 Take exit 19 on A51. Then follow N96 towards Manosque. After 7 km take D13. Campsite is located just past Dauphin.

💬 This campsite is peacefully located on a small river. Both shaded and sunny pitches. A pleasant outdoor seating area and restaurant with traditional cuisine next to the swimming pool.

CC 1/4-1/7   20/8-29/9

🏕 N 43°54'40''   E 5°46'53''

www.eurocampings.co.uk/104269

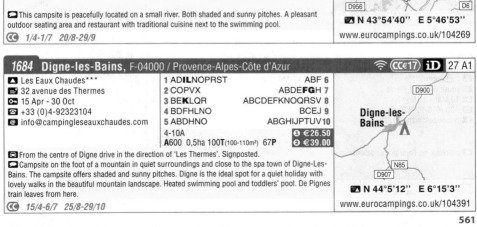

1684 Digne-les-Bains, F-04000 / Provence-Alpes-Côte d'Azur
📶 (CC€17) iD 27 A1

- ⛺ Les Eaux Chaudes***
- 🚐 32 avenue des Thermes
- 📅 15 Apr - 30 Oct
- ☎ +33 (0)4-92323104
- @ info@campingleseauxchaudes.com

1	ADILNOPRST	ABF	6
2	COPVX	ABDEFGH	7
3	BEKLQR	ABCDEFKNOQRSV	8
4	BDFHLNO	BCEJ	9
5	ABDHNO	ABGHIJPTUV	10

4-10A   ❶ €26.50
A600 0,5ha 100T(100-110m²) 67P   ❷ €39.00

🚗 From the centre of Digne drive in the direction of 'Les Thermes'. Signposted.
💬 Campsite on the foot of a mountain in quiet surroundings and close to the spa town of Digne-Les-Bains. The campsite offers shaded and sunny pitches. Digne is the ideal spot for a quiet holiday with lovely walks in the beautiful mountain landscape. Heated swimming pool and toddlers' pool. De Pignes train leaves from here.

CC 15/4-6/7   25/8-29/10

🏕 N 44°5'12''   E 6°15'3''

www.eurocampings.co.uk/104391

1685 Entrevaux, F-04320 / Provence-Alpes-Côte d'Azur ♿ 📶 (CC€15) iD 27 A1

🏠 du Brec**
📅 15 Mar - 15 Oct
☎ +33 (0)4-93054245
@ info@camping-dubrec.com

1 ADEJMNOPRST	LMNU 6
2 CDFJPRVWXY	ABDEFGH 7
3 AELQ	ABCDEFJKNQRSV 8
4 AFO	JQR 9
5 ADEFGHJNO	ABDHIJNPTUVZ 10
10A CEE	❶ €22.35
A500 3,8ha 76T(80-140m²) 11P	❷ €29.25

🚗 N202, 2.5 miles (4 km) west of Entrevaux. Follow the signs.

💬 The campsite is fairly basic, but good. Perfect for the active camper who feels at home in an area of natural beauty which has not yet been discovered by tourists. The nearby medieval town of Entrevaux is worth a visit. Set next to a 4-hectare lake with free use of canoes and kayaks. Top-quality swimming water. Perfectly suited to families with children. No entertainment, therefore quiet.

CC 15/3-6/7 24/8-14/10

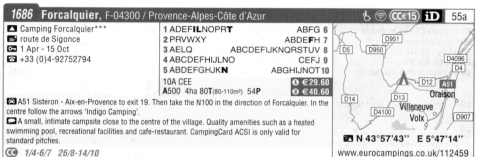

🧭 N 43°57'42'' E 6°47'56''

www.eurocampings.co.uk/110617

1686 Forcalquier, F-04300 / Provence-Alpes-Côte d'Azur ♿ 📶 (CC€15) iD 55a

🏠 Camping Forcalquier***
🛣 route de Sigonce
📅 1 Apr - 15 Oct
☎ +33 (0)4-92752794

1 ADEFILNOPRT	ABFG 6
2 PRVWXY	ABDEFH 7
3 AELQ	ABCDEFIJKNQRSTUV 8
4 ABCDEFHIJLNO	CEFJ 9
5 ABDEFGHJKN	ABGHIJNOT 10
10A CEE	❶ €29.60
A500 4ha 80T(80-110m²) 54P	❷ €40.60

🚗 A51 Sisteron - Aix-en-Provence to exit 19. Then take the N100 in the direction of Forcalquier. In the centre follow the arrows 'Indigo Camping'.

💬 A small, intimate campsite close to the centre of the village. Quality amenities such as a heated swimming pool, recreational facilities and cafe-restaurant. CampingCard ACSI is only valid for standard pitches.

CC 1/4-6/7 26/8-14/10

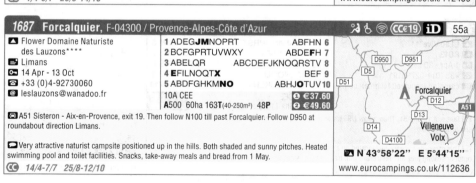

🧭 N 43°57'43'' E 5°47'14''

www.eurocampings.co.uk/112459

1687 Forcalquier, F-04300 / Provence-Alpes-Côte d'Azur ♨ ♿ 📶 (CC€19) iD 55a

🏠 Flower Domaine Naturiste des Lauzons****
🛣 Limans
📅 14 Apr - 13 Oct
☎ +33 (0)4-92730060
@ leslauzons@wanadoo.fr

1 ADEGJMNOPRT	ABFHN 6
2 BCFGPRTUVWXY	ABDEFH 7
3 ABELQR	ABCDEFJKNOQRSTV 8
4 EFILNOQTX	BEF 9
5 ABDFGHKMNO	ABHJOTUV 10
10A CEE	❶ €37.60
A500 60ha 163T(40-250m²) 48P	❷ €49.60

🚗 A51 Sisteron - Aix-en-Provence, exit 19. Then follow N100 till past Forcalquier. Follow D950 at roundabout direction Limans.

💬 Very attractive naturist campsite positioned up in the hills. Both shaded and sunny pitches. Heated swimming pool and toilet facilities. Snacks, take-away meals and bread from 1 May.

CC 14/4-7/7 25/8-12/10

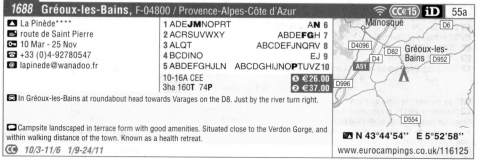

🧭 N 43°58'22'' E 5°44'15''

www.eurocampings.co.uk/112636

1688 Gréoux-les-Bains, F-04800 / Provence-Alpes-Côte d'Azur 📶 (CC€15) iD 55a

🏠 La Pinède****
🛣 route de Saint Pierre
📅 10 Mar - 25 Nov
☎ +33 (0)4-92780547
@ lapinede@wanadoo.fr

1 ADEJMNOPRT	AN 6
2 ACRSUVWXY	ABDEFGH 7
3 ALQT	ABCDEFJNQRV 8
4 BCDINO	EJ 9
5 ABDEFGHJLN	ABCDGHIJNOPTUVZ 10
10-16A CEE	❶ €26.00
3ha 160T 74P	❷ €37.00

🚗 In Gréoux-les-Bains at roundabout head towards Varages on the D8. Just by the river turn right.

💬 Campsite landscaped in terrace form with good amenities. Situated close to the Verdon Gorge, and within walking distance of the town. Known as a health retreat.

CC 10/3-11/6 1/9-24/11

🧭 N 43°44'54'' E 5°52'58''

www.eurocampings.co.uk/116125

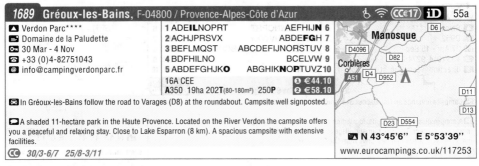

1689 Gréoux-les-Bains, F-04800 / Provence-Alpes-Côte d'Azur ♿ 🛜 (CC€17) iD 55a

- 🏕 Verdon Parc****
- 🏠 Domaine de la Paludette
- 🗓 30 Mar - 4 Nov
- ☎ +33 (0)4-82751043
- @ info@campingverdonparc.fr

1 ADE**IL**NOPRT	AEFHIJ**N** 6
2 ACHJPRSVX	ABDE**FGH** 7
3 BEFLMQST	ABCDEFIJNORSTUV 8
4 BDFHILNO	BCELVW 9
5 ABDEFGHJK**O**	ABGHIK**NOP**TUVZ 10
16A CEE	❸ €44.10
A350 19ha 202**T**(80-180m²) 250**P**	❷ €58.10

🚗 In Gréoux-les-Bains follow the road to Varages (D8) at the roundabout. Campsite well signposted.

💬 A shaded 11-hectare park in the Haute Provence. Located on the River Verdon the campsite offers you a peaceful and relaxing stay. Close to Lake Esparron (8 km). A spacious campsite with extensive facilities.

📍 N 43°45'6'' E 5°53'39''

(CC) 30/3-6/7 25/8-3/11

www.eurocampings.co.uk/117253

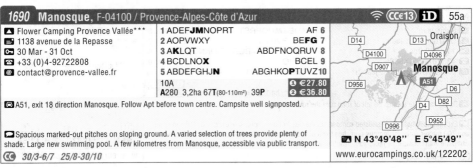

1690 Manosque, F-04100 / Provence-Alpes-Côte d'Azur 🛜 (CC€13) iD 55a

- 🏕 Flower Camping Provence Vallée***
- 🏠 1138 avenue de la Repasse
- 🗓 30 Mar - 31 Oct
- ☎ +33 (0)4-92722808
- @ contact@provence-vallee.fr

1 ADEF**JM**NOPRT	AF 6
2 AOPVWXY	BE**FG** 7
3 A**K**LQT	ABDFNOQRUV 8
4 BCDLNO**X**	BCEL 9
5 ABDEFGHJ**N**	ABGHKO**P**TUVZ 10
10A	❸ €27.80
A280 3,2ha 67**T**(80-110m²) 39**P**	❷ €36.80

🚗 A51, exit 18 direction Manosque. Follow Apt before town centre. Campsite well signposted.

💬 Spacious marked-out pitches on sloping ground. A varied selection of trees provide plenty of shade. Large new swimming pool. A few kilometres from Manosque, accessible via public transport.

📍 N 43°49'48'' E 5°45'49''

(CC) 30/3-6/7 25/8-30/10

www.eurocampings.co.uk/122202

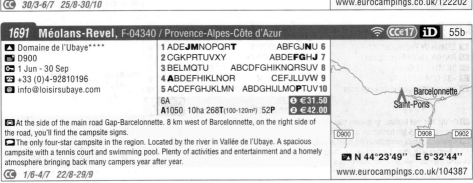

1691 Méolans-Revel, F-04340 / Provence-Alpes-Côte d'Azur 🛜 (CC€17) iD 55b

- 🏕 Domaine de l'Ubaye****
- 🏠 D900
- 🗓 1 Jun - 30 Sep
- ☎ +33 (0)4-92810196
- @ info@loisirsubaye.com

1 ADE**JM**NOPQR**T**	ABFGJ**N**U 6
2 CGKPRTUVXY	ABDE**FGH**J 7
3 BELMQTU	ABCDFGHIKNQRSUV 8
4 **A**BDEFHIKLNOR	CEFJLUVW 9
5 ACDEFGHJKLMN	ABDGHIJLMO**P**TUV 10
6A	❸ €31.50
A1050 10ha 268**T**(100-120m²) 52**P**	❷ €42.00

🚗 At the side of the main road Gap-Barcelonnette. 8 km west of Barcelonnette, on the right side of the road, you'll find the campsite signs.

💬 The only four-star campsite in the region. Located by the river in Vallée de l'Ubaye. A spacious campsite with a tennis court and swimming pool. Plenty of activities and entertainment and a homely atmosphere bringing back many campers year after year.

📍 N 44°23'49'' E 6°32'44''

(CC) 1/6-4/7 22/8-29/9

www.eurocampings.co.uk/104387

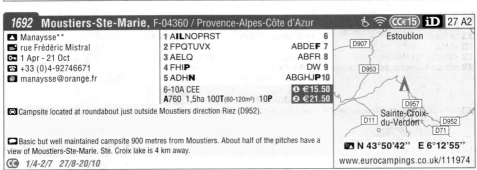

1692 Moustiers-Ste-Marie, F-04360 / Provence-Alpes-Côte d'Azur ♿ 🛜 (CC€15) iD 27 A2

- 🏕 Manaysse**
- 🏠 rue Frédéric Mistral
- 🗓 1 Apr - 21 Oct
- ☎ +33 (0)4-92746671
- @ manaysse@orange.fr

1 A**IL**NOPRST	6
2 FPQTUVX	ABDE**F** 7
3 AELQ	ABFR 8
4 FHI**P**	DW 9
5 ADH**N**	ABGHJ**P** 10
6-10A CEE	❸ €15.50
A760 1,5ha 100**T**(60-120m²) 10**P**	❷ €21.50

🚗 Campsite located at roundabout just outside Moustiers direction Riez (D952).

💬 Basic but well maintained campsite 900 metres from Moustiers. About half of the pitches have a view of Moustiers-Ste-Marie. Ste. Croix lake is 4 km away.

📍 N 43°50'42'' E 6°12'55''

(CC) 1/4-2/7 27/8-20/10

www.eurocampings.co.uk/111974

1693 Moustiers-Ste-Marie, F-04360 / Provence-Alpes-Côte d'Azur ⅋ 🛜 ⒸⒸ€17 🆔 27 A2

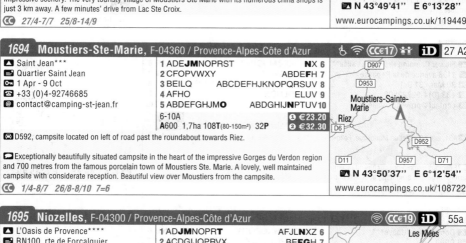

- ▲ Saint Clair***
- 🚏 D952
- ☀ 27 Apr - 15 Sep
- ☎ +33 (0)4-92746715
- @ direction@camping-st-clair.com

1 ADEJMNOPRT	X 6
2 BCFOPUVWXY	ABDEFH 7
3 BLQ	ABCDEFHJKNOPRS 8
4 F	EJL 9
5 ABDEFGMO	ABDGHIJPTUV 10
6A CEE	❶ €23.20
A525 3ha 93T(88-136m²) 12P	❷ €29.80

🅿 Campsite entrance on roundabout 3km south of Moustiers-Ste-Marie (D957).

💬 A congenial, shaded campsite, located on a river with magnificent panoramas of the very impressive scenery. The very touristy village of Moustiers Ste Marie with its numerous china shops is just 3 km away. A few minutes' drive from Lac Ste Croix.

ⓒⓒ 27/4-7/7 25/8-14/9

🏴 N 43°49'41'' E 6°13'28''

www.eurocampings.co.uk/119449

1694 Moustiers-Ste-Marie, F-04360 / Provence-Alpes-Côte d'Azur ⅋ 🛜 ⒸⒸ€17 ⋆⋆ 🆔 27 A2

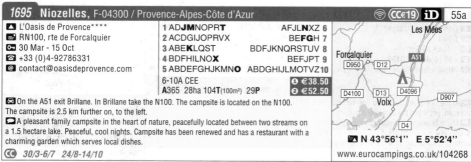

- ▲ Saint Jean***
- 🚏 Quartier Saint Jean
- ☀ 1 Apr - 9 Oct
- ☎ +33 (0)4-92746685
- @ contact@camping-st-jean.fr

1 ADEJMNOPRST	NX 6
2 CFOPVWXY	ABDEFH 7
3 BEILQ	ABCDEFHJKNOPQRSUV 8
4 AFHO	ELUV 9
5 ABDEFGHJMO	ABDGHIJNPTUV 10
6-10A	❶ €23.20
A600 1,7ha 108T(80-150m²) 32P	❷ €32.30

🅿 D592, campsite located on left of road past the roundabout towards Riez.

💬 Exceptionally beautifully situated campsite in the heart of the impressive Gorges du Verdon region and 700 metres from the famous porcelain town of Moustiers Ste. Marie. A lovely, well maintained campsite with considerate reception. Beautiful view over Moustiers from the campsite.

ⓒⓒ 1/4-8/7 26/8-8/10 7=6

🏴 N 43°50'37'' E 6°12'54''

www.eurocampings.co.uk/108722

1695 Niozelles, F-04300 / Provence-Alpes-Côte d'Azur 🛜 ⒸⒸ€19 🆔 55a

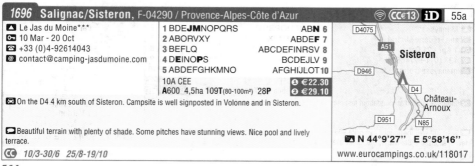

- ▲ L'Oasis de Provence****
- 🚏 RN100, rte de Forcalquier
- ☀ 30 Mar - 15 Oct
- ☎ +33 (0)4-92786331
- @ contact@oasisdeprovence.com

1 ADJMNOPRT	AFJLNXZ 6
2 ACDGIJOPRVX	BEFGH 7
3 ABEKLQST	BDFJKNQRSTUV 8
4 BDFHILNOX	BEFJPT 9
5 ABDEFGHJKMNO	ABDGHIJLMOTVZ 10
6-10A CEE	❶ €38.50
A365 28ha 104T(100m²) 29P	❷ €52.50

🅿 On the A51 exit Brillane. In Brillane take the N100. The campsite is located on the N100. The campsite is 2.5 km further on, to the left.

💬 A pleasant family campsite in the heart of nature, peacefully located between two streams on a 1.5 hectare lake. Peaceful, cool nights. Campsite has been renewed and has a restaurant with a charming garden which serves local dishes.

ⓒⓒ 30/3-6/7 24/8-14/10

🏴 N 43°56'1'' E 5°52'4''

www.eurocampings.co.uk/104268

1696 Salignac/Sisteron, F-04290 / Provence-Alpes-Côte d'Azur 🛜 ⒸⒸ€13 🆔 55a

- ▲ Le Jas du Moine***
- ☀ 10 Mar - 20 Oct
- ☎ +33 (0)4-92614043
- @ contact@camping-jasdumoine.com

1 BDEJMNOPQRS	ABN 6
2 ABORVXY	ABDEF 7
3 BEFLQ	ABCDEFINRSV 8
4 DEINOPS	BCDEJLV 9
5 ABDEFGHKMNO	AFGHIJLOT 10
10A CEE	❶ €22.30
A600 4,5ha 109T(80-100m²) 28P	❷ €29.10

🅿 On the D4 4 km south of Sisteron. Campsite is well signposted in Volonne and in Sisteron.

💬 Beautiful terrain with plenty of shade. Some pitches have stunning views. Nice pool and lively terrace.

ⓒⓒ 10/3-30/6 25/8-19/10

🏴 N 44°9'27'' E 5°58'16''

www.eurocampings.co.uk/118017

1697 Seyne-les-Alpes, F-04140 / Provence-Alpes-Côte d'Azur   🚶 📶 (CC€17) iD 27 A1

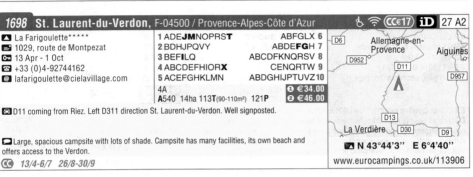

- 🔺 Sites & Paysages Les Prairies***
- 🏕 Haute Greyere
- 📅 8 May - 8 Sep
- ☎ +33 (0)4-92351021
- @ info@campinglesprairies.com

1 ADE**IL**NORT	AB**N** 6
2 CGPRVXY	ABE**FGH** 7
3 ABLQ**U**	ABCDFJKNOQRSTUV 8
4 FHINO	EJL 9
5 ABDEFGHK**N**	ABGHIJOTV 10
10A CEE	❶ €26.80
A1150 3,9ha 100T(100-140m²) 16P	❷ €36.80

🚗 From Gap direction Barcelonette. Then D900 direction Digne. Signposted at Seyne.

💬 This exceptionally beautiful campsite offers peace, comfort and relaxation. In addition to good toilet facilities this site has the advantage of being within walking distance of a typical Montagnard (mountain) village. The friendly owners will always have time for you.

CC 8/5-2/7 25/8-8/9 8=7, 16=14

📍 N 44°20'34" E 6°21'37"

www.eurocampings.co.uk/107575

1698 St. Laurent-du-Verdon, F-04500 / Provence-Alpes-Côte d'Azur   🚶 📶 (CC€17) iD 27 A2

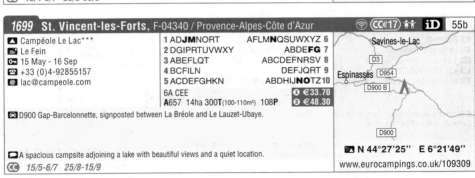

- 🔺 La Farigoulette*****
- 🏕 1029, route de Montpezat
- 📅 13 Apr - 1 Oct
- ☎ +33 (0)4-92744162
- @ lafarigoulette@cielavillage.com

1 ADE**JM**NOPRS**T**	ABFGLX 6
2 BDHJPQVY	ABDE**FGH** 7
3 BEF**IL**Q	ABCDFKNQRSV 8
4 ABCDEFHIOR**X**	CENQRTW 9
5 ACEFGHKLMN	ABDGHIJPTUVZ 10
4A	❶ €34.00
A540 14ha 113T(90-110m²) 121P	❷ €46.00

🚗 D11 coming from Riez. Left D311 direction St. Laurent-du-Verdon. Well signposted.

💬 Large, spacious campsite with lots of shade. Campsite has many facilities, its own beach and offers access to the Verdon.

CC 13/4-6/7 26/8-30/9

📍 N 43°44'3" E 6°4'40"

www.eurocampings.co.uk/113906

1699 St. Vincent-les-Forts, F-04340 / Provence-Alpes-Côte d'Azur   📶 (CC€17) 👫 iD 55b

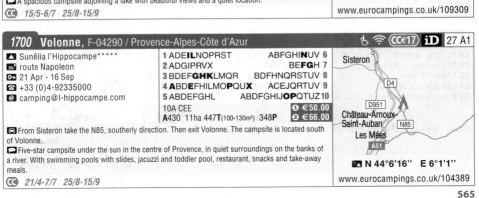

- 🔺 Campéole Le Lac***
- 🏕 Le Fein
- 📅 15 May - 16 Sep
- ☎ +33 (0)4-92855157
- @ lac@campeole.com

1 AD**JM**NORT	AFLMN**Q**SUWXYZ 6
2 DGIPRTUVWXY	ABDE**FG** 7
3 ABEFLQT	ABCDEFNRSV 8
4 BCFILN	DEFJQRT 9
5 ACDEFGHKN	ABDHIJ**NO**TZ 10
6A CEE	❶ €33.70
A657 14ha 300T(100-110m²) 108P	❷ €48.30

🚗 D900 Gap-Barcelonnette, signposted between La Bréole and Le Lauzet-Ubaye.

💬 A spacious campsite adjoining a lake with beautiful views and a quiet location.

CC 15/5-6/7 25/8-15/9

📍 N 44°27'25" E 6°21'49"

www.eurocampings.co.uk/109309

1700 Volonne, F-04290 / Provence-Alpes-Côte d'Azur   🚶 📶 (CC€17) iD 27 A1

- 🔺 Sunêlia l'Hippocampe*****
- 🏕 route Napoleon
- 📅 21 Apr - 16 Sep
- ☎ +33 (0)4-92335000
- @ camping@l-hippocampe.com

1 ADE**IL**NOPRST	ABFGHI**N**UV 6
2 ADGIPRVX	BEF**GH** 7
3 BDEF**GHK**LMQR	BDFHNQRSTUV 8
4 **A**BDE**F**HILMO**PQ**UX	ACEJQRTUV 9
5 ABDEFGHL	ABDFGHIJ**OP**QTUZ 10
10A CEE	❶ €50.00
A430 11ha 447T(100-130m²) 348P	❷ €66.00

🚗 From Sisteron take the N85, southerly direction. Then exit Volonne. The campsite is located south of Volonne.

💬 Five-star campsite under the sun in the centre of Provence, in quiet surroundings on the banks of a river. With swimming pools with slides, jacuzzi and toddler pool, restaurant, snacks and take-away meals.

CC 21/4-7/7 25/8-15/9

📍 N 44°6'16" E 6°1'1"

www.eurocampings.co.uk/104389

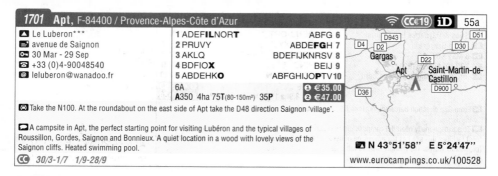

1701 Apt, F-84400 / Provence-Alpes-Côte d'Azur ≈ (CC€19) iD 55a

- ▲ Le Luberon***
- 🏠 avenue de Saignon
- 🗓 30 Mar - 29 Sep
- ☎ +33 (0)4-90048540
- @ leluberon@wanadoo.fr

1 ADEFILNORT	ABFG	6
2 PRUVY	ABDEFGH	7
3 AKLQ	BDEFIJKNRSV	8
4 BDFIOX	BEIJ	9
5 ABDEHKO	ABFGHIJOPTV	10
6A	❶ €35.00	
A350 4ha 75T(80-150m²) 35P	❷ €47.00	

🚗 Take the N100. At the roundabout on the east side of Apt take the D48 direction Saignon 'village'.

📖 A campsite in Apt, the perfect starting point for visiting Lubéron and the typical villages of Roussillon, Gordes, Saignon and Bonnieux. A quiet location in a wood with lovely views of the Saignon cliffs. Heated swimming pool.

CC 30/3-1/7 1/9-28/9

▨ N 43°51'58'' E 5°24'47''

www.eurocampings.co.uk/100528

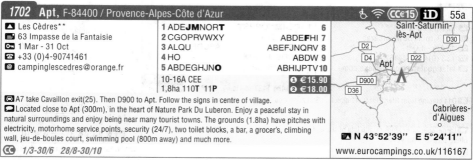

1702 Apt, F-84400 / Provence-Alpes-Côte d'Azur ♿ ≈ (CC€15) iD 55a

- ▲ Les Cèdres**
- 🏠 63 Impasse de la Fantaisie
- 🗓 1 Mar - 31 Oct
- ☎ +33 (0)4-90741461
- @ campinglescedres@orange.fr

1 ADEJMNORT		6
2 CGOPRVWXY	ABDEFHI	7
3 ALQU	ABEFJNQRV	8
4 HO	ABDW	9
5 ABDEGHJNO	ABHIJPTV	10
10-16A CEE	❶ €15.90	
1,8ha 110T 11P	❷ €18.00	

🚗 A7 take Cavaillon exit(25). Then D900 to Apt. Follow the signs in centre of village.
📖 Located close to Apt (300m), in the heart of Nature Park Du Luberon. Enjoy a peaceful stay in natural surroundings and enjoy being near many tourist towns. The grounds (1.8ha) have pitches with electricity, motorhome service points, security (24/7), two toilet blocks, a bar, a grocer's, climbing wall, jeu-de-boules court, swimming pool (800m away) and much more.

CC 1/3-30/6 28/8-30/10

▨ N 43°52'39'' E 5°24'11''

www.eurocampings.co.uk/116167

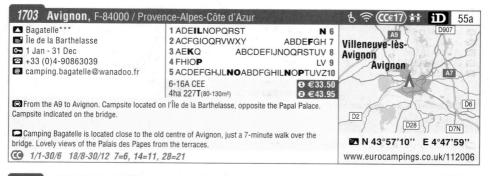

1703 Avignon, F-84000 / Provence-Alpes-Côte d'Azur ♿ ≈ (CC€17) ⚤ iD 55a

- ▲ Bagatelle***
- 🏠 Île de la Barthelasse
- 🗓 1 Jan - 31 Dec
- ☎ +33 (0)4-90863039
- @ camping.bagatelle@wanadoo.fr

1 ADEILNOPQRST	N	6
2 ACFGIOQRVWXY	ABDEFGH	7
3 AEKQ	ABCDEFIJNOQRSTUV	8
4 FHIOP	LV	9
5 ACDEFGHJLNOABDFGHILNOPTUVZ		10
6-16A CEE	❶ €33.50	
4ha 227T(80-130m²)	❷ €43.95	

🚗 From the A9 to Avignon. Campsite located on l'Île de la Barthelasse, opposite the Papal Palace. Campsite indicated on the bridge.

📖 Camping Bagatelle is located close to the old centre of Avignon, just a 7-minute walk over the bridge. Lovely views of the Palais des Papes from the terraces.

CC 1/1-30/6 18/8-30/12 7=6, 14=11, 28=21

▨ N 43°57'10'' E 4°47'59''

www.eurocampings.co.uk/112006

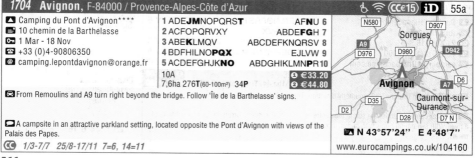

1704 Avignon, F-84000 / Provence-Alpes-Côte d'Azur ♿ ≈ (CC€15) iD 55a

- ▲ Camping du Pont d'Avignon****
- 🏠 10 chemin de la Barthelasse
- 🗓 1 Mar - 18 Nov
- ☎ +33 (0)4-90806350
- @ camping.lepontdavignon@orange.fr

1 ADEJMNOPQRST	AFNU	6
2 ACFOPQRVXY	ABDEFGH	7
3 ABEKLMQV	ABCDEFKNQRSV	8
4 BDFHILNOPQX	EJLVW	9
5 ACDEFGHJKNO	ABDGHIKLMNPR	10
10A	❶ €33.20	
7,6ha 276T(60-100m²) 34P	❷ €44.80	

🚗 From Remoulins and A9 turn right beyond the bridge. Follow 'Île de la Barthelasse' signs.

📖 A campsite in an attractive parkland setting, located opposite the Pont d'Avignon with views of the Palais des Papes.

CC 1/3-7/7 25/8-17/11 7=6, 14=11

▨ N 43°57'24'' E 4°48'7''

www.eurocampings.co.uk/104160

1705 Bédoin, F-84410 / Provence-Alpes-Côte d'Azur ♿ 📶 (CC€15) iD 55a

- ⛺ Camping Le Pastory**
- 🏠 1105 route de Malaucène
- 📅 1 Apr - 16 Oct
- ☎ +33 (0)4-90128583
- @ info@camping-le-pastory.com

1 ABDE**JM**NOPRS**T**		6
2 FPRSVWXY	ABDEF	7
3 ALQ	ABCDEFNRTU	8
4 D	E	9
5 ABDFGO	ABHJL**PV**	10
10A CEE	❶ €20.10	
A350 1,6ha 90**T**(100-130m²) 20**P**	❷ €26.10	

🚗 A7 exit Orange-Sud to Carpentras direction Bédoin. In centre of Bédoin follow signs.

💬 Ideal location at the foot of Mont Ventoux, 900 m from the Provence village of Bédoin. Le Pastory offers spacious, shaded pitches with a breathtaking view of Mont Ventoux. There is nature all around. Typical Provence market in Bédoin on Monday mornings. Swimming is possible in the surrounding lakes and the local swimming pool near the campsite.

(CC) 1/4-30/6 1/9-15/10 14=12, 30=26

📍 N 44°7'54'' E 5°10'15''

www.eurocampings.co.uk/120040

1706 Bollène, F-84500 / Provence-Alpes-Côte d'Azur ♿ 📶 (CC€15) iD 55a

- ⛺ La Simioune***
- 🏠 route de l'embisque
- 📅 1 Mar - 25 Oct
- ☎ +33 (0)4-90631791
- @ camping@la-simioune.fr

1 ADE**JM**NOPQRST	AF	6
2 ABFQRSUVWXY	ABDEFH	7
3 BEHLQS	ABCDEFKNRSTV	8
4 ABFGIKO	BEJKU	9
5 ABEFGHKMNO	ABHIJPTV	10
10A CEE	❶ €24.10	
A150 3ha 80**T**(100-200m²) 22**P**	❷ €31.60	

🚗 Leave A7 at Bollène. To roundabout direction Carpentras and follow signs from there (direction Suze la Rousse).

💬 A typically French, hospitable and natural campsite with spacious pitches. Located just outside the town of Bollène in a wood with tall pine trees. Close to Parcours Aventure (clambering and climbing). Wifi free at the campsite.

(CC) 1/3-6/7 24/8-24/10 15=13, 30=25

📍 N 44°17'50'' E 4°47'15''

www.eurocampings.co.uk/104152

1707 Carpentras, F-84200 / Provence-Alpes-Côte d'Azur ♿ 📶 (CC€15) 👬 iD 55a

- ⛺ Flower Camping Lou Comtadou***
- 🏠 881 av. Pierre de Coubertin
- 📅 15 Mar - 15 Oct
- ☎ +33 (0)4-90670316
- @ info@campingloucomtadou.com

1 AD**JM**NOPRST	AB**FH**	6
2 GPVXY	ABDE**F**	7
3 ABQ	ABCDFNRST	8
4 IO**P**	AE	9
5 ABDEFHKN	ABGHIJPTU	10
6A CEE	❶ €29.70	
A76 2ha 97**T**(100-110m²) 31**P**	❷ €40.70	

🚗 Follow ring road before Carpentras, then direction St. Didier. Right at second lights and follow signs. Left at sports complex on leaving the town.

💬 A campsite with lovely marked-out pitches and plenty of sun and shade. Good amenities and simple restaurant. Bus stop next to the site. Close to town centre with a large market on Fridays. Good paved roads.

(CC) 15/3-7/7 25/8-14/10 7=6, 14=11

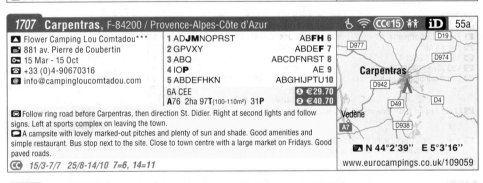

📍 N 44°2'39'' E 5°3'16''

www.eurocampings.co.uk/109059

1708 Cavaillon, F-84300 / Provence-Alpes-Côte d'Azur ♿ 📶 (CC€15) iD 55a

- ⛺ de la Durance***
- 🏠 495 avenue Boscodomini
- 📅 1 Apr - 30 Sep
- ☎ +33 (0)4-90711178
- @ contact@camping-durance.com

1 ADE**JM**NOPRST		6
2 APQRVWXY	ABDE**FG**H	7
3 AELM	ABCDFJNOPRSTUV	8
4	AEJ	9
5 ADE**NO**	ABDGHIO**PR**	10
4-12A CEE	❶ €18.60	
4ha 79**T**(80-120m²) 21**P**	❷ €24.20	

🚗 Take exit 25 to Cavaillon on the A7. Cross the River Durance. Right at the roundabout. Then follow camping signs.

💬 A campsite on the edge of the village of Cavaillon in the heart of Provence, between Alpilles and Luberon. In a park with plane trees. You will also be welcomed in English, German or Dutch.

(CC) 1/4-7/7 25/8-29/9

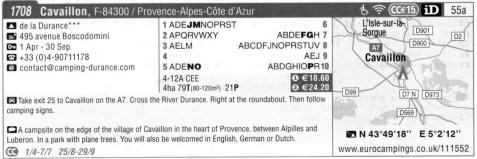

📍 N 43°49'18'' E 5°2'12''

www.eurocampings.co.uk/111552

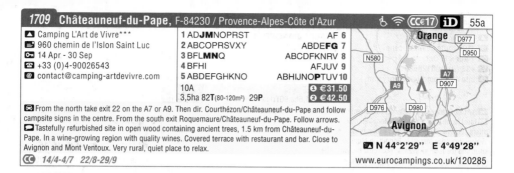

1709 Châteauneuf-du-Pape, F-84230 / Provence-Alpes-Côte d'Azur 🚍 🛜 (CC€17) iD 55a

Orange

- 🏕 Camping L'Art de Vivre***
- 🏠 960 chemin de l'Islon Saint Luc
- 🗓 14 Apr - 30 Sep
- ☎ +33 (0)4-90026543
- @ contact@camping-artdevivre.com

1 ADJMNOPRST	AF	6
2 ABCOPRSVXY	ABDEFG	7
3 BFLMNQ	ABCDFKNRV	8
4 BFHI	AFJUV	9
5 ABDEFGHKNO	ABHIJNOPTUV	10
10A	❶ €31.50	
3,5ha 82T(80-120m²) 29P	❷ €42.50	

🚗 From the north take exit 22 on the A7 or A9. Then dir. Courthézon/Châteauneuf-du-Pape and follow campsite signs in the centre. From the south exit Roquemaure/Châteauneuf-du-Pape. Follow arrows.
💬 Tastefully refurbished site in open wood containing ancient trees, 1.5 km from Châteauneuf-du-Pape. In a wine-growing region with quality wines. Covered terrace with restaurant and bar. Close to Avignon and Mont Ventoux. Very rural, quiet place to relax.
CC 14/4-4/7 22/8-29/9

📍 N 44°2'29" E 4°49'28"

www.eurocampings.co.uk/120285

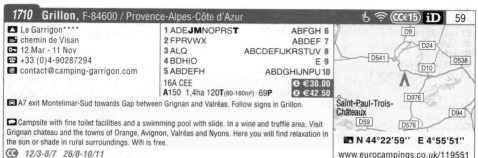

1710 Grillon, F-84600 / Provence-Alpes-Côte d'Azur 🚍 🛜 (CC€15) iD 59

- 🏕 Le Garrigon****
- 🏠 chemin de Visan
- 🗓 12 Mar - 11 Nov
- ☎ +33 (0)4-90287294
- @ contact@camping-garrigon.com

1 ADEJMNOPRST	ABFGH	6
2 FPRVWX	ABDEF	7
3 ALQ	ABCDEFIJKRSTUV	8
4 BDHIO	E	9
5 ABDEFH	ABDGHIJNPU	10
16A CEE	❶ €30.00	
A150 1,4ha 120T(80-160m²) 69P	❷ €42.50	

🚗 A7 exit Montelimar-Sud towards Gap between Grignan and Valréas. Follow signs in Grillon.

💬 Campsite with fine toilet facilities and a swimming pool with slide. In a wine and truffle area. Visit Grignan chateau and the towns of Orange, Avignon, Valréas and Nyons. Here you will find relaxation in the sun or shade in rural surroundings. Wifi is free.
CC 12/3-8/7 26/8-10/11

Saint-Paul-Trois-Châteaux

📍 N 44°22'59" E 4°55'51"

www.eurocampings.co.uk/119551

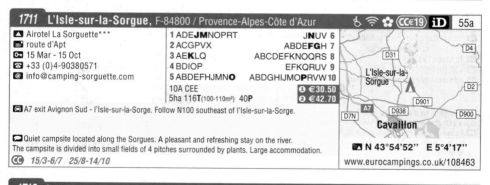

1711 L'Isle-sur-la-Sorgue, F-84800 / Provence-Alpes-Côte d'Azur 🚍 🛜 ❄ (CC€19) iD 55a

- 🏕 Airotel La Sorguette***
- 🏠 route d'Apt
- 🗓 15 Mar - 15 Oct
- ☎ +33 (0)4-90380571
- @ info@camping-sorguette.com

1 ADEJMNOPRT	JNUV	6
2 ACGPVX	ABDEFGH	7
3 AEKLQ	ABCDEFKNOQRS	8
4 BDIOP	EFKQRUV	9
5 ABDEFHJMNO	ABDGHIJMOPRVW	10
10A CEE	❶ €30.50	
5ha 116T(100-110m²) 40P	❷ €42.70	

🚗 A7 exit Avignon Sud - l'Isle-sur-la-Sorgue. Follow N100 southeast of l'Isle-sur-la-Sorgue.

💬 Quiet campsite located along the Sorgues. A pleasant and refreshing stay on the river. The campsite is divided into small fields of 4 pitches surrounded by plants. Large accommodation.
CC 15/3-6/7 25/8-14/10

L'Isle-sur-la-Sorgue

Cavaillon

📍 N 43°54'52" E 5°4'17"

www.eurocampings.co.uk/108463

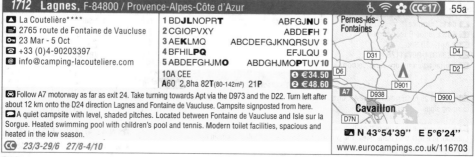

1712 Lagnes, F-84800 / Provence-Alpes-Côte d'Azur 🚍 🛜 ❄ (CC€17) 55a

Pernes-les-Fontaines

- 🏕 La Coutelière****
- 🏠 2765 route de Fontaine de Vaucluse
- 🗓 23 Mar - 5 Oct
- ☎ +33 (0)4-90203397
- @ info@camping-lacouteliere.com

1 BDJLNOPRT	ABFGJNU	6
2 CGIOPVXY	ABDEFH	7
3 AEKLMQ	ABCDEFGJKNQRSUV	8
4 BFHILPQ	EFJLQU	9
5 ABDEFGHJMO	ABDGHJMOPTUV	10
10A CEE	❶ €34.50	
A60 2,8ha 82T(80-142m²) 21P	❷ €48.60	

🚗 Follow A7 motorway as far as exit 24. Take turning towards Apt via the D973 and the D22. Turn left after about 12 km onto the D24 direction Lagnes and Fontaine de Vaucluse. Campsite signposted from here.
💬 A quiet campsite with level, shaded pitches. Located between Fontaine de Vaucluse and Isle sur la Sorgue. Heated swimming pool with children's pool and tennis. Modern toilet facilities, spacious and heated in the low season.
CC 23/3-29/6 27/8-4/10

Cavaillon

📍 N 43°54'39" E 5°6'24"

www.eurocampings.co.uk/116703

France

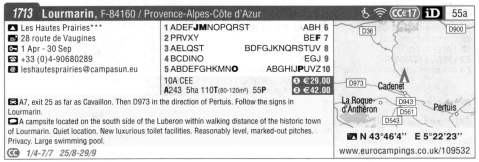

1713 Lourmarin, F-84160 / Provence-Alpes-Côte d'Azur

⛺ 🛜 (CC€17) iD 55a

- ⛺ Les Hautes Prairies***
- ✉ 28 route de Vaugines
- 🗓 1 Apr - 30 Sep
- ☎ +33 (0)4-90680289
- @ leshautesprairies@campasun.eu

1	ADEF**JM**NOPQRST	ABH 6
2	PRVXY	BE**F** 7
3	AELQST	BDFGJKNQRSTUV 8
4	BCDINO	EGJ 9
5	ABDEFGHKMN**O**	ABGHIJ**P**UVZ 10
10A CEE		❶ €29.00
A243 5ha 110**T**(80-120m²) 55**P**		❷ €42.00

🚗 A7, exit 25 as far as Cavaillon. Then D973 in the direction of Pertuis. Follow the signs in Lourmarin.

💬 A campsite located on the south side of the Luberon within walking distance of the historic town of Lourmarin. Quiet location. New luxurious toilet facilities. Reasonably level, marked-out pitches. Privacy. Large swimming pool.

CC 1/4-7/7 25/8-29/9

📍 N 43°46'4'' E 5°22'23''

www.eurocampings.co.uk/109532

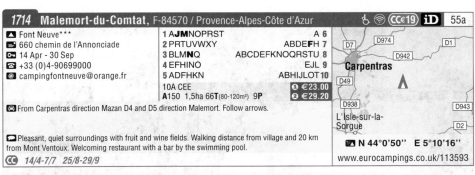

1714 Malemort-du-Comtat, F-84570 / Provence-Alpes-Côte d'Azur

⛺ 🛜 (CC€19) iD 55a

- ⛺ Font Neuve***
- ✉ 660 chemin de l'Annonciade
- 🗓 14 Apr - 30 Sep
- ☎ +33 (0)4-90699000
- @ campingfontneuve@orange.fr

1	A**JM**NOPRST	A 6
2	PRTUVWXY	ABDE**F**H 7
3	BLM**NQ**	ABCDEFKNOQRSTU 8
4	EFHINO	EJL 9
5	ADFHKN	ABHIJLOT 10
10A CEE		❶ €23.00
A150 1,5ha 66**T**(80-120m²) 9**P**		❷ €29.20

🚗 From Carpentras direction Mazan D4 and D5 direction Malemort. Follow arrows.

💬 Pleasant, quiet surroundings with fruit and wine fields. Walking distance from village and 20 km from Mont Ventoux. Welcoming restaurant with a bar by the swimming pool.

CC 14/4-7/7 25/8-29/9

📍 N 44°0'50'' E 5°10'16''

www.eurocampings.co.uk/113593

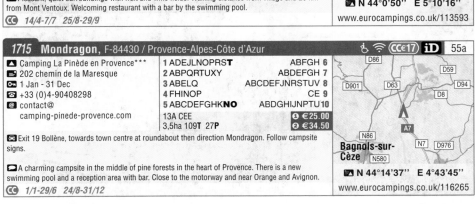

1715 Mondragon, F-84430 / Provence-Alpes-Côte d'Azur

⛺ 🛜 (CC€17) iD 55a

- ⛺ Camping La Pinède en Provence***
- ✉ 202 chemin de la Maresque
- 🗓 1 Jan - 31 Dec
- ☎ +33 (0)4-90408298
- @ contact@camping-pinede-provence.com

1	ADEJLNOPRS**T**	ABFGH 6
2	ABPQRTUXY	ABDEFGH 7
3	ABELQ	ABCDEFJNRSTUV 8
4	FHINOP	CE 9
5	ABCDEFGHK**NO**	ABDGHIJNPTU 10
13A CEE		❶ €25.00
3,5ha 109**T** 27**P**		❷ €34.50

🚗 Exit 19 Bollène, towards town centre at roundabout then direction Mondragon. Follow campsite signs.

💬 A charming campsite in the middle of pine forests in the heart of Provence. There is a new swimming pool and a reception area with bar. Close to the motorway and near Orange and Avignon.

CC 1/1-29/6 24/8-31/12

📍 N 44°14'37'' E 4°43'45''

www.eurocampings.co.uk/116265

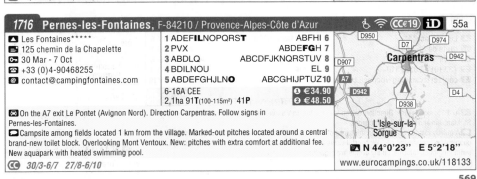

1716 Pernes-les-Fontaines, F-84210 / Provence-Alpes-Côte d'Azur

⛺ 🛜 (CC€19) iD 55a

- ⛺ Les Fontaines*****
- ✉ 125 chemin de la Chapelette
- 🗓 30 Mar - 7 Oct
- ☎ +33 (0)4-90468255
- @ contact@campingfontaines.com

1	ADEF**IL**NOPQRS**T**	ABFHI 6
2	PVX	ABDE**FG**H 7
3	ABDLQ	ABCDFJKNQRSTUV 8
4	BDILNOU	EL 9
5	ABDEFGHJLN**O**	ABCGHIJPTUZ 10
6-16A CEE		❶ €34.90
2,1ha 91**T**(100-115m²) 41**P**		❷ €48.50

🚗 On the A7 exit Le Pontet (Avignon Nord). Direction Carpentras. Follow signs in Pernes-les-Fontaines.

💬 Campsite among fields located 1 km from the village. Marked-out pitches located around a central brand-new toilet block. Overlooking Mont Ventoux. New: pitches with extra comfort at additional fee. New aquapark with heated swimming pool.

CC 30/3-6/7 27/8-6/10

📍 N 44°0'23'' E 5°2'18''

www.eurocampings.co.uk/118133

France

In the heart of the **Ochres du Luberon** and at the foot of the Mont **Ventoux**

CHÊNES BLANCS ★★★

☏ +33 (0)4 88 70 00 07   ✉ contact@leschenesblancs.com   🌐 www.leschenesblancs.com

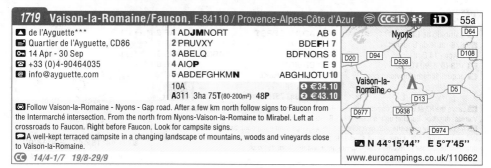

1719 Vaison-la-Romaine/Faucon, F-84110 / Provence-Alpes-Côte d'Azur 🛜 (CC€15) ⚐ iD 55a

- 🏕 de l'Ayguette***
- 🏠 Quartier de l'Ayguette, CD86
- 📅 14 Apr - 30 Sep
- ☎ +33 (0)4-90464035
- @ info@ayguette.com

1 AD**JM**NORT	AB	6
2 PRUVXY	BDE**F**H	7
3 ABELQ	BDFNORS	8
4 AIO**P**	E	9
5 ABDEFGHKM**N**	ABGHIJOTU	10
10A	❶ €34.10	
A311 3ha 75**T**(80-200m²) 48**P**	❷ €43.10	

🚗 Follow Vaison-la-Romaine - Nyons - Gap road. After a few km north follow signs to Faucon from the Intermarché intersection. From the north from Nyons-Vaison-la-Romaine to Mirabel. Left at crossroads to Faucon. Right before Faucon. Look for campsite signs.

💬 A well-kept terraced campsite in a changing landscape of mountains, woods and vineyards close to Vaison-la-Romaine.

CC 14/4-1/7 19/8-29/9

🧭 N 44°15'44'' E 5°7'45''

www.eurocampings.co.uk/110662

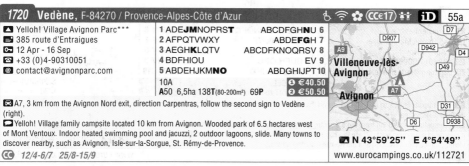

1720 Vedène, F-84270 / Provence-Alpes-Côte d'Azur ♿🛜❄ (CC€17) ⚐ iD 55a

- 🏕 Yelloh! Village Avignon Parc***
- 🏠 385 route d'Entraigues
- 📅 12 Apr - 16 Sep
- ☎ +33 (0)4-90310051
- @ contact@avignonparc.com

1 ADE**JM**NOPRS**T**	ABCDFGH**N**U	6
2 AFPQTVWXY	ABDE**FG**H	7
3 AEGH**K**LQTV	ABCDFKNOQRSV	8
4 BDFHIOU	EV	9
5 ABDEHJKM**NO**	ABDGHIJPT	10
10A	❶ €40.50	
A50 6,5ha 138**T**(80-200m²) 69**P**	❷ €50.50	

🚗 A7, 3 km from the Avignon Nord exit, direction Carpentras, follow the second sign to Vedène (right).

💬 Yelloh! Village family campsite located 10 km from Avignon. Wooded park of 6.5 hectares west of Mont Ventoux. Indoor heated swimming pool and jacuzzi, 2 outdoor lagoons, slide. Many towns to discover nearby, such as Avignon, Isle-sur-la-Sorgue, St. Rémy-de-Provence.

CC 12/4-6/7 25/8-15/9

🧭 N 43°59'25'' E 4°54'49''

www.eurocampings.co.uk/112721

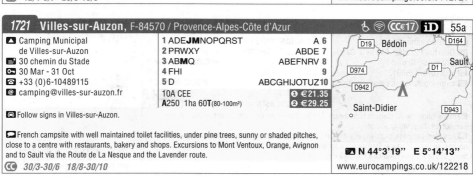

1721 Villes-sur-Auzon, F-84570 / Provence-Alpes-Côte d'Azur ♿🛜 (CC€17) iD 55a

- 🏕 Camping Municipal de Villes-sur-Auzon
- 🏠 30 chemin du Stade
- 📅 30 Mar - 31 Oct
- ☎ +33 (0)6-10489115
- @ camping@villes-sur-auzon.fr

1 ADE**JM**NOPQRST	A	6
2 PRWXY	ABDE	7
3 AB**M**Q	ABEFNRV	8
4 FHI		9
5 D	ABCGHIJOTUZ	10
10A CEE	❶ €21.35	
A250 1ha 60**T**(80-100m²)	❷ €29.25	

🚗 Follow signs in Villes-sur-Auzon.

💬 French campsite with well maintained toilet facilities, under pine trees, sunny or shaded pitches, close to a centre with restaurants, bakery and shops. Excursions to Mont Ventoux, Orange, Avignon and to Sault via the Route de La Nesque and the Lavender route.

CC 30/3-30/6 18/8-30/10

🧭 N 44°3'19'' E 5°14'13''

www.eurocampings.co.uk/122218

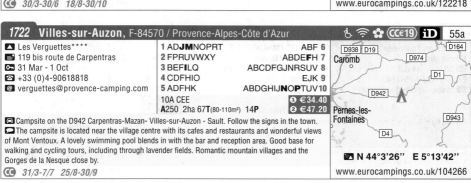

1722 Villes-sur-Auzon, F-84570 / Provence-Alpes-Côte d'Azur ♿🛜❄ (CC€19) iD 55a

- 🏕 Les Verguettes****
- 🏠 119 bis route de Carpentras
- 📅 31 Mar - 1 Oct
- ☎ +33 (0)4-90618818
- @ verguettes@provence-camping.com

1 AD**JM**NOPRT	ABF	6
2 FPRUVWXY	ABDE**F**H	7
3 BEF**I**LQ	ABCDFGJNRSUV	8
4 CDFHIO	EJK	9
5 ADFHK	ABDGHIJ**NOP**TUV	10
10A CEE	❶ €34.40	
A250 2ha 67**T**(80-110m²) 14**P**	❷ €47.20	

🚗 Campsite on the D942 Carpentras-Mazan- Villes-sur-Auzon - Sault. Follow the signs in the town.

💬 The campsite is located near the village centre with its cafes and restaurants and wonderful views of Mont Ventoux. A lovely swimming pool blends in with the bar and reception area. Good base for walking and cycling tours, including through lavender fields. Romantic mountain villages and the Gorges de la Nesque close by.

CC 31/3-7/7 25/8-30/9

🧭 N 44°3'26'' E 5°13'42''

www.eurocampings.co.uk/104266

1723 Visan, F-84820 / Provence-Alpes-Côte d'Azur ⚐ 📶 (CC€15) ⚥ iD 59

- ⛺ Camping de L'Hérein***
- ✉ 879 route de Bouchet
- 📅 6 Apr - 14 Oct
- ☎ +33 (0)4-90419599
- @ accueil@campingvisan.com

1 ADJMNOPRS**T**	AF	6
2 GPRVXY	ABDE**F**	7
3 BEQT	ABCDFKNORS	8
4 BDEIO**P**	E	9
5 ABDEFGHJKL	ABHIJPTU	10
6-16A CEE	❶ €22.00	
A200 3ha 75T(80-300m²) 31P	❷ €27.80	

🔲 Leave the A7 at Bollène, direction Suze-la-Rousse. At Tulette to Visan, then via signposts to Valreas, direction Bouchet on the route Visan-Bouche on the D161.

💬 A quiet family campsite with new toilet facilities, a large swimming pool, bar and new restaurant. Wifi on the entire site is free. Small shop selling fresh fruit from the site's orchard. Plenty of cycling opportunities, close to Nyons, Vaison-la-Romaine and the Mont Ventoux.

CC 6/4-5/7 23/8-13/10 21=18

⬛ N 44°18'44" E 4°56'9"

www.eurocampings.co.uk/104261

1724 Arles/Pont-de-Crau, F-13200 / Provence-Alpes-Côte d'Azur ⚐ 📶 (CC€17) ⚥ iD 55a

- ⛺ L'Arlesienne***
- ✉ 145 Draille Marseillaise
- 📅 1 Apr - 1 Nov
- ☎ +33 (0)4-90960212
- @ camping@larlesienne.com

1 ABDEF**JM**NOPQRST	ABFGH**N**	6
2 AOPQRVWX	ABDEF	7
3 A**K**LQT	ABCDFKNRSV	8
4 BDFHIO**PU**	EUV	9
5 ADEFGHJK**O**	ABDFGHJO**P**TU	10
6-10A CEE	❶ €28.20	
2,2ha 74T(80-90m²) 34P	❷ €39.50	

🔲 The campsite is located in Pont-de-Crau on the south-eastern edge of Arles, direction St. Martin-de-Crau. Signposted.

💬 A campsite located 3 km from the old centre of Arles. Attractive pitches, the campsite has lovely modernised swimming pools. There is a bus stop 200 metres from the site. Many activities in the vicinity, famous for Van Gogh and the Romans, among others.

CC 1/4-6/7 24/8-31/10 7=6

⬛ N 43°39'34" E 4°39'15"

www.eurocampings.co.uk/110354

1725 Beaurecueil, F-13100 / Provence-Alpes-Côte d'Azur 📶 (CC€17) iD 27 A2

- ⛺ Sainte Victoire**
- ✉ Quartier Paradou, 613 av J. Gautier
- 📅 5 Mar - 30 Nov
- ☎ +33 (0)4-42669131
- @ campingstevictoire@orange.fr

1 A**JM**NOPRST		6
2 ABCFGIORVWXY	ABDE**FH**	7
3 ALS	ABCDEFIJNORV	8
4 O	AEU	9
5 ABDGHM**O**	ABDGJ**NP**TU	10
6A CEE	❶ €21.50	
A253 2ha 85T(80-170m²) 27P	❷ €32.10	

🔲 In Aix follow the A8 towards Nice/Toulon. Exit 31. Then right and right again towards Palette/Beaurecueil. Then follow arrows.

💬 A modest campsite, picturesquely located at the foot of Sainte Victoire. Marked-out, shaded pitches, an oasis of peace. Starting point for lovely walks or for visiting Aix-en-Provence just 8 km away. Bus to Aix-en-Provence 13 times a day.

CC 1/4-6/7 25/8-14/10

⬛ N 43°31'2" E 5°32'26"

www.eurocampings.co.uk/113583

1726 Fontvieille, F-13990 / Provence-Alpes-Côte d'Azur 📶 (CC€17) iD 55a

- ⛺ Huttopia Fontvieille***
- ✉ rue Michelet
- 📅 30 Mar - 14 Oct
- ☎ +33 (0)4-90547869
- @ fontvieille@huttopia.com

1 ADE**JM**NOPQRST		6
2 BPQRTVWX	ABDE**FGH**	7
3 AE**K**LQ	ABCDEFNOQRSUV	8
4 FHIO		9
5 ADN	ABHIJPTU	10
6A	❶ €21.10	
4ha 150T(70-100m²)	❷ €23.10	

🔲 D33 from Avignon direction Arles. Campsite signposted in Fontvieille.

💬 Natural, quiet, basic campsite at walking distance from a lovely Provence village which is well known for Alphonse Daudet's mill, with nice restaurants.

CC 30/3-28/6 2/9-13/10

⬛ N 43°43'25" E 4°43'7"

www.eurocampings.co.uk/109530

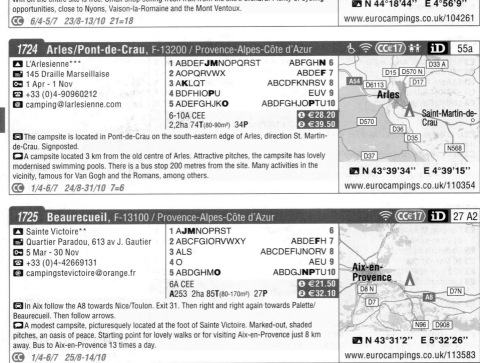

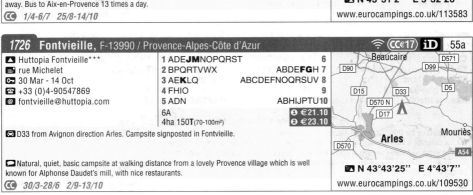

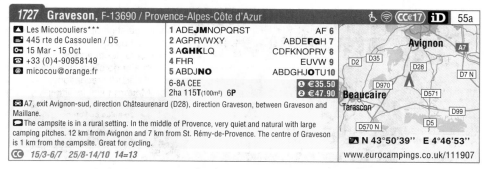

1727 Graveson, F-13690 / Provence-Alpes-Côte d'Azur

🚹 📶 (CC€17) iD 55a

- 🏕 Les Micocouliers***
- 📧 445 rte de Cassoulen / D5
- 📅 15 Mar - 15 Oct
- ☎ +33 (0)4-90958149
- @ micocou@orange.fr

1 ADE**JM**NOPQRST	AF	6
2 AGPRVWXY	ABDE**FG**H	7
3 A**GHK**LQ	CDFKNOPRV	8
4 FHR	EUVW	9
5 ABDJ**NO**	ABDGHJ**O**TU	10
6-8A CEE	❶ €35.50	
2ha 115**T**(100m²) 6**P**	❷ €47.90	

🚗 A7, exit Avignon-sud, direction Châteaurenard (D28), direction Graveson, between Graveson and Maillane.

💬 The campsite is in a rural setting. In the middle of Provence, very quiet and natural with large camping pitches. 12 km from Avignon and 7 km from St. Rémy-de-Provence. The centre of Graveson is 1 km from the campsite. Great for cycling.

(CC) 15/3-6/7 25/8-14/10 14=13

📍 N 43°50'39'' E 4°46'53''

www.eurocampings.co.uk/111907

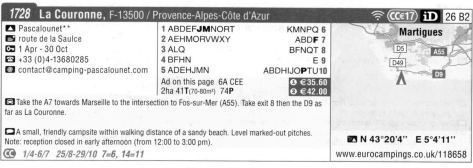

1728 La Couronne, F-13500 / Provence-Alpes-Côte d'Azur

📶 (CC€17) iD 26 B2

- 🏕 Pascalounet**
- 📧 route de la Saulce
- 📅 1 Apr - 30 Oct
- ☎ +33 (0)4-13680285
- @ contact@camping-pascalounet.com

1 ABDEF**JM**NORT	KMNPQ	6
2 AEHMORVWXY	ABD**F**	7
3 ALQ	BFNQT	8
4 BFHN	E	9
5 ADEHJMN	ABDHIJ**O**P TU	10
Ad on this page 6A CEE	❶ €35.60	
2ha 41**T**(70-80m²) 74**P**	❷ €42.00	

🚗 Take the A7 towards Marseille to the intersection to Fos-sur-Mer (A55). Take exit 8 then the D9 as far as La Couronne.

💬 A small, friendly campsite within walking distance of a sandy beach. Level marked-out pitches. Note: reception closed in early afternoon (from 12:00 to 3:00 pm).

(CC) 1/4-6/7 25/8-29/10 7=6, 14=11

📍 N 43°20'4'' E 5°4'11''

www.eurocampings.co.uk/118658

France

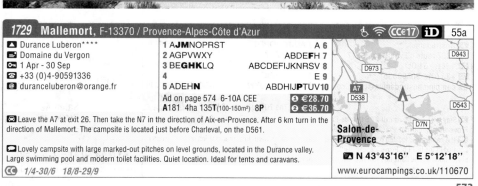

1729 Mallemort, F-13370 / Provence-Alpes-Côte d'Azur

🚹 📶 (CC€17) iD 55a

- 🏕 Durance Luberon****
- 📧 Domaine du Vergon
- 📅 1 Apr - 30 Sep
- ☎ +33 (0)4-90591336
- @ duranceluberon@orange.fr

1 A**JM**NOPRST	A	6
2 AGPVWXY	ABDE**F**H	7
3 BE**GHK**LQ	ABCDEFIJKNRSV	8
4	E	9
5 ADEH**N**	ABDHIJ**P**TUV	10
Ad on page 574 6-10A CEE	❶ €28.70	
A181 4ha 135**T**(100-150m²) 8**P**	❷ €36.70	

🚗 Leave the A7 at exit 26. Then take the N7 in the direction of Aix-en-Provence. After 6 km turn in the direction of Mallemort. The campsite is located just before Charleval, on the D561.

💬 Lovely campsite with large marked-out pitches on level grounds, located in the Durance valley. Large swimming pool and modern toilet facilities. Quiet location. Ideal for tents and caravans.

(CC) 1/4-30/6 18/8-29/9

📍 N 43°43'16'' E 5°12'18''

www.eurocampings.co.uk/110670

France

1730 Maussane-les-Alpilles, F-13520 / Provence-Alpes-Côte d'Azur   ♿ 🛜 (CC€17) iD   55a

▲ Les Romarins***
🚐 15 Mar - 3 Nov
☎ +33 (0)4-90543360
@ camping-municipal-maussane@
   wanadoo.fr

1 ADE**JM**NOPQRT	AF**N**	6
2 PRVWXY	ABDE**FGH**	7
3 A**KL**MQ	ABCDEFJKNQRSTUV	8
4 FHIO**P**	UVW	9
5 ABDN	ABDHIJPRVZ	10

10A CEE   ❶ €28.45
3ha 145**T**(70-100m²)   ❷ €32.15

🅿 The campsite is located on the D5. From Maussane via D17 direction Arles, then the D5. Located near the centre on the St. Rémy side.
🛏 Quiet, green campsite 200 m from the centre of a beautiful, authentic Provence village with a lovely shaded church square in the south of Les Alpilles. Heated indoor pool, open from 15 April to 15 October. Several bakers and restaurants in the village.
(CC) 3/4-30/4   14/5-30/6   1/9-2/11

Tarascon   D99
D33   D5
D570 N
Arles   Raphèle-les-Arles
A54   D113

🧭 N 43°43'16"   E 4°48'34"
www.eurocampings.co.uk/100523

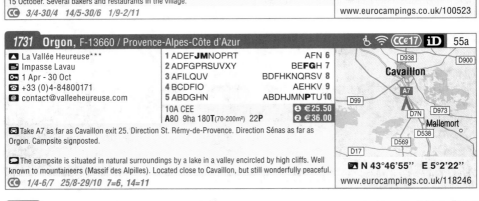

1731 Orgon, F-13660 / Provence-Alpes-Côte d'Azur   ♿ 🛜 (CC€17) iD   55a

▲ La Vallée Heureuse***
📧 Impasse Lavau
🚐 1 Apr - 30 Oct
☎ +33 (0)4-84800171
@ contact@valleeheureuse.com

1 ADEF**JM**NOPRT	AFN	6
2 ADFGPRSUVXY	BE**FGH**	7
3 AFILQUV	BDFHKNQRSV	8
4 BCDFIO	AEHKV	9
5 ABDGHN	ABDHJMN**P**TU	10

10A CEE   ❶ €25.50
A80 9ha 180**T**(70-200m²) 22**P**   ❷ €36.00

🅿 Take A7 as far as Cavaillon exit 25. Direction St. Rémy-de-Provence. Direction Sénas as far as Orgon. Campsite signposted.

🛏 The campsite is situated in natural surroundings by a lake in a valley encircled by high cliffs. Well known to mountaineers (Massif des Alpilles). Located close to Cavaillon, but still wonderfully peaceful.
(CC) 1/4-6/7   25/8-29/10   7=6, 14=11

D938   D900
Cavaillon
A7
D99   D7N   D973
   Mallemort
   D538
D17   D569

🧭 N 43°46'55"   E 5°2'22"
www.eurocampings.co.uk/118246

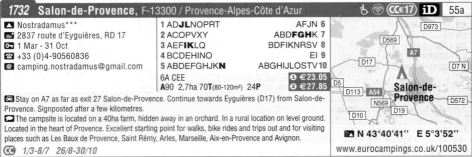

1732 Salon-de-Provence, F-13300 / Provence-Alpes-Côte d'Azur   ♿ 🛜 (CC€17) iD   55a

▲ Nostradamus***
📧 2837 route d'Eyguières, RD 17
🚐 1 Mar - 31 Oct
☎ +33 (0)4-90560836
@ camping.nostradamus@gmail.com

1 AD**JL**NOPRT	AFJN	6
2 ACOPVXY	ABD**FGH**K	7
3 AEF**I**KLQ	BDFIKNRSV	8
4 BCDEHINO	EI	9
5 ABDEFGHJK**N**	ABGHIJLOSTV	10

6A CEE   ❶ €23.05
A90 2,7ha 70**T**(80-120m²) 24**P**   ❷ €27.85

🅿 Stay on A7 as far as exit 27 Salon-de-Provence. Continue towards Eyguières (D17) from Salon-de-Provence. Signposted after a few kilometres.
🛏 The campsite is located on a 40ha farm, hidden away in an orchard. In a rural location on level ground. Located in the heart of Provence. Excellent starting point for walks, bike rides and trips out and for visiting places such as Les Baux de Provence, Saint Rémy, Arles, Marseille, Aix-en-Provence and Avignon.
(CC) 1/3-8/7   26/8-30/10

D973
D569
D17   A7   D7 N
D5   D113 A54
N569   **Salon-de-Provence**   D572
D10   D19

🧭 N 43°40'41"   E 5°3'52"
www.eurocampings.co.uk/100530

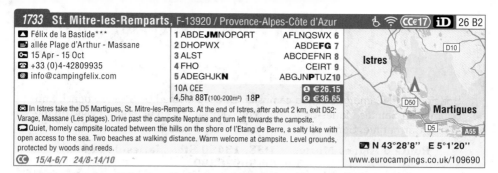

1733 St. Mitre-les-Remparts, F-13920 / Provence-Alpes-Côte d'Azur ♿ 📶 CC€17 iD 26 B2

- 🏕 Félix de la Bastide***
- 📧 allée Plage d'Arthur - Massane
- 📅 15 Apr - 15 Oct
- ☎ +33 (0)4-42809935
- @ info@campingfelix.com

1 ABDE**JM**NOPQRT	AFLNQSWX 6
2 DHOPWX	ABDE**FG** 7
3 ALST	ABCDEFNR 8
4 FHO	CEIRT 9
5 ADEGHJK**N**	ABGJN**P**TUZ10
10A CEE	❶ €26.15
4,5ha 88T(100-200m²) 18P	❷ €36.65

Istres · Martigues

🚗 In Istres take the D5 Martigues, St. Mitre-les-Remparts. At the end of Istres, after about 2 km, exit D52: Varage, Massane (Les plages). Drive past the campsite Neptune and turn left towards the campsite.
💬 Quiet, homely campsite located between the hills on the shore of l'Etang de Berre, a salty lake with open access to the sea. Two beaches at walking distance. Warm welcome at campsite. Level grounds, protected by woods and reeds.

◎ 15/4-6/7 24/8-14/10

🗺 N 43°28'8'' E 5°1'20''
www.eurocampings.co.uk/109690

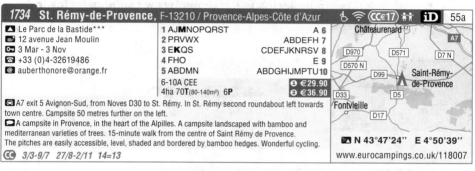

1734 St. Rémy-de-Provence, F-13210 / Provence-Alpes-Côte d'Azur ♿ 📶 CC€17 ♨ iD 55a

- 🏕 Le Parc de la Bastide***
- 📧 12 avenue Jean Moulin
- 📅 3 Mar - 3 Nov
- ☎ +33 (0)4-32619486
- @ auberthonore@orange.fr

1 AJ**JM**NOPQRST	A 6
2 PRVWX	ABDEFH 7
3 E**K**QS	CDEFJKNRSV 8
4 FHO	E 9
5 ABDMN	ABDGHIJMPTU10
6-10A CEE	❶ €29.90
4ha 70T(80-140m²) 6P	❷ €36.90

Châteaurenard · Saint-Rémy-de-Provence · Fontvieille

🚗 A7 exit 5 Avignon-Sud, from Noves D30 to St. Rémy. In St. Rémy second roundabout left towards town centre. Campsite 50 metres further on the left.
💬 A campsite in Provence, in the heart of the Alpilles. A campsite landscaped with bamboo and mediterranean varieties of trees. 15-minute walk from the centre of Saint Rémy de Provence. The pitches are easily accessible, level, shaded and bordered by bamboo hedges. Wonderful cycling.

◎ 3/3-9/7 27/8-2/11 14=13

🗺 N 43°47'24'' E 4°50'39''
www.eurocampings.co.uk/118007

France

1735 Stes Maries-de-la-Mer, F-13460 / Provence-Alpes-Côte d'Azur ♿ 📶 CC€17 ♨ iD 26 B2

- 🏕 Le Clos du Rhône****
- 📧 route d'Aigues-Mortes, CD38
- 📅 6 Apr - 11 Nov
- ☎ +33 (0)4-90978599
- @ info@camping-leclos.fr

1 ADE**JM**NOPQR**T**	ABFGHKMNOPQRX 6
2 EFHOQVWXY	ABDE**FG**H 7
3 BEGHLQ	ABCDFGIJKNQRSTUV 8
4 BCDFHILNO**PRUVX**Y	BEKLUVW 9
5 ACDEFGHJK**NO**	ABDGHIJLN**P**TUVZ10
Ad on page 576 16A CEE	❶ €33.30
7ha 248T(60-100m²) 124P	❷ €47.10

Saintes-Maries-de-la-Mer

🚗 From Arles beyond Chateau d'Avignon right onto D38c. Left after a few km on D38. Turn right before Stes Maries-de-la-Mer. Campsite signposted.

💬 A spacious campsite in traditional Camargue style. Positioned directly on a fine sandy beach 800 metres from Saintes Maries de la Mer. Views of the Camargue opposite the campsite.

◎ 6/4-8/7 26/8-10/11

🗺 N 43°27'0'' E 4°24'6''
www.eurocampings.co.uk/110569

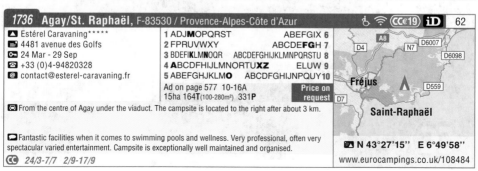

1736 Agay/St. Raphaël, F-83530 / Provence-Alpes-Côte d'Azur ♿ 📶 CC€19 iD 62

- 🏕 Estérel Caravaning*****
- 📧 4481 avenue des Golfs
- 📅 24 Mar - 29 Sep
- ☎ +33 (0)4-94820328
- @ contact@esterel-caravaning.fr

1 ADJ**M**OPQRST	ABEFGIX 6
2 FPRUVWXY	ABCDE**FG**H 7
3 BDEFI**KLMN**OQR	ABCDEFGHIJKLMNPQRSTU 8
4 **A**BCDFHIJLMNORTU**XZ**	ELUW 9
5 ABEFGHJKLM**O**	ABCDFGHIJNPQUY10
Ad on page 577 10-16A	Price on request
15ha 164T(100-280m²) 331P	

Fréjus · Saint-Raphaël

🚗 From the centre of Agay under the viaduct. The campsite is located to the right after about 3 km.

💬 Fantastic facilities when it comes to swimming pools and wellness. Very professional, often very spectacular varied entertainment. Campsite is exceptionally well maintained and organised.

◎ 24/3-7/7 2/9-17/9

🗺 N 43°27'15'' E 6°49'58''
www.eurocampings.co.uk/108484

Le Clos du Rhône

★ ★ ★ ★

Spacious and Camargue-styled campsite. Directly located by a sandy beach and 800m from Saintes-Maries-de-la-Mer. The campsite has a wonderful view on the Carmargue. Some of the pitches have a pergola to provide shade.

Route d'Aigues-Mortes, CD38, 13460 Stes Maries-de-la-Mer
Tel. 04-90978599
E-mail: info@camping-leclos.fr • Internet: www.camping-leclos.fr

France

577

1737 Aiguines, F-83630 / Provence-Alpes-Côte d'Azur   ♿ ⓦ (CCe15) iD   27 A2

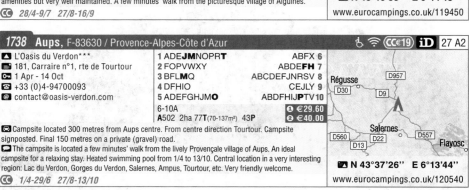

- ⛰ L'Aigle***
- 🏠 Quartier Saint Pierre
- 📅 28 Apr - 17 Sep
- ☎ +33 (0)4-94842375
- @ aigle@campasun.eu

1 ADE**JM**NOPR**T**	X	6
2 BFPTUVWXY	ABDE**FH**	7
3 BLPT	ABDFHNOPRSV	8
4 FHOU	AEF	9
5 ADFGHJKLNO	ABDFGHIJOVW	10
6A CEE	❶ €32.40	
A900 5ha 70**T**(80-120m²) 30**P**	❷ €45.40	

🅿 Campsite located 600 metres east of Aiguines (D19).

💬 A very nicely located campsite with breathtaking panoramas of Lac Sainte Croix. Relatively modest amenities but very well maintained. A few minutes' walk from the picturesque village of Aiguines.

ⓒⓒ 28/4-9/7 27/8-16/9

📍 N 43°46'35'' E 6°14'43''

www.eurocampings.co.uk/119450

1738 Aups, F-83630 / Provence-Alpes-Côte d'Azur   ♿ ⓦ (CCe19) iD   27 A2

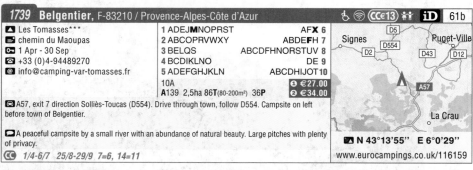

- ⛰ L'Oasis du Verdon***
- 🏠 181, Carraire n°1, rte de Tourtour
- 📅 1 Apr - 14 Oct
- ☎ +33 (0)4-94700093
- @ contact@oasis-verdon.com

1 ADE**JM**NOPR**T**	ABFX	6
2 FOPVWXY	ABDE**FH**	7
3 BFL**MQ**	ABCDEFJNRSV	8
4 DFHIO	CEJLY	9
5 ADEFGHJM**O**	ABDFHIJ**P**TV	10
6-10A	❶ €29.60	
A502 2ha 77**T**(70-137m²) 43**P**	❷ €40.00	

🅿 Campsite located 300 metres from Aups centre. From centre direction Tourtour. Campsite signposted. Final 150 metres on a private (gravel) road.

💬 The campsite is located a few minutes' walk from the lively Provençale village of Aups. An ideal campsite for a relaxing stay. Heated swimming pool from 1/4 to 13/10. Central location in a very interesting region: Lac du Verdon, Gorges du Verdon, Salernes, Ampus, Tourtour, etc. Very friendly welcome.

ⓒⓒ 1/4-29/6 27/8-13/10

📍 N 43°37'26'' E 6°13'44''

www.eurocampings.co.uk/120540

1739 Belgentier, F-83210 / Provence-Alpes-Côte d'Azur   ♿ ⓦ (CCe13) ♟♟ iD   61b

- ⛰ Les Tomasses***
- 🏠 chemin du Maoupas
- 📅 1 Apr - 30 Sep
- ☎ +33 (0)4-94489270
- @ info@camping-var-tomasses.fr

1 ADE**J**M**NOPRST**	AF**X**	6
2 ABCOPRVWXY	ABDE**FH**	7
3 BELQS	ABCDFHNORSTUV	8
4 BCDIKLNO	DE	9
5 ADEFGHJKLN	ABCDHIJOT	10
10A	❶ €27.00	
A139 2,5ha 86**T**(80-200m²) 36**P**	❷ €34.00	

🅿 A57, exit 7 direction Solliès-Toucas (D554). Drive through town, follow D554. Campsite on left before town of Belgentier.

💬 A peaceful campsite by a small river with an abundance of natural beauty. Large pitches with plenty of privacy.

ⓒⓒ 1/4-6/7 25/8-29/9 7=6, 14=11

📍 N 43°13'55'' E 6°0'29''

www.eurocampings.co.uk/116159

1740 Bormes-les-Mimosas, F-83230 / Provence-Alpes-Côte d'Azur   ♿ ⓦ iD   27 A2

- ⛰ Camp du Domaine*****
- 🏠 2581 route de Bénat / La Favière
- 📅 24 Mar - 31 Oct
- ☎ +33 (0)4-94710312
- @ mail@campdudomaine.com

1 ADE**J**K**NOPRST** KNOPQRSTVWXY		6
2 EFHPQRTUVWXY	ABDE**FG**H	7
3 BCEFL**MN**QR	ABCDEFHKNOPRSTUV	8
4 **A**BCDEILNOP**QR**T**VXZ** EJKLMNORST		9
5 ACDEFGHJKM**O** ABCFGHIJ**N**O**P**TUZ		10
Ad on page 579 10-16A	❶ €58.40	
45ha 1132**T**(80-200m²) 188**P**	❷ €75.80	

🅿 Between Bormes and Le Lavandou roundabout. At roundabout take direction La Favière and continue for 2.5 km.

💬 Heavenly location: in a pine forest of 45 ha and next to vineyards directly on a beautiful sandy beach across the Golden Isles. One of the most beautiful campsites in Europe, especially suitable for families.

📍 N 43°7'5'' E 6°21'7''

www.eurocampings.co.uk/104412

France

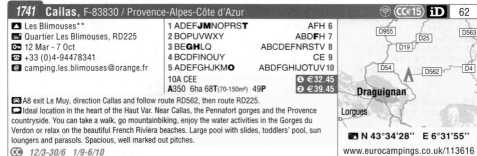

1741 Callas, F-83830 / Provence-Alpes-Côte d'Azur — (CC€15) iD 62

- Les Blimouses**
- Quartier Les Blimouses, RD225
- 12 Mar - 7 Oct
- +33 (0)4-94478341
- camping.les.blimouses@orange.fr

1 ADEF**JM**NOPRS**T**	AFH 6
2 BOPUVWXY	ABD**F**H 7
3 BE**GH**LQ	ABCDEFNRSTV 8
4 BCDFINOUY	CE 9
5 ADEFGHJKM**O**	ABDFGHIJOTUV 10

10A CEE
A350 6ha 68**T**(70-150m²) 49**P**

❶ €32.45
❷ €39.45

A8 exit Le Muy, direction Callas and follow route RD562, then route RD225.

Ideal location in the heart of the Haut Var. Near Callas, the Pennafort gorges and the Provence countryside. You can take a walk, go mountainbiking, enjoy the water activities in the Gorges du Verdon or relax on the beautiful French Riviera beaches. Large pool with slides, toddlers' pool, sun loungers and parasols. Spacious, well marked out pitches.

CC 12/3-30/6 1/9-6/10

D955 D563
D25
D19
D54 D562 D4

Draguignan

Lorgues

N 43°34'28" E 6°31'55"

www.eurocampings.co.uk/113616

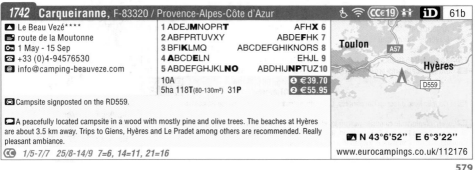

1742 Carqueiranne, F-83320 / Provence-Alpes-Côte d'Azur — ♿ 🛜 (CC€19) 🏃 iD 61b

- Le Beau Vezé****
- route de la Moutonne
- 1 May - 15 Sep
- +33 (0)4-94576530
- info@camping-beauveze.com

1 ADE**J**MNOPR**T**	AFH**X** 6
2 ABF**P**RTUVXY	ABD**E**FHK 7
3 BFI**K**LMQ	ABCDEFGHIKNORS 8
4 **A**BCD**E**LN	EHJL 9
5 ABDEFGHJKL**NO**	ABDHIJ**NP**TUZ 10

10A
5ha 118**T**(80-130m²) 31**P**

❶ €39.70
❷ €55.95

Campsite signposted on the RD559.

A peacefully located campsite in a wood with mostly pine and olive trees. The beaches at Hyères are about 3.5 km away. Trips to Giens, Hyères and Le Pradet among others are recommended. Really pleasant ambiance.

CC 1/5-7/7 25/8-14/9 7=6, 14=11, 21=16

Toulon A57

Hyères

D559

N 43°6'52" E 6°3'22"

www.eurocampings.co.uk/112176

1743 Cavalaire-sur-Mer, F-83240 / Provence-Alpes-Côte d'Azur   ⚕ 🛜 (CC€19) iD 62

- △ Bonporteau****
- 🏕 208 chemin Train des Pignes
- 📅 15 Mar - 15 Oct
- ☎ +33 (0)4-94640324
- @ contact@bonporteau.fr

1	AJMNOPRT	ABFGKNOPQSWX 6
2	EFHMOPQTUVWXY	ABDEF 7
3	BLQ	ABCDEFHJKNOPQRSTUV 8
4	BCDINOPU	EL 9
5	ACDEFGHJKLO	AFHIJNPTU10

10A CEE   ❶ €59.20
3ha 110T(80-120m²) 70P   ❷ €65.20

🪧 The campsite is clearly signposted in the centre of Cavalaire.

💬 A really lovely location, a well maintained campsite with good facilities and a genuine Mediterranean landscape. 200 metres from the beach and 800 metres from the centre of the popular seaside resort of Cavalaire-sur-Mer.

CC 15/3-7/7   1/9-14/10

📍 N 43°10'2"   E 6°31'9"

www.eurocampings.co.uk/108481

1744 Cavalaire-sur-Mer, F-83240 / Provence-Alpes-Côte d'Azur   ⚕ 🛜 (CC€19) iD 62

- △ Camping Cros de Mouton****
- 🏕 chemin du Cros de Mouton
- 📅 22 Mar - 28 Oct
- ☎ +33 (0)4-94641087
- @ campingcrosdemouton@wanadoo.fr

1	ADEJMNOPQRST	ABFGX 6
2	BFHMORTUVWXY	ABDEFH 7
3	BELQ	ABCDEFHJKNPQRSTUV 8
4	BCDEINOQUX	EJLUVW 9
5	ABDEFGHJKLMO	ABCDHIJNPTUZ10

10A   ❶ €37.60
A110 6ha 117T(60-200m²) 82P   ❷ €52.10

🪧 A8, exit Le Muy direction Ste Maxime. Direction St. Tropez then direction Cavalaire. Follow signs.

💬 A very attractive campsite with plenty of shade and fantastic views of the Mediterranean Sea and a beautiful nature reserve in the distant surroundings. 1.5 km from a lively seaside resort with beautiful sandy beaches. Restaurant and swimming pool with panoramic views.

CC 22/3-30/6   27/8-27/10

📍 N 43°10'56"   E 6°31'0"

www.eurocampings.co.uk/110122

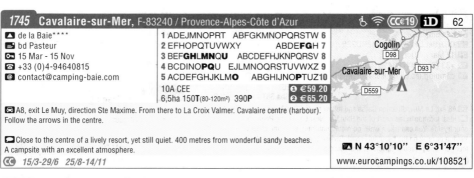

1745 Cavalaire-sur-Mer, F-83240 / Provence-Alpes-Côte d'Azur   ⚕ 🛜 (CC€19) iD 62

- △ de la Baie****
- 🏕 bd Pasteur
- 📅 15 Mar - 15 Nov
- ☎ +33 (0)4-94640815
- @ contact@camping-baie.com

1	ADEJMNOPRT	ABFGKMNOPQRSTW 6
2	EFHOPQTUVWXY	ABDEFGH 7
3	BEFGHLMNQU	ABCDEFHJKNPQRSV 8
4	BCDINOPQU	EJLMNOQRSTUVWXZ 9
5	ACDEFGHJKLMO	ABGHIJNOPTUZ10

10A CEE   ❶ €59.20
6,5ha 150T(80-120m²) 390P   ❷ €65.20

🪧 A8, exit Le Muy, direction Ste Maxime. From there to La Croix Valmer. Cavalaire centre (harbour). Follow the arrows in the centre.

💬 Close to the centre of a lively resort, yet still quiet. 400 metres from wonderful sandy beaches. A campsite with an excellent atmosphere.

CC 15/3-29/6   25/8-14/11

📍 N 43°10'10"   E 6°31'47"

www.eurocampings.co.uk/108521

1746 Cogolin, F-83310 / Provence-Alpes-Côte d'Azur   ⚕ 🛜 ✿ (CC€15) ♛♛ iD 62

- △ L'Argentière****
- 🏕 48 avenue Saint Maur
- 📅 1 Apr - 8 Oct
- ☎ +33 (0)4-94546363
- @ contact@camping-argentiere.com

1	AIKNOPRT	ABFHX 6
2	BFPRVWXY	ABDEFGH 7
3	BEKLMQ	ABCDEFKNRSV 8
4	BCDILNOU	EUV 9
5	ABDEFGHJKLMO	ABDHIJOPVZ10

Ad on page 581 6-10A   ❶ €46.20
5ha 100T(80-120m²) 150P   ❷ €54.20

🪧 In Cogolin keep direction Collobrières. Campsite entrance is next to Château Saint Maur.

💬 Lovely, comfortable campsite with an excellent ambiance. Very central location for trips, e.g. to St. Tropez, Sainte Maxime, Port Grimaud, the world-famous beaches of Pampelonne and Ramatuelle, Grimaud, Gassin. Campsite is located in a nature reserve.

CC 1/4-7/7   25/8-7/10

📍 N 43°15'27"   E 6°31'5"

www.eurocampings.co.uk/108480

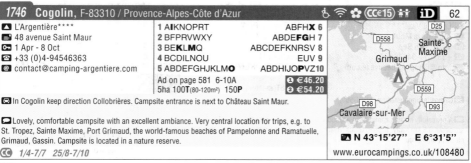

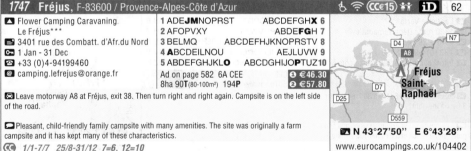

1747 Fréjus, F-83600 / Provence-Alpes-Côte d'Azur   ⚕ 🛜 (CC€15) ✸✸ **iD** | 62

- 🏕 Flower Camping Caravaning. Le Fréjus***
- 📧 3401 rue des Combatt. d'Afr.du Nord
- 🗓 1 Jan - 31 Dec
- ☎ +33 (0)4-94199460
- @ camping.lefrejus@orange.fr

1 ADE**JM**NOPRST	ABCDEFGH**X**	6
2 AFOPVXY	ABDE**FG**H	7
3 BELMQ	ABCDEFHJKNOPRSTV	8
4 **A**BCDEILNOU	AEJLUVW	9
5 ABDEFGHJKL**O**	ABCDGHIJO**P**TUZ	10

Ad on page 582 6A CEE
8ha 90**T**(80-100m²) 194**P**

❶ €46.30
❷ €57.80

🚗 Leave motorway A8 at Fréjus, exit 38. Then turn right and right again. Campsite is on the left side of the road.

💬 Pleasant, child-friendly family campsite with many amenities. The site was originally a farm campsite and it has kept many of these characteristics.

(CC) 1/1-7/7 25/8-31/12 7=6, 12=10

🏕 **Fréjus**
Saint-Raphaël

🏕 N 43°27'50'' E 6°43'28''

www.eurocampings.co.uk/104402

1748 Fréjus, F-83618 / Provence-Alpes-Côte d'Azur   ⚕ 🛜 (CC€19) **iD** | 62

- 🏕 La Baume/La Palmeraie*****
- 📧 3775 rue des Comb. d'Afr.du Nord
- 🗓 31 Mar - 28 Sep
- ☎ +33 (0)4-94198888
- @ reception@labaume-lapalmeraie.com

1 ADE**JM**NOPRST	ABEFGHI	6
2 ABFOPRVWXY	ABDE**FG**H	7
3 BEF**KL**MQR**ST**	ABCDEFHJKNOPQRSTUV	8
4 **A**BCD**E**ILMNO**PQ**RUV**XZ**	EIJLUV	9
5 ACDEFGHJKLM**O**	ABDHIJ**NO**P**Z**10	

Ad on page 583 6-10A
27ha 230**T**(90-130m²) 973**P**

❶ €57.20
❷ €80.20

🚗 A8, exit 38 Fréjus. Then right and right again. Campsite is on the left.

💬 A lovely campsite with fantastic swimming facilities and very professionally organised entertainment.

(CC) 31/3-22/6 8/9-27/9

🏕 **Fréjus**
Saint-Raphaël

🏕 N 43°27'59'' E 6°43'23''

www.eurocampings.co.uk/100553

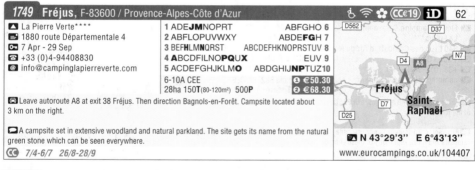
France

1749 Fréjus, F-83600 / Provence-Alpes-Côte d'Azur ♿ 📶 ✿ (CC€19) iD 62

- 🏕 La Pierre Verte★★★★
- 📧 1880 route Départementale 4
- 📅 7 Apr - 29 Sep
- ☎ +33 (0)4-94408830
- @ info@campinglapierreverte.com

1 ADE**JM**NOPRT	ABFGHO	6
2 ABFLOPUVWXY	ABDE**FG**H	7
3 BEF**HLMN**QRST	ABCDEFHKNOPRSTUV	8
4 **A**BCDFILNO**PQU**X	EUV	9
5 ACDEFGHJKLM**O**	ABDGHIJ**NP**TUZ	10

6-10A CEE
28ha 150T(80-120m²) 500P

❶ €50.30
❷ €68.30

🚗 Leave autoroute A8 at exit 38 Fréjus. Then direction Bagnols-en-Forêt. Campsite located about 3 km on the right.

💬 A campsite set in extensive woodland and natural parkland. The site gets its name from the natural green stone which can be seen everywhere.

CC 7/4-6/7 26/8-28/9

🗺 N 43°29'3'' E 6°43'13''
www.eurocampings.co.uk/104407

1750 Giens/Hyères, F-83400 / Provence-Alpes-Côte d'Azur 📶 (CC€19) iD 61b

- 🏕 La Tour Fondue
- 📧 1700 avenue des Arbanais
- 📅 16 Mar - 4 Nov
- ☎ +33 (0)4-94582359
- @ info@camping-latourfondue.com

1 ADE**JM**NOPRT	KNOPQSX	6
2 EFHJMOPRTVWX	ABDE**F**H	7
3 L	ABCDEFNRS	8
4 FO	ELUVW	9
5 ABDEFGHJK	AGHIJ**NP**U	10

16A
2,3ha 119T(50-120m²) 21P

❶ €35.15
❷ €50.15

🚗 On the peninsula campsite signs are posted.

💬 Ideal for fans of water sports. Diving club on site. The campsite is situated by the sea opposite the 'Golden Islands'.

CC 16/3-29/6 3/9-3/11

🗺 N 43°1'47'' E 6°9'22''
www.eurocampings.co.uk/110907

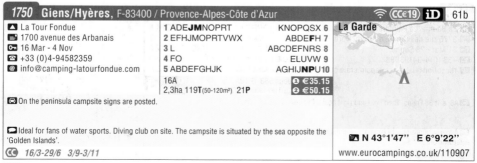

La Baume
CAMPING RESORT
★ ★ ★ ★ ★

La Palmeraie
RESIDENCE DE TOURISME
★ ★ ★

France

THE SOUTH
With its magnificent countryside

5 km from the sandy beaches of FRÉJUS and SAINT-RAPHAËL

COTTAGES - CARAVANS - APARTMENTS - VILLAS
An extensive selection of rental accommodation for 2 to 10 persons

Water parks, indoor and heated swimming pools.
Continuous entertainment

www.labaume-lapalmeraie.com

3775, Rue des Combattants d'Afrique du Nord 83618 FREJUS Cedex
Tel: +33 (0)4 94 19 88 88 - Fax: +33 (0)4 94 19 83 50
reception@labaume-lapalmeraie.com

583

1751 Giens/Hyères, F-83400 / Provence-Alpes-Côte d'Azur ♿ 🛜 (CC€19) iD | 61b

- ▲ Olbia★★★
- 🏠 545 ave René de Knyff, La Madrague
- 📅 31 Mar - 7 Oct
- ☎ +33 (0)4-94582196
- @ info@camping-olbia.com

1 ADE**IL**NORT	KNOPQSWX	6
2 BEHMOPRTUVXY	ABDE**F**H	7
3 BL	ABCDEFHKNOPRS	8
4 FO	ILNQRUVW	9
5 ABDEFGHJKM**O**	ABDGHIJ**NP**U	10
15A CEE		
110T 1P	❶ €36.90 ❷ €49.80	

🅿 Campsite located ± 500 metres east of the harbour at Madrague on the Giens headland.

💬 Grounds set in an attractive park in one of the loveliest parts of the Giens headland, rich in natural beauty. Trips to the Golden Islands and especially Porquerolles, to picturesque Giens and historically interesting Hyères are all highly recommended.

CC 31/3-29/6 3/9-6/10

La Garde A570
D559

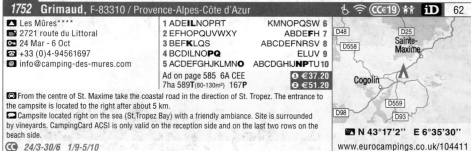

⛺ N 43°2'23'' E 6°6'12''

www.eurocampings.co.uk/119451

1752 Grimaud, F-83310 / Provence-Alpes-Côte d'Azur ♿ 🛜 (CC€19) ⚥ iD | 62

- ▲ Les Mûres★★★★
- 🏠 2721 route du Littoral
- 📅 24 Mar - 6 Oct
- ☎ +33 (0)4-94561697
- @ info@camping-des-mures.com

1 ADE**IL**NOPRT	KMNOPQSW	6
2 EFHOPQUVWXY	ABDE**F**H	7
3 BE**FK**LQS	ABCDEFNRSV	8
4 BCDILNO**PQ**	ELUV	9
5 ACDEFGHJKLMN**O**	ABCDGHIJ**NP**TU	10
Ad on page 585 6A CEE		
7ha 589T(80-130m²) 167P	❶ €37.20 ❷ €51.20	

🅿 From the centre of St. Maxime take the coastal road in the direction of St. Tropez. The entrance to the campsite is located to the right after about 5 km.

💬 Campsite located right on the sea (St.Tropez Bay) with a friendly ambiance. Site is surrounded by vineyards. CampingCard ACSI is only valid on the reception side and on the last two rows on the beach side.

CC 24/3-30/6 1/9-5/10

D48 D25 Sainte-Maxime
D558
Cogolin
D559
D98 D93

⛺ N 43°17'2'' E 6°35'30''

www.eurocampings.co.uk/104411

1753 La Croix-Valmer, F-83420 / Provence-Alpes-Côte d'Azur ♿ 🛜 (CC€19) iD | 62

- ▲ Sélection Camping★★★★
- 🏠 310 boulevard de la Mer
- 📅 15 Mar - 15 Oct
- ☎ +33 (0)4-94551030
- @ camping-selection@wanadoo.fr

1 ADE**J**KNOPRT	ABFGKNPQRSTWX	6
2 EFHOPQTUVXY	ABDE**FG**H	7
3 BE**IK**LQ	ABCDEFHJKNOPQRSV	8
4 BCDFHILNO**PQ**U	EHLMOQUVW	9
5 ACDEFGHJKLM**O**	ABCDGHIJ**NP**TU	10
10A		
4ha 117T(65-80m²) 79P	❶ €55.30 ❷ €65.15	

🅿 In La Croix-Valmer drive in the direction of Le Lavandou. Signposted at the roundabout 2 km down the road.

💬 The campsite has a magnificent location in an extensive Provençal park (pines, mimosa, etc.). Very good atmosphere. A few minutes walk to beach.

CC 15/3-7/7 25/8-14/10

D558 Cogolin
D559
D98 D93
Cavalaire-sur-Mer

⛺ N 43°11'40'' E 6°33'18''

www.eurocampings.co.uk/108490

1754 Le Lavandou, F-83980 / Provence-Alpes-Côte d'Azur ♿ 🛜 (CC€17) iD | 27 A2

- ▲ Beau Séjour★★★
- 🏠 route de Bénat, D298
- 📅 14 Apr - 1 Oct
- ☎ +33 (0)4-94712530
- @ caravaning.beau.sejour@gmail.com

1 A**JM**NOPRT		6
2 OPRVXY	ABDE**F**H	7
3 A**K**LQ	ABCDEFNOPRV	8
4		9
5 G**K**	ABDHIJOTU	10
10A		
1,8ha 135T(70-85m²)	❶ €27.80 ❷ €38.40	

🅿 A8, exit 35 direction Brignoles/Le Val D43. Then follow D14, D12 and D98 to D298 in Bormes-les-Mimosas. 2nd exit at roundabout.

💬 Very tidy, well maintained campsite within walking distance of the Mediterranean Sea. Le Lavandou is a very lively bathing resort. Ideal base for all kinds of outings.

CC 14/4-30/6 20/8-30/9

Bormes-les-Mimosas Le Canadel
D98
Les Salins

⛺ N 43°8'7'' E 6°21'6''

www.eurocampings.co.uk/116163

1755 Le Lavandou, F-83980 / Provence-Alpes-Côte d'Azur ♿ 🛜 (CC€19) iD 62

- 🏕 Parc Camping de Pramousquier**
- 🏠 chemin de la Faverolle
- 📅 14 Apr - 30 Sep
- ☎ +33 (0)4-94058395
- @ camping-lavandou@wanadoo.fr

1	ADEJMNORT	KNQSWX 6
2	EFHOPRTUVWXY	ABDEFGH 7
3	BKLQ	ABCDEFHNORV 8
4	BCDHOP	AEJL 9
5	ABDEFGHJKLMO	ABGHIKNPTUZ10

4-10A
4,5ha 146T(70-100m²) 22P

❶ €35.05
❷ €46.25

📷 The campsite is located on the coastal road, right at the front of the town Pramousquier (east side).

💬 A pleasant terraced campsite close to the Mediterranean and a few kilometres from the popular seaside resort of Le Lavandou. Very central location with regard to tourist attractions such as the Golden Islands and St. Tropez. Naturist beach close by.

CC 14/4-6/7 1/9-29/9

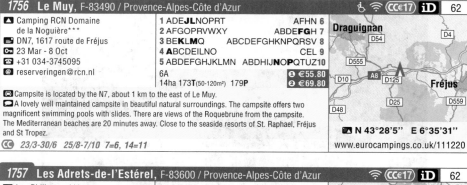

🧭 N 43°9'23'' E 6°26'53''

www.eurocampings.co.uk/104413

1756 Le Muy, F-83490 / Provence-Alpes-Côte d'Azur ♿ 🛜 (CC€17) iD 62

- 🏕 Camping RCN Domaine de la Noguière***
- 📍 DN7, 1617 route de Fréjus
- 📅 23 Mar - 8 Oct
- ☎ +31 034-3745095
- @ reserveringen@rcn.nl

1	ADEJLNOPRT	AFHN 6
2	AFGOPRVWXY	ABDEFGH 7
3	BEKLMQ	ABCDEFGHKNPQRSV 8
4	ABCDEILNO	CEL 9
5	ABDEFGHJKLMN	ABDHIJNOPQTUZ10

6A
14ha 173T(50-120m²) 179P

❶ €55.80
❷ €69.80

📷 Campsite is located by the N7, about 1 km to the east of Le Muy.

💬 A lovely well maintained campsite in beautiful natural surroundings. The campsite offers two magnificent swimming pools with slides. There are views of the Roquebrune from the campsite. The Mediterranean beaches are 20 minutes away. Close to the seaside resorts of St. Raphael, Fréjus and St Tropez.

CC 23/3-30/6 25/8-7/10 7=6, 14=11

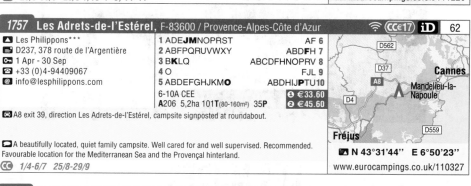

🧭 N 43°28'5'' E 6°35'31''

www.eurocampings.co.uk/111220

1757 Les Adrets-de-l'Estérel, F-83600 / Provence-Alpes-Côte d'Azur 🛜 (CC€17) iD 62

- 🏕 Les Philippons***
- 📍 D237, 378 route de l'Argentière
- 📅 1 Apr - 30 Sep
- ☎ +33 (0)4-94409067
- @ info@lesphilippons.com

1	ADEJMNOPRST	AF 6
2	ABFPQRUVWXY	ABDFH 7
3	BKLQ	ABCDFHNOPRV 8
4	O	FJL 9
5	ABDEFGHJKMO	ABDHIJPTU10

6-10A CEE
A206 5,2ha 101T(80-160m²) 35P

❶ €33.60
❷ €45.60

📷 A8 exit 39, direction Les Adrets-de-l'Estérel, campsite signposted at roundabout.

💬 A beautifully located, quiet family campsite. Well cared for and well supervised. Recommended. Favourable location for the Mediterranean Sea and the Provençal hinterland.

CC 1/4-6/7 25/8-29/9

🧭 N 43°31'44'' E 6°50'23''

www.eurocampings.co.uk/110327

1758 Les Issambres, F-83380 / Provence-Alpes-Côte d'Azur ♿ 🛜 (CC€17) iD 62

- 🏕 Au Paradis des Campeurs****
- 🏠 La Gaillarde-Plage
- 📅 1 Apr - 1 Oct
- ☎ +33 (0)4-94969355
- @ campingauparadisdescampeurs@gmail.com

1	ADEJMNOPRST	KMNOPQRX 6
2	EFHMOPTUVWXY	ABDEFGH 7
3	BEFJKLQ	ABCDEFHKNPRSTUV 8
4	FHIO	ELUV 9
5	ACDEFGHJKLMO	ABGHIJMNPTU10

6A CEE
2,7ha 180T(60-120m²) 17P

❶ €33.40
❷ €47.40

📷 On the N98 between St. Aygulf and Les Issambres.

💬 Direct access to the sandy beach from the campsite. A congenial family campsite. CampingCard ACSI is only valid for standard pitches. The discount card is not valid for comfort pitches.

CC 1/4-7/7 25/8-30/9

🧭 N 43°21'58'' E 6°42'43''

www.eurocampings.co.uk/108771

1759 Roquebrune-sur-Argens, F-83520 / Provence-Alpes-Côte d'Azur   ⚲ 📶 (CC€19) iD   62

- Domaine de la Bergerie*****
- 1960 D8
- 21 Apr - 10 Oct
- +33 (0)4-98114545
- info@domainelabergerie.com

1 ADE**JMN**OPRST	AEFHIN 6
2 ABCDFOPRTUVWXY	ABDE**FG**H 7
3 BDEFH**IKLMN**QR	ABCDEFHJKNOPQRSTUV 8
4 **A**BCD**E**FHIJKLMNO**PR**TU**VXZ**	ELUVW 9
5 ACDEFGHIJKLM**O**	ABDHIK**NP**TZ10

6-10A CEE
60ha 200T(80-200m²) 900P
❶ €46.70
❷ €67.70

From St. Aygulf to Roquebrune-sur-Argens. After about 3 miles (5 km) there's a roundabout.
Turn left to Col du Bougnon. After 1 km follow the signs.
Well positioned campsite set in a 60-hectare wood full of oak, fir and mimosa trees. Green hedges separate the pitches. Excellent (swimming) facilities including an indoor pool with jacuzzi, sauna and Turkish bath.

CC 21/4-3/7 26/8-9/10

N 43°23'55'' E 6°40'30''
www.eurocampings.co.uk/109261

1760 Roquebrune-sur-Argens, F-83520 / Provence-Alpes-Côte d'Azur   ⚲ 📶 (CC€17) ⚥ iD   62

- Flower Camping Les Pêcheurs****
- 1 Apr - 8 Oct
- +33 (0)4-94457125
- info@camping-les-pecheurs.com

1 ADE**JMN**OPRT	ABFGLNWXY 6
2 ACDFOPVWXY	ABDE**FG**H 7
3 BEI**K**LQR	ABCDEFHJKNPRSV 8
4 **A**BCDEILNO**PQTUXY**	EJLQTUV 9
5 ABDEFGHJKLM**O**	ABDGHIJ**NP**TZ10

10A CEE
5ha 123T(80-100m²) 67P
❶ €57.20
❷ €72.20

A8, exit Le Muy, direction Roquebrune. The campsite is located just before the village, opposite the lake.
A lovely, well-run campsite located by a river, 10 km from the sandy beaches of Fréjus and St. Raphaël. There is a lake opposite the hotel offering countless watersports opportunities. Lovely swimming pool with wellness facilities.

CC 1/4-1/7 26/8-7/10

N 43°27'4'' E 6°38'2''
www.eurocampings.co.uk/108497

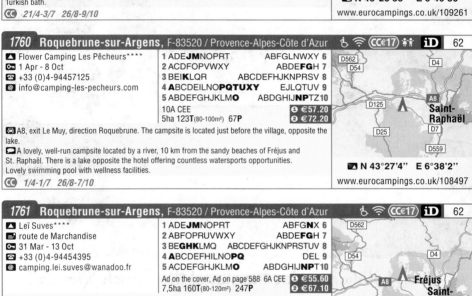

1761 Roquebrune-sur-Argens, F-83520 / Provence-Alpes-Côte d'Azur   ⚲ 📶 (CC€17) iD   62

- Leï Suves****
- route de Marchandise
- 31 Mar - 13 Oct
- +33 (0)4-94454395
- camping.lei.suves@wanadoo.fr

1 ADE**JMN**OPRT	ABFG**N**X 6
2 ABFOPRUVWXY	ABDE**FG**H 7
3 BE**GHK**LMQ	ABCDEFHJKNPRSTUV 8
4 **A**BCDEFHILNO**PQ**	DEL 9
5 ACDEFGHJKLM**O**	ABDGHIJ**NP**T10

Ad on the cover, Ad on page 588 6A CEE
7,5ha 160T(80-120m²) 247P
❶ €55.60
❷ €67.10

A8, exit Le Muy, direction Fréjus via the N7. Turn left at the roundabout at Roquebrune-sur-Argens, direction La Bouverie.
In every respect an excellently maintained and well organised campsite in the middle of the Provençal landscape. The site has a very appropriate name: 'Leï Suves', meaning cork trees. The campsite was once a cork plantation.

CC 31/3-30/6 27/8-12/10

N 43°28'40'' E 6°38'19''
www.eurocampings.co.uk/108496

1762 Roquebrune-sur-Argens, F-83520 / Provence-Alpes-Côte d'Azur   ⚲ 📶 (CC€17) iD   62

- Moulin des Iscles***
- 690 chemin du Moulin des Iscles
- 1 Apr - 30 Sep
- +33 (0)4-94457074
- moulin.iscles@wanadoo.fr

1 ADE**JMN**ORT	**N**X 6
2 ACFPVWXY	ABDE**FG**H 7
3 BEI**K**LQ	ABCDEFHJKNOPRSTUV 8
4 ABCDIOQ	EILQUV 9
5 ACDEFGJKM**O**	ABCDHIJ**NP**TUZ10

6A
1,3ha 79T(70-100m²) 11P
❶ €29.70
❷ €34.30

A8 exit Le Muy, then N7 direction Fréjus. After about 10 km right, Roquebrune. Campsite is located just to the south of the village, direction St. Aygulf.

A pleasant, quiet campsite on the banks of the Argens. Excellent food made by the owner!

CC 1/4-7/7 25/8-29/9 7=6

N 43°26'43'' E 6°39'28''
www.eurocampings.co.uk/109262

Leï Suves
CAMPING-CLUB CARAVANING ★★★★

Your holidays under the sun of the French Riviera !

lei-suves.com

Rte de Marchandise - 83520 Roquebrune sur Argens
Tél. : 04 94 45 43 95 - camping.lei.suves@wanadoo.fr

1763 Sanary-sur-Mer, F-83110 / Provence-Alpes-Côte d'Azur

  ♿ 📶 CC€19 iD   61b

- ⛺ Campasun Parc Mogador★★★★
- 🏕 167 chemin de Beaucours
- 📅 1 Mar - 31 Dec
- ☎ +33 (0)4-94745316
- @ mogador@campasun.eu

1 ADEF**JM**NOPRT		ABF 6
2 ABJOPRVX	ABDE**FGH** 7	
3 AB**KL**PQ	ABCDEFIJKNQRSTUV 8	
4 BDILNOPQU	EJLV 9	
5 ABDEFGHJM**N**	ABDFGHIJO**P**TUZ 10	
10A CEE		❶ €42.00
3ha 75**T**(80-100m²) 175**P**		❷ €58.90

🚗 A50, exit 12 Bandol. Follow D559 direction Sanary. Then take second right.

💬 A quiet campsite located 800 metres from the sea. Very conveniently located a few kilometres from Sanary and Bandol. Pitches with sufficient shade. Restaurant and toilet block with self-cleaning toilets.

CC 1/3-7/7   25/8-31/12

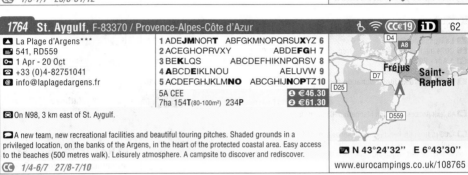

Toulon
Sanary-sur-Mer

📍 N 43°7'26''   E 5°47'16''
www.eurocampings.co.uk/111979

1764 St. Aygulf, F-83370 / Provence-Alpes-Côte d'Azur

  ♿ 📶 CC€19 iD   62

- ⛺ La Plage d'Argens★★★
- 🏕 541, RD559
- 📅 1 Apr - 20 Oct
- ☎ +33 (0)4-82751041
- @ info@laplagedargens.fr

1 ADE**JM**NOR**T**	ABFGKMNOPQRSU**X**YZ 6	
2 ACEGHOPRVXY	ABDE**FGH** 7	
3 BE**KL**QS	ABCDEFHIKNPQRSV 8	
4 **A**BCD**E**IKLNOU	AELUVW 9	
5 ACDEFGHJKLM**NO**	ABCGHIJ**NOP**TZ 10	
5A CEE		❶ €46.30
7ha 154**T**(80-100m²) 234**P**		❷ €61.30

🚗 On N98, 3 km east of St. Aygulf.

💬 A new team, new recreational facilities and beautiful touring pitches. Shaded grounds in a privileged location, on the banks of the Argens, in the heart of the protected coastal area. Easy access to the beaches (500 metres walk). Leisurely atmosphere. A campsite to discover and rediscover.

CC 1/4-6/7   27/8-7/10

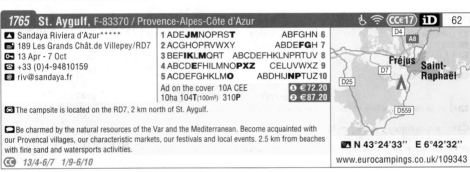

Fréjus
Saint-Raphaël

📍 N 43°24'32''   E 6°43'30''
www.eurocampings.co.uk/108765

1765 St. Aygulf, F-83370 / Provence-Alpes-Côte d'Azur

  ♿ 📶 CC€17 iD   62

- ⛺ Sandaya Riviera d'Azur★★★★★
- 🏕 189 Les Grands Chât.de Villepey/RD7
- 📅 13 Apr - 7 Oct
- ☎ +33 (0)4-94810159
- @ riv@sandaya.fr

1 ADE**JM**NOPRS**T**	ABFGHN 6	
2 ACGHOPRVWXY	ABDE**FGH** 7	
3 BEF**IKLM**QRT	ABCDEFHKLNPRTUV 8	
4 ABCD**E**FHILMNO**PXZ**	CELUVWXZ 9	
5 ACDEFGHKLM**O**	ABDHIJ**NP**TUZ 10	
Ad on the cover 10A CEE		❶ €72.20
10ha 104**T**(100m²) 310**P**		❷ €87.20

🚗 The campsite is located on the RD7, 2 km north of St. Aygulf.

💬 Be charmed by the natural resources of the Var and the Mediterranean. Become acquainted with our Provencal villages, our characteristic markets, our festivals and local events. 2.5 km from beaches with fine sand and watersports activities.

CC 13/4-6/7   1/9-6/10

Fréjus
Saint-Raphaël

📍 N 43°24'33''   E 6°42'32''
www.eurocampings.co.uk/109343

1766 St. Cyr-sur-Mer, F-83270 / Provence-Alpes-Côte d'Azur

  ♿ 📶 CC€17 iD   61b

- ⛺ Le Clos Ste Thérèse★★★★
- 🏕 route de Bandol
- 📅 2 Apr - 30 Sep
- ☎ +33 (0)4-94321221
- @ camping@clos-therese.com

1 ADE**IL**NOR**T**		AF 6
2 AFORUVX	ABDE**FH** 7	
3 AE**KL**Q	ABCDFJNOQRSV 8	
4 BCDFINO**PUX**	BCEFIL 9	
5 ADEFGHJK**NO**	ABFGHIKMOUZ 10	
6-10A CEE		❶ €36.90
A100 4ha 80**T**(65-150m²) 40**P**		❷ €46.80

🚗 Follow A50 as far as St. Cyr-sur-Mer exit, then continue towards Bandol. Campsite is located 3.5 km from the village, on the left.

💬 A small, well-shaded family campsite protruding high above the sea and the Gulf of Frégate. 4 km from a sandy beach. Two swimming pools, one of which is heated. 15 km from the medieval village of Castellet and 25 km from Cassis and its magnificent bays.

CC 2/4-6/7   27/8-29/9

La Seyne-sur-Mer

📍 N 43°9'35''   E 5°43'46''
www.eurocampings.co.uk/112551

1767 St. Raphaël, F-83700 / Provence-Alpes-Côte d'Azur — ♿ 🛜 ✿ CC€17 iD 62

▲ Sandaya Douce Quiétude*****
🏠 3435, bd Jacques Baudino
🗓 13 Apr - 16 Sep
☎ +33 (0)4-94443000
@ dou@sandaya.fr

1 ADE**JM**NOPRT	ABFGHIX	6
2 BOPUVWXY	ABDE**FGH**	7
3 BEI**KLM**QR	ABCDEFJKLNQRSTUV	8
4 BCDILMNO**RUXZ**	BEFLUVWX	9
5 ACDEFGHIJL	ABCDEHIJ**P**TUZ	10

Ad on the cover 16A CEE ❶ €64.30
A63 10ha 84T(60-100m²) 277P ❷ €84.30

🚗 A8, exit Fréjus exit 38. At all roundabouts follow dir. St. Raphaël, then direction Boulouris/Agay. Turn left after the second roundabout at the Valescure stadium: Boulevard Baudino.
🏕 Five-star campsite close to the Mediterranean coast in wooded surroundings on the edge of the Esterel volcanic massif. The Var area is a dream location for many for a successful holiday. Relaxation, sports and discovery are the keywords for a holiday in the Provence.
CC 13/4-6/7 1/9-15/9

📍 N 43°26'52'' E 6°48'20''
www.eurocampings.co.uk/104409

1768 Antibes, F-06600 / Rivièra-Côte d'Azur — ♿ 🛜 CC€19 iD 62

▲ Le Rossignol***
🏠 2074 av. M. Pellissier/av. J. Grec
🗓 1 Apr - 29 Sep
☎ +33 (0)4-93335698
@ campinglerossignol@wanadoo.fr

1 AD**IL**NOPR**T**	ABF	6
2 AJOPRUVY	ABDE**FGH**	7
3 A**K**LQ	ABCDEFKNQRSTUV	8
4 IO	EFL	9
5 ABDH**O**	ABDGHIJ**NP**TU	10

10A CEE ❶ €32.60
1,8ha 111T(90-110m²) 27P ❷ €44.60

🚗 A8, exit Antibes; direction Marineland. Campsite is signposted.

🏕 1200 m from the beach, close to Atibes and the Picasso and Léger museums, in natural and pleasant surroundings, Le Rossignol offers pitches marked out by small hedges. Satellite TV connection. Heated swimming pool. Reception open between 9:30 am and 7:00 pm.
CC 1/4-12/7 30/8-28/9

📍 N 43°36'23'' E 7°6'43''
www.eurocampings.co.uk/109219

1769 Cagnes-sur-Mer, F-06800 / Rivièra-Côte d'Azur — 🛜 CC€17 iD 62

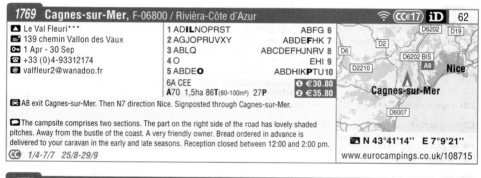

▲ Le Val Fleuri***
🏠 139 chemin Vallon des Vaux
🗓 1 Apr - 30 Sep
☎ +33 (0)4-93312174
@ valfleur2@wanadoo.fr

1 AD**IL**NOPRST	ABFG	6
2 AGJOPRUVXY	ABDE**F**HK	7
3 A**B**LQ	ABCDEFHJNRV	8
4 O	EHI	9
5 ABDE**O**	ABDHIK**P**TU	10

6A CEE ❶ €30.80
A70 1,5ha 86T(80-100m²) 27P ❷ €35.80

🚗 A8 exit Cagnes-sur-Mer. Then N7 direction Nice. Signposted through Cagnes-sur-Mer.

🏕 The campsite comprises two sections. The part on the right side of the road has lovely shaded pitches. Away from the bustle of the coast. A very friendly owner. Bread ordered in advance is delivered to your caravan in the early and late seasons. Reception closed between 12:00 and 2:00 pm.
CC 1/4-7/7 25/8-29/9

📍 N 43°41'14'' E 7°9'21''
www.eurocampings.co.uk/108715

1770 La Colle-sur-Loup, F-06480 / Rivièra-Côte d'Azur — ⊗ 🛜 CC€17 iD 62

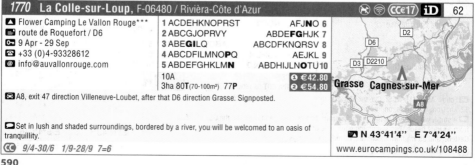

▲ Flower Camping Le Vallon Rouge***
🏠 route de Roquefort / D6
🗓 9 Apr - 29 Sep
☎ +33 (0)4-93328612
@ info@auvallonrouge.com

1 ACDEHKNOPRST	AFJ**N**O	6
2 ABCGJOPRVY	ABDE**FG**HJK	7
3 ABE**GIL**Q	ABCDFKNQRSV	8
4 ABCDFILMNOP**Q**	AEJKL	9
5 ABDEFGHKLM**N**	ABDHIJLNO**T**U	10

10A ❶ €42.80
3ha 80T(70-100m²) 77P ❷ €54.80

🚗 A8, exit 47 direction Villeneuve-Loubet, after that D6 direction Grasse. Signposted.

🏕 Set in lush and shaded surroundings, bordered by a river, you will be welcomed to an oasis of tranquillity.
CC 9/4-30/6 1/9-28/9 7=6

📍 N 43°41'4'' E 7°4'24''
www.eurocampings.co.uk/108488

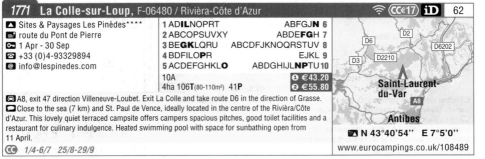

1771 La Colle-sur-Loup, F-06480 / Rivièra-Côte d'Azur 🛜 CC€17 iD 62

- ▲ Sites & Paysages Les Pinèdes★★★★
- 🚏 route du Pont de Pierre
- 📅 1 Apr - 30 Sep
- ☎ +33 (0)4-93329894
- @ info@lespinedes.com

1 ADILNOPRT	ABFGJN	6
2 ABCOPSUVXY	ABDEFGH	7
3 BEGKLQRU ABCDFJKNOQRSTUV		8
4 BDFILOPR	EJKL	9
5 ACDEFGHKLO	ABDGHIJLNPTU	10
10A		❶ €43.20
4ha 106T(80-110m²) 41P		❷ €55.80

🚗 A8, exit 47 direction Villeneuve-Loubet. Exit La Colle and take route D6 in the direction of Grasse.
💬 Close to the sea (7 km) and St. Paul de Vence, ideally located in the centre of the Rivièra/Côte d'Azur. This lovely quiet terraced campsite offers campers spacious pitches, good toilet facilities and a restaurant for culinary indulgence. Heated swimming pool with space for sunbathing open from 11 April.

CC 1/4-6/7 25/8-29/9

Saint-Laurent-du-Var
Antibes

📍 N 43°40'54'' E 7°5'0''

www.eurocampings.co.uk/108489

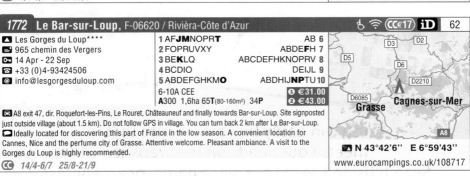

1772 Le Bar-sur-Loup, F-06620 / Rivièra-Côte d'Azur ♿ 🛜 CC€17 iD 62

- ▲ Les Gorges du Loup★★★★
- 🚏 965 chemin des Vergers
- 📅 14 Apr - 22 Sep
- ☎ +33 (0)4-93424506
- @ info@lesgorgesduloup.com

1 AFJMNOPRT	AB	6
2 FOPRUVXY	ABDEFH	7
3 BEKLQ ABCDEFHKNOPRV		8
4 BCDIO	DEIJL	9
5 ABDEFGHKMO	ABDHIJNPTU	10
6-10A CEE		❶ €31.00
A300 1,6ha 65T(80-160m²) 34P		❷ €43.00

🚗 A8 exit 47, dir. Roquefort-les-Pins, Le Rouret, Châteauneuf and finally towards Bar-sur-Loup. Site signposted just outside village (about 1.5 km). Do not follow GPS in village. You can turn back 2 km after Le Bar-sur-Loup.
💬 Ideally located for discovering this part of France in the low season. A convenient location for Cannes, Nice and the perfume city of Grasse. Attentive welcome. Pleasant ambiance. A visit to the Gorges du Loup is highly recommended.

CC 14/4-6/7 25/8-21/9

Grasse Cagnes-sur-Mer

📍 N 43°42'6'' E 6°59'43''

www.eurocampings.co.uk/108717

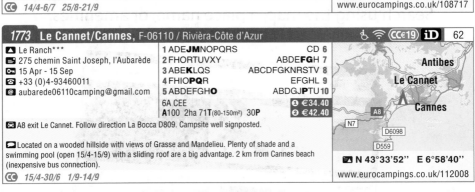

1773 Le Cannet/Cannes, F-06110 / Rivièra-Côte d'Azur ♿ 🛜 CC€19 iD 62

- ▲ Le Ranch★★★
- 🚏 275 chemin Saint Joseph, l'Aubarède
- 📅 15 Apr - 15 Sep
- ☎ +33 (0)4-93460011
- @ aubarede06110camping@gmail.com

1 ADEJMNOPQRS	CD	6
2 FHORTUVXY	ABDEFGH	7
3 ABEKLQS ABCDFGKNRSTV		8
4 FHIOPQR	EFGHL	9
5 ABDEFGHO	ABDGJPTU	10
6A CEE		❶ €34.40
A100 2ha 71T(80-150m²) 30P		❷ €42.40

🚗 A8 exit Le Cannet. Follow direction La Bocca D809. Campsite well signposted.

💬 Located on a wooded hillside with views of Grasse and Mandelieu. Plenty of shade and a swimming pool (open 15/4-15/9) with a sliding roof are a big advantage. 2 km from Cannes beach (inexpensive bus connection).

CC 15/4-30/6 1/9-14/9

Antibes
Le Cannet
Cannes

📍 N 43°33'52'' E 6°58'40''

www.eurocampings.co.uk/112008

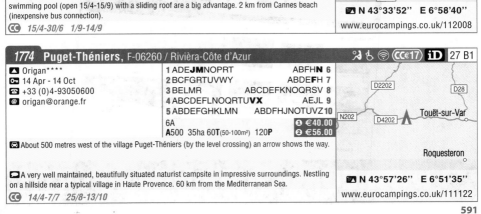

1774 Puget-Théniers, F-06260 / Rivièra-Côte d'Azur 🌐 ♿ 🛜 CC€17 iD 27 B1

- ▲ Origan★★★★
- 📅 14 Apr - 14 Oct
- ☎ +33 (0)4-93050600
- @ origan@orange.fr

1 ADEJMNOPRT	ABFHN	6
2 BCFGRTUVWY	ABDEFH	7
3 BELMR ABCDEFKNOQRSV		8
4 ABCDEFLNOQRTUVX	AEJL	9
5 ABDEFGHKLMN ABDFHJNOTUVZ		10
6A		❶ €40.00
A500 35ha 60T(50-100m²) 120P		❷ €56.00

🚗 About 500 metres west of the village Puget-Théniers (by the level crossing) an arrow shows the way.

💬 A very well maintained, beautifully situated naturist campsite in impressive surroundings. Nestling on a hillside near a typical village in Haute Provence. 60 km from the Mediterranean Sea.

CC 14/4-7/7 25/8-13/10

Touët-sur-Var
Roquesteron

📍 N 43°57'26'' E 6°51'35''

www.eurocampings.co.uk/111122

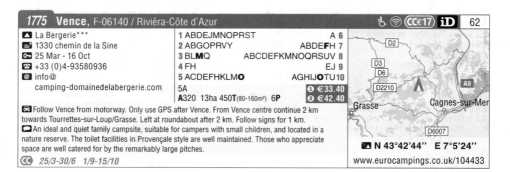

1775 **Vence**, F-06140 / Rivièra-Côte d'Azur

- La Bergerie★★★
- 1330 chemin de la Sine
- 25 Mar - 16 Oct
- +33 (0)4-93580936
- info@
  camping-domainedelabergerie.com

1 ABDEJMNOPRST	A 6
2 ABGOPRVY	ABDE**F**H 7
3 BL**M**Q	ABCDEFKMNOQRSUV 8
4 FH	EJ 9
5 ACDEFHKLM**O**	AGHIJ**O**TU10
5A	❶ €33.40
A320 13ha 450**T**(80-160m²) 6**P**	❷ €42.40

Follow Vence from motorway. Only use GPS after Vence. From Vence centre continue 2 km towards Tourrettes-sur-Loup/Grasse. Left at roundabout after 2 km. Follow signs for 1 km.
An ideal and quiet family campsite, suitable for campers with small children, and located in a nature reserve. The toilet facilities in Provençale style are well maintained. Those who appreciate space are well catered for by the remarkably large pitches.

CC 25/3-30/6 1/9-15/10

N 43°42'44'' E 7°5'24''

www.eurocampings.co.uk/104433

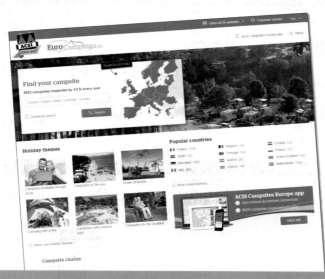
France

Corsica

Island of Beauty

Tough, mountainous, yet beautiful – Corse's landscape and strategic location have shaped its history. Standing stones near Filitosa indicate Stone Age habitation, and the Island of Beauty has been ruled by Romans, Etruscans, Carthaginians, Greeks, Pisans, Genovese, Italians, and French. Today the island is home to many rare species of plants, and everywhere you look is the wild evergreen shrub known as maquis.

History all around

At the coast, look around – you won't be far from one of the watch towers built by the Genovese. They also built the citadel at Bonifacio, and you can walk up there or take the little train and stroll around. Sit at a café to soak up the atmosphere in the maze of mediaeval streets of the Old Town. The Corsican capital Ajaccio, set against a backdrop of forested mountains, also has a citadel, but this is still used by the military. Not to worry – there are plenty of other interesting places! Admire the beautiful Baroque cathedral, and the attractive and shaded Foch Square near the seafront. Ajaccio is the birthplace of Napoleon Bonaparte, and you can see the marble font in the cathedral where he was baptised. Naturally the town has amazing beaches, and children's playgrounds along the seafront promenade will keep the smallies happy.

Day trips and things to do

How about swimming in a natural river pool at Vallée du Fango near Galeria? Porto-Vecchio, with its lovely bays and white beaches, is a great base for walking the Alta Rocca and Bavella Massif. Further north is Parc de la Solenzara which offers canyoning, paintballing, and kayaking – so everybody's happy. Western Corse has the village of Girolata, which you can only reach on foot or by boat. Cap Corse in the north

is also interesting: just offshore from Barcaggio is the island of Giraglia, home to one of the largest lighthouses in the Mediterranean.

Did you know ...?
According to legend, explorer Christopher Columbus was originally from Calvi, Corsica.

Our tips

1. *See the mysterious black beach at Nonza, Cap Corse*
2. *Visit the fortress and Museum of Corse in the inland hilltop town of Corte*
3. *Go hiking on Les Calanches cliffs overlooking Golfe de Porto*
4. *Wander around the megalithic standing stones at Filitosa and Sartene*
5. *Music lover? Check out the Polyfonie Festival of World Music*

What to eat and drink

With all these wild forests, wild boar is widely available. Seafood and freshwater trout are also abundant. Local dishes are figatellu (liver), lonzu (pork), cured meats, brocciu cheese, chestnuts and local fruit. To drink, try aquavita, a type of brandy that burns as it goes down. Be sure to take home some Corsican honey.

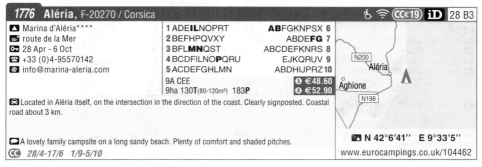

1776 Aléria, F-20270 / Corsica

  🚴 🛜 CC€19 iD 28 B3

🏕 Marina d'Aléria★★★★
📧 route de la Mer
📅 28 Apr - 6 Oct
☎ +33 (0)4-95570142
@ info@marina-aleria.com

1 ADE**IL**NOPRT	**AB**FGKNPSX **6**
2 BEFHPQVXY	ABDE**FG 7**
3 BFL**MN**QST	ABCDEFKNRS **8**
4 BCDFILNO**P**QRU	EJKQRUV **9**
5 ACDEFGHLMN	ABDHIJPRZ **10**
9A CEE	💶 €48.60
9ha 130**T**(80-120m²) 183**P**	💶 €52.90

🛏 Located in Aléria itself, on the intersection in the direction of the coast. Clearly signposted. Coastal road about 3 km.

💬 A lovely family campsite on a long sandy beach. Plenty of comfort and shaded pitches.
CC *28/4-17/6 1/9-5/10*

📍 **N 42°6'41'' E 9°33'5''**

www.eurocampings.co.uk/104462

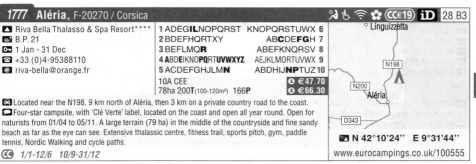

1777 Aléria, F-20270 / Corsica

  🍴 🚴 🛜 ✿ CC€19 iD 28 B3

🏕 Riva Bella Thalasso & Spa Resort★★★★
📧 B.P. 21
📅 1 Jan - 31 Dec
☎ +33 (0)4-95388110
@ riva-bella@orange.fr

1 ADEG**IL**NOPQRST	KNOPQRSTUWX **6**
2 BDEFHQRTXY	AB**CDEFGH 7**
3 BEFLMQ**R**	ABEFKNQRSV **8**
4 **ABD**EI**K**NO**P**QRT**UVWXYZ**	AEJKLMORTUVWX **9**
5 ACDEFGHJLM**N**	ABDHIJ**NP**TUZ **10**
10A CEE	💶 €47.70
78ha 200**T**(100-160m²) 166**P**	💶 €66.30

🛏 Located near the N198, 9 km north of Aléria, then 3 km on a private country road to the coast.
💬 Four-star campsite, with 'Clé Verte' label. Located on the coast and open all year round. Open for naturists from 01/04 to 05/11. A large terrain (79 ha) in the middle of the countryside and fine sandy beach as far as the eye can see. Extensive thalassic centre, fitness trail, sports pitch, gym, paddle tennis, Nordic Walking and cycle paths.
CC *1/1-12/6 10/9-31/12*

📍 **N 42°10'24'' E 9°31'44''**

www.eurocampings.co.uk/100555

1778 Bonifacio, F-20169 / Corsica

  🚴 🛜 CC€17 ♟ iD 35 A1

🏕 Pian del Fosse★★★
📧 route de Santa Manza
📅 20 Apr - 15 Oct
☎ +33 (0)4-95731634
@ pian.del.fosse@wanadoo.fr

1 ACDE**JM**NOR**T**	X **6**
2 PUVY	ABDE**FG**H **7**
3 B**GHK**LQ	ABCDEFKNORSV **8**
4 OR	FJ **9**
5 ABDEHJM**NO**	ABDFGHIJLO**Q**V **10**
10A CEE	💶 €35.30
A100 5ha 100**T**(40-80m²) 19**P**	💶 €45.10

🛏 From Porto Vecchio N198 dir. Bonifacio. Left at white Sant' Amanza (D60) sign close to Bonifacio. Right at end of road (D58). Follow campsite sign. For Satnav enter: Pian del Fosse/Bonifacio or coordinates.
💬 Very well maintained campsite with a friendly welcome and plenty of shade. The perfect starting point for visiting bays, beaches and towns. A quiet campsite. Cycle or walk inland from the campsite to Bonifacio along marked-out paths.
CC *20/4-14/7 1/9-14/10*

📍 **N 41°23'59'' E 9°12'4''**

www.eurocampings.co.uk/101400

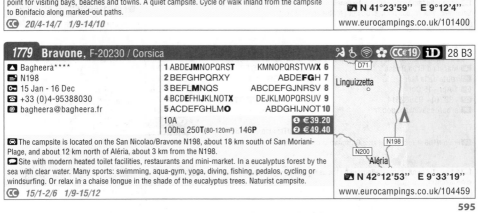

1779 Bravone, F-20230 / Corsica

  🍴 🚴 🛜 ✿ CC€19 iD 28 B3

🏕 Bagheera★★★★
📧 N198
📅 15 Jan - 16 Dec
☎ +33 (0)4-95388030
@ bagheera@bagheera.fr

1 ABDE**JM**NOPQRST	KMNOPQRSTVW**X 6**
2 BEFGHPQRXY	ABDE**FG**H **7**
3 BEFL**M**NQS	ABCDEFGJNRSV **8**
4 BCD**E**FHIJKLNOT**X**	DEJKLMOPQRSUV **9**
5 ACDEFGHLM**O**	ABDGHIJNOT **10**
10A	💶 €39.20
100ha 250**T**(80-120m²) 146**P**	💶 €49.40

🛏 The campsite is located on the San Nicolao/Bravone N198, about 18 km south of San Moriani-Plage, and about 12 km north of Aléria, about 3 km from the N198.
💬 Site with modern heated toilet facilities, restaurants and mini-market. In a eucalyptus forest by the sea with clear water. Many sports: swimming, aqua-gym, yoga, diving, fishing, pedalos, cycling or windsurfing. Or relax in a chaise longue in the shade of the eucalyptus trees. Naturist campsite.
CC *15/1-2/6 1/9-15/12*

📍 **N 42°12'53'' E 9°33'19''**

www.eurocampings.co.uk/104459

France

1780 Calvi, F-20260 / Corsica

🚷 📶 (CC€15) **iD** 28 A3

🔺 Dolce Vita***
🚌 route de Bastia, N197
📅 27 Apr - 30 Sep
☎ +33 (0)4-95650599
@ dolce-vita.office@orange.fr

1 ADEILNOPQRST	KNOPQSW**X**YZ 6
2 BCEHOQVWXY	BE**FG**H 7
3 BCEGHLMQ	ABCDEFGJKNOQRSV 8
4 OT	EJL 9
5 ABDEGHJLM**O**	ABGHIJPTUVZ 10

10A CEE   ❶ €36.40
6ha 161**T**(80-100m²) 59**P**   ❷ €51.70

🚗 Located on the N197, l'Île Rousse-Calvi, about 4 km north of Calvi.

💬 Quiet family campsite, located directly on the coast only 3 km from Calvi. Shaded pitches. Fully renovated toilet facilities.

(CC) 27/4-30/6 1/9-29/9 7=6, 14=11

Calvi N197   D151   D81   Monticello

🗺 N 42°33'15'' E 8°47'19''

www.eurocampings.co.uk/104435

1781 Calvi, F-20260 / Corsica

🚷 📶 (CC€19) **iD** 28 A3

🔺 La Pinède****
🚌 route de la Pinède
📅 31 Mar - 10 Nov
☎ +33 (0)4-95651780
@ info@camping-calvi.com

1 ADEILNOPRST	ABFGHIKNOPQRSTW**X** 6
2 EHOQRVXY	ABDE**FG**H 7
3 BDEGHILMQ	ABCDEFNORSV 8
4 ABCDEILNOR**TUVXZ**	EJKL 9
5 ACDEFGHJLMN**O**	ABGHIJO**P**TVZ 10

12A CEE   ❶ €44.80
5ha 123**T**(80-100m²) 139**P**   ❷ €64.60

🚗 N197 from l'Île Rousse dir. Calvi. At Calvi (after the place name sign) turn right after 200 metres. Follow campsite signs. Campsite situated in La Pinède woods.
💬 Situated at one of the most beautiful fine sandy beaches in Europe. Campsite La Pinède welcomes you to a forest of pine and eucalyptus trees. A 20-minute walk from the centre of Calvi. Experience an unforgettable holiday under the Corsican sun in this 5ha oasis full of flowers and greenery.

(CC) 31/3-30/6 1/9-9/11 7=6, 14=11

L'Île-Rousse Calvi D71 N197 D151 D81

🗺 N 42°33'13'' E 8°46'7''

www.eurocampings.co.uk/104437

1782 Ghisonaccia, F-20240 / Corsica

🚷 📶 (CC€19) **iD** 28 B3

🔺 Arinella Bianca*****
🚌 route de la Mer
📅 28 Apr - 13 Oct
☎ +33 (0)4-95560478
@ arinella@arinellabianca.com

1 ADE**IL**NOPRST	ABF**K**MNPQRSTWX 6
2 CEFHOPQVY	ABDE**FG**H 7
3 BEF**GH**LMQ	ABCDEFNQRSV 8
4 BCD**E**ILN**PQUXYZ**	EJLMOQRT 9
5 ACDEFGHKLMN	ABDGHIJM**P**TUVZ 10

10A CEE   ❶ €57.30
10ha 100**T**(80-100m²) 225**P**   ❷ €80.60

🚗 From the N198 roundabout after Ghisonaccia centre, take route de la Mer 5 km, and turn right at the roundabout. Follow campsite signs.

💬 A beautiful family campsite on the beach with a swimming pool and plenty of entertainment. Separated, well shaded pitches. Charges for the spa and pool.

(CC) 28/4-6/7 1/9-12/10

D344 D343 Ghisonaccia Prunelli-di-Fiumorbo N198

🗺 N 41°59'56'' E 9°26'32''

www.eurocampings.co.uk/104463

1783 Ghisonaccia, F-20240 / Corsica

📶 (CC€17) **iD** 28 B3

🔺 Marina d'Erba Rossa****
🚌 route de la Mer
📅 1 Apr - 15 Oct
☎ +33 (0)4-95562514
@ erbarossa@wanadoo.fr

1 ADE**IL**NOPRST	AKMNOPQ 6
2 BEFHPQRVWXY	ABDE**FG**H 7
3 ABEFILMQ	ABCDEFNQRS 8
4 ABCDHIKLNO**P**Q**TUXYZ**	EJKLV 9
5 ACDEFGHJL	ABDHIJO**P**STZ 10

10A CEE   ❶ €60.10
20ha 70**T**(80-120m²) 538**P**   ❷ €72.10

🚗 From N198 at roundabout after Ghisonaccia centre. Route de la Mer 5 km.

💬 A beautiful family campsite located on the beach, with every comfort, shady pitches and lots of entertainment.

(CC) 7/4-7/7 2/9-13/10

D343 D344 Ghisonaccia Prunelli-di-Fiumorbo N198

🗺 N 42°0'2'' E 9°26'49''

www.eurocampings.co.uk/101264

1784 Ghisonaccia, F-20240 / Corsica

🛜 CC€17 **iD** 28 B3

- 🏕 U Casone
- 🚩 route de la Mer
- 📅 1 May - 1 Oct
- ☎ +33 (0)4-95560241
- @ info@ucasone.net

1 ADE**JM**NOPRST	A**N**OPQSUW**X** 6
2 CFHQRVXY	ABDE**F**H 7
3 AFL	ABEFNQRSTV 8
4 D**E**O**X**	ABEIJRVZ 9
5 ABDGHKN	ABGHIJOTUV 10

4-16A CEE
4ha 100T(100-160m²) 42**P**

❶ €31.40
❷ €44.00

🗺 From N198, after centre at roundabout take route de la Mer. Turn right after about 4 km and follow campsite signs.

💬 Very quiet campsite with friendly welcome. Basic toilet facilities. Shaded and sunny marked-out pitches. Swimming pool and cocktail bar. Beach 700 metres away, accessible via a path.

🗺 **N 41°59'58'' E 9°26'10''**

CC 1/5-30/6 1/9-30/9

www.eurocampings.co.uk/121074

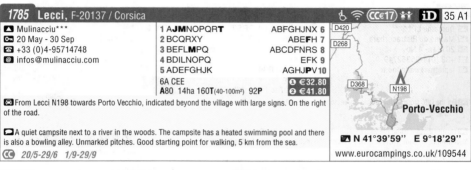

1785 Lecci, F-20137 / Corsica

♿ 🛜 CC€17 ♟ **iD** 35 A1

- 🏕 Mulinacciu***
- 📅 20 May - 30 Sep
- ☎ +33 (0)4-95714748
- @ infos@mulinacciu.com

1 A**JM**NOPQR**T**	ABFGHJNX 6
2 BCQRXY	ABE**F**H 7
3 BEFL**M**PQ	ABCDFNRS 8
4 BDILNOPQ	EFK 9
5 ADEFGHJK	AGHJ**P**V 10

6A CEE
A80 14ha 160T(40-100m²) 92**P**

❶ €32.80
❷ €41.80

🗺 From Lecci N198 towards Porto Vecchio, indicated beyond the village with large signs. On the right of the road.

💬 A quiet campsite next to a river in the woods. The campsite has a heated swimming pool and there is also a bowling alley. Unmarked pitches. Good starting point for walking, 5 km from the sea.

🗺 **N 41°39'59'' E 9°18'29''**

CC 20/5-29/6 1/9-29/9

www.eurocampings.co.uk/109544

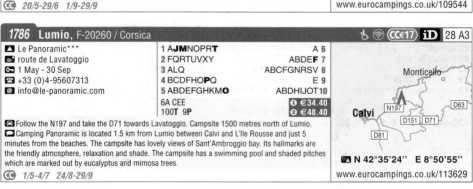

1786 Lumio, F-20260 / Corsica

♿ 🛜 CC€17 **iD** 28 A3

- 🏕 Le Panoramic***
- 🚩 route de Lavatoggio
- 📅 1 May - 30 Sep
- ☎ +33 (0)4-95607313
- @ info@le-panoramic.com

1 A**JM**NOPR**T**	A 6
2 FQRTUVXY	ABDE**F** 7
3 ALQ	ABCFGNRSV 8
4 BCDFHO**PQ**	E 9
5 ABDEFGHKM**O**	ABDHIJOT 10

6A CEE
100T 9**P**

❶ €34.40
❷ €48.40

🗺 Follow the N197 and take the D71 towards Lavatoggio. Campsite 1500 metres north of Lumio.
💬 Camping Panoramic is located 1.5 km from Lumio between Calvi and L'Ile Rousse and just 5 minutes from the beaches. The campsite has lovely views of Sant'Ambroggio bay. Its hallmarks are the friendly atmosphere, relaxation and shade. The campsite has a swimming pool and shaded pitches which are marked out by eucalyptus and mimosa trees.

🗺 **N 42°35'24'' E 8°50'55''**

CC 1/5-4/7 24/8-29/9

www.eurocampings.co.uk/113629

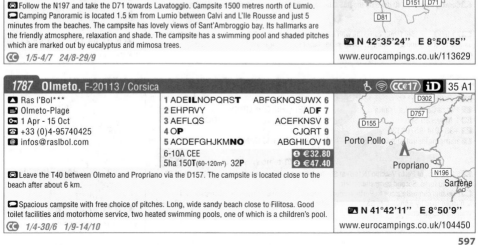

1787 Olmeto, F-20113 / Corsica

♿ 🛜 CC€17 **iD** 35 A1

- 🏕 Ras l'Bol***
- 🚩 Olmeto-Plage
- 📅 1 Apr - 15 Oct
- ☎ +33 (0)4-95740425
- @ infos@raslbol.com

1 ADE**IL**NOPQRS**T**	ABFGKNQSUW**X** 6
2 EHPRVY	AD**F** 7
3 AEFLQS	ACEFKNSV 8
4 O**P**	CJQRT 9
5 ACDEFGHJKM**NO**	ABGHILOV 10

6-10A CEE
5ha 150T(60-120m²) 32**P**

❶ €32.80
❷ €47.40

🗺 Leave the T40 between Olmeto and Propriano via the D157. The campsite is located close to the beach after about 6 km.

💬 Spacious campsite with free choice of pitches. Long, wide sandy beach close to Filitosa. Good toilet facilities and motorhome service, two heated swimming pools, one of which is a children's pool.

🗺 **N 41°42'11'' E 8°50'9''**

CC 1/4-30/6 1/9-14/10

www.eurocampings.co.uk/104450

France

1788 Olmeto, F-20113 / Corsica

♿ 📶 (CC€15) iD 35 A1

- 🏕 Vigna Maggiore***
- 🏠 T40/D157
- 📅 1 Apr - 30 Oct
- ☎ +33 (0)6-85930106
- @ vignamaggiore@gmail.com

1	ACILNOPQRST	AB	6
2	FGQRTWXY	ABDEFH	7
3	ABLQ	ABCDEFKNV	8
4	F	F	9
5	ABCDEFGHJKMN	AGHIJNOST	10

6A CEE ❶ €32.30
A50 5,5ha 140T(70-180m²) 40P ❷ €45.30

🚗 From Propriano dir. Olmeto, site on a bend on the left just after the D157 intersection. From Ajaccio on T40, site on a bend after Olmeto, 2nd entrance on the right. After bend take D157 exit, site on the right after the filling station.

💬 A peaceful campsite on the southwest coast close to Olmeto and about 5 km from Propriano. Beach 5 minutes towards Porto Pollo. Lovely swimming pools, the smallest of which is heated, with bar, patio and sea views.

(CC) 1/4-7/7 25/8-29/10

📷 N 41°41'53'' E 8°53'47''

www.eurocampings.co.uk/121407

1789 Pietracorbara, F-20233 / Corsica

♿ 📶 (CC€17) iD 28 A2

- 🏕 Domaine LP****
- 🏠 Marine de Pietracorbara
- 📅 20 Mar - 4 Nov
- ☎ +33 (0)4-95352749
- @ lapietra@wanadoo.fr

1	ADEJMNOPQRST	AOPQX	6
2	FGHMOQVWXY	ABDEF	7
3	BLQ	ABCDEFNOQRS	8
4	IOU	J	9
5	ABDEHJKN	AFGHIJOTUZ	10

10A CEE ❶ €38.30
5ha 170T(95-120m²) 13P ❷ €50.10

🚗 On the D80 from Bastia to Cap Corse, turn left after 20 km, well signposted.

💬 Quietly located campsite with excellent toilet facilities on Cap Corse, a unique part of Corsica. New swimming pool. There is a lovely beach 600 metres away via a footpath.

(CC) 20/3-30/6 10/9-3/11

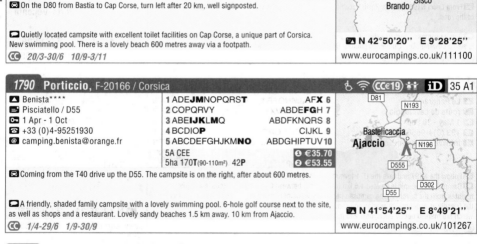

📷 N 42°50'20'' E 9°28'25''

www.eurocampings.co.uk/111100

1790 Porticcio, F-20166 / Corsica

♿ 📶 (CC€19) ✹✹ iD 35 A1

- 🏕 Benista****
- 🏠 Pisciatello / D55
- 📅 1 Apr - 1 Oct
- ☎ +33 (0)4-95251930
- @ camping.benista@orange.fr

1	ADEJMNOPQRST	AFX	6
2	COPQRVY	ABDEFGH	7
3	ABEIJKLMQ	ABDFKNQRS	8
4	BCDIOP	CIJKL	9
5	ABCDEFGHJKMNO	ABDGHIPTUV	10

5A CEE ❶ €35.70
5ha 170T(90-110m²) 42P ❷ €53.55

🚗 Coming from the T40 drive up the D55. The campsite is on the right, after about 600 metres.

💬 A friendly, shaded family campsite with a lovely swimming pool. 6-hole golf course next to the site, as well as shops and a restaurant. Lovely sandy beaches 1.5 km away. 10 km from Ajaccio.

(CC) 1/4-29/6 1/9-30/9

📷 N 41°54'25'' E 8°49'21''

www.eurocampings.co.uk/101267

1791 Porto Vecchio, F-20137 / Corsica

♿ 📶 (CC€17) iD 35 A1

- 🏕 Les Ilots d'Or***
- 🏠 Pezza Cardo - La Trinité
- 📅 2 May - 30 Sep
- ☎ +33 (0)4-95700130
- @ campinglesilotsdor@sfr.fr

1	ADILNORST	KMNQSTWX	6
2	BEFGHIPQRSUVXY	ABDEFH	7
3	ABLQ	ABCDEFLNORS	8
4	O	EHJ	9
5	ACDEFGHJKMNO	ABGHIJOT	10

6A CEE ❶ €26.30
4ha 180T(20-110m²) 51P ❷ €36.80

🚗 5 km north of Porto Vecchio (N198) at Ste Trinité, exit in direction of ocean (D468), take D568 when road forks. Second campsite on left.

💬 Beautiful campsite close to Porto Vecchio. Spacious, well maintained beach campsite with asphalted road by a small bay. Sandy beach inclines only slightly. Suitable for families with children. Watersports options.

(CC) 2/5-29/6 1/9-29/9

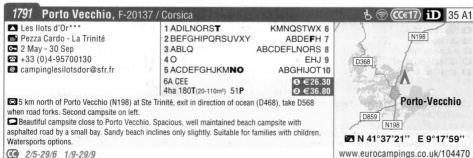

📷 N 41°37'21'' E 9°17'59''

www.eurocampings.co.uk/104470

1792 Sagone, F-20118 / Corsica

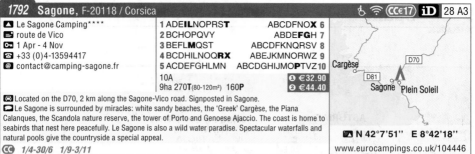

♿ 📶 (CC€17) iD 28 A3

- ⛺ Le Sagone Camping****
- 🛣 route de Vico
- 📅 1 Apr - 4 Nov
- ☎ +33 (0)4-13594417
- @ contact@camping-sagone.fr

1	ADE**IL**NOPRS**T**	ABCDFNO**X**	6
2	BCHOPQVY	ABDE**FG**H	7
3	BEFL**M**QST	ABCDFKNQRSV	8
4	BCDHILNOQ**RX**	ABEJKMNORWZ	9
5	ACDEFGHLMN	ABCDGHIJMO**P**TVZ	10

10A   ❸ €32.90
9ha 270T(80-120m²) 160P   ❷ €44.40

🔲 Located on the D70, 2 km along the Sagone-Vico road. Signposted in Sagone.

🔲 Le Sagone is surrounded by miracles: white sandy beaches, the 'Greek' Cargèse, the Piana Calanques, the Scandola nature reserve, the tower of Porto and Genoese Ajaccio. The coast is home to seabirds that nest here peacefully. Le Sagone is also a wild water paradise. Spectacular waterfalls and natural pools give the countryside a special appeal.

(CC) 1/4-30/6 1/9-3/11

N 42°7'51'' E 8°42'18''

www.eurocampings.co.uk/104446

1793 Sartène, F-20100 / Corsica

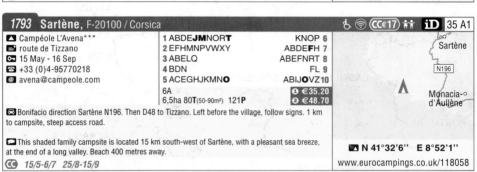

♿ 📶 (CC€17) ♟♟ iD 35 A1

- ⛺ Campéole L'Avena***
- 🛣 route de Tizzano
- 📅 15 May - 16 Sep
- ☎ +33 (0)4-95770218
- @ avena@campeole.com

1	ABDE**JM**NOR**T**	KNOP	6
2	EFHMNPVWXY	ABDE**F**H	7
3	ABELQ	ABEFNRT	8
4	BDN	FL	9
5	ACEGHJKMN**O**	ABIJ**O**VZ	10

6A   ❸ €35.20
6,5ha 80T(50-90m²) 121P   ❷ €48.70

🔲 Bonifacio direction Sartène N196. Then D48 to Tizzano. Left before the village, follow signs. 1 km to campsite, steep access road.

🔲 This shaded family campsite is located 15 km south-west of Sartène, with a pleasant sea breeze, at the end of a long valley. Beach 400 metres away.

(CC) 15/5-6/7 25/8-15/9

N 41°32'6'' E 8°52'1''

www.eurocampings.co.uk/118058

1794 Solaro, F-20240 / Corsica

♿ 📶 (CC€17) ♟♟ iD 35 A1

- ⛺ Les Eucalyptus**
- 🛣 N198
- 📅 1 May - 15 Oct
- ☎ +33 (0)6-86810371
- @ camping.eucalyptus@orange.fr

1	ABJMNOPQRST	KX	6
2	CEFHRWX	ABDE**F**	7
3	FL	ABEFNR	8
4		D	9
5	ADHJN**O**	AHOR	10

15A   ❸ €28.30
3ha 60T(100m²) 4P   ❷ €35.30

🔲 Campsite is on N198, 2 km north of Solenzara.

🔲 A beautiful campsite situated on the beach. Shaded pitches under eucalyptus trees. Pick your own pitch.

(CC) 1/5-30/6 1/9-14/10

N 41°52'38'' E 9°23'47''

www.eurocampings.co.uk/119459

Spain

Bay of Biscay

Bordeaux

FRANCE

A Coruña
Santiago de Compostela
705
GALICIA
Vigo
Porto

ASTURIAS
715 Oviedo
León
CANTABRIA
Santander
699

BASQUE COUNTRY/
NAVARRE/
LA RIOJA
Bilbao San Sebastián
Pamplona
688
Logroño

Toulouse

LLEIDA
ANDORRA
LA VELLA
ANDORRA

Burgos

720
Valladolid

Zaragoza

Lleida

651

BARCELONA/
GIRONA
605
Barcelona

CASTILE AND LEON/MADRID
Salamanca

PORTUGAL

MADRID
Alcalá de Henares
Toledo

ARAGON
679

638
Tarragona

TARRAGONA

ESTREMADURA/
CASTILE-LA MANCHA
Badajoz

Castellón de la Plana

Valencia

Albacete
731

VALENCIAN
COMMUNITY
658
Alicante

Córdoba

Sevilla
Huelva
Jerez de la Frontera
ANDALUSIA
738
Granada
Málaga
Marbella
GIBRALTAR
Tanger Ceuta

MOROCCO

758
Murcia
MURCIA
Cartagena

Almería

Mediterranean Sea

CS-WEU

General
Spain is a member of the EU. The capital city is Madrid.

Time
The time in Spain is one hour ahead of London.

Languages
Spanish.

Crossings
There are direct ferry connections between the UK and Spain. On page 36, you can see at a glance where the ferries depart and arrive.

Currency

The currency in Spain is the euro. Approximate exchange rates September 2017: € 1 = £ 0.92. ATMs are present in all Spanish cities and towns, shopping centres and popular tourist destinations. Occasionally they are also located at train and bus stations and gas stations.

Credit cards

Credit cards, like Visa en Mastercard, are widely accepted in most places, including toll roads.

(Mobile) phones

The mobile network works well throughout Spain. There is a 4G network for mobile internet.

Wifi, internet

You can use a wifi networks at many public locations, often for free.

Opening times /Public holidays

Banks

Banks are open from Monday to Friday until 2:00 pm, Saturday until 1:00 pm. Banks are closed on Saturdays in June, July and August.

Shops (including pharmacies)

Most shops are open from Monday to Friday until 1:30 pm and from 4:30 pm to 8:00 pm, on Saturdays from 9:30 am to 1:30 pm. Department stores and shopping centres in big towns are open all day from 10:00 am to 9:00 pm or 10:00 pm. During the tourist season shops in the coastal areas are often open until after 10:00 pm. In the week before Easter (the 'Semana Santa') the shops open for half the day. Spanish pharmacies, which can be recognised by a green cross, are open from Monday to Friday until 1:30 pm and from 4:30 pm to 8:00 pm.

Post

In general post offices are open on weekdays until 12:30 pm and from 5:00 pm to 8:00 pm, on Saturdays until 1:00 pm.

Public holidays

New Year's Day, 6 January (Epiphany), Maundy Thursday, Good Friday, Easter, 1 May (Labour Day), Whitsunday, 31 May (Corpus Christi), 15 August (The Assumption), 12 October (National Day), All Saints Day, 6 December

(Constitution Day), 8 December (Immaculate Conception), Christmas Day.

Roads and traffic

Traffic regulations

Remember, all traffic in Spain drives on the right and overtakes on the left! Headlight deflectors are advisable to prevent annoying oncoming drivers. If you are from Britain you will need to attach a GB sticker to the rear, unless your number plate incorporates a GB identifier.

You must give way to traffic from the right, except on priority routes. This also applies to slow traffic. Traffic on a roundabout (coming from the left!) has priority over traffic entering it. Trams always have priority.

If you go to Spain by car, make sure that you have the correct documents with you. See page 8. Furthermore, in Spain it is compulsory to have the following items in your car:

- Reflective jackets: one for each occupant, these must be kept inside the vehicle within easy reach.
- Warning triangle: compulsory in every vehicle with 4 wheels or more. It is best to have two warning triangles with you. For Spanish cars this is compulsory.
- Spare wheel: it is compulsory to have a spare wheel or tyre repair kit in your car, unless you have run-flat tires.

The maximum permitted alcohol level is 0.5 promille. Dipped headlights are compulsory in tunnels. Phones may only be used hands-free. Use of the horn is compulsory on blind corners in mountain areas. Carrying a spare set of lights is mandatory and drivers who wear spectacles must carry a spare pair. Radios and mobile phones

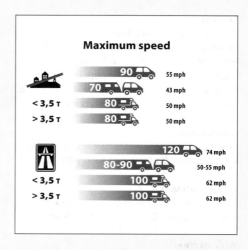

must be switched off when refuelling your vehicle. Use of a head set in cars is not permitted.

Road network

Spain uses the metric system, so distances are measured in kilometres (km) and speeds in kilometres per hour (km/h) 1 mile = 1.609 km and 1 km = 0.621 mile.

You are not advised to drive in the dark except on main roads. If you break down you can contact the Spanish motoring organisation RACE (in Catalonia the RACC) using the emergency phones.

Caravans, motorhomes

If your outfit (motorhome or car + caravan combination) exceeds 12 metres or has a total weight of 3,500 kg or more, you are required to fit ECE 70 marking plates. These are retro-reflective stickers that are to be placed at the back of your outfit. If your caravan is longer than 12 metres you must keep a distance of at least 50 metres from another vehicle outside built up areas.

Maximum permitted measurements of combined length

Height 4 metres, width 2.55 metres and maximum length 18.75 metres (of which the trailer is 12 metres maximum).

Fuel

Unleaded petrol and diesel are easily available everywhere. LPG is reasonably easily available.

Filling stations

Most filling stations along motorways are open between 6:00 am and 12:00 am. Elsewhere they are open between 7:00 am and 10:00 pm. Pay attention when filling up: 'gasolina' means petrol and 'gasóleo' means diesel! You can pay by credit card at all service stations on motorways.

Charging stations

Most charging stations, or estaciónes de carga eléctrical (ectrolineras), are located in and around the major Spanish cities. The network of public charging stations does not yet cover the whole country. Thus, it is definitely advisable to plan your trip carefully. For the exact location of charging stations check websites like ▶ *www.chargemap.com* ◀, ▶ *www.plugsurfing.com* ◀ or ▶ *openchargemap.org* ◀.

Tolls

Most motorways in Spain charge a toll. You can pay in cash, by credit card or automatically with an electronic (ETC) box. Toll roads are indicated by the letters AP, while toll-free motorways are

indicated by the letter A. More information:
▶ *www.autopistas.com* ◀.

Mountain passes with caravans

The Bonaigua Pass: is not prohibited for caravans, but snow chains must be used in the winter months when there is snow on the ground, and the pass may sometimes be closed.

The Portillón Pass: is not prohibited for caravans, but the road is not very wide and going in the direction of France is even narrower; so driving with a large(r) caravan may be difficult.

Emergency number

112: the national emergency number for fire, police or ambulance.

Camping

Spain has more than 1000 campsites, of which the sites on the northern Mediterranean coast are the busiest. Reservations are recommended here! Trees, bushes and flowers ensure beautiful campsites, and also provide marked out pitches which increase privacy.

Campsites in Spain are classified by category. Category 1 is the most luxurious. Free camping is not allowed. If you still want to camp where there is no campsite, permission from the landowner must be sought.

Practical

- The Spanish are renowned for eating late; quite often people eat at home and in catering establishments between 8:30 pm and 10:30 pm.
- Blue camping gas bottles cannot be refilled in Spain. You are advised to buy a Spanish container which can be returned when you leave the country.
- Make sure you have a world adaptor for electrical appliances.
- You are advised to drink bottled (mineral) water in preference to mains water.

Miles and miles of coastline

The two coastal provinces of Barcelona and Girona are part of the autonomous region of Catalonia, and border the Balearic Sea to the east. Girona – or Gerona in Catalan – is more mountainous, and includes the Mediterranean Pyrenees, with dizzying mountain peaks, forests and lakes. The two provinces share 580 km of coastline (360 miles). You'll find plenty of beaches and cliffs for hikes, and great villages to explore.

Cities of Barcelona and Girona

Gaudi is synonymous with Barcelona: The architect is responsible for Casa Milà, Casa Batlló, Parc Guëll and the Sagrada Familia, the cathedral that dominates the city skyline. Enjoy street performances from a Gothic Quarter café, stroll down La Rambla and admire the shops, or

take the cable car up to Montjuic Hill. The city of Girona is just as attractive: the Old Town is made up of buildings which date from Roman and Moorish times: the cathedral, once a mosque, is now an example of Catalan Gothic architecture. Did you know you can walk the ancient Roman walls of Girona? The Passeig de la Muralla, as this is called, is a great way to look over the maze of narrow streets, stairs and courtyards of mediaeval Girona.

Wild Catalonia

Walkers and nature-lovers visit Aiguamolls de l'Empordà National Park, which is mainly wetland with a beach, dune area, salt pans and freshwater lagoons. Walking routes bring you to the picturesque town of Castelló d'Empuries. For relaxing beach time in a historic location, try Tossa de Mar, where the beach is right beside the picturesque rocky fortified walls of town Vila Vella. Prefer someplace a little more active? Check out the water sports options at Roses, or hike the nearby rocky headland and wild bird sanctuary Cap de Creus.

> **Did you know ...?**
> Gustav Eiffel constructed a bridge - called the Pont de les Peixateries Velles - in Girona just before the Eiffel Tower was built.

Our tips

1. *The Dalí triangle: Portlligat House, Púbol castle and the Dalí Theatre-Museum in Figueres.*
2. *Spend a day in Montserrat Nature Park*
3. *The theme park on Tibidabo mountain is a guaranteed hit with kids*
4. *Walk around Pals, a beautiful mediaeval town with a great beach*
5. *Walk with giants during La Merce festival, Barcelona*

Bon profit!

A handy snack is pa amb tomàquet (country bread with tomato and olive oil), and you can also try patates d'Olot, Xuixo pastries and Botifarra sausage. Suqet de Peix is fish stew, and escudella d'Olla is a hearty winter stew, while esquietxada is a summer salad with fish. Also delicious is escalivada vegetable dish with aubergine and peppers. If you have room, have Crema Catalan or Mel I Mato for dessert.

1795 Albanyà, E-17733 / Cataluña ♿ 🤵 (CC€17) iD 25 B3

- 🏕 Bassegoda Park Cat. 1
- 📧 Camí de Bassegoda s/n
- 🗓 16 Mar - 9 Dec
- ☎ +34 972-542021
- @ info@bassegodapark.com

1	ADE**JM**NOPRS**T**	AJN 6
2	BCGRTVXY	ABDE**FG** 7
3	ABCE**GHIL**QT	ABEFJKNQRSTU 8
4	ABCD**EFG**HILNO**PQ**Y	CGJLUV 9
5	ABDEFGHJLMN**O**	ABHIJL**NP**V10

| 10-16A | | ❶ €37.00 |
| 4,5ha 126**T**(70-110m²) 78**P** | | ❷ €47.70 |

🚗 From France exit 3, from Spain exit 4 direction Llers, then Terrades and Sant Llorenç de la Muga and finally Albanyà, keep straight ahead; the road is a dead end.

💬 A campsite in wooded hilly surroundings with amenities that will surprise you. Only open at weekends from March to May and from October to December. Open every day from June to September.

CC 16/3-8/7 12/9-8/12 7=6, 14=10

Castellfollit De La Roca [A-26] Navata [N-260]

📍 **N 42°18'25'' E 2°42'31''**

www.eurocampings.co.uk/113335

1796 Begur/Girona, E-17255 / Cataluña 🤵 64

- 🏕 Begur
- 📧 Ctra d'Esclanyà km 4
- 🗓 1 Apr - 30 Sep
- ☎ +34 972-623201
- @ info@campingbegur.com

1	B**JM**NOPQRST	AB 6
2	GTVY	ABDE**FG**H 7
3	BE**KLM**	ABCDEFKNSTUV 8
4	BDFHILN**PQ**R	CHIJVWXZ 9
5	ACDEHJK	ABIKNOQSTVYZ10

| 10A | | ❶ €52.60 |
| 317**T**(90-150m²) 61**P** | | ❷ €64.10 |

🚗 Motorway, exit 6 direction Bisbal, from Pals direction Begur. In Begur drive in the direction of Aiguablava, then Palafrugell.

💬 A quiet campsite in a forest on a hilly terrain.

[C-66]

Palafrugell

📍 **N 41°56'25'' E 3°12'0''**

www.eurocampings.co.uk/109354

Spain

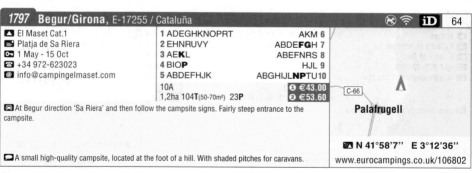

1797 Begur/Girona, E-17255 / Cataluña ⊗ 🤵 iD 64

- 🏕 El Maset Cat.1
- 📧 Platja de Sa Riera
- 🗓 1 May - 15 Oct
- ☎ +34 972-623023
- @ info@campingelmaset.com

1	ADEGHKNOPRT	AKM 6
2	EHNRUVY	ABDE**FG**H 7
3	AE**KL**	ABEFNRS 8
4	BIO**P**	HJL 9
5	ABDEFHJK	ABGHIJL**NP**TU10

| 10A | | ❶ €43.00 |
| 1,2ha 104**T**(50-70m²) 23**P** | | ❷ €53.60 |

🚗 At Begur direction 'Sa Riera' and then follow the campsite signs. Fairly steep entrance to the campsite.

💬 A small high-quality campsite, located at the foot of a hill. With shaded pitches for caravans.

[C-66]

Palafrugell

📍 **N 41°58'7'' E 3°12'36''**

www.eurocampings.co.uk/106802

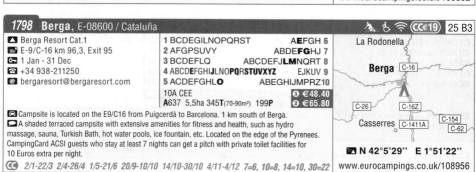

1798 Berga, E-08600 / Cataluña ♿ 🤵 (CC€19) 25 B3

- 🏕 Berga Resort Cat.1
- 📧 E-9/C-16 km 96,3, Exit 95
- 🗓 1 Jan - 31 Dec
- ☎ +34 938-211250
- @ bergaresort@bergaresort.com

1	BCDEGILNOPQRST	A**E**FGH 6
2	AFGPSUVY	ABDE**FG**HJ 7
3	BCDEFLQ	ABCDEFJ**LMN**QRT 8
4	ABCD**EFG**HIJLNO**PQRS TUVXYZ**	EJKUV 9
5	ACDEFGHL**O**	ABEGHIJMPRZ10

| 10A CEE | | ❶ €48.40 |
| A637 5,5ha 345**T**(70-90m²) 199**P** | | ❷ €65.80 |

🚗 Campsite is located on the E9/C16 from Puigcerdà to Barcelona. 1 km south of Berga.

💬 A shaded terraced campsite with extensive amenities for fitness and health, such as hydro massage, sauna, Turkish Bath, hot water pools, ice fountain, etc. Located on the edge of the Pyrenees. CampingCard ACSI guests who stay at least 7 nights can get a pitch with private toilet facilities for 10 Euros extra per night.

CC 2/1-22/3 2/4-26/4 1/5-21/6 20/9-10/10 14/10-30/10 4/11-4/12 7=6, 10=8, 14=10, 30=22

La Rodonella [C-16] **Berga** [C-26] [C-16Z] Casserres [C-1411A] [C-154] [C-62]

📍 **N 42°5'29'' E 1°51'22''**

www.eurocampings.co.uk/108956

1799 Besalú, E-17850 / Cataluña 📶 iD 25 B3

🏕 Camping de Besalú, S.L.
🏠 Camí de Besalú a Sant Ferriol, s/n
📅 1 Jan - 31 Dec
☎ +34 618-872444
@ campingdebesalu@gmail.com

1 ABDE**JM**NOPRS**T**		AN 6
2 BCFGPVXY		ABDE**FG** 7
3 ABLQ		ABEFNQRSUV 8
4 BFHO**XZ**		EJ 9
5 ABDEFGHJKL**O**		ABHIJPR10

8-16A
A250 68**T** 40**P**

❶ €31.50
❷ €40.50

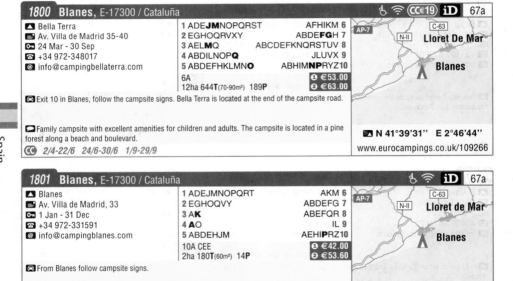

🅿 From Figueres take the N260, exit Besalú. Campsite signposted before the old bridge, another 3 km, direction Sant Ferriol. Partly unpaved road.

💬 Lovely stay in the forests with a view of the renowned historic city of Besalú. With various options for some relaxation.

📍 N 42°11'45'' E 2°41'14''
www.eurocampings.co.uk/122219

1800 Blanes, E-17300 / Cataluña ♿ 📶 (CC€19) iD 67a

🏕 Bella Terra
🏠 Av. Villa de Madrid 35-40
📅 24 Mar - 30 Sep
☎ +34 972-348017
@ info@campingbellaterra.com

1 ADE**JM**NOPQRST		AFHIKM 6
2 EGHOQRVXY		ABDE**FG**H 7
3 AEL**MQ**		ABCDEFKNQRSTUV 8
4 ABDILNOP**Q**		JLUVX 9
5 ABDEFHKLMN**O**		ABHIM**NP**RYZ10

6A
12ha 644**T**(70-90m²) 189**P**

❶ €53.00
❷ €63.00

🅿 Exit 10 in Blanes, follow the campsite signs. Bella Terra is located at the end of the campsite road.

💬 Family campsite with excellent amenities for children and adults. The campsite is located in a pine forest along a beach and boulevard.

📍 N 41°39'31'' E 2°46'44''
www.eurocampings.co.uk/109266

CC 2/4-22/6 24/6-30/6 1/9-29/9

1801 Blanes, E-17300 / Cataluña ♿ 📶 iD 67a

🏕 Blanes
🏠 Av. Villa de Madrid, 33
📅 1 Jan - 31 Dec
☎ +34 972-331591
@ info@campingblanes.com

1 ADEJMNOPQRT		AKM 6
2 EGHOQVY		ABDEFG 7
3 A**K**		ABEFQR 8
4 **A**O		IL 9
5 ABDEHJM		AEHI**P**RZ10

10A CEE
2ha 180**T**(60m²) 14**P**

❶ €42.00
❷ €53.60

🅿 From Blanes follow campsite signs.

💬 Small family campsite in a pine forest with reasonable toilet facilities.

📍 N 41°39'33'' E 2°46'48''
www.eurocampings.co.uk/108188

1802 Blanes, E-17300 / Cataluña 📶 (CC€19) iD 67a

🏕 Camping El Pinar
🏠 Av. Villa de Madrid, 39
📅 30 Mar - 30 Sep
☎ +34 972-331083
@ camping@elpinarbeach.com

1 ADE**JM**NOPQR**T**		AFKM 6
2 EGHOPQVWXY		ABDEFGH 7
3 AEL		ABEFNQRS 8
4 BCDIKLNO**RS**		JLVZ 9
5 ACDEFHKM		ABHIJ**P**RZ10

Ad on page 609 6-10A
6,8ha 449**T**(60-80m²) 63**P**

❶ €46.90
❷ €55.30

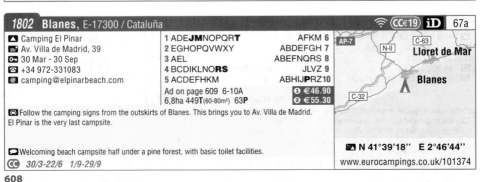

🅿 Follow the camping signs from the outskirts of Blanes. This brings you to Av. Villa de Madrid. El Pinar is the very last campsite.

💬 Welcoming beach campsite half under a pine forest, with basic toilet facilities.

CC 30/3-22/6 1/9-29/9

📍 N 41°39'18'' E 2°46'44''
www.eurocampings.co.uk/101374

BEACH CAMP

el Pinar

C O S T A   B R A V A

Holiday at the beach

The campsite EL PINAR is located on a 300m long fine sandy beach, and in a dense pine forest. There are daily activities for young and old and we have a beautiful swimming pool in a beautiful landscaped garden.

C. Villa de Madrid I E-17300 Blanes (Girona) Tel.: (34) 972 33 10 83 I www.campingelpinar.com

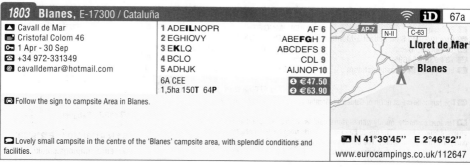

1803 Blanes, E-17300 / Cataluña 📶 iD 67a

- ▲ Cavall de Mar
- 🏠 Cristofal Colom 46
- 📅 1 Apr - 30 Sep
- ☎ +34 972-331349
- @ cavalldemar@hotmail.com

1 ADEILNOPR	AF 6
2 EGHIOVY	ABEFGH 7
3 EKLQ	ABCDEFS 8
4 BCLO	CDL 9
5 ADHJK	AIJNOP 10
6A CEE	❶ €47.50
1,5ha 150T 64P	❷ €63.90

🅿 Follow the sign to campsite Area in Blanes.

💬 Lovely small campsite in the centre of the 'Blanes' campsite area, with splendid conditions and facilities.

Lloret de Mar
Blanes

◤ N 41°39'45''   E 2°46'52''
www.eurocampings.co.uk/112647

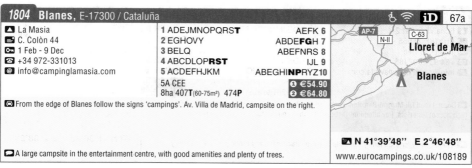

1804 Blanes, E-17300 / Cataluña ♿ 📶 iD 67a

- ▲ La Masia
- 🏠 C. Colòn 44
- 📅 1 Feb - 9 Dec
- ☎ +34 972-331013
- @ info@campinglamasia.com

1 ADEJMNOPQRST	AEFK 6
2 EGHIOVY	ABDEFGH 7
3 BELQ	ABEFNRS 8
4 ABCDLOPRST	IJL 9
5 ACDEFHJKM	ABEGHINPRYZ 10
5A CEE	❶ €54.90
8ha 407T (60-75m²) 474P	❷ €64.80

🅿 From the edge of Blanes follow the signs 'campings'. Av. Villa de Madrid, campsite on the right.

💬 A large campsite in the entertainment centre, with good amenities and plenty of trees.

Lloret de Mar
Blanes

◤ N 41°39'48''   E 2°46'48''
www.eurocampings.co.uk/108189

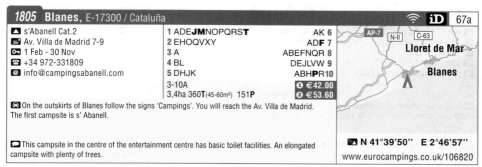

1805 Blanes, E-17300 / Cataluña 📶 iD 67a

- ▲ s'Abanell Cat.2
- 🏠 Av. Villa de Madrid 7-9
- 📅 1 Feb - 30 Nov
- ☎ +34 972-331809
- @ info@campingsabanell.com

1 ADEJMNOPQRST	AK 6
2 EHOQVXY	ADF 7
3 A	ABEFNQR 8
4 BL	DEJLVW 9
5 DHJK	ABHPR 10
3-10A	❶ €42.00
3,4ha 360T (45-60m²) 151P	❷ €53.60

🅿 On the outskirts of Blanes follow the signs 'Campings'. You will reach the Av. Villa de Madrid. The first campsite is s' Abanell.

💬 This campsite in the centre of the entertainment centre has basic toilet facilities. An elongated campsite with plenty of trees.

Lloret de Mar
Blanes

◤ N 41°39'50''   E 2°46'57''
www.eurocampings.co.uk/106820

Spain

1806 Blanes, E-17300 / Cataluña ⏺ (CC€17) iD 67a

- 🏠 Solmar
- 📧 Colom 48
- 📅 24 Mar - 14 Oct
- ☎ +34 972-348034
- @ campingsolmar@campingsolmar.com

1 ADEJMNOPQR**T**	AFK	6
2 EHOPRVXY	ABDE**FGH**	7
3 BEL**MQ**	ABEFS	8
4 **A**BDLNOP**Q**	DIJL	9
5 ACDEFGHJKM	ABDHIL**P**ST	10
6A		
6ha 200**T**(65-85m²) 289**P**	❶ €45.00 ❷ €58.40	

🔧 From the edge of Blanes follow 'camping' signs. Arrive in Av. Villa de Madrid. Sign to the right 'Solmar'.

💬 Campsite in the centre of the nightlife area with reasonably good toilet facilities and plenty of shade.

CC 1/4-22/6 1/9-13/10

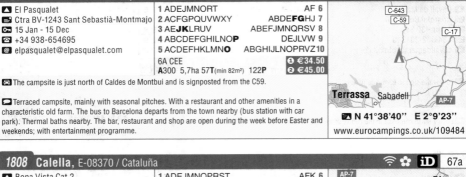

🧭 N 41°39'43'' E 2°46'50''

www.eurocampings.co.uk/108190

1807 Caldes de Montbui, E-08140 / Cataluña ⏺ iD 33 B1

- 🏠 El Pasqualet
- 📧 Ctra BV-1243 Sant Sebastià-Montmajo
- 📅 15 Jan - 15 Dec
- ☎ +34 938-654695
- @ elpasqualet@elpasqualet.com

1 ADEJMNORT	AF	6
2 ACFGPQUVWXY	ABDE**FG**HJ	7
3 AE**JK**LRUV	ABEFJMNQRSV	8
4 ABCDEFGHILNO**P**	DEJLVW	9
5 ACDEFHKLMN**O**	ABGHIJLNOPRVZ	10
6A CEE		
A300 5,7ha 57**T**(min 82m²) 122**P**	❶ €34.50 ❷ €45.00	

🔧 The campsite is just north of Caldes de Montbui and is signposted from the C59.

💬 Terraced campsite, mainly with seasonal pitches. With a restaurant and other amenities in a characteristic old farm. The bus to Barcelona departs from the town nearby (bus station with car park). Thermal baths nearby. The bar, restaurant and shop are open during the week before Easter and weekends; with entertainment programme.

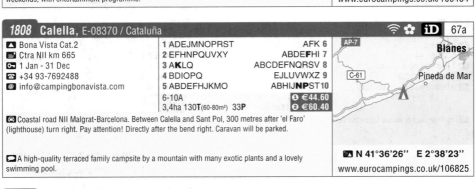

🧭 N 41°38'40'' E 2°9'23''

www.eurocampings.co.uk/109484

1808 Calella, E-08370 / Cataluña ⏺ ❀ iD 67a

- 🏠 Bona Vista Cat.2
- 📧 Ctra NII km 665
- 📅 1 Jan - 31 Dec
- ☎ +34 93-7692488
- @ info@campingbonavista.com

1 ADEJMNOPRST	AFK	6
2 EFHNPQUVXY	ABDE**F**HI	7
3 A**K**LQ	ABCDEFNQRSV	8
4 BDIOPQ	EJLUVWXZ	9
5 ABDEFHJKMO	ABHIJ**NP**ST	10
6-10A		
3,4ha 130**T**(60-80m²) 33**P**	❶ €44.60 ❷ €60.40	

🔧 Coastal road NII Malgrat-Barcelona. Between Calella and Sant Pol, 300 metres after 'el Faro' (lighthouse) turn right. Pay attention! Directly after the bend right. Caravan will be parked.

💬 A high-quality terraced family campsite by a mountain with many exotic plants and a lovely swimming pool.

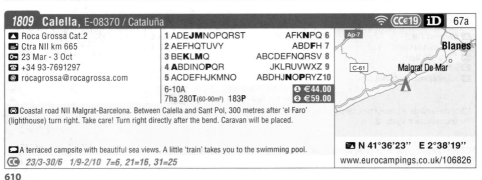

🧭 N 41°36'26'' E 2°38'23''

www.eurocampings.co.uk/106825

1809 Calella, E-08370 / Cataluña ⏺ (CC€19) iD 67a

- 🏠 Roca Grossa Cat.2
- 📧 Ctra NII km 665
- 📅 23 Mar - 3 Oct
- ☎ +34 93-7691297
- @ rocagrossa@rocagrossa.com

1 ADE**JM**NOPQRST	AFK**N**PQ	6
2 AEFHQTUVVY	ABD**F**H	7
3 BE**KL**MQ	ABCDEFNQRSV	8
4 **A**BDINO**P**QR	JKLRUVWXZ	9
5 ACDEFHJKMNO	ABDHJ**NOP**RYZ	10
6-10A		
7ha 280**T**(60-90m²) 183**P**	❶ €44.00 ❷ €59.00	

🔧 Coastal road NII Malgrat-Barcelona. Between Calella and Sant Pol, 300 metres after 'el Faro' (lighthouse) turn right. Take care! Turn right directly after the bend. Caravan will be placed.

💬 A terraced campsite with beautiful sea views. A little 'train' takes you to the swimming pool.

CC 23/3-30/6 1/9-2/10 7=6, 21=16, 31=25

🧭 N 41°36'23'' E 2°38'19''

www.eurocampings.co.uk/106826

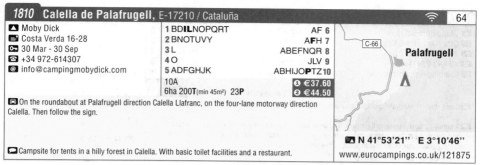

1810 Calella de Palafrugell, E-17210 / Cataluña — 64

- ▲ Moby Dick
- 🏠 Costa Verda 16-28
- 📅 30 Mar - 30 Sep
- ☎ +34 972-614307
- @ info@campingmobydick.com

1 BDILNOPQRT	AF	6
2 BNOTUVY	AFH	7
3 L	ABEFNQR	8
4 O	JLV	9
5 ADFGHJK	ABHIJOPTZ	10
10A		
6ha 200T(min 45m²)	23P	

- ❶ €37.60
- ❷ €44.50

On the roundabout at Palafrugell direction Calella Llafranc, on the four-lane motorway direction Calella. Then follow the sign.

Campsite for tents in a hilly forest in Calella. With basic toilet facilities and a restaurant.

Palafrugell
C-66

N 41°53'21'' E 3°10'46''
www.eurocampings.co.uk/121875

1811 Calonge, E-17251 / Cataluña — CC€19 iD 64

- ▲ Sènia Cala Gogo Cat.1
- 🏠 Av. Andorra 13
- 📅 21 Apr - 24 Sep
- ☎ +34 972-651564
- @ calagogo@calagogo.es

1 ADEJKNOPQRST	ABFGHIKMNOPQS	6
2 EFHOPQRTUVWXY	ABDEFGH	7
3 BEKLMT	ABCDEFKLMNQRSTUV	8
4 ABCDFILNOPQ	CEJLUVWXZ	9
5 ACDEFHJKLMO	ABDGHIJOPRXYZ	10
6-10A		
20ha 670T(60-115m²)	197P	

- ❶ €65.40
- ❷ €74.80

Exit 6 Palafrugell-Palamós. Direction San Feliu, then Palamós-est. Then Platja d'Aro. Campsite on the right side of the road. Campsite clearly signposted.

A friendly family campsite backing onto a hillside with plenty of shade. Designer toilet facilities, a lively swimming pool and plenty of free entertainment.

CC 21/4-29/6 1/9-23/9

Sant Feliu De Guíxols

N 41°49'49'' E 3°5'2''
www.eurocampings.co.uk/101068

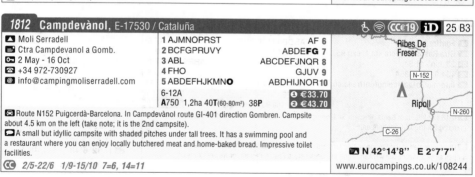

1812 Campdevànol, E-17530 / Cataluña — CC€19 iD 25 B3

- ▲ Moli Serradell
- 🏠 Ctra Campdevanol a Gomb.
- 📅 2 May - 16 Oct
- ☎ +34 972-730927
- @ info@campingmoliserradell.com

1 AJMNOPRST	AF	6
2 BCFGPRUVY	ABDEFG	7
3 ABL	ABCDEFJNQR	8
4 FHO	GJUV	9
5 ABDEFHJKMNO	ABDHIJNOR	10
6-12A		
A750 1,2ha 40T(60-80m²)	38P	

- ❶ €33.70
- ❷ €43.70

Route N152 Puigcerdà-Barcelona. In Campdevànol route GI-401 direction Gombren. Campsite about 4.5 km on the left (take note; it is the 2nd campsite).

A small but idyllic campsite with shaded pitches under tall trees. It has a swimming pool and a restaurant where you can enjoy locally butchered meat and home-baked bread. Impressive toilet facilities.

CC 2/5-22/6 1/9-15/10 7=6, 14=11

Ribes De Freser
N-152
Ripoll
N-260
C-26

N 42°14'8'' E 2°7'7''
www.eurocampings.co.uk/108244

1813 Camprodon, E-17867 / Cataluña — iD 25 B3

- ▲ Vall de Camprodon Cat.1
- 🏠 Ctra 38 Ripoll-Camprodon, km 7,5
- 📅 1/1 - 10/12, 26/12 - 31/12
- ☎ +34 972-740507
- @ info@valldecamprodon.net

1 ABDJMNOPQRST	AFJN	6
2 BCFGOPSVX	ABDEFGH	7
3 ABEFGHJKLMQU	ABEFJKNQRSV	8
4 BCEFHIKLOP	EFJL	9
5 ABCDEFGHJKLMNO	ABFGHIJPRV	10
4-10A		
A950 4,8ha 106T(80m²)	115P	

- ❶ €42.50
- ❷ €51.50

From Ripoll direction Camprodon. Campsite located on the C38, km 7.5. From Figueres take A26 which becomes the N260. Campsite 2 km after the Camprodon roundabout. Signposted.

A spacious campsite with level pitches. Separate field for tents, plenty of sports facilities, animal park and children's playground. Modern toilet facilities and a good restaurant. Established walks, for example to Camprodon. Open only at weekends January-May and October-December.

Setcases
D115
C-38
C-26
Sant Pau de Segúries

N 42°17'22'' E 2°21'50''
www.eurocampings.co.uk/110865

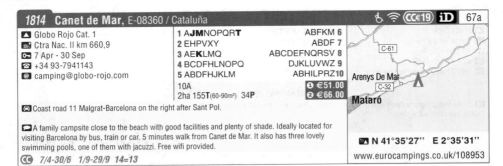

1814 Canet de Mar, E-08360 / Cataluña

🕭 📶 (CC€19) iD 67a

- 🏕 Globo Rojo Cat. 1
- 🚏 Ctra. Nac. II km 660,9
- 📅 7 Apr - 30 Sep
- ☎ +34 93-7941143
- @ camping@globo-rojo.com

1 A**JM**NOPQR**T**		ABFKM	6
2 EHPVXY		ABDF	7
3 AE**K**LMQ		ABCDEFNQRSV	8
4 BCDFHLNOPQ		DJKLUVWZ	9
5 ABDFHJKLM		ABHILPRZ	10
10A		❶ €51.00	
2ha 155**T**(60-90m²) 34**P**		❷ €66.00	

🗺 Coast road 11 Malgrat-Barcelona on the right after Sant Pol.

💬 A family campsite close to the beach with good facilities and plenty of shade. Ideally located for visiting Barcelona by bus, train or car. 5 minutes walk from Canet de Mar. It also has three lovely swimming pools, one of them with jacuzzi. Free wifi provided.

(CC) 7/4-30/6   1/9-29/9 14=13

🧭 N 41°35'27''   E 2°35'31''

www.eurocampings.co.uk/108953

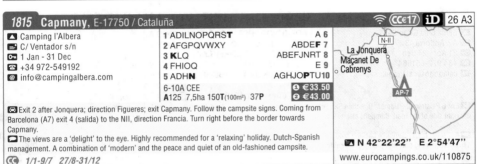

1815 Capmany, E-17750 / Cataluña

📶 (CC€17) iD 26 A3

- 🏕 Camping l'Albera
- 🚏 C/ Ventador s/n
- 📅 1 Jan - 31 Dec
- ☎ +34 972-549192
- @ info@campingalbera.com

1 ADILNOPQRS**T**		A	6
2 AFGPQVWXY		ABDE**F**	7
3 **K**LQ		ABEFJNRT	8
4 FHIOQ		E	9
5 ADH**N**		AGHJO**P**T**U**	10
6-10A CEE		❶ €33.50	
A125 7,5ha 150**T**(100m²) 37**P**		❷ €43.00	

🗺 Exit 2 after Jonquera; direction Figueres; exit Capmany. Follow the campsite signs. Coming from Barcelona (A7) exit 4 (salida) to the NII, direction Francia. Turn right before the border towards Capmany.

💬 The views are a 'delight' to the eye. Highly recommended for a 'relaxing' holiday. Dutch-Spanish management. A combination of 'modern' and the peace and quiet of an old-fashioned campsite.

(CC) 1/1-9/7   27/8-31/12

🧭 N 42°22'22''   E 2°54'47''

www.eurocampings.co.uk/110875

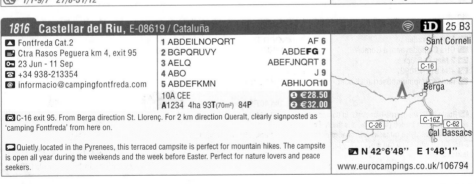

1816 Castellar del Riu, E-08619 / Cataluña

📶 iD 25 B3

- 🏕 Fontfreda Cat.2
- 🚏 Ctra Rasos Peguera km 4, exit 95
- 📅 23 Jun - 11 Sep
- ☎ +34 938-213354
- @ informacio@campingfontfreda.com

1 ABDEILNOPQRT		AF	6
2 BGPQRUVY		ABDE**FG**	7
3 AELQ		ABEFJNQRT	8
4 ABO		J	9
5 ABDEFKMN		ABHIJOR	10
10A CEE		❶ €28.50	
A1234 4ha 93**T**(70m²) 84**P**		❷ €32.00	

🗺 C-16 exit 95. From Berga direction St. Llorenç. For 2 km direction Queralt, clearly signposted as 'camping Fontfreda' from here on.

💬 Quietly located in the Pyrenees, this terraced campsite is perfect for mountain hikes. The campsite is open all year during the weekends and the week before Easter. Perfect for nature lovers and peace seekers.

🧭 N 42°6'48''   E 1°48'1''

www.eurocampings.co.uk/106794

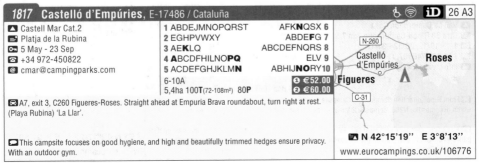

1817 Castelló d'Empúries, E-17486 / Cataluña

🕭 📶 iD 26 A3

- 🏕 Castell Mar Cat.2
- 🚏 Platja de la Rubina
- 📅 5 May - 23 Sep
- ☎ +34 972-450822
- @ cmar@campingparks.com

1 ABDEJMNOPQRST		AFK**N**QSX	6
2 EGHPVWXY		ABDE**FG**	7
3 AE**K**LQ		ABCDEFNQRS	8
4 A**BCDFHILNOPQ**		ELV	9
5 ACDEFGHJKLM**N**		ABHIJ**NOR**Y	10
6-10A		❶ €52.00	
5,4ha 100**T**(72-108m²) 80**P**		❷ €60.00	

🗺 A7, exit 3, C260 Figueres-Roses. Straight ahead at Empuria Brava roundabout, turn right at rest. (Playa Rubina) 'La Llar'.

💬 This campsite focuses on good hygiene, and high and beautifully trimmed hedges ensure privacy. With an outdoor gym.

🧭 N 42°15'19''   E 3°8'13''

www.eurocampings.co.uk/106776

1818 Castelló d'Empúries, E-17486 / Cataluña ⇒ ✿ 26 A3

- 🏕 Laguna Cat.1
- ✉ Apartado de Correos 55
- 📅 27 Mar - 28 Oct
- ☎ +34 972-452033
- @ info@campinglaguna.com

1 BCDEJMNOPQRST	ABFKMNQRSTWXY 6	
2 CDEGHPVWXY	ABDEFGH 7	
3 BEFGHIKLMQ	ABCDEFKNRSV 8	
4 ABCDFHILMOPQ	ELMOUV 9	
5 ACDEFGHJKLMNO	ABGHIJNPRYZ10	
5-10A CEE	❶ €61.00	
12,5ha 709T(90-120m²) 109P	❷ €69.00	

🔲 Exit 3 direction Castelló d'Empúries, Roses (C260). Then roundabout with exit Camping 4.

🔲 The quiet Laguna campsite is located by the bay of Roses. The environs are perfect for excursions, such as to Figerueres (Dali museum) and Barcelona. The pitches are well-divided and have sufficient trees to provide some shade.

Figueres — Roses

🧭 N 42°14'42'' E 3°6'14''

www.eurocampings.co.uk/106781

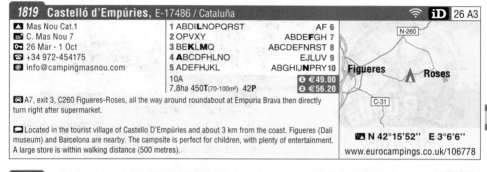

1819 Castelló d'Empúries, E-17486 / Cataluña ⇒ iD 26 A3

- 🏕 Mas Nou Cat.1
- ✉ C. Mas Nou 7
- 📅 26 Mar - 1 Oct
- ☎ +34 972-454175
- @ info@campingmasnou.com

1 ABDILNOPQRST	AF 6	
2 OPVXY	ABDEFGH 7	
3 BEKLMQ	ABCDEFNRST 8	
4 ABCDFHLNO	EJLUV 9	
5 ADEFHJKL	ABGHIJNPRY10	
10A	❶ €49.00	
7,8ha 450T(70-100m²) 42P	❷ €56.20	

🔲 A7, exit 3, C260 Figueres-Roses, all the way around roundabout at Empuria Brava then directly turn right after supermarket.

🔲 Located in the tourist village of Castello D'Empùries and about 3 km from the coast. Figueres (Dali museum) and Barcelona are nearby. The campsite is perfect for children, with plenty of entertainment. A large store is within walking distance (500 metres).

Figueres — Roses

🧭 N 42°15'52'' E 3°6'6''

www.eurocampings.co.uk/106778

1820 Castelló d'Empúries, E-17486 / Cataluña ♿ ⇒ 64

- 🏕 Nautic Almata Cat.1
- 📅 19 May - 17 Sep
- ☎ +34 972-454477
- @ info@almata.com

1 BCDEJMNOPQRST	AFKMNOPQRSTUVXYZ 6	
2 CEGHPVWXY	ABDEFGH 7	
3 ABEIKLMNQR	ABCDEFNQRSTU 8	
4 ABCDEFHILMNOPQUXYZ	ABIJKLMNOPQRSUVXZ 9	
5 ACDEFGHJKLM	ABCGHIJMNPSUWYZ10	
10A CEE	❶ €64.50	
22ha 1159T(90-100m²) 62P	❷ €76.70	

🔲 C260 Figueres-Roses. After 9 km turn right to Sant Pere Pescador. Then after 4 km left (indicated with signs and flags). Another few kilometres to the campsite.

🔲 Located on the beach, neighbouring a nature reserve. Wonderful landscaping with a feast of flowering oleanders. Access to the sea for small boats through a connecting channel. This campsite is particularly noted for its water sports (surfing, diving).

Figueres — Roses

🧭 N 42°12'22'' E 3°6'14''

www.eurocampings.co.uk/106782

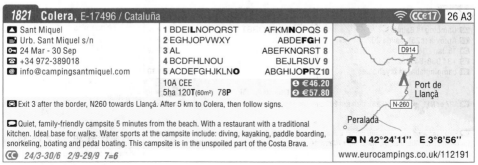

1821 Colera, E-17496 / Cataluña ⇒ CC€17 26 A3

- 🏕 Sant Miquel
- ✉ Urb. Sant Miquel s/n
- 📅 24 Mar - 30 Sep
- ☎ +34 972-389018
- @ info@campingsantmiquel.com

1 BDEILNOPQRST	AFKMNOPQS 6	
2 EGHJOPVWXY	ABDEFGH 7	
3 AL	ABEFKNQRST 8	
4 BCDFHLNOU	BEJLRSUV 9	
5 ACDEFGHJKLNO	ABGHIJOPRZ10	
10A CEE	❶ €46.20	
5ha 120T(60m²) 78P	❷ €57.80	

🔲 Exit 3 after the border, N260 towards Llançà. After 5 km to Colera, then follow signs.

🔲 Quiet, family-friendly campsite 5 minutes from the beach. With a restaurant with a traditional kitchen. Ideal base for walks. Water sports at the campsite include: diving, kayaking, paddle boarding, snorkeling, boating and pedal boating. This campsite is in the unspoiled part of the Costa Brava.

CC 24/3-30/6 2/9-29/9 7=6

Port de Llançà

Peralada

🧭 N 42°24'11'' E 3°8'56''

www.eurocampings.co.uk/112191

1822 Cubelles, E-08880 / Cataluña

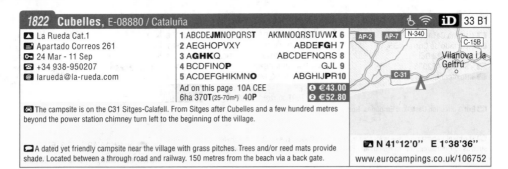

- ▲ La Rueda Cat.1
- ✉ Apartado Correos 261
- 📅 24 Mar - 11 Sep
- ☎ +34 938-950207
- @ larueda@la-rueda.com

1 ABCDE**JM**NOPQRS**T**	AKMNOQRSTUVW**X** 6
2 AEGHOPVXY	ABDE**FGH** 7
3 A**GHK**Q	ABCDEFNQRS 8
4 BCDFINO**P**	GJL 9
5 ACDEFGHIKMN**O**	ABGHIJ**P**R10
Ad on this page 10A CEE	❶ €43.00
6ha 370**T**(25-70m²) 40**P**	❷ €52.80

🚗 The campsite is on the C31 Sitges-Calafell. From Sitges after Cubelles and a few hundred metres beyond the power station chimney turn left to the beginning of the village.

💬 A dated yet friendly campsite near the village with grass pitches. Trees and/or reed mats provide shade. Located between a through road and railway. 150 metres from the beach via a back gate.

🏁 **N 41°12'0''   E 1°38'36''**

www.eurocampings.co.uk/106752

1823 Empuriabrava, E-17487 / Cataluña

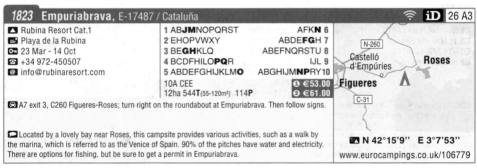

- ▲ Rubina Resort Cat.1
- ✉ Playa de la Rubina
- 📅 23 Mar - 14 Oct
- ☎ +34 972-450507
- @ info@rubinaresort.com

1 AB**JM**NOPQRST	AFK**N** 6
2 EHOPVWXY	ABDE**FGH** 7
3 BE**GH**KLQ	ABEFNQRSTU 8
4 BCDFHILO**PQR**	IJL 9
5 ABDEFGHIJKLM**O**	ABGHIJMN**NPR**Y10
10A CEE	❶ €53.00
12ha 544**T**(55-120m²) 114**P**	❷ €61.00

🚗 A7 exit 3, C260 Figueres-Roses; turn right on the roundabout at Empuriabrava. Then follow signs.

💬 Located by a lovely bay near Roses, this campsite provides various activities, such as a walk by the marina, which is referred to as the Venice of Spain. 90% of the pitches have water and electricity. There are options for fishing, but be sure to get a permit in Empuriabrava.

🏁 **N 42°15'9''   E 3°7'53''**

www.eurocampings.co.uk/106779

1824 Espinelves, E-17405 / Cataluña

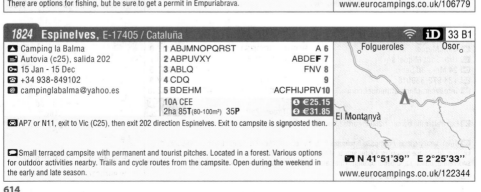

- ▲ Camping la Balma
- ✉ Autovia (c25), salida 202
- 📅 15 Jan - 15 Dec
- ☎ +34 938-849102
- @ campinglabalma@yahoo.es

1 ABJMNOPQRST	A 6
2 ABPUVXY	ABDE**F** 7
3 ABLQ	FNV 8
4 CDQ	9
5 BDEHM	ACFHIJPRV10
10A CEE	❶ €25.15
2ha 85**T**(80-100m²) 35**P**	❷ €31.85

🚗 AP7 or N11, exit to Vic (C25), then exit 202 direction Espinelves. Exit to campsite is signposted then.

💬 Small terraced campsite with permanent and tourist pitches. Located in a forest. Various options for outdoor activities nearby. Trails and cycle routes from the campsite. Open during the weekend in the early and late season.

🏁 **N 41°51'39''   E 2°25'33''**

www.eurocampings.co.uk/122344

Spain

1825 Esponellà (Girona), E-17832 / Cataluña ⟨CC€19⟩ ♦ 26 A3

- ⛺ Esponellà Cat.2
- 🛣 Ctra de Banyoles a Figueres, km 8
- 🗓 1 Jan - 31 Dec
- ☎ +34 972-597074
- @ informa@campingesponella.com

1	BDEILNOPQRT	ABCDFN 6
2	CPQRVXY	ABDEF 7
3	BEIKLMQ	ABEFJNRT 8
4	BFHIMOQ	JRU 9
5	ABDEFHKLMNO	ABDGHIJPSVZ 10
5-10A		❶ €38.25
A116 4,5ha 130T(60m²) 85P		❷ €49.55

🚗 A7 exit 3, dir. Figueres N260 Figueres-Besalu. After Navata past service station turn left dir. Banyoles. At hairpin bend after bridge over Fluvia turn right. Signposted.
⛱ Located in hinterland of Figueres on River Fluviá. Marked-out walks and mountain bike routes. Trips out in the area, e.g. Nuria (cog railway to an altitude of 2 km). River close to the campsite for fishing or kayaking. Special birds for spotting. Covered heated swimming pool.

CC 1/1-30/6 1/9-31/12 7=6, 14=11

N 42°10'54'' E 2°47'42''

www.eurocampings.co.uk/106786

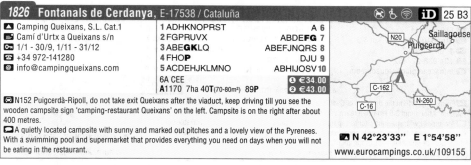

1826 Fontanals de Cerdanya, E-17538 / Cataluña ⊗ ♿ 🛜 iD 25 B3

- ⛺ Camping Queixans, S.L. Cat.1
- 🛣 Camí d'Urtx a Queixans s/n
- 🗓 1/1 - 30/9, 1/11 - 31/12
- ☎ +34 972-141280
- @ info@campingqueixans.com

1	ADHKNOPRST	A 6
2	FGPRUVX	ABDEFG 7
3	ABEGKLQ	ABEFJNQRS 8
4	FHOP	DJU 9
5	ACDEHJKLMNO	ABHIJOSV 10
6A CEE		❶ €34.00
A1170 7ha 40T(70-80m²) 89P		❷ €43.00

🚗 N152 Puigcerdà-Ripoll, do not take exit Queixans after the viaduct, keep driving till you see the wooden campsite sign 'camping-restaurant Queixans' on the left. Campsite is on the right after about 400 metres.
⛱ A quietly located campsite with sunny and marked out pitches and a lovely view of the Pyrenees. With a swimming pool and supermarket that provides everything you need on days when you will not be eating in the restaurant.

N 42°23'33'' E 1°54'58''

www.eurocampings.co.uk/109155

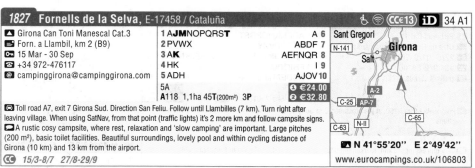

1827 Fornells de la Selva, E-17458 / Cataluña ♿ 🛜 ⟨CC€13⟩ iD 34 A1

- ⛺ Girona Can Toni Manescal Cat.3
- 🛣 Forn. a Llambil, km 2 (B9)
- 🗓 15 Mar - 30 Sep
- ☎ +34 972-476117
- @ campinggirona@campinggirona.com

1	AJMNOPQRST	A 6
2	PVWX	ABDF 7
3	AK	AEFNQR 8
4	HK	I 9
5	ADH	AJOV 10
5A		❶ €24.00
A118 1,1ha 45T(200m²) 3P		❷ €32.80

🚗 Toll road A7, exit 7 Girona Sud. Direction San Feliu. Follow until Llambilles (7 km). Turn right after leaving village. When using SatNav, from that point (traffic lights) it's 2 more km and follow campsite signs.
⛱ A rustic cosy campsite, where rest, relaxation and 'slow camping' are important. Large pitches (200 m²), basic toilet facilities. Beautiful surroundings, lovely pool and within cycling distance of Girona (10 km) and 13 km from the airport.

CC 15/3-8/7 27/8-29/9

N 41°55'20'' E 2°49'42''

www.eurocampings.co.uk/106803

1828 Garriguella, E-17780 / Cataluña 🛜 ⟨CC€17⟩ 26 A3

- ⛺ Vell Empordà Cat.2
- 🛣 Ctra Roses-La Jonquera s/n
- 🗓 24 Mar - 28 Oct
- ☎ +34 972-530200
- @ vellemporda@vellemporda.com

1	BDEILNORT	AF 6
2	GPRUVXY	ABDEFGH 7
3	ABEL	AEFNQRST 8
4	ABCDEFHIMOQ	ABJLUV 9
5	ACDEFHKLMNO	ABGHIJLMOPR 10
6-10A		❶ €43.00
7ha 230T(80-100m²) 65P		❷ €56.00

🚗 A7, exit 3, N260 Figueres Llançà. After 9 km, the campsite is signposted. Turn right, C252 then turn left under the viaduct direction La Jonquera. Then another 2 km.
⛱ A quiet campsite not quite on the coast. You can visit it close by. In just 10 km you can be on the beach or in the mountains. A family business where the mother manages the kitchen. Spanish, friendly atmosphere. Beautiful large swimming pool with a separate children's pool.

CC 24/3-21/6 1/9-27/10 7=6, 14=11

N 42°20'21'' E 3°4'4''

www.eurocampings.co.uk/106775

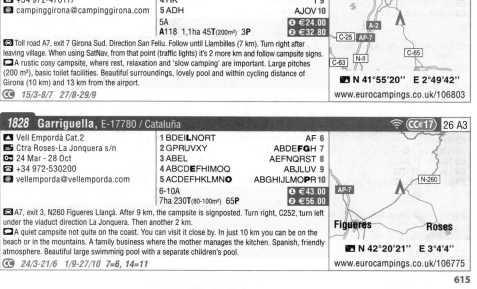

1829 Gavà (Barcelona), E-08850 / Cataluña   ♿ 📶 (CC€19) iD 33 B1

- ⛰ 3 Estrellas Cat.1
- ✉ C-31, km 186,2/Aptdo de Correos 238
- 📅 12 Jan - 16 Dec
- ☎ +34 936-330637
- @ info@camping3estrellas.com

1 ABCDE**JM**NOPRST	AFKMN**QSTX** 6
2 ABEGHOPQVWXY	ABDE**FG**H 7
3 AELMQ	ABCDEFJNQRSTUV 8
4 BMOQ	ABCDEFGJL 9
5 ACDEFHIKLM**O**	ABDGHIKLMPRVY 10

5A	❶ €49.00
8ha 240T(70-100m²) 229P	❷ €60.50

🚗 In Barcelona follow 'Ronda de Dalt' (B20), dir. airport. C-31 dir. Castelldefels, exit Gavà Mar (on the left along the beach), with viaduct over C-31, then three times to the right and back dir. Barcelona to the site.
⛺ A perfect campsite for visiting Barcelona, bus stop from at the site, a lovely swimming pool and good toilet facilities. Right by a sandy beach. 25% discount from 23/6 to 15/7 for CampingCard ACSI holders. Discount only for standard pitches.
CC 12/1-22/6 1/9-15/12

L'Hospitalet de Llobregat

📍 N 41°16'21'' E 2°2'35''
www.eurocampings.co.uk/106773

1830 Guardiola de Berguedà, E-08694 / Cataluña   ♿ 📶 (CC€17) iD 25 B3

- ⛰ El Berguedà
- ✉ Ctra B400 a Saldes, km 3,5
- 📅 1 Apr - 1 Nov
- ☎ +34 938-227432
- @ info@campingbergueda.com

1 ADEJMNOPRST	AF 6
2 BCFGPRTUVWXY	ABDE**FG** 7
3 ABELQ	ABCDEFJNQRSV 8
4 **EFHOPQ**	GJ 9
5 ABCDEHJM**NO**	ABCHIJOP**V** 10

6A CEE	❶ €30.00
A900 2ha 40T(70-110m²) 35P	❷ €39.30

🚗 From Berga C16 in the direction of Cadi Tunnel. Just before Guardiola de Berguedà turn left (Saldes). After about 3.5 km you'll reach the campsite.
⛺ A campsite with spacious pitches separated by trees and bushes. Simple meals available out of season at weekends or on special occasions. Lovely area for mountain walks. The reception staff gladly provide you with maps of the area.
CC 3/4-26/4 2/5-6/7 27/8-6/9 12/9-10/10 15/10-30/10

Bagà   La Pobla De Lillet
C-16
C-26

📍 N 42°12'59'' E 1°50'13''
www.eurocampings.co.uk/110246

1831 Guils de Cerdanya, E-17528 / Cataluña   ⊗ ⛷ ♿ 📶 iD 25 B3

- ⛰ Pirineus Cat.1
- ✉ Ctra de Guils de Cerdanya km 2
- 📅 22/6 - 11/9, 20/10 - 1/5
- ☎ +34 972-881062
- @ guils@stel.es

1 ADEHKNOPRST	ABF 6
2 CFGPRVXY	ABDE**FG** 7
3 ABE**GJKL**QV	ABCDEFJKNQRSV 8
4 FHIO**PQ**	JU 9
5 ACDEFHJKLMN**O**	ABHIJPR 10

7.5A	❶ €44.50
A1300 5ha 250T(70m²) 30P	❷ €55.90

🚗 Puigcerdà - Ctra N260, at the crossroad Ctra Guils de Cerdanya-Puigcerdà, km 2. Follow the directions.
⛺ Very quiet campsite with marked out pitches near the mediaeval town of Puigcerdà. With excellent toilet facilities and a heated outdoor pool.

D618
N20   Saillagouse
Puigcerdà
N-260
C-162

📍 N 42°26'35'' E 1°54'22''
www.eurocampings.co.uk/106772

1832 Isovol, E-17539 / Cataluña   📶 iD 25 B3

- ⛰ Bellver
- ✉ N260, km 193,7
- 📅 23 Jun - 11 Sep
- ☎ +34 973-510239
- @ campingbellver@campingbellver.com

1 ADEJMNOPRST	AF**JN** 6
2 CFGOPRUVY	ABDE**FG** 7
3 ABELQ	ABEFJNQRV 8
4 BFHIO**P**	IJL 9
5 ABDEGHJMN**O**	ABHIJPR 10

5A	❶ €26.80
A1100 3ha 50T(50-70m²) 112P	❷ €37.00

🚗 On the N260 between Bellver and Puigcerdà, km 194.
⛺ Small campsite located by a river. With a swimming pool and bar. Here and there some trees that provide the pitches with a little shade.

N20
Puigcerdà
Bourg-Madame
C-162
N-260
C-16

📍 N 42°22'16'' E 1°48'29''
www.eurocampings.co.uk/106748

Spain

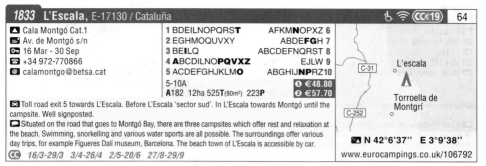

1833 L'Escala, E-17130 / Cataluña   ♿ 📶 CCe19   64

- 🏔 Cala Montgó Cat.1
- 🏠 Av. de Montgó s/n
- 📅 16 Mar - 30 Sep
- ☎ +34 972-770866
- @ calamontgo@betsa.cat

1 BDEILNOPQRST	AFKMNOPXZ	6
2 EGHMOQUVXY	ABDEFGH	7
3 BEILQ	ABCDEFNQRST	8
4 ABCDILNOPQVXZ	EJLW	9
5 ACDEFGHJKLMO	ABGHIJNPRZ	10
5-10A		
A182 12ha 525T(80m²) 223P	❶ €48.80	
	❷ €57.70	

🛣 Toll road exit 5 towards L'Escala. Before L'Escala 'sector sud'. In L'Escala towards Montgó until the campsite. Well signposted.

💬 Situated on the road that goes to Montgó Bay, there are three campsites which offer rest and relaxation at the beach. Swimming, snorkelling and various water sports are all possible. The surroundings offer various day trips, for example Figueres Dalí museum, Barcelona. The beach town of L'Escala is accessible by car.

CC 16/3-29/3 3/4-26/4 2/5-20/6 27/8-29/9

📍 N 42°6'37'' E 3°9'38''

www.eurocampings.co.uk/106792

1834 L'Escala, E-17130 / Cataluña   📶   64

- 🏔 Camping Punta Milà
- 🏠 Cala Montgó
- 📅 17 May - 25 Sep
- ☎ +34 638-652712
- @ info@campingpuntamila.com

1 BDEJMNOPQRST	AF	6
2 BHMQRUVWXY	ABDEFGH	7
3 BFMNQ	ABCDEFNQRSV	8
4 ABCDFHLO	ABCKLU	9
5 ACDEFGHJKLMNO	ABGHIJOPTUY	10
6-10A CEE		
3,8ha 143T(40-120m²) 60P	❶ €51.00	
	❷ €61.00	

🛣 Exit 5 direction centre of L'Escala, direction Cala Montgó and then follow the signs.

💬 Located in a pine forest and equipped with a swimming pool, where silence and tranquillity prevail. There is a friendly and spontaneous interaction among the campers. The attractive seaside town of L'Escala is easily accessible by car.

📍 N 42°6'18'' E 3°9'30''

www.eurocampings.co.uk/109487

1835 L'Escala, E-17130 / Cataluña   ♿ 📶 CCe19 ⛹ iD   64

- 🏔 Illa Mateua Cat.1
- 🏠 Avda. de Montgó, 260
- 📅 24 Mar - 21 Oct
- ☎ +34 972-770200
- @ info@campingillamateua.com

1 ABILNORT	ABFGKMNOPQSUVWX	6
2 BEGHKOPQUVY	ABDEFGH	7
3 BELMQ	ABCDEFJNQRS	8
4 AFHILO	JLQRS	9
5 ACDEFHKLM	ABHIJNPRY	10
6A	❶ €56.65	
A182 6,4ha 318T(80-90m²) 104P	❷ €67.15	

🛣 Toll road exit 5 direction L'Escala. Before L'Escala direction Escala Riells. Then follow camping signs and Montgó. Clearly signposted.

💬 A family site, spectacularly located on the sandy beach at Montgó and bordering the Montgri nature park and the rocky beach at Illa Mateua, which has excellent snorkelling. Breathtaking views of Roses Bay. Picturesque villages inland. A friendly welcome in various languages.

CC 24/3-30/6 30/8-20/10 7=6, 15=12, 28=22

📍 N 42°6'37'' E 3°9'56''

www.eurocampings.co.uk/106793

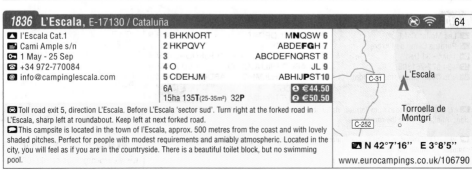

1836 L'Escala, E-17130 / Cataluña   ⌀ 📶   64

- 🏔 l'Escala Cat.1
- 🏠 Cami Ample s/n
- 📅 1 May - 25 Sep
- ☎ +34 972-770084
- @ info@campinglescala.com

1 BHKNORT	MNQSW	6
2 HKPQVY	ABDEFGH	7
3	ABCDEFNQRST	8
4 O	JL	9
5 CDEHJM	ABHIJPST	10
6A	❶ €44.50	
15ha 135T(25-35m²) 32P	❷ €50.50	

🛣 Toll road exit 5, direction L'Escala. Before L'Escala 'sector sud'. Turn right at the forked road in L'Escala, sharp left at roundabout. Keep left at next forked road.

💬 This campsite is located in the town of l'Escala, approx. 500 metres from the coast and with lovely shaded pitches. Perfect for people with modest requirements and amiably atmospheric. Located in the city, you will feel as if you are in the countryside. There is a beautiful toilet block, but no swimming pool.

📍 N 42°7'16'' E 3°8'5''

www.eurocampings.co.uk/106790

1837 L'Estartit, E-17258 / Cataluña 🚶 🛜 (CC€17) iD 64

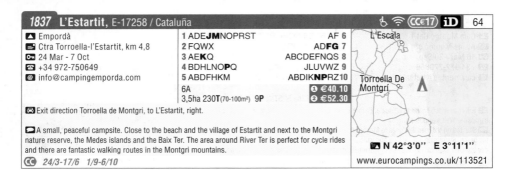

- 🏕 Empordà
- 📧 Ctra Torroella-l'Estartit, km 4,8
- 📅 24 Mar - 7 Oct
- ☎ +34 972-750649
- @ info@campingemporda.com

1 ADE**JM**NOPRST	AF	6
2 FQWX	AD**FG**	7
3 AE**KQ**	ABCDEFNQS	8
4 BDHLNOPQ	JLUVWZ	9
5 ABDFHKM	ABDIK**NP**RZ	10
6A	❶ €40.10	
3,5ha 230T(70-100m²) 9P	❷ €52.30	

L'Escala

Torroella De Montgrí

🔲 Exit direction Torroella de Montgri, to L'Estartit, right.

💬 A small, peaceful campsite. Close to the beach and the village of Estartit and next to the Montgri nature reserve, the Medes islands and the Baix Ter. The area around River Ter is perfect for cycle rides and there are fantastic walking routes in the Montgri mountains.

N 42°3'0"   E 3°11'1"

CC 24/3-17/6 1/9-6/10

www.eurocampings.co.uk/113521

1838 L'Estartit, E-17258 / Cataluña 🛜 iD 64

- 🏕 Estartit
- 📧 Pujada de la Primavera 12
- 📅 1 Apr - 1 Oct
- ☎ +34 972-751909
- @ info@campingestartit.com

1 AJKNOPR**T**	ABF	6
2 ERTUVY	ABE**FH**	7
3 AK	ACDE**FNRSV**	8
4 BDOPQ	ACDEFILUVXZ	9
5 ABDEHK**N**	ABHIJ**PT**	10
6A	❶ €35.20	
2,5ha 160T(60-80m²) 37P	❷ €45.00	

C-31

Torroella de Montgrí

🔲 L'Estartit, follow signs or straight ahead until pedestrian area on the left.

💬 Campsite located in a valley, sheltered from the wind and near a village and beach. With glamping and a Gold Award for most satisfied guests.

N 42°3'25"   E 3°11'51"

www.eurocampings.co.uk/110689

1839 L'Estartit, E-17258 / Cataluña 🛜 (CC€17) 64

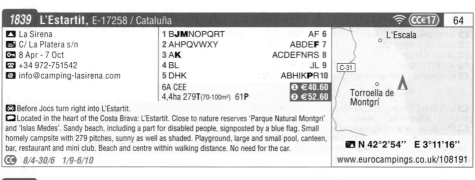

- 🏕 La Sirena
- 📧 C/ La Platera s/n
- 📅 8 Apr - 7 Oct
- ☎ +34 972-751542
- @ info@camping-lasirena.com

1 B**JM**NOPQRT	AF	6
2 AHPQVWXY	ABDE**F**	7
3 A**K**	ACDEFNRS	8
4 BL	JL	9
5 DHK	ABHIK**PR**	10
6A CEE	❶ €40.60	
4,4ha 279T(70-100m²) 61P	❷ €52.60	

L'Escala

C-31

Torroella de Montgrí

🔲 Before Jocs turn right into L'Estartit.

💬 Located in the heart of the Costa Brava: L'Estartit. Close to nature reserves 'Parque Natural Montgri' and 'Islas Medes'. Sandy beach, including a part for disabled people, signposted by a blue flag. Small homely campsite with 279 pitches, sunny as well as shaded. Playground, large and small pool, canteen, bar, restaurant and mini club. Beach and centre within walking distance. No need for the car.

N 42°2'54"   E 3°11'16"

CC 8/4-30/6 1/9-6/10

www.eurocampings.co.uk/108191

1840 L'Estartit, E-17258 / Cataluña 🚶 🛜 ♣ (CC€19) 64

- 🏕 Les Medes Cat.1
- 📧 Paratge Camp de l'Arbre
- 📅 1 Jan - 31 Dec
- ☎ +34 972-751805
- @ info@campinglesmedes.com

1 DE**J**KNOPRST	AEFOP	6
2 GOPVXY	ABDEFGH	7
3 BEF**KLMQ**	ABCDEFJKNQRSTUV	8
4 **A**BCDFHILNOQ**STX**	HLUVWXZ	9
5 ACDEFHJLMN**O**	ABDGHIJ**NP**QRZ	10
6-16A CEE	❶ €48.50	
2,6ha 170T(70-80m²) 14P	❷ €61.10	

C-31
L'Escala

Torroella De Montgrí

C-66

🔲 A7, exit 5. On the road from Torroella de Montgrí to Estartit turn right before 'Jocs' and follow signs. Another 2 km to the campsite.

💬 A top-class campsite, open all year. Indoor swimming pool in early and late seasons. An excellent campsite for winter guests.

N 42°2'33"   E 3°11'0"

CC 1/1-28/3 2/4-27/4 1/5-30/6 1/9-8/9 11/9-31/12

www.eurocampings.co.uk/106796

1841 L'Estartit, E-17258 / Cataluña

🛜 iD 64

- 🏕 Rifort
- 📧 Cami Vell 2
- 📅 24 Mar - 28 Oct
- ☎ +34 972-750406
- @ campingrifort@campingrifort.com

1 ADE**JM**NOPQRT	A **6**
2 HORUWXY	ABD**F**H **7**
3 **K**	ABEFNST **8**
4 CO	IJLZ **9**
5 DEHJK	ABI**PR**10
6-10A CEE	❶ €33.50
1,7ha 120**T**(60m²) 12**P**	❷ €42.30

🚗 A7, exit 6 direction L'Escala. Then via Torroella de Montgri to L'Estartit.

💬 A shaded city campsite on a hilly terrain with a swimming pool.

L'Escala

Torroella de Montgrí

📌 **N 42°3'8'' E 3°11'29''**

www.eurocampings.co.uk/111689

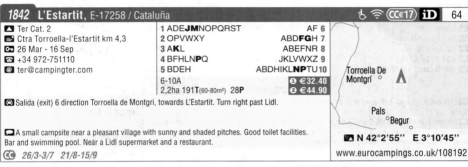

1842 L'Estartit, E-17258 / Cataluña

♿ 🛜 (CC€17) iD 64

- 🏕 Ter Cat. 2
- 📧 Ctra Torroella-l'Estartit km 4,3
- 📅 26 Mar - 16 Sep
- ☎ +34 972-751110
- @ ter@campingter.com

1 ADE**JM**NOPQRST	AF **6**
2 OPVWXY	ABD**FG**H **7**
3 A**K**L	ABEFNR **8**
4 BFHLN**PQ**	JKLVWXZ **9**
5 BDEH	ABDHIKL**NP**TU10
6-10A	❶ €32.40
2,2ha 191**T**(60-80m²) 28**P**	❷ €44.90

🚗 Salida (exit) 6 direction Torroella de Montgri, towards L'Estartit. Turn right past Lidl.

💬 A small campsite near a pleasant village with sunny and shaded pitches. Good toilet facilities. Bar and swimming pool. Near a Lidl supermarket and a restaurant.

CC *26/3-3/7 21/8-15/9*

Torroella De Montgrí

Pals
Begur

📌 **N 42°2'55'' E 3°10'45''**

www.eurocampings.co.uk/108192

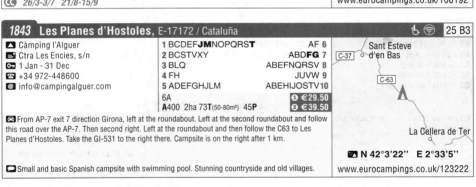

1843 Les Planes d'Hostoles, E-17172 / Cataluña

♿ 🛜 25 B3

- 🏕 Càmping l'Alguer
- 📧 Ctra Les Encies, s/n
- 📅 1 Jan - 31 Dec
- ☎ +34 972-448600
- @ info@campingalguer.com

1 BCDEF**JM**NOPQRS**T**	AF **6**
2 BCSTVXY	ABD**FG** **7**
3 BLQ	ABEFNQRSV **8**
4 FH	JUVW **9**
5 ADEFGHJLM	ABEHIJOSTV10
6A	❶ €29.50
A400 2ha 73**T**(50-80m²) 45**P**	❷ €39.50

🚗 From AP-7 exit 7 direction Girona, left at the roundabout. Left at the second roundabout and follow this road over the AP-7. Then second right. Left at the roundabout and then follow the C63 to Les Planes d'Hostoles. Take the GI-531 to the right there. Campsite is on the right after 1 km.

💬 Small and basic Spanish campsite with swimming pool. Stunning countryside and old villages.

Sant Esteve d'en Bas

La Cellera de Ter

📌 **N 42°3'22'' E 2°33'5''**

www.eurocampings.co.uk/123222

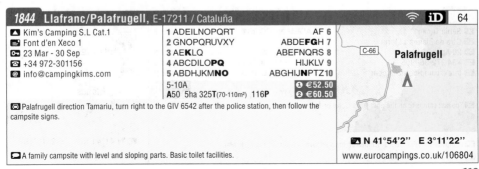

1844 Llafranc/Palafrugell, E-17211 / Cataluña

🛜 iD 64

- 🏕 Kim's Camping S.L Cat.1
- 📧 Font d'en Xeco 1
- 📅 23 Mar - 30 Sep
- ☎ +34 972-301156
- @ info@campingkims.com

1 ADEILNOPQRT	AF **6**
2 GNOPQRUVXY	ABDE**FG**H **7**
3 AE**K**LQ	ABEFNQRS **8**
4 ABCDILO**PQ**	HIJKLV **9**
5 ABDHJKM**NO**	ABGHIJ**N**PTZ10
5-10A	❶ €52.50
A50 5ha 325**T**(70-110m²) 116**P**	❷ €60.50

🚗 Palafrugell direction Tamariu, turn right to the GIV 6542 after the police station, then follow the campsite signs.

💬 A family campsite with level and sloping parts. Basic toilet facilities.

Palafrugell

📌 **N 41°54'2'' E 3°11'22''**

www.eurocampings.co.uk/106804

Spain

1845 Llagostera, E-17240 / Cataluña ⊗ ♿ 🛜 (CC€17) ⚎ iD 64

- ▲ Ridaura
- 🖃 Ctra Girona-Platja d'Aro C65 km 6,5
- 📅 2 Mar - 14 Oct
- ☎ +34 639-434557
- @ info@campingridaura.com

1 ADEHKNOPQRST		AF 6
2 BRTXY		ABDEFH 7
3 BEJK		ABEFNRST 8
4 **A**BFHLNO		ELUV 9
5 ABDEGHJKM**NO**		ABDHIKO**P**TUV 10
10A CEE		
4ha 202T(60-110m²) 187P	❶ €36.00	
	❷ €44.00	

🚳 AP7 exit 9 direction Playa d'Aro (25 km). Ridaura campsite is on the left.

📖 A campsite located in woods alongside the C65. Close to Sant Feliu and Playa d'Aro. It has good toilet facilities and a very attractive swimming pool with a chair hoist. Located next to natural woodland paths and walking and cycling routes from Girona (Voies Vertes, i Ruta Pirinexus).

CC 27/4-14/7 1/9-16/9

🧭 N 41°49'39'' E 2°57'29''

www.eurocampings.co.uk/111045

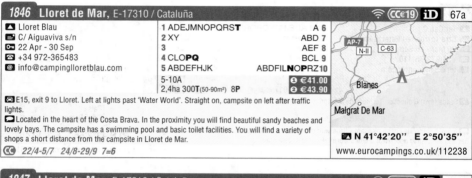

1846 Lloret de Mar, E-17310 / Cataluña 🛜 (CC€19) iD 67a

- ▲ Lloret Blau
- 🖃 C/ Aiguaviva s/n
- 📅 22 Apr - 30 Sep
- ☎ +34 972-365483
- @ info@campinglloretblau.com

1 ADEJMNOPQRS**T**		A 6
2 XY		ABD 7
3		AEF 8
4 CLO**PQ**		BCL 9
5 ABDEFHJK		ABDFIL**NO**PRZ 10
5-10A		
2,4ha 300T(50-90m²) 8P	❶ €41.00	
	❷ €43.90	

🚳 E15, exit 9 to Lloret. Left at lights past 'Water World'. Straight on, campsite on left after traffic lights.

📖 Located in the heart of the Costa Brava. In the proximity you will find beautiful sandy beaches and lovely bays. The campsite has a swimming pool and basic toilet facilities. You will find a variety of shops a short distance from the campsite in Lloret de Mar.

CC 22/4-5/7 24/8-29/9 7=6

🧭 N 41°42'20'' E 2°50'35''

www.eurocampings.co.uk/112238

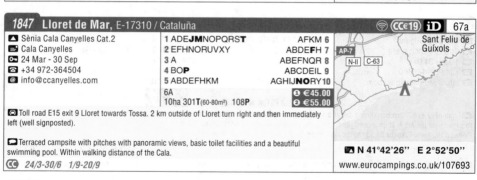

1847 Lloret de Mar, E-17310 / Cataluña ⊚ (CC€19) iD 67a

- ▲ Sènia Cala Canyelles Cat.2
- 🖃 Cala Canyelles
- 📅 24 Mar - 30 Sep
- ☎ +34 972-364504
- @ info@ccanyelles.com

1 ADE**JM**NOPQRS**T**		AFKM 6
2 EFHNORUVXY		ABDE**F**H 7
3 A		ABEFNQR 8
4 BO**P**		ABCDEIL 9
5 ABDEFHKM		AGHIJ**NO**RY 10
6A		
10ha 301T(60-80m²) 108P	❶ €45.00	
	❷ €55.00	

🚳 Toll road E15 exit 9 Lloret towards Tossa. 2 km outside of Lloret turn right and then immediately left (well signposted).

📖 Terraced campsite with pitches with panoramic views, basic toilet facilities and a beautiful swimming pool. Within walking distance of the Cala.

CC 24/3-30/6 1/9-20/9

🧭 N 41°42'26'' E 2°52'50''

www.eurocampings.co.uk/107693

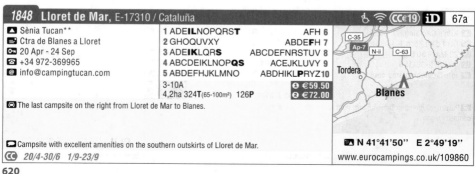

1848 Lloret de Mar, E-17310 / Cataluña ♿ 🛜 (CC€19) iD 67a

- ▲ Sènia Tucan**
- 🖃 Ctra de Blanes a Lloret
- 📅 20 Apr - 24 Sep
- ☎ +34 972-369965
- @ info@campingtucan.com

1 ADE**IL**NOPQRS**T**		AFH 6
2 GHOQUVXY		ABDE**F**H 7
3 ADE**IKL**QRS		ABCDEFNRSTUV 8
4 ABCDEIKLNOP**QS**		ACEJKLUVY 9
5 ABDEFHJKLMNO		ABDHIKL**P**RYZ 10
3-10A		
4,2ha 324T(65-100m²) 126P	❶ €59.50	
	❷ €72.00	

🚳 The last campsite on the right from Lloret de Mar to Blanes.

📖 Campsite with excellent amenities on the southern outskirts of Lloret de Mar.

CC 20/4-30/6 1/9-23/9

🧭 N 41°41'50'' E 2°49'19''

www.eurocampings.co.uk/109860

Spain

1849 Malgrat de Mar, E-08380 / Cataluña

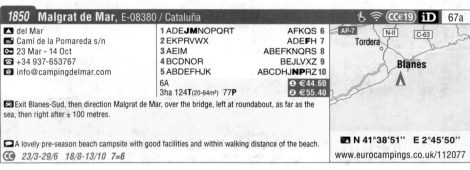

🏕 Camping Resort Els Pins
🏠 Avda Pomareda s/n
📅 1 Apr - 31 Oct
☎ +34 937-653173
@ pinsresort@campingelspins.es

1 ADE**JM**NOPQRT	AF	6
2 EHOQWX	ABDEFGH	7
3 AELS	ABCDE**F**NQRSTUV	8
4 BCDLO**T**	EJLVX	9
5 ABDFHJKM	AB**I**J**P**RV	10
6A CEE	❶ €47.00	
3,2ha 220T(70-110m²) 146P	❷ €58.50	

🛣 Past Blanes-sud towards centre of Malgrat de Mar. Cross river, left at roundabout, left again at beach. Site on the left.

💬 Malgrat de Mar is a town with more than 5 km of paradisiacal beaches. 1.5 km from the market, shopping and touristic areas. Near the Tordera river with its natural diversity of animals and nature. 40 km from Gerona and 60 km from Barcelona. 50m from the beaches. Pitches (approx. 80 m²) bordered by trees. Good toilet facilities.

ⓒ 1/4-19/6 25/6-30/6 1/9-30/10 7=6

📍 N 41°38'54" E 2°46'12"

www.eurocampings.co.uk/118703

1850 Malgrat de Mar, E-08380 / Cataluña

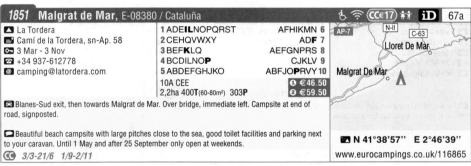

🏕 del Mar
🏠 Camí de la Pomareda s/n
📅 23 Mar - 14 Oct
☎ +34 937-653767
@ info@campingdelmar.com

1 ADE**JM**NOPQRT	AFKQS	6
2 EKPRVWX	ADE**F**H	7
3 AEIM	ABEFKNQRS	8
4 BCDNOR	BEJLVXZ	9
5 ABDEFHJK	ABCDHJ**NP**RZ	10
6A	❶ €44.60	
3ha 124T(20-64m²) 77P	❷ €55.40	

🛣 Exit Blanes-Sud, then direction Malgrat de Mar, over the bridge, left at roundabout, as far as the sea, then right after ± 100 metres.

💬 A lovely pre-season beach campsite with good facilities and within walking distance of the beach.

ⓒ 23/3-29/4 18/8-13/10 7=6

📍 N 41°38'51" E 2°45'50"

www.eurocampings.co.uk/112077

1851 Malgrat de Mar, E-08380 / Cataluña

🏕 La Tordera
🏠 Camí de la Tordera, sn-Ap. 58
📅 3 Mar - 3 Nov
☎ +34 937-612778
@ camping@latordera.com

1 ADE**IL**NOPQRST	AFHIKMN	6
2 CEHQVWXY	AD**F**	7
3 BEF**K**LQ	AEFGNPRS	8
4 BCDILNO**P**	CJKLV	9
5 ABDEFGHJKO	ABFJO**P**RVY	10
10A CEE	❶ €46.50	
2,2ha 400T(60-80m²) 303P	❷ €59.50	

🛣 Blanes-Sud exit, then towards Malgrat de Mar. Over bridge, immediate left. Campsite at end of road, signposted.

💬 Beautiful beach campsite with large pitches close to the sea, good toilet facilities and parking next to your caravan. Until 1 May and after 25 September only open at weekends.

ⓒ 3/3-21/6 1/9-2/11

📍 N 41°38'57" E 2°46'39"

www.eurocampings.co.uk/116865

1852 Mataró, E-08304 / Cataluña

🏕 Barcelona Cat.1
🏠 Ctra N-II, km 650
📅 1 Mar - 1 Nov
☎ +34 93-7904720
@ info@campingbarcelona.com

1 ADEJMNOPQRST	AF**N**OPQRSTUVX	6
2 AEFGHMOPVWXY	ABDE**FG**H	7
3 AEKLQ	ABEFNQRSTU	8
4 **A**BDFHIKLO**PQSX**	JLMOQRSUV	9
5 ACDEFGHKLMN**O**	ABDEGHIKL**N**PRZ	10
Ad on page 622 10-16A CEE	❶ €51.60	
7ha 320T(60-120m²) 53P	❷ €64.50	

🛣 C32, exits 103 or 104. Or via AP-7 at km 12B exit to Mataró via C60.

💬 The campsite is located on the coast. Free bus service to the beach, the beach club, Mataró, the train and swimming pool complex. The campsite also offers a free bus service to Barcelona (take note: the bus service to Barcelona is not free 1/6 - 30/9, 2.90 Euros per person). Free activities in the pre-season. Swimming pool always open.

ⓒ 1/3-30/6 1/9-31/10

📍 N 41°33'2" E 2°29'0"

www.eurocampings.co.uk/111881

Spain

Camping Barcelona is the best campsite for visiting Barcelona: FREE shuttle bus to Barcelona every day. (Not free from 1st June to 30th September: €2,90 one way). Public transport to Barcelona is also available 24h. Our free buses also take you to several beaches, to our Beach Club, beach restaurant, train station and local markets. Swimming pool open all season. Entertainment all year round; for children in July and August. Free Wi-Fi in all the pitches. 107 to 120 sq. yard pitches with 16 amp electric power connection point.

Spain

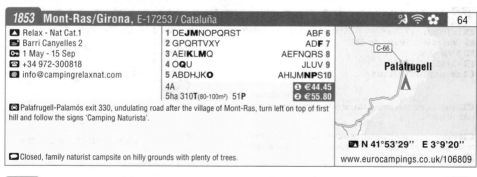

1853 Mont-Ras/Girona, E-17253 / Cataluña   64

- 🏕 Relax - Nat Cat.1
- Barri Canyelles 2
- 1 May - 15 Sep
- +34 972-300818
- @ info@campingrelaxnat.com

1 DE**JM**NOPQRST	ABF **6**
2 GPQRTVXY	AD**F 7**
3 AEI**KLM**Q	AEFNQRS **8**
4 O**QU**	JLUV **9**
5 ABDHJK**O**	AHIJM**NPS**10

4A
5ha 310**T**(80-100m²) 51**P**

❶ €44.45
❷ €55.80

Palafrugell-Palamós exit 330, undulating road after the village of Mont-Ras, turn left on top of first hill and follow the signs 'Camping Naturista'.

Palafrugell

Closed, family naturist campsite on hilly grounds with plenty of trees.

🧭 N 41°53'29" E 3°9'20"

www.eurocampings.co.uk/106809

1854 Mont-Ras/Girona, E-17253 / Cataluña   iD 64

- 🏕 Relax-Ge
- Ctra C31, sortida 330
- 26 May - 2 Sep
- +34 972-301549
- @ info@campingrelaxge.com

1 ADE**JM**NOPQRST	AF **6**
2 HMOPVX	ABDEFH **7**
3 AE**KL**	ABEFNQRSV **8**
4 O**Q**	JLV **9**
5 ABDEHJK**O**	AHIM**NP**RV10

6A
2,7ha 140**T**(90-100m²) 55**P**

❶ €41.80
❷ €53.00

Palafrugell-Palamós C31, exit 330, see Relax-Ge.

Palafrugell

Platja d'Aro

Family campsite with a large swimming pool in a lovely environment near Palamós. Basic toilet facilities.

🧭 N 41°53'32" E 3°8'38"

www.eurocampings.co.uk/113522

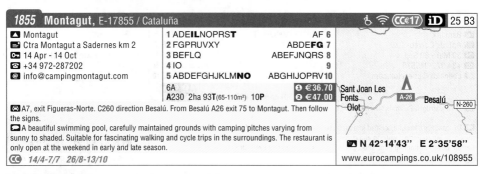

1855 Montagut, E-17855 / Cataluña
  ♿ 🛜 (CC€17) iD   25 B3

- 🏕 Montagut
- 🛏 Ctra Montagut a Sadernes km 2
- 📅 14 Apr - 14 Oct
- ☎ +34 972-287202
- @ info@campingmontagut.com

1	ADE**IL**NOPRS**T**	AF 6
2	FGPRUVXY	ABDE**FG** 7
3	BEFLQ	ABEFJNQRS 8
4	IO	9
5	ABDEFGHJKLMN**O**	ABGHIJOPRV 10
6A		❶ €36.70
A230	2ha 93**T**(65-110m²) 10**P**	❷ €47.00

🅰 A7, exit Figueras-Norte. C260 direction Besalú. From Besalú A26 exit 75 to Montagut. Then follow the signs.

💬 A beautiful swimming pool, carefully maintained grounds with camping pitches varying from sunny to shaded. Suitable for fascinating walking and cycle trips in the surroundings. The restaurant is only open at the weekend in early and late season.

(CC) 14/4-7/7 26/8-13/10

▦ N 42°14'43" E 2°35'58"

www.eurocampings.co.uk/108955

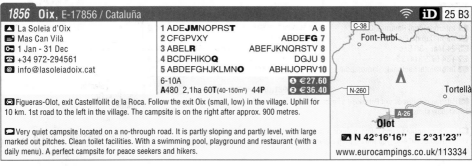

1856 Oix, E-17856 / Cataluña
  🛜 iD   25 B3

- 🏕 La Soleia d'Oix
- 🛏 Mas Can Vilà
- 📅 1 Jan - 31 Dec
- ☎ +34 972-294561
- @ info@lasoleiadoix.cat

1	ADE**JM**NOPRS**T**	A 6
2	CFGPVXY	ABDE**FG** 7
3	ABEL**R**	ABEFJKNQRSTV 8
4	BCDFHIKO**Q**	DGJU 9
5	ABDEFGHJKLMN**O**	ABHIJOPRV 10
6-10A		❶ €27.60
A480	2,1ha 60**T**(40-150m²) 44**P**	❷ €36.40

🅰 Figueras-Olot, exit Castellfollit de la Roca. Follow the exit Oix (small, low) in the village. Uphill for 10 km. 1st road to the left in the village. The campsite is on the right after approx. 900 metres.

💬 Very quiet campsite located on a no-through road. It is partly sloping and partly level, with large marked out pitches. Clean toilet facilities. With a swimming pool, playground and restaurant (with a daily menu). A perfect campsite for peace seekers and hikers.

▦ N 42°16'16" E 2°31'23"

www.eurocampings.co.uk/113334

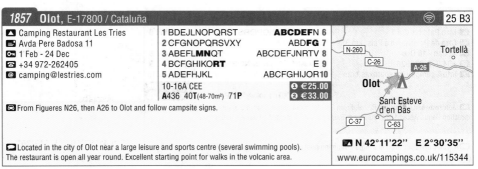

1857 Olot, E-17800 / Cataluña
  🛜   25 B3

- 🏕 Camping Restaurant Les Tries
- 🛏 Avda Pere Badosa 11
- 📅 1 Feb - 24 Dec
- ☎ +34 972-262405
- @ camping@lestries.com

1	BDEJLNOPQRST	**ABCDEF**N 6
2	CFGNOPQRSVXY	ABD**FG** 7
3	ABEFL**MN**QT	ABCDEFJNRTV 8
4	BCFGHIKO**RT**	E 9
5	ADEFHJKL	ABCFGHIJOR 10
10-16A CEE		❶ €25.00
A436	40**T**(48-70m²) 71**P**	❷ €33.00

🅰 From Figueres N26, then A26 to Olot and follow campsite signs.

💬 Located in the city of Olot near a large leisure and sports centre (several swimming pools). The restaurant is open all year round. Excellent starting point for walks in the volcanic area.

▦ N 42°11'22" E 2°30'35"

www.eurocampings.co.uk/115344

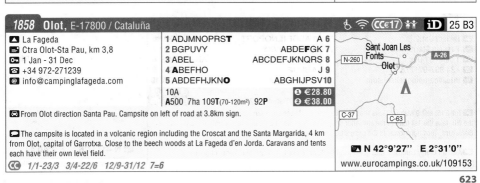

1858 Olot, E-17800 / Cataluña
  ♿ 🛜 (CC€17) ⚦ iD   25 B3

- 🏕 La Fageda
- 🛏 Ctra Olot-Sta Pau, km 3,8
- 📅 1 Jan - 31 Dec
- ☎ +34 972-271239
- @ info@campinglafageda.com

1	ADJMNOPRS**T**	A 6
2	BGPUVY	ABDE**FG**K 7
3	ABEL	ABCDEFJKNQRS 8
4	**A**BEFHO	J 9
5	ABDEFHJKN**O**	ABGHIJPSV 10
10A		❶ €28.80
A500	7ha 109**T**(70-120m²) 92**P**	❷ €38.00

🅰 From Olot direction Santa Pau. Campsite on left of road at 3.8km sign.

💬 The campsite is located in a volcanic region including the Croscat and the Santa Margarida, 4 km from Olot, capital of Garrotxa. Close to the beech woods at La Fageda d'en Jorda. Caravans and tents each have their own level field.

(CC) 1/1-23/3 3/4-22/6 12/9-31/12 7=6

▦ N 42°9'27" E 2°31'0"

www.eurocampings.co.uk/109153

1859 Palamós, E-17230 / Cataluña ⓦ (CC€19) iD 64

- 🏕 Benelux
- ✉ Apt. de Correos 270
- 📅 30 Mar - 30 Sep
- ☎ +34 972-315575
- @ cbenelux@cbenelux.com

1 ADEJMNORST	AFOP 6
2 GHQRTVY	ABDEF 7
3 AQ	ABCDEFNQRS 8
4 BDO	AKLSUVWX 9
5 ABDHJKM	ABDHIJNORZ 10
6A	❶ €45.20
4,6ha 250T(50-80m²) 82P	❷ €59.20

🚗 C31 Palafrugell-Palamós take exit 328. Then follow campsite signs.

💬 An attractive campsite, located in a protected nature reserve in one of the loveliest locations on the Costa Brava. Perfect walking and cycling opportunities. Within walking distance of the sea: Platja Castell. Lovely swimming pool, shop, bar, good restaurant and free wifi. Diving school.

CC 30/3-10/7 28/8-29/9

🧭 N 41°52'21" E 3°9'4"

www.eurocampings.co.uk/107754

1860 Palamós, E-17230 / Cataluña ♿ ⓦ (CC€17) 64

- 🏕 Internacional Palamós Cat.1
- ✉ Camí Cap de Planes s/n
- 📅 24 Mar - 30 Sep
- ☎ +34 972-314736
- @ info@internacionalpalamos.com

1 BJMNOPQRST	AFK 6
2 EPQVXY	ABDEFH 7
3 AK	ABCDEFNQRSTUV 8
4 ABLO	BEJLUVZ 9
5 ABDEFHJKO	ABDGHIJNPRYZ 10
6-10A	❶ €52.30
5,2ha 398T(60-80m²) 93P	❷ €60.60

🚗 Palafrugell-Palamós exit Palamós-La Fosca. Direction La Fosca. Turn right before King's campsite. Then follow signs.

💬 Family campsite on undulating grounds with many trees and good toilet facilities. With CampingCard ACSI you will be given a gran-confort pitch.

CC 24/3-6/7 28/8-29/9

🧭 N 41°51'26" E 3°8'17"

www.eurocampings.co.uk/106806

1861 Pals, E-17256 / Cataluña ♿ ⓦ (CC€17) iD 64

- 🏕 Mas Patoxas Cat.1
- ✉ Ctra de Palafrugell a Pals, km 339
- 📅 12 Jan - 16 Dec
- ☎ +34 972-636928
- @ info@campingmaspatoxas.com

1 ADEJMNOPQRST	AFH 6
2 GPUVWXY	ABDEFGH 7
3 BEFKLMQ	ABEFJKNQRSTUV 8
4 ABCDFHIKLMNOPQR	AEJLUVWXZ 9
5 ACDEFHJLMNO	ABDHIJMPRYZ 10
6-10A	❶ €59.00
11ha 400T(72-100m²) 339P	❷ €70.70

🚗 Motorway exit 6 direction Bisbal. From Pals follow direction Begur/Palamos. At roundabout direction Begur. About 1 km further on, Pals campsite is located on the left of the road.

💬 A family campsite around a large swimming pool on hilly grounds with trees.

CC 12/1-9/7 27/8-15/12 7=6, 14=10

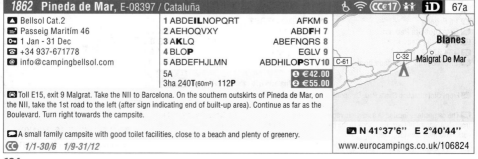

🧭 N 41°57'19" E 3°9'26"

www.eurocampings.co.uk/106800

1862 Pineda de Mar, E-08397 / Cataluña ♿ ⓦ (CC€17) ⚤ iD 67a

- 🏕 Bellsol Cat.2
- ✉ Passeig Marítím 46
- 📅 1 Jan - 31 Dec
- ☎ +34 937-671778
- @ info@campingbellsol.com

1 ABDEILNOPQRT	AFKM 6
2 AEHOQVXY	ABDFH 7
3 AKLQ	ABEFNQRS 8
4 BLOP	EGLV 9
5 ABDEFHJLMN	ABDHILOPSTV 10
5A	❶ €42.00
3ha 240T(60m²) 112P	❷ €55.00

🚗 Toll E15, exit 9 Malgrat. Take the NII to Barcelona. On the southern outskirts of Pineda de Mar, on the NII, take the 1st road to the left (after sign indicating end of built-up area). Continue as far as the Boulevard. Turn right towards the campsite.

💬 A small family campsite with good toilet facilities, close to a beach and plenty of greenery.

CC 1/1-30/6 1/9-31/12

🧭 N 41°37'6" E 2°40'44"

www.eurocampings.co.uk/106824

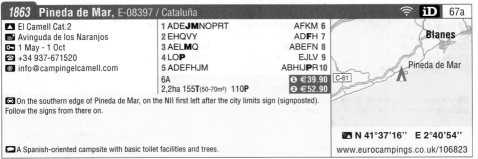

1863 Pineda de Mar, E-08397 / Cataluña 67a

- El Camell Cat.2
- Avinguda de los Naranjos
- 1 May - 1 Oct
- +34 937-671520
- @ info@campingelcamell.com

1 ADEJMNOPRT	AFKM 6
2 EHQVY	ADFH 7
3 AELMQ	ABEFN 8
4 LOP	EJLV 9
5 ADEFHJM	ABHIJPR 10

6A   ❶ €39.90
2,2ha 155T(50-70m²) 110P   ❷ €52.90

On the southern edge of Pineda de Mar, on the NII first left after the city limits sign (signposted). Follow the signs from there on.

A Spanish-oriented campsite with basic toilet facilities and trees.

Blanes
Pineda de Mar

N 41°37'16'' E 2°40'54''
www.eurocampings.co.uk/106823

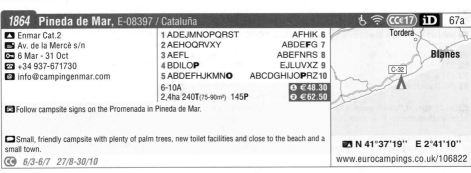

1864 Pineda de Mar, E-08397 / Cataluña 67a

- Enmar Cat.2
- Av. de la Mercè s/n
- 6 Mar - 31 Oct
- +34 937-671730
- @ info@campingenmar.com

1 ADEJMNOPQRST	AFHIK 6
2 AEHOQRVXY	ABDEFG 7
3 AEFL	ABEFNRS 8
4 BDILOP	EJLUVXZ 9
5 ABDEFHJKMNO	ABCDGHIJOPRZ 10

6-10A   ❶ €48.30
2,4ha 240T(75-90m²) 145P   ❷ €62.50

Follow campsite signs on the Promenada in Pineda de Mar.

Small, friendly campsite with plenty of palm trees, new toilet facilities and close to the beach and a small town.

CC 6/3-6/7 27/8-30/10

Tordera
Blanes

N 41°37'19'' E 2°41'10''
www.eurocampings.co.uk/106822

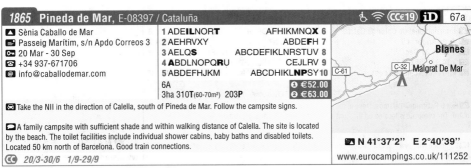

1865 Pineda de Mar, E-08397 / Cataluña 67a

- Sènia Caballo de Mar
- Passeig Marítim, s/n Apdo Correos 3
- 20 Mar - 30 Sep
- +34 937-671706
- @ info@caballodemar.com

1 ADEILNORT	AFHIKMNQX 6
2 AEHRVXY	ABDEFH 7
3 AELQS	ABCDEFIKLNRSTUV 8
4 ABDLNOPQRU	CEJLRV 9
5 ABDEFHJKM	ABCDHIKLNPSY 10

6A   ❶ €52.00
3ha 310T(60-70m²) 203P   ❷ €63.00

Take the NII in the direction of Calella, south of Pineda de Mar. Follow the campsite signs.

A family campsite with sufficient shade and within walking distance of Calella. The site is located by the beach. The toilet facilities include individual shower cabins, baby baths and disabled toilets. Located 50 km north of Barcelona. Good train connections.

CC 20/3-30/6 1/9-29/9

Blanes
Malgrat De Mar

N 41°37'2'' E 2°40'39''
www.eurocampings.co.uk/111252

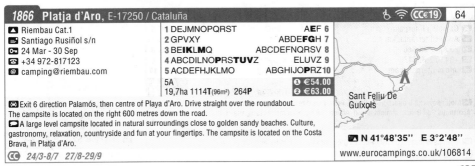

1866 Platja d'Aro, E-17250 / Cataluña 64

- Riembau Cat.1
- Santiago Rusiñol s/n
- 24 Mar - 30 Sep
- +34 972-817123
- @ camping@riembau.com

1 DEJMNOPQRST	AEF 6
2 GPVXY	ABDEFGH 7
3 BEIKLMQ	ABCDEFNQRSV 8
4 ABCDILNOPRSTUVZ	ELUVZ 9
5 ACDEFHJKLMO	ABGHIJOPRZ 10

5A   ❶ €54.00
19,7ha 1114T(96m²) 264P   ❷ €63.00

Exit 6 direction Palamós, then centre of Playa d'Aro. Drive straight over the roundabout. The campsite is located on the right 600 metres down the road.

A large level campsite located in natural surroundings close to golden sandy beaches. Culture, gastronomy, relaxation, countryside and fun at your fingertips. The campsite is located on the Costa Brava, in Platja d'Aro.

CC 24/3-8/7 27/8-29/9

Sant Feliu De Guíxols

N 41°48'35'' E 3°2'48''
www.eurocampings.co.uk/106814

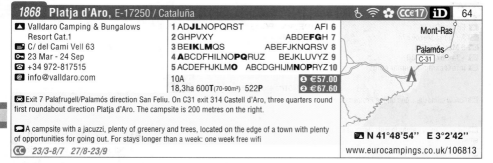

1867 Platja d'Aro, E-17250 / Cataluña

🚩 Treumal Cat.1
✉ Apartado Correos 348
📅 23 Mar - 30 Sep
☎ +34 972-651095
@ info@campingtreumal.com

1 ADEHKNOPRT	FKMNPQWX 6
2 EFHNPQRTUVXY	ABDE**FG**H 7
3 BEF**K**LQ	ABCDEFNQRS 8
4 **ABCDFHLNOPQ**	EGHLQRUVWXZ 9
5 ACDEFHJLMN**O**	ABHIJ**NP**RY 10

6-10A
8ha 544**T**(70-90m²) 187**P**
❶ €55.20
❷ €65.40

Palafrugell

📍 Palafrugell-Palamós, direction San Feliu, then Palamós-est. Then Platja d'Aro. The campsite is located on the left side of the road at Torre Valentina. Clearly signposted.

💬 A campsite on a country estate with excellent amenities.

📌 N 41°50'11'' E 3°5'14''

www.eurocampings.co.uk/106808

64

1868 Platja d'Aro, E-17250 / Cataluña

🚩 Valldaro Camping & Bungalows Resort Cat.1
✉ C/ del Cami Vell 63
📅 23 Mar - 24 Sep
☎ +34 972-817515
@ info@valldaro.com

1 AD**JL**NOPQRST	AFI 6
2 GHPVXY	ABDE**FG**H 7
3 BE**IK**LMQS	ABEFJKNQRSV 8
4 **ABCDFHILNOPQ**RUZ	BEJKLUVYZ 9
5 ACDEFHJKLM**O**	ABCDGHIJMN**OP**RYZ 10

10A
18,3ha 600**T**(70-90m²) 522**P**
❶ €57.00
❷ €67.60

Mont-Ras
Palamós
C-31

📍 Exit 7 Palafrugell/Palamós direction San Feliu. On C31 exit 314 Castell d'Aro, three quarters round first roundabout direction Platja d'Aro. The campsite is 200 metres on the right.

💬 A campsite with a jacuzzi, plenty of greenery and trees, located on the edge of a town with plenty of opportunities for going out. For stays longer than a week: one week free wifi
CC 23/3-8/7 27/8-23/9

📌 N 41°48'54'' E 3°2'42''

www.eurocampings.co.uk/106813

64

1869 Platja d'Aro/Calonge, E-17251 / Cataluña

🚩 Internacional de Calonge Cat.1
✉ Avda Andorra 9
📅 1 Jan - 31 Dec
☎ +34 972-651233
@ info@intercalonge.com

1 ADE**JM**NOPQRST	AFKMNOPQSW 6
2 EHOPQRTUVXY	ABDE**FG**H 7
3 BEF**KLMN**Q	ABCDEFIJKNQRSTUV 8
4 **ABCDEFHILNOPQ**	ACEJLRSUVWXZ 9
5 ACDEFHJKLMN**O**	ABFHIJMN**OP**RYZ 10

5-10A
15ha 771**T**(60-90m²) 178**P**
❶ €55.00
❷ €64.80

Palafrugell
C-31
Platja D'Aro

📍 Exit 6 Palafrugell-Palamós. Drive in the direction of San Feliu, then Palamós-est and then Platja d'Aro. The campsite is located on the right side of the road. Clearly signposted.

💬 Campsite with everything a camper could wish for. Situated against a hill with lots of trees.
CC 1/1-29/3 2/4-8/7 26/8-31/12

📌 N 41°50'0'' E 3°5'4''

www.eurocampings.co.uk/106812

64

1870 Platja de Pals, E-17256 / Cataluña

🚩 Camping Interpals
✉ Av. Mediterrània, km 4,5
📅 20 Apr - 23 Sep
☎ +34 972-636179
@ info@interpals.com

1 ADE**JM**NOPRST	AF 6
2 BGHNQTUVY	ABDE**FG**H 7
3 AE**KLM**	ABDEFNQRS 8
4 **ABCD**LO**PU**	AJLUVXZ 9
5 ACDEFHJKM	ABDHIJLMN**NP**RYZ 10

5A
7ha 560**T**(60-200m²) 131**P**
❶ €59.00
❷ €68.40

Begur
Mont-Ras

📍 Motorway, exit 6 direction La Bisbal. From Pals direction Platja de Pals. At roundabout after 'Aparthotel Golf Beach' straight ahead. After a few hundred metres campsite on the right.

💬 A campsite located on hilly wooded grounds with good toilet facilities.
CC 20/4-8/7 27/8-22/9

📌 N 41°58'52'' E 3°12'4''

www.eurocampings.co.uk/106801

64

Spain

1871 Platja de Pals, E-17256 / Cataluña

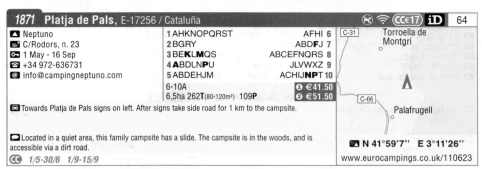

🏕 Neptuno
📫 C/Rodors, n. 23
📅 1 May - 16 Sep
☎ +34 972-636731
@ info@campingneptuno.com

1 AHKNOPQRST	AFHI	6
2 BGRY	ABDFJ	7
3 BEKLMQS	ABCEFNQRS	8
4 ABDLNPU	JLVWXZ	9
5 ABDEHJM	ACHIJNPT	10

6-10A   ❶ €41.50
6,5ha 262T(80-120m²) 109P   ❷ €51.50

🚗 Towards Platja de Pals signs on left. After signs take side road for 1 km to the campsite.

💬 Located in a quiet area, this family campsite has a slide. The campsite is in the woods, and is accessible via a dirt road.
CC 1/5-30/6 1/9-15/9

C-31 | Torroella de Montgrí
C-66
Palafrugell
📍 N 41°59'7" E 3°11'26"
www.eurocampings.co.uk/110623

iD 64

1872 Platja de Pals, E-17256 / Cataluña

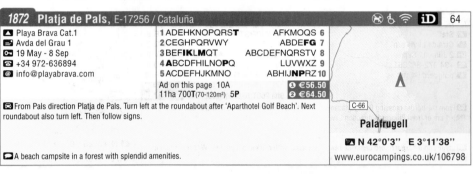

🏕 Playa Brava Cat.1
📫 Avda del Grau 1
📅 19 May - 8 Sep
☎ +34 972-636894
@ info@playabrava.com

1 ADEHKNOPQRST	AFKMOQS	6
2 CEGHPQRVWY	ABDEFG	7
3 BEFIKLMQT	ABCDEFNQRSTV	8
4 ABCDFHILNOPQ	LUVWXZ	9
5 ACDEFHJKMNO	ABHIJNPRZ	10

Ad on this page 10A   ❶ €56.50
11ha 700T(70-120m²) 5P   ❷ €64.50

🚗 From Pals direction Platja de Pals. Turn left at the roundabout after 'Aparthotel Golf Beach'. Next roundabout also turn left. Then follow signs.

💬 A beach campsite in a forest with splendid amenities.

C-66
Palafrugell
📍 N 42°0'3" E 3°11'38"
www.eurocampings.co.uk/106798

iD 64

1873 Platja de Pals, E-17256 / Cataluña

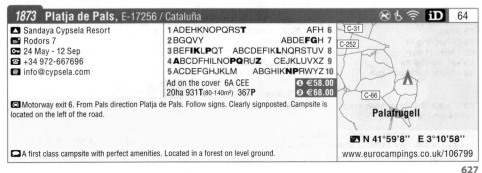

🏕 Sandaya Cypsela Resort
📫 Rodors 7
📅 24 May - 12 Sep
☎ +34 972-667696
@ info@cypsela.com

1 ADEHKNOPQRST	AFH	6
2 BGQVY	ABDEFGH	7
3 BEFIKLPQT	ABCDEFIKLNQRSTUV	8
4 ABCDFHILNOPQRUZ	CEJKLUVXZ	9
5 ACDEFGHJKLM	ABGHIKNPRWYZ	10

Ad on the cover 6A CEE   ❶ €58.00
20ha 931T(80-140m²) 367P   ❷ €68.00

🚗 Motorway exit 6. From Pals direction Platja de Pals. Follow signs. Clearly signposted. Campsite is located on the left of the road.

💬 A first class campsite with perfect amenities. Located in a forest on level ground.

C-31
C-252
C-66
Palafrugell
📍 N 41°59'8" E 3°10'58"
www.eurocampings.co.uk/106799

iD 64

Spain

1874 Porqueres/Banyoles, E-17834 / Cataluña ♿ 📶 CC€17 ⚤ 26 A3

- ⛺ El Llac Cat. 2
- 🅿 Ctra Circumal.lació de l'Estany
- 📅 16 Jan - 14 Dec
- ☎ +34 972-570305
- @ info@campingllac.com

1 BCDEILNOPQRST	AFGLN	6
2 BDIPRVWXY	ABDFG	7
3 ABEFLQ	ABCDEFJQRSV	8
4 BCDFHINOPQ	EJ	9
5 ABEFHJKLMNO	ABDGHIJPTUV	10
6-10A	❶ €32.15	
A175 6ha 300T(70-100m²) 143P	❷ €41.45	

🚗 From Figueres exit 6 towards Banyoles/Porqueres.

💬 Camping El Llac is situated by Banyoles Lake and close to Porqueres. Lovely area for walking and cycling around the lake.

CC 16/1-25/3 2/4-15/6 11/9-13/12 7=6, 14=11

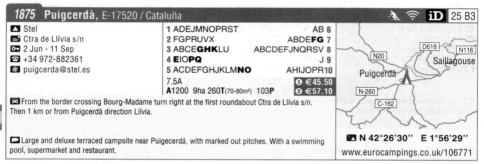

📷 N 42°7'14'' E 2°44'51''

www.eurocampings.co.uk/112646

1875 Puigcerdà, E-17520 / Cataluña 🎿 📶 iD 25 B3

- ⛺ Stel
- 🅿 Ctra de Llívia s/n
- 📅 2 Jun - 11 Sep
- ☎ +34 972-882361
- @ puigcerda@stel.es

1 ADEJMNOPRST	AB	6
2 FGPRUVX	ABDEFG	7
3 ABCEGHKLU	ABCDEFJNQRSV	8
4 EIOPQ	J	9
5 ACDEFGHJKLMNO	AHIJOPR	10
7.5A	❶ €45.50	
A1200 9ha 260T(70-80m²) 103P	❷ €57.10	

🚗 From the border crossing Bourg-Madame turn right at the first roundabout Ctra de Llívia s/n. Then 1 km or from Puigcerdà direction Llívia.

💬 Large and deluxe terraced campsite near Puigcerdá, with marked out pitches. With a swimming pool, supermarket and restaurant.

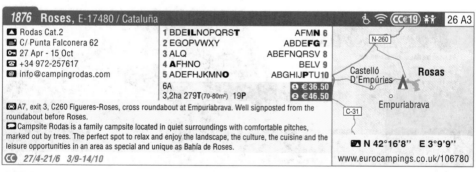

📷 N 42°26'30'' E 1°56'29''

www.eurocampings.co.uk/106771

1876 Roses, E-17480 / Cataluña ♿ 📶 CC€19 ⚤ 26 A3

- ⛺ Rodas Cat.2
- 🅿 C/ Punta Falconera 62
- 📅 27 Apr - 15 Oct
- ☎ +34 972-257617
- @ info@campingrodas.com

1 BDEILNOPQRST	AFMN	6
2 EGOPVWXY	ABDEFG	7
3 ALQ	ABEFNQRSV	8
4 AFHNO	BELV	9
5 ADEFHJKMNO	ABGHIJPTU	10
6A	❶ €36.50	
3,2ha 279T(70-80m²) 19P	❷ €46.50	

🚗 A7, exit 3, C260 Figueres-Roses, cross roundabout at Empuriabrava. Well signposted from the roundabout before Roses.

💬 Campsite Rodas is a family campsite located in quiet surroundings with comfortable pitches, marked out by trees. The perfect spot to relax and enjoy the landscape, the culture, the cuisine and the leisure opportunities in an area as special and unique as Bahía de Roses.

CC 27/4-21/6 3/9-14/10

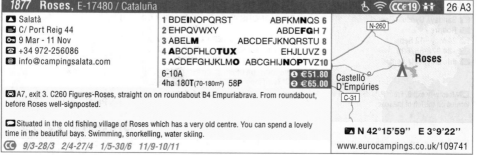

📷 N 42°16'8'' E 3°9'9''

www.eurocampings.co.uk/106780

1877 Roses, E-17480 / Cataluña ♿ 📶 CC€19 ⚤ 26 A3

- ⛺ Salatà
- 🅿 C/ Port Reig 44
- 📅 9 Mar - 11 Nov
- ☎ +34 972-256086
- @ info@campingsalata.com

1 BDEINOPQRST	ABFKMNQS	6
2 EHPQVWXY	ABDEFGH	7
3 ABELM	ABCDEFJKNQRSTU	8
4 ABCDFHLOTUX	EHJLUVZ	9
5 ACDEFGHJKLMO	ABCGHIJNOPTVZ	10
6-10A	❶ €51.80	
4ha 180T(70-180m²) 58P	❷ €65.00	

🚗 A7, exit 3. C260 Figures-Roses, straight on on roundabout B4 Empuriabrava. From roundabout, before Roses well-signposted.

💬 Situated in the old fishing village of Roses which has a very old centre. You can spend a lovely time in the beautiful bays. Swimming, snorkelling, water skiing.

CC 9/3-28/3 2/4-27/4 1/5-30/6 11/9-10/11

📷 N 42°15'59'' E 3°9'22''

www.eurocampings.co.uk/109741

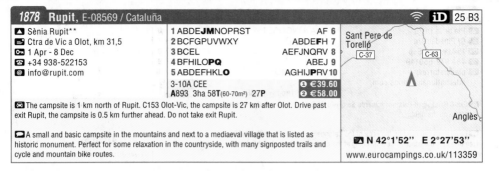

1878 Rupit, E-08569 / Cataluña 📶 iD 25 B3

- 🏕 Sènia Rupit**
- 📍 Ctra de Vic a Olot, km 31,5
- 📅 1 Apr - 8 Dec
- ☎ +34 938-522153
- @ info@rupit.com

1 ABDE**JM**NOPRST	AF	6
2 BCFGPUVWXY	ABDE**F**H	7
3 BCEL	AEFJNQRV	8
4 BFHILO**PQ**	ABEJ	9
5 ABDEFHKL**O**	AGHIJ**P**RV	10
3-10A CEE	❶ €39.60	
A893 3ha 58T(60-70m²) 27P	❷ €58.00	

🛣 The campsite is 1 km north of Rupit. C153 Olot-Vic, the campsite is 27 km after Olot. Drive past exit Rupit, the campsite is 0.5 km further ahead. Do not take exit Rupit.

💬 A small and basic campsite in the mountains and next to a mediaeval village that is listed as historic monument. Perfect for some relaxation in the countryside, with many signposted trails and cycle and mountain bike routes.

📌 N 42°1'52'' E 2°27'53''

www.eurocampings.co.uk/113359

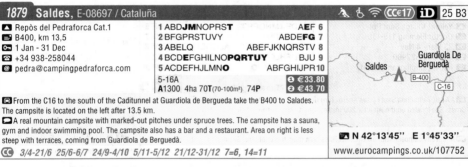

1879 Saldes, E-08697 / Cataluña ⛷ ♿ 📶 (CC€17) iD 25 B3

- 🏕 Repòs del Pedraforca Cat.1
- 📍 B400, km 13,5
- 📅 1 Jan - 31 Dec
- ☎ +34 938-258044
- @ pedra@campingpedraforca.com

1 ABD**JM**NOPRS**T**	AEF	6
2 BFGPRSTUVY	ABDE**FG**	7
3 ABELQ	ABEFJKNQRSTV	8
4 BCD**EFGHILNO**PQRTUY**	BJU	9
5 ACDEFHJLMN**O**	ABFGHIJPR	10
5-16A	❶ €33.80	
A1300 4ha 70T(70-100m²) 74P	❷ €43.70	

🛣 From the C16 to the south of the Caditunnel at Guardiola de Bergueda take the B400 to Salades. The campsite is located on the left after 13.5 km.

💬 A real mountain campsite with marked-out pitches under spruce trees. The campsite has a sauna, gym and indoor swimming pool. The campsite also has a bar and a restaurant. Area on right is less steep with terraces, coming from Guardiola de Bergueda.

CC 3/4-21/6 25/6-6/7 24/9-4/10 5/11-5/12 21/12-31/12 7=6, 14=11

📌 N 42°13'45'' E 1°45'33''

www.eurocampings.co.uk/107752

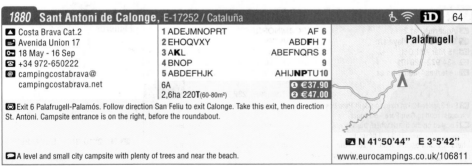

1880 Sant Antoni de Calonge, E-17252 / Cataluña ♿ 📶 iD 64

- 🏕 Costa Brava Cat.2
- 📍 Avenida Union 17
- 📅 18 May - 16 Sep
- ☎ +34 972-650222
- @ campingcostabrava@
  campingcostabrava.net

1 ADEJMNOPRT	AF	6
2 EHOQVXY	ABDF**H**	7
3 A**K**L	ABEFNQRS	8
4 BNOP		9
5 ABDEFHJK	AHIJ**NP**TU	10
6A	❶ €37.90	
2,6ha 220T(60-80m²)	❷ €47.00	

🛣 Exit 6 Palafrugell-Palamós. Follow direction San Feliu to exit Calonge. Take this exit, then direction St. Antoni. Campsite entrance is on the right, before the roundabout.

💬 A level and small city campsite with plenty of trees and near the beach.

📌 N 41°50'44'' E 3°5'42''

www.eurocampings.co.uk/106811

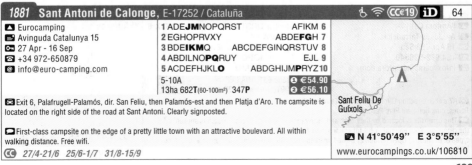

1881 Sant Antoni de Calonge, E-17252 / Cataluña ♿ 📶 (CC€19) iD 64

- 🏕 Eurocamping
- 📍 Avinguda Catalunya 15
- 📅 27 Apr - 16 Sep
- ☎ +34 972-650879
- @ info@euro-camping.com

1 ADE**JM**NOPQRST	AFIKM	6
2 EGHOPRVXY	ABDE**FG**H	7
3 BDE**IKM**Q	ABCDEFGINQRSTUV	8
4 ABDILNO**PQ**RUY	EJL	9
5 ACDEFHJKL**O**	ABDGHIJMP**R**YZ	10
5-10A	❶ €54.90	
13ha 682T(60-100m²) 347P	❷ €56.10	

🛣 Exit 6, Palafrugell-Palamós, dir. San Feliu, then Palamós-est and then Platja d'Aro. The campsite is located on the right side of the road at Sant Antoni. Clearly signposted.

💬 First-class campsite on the edge of a pretty little town with an attractive boulevard. All within walking distance. Free wifi.

CC 27/4-21/6 25/6-1/7 31/8-15/9

📌 N 41°50'49'' E 3°5'55''

www.eurocampings.co.uk/106810

Spain

1882 Sant Antoni de Calonge, E-E17251 / Cataluña 🛜 (CC€13) iD 64

- 🏔 Pla de la Torre
- 🏢 C/ Pinedes s/n
- 🗓 15 May - 16 Sep
- ☎ +34 972-650149
- @ pladelatorre@
  internationalpalamos.com

1 AJMNOQRST		6
2 ABHOQVY	ABDEFH	7
3 K	ABCDEFNPR	8
4	AEUVZ	9
5 ABDHJNO	GHIJNOPRW	10
6A		❶ €35.25
1ha 140T(60-75m²) 18P		❷ €43.25

🚗 Exit 6 Palafrugell-Palamos towards San Feliu de Guíxols until exit Calonge towards St. Antoni. Campsite on the right.

💬 Level town campsite on the edge of the Calonge. In the woods, with modern toilet facilities. Free bikes for the beach. Free swimming at the campsite. International Palamos.

CC 15/5-14/7 1/9-15/9

🏔 N 41°50'59'' E 3°5'15''

www.eurocampings.co.uk/117594

1883 Sant Feliu de Guixols, E-17220 / Cataluña 🛜 iD 64

- 🏔 Yelloh! Village Sant Pol
- 🏢 Doctor Fleming 118-130
- 🗓 23 Mar - 4 Nov
- ☎ +34 682-627900
- @ info@campingsantpol.cat

1 ADEJMNOPRT	ABF	6
2 ENOPRUY	ABDEFG	7
3 BKL	ABCDEFNQRSTUV	8
4 BDFHJKLO	CJLUVWXZ	9
5 ABDFHJKNO	ABGHIJNPR	10
10A		❶ €53.00
1,7ha 77T(50-80m²) 59P		❷ €71.00

🚗 A7 exit 7 direction Sant Feliu/s'Agaro. Turn right at roundabout, past service station and Red Cross. Site located on the left after 200 metres. Short bend with slight slope.

💬 A real city campsite with excellent facilities on a main thoroughfare. Swimming pool with flowers and palms.

🏔 N 41°47'12'' E 3°2'29''

www.eurocampings.co.uk/107753

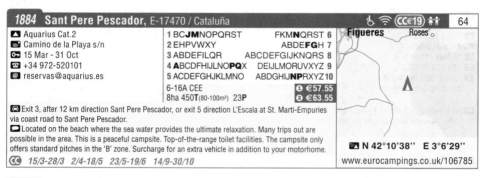

1884 Sant Pere Pescador, E-17470 / Cataluña ♿ 🛜 (CC€19) ♟♟ 64

- 🏔 Aquarius Cat.2
- 🏢 Camino de la Playa s/n
- 🗓 15 Mar - 31 Oct
- ☎ +34 972-520101
- @ reservas@aquarius.es

1 BCJMNOPQRST	FKMNQRST	6
2 EHPVWXY	ABDEFGH	7
3 ABDEFILQR	ABCDEFGIJKNQRS	8
4 ABCDFHIJLNOPQX	DEIJLMORUVXYZ	9
5 ACDEFGHJKLMNO	ABDGHIJNPRXYZ	10
6-16A CEE		❶ €57.55
8ha 450T(80-100m²) 23P		❷ €63.55

🚗 Exit 3, after 12 km direction Sant Pere Pescador, or exit 5 direction L'Escala at St. Marti-Empuries via coast road to Sant Pere Pescador.

💬 Located on the beach where the sea water provides the ultimate relaxation. Many trips out are possible in the area. This is a peaceful campsite. Top-of-the-range toilet facilities. The campsite only offers standard pitches in the 'B' zone. Surcharge for an extra vehicle in addition to your motorhome.

CC 15/3-28/3 2/4-18/5 23/5-19/6 14/9-30/10

🏔 N 42°10'38'' E 3°6'29''

www.eurocampings.co.uk/106785

1885 Sant Pere Pescador, E-17470 / Cataluña ♿ 🛜 64

- 🏔 l'Àmfora Cat.1
- 🏢 Av. Josep Tarradellas, 2
- 🗓 15 Apr - 28 Sep
- ☎ +34 972-520540
- @ info@campingamfora.com

1 BCJMNOPQRST	AFHKMNOPQRSTX	6
2 EGHPRVWXY	ABDEFGH	7
3 ABDEFILMQR	ABCDEFGJKLMNQRST	8
4 ABCDFHLMOPQUYZ	EIJKLMORUVW	9
5 ACDEFGHJKLMO	ABGHIJNPRYZ	10
Ad on page 631 10A CEE		❶ €67.80
12ha 700T(90-180m²) 142P		❷ €76.20

🚗 A7 exit 3, direction Girona/Barcelona. Third exit Figueres/Roses (C260). Turn right 9 km before Roses, direction Sant Pere Pescador.

💬 This campsite is located by the beach and near various places of interest. Dutch is spoken at the reception. With entertainment for children and adults and well-cared for toilet facilities. Various types of pitches: 1) Open terrain, 2) Closed, marked out, with high hedges, 3) Separate toilet facilities (limited).

🏔 N 42°10'55'' E 3°6'15''

www.eurocampings.co.uk/106784

Spain

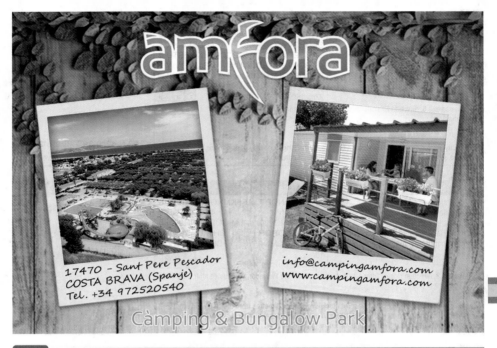

amfora

17470 - Sant Pere Pescador
COSTA BRAVA (Spanje)
Tel. +34 972520540

info@campingamfora.com
www.campingamfora.com

Càmping & Bungalow Park

1886 Sant Pere Pescador, E-17470 / Cataluña ♿ 🛜 ✿ 64

🔺 La Ballena Alegre Costa Brava Cat.1
⊙ 11 May - 31 Oct
☎ +34 972-520302
@ info@ballena-alegre.com

1 BCI**L**NOPQRST	AFKM**N**OPQRSTWX 6	
2 EGHPVXY	ABC**DEFG**H 7	
3 ABDEFL**MN**	ABCDEFGKNQRSTU 8	
4 **ABCD**HILMNOP**QRTU**VW**XY**	JLMORSUV 9	
5 ACDEFGHIJKLMN**O**	ABGHIJM**NP**RWXYZ**10**	
10A CEE	❶ €78.00	
24ha 821**T**(100-120m²) 337**P**	❷ €85.00	

Les Forques
C-31
Λ L'Escala

🚗 Exit 5 direction L'Escala. Then San Marti de Empuries (km 18.5).

💬 Located by the beach, with beautiful pitches and clean toilet facilities. There is plenty to do for young people. The perfect place for a relaxing holiday. An almost 2 km long magnificent sandy beach. A special family campsite. This campsite is at one with the beach and the sea.

🔺 N 42°9'12'' E 3°6'43''
www.eurocampings.co.uk/106788

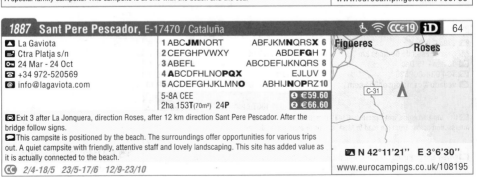

1887 Sant Pere Pescador, E-17470 / Cataluña ♿ 🛜 (CC€19) iD 64

🔺 La Gaviota
🏢 Ctra Platja s/n
⊙ 24 Mar - 24 Oct
☎ +34 972-520569
@ info@lagaviota.com

1 ABC**JM**NORT	ABFJKM**N**QRS**X** 6	
2 CEFGHPVWXY	ABD**EFG**H 7	
3 ABEFL	ABCDEFIJKNQRS 8	
4 **ABCD**FHLNOP**QX**	EJLUV 9	
5 ACDEFGHJKLMN**O**	ABHIJ**NO**PRZ**10**	
5-8A CEE	❶ €59.60	
2ha 153**T**(70m²) 24**P**	❷ €66.60	

Figueres   Roses
C-31
Λ

🚗 Exit 3 after La Jonquera, direction Roses, after 12 km direction Sant Pere Pescador. After the bridge follow signs.

💬 This campsite is positioned by the beach. The surroundings offer opportunities for various trips out. A quiet campsite with friendly, attentive staff and lovely landscaping. This site has added value as it is actually connected to the beach.

(CC) 2/4-18/5 23/5-17/6 12/9-23/10

🔺 N 42°11'21'' E 3°6'30''
www.eurocampings.co.uk/108195

1888 Sant Pere Pescador, E-17470 / Cataluña ♿ 🛜 iD 64

🔺 Las Dunas Cat.1
🗓 15 May - 15 Sep
☎ +34 972-521717
@ info@campinglasdunas.com

1	ABILNOPQRST	AFHIKMNQRSTWX	6
2	EGHPVWXY	ABDEFGHK	7
3	ABDEFILMQR	ABCDEFKNQRSTU	8
4	ABCDFHLMNOPQUY	AEJLMUVW	9
5	ACDEFGHJKLMN	ABGHIJMNPRYZ	10

6-10A CEE ❶ €70.50
27ha 1500T(75-100m²) 262P ❷ €77.50

Castelló
d'Empúries

C-31

🔺 L'Escala

🛣 Toll road exit 5, direction L'Escala. Just before L'Escala turn left at roundabout. Follow signs 'Las Dunas'.

💬 Directly located by a wide sandy beach of almost 2 km long. A holiday park with the best amenities. With a separate discothèque with soundless construction.

📍 N 42°9'39'' E 3°6'28''
www.eurocampings.co.uk/106787

1889 Sant Pere Pescador, E-17470 / Cataluña 🛜 iD 64

🔺 Las Palmeras Cat.1
🗓 Carr. de la Playa s/n
🗓 24 Apr - 27 Oct
☎ +34 972-520506
@ info@campinglaspalmeras.com

1	ABCDILNORT	ABFKMNOPQRSTWX	6
2	EGHPVY	ABCDEFGH	7
3	ABFLMNQ	ABCDEFIKNRSTU	8
4	AEHILNOPQR	BHJKLMOSUV	9
5	CDEFHKLMN	ABGHIJNPRYZ	10

10A ❶ €59.10
5ha 250T(90-120m²) 44P ❷ €66.10

Figueres   Roses

C-31

🔺

🛣 Take exit 3, direction Roses. After 12 km direction Sant Pere Pescador. Signposted after the bridge.

💬 This quiet campsite with distinctive toilet block is located 500 metres from the coast and among sunflowers. The planting is perfectly maintained. A quiet, attractive and well-maintained campsite. Highly recommended. With plenty of entertainment for children of all ages.

📍 N 42°11'17'' E 3°6'9''
www.eurocampings.co.uk/106783

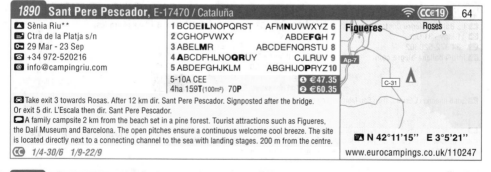

1890 Sant Pere Pescador, E-17470 / Cataluña 🛜 (CC€19) 64

🔺 Sènia Riu**
🗓 Ctra de la Platja s/n
🗓 29 Mar - 23 Sep
☎ +34 972-520216
@ info@campingriu.com

1	BCDEILNOPQRST	AFMNUVWXYZ	6
2	CGHOPVWXY	ABDEFGH	7
3	ABELMR	ABCDEFNQRSTU	8
4	ABCDFHLNOQRUY	CJLRUV	9
5	ABDEFGHJKLM	ABGHIJOPRYZ	10

5-10A CEE ❶ €47.35
4ha 159T(100m²) 70P ❷ €60.35

Figueres   Roses

Ap-7

C-31

🔺

🛣 Take exit 3 towards Rosas. After 12 km dir. Sant Pere Pescador. Signposted after the bridge.
Or exit 5 dir. L'Escala then dir. Sant Pere Pescador.

💬 A family campsite 2 km from the beach set in a pine forest. Tourist attractions such as Figueres, the Dalí Museum and Barcelona. The open pitches ensure a continuous welcome cool breeze. The site is located directly next to a connecting channel to the sea with landing stages. 200 m from the centre.

CC 1/4-30/6 1/9-22/9

📍 N 42°11'15'' E 3°5'21''
www.eurocampings.co.uk/110247

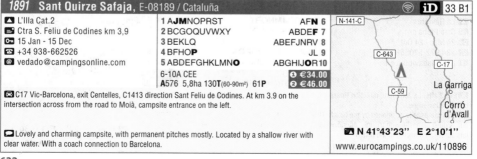

1891 Sant Quirze Safaja, E-08189 / Cataluña 🛜 iD 33 B1

🔺 L'Illa Cat.2
🗓 Ctra S. Feliu de Codines km 3,9
🗓 15 Jan - 15 Dec
☎ +34 938-662526
@ vedado@campingsonline.com

1	AJMNOPRST	AFN	6
2	BCGOQUVWXY	ABDEF	7
3	BEKLQ	ABEFJNRV	8
4	BFHOP	JL	9
5	ABDEFGHKLMNO	ABGHIJOR	10

6-10A CEE ❶ €34.00
A576 5,8ha 130T(60-90m²) 61P ❷ €46.00

N-141-C

C-643

🔺

C-59   C-17

La Garriga

Corró
d'Avall

🛣 C17 Vic-Barcelona, exit Centelles, C1413 direction Sant Feliu de Codines. At km 3.9 on the intersection across from the road to Moià, campsite entrance on the left.

💬 Lovely and charming campsite, with permanent pitches mostly. Located by a shallow river with clear water. With a coach connection to Barcelona.

📍 N 41°43'23'' E 2°10'1''
www.eurocampings.co.uk/110896

Spain

1892 Santa Cristina d'Aro, E-17246 / Cataluña 🦽 🛜 64

- Mas St. Josep
- Ctra Sta Cristina-Platja d'Aro, km2
- 18 May - 16 Sep
- ☎ +34 972-835108
- @ info@campingmassantjosep.com

1	BDE**JM**NOQRST	AF 6
2	GPQRVXY	ABDEFGH 7
3	BDEF**IKLMNOP**Q	ABCDEFGIJKNQRSTV 8
4	**A**BDFHILNO**PQRSTU**Z	EJLUVWZ 9
5	ACDEFHJKO	ABFGHIJM**N**PRYZ 10
10A CEE		❶ €57.00
35ha 1030**T**(75-108m²) 690**P**		❷ €73.00

From the motorway direction Platja d'Aro and San Feliu, then Santa Cristina d'Aro. Drive straight ahead for 1.5 km and turn left.

A large campsite (basic grounds) with plenty of amenities around a large swimming pool.

N 41°48'40'' E 3°1'6''

www.eurocampings.co.uk/108196

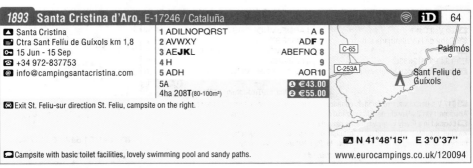

1893 Santa Cristina d'Aro, E-17246 / Cataluña 🛜 iD 64

- Santa Cristina
- Ctra Sant Felíu de Guíxols km 1,8
- 15 Jun - 15 Sep
- ☎ +34 972-837753
- @ info@campingsantacristina.com

1	ADILNOPQRST	A 6
2	AVWXY	ADF 7
3	AE**JK**L	ABEFNQ 8
4	H	9
5	ADH	AOR 10
5A		❶ €43.00
4ha 208**T**(80-100m²)		❷ €55.00

Exit St. Felíu-sur direction St. Felíu, campsite on the right.

Campsite with basic toilet facilities, lovely swimming pool and sandy paths.

N 41°48'15'' E 3°0'37''

www.eurocampings.co.uk/120094

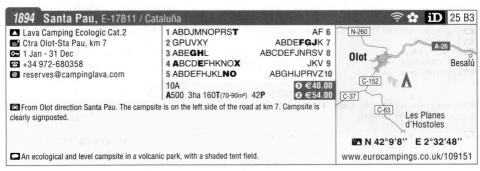

1894 Santa Pau, E-17811 / Cataluña 🛜 ✿ iD 25 B3

- Lava Camping Ecologic Cat.2
- Ctra Olot-Sta Pau, km 7
- 1 Jan - 31 Dec
- ☎ +34 972-680358
- @ reserves@campinglava.com

1	ABDJMNOPRS**T**	AF 6
2	GPUVXY	ABDE**FGJ**K 7
3	ABE**GH**L	ABCDEFJNRSV 8
4	**A**BCDE**F**HKNO**X**	JKV 9
5	ABDEFHJKL**NO**	ABGHIJPRVZ 10
10A		❶ €40.00
A500 3ha 160**T**(70-90m²) 42**P**		❷ €54.00

From Olot direction Santa Pau. The campsite is on the left side of the road at km 7. Campsite is clearly signposted.

An ecological and level campsite in a volcanic park, with a shaded tent field.

N 42°9'8'' E 2°32'48''

www.eurocampings.co.uk/109151

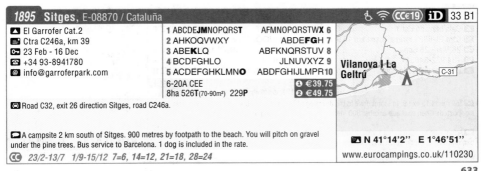

1895 Sitges, E-08870 / Cataluña 🦽 🛜 CC€19 iD 33 B1

- El Garrofer Cat.2
- Ctra C246a, km 39
- 23 Feb - 16 Dec
- ☎ +34 93-8941780
- @ info@garroferpark.com

1	ABCDE**JM**NOPQRST	AFMNOPQRSTW**X** 6
2	AHKOQVWXY	ABDE**FG**H 7
3	ABE**K**LQ	ABFKNQRSTUV 8
4	BCDFGHLO	JLNUVXYZ 9
5	ACDEFGHKLMN**O**	ABDFGHIJLMPR 10
6-20A CEE		❶ €39.75
8ha 526**T**(70-90m²) 229**P**		❷ €49.75

Road C32, exit 26 direction Sitges, road C246a.

A campsite 2 km south of Sitges. 900 metres by footpath to the beach. You will pitch on gravel under the pine trees. Bus service to Barcelona. 1 dog is included in the rate.

CC 23/2-13/7 1/9-15/12 7=6, 14=12, 21=18, 28=24

N 41°14'2'' E 1°46'51''

www.eurocampings.co.uk/110230

Spain

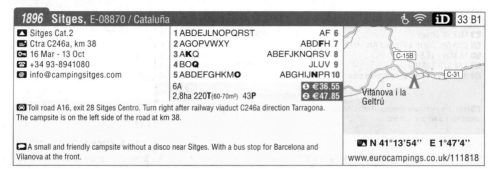

1896 Sitges, E-08870 / Cataluña ♿ 🛜 **iD** 33 B1

- ▲ Sitges Cat.2
- 📷 Ctra C246a, km 38
- 📅 16 Mar - 13 Oct
- ☎ +34 93-8941080
- @ info@campingsitges.com

1 ABDEJLNOPQRST	AF	6
2 AGOPVWXY	ABD**F**H	7
3 A**K**Q	ABEFJKNQRSV	8
4 BO**Q**	JLUV	9
5 ABDEFGHKM**O**	ABGHIJN**P**R	10
6A		❶ €36.55
2,8ha 220**T**(60-70m²) 43**P**		❷ €47.85

🛣 Toll road A16, exit 28 Sitges Centro. Turn right after railway viaduct C246a direction Tarragona. The campsite is on the left side of the road at km 38.

💬 A small and friendly campsite without a disco near Sitges. With a bus stop for Barcelona and Vilanova at the front.

📍 N 41°13'54'' E 1°47'4''

www.eurocampings.co.uk/111818

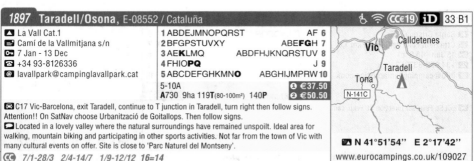

1897 Taradell/Osona, E-08552 / Cataluña ♿ 🛜 **(CC€19)** **iD** 33 B1

- ▲ La Vall Cat.1
- 📷 Camí de la Vallmitjana s/n
- 📅 7 Jan - 13 Dec
- ☎ +34 93-8126336
- @ lavallpark@campinglavallpark.cat

1 ABDEJMNOPQRST	AF	6
2 BFGPSTUVXY	ABE**FGH**	7
3 AE**KLMQ**	ABDFHJKNQRSTUV	8
4 FHIO**PQ**	J	9
5 ABCDEFGHKMN**O**	ABGHIJMPRW	10
5-10A		❶ €37.50
A730 9ha 119**T**(80-100m²) 140**P**		❷ €50.50

🛣 C17 Vic-Barcelona, exit Taradell, continue to T junction in Taradell, turn right then follow signs. Attention!! On SatNav choose Urbanització de Goitallops. Then follow signs.

💬 Located in a lovely valley where the natural surroundings have remained unspoilt. Ideal area for walking, mountain biking and participating in other sports activities. Not far from the town of Vic with many cultural events on offer. Site is close to 'Parc Naturel del Montseny'.

CC 7/1-28/3 2/4-14/7 1/9-12/12 16=14

📍 N 41°51'54'' E 2°17'42''

www.eurocampings.co.uk/109027

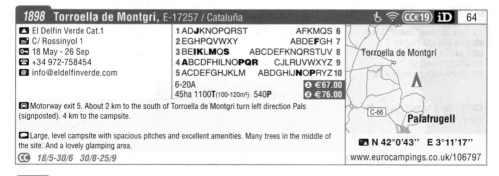

1898 Torroella de Montgri, E-17257 / Cataluña ♿ 🛜 **(CC€19)** **iD** 64

- ▲ El Delfin Verde Cat.1
- 📷 C/ Rossinyol 1
- 📅 18 May - 26 Sep
- ☎ +34 972-758454
- @ info@eldelfinverde.com

1 ADJKNOPQRST	AFKMQS	6
2 EGHPQVWXY	ABD**EFGH**	7
3 BE**IKLMQS**	ABCDEFKNQRSTUV	8
4 **A**BCDFHILNO**PQR**	CJLRUVWXYZ	9
5 ACDEFGHJKLM	ABDGHIJ**NOP**RYZ	10
6-20A		❶ €67.00
45ha 1100**T**(100-120m²) 540**P**		❷ €76.00

🛣 Motorway exit 5. About 2 km to the south of Torroella de Montgri turn left direction Pals (signposted). 4 km to the campsite.

💬 Large, level campsite with spacious pitches and excellent amenities. Many trees in the middle of the site. And a lovely glamping area.

CC 18/5-30/6 30/8-25/9

📍 N 42°0'43'' E 3°11'17''

www.eurocampings.co.uk/106797

1899 Tossa de Mar, E-17320 / Cataluña 🛜 ✿ **(CC€19)** **iD** 67a

- ▲ Cala Llevadó Cat.1
- 📷 Ctra GI-682 Lloret a Tossa km 18,9
- 📅 26 Mar - 26 Sep
- ☎ +34 972-340314
- @ info@calallevado.com

1 ADE**JM**NORT	AFKMNOPQRSWXZ	6
2 BEFHKMNOQRTUVXY	ABD**EFGH**	7
3 BEFL	ABCDEFNQRSTUV	8
4 **A**BDEFHILNO	EJKLMQRS	9
5 ACDEFGHJKLMNO	ABDGHIJ**NOP**TUVYZ	10
10A CEE		❶ €53.45
17ha 612**T**(40-100m²) 117**P**		❷ €64.95

🛣 Toll road E15 exit 9. In Lloret drive in the direction of Tossa. Turn to the right after 8 km (clearly signposted). Then continue another 800 metres to the campsite on the private road.

💬 A fantastic location in the loveliest part of the Costa Brava. Quiet, four beaches, swimming pool, bar, restaurant, supermarket and excellent toilet facilities.

CC 26/3-6/7 27/8-25/9

📍 N 41°42'47'' E 2°54'23''

www.eurocampings.co.uk/106819

Spain

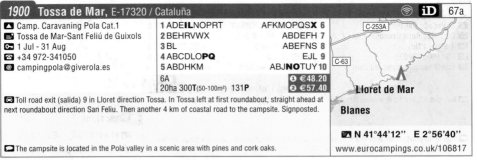

1900 Tossa de Mar, E-17320 / Cataluña 🛜 iD 67a

- ▲ Camp. Caravaning Pola Cat.1
- 🛏 Tossa de Mar-Sant Feliú de Guixols
- ⌖ 1 Jul - 31 Aug
- ☎ +34 972-341050
- @ campingpola@giverola.es

1 ADE**IL**NOPRT	AFKMOPQS**X** 6
2 BEHRVWX	ABDEFH 7
3 BL	ABEFNS 8
4 ABCDLO**PQ**	EJL 9
5 ABDHKM	ABJ**NO**TUY 10
6A	❶ €48.20
20ha 300**T**(50-100m²) 131**P**	❷ €57.40

🔟 Toll road exit (salida) 9 in Lloret direction Tossa. In Tossa left at first roundabout, straight ahead at next roundabout direction San Feliu. Then another 4 km of coastal road to the campsite. Signposted.

💬 The campsite is located in the Pola valley in a scenic area with pines and cork oaks.

Lloret de Mar
Blanes

📷 N 41°44'12" E 2°56'40"

www.eurocampings.co.uk/106817

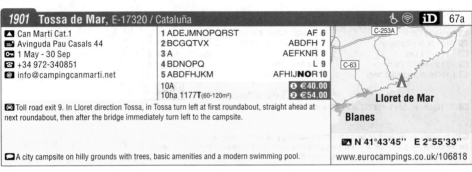

1901 Tossa de Mar, E-17320 / Cataluña ♿ 🛜 iD 67a

- ▲ Can Marti Cat.1
- 🛏 Avinguda Pau Casals 44
- ⌖ 1 May - 30 Sep
- ☎ +34 972-340851
- @ info@campingcanmarti.net

1 ADEJMNOPQRST	AF 6
2 BCGQTVX	ABDFH 7
3 A	AEFKNR 8
4 BDNOPQ	L 9
5 ABDFHJKM	AFHIJ**NOR** 10
10A	❶ €40.00
10ha 1177**T**(60-120m²)	❷ €54.00

🔟 Toll road exit 9. In Lloret direction Tossa, in Tossa turn left at first roundabout, straight ahead at next roundabout, then after the bridge immediately turn left to the campsite.

💬 A city campsite on hilly grounds with trees, basic amenities and a modern swimming pool.

Lloret de Mar
Blanes

📷 N 41°43'45" E 2°55'33"

www.eurocampings.co.uk/106818

Spain

1902 Tossa de Mar, E-17320 / Cataluña 🛜 iD 67a

- ▲ Tossa
- 🛏 Ctra Llagostera, km 13
- ⌖ 1 Mar - 30 Nov
- ☎ +34 972-340547
- @ manel@campingtossa.com

1 ADEJMNOPQRT	A 6
2 BQRUVY	A**BDEF** 7
3 AE**M**Q	AEFR 8
4 BOP	9
5 BDEFHKM	ABHIJL**NOR**Z 10
5A	❶ €35.00
10ha 431**T**(80-150m²) 280**P**	❷ €46.00

🔟 In Tossa de Mar follow the signs for 3.5 km direction Llagostera.

💬 Spanish-oriented campsite in a forest.

Lloret de Mar
Blanes

📷 N 41°43'44" E 2°53'33"

www.eurocampings.co.uk/108197

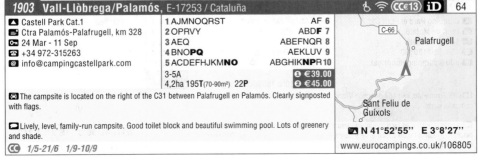

1903 Vall-Llòbrega/Palamós, E-17253 / Cataluña ♿ 🛜 (CC€13) iD 64

- ▲ Castell Park Cat.1
- 🛏 Ctra Palamós-Palafrugell, km 328
- ⌖ 24 Mar - 11 Sep
- ☎ +34 972-315263
- @ info@campingcastellpark.com

1 AJMNOQRST	AF 6
2 OPRVY	ABD**F** 7
3 AEQ	ABEFNQR 8
4 BNO**PQ**	AEKLUV 9
5 ACDEFHJKM**NO**	ABGHIK**NP**R 10
3-5A	❶ €39.00
4,2ha 195**T**(70-90m²) 22**P**	❷ €45.00

🔟 The campsite is located on the right of the C31 between Palafrugell en Palamós. Clearly signposted with flags.

💬 Lively, level, family-run campsite. Good toilet block and beautiful swimming pool. Lots of greenery and shade.

🆑 1/5-21/6   1/9-10/9

Palafrugell

Sant Feliu de Guíxols

📷 N 41°52'55" E 3°8'27"

www.eurocampings.co.uk/106805

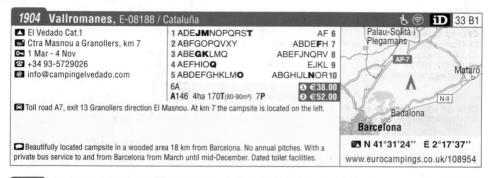

1904 Vallromanes, E-08188 / Cataluña
🛡️ 📶 iD 33 B1

🏕️ El Vedado Cat.1
🚌 Ctra Masnou a Granollers, km 7
📅 1 Mar - 4 Nov
☎️ +34 93-5729026
@ info@campingelvedado.com

1 ADE**JM**NOPQRS**T**	AF **6**
2 ABFGOPQVXY	ABDE**F**H **7**
3 ABE**GK**LMQ	ABEFJNQRV **8**
4 AEFHIO**Q**	EJKL **9**
5 ABDEFGHKLM**O**	ABGHIJL**N**OR**10**
6A	❶ €38.00
A146 4ha 170T(80-90m²) 7P	❷ €52.00

🔄 Toll road A7, exit 13 Granollers direction El Masnou. At km 7 the campsite is located on the left.

💬 Beautifully located campsite in a wooded area 18 km from Barcelona. No annual pitches. With a private bus service to and from Barcelona from March until mid-December. Dated toilet facilities.

🧭 N 41°31'24'' E 2°17'37''
www.eurocampings.co.uk/108954

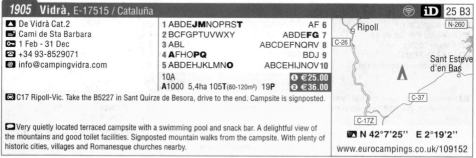

1905 Vidrà, E-17515 / Cataluña
📶 iD 25 B3

🏕️ De Vidrà Cat.2
🚌 Cami de Sta Barbara
📅 1 Feb - 31 Dec
☎️ +34 93-8529071
@ info@campingvidra.com

1 ABDE**JM**NOPRS**T**	AF **6**
2 BCFGPTUVWXY	ABDE**FG 7**
3 ABL	ABCDEFNQRV **8**
4 **A**FHO**PQ**	BDJ **9**
5 ABDEHJKLMN**O**	ABCEHIJNOV**10**
10A	❶ €25.00
A1000 5,4ha 105T(80-120m²) 19P	❷ €36.00

🔄 C17 Ripoll-Vic. Take the B5227 in Sant Quirze de Besora, drive to the end. Campsite is signposted.

💬 Very quietly located terraced campsite with a swimming pool and snack bar. A delightful view of the mountains and good toilet facilities. Signposted mountain walks from the campsite. With plenty of historic cities, villages and Romanesque churches nearby.

🧭 N 42°7'25'' E 2°19'2''
www.eurocampings.co.uk/109152

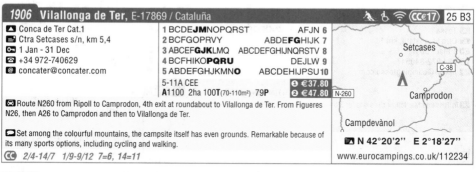

1906 Vilallonga de Ter, E-17869 / Cataluña
🎿 🛡️ 📶 (CC€17) 25 B3

🏕️ Conca de Ter Cat.1
🚌 Ctra Setcases s/n, km 5,4
📅 1 Jan - 31 Dec
☎️ +34 972-740629
@ concater@concater.com

| 1 BCDE**JM**NOPQRST | AF**JN 6** |
| 2 BCFGOPRVY | ABDE**FG**HIJK **7** |
| 3 ABCEF**GJK**LMQ   ABCDEFGHIJNQRSTV **8** |
| 4 BCFHIKO**PQRU** | DEJLW **9** |
| 5 ABDEFGHJKMN**O**   ABCDEHIJPSU**10** |
| 5-11A CEE | ❶ €37.80 |
| A1100 2ha 100T(70-110m²) 79P | ❷ €47.80 |

🔄 Route N260 from Ripoll to Camprodon, 4th exit at roundabout to Vilallonga de Ter. From Figueres N26, then A26 to Camprodon and then to Vilallonga de Ter.

💬 Set among the colourful mountains, the campsite itself has even grounds. Remarkable because of its many sports options, including cycling and walking.

ⓒ 2/4-14/7 1/9-9/12 7=6, 14=11

🧭 N 42°20'2'' E 2°18'27''
www.eurocampings.co.uk/112234

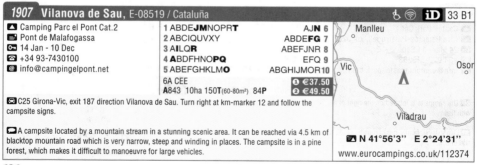

1907 Vilanova de Sau, E-08519 / Cataluña
🛡️ 📶 iD 33 B1

🏕️ Camping Parc el Pont Cat.2
🚌 Pont de Malafogassa
📅 14 Jan - 10 Dec
☎️ +34 93-7430100
@ info@campingelpont.net

1 ABDE**JM**NOPR**T**	AJ**N 6**
2 ABCIQUVXY	ABDE**FG 7**
3 AILQ**R**	ABEFJNR **8**
4 **A**BDFHNO**PQ**	EFQ **9**
5 ABEFGHKLM**O**	ABGHIJMOR**10**
6A CEE	❶ €37.50
A843 10ha 150T(60-80m²) 84P	❷ €49.50

🔄 C25 Girona-Vic, exit 187 direction Vilanova de Sau. Turn right at km-marker 12 and follow the campsite signs.

💬 A campsite located by a mountain stream in a stunning scenic area. It can be reached via 4.5 km of blacktop mountain road which is very narrow, steep and winding in places. The campsite is in a pine forest, which makes it difficult to manoeuvre for large vehicles.

🧭 N 41°56'3'' E 2°24'31''
www.eurocampings.co.uk/112374

Spain

1908 Vilanova i la Geltrú, E-08800 / Cataluña ♿ 📶 (CC€19) iD 33 B1

🔺 Vilanova Park Cat.1
📧 Carretera Arboç km 2,5
📅 1 Jan - 31 Dec
☎ +34 93-8933402
@ info@vilanovapark.com

1 ABCDE**IL**NOPRS**T**	AEFHOPQRSTUVW 6
2 AGOQRSUVXY	ABDE**FG**H 7
3 BCE**IKLMNQT**	ABCDEFJNQRSTU 8
4 A**B**DE**F**HILNO**PRTUVXY**	ABEJKLMNORSUVXZ 9
5 ACDEFGHIKLM**NO**	ABDEFGHIJL**NOP**STYZ 10

10A
A96 40ha 348**T**(70-100m²) 1040**P**

❶ €56.00
❷ €70.00

🛣 Toll road A7, exit 29 direction Vilanova. Before Vilanova turn right on roundabout direction Cubelles C31. After km-marker 153 exit right direction Arboç. Then follow signs.
💬 On a hillside, 2 km from Vilanova i la Geltrú and 3.5 km from the beach. Enjoyable stays in early and late season with adapted facilities including an indoor pool, sauna, jacuzzi and fitness. Bus stop at the entrance for the beach, village and station. Daily bus to Barcelona.
(CC) 3/1-22/6 25/6-1/7 27/8-31/12 **14=12**

🏁 N 41°13'54" E 1°41'28"

www.eurocampings.co.uk/106750

Spain

Tarragona

Two sides of Tarragona

Located on the Costa Dorada, south of Barcelona, you'll notice that the province of Tarragona is more rural and hilly inland, while the coast is more developed. You'll also see traces of Roman and Moorish occupation, as well as lots of beaches and nature parks. Tarragona's safe beaches are ideal for families, while the resort towns have plenty of nightlife – including great food and wine – for everyone.

Historical city of Tarragona

You can't miss Les Ferres Aqueduct just north of the city, and in Tarragona city itself there's the Tárraco Archaeological site and an archaeological walk that includes the Roman theatre and circus. Admire the mediaeval cathedral of Santa Maria, formerly a Roman temple, later a mosque. Modernist buildings include the city's Central

Market, and artist/architect Gaudi was involved in building Colegio Jesus I Maria. Walk up to the Mediterranean Balcony and touch the iron railings, it's said to bring good luck. Bring the kids to the Festival de Santa Tecla, with dragons parading the streets, music, dancing and fireworks – and human castles!

Take the long way home

Family holiday destinations include the seaside towns of Cambrils and Salou, which also has the Port Aventura theme park. History and culture vultures should check out historic Montblanc – but leave your car outside the walls – or Tortosa, which has mediaeval, Renaissance, Baroque and Modernist architecture, while Reus is worth visiting for the Gaudi Centre alone! Mountain town Prades is a good base for hikers, mountain bikers and climbers. Can't stay away from the sea?

with Romanesco sauce. Daredevil diners order Pataco, a stew of snails with potatoes, tuna, almonds, garlic and ham, preferably with a bottle of Tarragona wine - world famous for good reasons.

Visit historic Moleta del Remei, and enjoy water sports on the nearby beach. Explore the Ebro Delta on foot, by bike, on horseback or by boat, and admire the flamingos and other birds, the lighthouse on Fangar Head; or go to Trubacador, the long, narrow beach that connects Punta de la Banya with the rest of the delta.

After a day in the sea air

Try some calçots – grilled leeks, fish served with Xató sauce, or endive salad. Local delicacies include crustaceans, langoustines, or eels served

Our tips

1. Go back 2500 years in the village of Les Toixoneres and experience life then
2. L'Ametlla de Mar: for scuba diving, rocky coves, and a Ceramics Museum
3. Visit the Old Tower at Salou and the Contemporary Enamel Art Museum
4. Wander around the mediaeval castle of Altafulla
5. Enjoy delicious food and stunning views in the floating restaurant Xiringuito de la Costa

1909 Amposta, E-43870 / Cataluña   ♿ 🛜 ⒸⒸ€17   66b

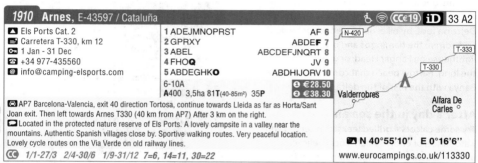

🔺 Eucaliptus Cat.2
🏖 Platja Eucaliptus
🗓 16 Mar - 23 Sep
☎ +34 977-479046
@ eucaliptus@campingeucaliptus.com

1 BCDEJMNOPRST	AFKNQRSWX 6
2 EGHOPVXY	ABDEFGH 7
3 BEL	ABEFKNQRST 8
4 FHOPQR	JLPUV 9
5 ACDEFHKLM	ABDGHIJMOPSTV 10
6A	➊ €37.20
4,5ha 240T(60-90m²) 125P	➋ €48.00

Deltebre   Sant Jaume D'Enveja

⛴ On the A7 take exit 41 to Amposta and Deltebre. On the N340 take the Amposta exit, turn right at Amposta. Take the TV3405 to Platja dels Eucaliptus, then follow the campsite signs.
🏕 A campsite located in the Ebro delta with excellent toilet facilities, outdoor swimming pool from the beginning of May. Good opportunities for windsurfing and cycle trips in the 'Delta del Ebre' nature reserve. A paradise for bird enthusiasts.

ⒸⒸ 16/3-28/3 2/4-26/4 1/5-5/7 24/8-6/9 11/9-22/9 7=6, 14=12, 21=18

📍 N 40°39'24''   E 0°46'47''

www.eurocampings.co.uk/112708

1910 Arnes, E-43597 / Cataluña   ♿ 🛜 ⒸⒸ€19 iD   33 A2

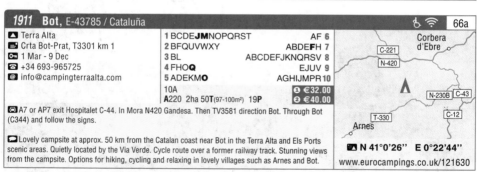

🔺 Els Ports Cat. 2
🏖 Carretera T-330, km 12
🗓 1 Jan - 31 Dec
☎ +34 977-435560
@ info@camping-elsports.com

1 ADEJMNOPRST	AF 6
2 GPRXY	ABDEF 7
3 ABEL	ABCDEFJNQRT 8
4 FHOQ	JV 9
5 ABDEGHKO	ABDHIJORV 10
6-10A	➊ €28.50
A400 3,5ha 81T(40-85m²) 35P	➋ €38.30

N-420   T-333   T-330   Valderrobres   Alfara De Carles

⛴ AP7 Barcelona-Valencia, exit 40 direction Tortosa, continue towards Lleida as far as Horta/Sant Joan exit. Then left towards Arnes T330 (40 km from AP7) After 3 km on the right.
🏕 Located in the protected nature reserve of Els Ports. A lovely campsite in a valley near the mountains. Authentic Spanish villages close by. Sportive walking routes. Very peaceful location. Lovely cycle routes on the Via Verde on old railway lines.

ⒸⒸ 1/1-27/3 2/4-30/6 1/9-31/12 7=6, 14=11, 30=22

📍 N 40°55'10''   E 0°16'6''

www.eurocampings.co.uk/113330

1911 Bot, E-43785 / Cataluña   ♿ 🛜   66a

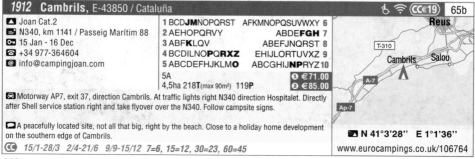

🔺 Terra Alta
🏖 Crta Bot-Prat, T3301 km 1
🗓 1 Mar - 9 Dec
☎ +34 693-965725
@ info@campingterraalta.com

1 BCDEJMNOPQRST	AF 6
2 BFQUVWXY	ABDEFH 7
3 BL	ABCDEFJKNQRSV 8
4 FHOQ	EJUV 9
5 ADEKMO	AGHIJMPR 10
10A	➊ €32.00
A220 2ha 50T(97-100m²) 19P	➋ €40.00

Corbera d'Ebre   C-221   N-420   N-230B   C-43   T-330   C-12   Arnes

⛴ A7 or AP7 exit Hospitalet C-44. In Mora N420 Gandesa. Then TV3581 direction Bot. Through Bot (C344) and follow the signs.

🏕 Lovely campsite at approx. 50 km from the Catalan coast near Bot in the Terra Alta and Els Ports scenic areas. Quietly located by the Via Verde. Cycle route over a former railway track. Stunning views from the campsite. Options for hiking, cycling and relaxing in lovely villages such as Arnes and Bot.

📍 N 41°0'26''   E 0°22'44''

www.eurocampings.co.uk/121630

1912 Cambrils, E-43850 / Cataluña   ♿ 🛜 ⒸⒸ€19   65b

🔺 Joan Cat.2
🏖 N340, km 1141 / Passeig Marítim 88
🗓 15 Jan - 16 Dec
☎ +34 977-364604
@ info@campingjoan.com

1 BCDJMNOPQRST	AFKMNOPQSUVWXY 6
2 AEHOPQRVY	ABDEFGH 7
3 ABFKLQV	ABEFJNQRST 8
4 BCDILNOPQRXZ	EHIJLORTUVXZ 9
5 ABCDEFHJKLMO	ABCGHIJNPRYZ 10
5A	➊ €71.00
4,5ha 218T(max 90m²) 119P	➋ €85.00

Reus   T-310   Cambrils   Salou   A-7   Ap-7

⛴ Motorway AP7, exit 37, direction Cambrils. At traffic lights right N340 direction Hospitalet. Directly after Shell service station right and take flyover over the N340. Follow campsite signs.

🏕 A peacefully located site, not all that big, right by the beach. Close to a holiday home development on the southern edge of Cambrils.

ⒸⒸ 15/1-28/3 2/4-21/6 9/9-15/12 7=6, 15=12, 30=23, 60=45

📍 N 41°3'28''   E 1°1'36''

www.eurocampings.co.uk/106764

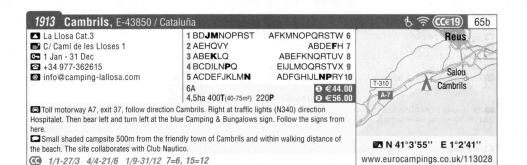

1913 Cambrils, E-43850 / Cataluña ⚼ 🛜 (CC€19) 65b

- 🏕 La Llosa Cat.3
- 🏠 C/ Camí de les Lloses 1
- 📅 1 Jan - 31 Dec
- ☎ +34 977-362615
- @ info@camping-lalosa.com

1 BDJMNOPRST	AFKMNOPQRSTW 6
2 AEHQVY	ABDEFH 7
3 ABEKLQ	ABEFKNQRTUV 8
4 BCDILNPQ	EIJLMOQRSTVX 9
5 ACDEFJKLMN	ADFGHIJLNPRY 10

6A
4,5ha 400T(40-75m²) 220P

| ❶ €44.00 |
| ❷ €56.00 |

🅿 Toll motorway A7, exit 37, follow direction Cambrils. Right at traffic lights (N340) direction Hospitalet. Then bear left and turn left at the blue Camping & Bungalows sign. Follow the signs from here.

💬 Small shaded campsite 500m from the friendly town of Cambrils and within walking distance of the beach. The site collaborates with Club Nautico.

CC 1/1-27/3 4/4-21/6 1/9-31/12 7=6, 15=12

🗺 N 41°3'55'' E 1°2'41''

www.eurocampings.co.uk/113028

1914 Cambrils, E-43850 / Cataluña ⚼ 🛜 (CC€17) ♟♟ 65b

- 🏕 Platja Cambrils Cat.2
- 🏠 Av. Oleastrum 12
- 📅 15 Mar - 16 Oct
- ☎ +34 977-361490
- @ info@playacambrils.com

1 BCDJMNOPQRST	AFKMNOPQRSTWX 6
2 AEHOQRVY	ABDFGH 7
3 BEKLMQ	ABCDEFHNPQRSTU 8
4 ABDFILNOPQXZ	EJKLV 9
5 ACDEFGHIJKLMO	ABHIMNORZ 10

Ad on this page 5A CEE
8ha 400T(45-70m²) 302P

| ❶ €46.80 |
| ❷ €54.50 |

🅿 Toll motorway AP7, exit 35 Salou. N340 or AP7 to Cambrils. At the roundabout in the direction of Vilafortuny, at the end of the road at traffic lights to the right. Then follow signs to the campsite.

💬 This campsite is located on the outskirts of Cambrils near Salou 250m from the beach. There is a large swimming pool and a solarium. Shaded but small pitches. Close to railway line.

CC 15/3-23/3 3/4-22/6 25/8-15/10 7=6

🗺 N 41°4'1'' E 1°4'59''

www.eurocampings.co.uk/106763

1915 Coma-Ruga/El Vendrell, E-43880 / Cataluña ⚼ 🛜 (CC€17) ♟♟ 33 B1

- 🏕 Vendrell Platja Cat.1
- 🏠 Av. Sanatori, s/n
- 📅 23 Mar - 14 Oct
- ☎ +34 977-694009
- @ vendrell@camping-vendrellplatja.com

1 BDEJMNOPQRST	AFHKMNOPQSWX 6
2 AEGHOQRVX	ABDEFGH 7
3 ABEFKLQ	ABCDEFKMNQRS 8
4 ABCDILNOPQ	EJKLV 9
5 ABCDEFHJKLNO	ABGHIJMPR10

6A
7ha 421T(70-105m²) 347P

| ❶ €48.00 |
| ❷ €62.00 |

🅿 Toll motorway sortida (exit) 31. Then take dir. Coma-Ruga. Continue to the coast, turn left and follow the signs.

💬 The campsite is 50m from the beach and has various swimming pools and lawns. Make trips out to Barcelona (70 km), Tarragona (30 km) or Port Aventura theme park. Entertainment at weekends in the low season. Shaded pitches. Additional facilities on the campsite: modern toilet facilities, restaurant and supermarket. Close to railway line.

CC 23/3-29/6 27/8-13/10 7=6, 14=12, 21=18

🗺 N 41°11'8'' E 1°33'19''

www.eurocampings.co.uk/106753

Spain

1916 Creixell, E-43839 / Cataluña   65b

- ▲ Gavina Camping & Resort Cat.2
- ▣ Platja Creixell
- ☰ 20 Mar - 30 Oct
- ☎ +34 977-801503
- @ contact@campinggavina.com

1 BDJMNOPQRST	AFKMNPQS 6
2 AEHOQVX	ABDEFGH 7
3 ABEFKLMQ	ABEFNQRS 8
4 BCDGHLNOQU	BEJLMUZ 9
5 ACDEFHJLMNO	ABGHIJPRZ10
6A	❶ €46.00
7ha 190T(50-70m²) 194P	❷ €59.00

Toll road exit 31. N340 direction Tarragona. 2 km after the Roman arch, exit to the right after km 1181, left with tunnel under the N340. Follow the signs from there on.

Level campsite located between the railway and the beach, with semi-shaded pitches and many pitches at a wide sandy beach.

📍 N 41°9'24'' E 1°26'29''

www.eurocampings.co.uk/106756

1917 Hospitalet del Infante, E-43890 / Cataluña   66a

- ▲ El Templo del Sol Cat.2
- ▣ Ant. Crta de Valencia
- ☰ 15 Mar - 31 Oct
- ☎ +34 977-823434
- @ info@eltemplodelsol.com

1 ACDEHKNOPRT	AFGKMNPQSWXY 6
2 AEGHPRSVXY	ABDEFGH 7
3 BEFIKLMQR	ABCDEFIKNQRSTV 8
4 ABDEFHILNOQRSUXZ	ACJLU 9
5 ACDEFGHKLNO	ABGHIJNPRY10
6A	❶ €45.10
14ha 300T(50-81m²) 132P	❷ €58.50

On the N340 from Valencia, first exit Hospitalet del Infante. Campsite is on the right after 200 metres. From Tarragona past the village, then second campsite left. From A7 exit 38 Hospitalet del Infante, then signposted.

Large, beautiful and quiet naturist family campsite by the Mediterranean Sea. Amenities included large swimming pools and a jacuzzi with sea water. Marked out pitches with some shade. Naturist membership card mandatory.

📍 N 40°58'37'' E 0°54'3''

www.eurocampings.co.uk/107697

1918 Hospitalet del Infante, E-43890 / Cataluña   66a

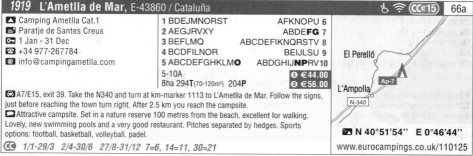

- ▲ La Masia***
- ▣ Ctra N340, km 1121
- ☰ 1 Feb - 30 Nov
- ☎ +34 977-820588
- @ admon@camping-lamasia.com

1 BDEILNOPRST	AFKMNPQS 6
2 AEFGHOQRSVWXY	ABDEFG 7
3 BEFKLMQ	ABEFNQRSV 8
4 BDFHILOQRU	CDEJUVXYZ 9
5 ABDEGHKLMO	ABDGHIJPR10
6A	❶ €44.00
2,6ha 264T(60-90m²) 158P	❷ €52.00

On the N340 (Tarragona-Valencia) at the 1120.5 km post direction Platja de l'Almadrava. Coming via Autopista Salida 38. Take note: new road under construction.

A campsite on the Playa de l'Almadrava, a beautiful sandy beach. New swimming pool and jacuzzi, lawn and tennis court. Very good toilet facilities. Very peaceful location. Free Spa and wifi from 01/02 to 31/05 and from 01/09 to 30/11.

CC 1/2-28/3 2/4-8/7 1/9-29/11

📍 N 40°56'25'' E 0°51'25''

www.eurocampings.co.uk/101376

1919 L'Ametlla de Mar, E-43860 / Cataluña   66a

- ▲ Camping Ametlla Cat.1
- ▣ Paratje de Santes Creus
- ☰ 1 Jan - 31 Dec
- ☎ +34 977-267784
- @ info@campingametlla.com

1 BDEJMNORST	AFKNOPU 6
2 AEGJRVXY	ABDEFG 7
3 BEFLMQ	ABCDEFIKNQRSTV 8
4 BCDFILNOR	BEIJLSU 9
5 ABCDEFGHKLMO	ABDGHIJNPRV10
5-10A	❶ €44.00
8ha 294T(70-120m²) 204P	❷ €56.00

A7/E15, exit 39. Take the N340 and turn at km-marker 1113 to L'Ametlla de Mar. Follow the signs, just before reaching the town turn right. After 2.5 km you reach the campsite.

Attractive campsite. Set in a nature reserve 100 metres from the beach, excellent for walking. Lovely, new swimming pools and a very good restaurant. Pitches separated by hedges. Sports options: football, basketball, volleyball, padel.

CC 1/1-29/3 2/4-30/6 27/8-31/12 7=6, 14=11, 30=21

📍 N 40°51'54'' E 0°46'44''

www.eurocampings.co.uk/110125

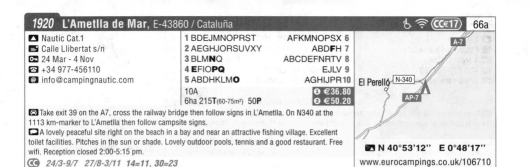

1920 L'Ametlla de Mar, E-43860 / Cataluña   ♿ 🛜 (CC€17) 66a

- ▲ Nautic Cat.1
- 🏢 Calle Llibertat s/n
- 📅 24 Mar - 4 Nov
- ☎ +34 977-456110
- @ info@campingnautic.com

1 BDEJMNOPRST	AFKMNOPSX 6
2 AEGHJORSUVXY	ABDFH 7
3 BLMNQ	ABCDEFNRTV 8
4 EFIOPQ	EJLV 9
5 ABDHKLMO	AGHIJPR 10
10A	
6ha 215T(60-75m²) 50P	❶ €36.80
	❷ €50.20

🚗 Take exit 39 on the A7, cross the railway bridge then follow signs in L'Ametlla. On N340 at the 1113 km-marker to L'Ametlla then follow campsite signs.

💬 A lovely peaceful site right on the beach in a bay and near an attractive fishing village. Excellent toilet facilities. Pitches in the sun or shade. Lovely outdoor pools, tennis and a good restaurant. Free wifi. Reception closed 2:00-5:15 pm.

(CC) 24/3-9/7 27/8-3/11 14=11, 30=23

📷 N 40°53'12" E 0°48'17"

www.eurocampings.co.uk/106710

1921 L'Ampolla, E-43895 / Cataluña   ♿ 🛜 (CC€17) 66a

- ▲ Camping Ampolla Playa Cat. 2
- 🏢 Playa Arenal s/n
- 📅 16 Mar - 4 Nov
- ☎ +34 977-460535
- @ reservas@campingampolla.es

1 BDEJMNOPRST	AKMNOPQRSTVWX 6
2 AEGHJOPQVWXY	ABDEF 7
3 ABEFGHIKLQ	ABEFGHIKNQRSTV 8
4 ABCDEFHILMNOPQR	JLNORUVWXZ 9
5 ABCDEFGHKLMN0	ABDEFHIJLMOPRVZ 10
Ad on this page 10A	
5ha 85T(60-80m²) 45P	❶ €34.00
	❷ €42.00

🚗 On A7 exit 39a. From N340 1096 km-marker. Keep south in L'Ampolla. Follow camping signs on beach road.

💬 A campsite on a bay right next to a sandy beach near a fishing village. Close to the Ebro delta with its unusual flora and fauna, including flamingos. Lovely cycle routes. Watersports. Close to the N340 so suitable as a stopover site.

(CC) 16/3-28/3 2/4-10/7 28/8-3/11 7=6, 14=11, 30=20

📷 N 40°47'58" E 0°41'59"

www.eurocampings.co.uk/115359

1922 La Pineda, E-43481 / Cataluña   ♿ 🛜 65b

- ▲ Camping la Pineda de Salou Cat.2
- 🏢 Ctra Costa Tarragona-Salou km 5
- 📅 1 Apr - 24 Sep
- ☎ +34 977-373080
- @ info@campinglapineda.com

1 BCDEJKNOPQRST	ABFGKMNQRSTWX 6
2 AEHOPRVXY	ABDFGH 7
3 ABEJL	ABCEFNQRS 8
4 ABHLOPTUVY	EJLY 9
5 ACDEFHJKLMNO	ABHIKMPR 10
5A	
4ha 250T(50-100m²) 84P	❶ €54.40
	❷ €67.20

🚗 Motorway C31-B from Tarragona to Salou; signposted from the exit La Pineda.

💬 Medium and well-maintained campsite located between Pineda de Salou and the Tarragona petroleum port, 500 metres from the beach and near the Port Aventura theme park. New toilet facilities.

📷 N 41°5'19" E 1°10'56"

www.eurocampings.co.uk/108957

Spain

1923 Les Cases d'Alcanar, E-43569 / Cataluña — 66b

▲ Estanyet
✉ Paseig del Marjal s/n
🗓 1 Mar - 5 Nov
☎ +34 977-737268
@ info@estanyet.com

1 BDEJMNOPQRST	AFKNOPQRSTV**X**	6
2 AEHJPRSVWXY	ABDE**FG**H	7
3 B**K**QRT	ABEFJKNQRSV	8
4 ABCDFHIJLNO**P**	JLRUV	9
5 ABDEFGHKLMN**O**	ABDFHIJNPRZ	10

5-10A
1,5ha 120**T**(55-100m²) 26**P**

❶ €41.40
❷ €54.05

Sant Carles De La Ràpita
T-331
AP-7
N-238 N-340
N-232

🚗 From the north A7 take exit 41, from the south take exit 43, then on N340 past the petrol station (there is a campsite sign on the right), turn right and after ±300 metres is campsite Estanyet.

💬 An attractive, quietly situated campsite with excellent toilet facilities located right on the beach. Lovely new swimming pool and very good restaurant. Close to the Ebro and Els Ports nature reserves.

CC 1/3-28/3 3/4-20/6 10/9-4/11

📷 N 40°32'25'' E 0°31'11''
www.eurocampings.co.uk/115212

1925 Mont-roig (Tarragona), E-43300 / Cataluña — 65b

▲ Playa Montroig Camping Resort Cat.1
✉ Apartado de Correos 3
🗓 23 Mar - 28 Oct
☎ +34 977-810637
@ info@playamontroig.com

1 BCDEHKNOPQRST	ABFGHIKMNOPQRSTW**X**YZ	6
2 AEGHOPRVY	ABDE**FG**H	7
3 BDEFI**KLM**QT	ABCDEFJKNQRSTUV	8
4 AB**C**DEFHILMNOP**QRSTUVWXYZ**	EJLMQRSTUVWZ	9
5 ACDEFGHJLM**NO**	ABGHIJ**NOP**RXYZ	10

10A CEE
35ha 1200**T**(80-110m²) 202**P**

❶ €65.00
❷ €77.00

Mont-Roig Del Camp
Cambrils
T-310
AP-7
C-44
A-7
N-340

🚗 AP7, exit 37 Cambrils. Follow dir. Cambrils as far as roundabout then right onto N340 direction Hospitalet. Right after km 1137 sign and follow signs off the N340.
💬 A luxuriously laid out, well maintained campsite with a lovely swimming pool. On the Costa Dorada with beaches of fine golden sand and an ideal climate for most of the year. Partly between the N340 and a railway line. Salt-water swimming pool with 6 slides and a new toddlers' play pool.

CC 23/3-27/3 2/4-21/6 2/9-27/10 21=20, 30=27, 45=36

📷 N 41°2'1'' E 0°58'5''
www.eurocampings.co.uk/106770

1924 Mont-roig del Camp, E-43892 / Cataluña — 65b

▲ Els Prats Village Cat.1
✉ Ctra N340, km 1137
🗓 16 Mar - 4 Nov
☎ +34 977-810027
@ info@campingelsprats.com

1 BCD**JM**NOPQRST	AFHIKMNOPQRSTUVWXY	6
2 AEGHOPRVY	ABDE**FG**H	7
3 BEFI**KLM**QT	ABCDEFGIKNQRSTUV	8
4 AB**C**DEFHIJLNO**PQRSTUVX**	CEHIJKLMORSTUVXZ	9
5 ACDEFGHIJKLM**NO**	ABCDFHIJMN**NP**RYZ	10

5-10A
8,5ha 391**T**(80-115m²) 75**P**

❶ €56.00
❷ €69.00

T-310
Vila-Seca
Cambrils
C-44
Ap-7
A-7

🚗 AP7, exit 37 Cambrils. Follow Cambrils as far as roundabout, then right onto N340 towards Hospitalet. Follow camping signs after km 1137.

💬 A really friendly family campsite with spacious pitches right by the sea. Most suitable for swimming enthusiasts, both in the sea and in the modern swimming pool.

CC 16/3-27/3 2/4-21/6 26/8-3/11 21=20, 28=25

📷 N 41°2'24'' E 0°58'50''
www.eurocampings.co.uk/106768

1926 Mont-roig del Camp, E-43300 / Cataluña — 65b

▲ La Torre del Sol Cat.1
✉ Ctra N340 km 1136
🗓 15 Mar - 30 Oct
☎ +34 977-810486
@ info@latorredelsol.com

1 BDEHKNOPQR**T**	ABFGKMNOPQSWX	6
2 AEGHOPRVWXY	ABDE**FG**H	7
3 ABEFI**KLMO**QRST	ABCDEFGIKNQRSTU	8
4 AB**C**DEHIJLMNOP**QRTUVWX**	ABCDEJLMOQRSTUV	9
5 ACDEFGHJKL**NO**	ABGHIJ**NP**QRYZ	10

Ad on page 645 6-10A
24ha 600**T**(70-100m²) 429**P**

❶ €56.00
❷ €70.00

Mont-Roig Del Camp
Cambrils
Salou
T-310
Ap-7
C-44
A-7
N-340

🚗 AP7 exit 37 Cambrils direction Cambrils as far as roundabout, then right onto N340 direction Hospitalet. Right after km 1137 sign and follow signs off the N3.
💬 This campsite is located on the Costa Dorada with a long, beautiful white sandy beach, in a heavenly park with palm trees and mulberry trees. Excellent amenities for all ages. Swimming pool decorated as a tropical lagoon.

CC 15/3-29/3 2/4-22/6 27/8-29/10 21=20, 28=25

📷 N 41°2'15'' E 0°58'29''
www.eurocampings.co.uk/106769

Spain

CAMPING BUNGALOW WELLNESS RESORT
LA TORRE DEL SOL
Cat.1 ★★★★

WiFi ZONE

CATALUNYA

Catalunya Sud

SEA, WELLNESS AND ANIMATION

ANIMATION NON-STOP
15.03/31.10

TROPICAL OPEN AIR JACUZZI
JACUZZIS WITH WARM SEA WATER

CC CampingCard ACSI

2018 DISCOUNT CARD
11 13 15 17 19

✉ **E-43892 MIAMI PLATJA (TARRAGONA)**
Tel.: +34 977 810 486 · Fax: +34 977 811 306
www.latorredelsol.com · info@latorredelsol.com

CAMPING RESORTS
soleil VILLAGE

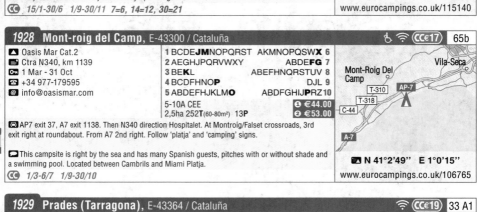

1927 Mont-roig del Camp, E-43892 / Cataluña 🛜 CC€13 65b

- 🔺 Miramar Cat.2
- 🚏 Ctra N340, km 1134
- 📅 15 Jan - 1 Dec
- ☎ +34 977-811203
- @ recepcio@camping-miramar.com

1	BDJMNOPQRST	KMNPQSW	6
2	AEHOQVX	BEF	7
3	AFQ	ABDFHKNPQRS	8
4	BDFHNOPQ	DEV	9
5	ABDEFHJK	ABCDFHIJPSTZ	10
6-10A		❶ €35.50	
3,7ha 50T(80-100m²) 202P		❷ €45.50	

🚗 AP7, exit 37 Cambrils. Follow direction Cambrils as far as roundabout then right onto N340 direction Hospitalet. Left after 1137 km-marker to the campsite.

📑 Rural location on the Costa Daurada with spacious touring pitches right by the sea, and close to the lively town of Miami Platja with many Spanish guests.

CC 15/1-30/6 1/9-30/11 7=6, 14=12, 30=21

Mont-Roig Del Camp · T-310 · AP-7 · C-44 · A-7 · N-340

🔺 N 41°1'31" E 0°57'33"

www.eurocampings.co.uk/115140

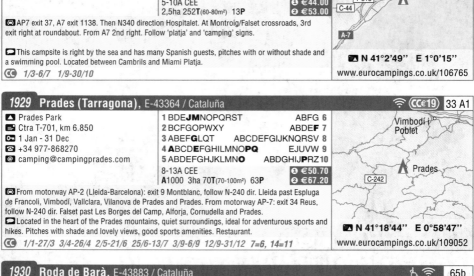

1928 Mont-roig del Camp, E-43300 / Cataluña ♿ 🛜 CC€17 65b

- 🔺 Oasis Mar Cat.2
- 🚏 Ctra N340, km 1139
- 📅 1 Mar - 31 Oct
- ☎ +34 977-179595
- @ info@oasismar.com

1	BCDEJMNOPQRST	AKMNOPQSWX	6
2	AEGHJPQRVWXY	ABDEFG	7
3	BEKL	ABEFHNQRSTUV	8
4	BCDFHNOP	DJL	9
5	ABDEFHJKLMO	ABDFGHIJPRZ	10
5-10A CEE		❶ €44.00	
2,5ha 252T(60-80m²) 13P		❷ €53.00	

🚗 AP7 exit 37, A7 exit 1138. Then N340 direction Hospitalet. At Montroig/Falset crossroads, 3rd exit right at roundabout. From A7 2nd right. Follow 'platja' and 'camping' signs.

📑 This campsite is right by the sea and has many Spanish guests, pitches with or without shade and a swimming pool. Located between Cambrils and Miami Platja.

CC 1/3-6/7 1/9-30/10

Mont-Roig Del Camp · Vila-Seca · T-310 · AP-7 · T-318 · C-44 · A-7

🔺 N 41°2'49" E 1°0'15"

www.eurocampings.co.uk/106765

1929 Prades (Tarragona), E-43364 / Cataluña 🛜 CC€19 33 A1

- 🔺 Prades Park
- 🚏 Ctra T-701, km 6.850
- 📅 1 Jan - 31 Dec
- ☎ +34 977-868270
- @ camping@campingprades.com

1	BDEJMNOPQRST	ABFG	6
2	BCFGOPWXY	ABDEF	7
3	ABEFGLQT	ABCDEFGIJKNQRSV	8
4	ABCDEFGHILMNOPQ	EJUVW	9
5	ABDEFGHJKLMNO	ABDGHIJPRZ	10
8-13A CEE		❶ €50.70	
A1000 3ha 70T(70-100m²) 63P		❷ €67.20	

🚗 From motorway AP-2 (Lleida-Barcelona): exit 9 Montblanc, follow N-240 dir. Lleida past Espluga de Francolí, Vimbodí, Vallclara, Vilanova de Prades and Prades. From motorway AP-7: exit 34 Reus, follow N-240 dir. Falset past Les Borges del Camp, Alforja, Cornudella and Prades.

📑 Located in the heart of the Prades mountains, quiet surroundings, ideal for adventurous sports and hikes. Pitches with shade and lovely views, good sports amenities. Restaurant.

CC 1/1-27/3 3/4-26/4 2/5-21/6 25/6-13/7 3/9-6/9 12/9-31/12 7=6, 14=11

Vimbodí i Poblet · Prades · C-242

🔺 N 41°18'44" E 0°58'47"

www.eurocampings.co.uk/109052

1930 Roda de Barà, E-43883 / Cataluña ♿ 🛜 65b

- 🔺 Park Playa Barà Cat.1
- 🚏 Ctra N340 km 1183
- 📅 31 Mar - 1 Oct
- ☎ +34 977-802701
- @ info@barapark.es

1	BCDEJMNOPQRST	ABFGHIKMNOPQRSTWX	6
2	AEFGHKOQRUVXY	ABDEFGH	7
3	ABIKLMOPQR	ABCDEFIKLNQRSTUV	8
4	ABCDILMNOPQRSTUVWXYZ	EJLMTVZ	9
5	ACDEFGHIJKLMNO	AGHIJMNPRYZ	10
5-10A		❶ €52.10	
14,5ha 650T(60-120m²) 160P		❷ €59.80	

🚗 Toll road exit 31 El Vendrell/Coma-Ruga. N340 direction Tarragona. The campsite entrance is directly left of a Roman archway in the middle of the road.

📑 The campsite is located between the N340 and the railway line, close to the beach, and is partly level and partly terraced. It is set in parkland, resembling a sort of open-air Center Parcs. There is an amphitheatre for staging shows and a jacuzzi at the highest point of the sun terrace.

El Vendrell · AP-7 · La Móra

🔺 N 41°10'20" E 1°28'10"

www.eurocampings.co.uk/106754

1931 Roda de Barà, E-43883 / Cataluña 65b

- Stel Cat.1
- Ctra N340 km 1182
- 1 Apr - 29 Sep
- +34 977-802002
- @ rodadebara@stel.es

1	BCDHKNOQRST	ABFHKMNPQRSTWX	6
2	AEGHOQRVWXY	ABDE**FG**H	7
3	ABDE**KLM**QR	ABCDEFGIKLMNQRSTUV	8
4	BCDILNO**PRUX**	EJKLMRTV	9
5	ABCDEFGHIJKLM**NO**	ABEHIJPRYZ	10

5-10A   ❶ €52.50
12ha 520T(60-95m²)   178P   ❷ €65.50

Toll road exit 31 El Vendrell/Coma-Ruga. N340 direction Tarragona, a few hundred metres past a Roman archway, campsite Stel on the left.

Beautifully laid out campsite between the N340 and the railway with a private subway to the beach. Planting consists of various bushes, pines, mulberry trees and many palms.

N 41°10'12'' E 1°27'52''

www.eurocampings.co.uk/106755

1932 Salou/Tarragona, E-43840 / Cataluña 65b

- Camping & Resort Sangulí Salou Cat.1
- Paseo Miramar-Plaça Venus
- 23 Mar - 3 Oct
- +34 977-381641
- @ mail@sangulisalou.com

1	BCDEJMNOPQRST	AFHIKMNOPQRSTW	6
2	AEFGHOPQRVXY	BE**FG**H	7
3	BCDEF**IKLM**QS	BDFJKNQRSTUV	8
4	**A**BCDFHILNO**PQRS**U	CEJLOTUVWZ	9
5	ACDEFGHJKL**O**	ABCFGHIJMPQRYZ	10

8-10A   ❶ €75.00
23ha 976T(75-135m²)   417P   ❷ €85.00

Toll road A7, exit 35 Salou. Direction Salou, turn right at first roundabout direction Cambrils, turn left at next roundabout, then right at the end of the road. Follow the signs.

An excellent campsite, located near the boulevard, the beach and the Salou sea. With five swimming/amusement parks, various sports facilities and a wonderful amphitheatre, this unparalleled campsite is a true paradise for the entire family.

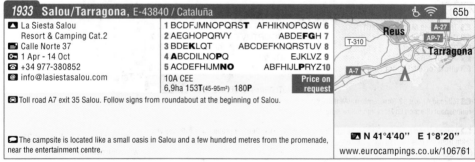

N 41°4'31'' E 1°7'2''

www.eurocampings.co.uk/101069

1933 Salou/Tarragona, E-43840 / Cataluña 65b

- La Siesta Salou Resort & Camping Cat.2
- Calle Norte 37
- 1 Apr - 14 Oct
- +34 977-380852
- @ info@lasiestasalou.com

1	BCDFJMNOPQRS**T**	AFHIKNOPQSW	6
2	AEGHOPQRVY	ABDE**FG**H	7
3	BDE**K**LQT	ABCDEFKNQRSTUV	8
4	**A**BCDILNO**PQ**	EJKLVZ	9
5	ACDEFHIJM**NO**	ABFHIJL**P**RYZ	10

10A CEE   **Price on**
6,9ha 153T(45-95m²)   180P   **request**

Toll road A7 exit 35 Salou. Follow signs from roundabout at the beginning of Salou.

The campsite is located like a small oasis in Salou and a few hundred metres from the promenade, near the entertainment centre.

N 41°4'40'' E 1°8'20''

www.eurocampings.co.uk/106761

1934 Sant Carles de la Ràpita, E-43530 / Cataluña CC€17 66b

- Alfacs Cat.2
- Ctra Alcanar Platja
- 23 Mar - 14 Oct
- +34 977-740561
- @ info@alfacs.com

1	BDE**JM**NOP**R**T	**AF**KNPQSWX	6
2	ABEKMORVXY	ABD**F**	7
3	AELMQ	ABEFNRV	8
4	HLO	IJU	9
5	ACDEFHKLMN	ABDGHIJPSTV	10

7-10A   ❶ €34.60
2,5ha 155T(45-70m²)   119P   ❷ €44.60

North: on the A7 exit 41 dir. Sant Carles de la Ràpita. N340 at the 1072 km marker, exit to Sant Carles de la Ràpita. Turn right at 2nd roundabout to Calle Sant/Sidre. South: exit 43 on A7, N340 between 1066 and 1065 km markers dir. Sant Carles de la Ràpita. Site 2 km on the right.

Right by the Mediterranean coast. 6 km from Ebro Delta nature reserve past the rice fields with unusual flora and fauna. Excellent walking, cycling and fishing in the Delta.

CC 23/3-28/3   3/4-22/6   11/9-13/10   7=6

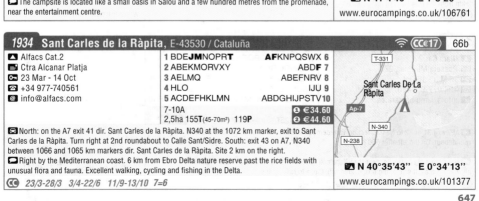

N 40°35'43'' E 0°34'13''

www.eurocampings.co.uk/101377

Spain

1935 Tamarit/Tarragona, E-43008 / Cataluña   ♿ 🛜 (CC€19) ⚥ | 65b

- ⛺ Tamarit Beach Resort Cat.1
- 🏖 Platja de Tamarit, N340a km 1172
- 📅 21 Mar - 4 Nov
- ☎ +34 977-650128
- @ resort@tamarit.com

1 BCDE**JM**NOPQRST	AFHKMNOPQSTUVW**X**YZ	6
2 ABCEFGHMOQRVWXY	ABCDE**F**GHJ	7
3 ABDE**IKLM**NQTU	ABCDEFGIJ**KLM**NQRSTUV	8
4 **A**BCDFHILNO**PQRX**Z	CEJKLORSTUVZ	9
5 ACDEFGHJKLM**O**	ABDEFGHIJMOPRVXYZ	10
10-16A CEE	❶ €68.00	
17ha 476**T**(66-200m²) 254**P**	❷ €75.00	

🅰 AP7 exit 32, dir. Altafulla/Torredembarra/Tamarit. N340a dir. Tarragona, 1st exit at roundabout, 4th exit next roundabout dir. Tamarit/Altafulla. Right after 250m, follow 'Tamarit Park' signs. Campsite on the left.
🗨 The campsite is beautifully located at the foot of Tamarit castle, right on the beach and some distance from the coast road and railway line. Restaurant/bar with roof garden and sea views where the sandy beach meets the rocky coast.

(CC) 21/3-21/6 11/9-3/11

Tarragona

📍 N 41°7'57'' E 1°21'37''

www.eurocampings.co.uk/106758

1936 Tarragona, E-43080 / Cataluña   ♿ 🛜 (CC€17) | 65b

- ⛺ Las Palmeras Cat.1
- 🏖 Ctra N340, km 1168
- 📅 24 Mar - 14 Oct
- ☎ +34 977-208081
- @ laspalmeras@laspalmeras.com

1 BCD**IL**NOPQRST	AFKMNOPQRSTUVWXZ	6
2 AEFGHOPQRVWXY	ABDE**FG**	7
3 BEF**KLMN**Q	ABCDEFKNQRST	8
4 BCDILNO**P**	BELMRUV	9
5 ACDEFGHIJKLM**O**	ABDGHIKM**P**RVXYZ	10
5-10A	❶ €60.00	
17ha 140**T**(70-110m²) 209**P**	❷ €78.00	

🅰 Toll road A7, exit 32, roundabout dir. Tarragona N340. After a few kilometres on the left restaurant 'El Trull'. Then beyond km-marker 1168 turn left through the tunnel under the railway track to the site.
🗨 Paradise for beach lovers. You can camp beside or up to 50m from the beautiful sandy beach. At the end of the site is the Punta de la Mora walking area. 4 km from the historic city of Tarragona. All this compensates for the noise of the railway.

(CC) 3/4-14/6 12/9-13/10

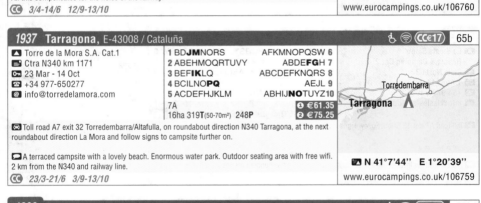

Torredembarra

Tarragona

📍 N 41°7'49'' E 1°18'43''

www.eurocampings.co.uk/106760

1937 Tarragona, E-43008 / Cataluña   ♿ 🛜 (CC€17) | 65b

- ⛺ Torre de la Mora S.A. Cat.1
- 🏖 Ctra N340 km 1171
- 📅 23 Mar - 14 Oct
- ☎ +34 977-650277
- @ info@torredelamora.com

1 BD**JM**NORS	AFKMNOPQSW	6
2 ABEHMOQRTUVY	ABDE**FG**H	7
3 BEF**IK**LQ	ABCDEFKNQRS	8
4 BCILNO**PQ**	AEJL	9
5 ACDEFHJKLM	ABHIJ**NO**TUYZ	10
7A	❶ €61.35	
16ha 319**T**(50-70m²) 248**P**	❷ €75.25	

🅰 Toll road A7 exit 32 Torredembarra/Altafulla, on roundabout direction N340 Tarragona, at the next roundabout direction La Mora and follow signs to campsite further on.

🗨 A terraced campsite with a lovely beach. Enormous water park. Outdoor seating area with free wifi. 2 km from the N340 and railway line.

(CC) 23/3-21/6 3/9-13/10

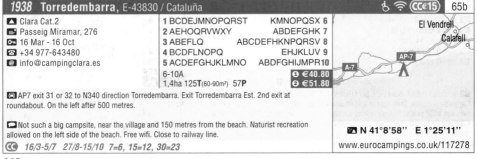

Torredembarra

Tarragona

📍 N 41°7'44'' E 1°20'39''

www.eurocampings.co.uk/106759

1938 Torredembarra, E-43830 / Cataluña   ♿ 🛜 (CC€15) | 65b

- ⛺ Clara Cat.2
- 🏖 Passeig Miramar, 276
- 📅 16 Mar - 16 Oct
- ☎ +34 977-643480
- @ info@campingclara.es

1 BCDE**JM**NOPQRST	KMNOPQSX	6
2 AEHOQRVWXY	ABDEFGHK	7
3 ABEFLQ	ABCDEFHKNPQRSV	8
4 BCDFLNOPQ	EHJKLUV	9
5 ACDEFGHJKLMNO	ABDFGHIJMPR	10
6-10A	❶ €40.80	
1,4ha 125**T**(60-90m²) 57**P**	❷ €51.80	

🅰 AP7 exit 31 or 32 to N340 direction Torredembarra. Exit Torredembarra Est. 2nd exit at roundabout. On the left after 500 metres.

🗨 Not such a big campsite, near the village and 150 metres from the beach. Naturist recreation allowed on the left side of the beach. Free wifi. Close to railway line.

(CC) 16/3-5/7 27/8-15/10 7=6, 15=12, 30=23

El Vendrell
Calafell

📍 N 41°8'58'' E 1°25'11''

www.eurocampings.co.uk/117278

1939 Torredembarra, E-43830 / Cataluña   (CC€15)   65b

- La Noria Cat.2
- Passeig Miramar 278
- 24 Mar - 1 Oct
- +34 977-640453
- info@camping-lanoria.com

1 BDEJMNOPQRT	KMNPQS 6
2 AEHOPQRVXY	ABDEFGH 7
3 ABEFLQ	ABEFKNQRSV 8
4 BDFHLNOQ	DEJLV 9
5 ACDEFGHJKLMNO	AGHIJNPRZ 10

6A
5ha 440T(50-60m²) 219P
❶ €41.40
❷ €52.20

AP7 exit 31 or 32 to N340 direction Torredembarra Est. 2nd exit on roundabout and campsite 400 metres on the left of the road.

A well maintained campsite. Close to a village and beach. Naturist recreation is permitted on the left side of the beach. Free wifi. Attractive outdoor cafe and a good restaurant. There is a railway track next to the campsite.

CC 24/3-5/7 27/8-29/9 7=6, 14=12, 21=18, 30=23

N 41°9'1" E 1°25'16"
www.eurocampings.co.uk/108181

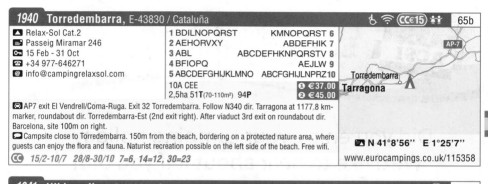

El Vendrell — AP-7, A-7

1940 Torredembarra, E-43830 / Cataluña   (CC€15)   65b

- Relax-Sol Cat.2
- Passeig Miramar 246
- 15 Feb - 31 Oct
- +34 977-646271
- info@campingrelaxsol.com

1 BDILNOPQRST	KMNOPQRST 6
2 AEHORVXY	ABDEFHIK 7
3 ABL	ABCDEFHKNPQRSTV 8
4 BFIOPQ	AEJLW 9
5 ABCDEFGHIJKLMNO	ABCFGHIJLNPRZ 10

10A CEE
2,5ha 51T(70-110m²) 94P
❶ €37.00
❷ €45.00

AP7 exit El Vendrell/Coma-Ruga. Exit 32 Torredembarra. Follow N340 dir. Tarragona at 1177.8 km-marker, roundabout dir. Torredembarra-Est (2nd exit right). After viaduct 3rd exit on roundabout dir. Barcelona, site 100m on right.

Campsite close to Torredembarra. 150m from the beach, bordering on a protected nature area, where guests can enjoy the flora and fauna. Naturist recreation possible on the left side of the beach. Free wifi.

CC 15/2-10/7 28/8-30/10 7=6, 14=12, 30=23

N 41°8'56" E 1°25'7"
www.eurocampings.co.uk/115358

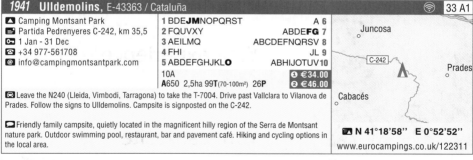

Torredembarra, Tarragona — AP-7

1941 Ulldemolins, E-43363 / Cataluña   33 A1

- Camping Montsant Park
- Partida Pedrenyeres C-242, km 35,5
- 1 Jan - 31 Dec
- +34 977-561708
- info@campingmontsantpark.com

1 BDEJMNOPQRST	A 6
2 FQUVXY	ABDEFG 7
3 AEILMQ	ABCDEFNQRSV 8
4 FHI	JL 9
5 ABDEFGHJKLO	ABHIJOTUV 10

10A
A650 2,5ha 99T(70-100m²) 26P
❶ €34.00
❷ €46.00

Leave the N240 (Lleida, Vimbodi, Tarragona) to take the T-7004. Drive past Vallclara to Vilanova de Prades. Follow the signs to Ulldemolins. Campsite is signposted on the C-242.

Friendly family campsite, quietly located in the magnificent hilly region of the Serra de Montsant nature park. Outdoor swimming pool, restaurant, bar and pavement café. Hiking and cycling options in the local area.

N 41°18'58" E 0°52'52"
www.eurocampings.co.uk/122311

Juncosa, C-242, Prades, Cabacés

1942 Vilanova de Prades, E-43439 / Cataluña   (CC€17)   33 A1

- Serra de Prades Resort Cat.1
- Sant Antonio s/n
- 1 Jan - 31 Dec
- +34 977-869050
- info@serradeprades.com

1 BDEJMNOPQRST	ABFG 6
2 FGPQRUVWXY	ABDFGHK 7
3 BCEFHLMNQRSTU	ABCDEFJNQRSV 8
4 ABCDEFHIJKLNOPQRTUX	EGHJUVW 9
5 ACEFGHJKLMNO	ABDGHIJNOPRV 10

6A
A920 5ha 215T(92-100m²) 89P
❶ €38.00
❷ €52.00

From Barcelona AP-7 to Tarragona, AP-2 to Lleida, exit 9 Montblanc, N240 Lleida, Vimbodi, Vilanova de Prades. From Lleida N240, Vimbodi, Vilanova de Prades. From Vimbodi dir. Vallclara. Don't use SatNav but follow directions.

Quietly located campsite with heated pool, own wine production, wellness area and restaurant. Surroundings: museums, wine cellars, sports activities. Organised themed activities such as photography, nature, animals, etc.

CC 1/1-26/4 2/5-21/6 25/6-14/7 7/9-26/10 5/11-31/12 7=6, 14=11

N 41°20'59" E 0°57'30"
www.eurocampings.co.uk/108185

AP-2, Vimbodi i Poblet, Prades, C-242

1943 Vinyols i Els Arcs, E-43391 / Cataluña

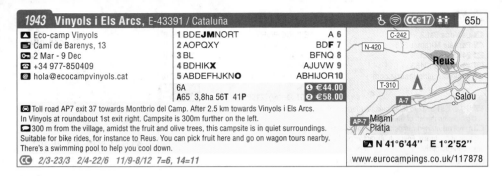

- ▲ Eco-camp Vinyols
- ✉ Camí de Barenys, 13
- 🗓 2 Mar - 9 Dec
- ☎ +34 977-850409
- @ hola@ecocampvinyols.cat

1	BDE**JM**NORT	A 6
2	AOPQXY	BD**F** 7
3	BL	BFNQ 8
4	BDHIK**X**	AJUVW 9
5	ABDEFHJKN**O**	ABHIJOR 10
	6 A	❶ €44.00
A 65	3,8ha 56**T** 41**P**	❷ €58.00

🚗 Toll road AP7 exit 37 towards Montbrio del Camp. After 2.5 km towards Vinyols i Els Arcs. In Vinyols at roundabout 1st exit right. Campsite is 300m further on the left.
💬 300 m from the village, amidst the fruit and olive trees, this campsite is in quiet surroundings. Suitable for bike rides, for instance to Reus. You can pick fruit here and go on wagon tours nearby. There's a swimming pool to help you cool down.

CC 2/3-23/3 2/4-22/6 11/9-8/12 7=6, 14=11

📷 N 41°6'44" E 1°2'52"

www.eurocampings.co.uk/117878

65b

Reus
Salou
Miami Platja

Spain

Lleida

Rich and diverse land

Lleida is a province that's part of the autonomous region of Catalonia, and borders France in the north. Mountainous and forested to the north and arid in the south, Lleida is rich and fertile in between. No wonder then that it was invaded so many times, and you'll see traces of Romans, Moors, and even prehistoric tribes.

What's in a name?

Lleida, or Lérida in Catalan, is also the name of the main city, it has been Iberian, Roman, Visigothic, Moorish, Spanish and eventually it became Catalan. Today, the city's old quarter is dominated by La Alcazaba castle, built in 1149. Also admire La Seu d'Urgell, the Byzantine-Gothic Cathedral with Moorish influences. Lleida is a vibrant city with great local festivals – take

the kids to Moros i Cristians, where they can watch re-enactments of battles between Moors and Christians. Or go to Aplec del Caragol, a food festival involving snails.

Little towns, big country

You'll find some interesting museums in the province: Os de Balaguer, just north of Serra Llarga-Secans de la Noguera. It is overlooked by Moorish stronghold d'Os Castle, which houses the Bells of Catalonia Museum – a fun, if noisy, place to bring the kids! In Mollerussa, there's a Paper Dress Museum, which sure is fascinating for artists and fashionistas alike. And the great outdoors is an open-air museum in its own right: Cadí-Moixero Nature Park has many pretty traditional towns like Saldes, Cava and Gósol. It's also got El Pedraforca, perfect for hikers and climbers, as well as routes for cross-country hikers of all levels. Thrill-seekers won't want to miss subterranean La Cigalera de l'Obage de

Our tips

1. *Follow the Castles Route and see Arab and Christian mediaeval fortresses*

2. *A fun evening activity for all the family: The Labyrinth near La Fuliola*

3. *Buy olive oil at the source: the oil produced in Borjas Blancas is famous for its purity*

4. *Bit of a petrol head? Visit the Roda Roda Museum for the cars and motorbikes*

5. *Be a knight for a day in Lleida: discover for yourself what life as a Templar knight was like*

Veleran in Alt Pirineu Nature Park, which contains several large underground caverns, various galleries and an underground lake.

What to eat and drink

Rice with rabbit and hearty meat stews are very popular. A typical dish of Noguera is Cassoletes, while in the Arán valley, La Olla Aranesa (a casserole dish) is served. Costers del Segre wines are produced here, mushrooms grow in the Pyrenees and the foothills, and you simply must try the local honey and delicious fruit!

1944 Aristot, E-25722 / Cataluña ⊚ iD 25 B3

- ▲ Pont d'Ardaix Cat.2
- ▥ Ctra N260 km 210
- ☷ 1 Jan - 31 Dec
- ☎ +34 973-384098
- @ pontdardaix@clior.es

1	ADILNORST	AFHN	6
2	CGOPUVXY	ABDEFG	7
3	ABELQ	ABEFJNQRV	8
4	ABCFHIO	DGJ	9
5	ACDEFHJKLMNO	ABHIKOSUV	10
6A		❶ €27.75	
A900 3ha 100T(42-60m²) 96P		❷ €37.25	

🖭 Puigcerda - La Seo de Urgell - Crta N260 km 210.

Sant Julià de Lòria

Bellver de Cerdanya

N-260 ▲

▱ Small terraced campsite located on the river Segre with excellent toilet facilities, a swimming pool and a restaurant.

🖼 N 42°22'27'' E 1°38'13''
www.eurocampings.co.uk/106746

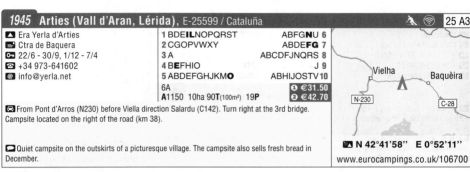

1945 Arties (Vall d'Aran, Lérida), E-25599 / Cataluña ⚲ ⊚ 25 A3

- ▲ Era Yerla d'Arties
- ▥ Ctra de Baquera
- ☷ 22/6 - 30/9, 1/12 - 7/4
- ☎ +34 973-641602
- @ info@yerla.net

1	BDEILNOPQRST	ABFGNU	6
2	CGOPVWXY	ABDEFG	7
3	A	ABCDFJNQRS	8
4	BEFHIO	J	9
5	ABDEFGHJKMO	ABHIJOSTV	10
6A		❶ €31.50	
A1150 10ha 90T(100m²) 19P		❷ €42.70	

🖭 From Pont d'Arros (N230) before Viella direction Salardu (C142). Turn right at the 3rd bridge. Campsite located on the right of the road (km 38).

Vielha Baquèira

N-230 C-28

▱ Quiet campsite on the outskirts of a picturesque village. The campsite also sells fresh bread in December.

🖼 N 42°41'58'' E 0°52'11''
www.eurocampings.co.uk/106700

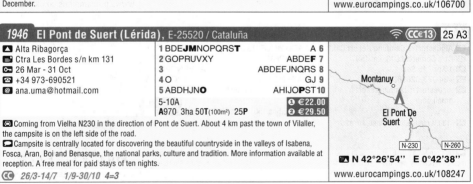

1946 El Pont de Suert (Lérida), E-25520 / Cataluña ⊚ CC€13 25 A3

- ▲ Alta Ribagorça
- ▥ Ctra Les Bordes s/n km 131
- ☷ 26 Mar - 31 Oct
- ☎ +34 973-690521
- @ ana.uma@hotmail.com

1	BDEJMNOPQRST	A	6
2	GOPRUVXY	ABDEF	7
3		ABDEFJNQRS	8
4	O	GJ	9
5	ABDHJNO	AHIJOPST	10
5-10A		❶ €22.00	
A970 3ha 50T(100m²) 25P		❷ €29.50	

🖭 Coming from Vielha N230 in the direction of Pont de Suert. About 4 km past the town of Vilaller, the campsite is on the left side of the road.

▱ Campsite is centrally located for discovering the beautiful countryside in the valleys of Isabena, Fosca, Aran, Boi and Benasque, the national parks, culture and tradition. More information available at reception. A free meal for paid stays of ten nights.

ⓒ 26/3-14/7 1/9-30/10 4=3

Montanuy

El Pont De Suert

N-230 N-260

🖼 N 42°26'54'' E 0°42'38''
www.eurocampings.co.uk/108247

1947 Era Bordeta/Val d'Aran, E-25551 / Cataluña ⊗ ⊚ 25 A2

- ▲ Bedurá Park
- ▥ CN230 km 174,5
- ☷ 28 Mar - 30 Sep
- ☎ +34 973-648293
- @ info@bedurapark.com

1	BHKNOPQRST	ABNUV	6
2	BCFGOPRUVWXY	ABDEFGH	7
3	ABEL	ABCDEFIKNQRSV	8
4	BFHILO	FJ	9
5	ACDEFHJKLMNO	ABHIJOSTV	10
6A		❶ €34.20	
A795 5ha 150T(50-90m²) 32P		❷ €45.00	

🖭 From Bossóst (N230), km-marker 174,5, directly after sign Era Bordeta turn right over the bridge, then follow the road left to the campsite on the right (past the small campsite on the left).

Bagnères-de-Luchon

D618
D618 A
N-141

N-230 ▲

▱ Friendly and quiet campsite with a playground and heated swimming pool. Perfect for a stopover to enjoy the day's menu in the restaurant. Stunning trails in the environs.

🖼 N 42°45'1'' E 0°41'53''
www.eurocampings.co.uk/101072

Spain

1948 Espot, E-25597 / Cataluña   25 A3

- ▲ La Mola Cat.2
- ▣ Ctra de Espot LV-5004, km 5
- ☛ 1 Jun - 15 Sep
- ☎ +34 973-624024
- @ info@campinglamola.com

1	ABDJMNOPRST	ANU 6
2	CGPVXY	ABDEFGH 7
3	ABELM	ABDEFGHLNPQRSV 8
4	FHIO**PQ**	IJL 9
5	ABCDEGHJMN**O**	ABHIJLNORV 10

4-6A   ❶ €28.45
A1300 2,2ha 166T(60-120m²) 11P   ❷ €38.45

On the C13 Pobla de Segur-Esterri d'Aneu, 26 km north of Sort, continue for another 5 km up the mountain, an incline of 10% direction Espot. The campsite is clearly signposted on the left side of the road.

Small shaded campsite located by a river and with excellent toilet facilities, a pool and snack bar. Homemade bread available in the high season. Perfect operating base for a visit to Aigües Tortes.

N 42°34'9" E 1°6'37"
www.eurocampings.co.uk/106739

1949 Espot, E-25597 / Cataluña   25 A3

- ▲ Voraparc
- ▣ Ctra Sant Maurici s/n
- ☛ 4/2 - 26/3, 27/4 - 14/10
- ☎ +34 973-624108
- @ info@voraparc.com

1	ADEJMNOPRS**T**	AF**N**UVX 6
2	CGPRVY	ABDE**FG**HK 7
3	AB**G**LQ	ABCDF**N**QRSV 8
4	ABD**EF**HILO**PQ**	BIJQRU 9
5	ABDEFGHIJMN**O**	ABHIJNPRV 10

4-10A   ❶ €28.50
A1400 3,3ha 129T(68-150m²) 8P   ❷ €39.30

On the C13 Pobla de Segur-Esterri d'Àneu, 26 km north of Sort at the service station 9 km uphill, 10% incline, to Espot, then another 1.8 km uphill.

Lovely located mountain campsite, partly level and partly terraced with marked out and mostly shaded pitches. With a swimming pool, bar and snack bar. Splendid toilet facilities. The campsite is near the entrance to Aigües Fortes. Tents with kitchen on a support.

N 42°34'57" E 1°4'28"
www.eurocampings.co.uk/115937

1950 Esterri d'Àneu, E-25580 / Cataluña   25 A3

- ▲ Aigüestortes Camping Resort Cat.2
- ▣ Ctra Comercal C13, km 159
- ☛ 1 Apr - 15 Sep
- ☎ +34 973-626263
- @ aiguestortescampingresort@
  gmail.com

1	AD**JM**NOPRST	AF**J**NUVX 6
2	CFGPRVXY	ABDE**FG**H 7
3	ABE	ABEF**N**QRSV 8
4	A**E**FHO**PQ**	FJQRUV 9
5	ABDEFGHJKLMN**O**	ABFGHIJ**O**ST 10

6A   ❶ €28.50
A970 2,5ha 150T(70m²) 31P   ❷ €39.00

C13 Llavorsi-Esterri d'Àneu, km 125.

This renewed (2016) campsite in Esterri d' Aneu is the first you will see when entering from the mountain scenery near the Port de la Bonaigua (known from the Tour). A bit further is the Aigüestortes national park and the Noguera Pallaresa.

N 42°36'53" E 1°7'28"
www.eurocampings.co.uk/100918

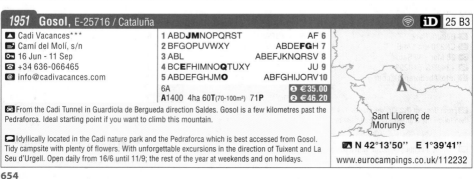

1951 Gosol, E-25716 / Cataluña   25 B3

- ▲ Cadi Vacances***
- ▣ Camí del Molí, s/n
- ☛ 16 Jun - 11 Sep
- ☎ +34 636-066465
- @ info@cadivacances.com

1	ABD**JM**NOPQRST	AF 6
2	BFGOPUVWXY	ABDE**FG**H 7
3	ABL	ABEFJKNQRSV 8
4	BC**E**FHIMNO**Q**TUXY	JU 9
5	ABDEFGHJM**O**	ABFGHIJORV 10

6A   ❶ €35.00
A1400 4ha 60T(70-100m²) 71P   ❷ €46.20

From the Cadi Tunnel in Guardiola de Bergueda direction Saldes. Gosol is a few kilometres past the Pedraforca. Ideal starting point if you want to climb this mountain.

Idyllically located in the Cadi nature park and the Pedraforca which is best accessed from Gosol. Tidy campsite with plenty of flowers. With unforgettable excursions in the direction of Tuixent and La Seu d'Urgell. Open daily from 16/6 until 11/9; the rest of the year at weekends and on holidays.

N 42°13'50" E 1°39'41"
www.eurocampings.co.uk/112232

Spain

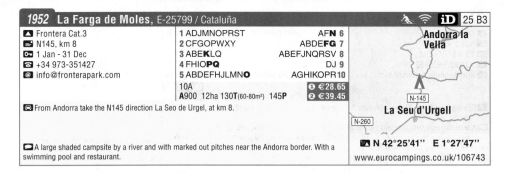

1952 La Farga de Moles, E-25799 / Cataluña 25 B3

- ▲ Frontera Cat.3
- 🚐 N145, km 8
- 📅 1 Jan - 31 Dec
- ☎ +34 973-351427
- @ info@fronterapark.com

1 ADJMNOPRST	AF**N** 6
2 CFGOPWXY	ABDE**FG** 7
3 ABE**KLQ**	ABEFJNQRSV 8
4 FHIO**PQ**	DJ 9
5 ABDEFHJLMN**O**	AGHIKOPR 10

10A | ❶ €28.65
A900 12ha 130**T**(60-80m²) 145**P** | ❷ €39.45

🗺 From Andorra take the N145 direction La Seo de Urgel, at km 8.

💬 A large shaded campsite by a river and with marked out pitches near the Andorra border. With a swimming pool and restaurant.

Andorra la Vella

N-145

La Seu d'Urgell

N-260

📷 N 42°25'41'' E 1°27'47''

www.eurocampings.co.uk/106743

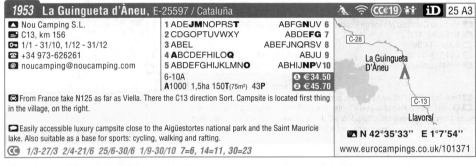

1953 La Guingueta d'Àneu, E-25597 / Cataluña 25 A3

- ▲ Nou Camping S.L.
- 🚐 C13, km 156
- 📅 1/1 - 31/10, 1/12 - 31/12
- ☎ +34 973-626261
- @ noucamping@noucamping.com

1 ADE**JM**NOPRS**T**	ABFG**N**UV 6
2 CDGOPTUVWXY	ABDE**FG** 7
3 ABEL	ABEFJNQRSV 8
4 **A**BCDEFHILO**Q**	ABJU 9
5 ABDEFGHIJKLMN**O**	ABHIJ**NP**V 10

6-10A | ❶ €34.50
A1000 1,5ha 150**T**(75m²) 43**P** | ❷ €45.70

🗺 From France take N125 as far as Viella. There the C13 direction Sort. Campsite is located first thing in the village, on the right.

💬 Easily accessible luxury campsite close to the Aigüestortes national park and the Saint Mauricie lake. Also suitable as a base for sports: cycling, walking and rafting.

Ⓒ 1/3-27/3 2/4-21/6 25/6-30/6 1/9-30/10 7=6, 14=11, 30=23

C-28

La Guingueta D'Àneu

C-13

Llavorsí

📷 N 42°35'33'' E 1°7'54''

www.eurocampings.co.uk/101371

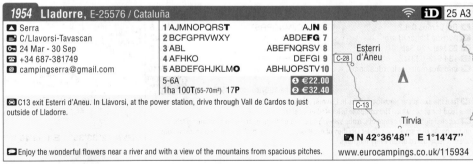

1954 Lladorre, E-25576 / Cataluña 25 A3

- ▲ Serra
- 🚐 C/Llavorsi-Tavascan
- 📅 24 Mar - 30 Sep
- ☎ +34 687-381749
- @ campingserra@gmail.com

1 AJMNOPQRS**T**	AJ**N** 6
2 BCFGPRVWXY	ABDE**FG** 7
3 ABL	ABEFNQRSV 8
4 AFHKO	DEFGI 9
5 ABDEFGHJKLM**O**	ABHIJOPSTV 10

5-6A | ❶ €22.00
1ha 100**T**(55-70m²) 17**P** | ❷ €32.40

🗺 C13 exit Esterri d'Aneu. In Llavorsi, at the power station, drive through Vall de Cardos to just outside of Lladorre.

💬 Enjoy the wonderful flowers near a river and with a view of the mountains from spacious pitches.

Esterri d'Aneu

C-28

C-13

Tírvia

📷 N 42°36'48'' E 1°14'47''

www.eurocampings.co.uk/115934

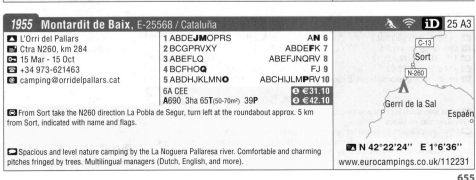

1955 Montardit de Baix, E-25568 / Cataluña 25 A3

- ▲ L'Orri del Pallars
- 🚐 Ctra N260, km 284
- 📅 15 Mar - 15 Oct
- ☎ +34 973-621463
- @ camping@orridelpallars.cat

1 ABDE**JM**OPRS	A**N** 6
2 BCGPRVXY	ABDE**FK** 7
3 ABEFLQ	ABEFJNQRV 8
4 BCFHO**Q**	FJ 9
5 ABDHJKLMN**O**	ABCHIJLM**P**RV 10

6A CEE | ❶ €31.10
A690 3ha 65**T**(50-70m²) 39**P** | ❷ €42.10

🗺 From Sort take the N260 direction La Pobla de Segur, turn left at the roundabout approx. 5 km from Sort, indicated with name and flags.

💬 Spacious and level nature camping by the La Noguera Pallaresa river. Comfortable and charming pitches fringed by trees. Multilingual managers (Dutch, English, and more).

C-13

Sort

N-260

Gerri de la Sal

Espaén

📷 N 42°22'24'' E 1°6'36''

www.eurocampings.co.uk/112231

Spain

1956 Montferrer, E-25711 / Cataluña

🛰 ((€19)) iD | 25 B3

- 🅰 Gran Sol
- 📧 N260, km 230
- 📅 23 Mar - 14 Oct
- ☎ +34 973-351332
- @ info@campinggransol.com

1 ABDE**JM**NOPRS**T**	AFNUV	6
2 GPVWXY	ABDE**F**	7
3 ABCE**KL**	ABEFJNQRSV	8
4 BFHILO	HIJ	9
5 ABDEFHJKLMN**O**	AHIJPRV	10

3-10A
A900 1,7ha 160**T**(70-140m²) 44**P**

❶ €31.45
❷ €42.65

🔲 Coming from Bourg Madame (F) until 3 km beyond La Seu d'Urgell on the N260.

💬 A level campsite with spacious pitches between trees. Lovely swimming pool, good restaurant. Most suitable as a starting point for visiting Seu d'Urgell/Seo de Urgel, Puigcerdá and Andorra. Also excellent for visiting the mountains.

CC 3/4-8/7 27/8-11/10 7=6, 14=11

🔲 N 42°20'52" E 1°25'51"

www.eurocampings.co.uk/109154

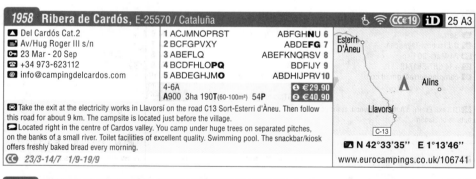

1957 Pont d'Arros, E-25537 / Cataluña

🛰 ((€17)) | 25 A3

- 🅰 Verneda Camping Mountain Resort
- 📧 N230, km 171
- 📅 2 Apr - 14 Oct
- ☎ +34 973-641024
- @ info@campingverneda.com

1 BCDE**JM**NOPQRST	ABFG**N**U	6
2 CGOPVWXY	ABDE**FG**	7
3 ABEHL	ABFKNQRSV	8
4 **A**BEFHIO**PQ**	IJUW	9
5 ABDEFGHJKLMN**O**	ABDHIJO**P**TV	10

5A
180**T**(40-80m²) 33**P**

❶ €35.00
❷ €48.00

🔲 From Bossost (N230) the campsite is clearly signposted on the right.

💬 A lovely, well maintained campsite by the river. Ideal area for walking and cycling. Wild-water activities, canoeing and rafting. Free wifi during opening times at the bar. Val d'Aran offers unforgettable locations with challenges and activities for the whole family. Also great as a stopover campsite.

CC 2/4-30/6 1/9-13/10

🔲 N 42°44'12" E 0°44'47"

www.eurocampings.co.uk/112229

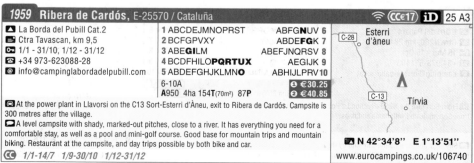

1958 Ribera de Cardós, E-25570 / Cataluña

♿ 🛰 ((€19)) iD | 25 A3

- 🅰 Del Cardós Cat.2
- 📧 Av/Hug Roger III s/n
- 📅 23 Mar - 20 Sep
- ☎ +34 973-623112
- @ info@campingdelcardos.com

1 ACJMNOPRST	ABFGH**N**U	6
2 BCFGPVXY	ABDE**FG**	7
3 ABEFLQ	ABEFKNQRSV	8
4 BCDFHLO**PQ**	BDFIJY	9
5 ABDEGHJM**O**	ABDHIJPRV	10

4-6A
A900 3ha 190**T**(60-100m²) 54**P**

❶ €29.90
❷ €40.90

🔲 Take the exit at the electricity works in Llavorsí on the road C13 Sort-Esterri d'Àneu. Then follow this road for about 9 km. The campsite is located just before the village.

💬 Located right in the centre of Cardos valley. You camp under huge trees on separated pitches, on the banks of a small river. Toilet facilities of excellent quality. Swimming pool. The snackbar/kiosk offers freshly baked bread every morning.

CC 23/3-14/7 1/9-19/9

🔲 N 42°33'35" E 1°13'46"

www.eurocampings.co.uk/106741

1959 Ribera de Cardós, E-25570 / Cataluña

🛰 ((€17)) iD | 25 A3

- 🅰 La Borda del Pubill Cat.2
- 📧 Ctra Tavascan, km 9,5
- 📅 1/1 - 31/10, 1/12 - 31/12
- ☎ +34 973-623088-28
- @ info@campinglabordadelpubill.com

1 ABCDE**JM**NOPRST	ABFG**N**UV	6
2 BCFGPVXY	ABDE**FG**K	7
3 ABE**G**ILM	ABEFJNQRSV	8
4 BCDFHILO**PQRTUX**	AEGIJK	9
5 ABDEFGHJKLMN**O**	ABHIJLPRV	10

6-10A
A950 4ha 154**T**(70m²) 87**P**

❶ €30.25
❷ €40.85

🔲 At the power plant in Llavorsí on the C13 Sort-Esterri d'Àneu, exit to Ribera de Cardós. Campsite is 300 metres after the village.

💬 A level campsite with shady, marked-out pitches, close to a river. It has everything you need for a comfortable stay, as well as a pool and mini-golf course. Good base for mountain trips and mountain biking. Restaurant at the campsite, and day trips possible by both bike and car.

CC 1/1-14/7 1/9-30/10 1/12-31/12

🔲 N 42°34'8" E 1°13'51"

www.eurocampings.co.uk/106740

1960 Sant Llorenc de Montgai, E-25613 / Cataluña

📶 (CC€19) | 33 A1

- 🏔 La Noguera
- 📧 Partida La Solana s/n
- 📅 2/1 - 7/1, 26/1 - 31/12
- ☎ +34 973-420334
- @ info@campinglanoguera.com

1 BDE**JM**NOPQRST — A**E**FN**U** 6
2 FGPRUVWXY — ABDE**FG** 7
3 **BC**DELQT — ABEFJKNQRSV 8
4 BCDFGHILMOR**SZ** — AJRUY 9
5 ABDEFGHJKLMN**O** — ABDGHIKMO**PR**V 10

10A — ❶ €35.50
A244 2,5ha 220T 117P — ❷ €46.90

🚗 C13 from Lleida via Balaguer to Sant Llorenc de Montgai.

💬 Modern terraced campsite in the nature reserve around the lake of Sant Llorenç de Montgai. Many facilities for sports and leisure activities at the site and in the area. Restaurant with local products.

CC 26/1-28/3 2/4-26/4 1/5-21/6 11/9-10/10 14/10-30/10 4/11-5/12 7=6

🏔 N 41°51'37" E 0°49'57"
www.eurocampings.co.uk/112228

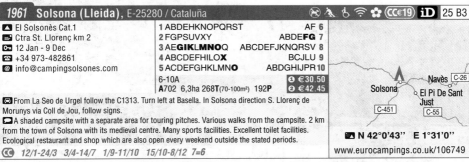

1961 Solsona (Lleida), E-25280 / Cataluña

🚫 ⛷ ♿ 📶 ✿ (CC€19) **iD** | 25 B3

- 🏔 El Solsonès Cat.1
- 📧 Ctra St. Llorenç km 2
- 📅 12 Jan - 9 Dec
- ☎ +34 973-482861
- @ info@campingsolsones.com

1 ABDEHKNOPQRST — AF 6
2 FGPSUVXY — ABDE**FG** 7
3 AE**GIKLMNO**Q — ABCDEFJKNQRSV 8
4 ABCDEFHILO**X** — BCJLU 9
5 ACDEFGHKLMN**O** — ABDGHIJPR 10

6-10A — ❶ €30.50
A702 6,3ha 268T(70-100m²) 192P — ❷ €42.45

🚗 From La Seo de Urgel follow the C1313. Turn left at Basella. In Solsona direction S. Llorenç de Morunys via Coll de Jou, follow signs.

💬 A shaded campsite with a separate area for touring pitches. Various walks from the campsite. 2 km from the town of Solsona with its medieval centre. Many sports facilities. Excellent toilet facilities. Ecological restaurant and shop which are also open every weekend outside the stated periods.

CC 12/1-24/3 3/4-14/7 1/9-11/10 15/10-8/12 7=6

🏔 N 42°0'43" E 1°31'0"
www.eurocampings.co.uk/106749

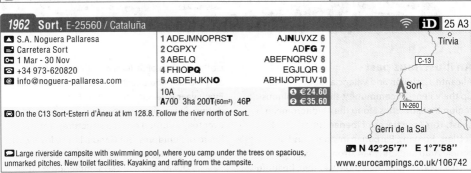

1962 Sort, E-25560 / Cataluña

📶 **iD** | 25 A3

- 🏔 S.A. Noguera Pallaresa
- 📧 Carretera Sort
- 📅 1 Mar - 30 Nov
- ☎ +34 973-620820
- @ info@noguera-pallaresa.com

1 ADEJMNOPRST — AJN**U**VXZ 6
2 CGPXY — AD**FG** 7
3 ABELQ — ABEFNQRSV 8
4 FHIO**PQ** — EGJLQR 9
5 ABDEHJKN**O** — ABHIJOPTUV 10

10A — ❶ €24.60
A700 3ha 200T(60m²) 46P — ❷ €35.60

🚗 On the C13 Sort-Esterri d'Àneu at km 128.8. Follow the river north of Sort.

💬 Large riverside campsite with swimming pool, where you camp under the trees on spacious, unmarked pitches. New toilet facilities. Kayaking and rafting from the campsite.

🏔 N 42°25'7" E 1°7'58"
www.eurocampings.co.uk/106742

Spain

An illustrious past

Alicante, Castellón and Valencia together make up the Valencian community, the mountainous region that stretches along the Mediterranean coast. You'll see traces of Iberian tribes, Greek settlers, Romans, Barbarian invaders, and of course Arab and Christian strongholds. With such a vivid history, incredible weather, beautiful towns and glorious beaches, you can see why so many visitors come to Valenciana.

Cities by the sea

The city of Valencia, located on the thin fertile coastal plain, is divided by the Turia Gardens, formerly the riverbed, which take you to the Institute of Modern Art and the City of the Arts and Sciences. Leave the park to see the mediaeval Palau de la Generalitatat and Gothic Church of St Juan del Hospital, or you and the kids could just head for the beach! Every year Valencia holds Las Fallas festival, during which giant puppets are paraded and eventually burned on falla structures. You've heard of Benidorm, but Gandia is also lovely, with great shopping, as well as historic sites like the Palacio Ducal, and you can sample some tapas along the tree-shaded Passeig de les Germanies.

Valenciana: a huge open-air museum

History buffs head to Sagunto to explore its Roman Amphitheatre, Moorish castle ruin and mediaeval Jewish Quarter, and climb up to the Castello at Xativa, (as an added bonus). In the mountain village Guadalest, the houses seem to grow from the very rocks. Walk to the town's other half via a tunnel and climb to the

17th century San Jose castle. Climbers and hikers are drawn to Chera-Sot de Chera Nature Park, with waterfalls and lakes – watch out for raptors and reptiles. At the coast, explore the wetlands and rice fields of Albufera Nature Park by boat, and relish the shade of the planted forests at the coastal dunes of nearby Saler.

With a pinch of salt ...

The abundance of salt allows for delicious salt-cured tuna. Valenciana is also home of paella, but other rice-based dishes you might like to sample are arros negre (cuttlefish) or arros am

costra. Everywhere you look are Citrus fruits like oranges, and of course the local wines are excellent, but try the liqueur horchata. Sweets include turrón, a soft nougat, while pumpkins are included in dessert menus.

Our tips

1. Explore the maze of canals at Port Saplaya, Valenciana's 'Little Venice'
2. Take a boat trip to Tabarca Island, once a pirate hangout
3. Soak in the warm water springs at Montanejos
4. Hop on the train from Benidorm to Denia for great views
5. Visit the Museum of Rice, in Valencia, housed in an old rice mill

🔺 Playa Tropicana Cat.1
🏠 Camino de l'Atall s/n
📅 1 Jan - 31 Dec
☎ +34 964-412463
@ info@playatropicana.com

1	BCDEJMNOPQRT	ACDFHKMNPQSWX	6
2	AEHJORSVXY	ABDE**FGH**J	7
3	BFL**MNQ**	ABCDEFJKNQRSV	8
4	**A**BCDILNO**PQUZ**	IJLRVZ	9
5	ACDEFGHKLM**O**	ABDGHIJ**NPR**	10

Ad on page 661 10A
3ha 380T(50-100m²) 69P

❶ €56.50
❷ €68.50

Alcalà De Xivert

🔲 On A7 take exit 44; on N340 at km-marker 1018 to Alcossebre. Follow signs. Take 1st exit at roundabout. Enter village, turn right at 2nd traffic lights. Right at the T junction, then follow signs on coast road to the campsite. 📖 A large campsite on a sandy beach. New toilet facilities. Pitches separated by hedges. Swimming pool, covered and heated in winter and a good restaurant and supermarket. 4 km from Alcossebre. Good cycling and challenging walks.

CC 1/1-28/3 3/4-21/6 1/9-31/12 14=12, 21=18, 28=24

🗺 N 40°13'13'' E 0°16'6''

www.eurocampings.co.uk/108186

🔺 Ribamar Cat.1
🏠 Partida Ribamar s/n
📅 1 Jan - 31 Dec
☎ +34 964-761601
@ info@campingribamar.com

1	BDE**JM**NOPRS**T**	AFKNOPQSX	6
2	EJKMRSTVX	ABDE**FGH**	7
3	BEL**MQ**	ABCDEFJKNQRSTUV	8
4	BDFHILO	JLU	9
5	ABDHLMN**O**	ABDHIJ**NPT**U	10

6-10A CEE
2,2ha 71T(40-100m²) 41P

❶ €51.50
❷ €60.90

Alcalà De Xivert

🔲 A7, exit 44. Via the N340 to Alcoceber at the 1018 km sign along Las Fuentes. Follow campsite signs. The final km is unsurfaced road. 📖 Excellent amenities. Very quiet and 150m from the beach in the 'Sierra de Irta' nature reserve excellent for walking and cycling. Swimming pool, tennis and basketball. Pitches with water tap. Heated toilet facilities. Site only accessible along a 1 km unsurfaced road, but worth the effort to stay at this lovely site!

CC 1/1-28/3 2/4-21/6 9/9-31/12

🗺 N 40°16'13'' E 0°18'24''

www.eurocampings.co.uk/106720

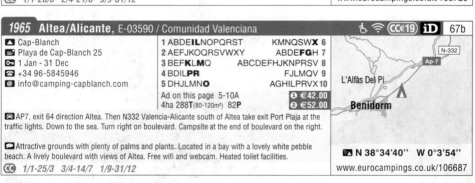

🔺 Cap-Blanch
🏠 Playa de Cap-Blanch 25
📅 1 Jan - 31 Dec
☎ +34 96-5845946
@ info@camping-capblanch.com

1	ABDE**IL**NOPQRST	KMNQSW**X**	6
2	AEFJKOQRSVWXY	ABDE**FGH**	7
3	BEF**KLMQ**	ABCDEFHJKNPRSV	8
4	BDIL**PR**	FJLMQV	9
5	DHJLMN**O**	AGHILPRVX	10

Ad on this page 5-10A
4ha 288T(80-120m²) 82P

❶ €42.00
❷ €52.00

L'Alfàs Del Pi

Benidorm

🔲 AP7, exit 64 direction Altea. Then N332 Valencia-Alicante south of Altea take exit Port Plaja at the traffic lights. Down to the sea. Turn right on boulevard. Campsite at the end of boulevard on the right.

📖 Attractive grounds with plenty of palms and plants. Located in a bay with a lovely white pebble beach. A lively boulevard with views of Altea. Free wifi and webcam. Heated toilet facilities.

CC 1/1-25/3 3/4-14/7 1/9-31/12

🗺 N 38°34'40'' W 0°3'54''

www.eurocampings.co.uk/106687

Spain

1966 Benicarlo, E-12580 / Comunidad Valenciana   ♿ 📶 CC€17   66b

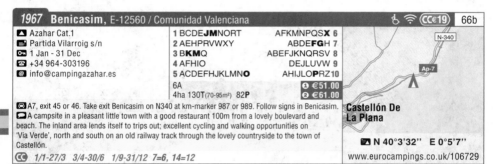

- 🏕 Alegria del Mar Cat.2
- 🛣 Ctra Nacional 340a km 1046
- 📅 1 Jan - 31 Dec
- ☎ +34 964-470871
- @ info@campingalegria.com

1 BDEJMNOPQRST	AFKNPQSUW**X** 6
2 AEHJRSVWX	ABDE**FG** 7
3 BQT	ABEFJNQRSTV 8
4 BCDNOP**Q**	JZ 9
5 ACDEFGHKLM**O**	ABEFGHIJ**PR**10

6-10A   ❶ €33.00
0,8ha 145**T**(60-135m²) 25**P**   ❷ €44.00

🚗 Take exit 42 on the A7. On the N340 (Tarragona-Valencia) follow signs to N340a. Take exit on N340a at km 1046 towards the sea. Then about 1 km on a minor road.

💬 A medium-sized campsite right by the sea, good facilities, swimming pool, restaurant. Very peaceful location, close to Benicarlo. Good walking and cycling opportunities.

CC 1/1-1/7   20/8-31/12

Vinaròs
Benicarló

📍 N 40°25'36''   E 0°26'17''
www.eurocampings.co.uk/106715

1967 Benicasim, E-12560 / Comunidad Valenciana   ♿ 📶 CC€19   66b

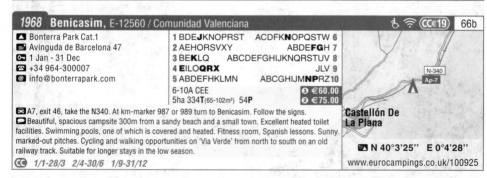

- 🏕 Azahar Cat.1
- 🛣 Partida Vilarroig s/n
- 📅 1 Jan - 31 Dec
- ☎ +34 964-303196
- @ info@campingazahar.es

1 BCDE**JM**NORT	AFKMNPQS**X** 6
2 AEHPRVWXY	ABDE**FG**H 7
3 B**KMQ**	ABEFJKNQRSV 8
4 AFHIO	DEJLUVW 9
5 ACDEFHJKLMN**O**	AHIJLO**PR**Z10

6A   ❶ €51.00
4ha 130**T**(70-95m²) 82**P**   ❷ €61.00

🚗 A7, exit 45 or 46. Take exit Benicasim on N340 at km-marker 987 or 989. Follow signs in Benicasim.
💬 A campsite in a pleasant little town with a good restaurant 100m from a lovely boulevard and beach. The inland area lends itself to trips out; excellent cycling and walking opportunities on 'Via Verde', north and south on an old railway track through the lovely countryside to the town of Castellón.

CC 1/1-27/3   3/4-30/6   1/9-31/12   7=6, 14=12

Castellón De La Plana

📍 N 40°3'32''   E 0°5'7''
www.eurocampings.co.uk/106729

1968 Benicasim, E-12560 / Comunidad Valenciana   ♿ 📶 CC€19   66b

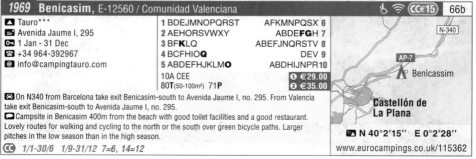

- 🏕 Bonterra Park Cat.1
- 🛣 Avinguda de Barcelona 47
- 📅 1 Jan - 31 Dec
- ☎ +34 964-300007
- @ info@bonterrapark.com

1 BDE**J**KNOPRST	ACDFK**N**OPQSTW 6
2 AEHORSVXY	ABDE**FG**H 7
3 BE**KLQ**	ABCDEFGHIJKNQRSTUV 8
4 E**ILO**Q**RX**	JLV 9
5 ABDEFHKLMN	ABCGHIJM**N**PRZ10

6-10A CEE   ❶ €60.00
5ha 334**T**(65-102m²) 54**P**   ❷ €75.00

🚗 A7, exit 46, take the N340. At km-marker 987 or 989 turn to Benicasim. Follow the signs.
💬 Beautiful, spacious campsite 300m from a sandy beach and a small town. Excellent heated toilet facilities. Swimming pools, one of which is covered and heated. Fitness room, Spanish lessons. Sunny marked-out pitches. Cycling and walking opportunities on 'Via Verde' from north to south on an old railway track. Suitable for longer stays in the low season.

CC 1/1-28/3   2/4-30/6   1/9-31/12

Castellón De La Plana

📍 N 40°3'25''   E 0°4'28''
www.eurocampings.co.uk/100925

1969 Benicasim, E-12560 / Comunidad Valenciana   ♿ 📶 CC€15   66b

- 🏕 Tauro***
- 🛣 Avenida Jaume I, 295
- 📅 1 Jan - 31 Dec
- ☎ +34 964-392967
- @ info@campingtauro.com

1 BDEJMNOPQRST	AFKMNPQSX 6
2 AEHORSVWXYY	ABDE**FG**H 7
3 BF**KLQ**	ABEFJNQRSTV 8
4 BCFHIO**Q**	DEV 9
5 ABDEFHJKLM**O**	ABDHIJNPR10

10A CEE   ❶ €29.00
80**T**(50-100m²) 71**P**   ❷ €35.00

🚗 On N340 from Barcelona take exit Benicasim-south to Avenida Jaume I, no. 295. From Valencia take exit Benicasim-south to Avenida Jaume I, no. 295.
💬 Campsite in Benicasim 400m from the beach with good toilet facilities and a good restaurant. Lovely routes for walking and cycling to the north or the south over green bicycle paths. Larger pitches in the low season than in the high season.

CC 1/1-30/6   1/9-31/12   7=6, 14=12

Benicassim
Castellón de La Plana

📍 N 40°2'15''   E 0°2'28''
www.eurocampings.co.uk/115362

1970 Benidorm, E-03503 / Comunidad Valenciana ⊗ & 🛜 (CC€19) iD 67b

🔺 Villasol
🏠 Avda Bernat de Sarriá 13
📅 1 Jan - 31 Dec
☎ +34 965-850422
@ info@camping-villasol.com

1 ABDEHKNOPQRS**T**	AEF 6
2 AGOQSUVWXY	ABDE**FG** 7
3 AE**KQ**	ABEFJNQRSV 8
4 BDILO**PQ**	JL 9
5 ACDEFHJK**O**	ABCDEHI**N**PRXY 10

16A   ❶ €36.60
7ha 506**T**(70-90m²) 206**P**   ❷ €48.40

🅡 On N332 between 151 and 152 km-markers, take Benidorm/Playa de Levante exit. Then follow campsite signs.

💬 Large campsite, spaciously appointed with all amenities, open all year. Varied foliage and many flowering plants. Outdoor seating area with a view of the pool and the Benidorm skyline.

CC 7/1-22/3   2/4-12/7   2/9-20/12

🔺 N 38°32'51''   W 0°6'37''
www.eurocampings.co.uk/106688

1971 Benidorm/Alicante, E-03503 / Comunidad Valenciana & 🛜 ✿ (CC€17) iD 67b

🔺 Arena Blanca★★★★
🏠 Avda Doctor Severa Ochoa 44
📅 1 Jan - 31 Dec
☎ +34 96-5861889
@ info@camping-arenablanca.es

1 ABDEJMNOQR**T**	ACDX 6
2 AGOQRSUVWXY	ABDE**FGH** 7
3 A**KQ**	ABCDEFHJNQRSTU 8
4 BDLO**PQ**	EHIJL 9
5 ABDEFGHJKMN**O**	ABCDEGHIK**N**PTUX 10

16A   ❶ €33.60
A150 2,5ha 95**T**(60-80m²) 63**P**   ❷ €38.60

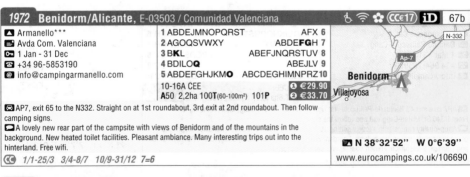

🅡 On the N332 Valencia-Alicante take Benidorm/Playa de Levante exit between 151 and 152 km-markers. Then follow campsite signs.

💬 A charming campsite. Small-scale. Swimming all year. Wonderful sunbathing on real lawns when the weather is good. Pool covered and heated in winter. Very clean toilet facilities. Free wifi.

CC 1/1-25/3   3/4-8/7   10/9-31/12

🔺 N 38°33'4''   W 0°5'47''
www.eurocampings.co.uk/101612

1972 Benidorm/Alicante, E-03503 / Comunidad Valenciana & 🛜 ✿ (CC€17) iD 67b

🔺 Armanello★★★
🏠 Avda Com. Valenciana
📅 1 Jan - 31 Dec
☎ +34 96-5853190
@ info@campingarmanello.com

1 ABDEJMNOPQRST	AFX 6
2 AGOQSVWXY	ABDE**FG** 7
3 B**KL**	ABEFJNQRSTUV 8
4 BDILO**Q**	ABEJLV 9
5 ABDEFGHJKM**O**	ABCDEGHIMNPRZ 10

10-16A CEE   ❶ €29.90
A50 2,2ha 100**T**(60-100m²) 101**P**   ❷ €33.70

🅡 AP7, exit 65 to the N332. Straight on at 1st roundabout. 3rd exit at 2nd roundabout. Then follow camping signs.
💬 A lovely new rear part of the campsite with views of Benidorm and of the mountains in the background. New heated toilet facilities. Pleasant ambiance. Many interesting trips out into the hinterland. Free wifi.

CC 1/1-25/3   3/4-8/7   10/9-31/12   7=6

🔺 N 38°32'52''   W 0°6'39''
www.eurocampings.co.uk/106690

1973 Benidorm/Alicante, E-03503 / Comunidad Valenciana & 🛜 (CC€17) iD 67b

🔺 Benisol
🏠 Av. Com. Valenciana s/n
📅 1 Jan - 31 Dec
☎ +34 96-5851673
@ info@campingbenisol.com

1 ABDEJMNOQR**T**	AEFH**X** 6
2 AOQRSUVWXY	ABDE**FGH** 7
3 **KLMQ**	ABCDEFJNORSTU 8
4 DILO**PU**	L 9
5 ABDEFGHJKLMN**O**	ABCDEFHIJ**N**PRY 10

6-10A CEE   ❶ €34.80
7ha 100**T**(60-80m²) 180**P**   ❷ €44.50

🅡 AP7, exit 65. Turn right and right again after toll booth. Then keep right again (= exit).
The campsite is located on the left a few hundred metres down the road.
💬 A campsite with very friendly reception. Ideal for visiting Benidorm and its beautiful surroundings. Heated swimming pool in the winter and a large outdoor pool in summer, with bar and terrace by the pool.

CC 1/1-28/3   2/4-10/7   1/9-31/12   7=6

🔺 N 38°33'36''   W 0°5'54''
www.eurocampings.co.uk/100929

1974 Bétera, E-46117 / Comunidad Valenciana

   ♿ 📶 (CC€15)   32 B3

🔼 Valencia Camper Park***
📧 Calle Universo s/n
🗓 1 Jan - 31 Dec
☎ +34 960-718095
@ valcampark@gmail.com

1 BDEJMNOPQRST	AFX 6
2 AGOQRSVWX	ABDEFH 7
3 BKLQ	ABCDEFGHJNQRS 8
4 FHO	9
5 ABDEFHLO	ABGHIJPR10
4-6A CEE	❶ €15.00
1,4ha 64T(40-80m²)	❷ €21.00

Rafelbunyol
A-7
Paterna

🚩 On A7 exit Bétera, then follow signs.
📖 Campsite with good amenities for motorhomes but also for caravans, situated on the north-west side. If you arrive with your caravan, you can park your car on the car park not far from the touring pitch. The campsite is also very suitable as a stopover campsite for people headed to the south of Spain. Ask reception about the extra discounts for a longer stay.

(CC) 15/5-30/6 15/9-30/9

📍 N 39°34'46'' W 0°26'44''

www.eurocampings.co.uk/122069

1975 Bigastro/Alicante, E-03380 / Comunidad Valenciana

  📶 (CC€17) iD   39 A2

🔼 La Pedrera*
📧 Cañada de Andrea 100
🗓 1 Jan - 31 Dec
☎ +34 966-183020
@ info@campinglapedrera.com

1 ABDEJMNOPQRST	AF 6
2 BFGQSUVWX	ABDEFG 7
3 ABEKLQ	ABEFJNQRSTU 8
4 BDFHJLNOPQUY	J 9
5 ABDEFGHJKLMNO	ABCDFGHIJOPTUV10
16A	❶ €29.00
A400 4,4ha 46T(50-185m²) 28P	❷ €21.00

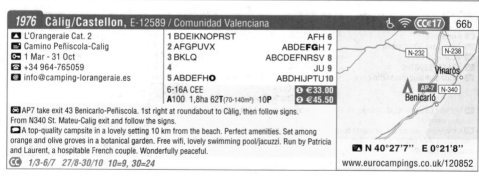

Cox
A-7 N-340
Orihuela
El Raal
AP-7

🚩 AP7, exit 740. 1st roundabout direction Orihuela (CV921). 2nd roundabout direction Benejúzar. 3rd roundabout direction Jacarilla. In Jacarilla direction Bigastro. Follow campsiteg signs in Biagastro.

📖 A small campsite, spacious pitches with plenty of sun and lovely views across the valley. A pleasant friendly atmosphere and a brand-new swimming pool with lawn (2014).

(CC) 1/1-24/3 2/4-5/7 27/8-31/12 7=6

📍 N 38°3'4'' W 0°53'54''

www.eurocampings.co.uk/122117

1976 Càlig/Castellon, E-12589 / Comunidad Valenciana

  ♿ 📶 (CC€17)   66b

🔼 L'Orangeraie Cat. 2
📧 Camino Peñiscola-Calig
🗓 1 Mar - 31 Oct
☎ +34 964-765059
@ info@camping-lorangeraie.es

1 BDEIKNOPRST	AFH 6
2 AFGPUVX	ABDEFGH 7
3 BKLQ	ABCDEFNRSV 8
4	JU 9
5 ABDEFHO	ABDHIJPTU10
6-16A CEE	❶ €33.00
A100 1,8ha 62T(70-140m²) 10P	❷ €45.50

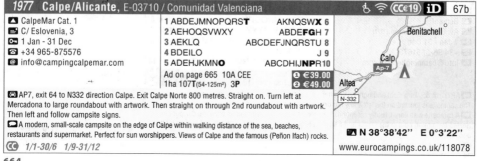

N-232 N-238
Vinaròs
AP-7 N-340
Benicarló

🚩 AP7 take exit 43 Benicarlo-Peñiscola. 1st right at roundabout to Càlig, then follow signs. From N340 St. Mateu-Calig exit and follow the signs.
📖 A top-quality campsite in a lovely setting 10 km from the beach. Perfect amenities. Set among orange and olive groves in a botanical garden. Free wifi, lovely swimming pool/jacuzzi. Run by Patricia and Laurent, a hospitable French couple. Wonderfully peaceful.

(CC) 1/3-6/7 27/8-30/10 10=9, 30=24

📍 N 40°27'7'' E 0°21'8''

www.eurocampings.co.uk/120852

1977 Calpe/Alicante, E-03710 / Comunidad Valenciana

  ♿ 📶 (CC€19) iD   67b

🔼 CalpeMar Cat. 1
📧 C/ Eslovenia, 3
🗓 1 Jan - 31 Dec
☎ +34 965-875576
@ info@campingcalpemar.com

1 ABDEJMNOPQRST	AKNQSWX 6
2 AEHOQSVWXY	ABDEFGH 7
3 AEKLQ	ABCDEFJNQRSTU 8
4 BDEILO	J 9
5 ADEHJKMNO	ABCDHIJNPR10
Ad on page 665 10A CEE	❶ €39.00
1ha 107T(54-125m²) 3P	❷ €49.00

Benitachell
Calp
Ap-7
Altea
N-332

🚩 AP7, exit 64 to N332 direction Calpe. Exit Calpe Norte 800 metres. Straight on. Turn left at Mercadona to large roundabout with artwork. Then straight on through 2nd roundabout with artwork. Then left and follow campsite signs.
📖 A modern, small-scale campsite on the edge of Calpe within walking distance of the sea, beaches, restaurants and supermarket. Perfect for sun worshippers. Views of Calpe and the famous (Peñon Ifach) rocks.

(CC) 1/1-30/6 1/9-31/12

📍 N 38°38'42'' E 0°3'22''

www.eurocampings.co.uk/118078

Spain

CalpeMar CAMPING

C/ Eslovenia, 3 • 03710 Calpe/Alicante • Tel. 965-875576
E-mail: info@campingcalpemar.com • Internet: www.campingcalpemar.com

1st Category

- Special pitches.
- Located just 300m from the beach of Arenal and Calpe centre.
- 1 km from Parque Natural del Peñón de Ifach.
- Spacious pitches and bungalows.
- All pitches have a water, waste water and electricity connection (10A).

1978 Crevillente/Alicante, E-03330 / Comunidad Valenciana
  ♿ 🛜 (CC€17) iD 39 B1

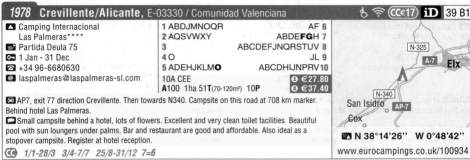

🏕 Camping Internacional
Las Palmeras****
✉ Partida Deula 75
📅 1 Jan - 31 Dec
☎ +34 96-6680630
@ laspalmeras@laspalmeras-sl.com

1 ABDJMNOQR	AF **6**
2 AQSVWXY	ABDE**FGH 7**
3	ABCDEFJNQRSTUV **8**
4 O	JL **9**
5 ADEHJKLM**O**	ABCDHIJNPRV**10**
10A CEE	❶ €27.80
A100 1ha 51**T**(70-120m²) 10**P**	❷ €37.40

🚗 AP7, exit 77 direction Crevillente. Then towards N340. Campsite on this road at 708 km marker. Behind hotel Las Palmeras.
🏕 Small campsite behind a hotel, lots of flowers. Excellent and very clean toilet facilities. Beautiful pool with sun loungers under palms. Bar and restaurant are good and affordable. Also ideal as a stopover campsite. Register at hotel reception.
CC 1/1-28/3 3/4-7/7 25/8-31/12 7=6

N-325 · A-7 · **Elx** · N-340 · San Isidro · AP-7 · Cox
🏕 **N 38°14'26'' W 0°48'42''**
www.eurocampings.co.uk/100934

1979 Crevillente/Alicante, E-03330 / Comunidad Valenciana
  ♿ 🛜 (CC€19) iD 39 B2

🏕 Marjal Costa Blanca
Camping & Resort*****
✉ Partida de las Casicas, 5
📅 1 Jan - 31 Dec
☎ +34 965-484945
@ reservas@marjal.com

1 ABDE**JM**NOPQRST	A**E**FGHIX **6**
2 AGOQRSVWX	ABDE**FGH 7**
3 BCE**IKLM**NQRT	ABCDEFGHIJKNPQRSTUV **8**
4 BCDEFHILNO**PQRSTUVWXYZ**	DEJLVWXYZ **9**
5 ACDEFGHIJKLM**O**	ABCDEFGHIM**NO**PRVYZ**10**
16A	❶ €55.00
35ha 1202**T**(90-180m²) 356**P**	❷ €69.00

🚗 AP-7 Alicante-Cartagena, exit 730. Follow campsite signs.

🏕 A very comprehensive, luxurious campsite for long or short stays. Comfortable pitches with all amenities. The most important towns are not far away. Friendly ambiance in the main square with pavement cafes and fountains. Seeing is believing. You will come again.
CC 1/1-28/3 2/4-28/6 9/9-31/10 4/11-27/12

N-325 · **Elx** · A-7 · N-340 · AP-7 · Callosa De Segura · **Orihuela**
🏕 **N 38°10'44'' W 0°48'30''**
www.eurocampings.co.uk/117642

1980 Cullera/Valencia, E-46400 / Comunidad Valenciana
  ♿ 🛜 (CC€15) iD 32 B3

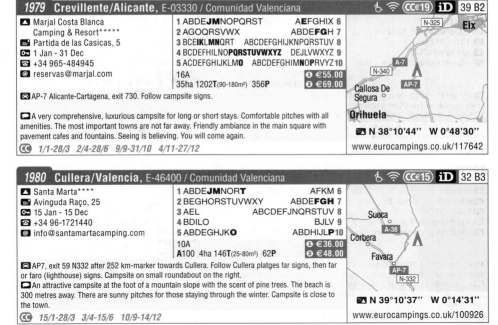

🏕 Santa Marta****
✉ Avinguda Raço, 25
📅 15 Jan - 15 Dec
☎ +34 96-1721440
@ info@santamartacamping.com

1 ABDE**JM**NOR**T**	AFKM **6**
2 BEGHORSTUVWXY	ABDE**FGH 7**
3 AEL	ABCDEFJNQRSTUV **8**
4 BDILO	BJLV **9**
5 ABDEGHJK**O**	ABDHIJL**P10**
10A	❶ €36.00
A100 4ha 146**T**(25-80m²) 62**P**	❷ €48.00

🚗 AP7, exit 59 N332 after 252 km-marker towards Cullera. Follow Cullera platges far signs, then far or faro (lighthouse) signs. Campsite on small roundabout on the right.
🏕 An attractive campsite at the foot of a mountain slope with the scent of pine trees. The beach is 300 metres away. There are sunny pitches for those staying through the winter. Campsite is close to the town.
CC 15/1-28/3 3/4-15/6 10/9-14/12

Sueca · A-38 · Corbera · Favara · AP-7 · N-332
🏕 **N 39°10'37'' W 0°14'31''**
www.eurocampings.co.uk/100926

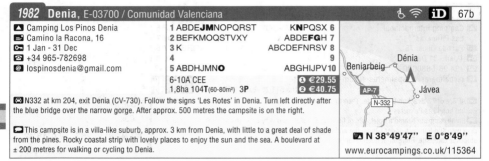

1981 Daimús/Valencia, E-46710 / Comunidad Valenciana ♿ 📶 (CC€15) 👫 iD 67b

- ▲ L'Aventura
- 🏠 Ctra Playa Daimús s/n
- 🗓 1 Jan - 31 Dec
- ☎ +34 962-818330
- @ info@campinglaventuraplaya.com

1 ABDEJMNOR	AF 6
2 ABQVXY	ABDE**FGH** 7
3 A**K**	ABEFNQRSV 8
4 BIO	JV 9
5 ADEHJKMO	ABCDHIKPRV 10
6-10A	❶ €36.00
1,8ha 130**T**(60-65m²) 26**P**	❷ €45.20

🗺 Route A7 Salida 60 to Gandía on the N332. Continue to Grao de Gándia. Then towards Daimús. In Daimús left at 2nd roundabout. Campsite about 300 metres on the right.

💬 Campsite is 600 metres from the beach. Deciduous trees offer plenty of shade in summer and sufficient sun in winter. Brand-new toilet block (2016).

CC 1/1-28/3 3/4-15/6 1/9-31/12 15=10

🗺 N 38°58'25'' W 0°9'3''

www.eurocampings.co.uk/108187

1982 Denia, E-03700 / Comunidad Valenciana ♿ 📶 iD 67b

- ▲ Camping Los Pinos Denia
- 🏠 Camino la Racona, 16
- 🗓 1 Jan - 31 Dec
- ☎ +34 965-782698
- @ lospinosdenia@gmail.com

1 ABDE**JM**NOPQRST	K**N**PQSX 6
2 BEFKMOQSTVXY	ABDE**FGH** 7
3 K	ABCDEFNRSV 8
4	9
5 ABDHJMN**O**	ABGHIJPV 10
6-10A CEE	❶ €29.55
1,8ha 104**T**(60-80m²) 3**P**	❷ €40.75

🗺 N332 at km 204, exit Denia (CV-730). Follow the signs 'Les Rotes' in Denia. Turn left directly after the blue bridge over the narrow gorge. After approx. 500 metres the campsite is on the right.

💬 This campsite is in a villa-like suburb, approx. 3 km from Denia, with little to a great deal of shade from the pines. Rocky coastal strip with lovely places to enjoy the sun and the sea. A boulevard at ± 200 metres for walking or cycling to Denia.

🗺 N 38°49'47'' E 0°8'49''

www.eurocampings.co.uk/115364

1983 El Campello/Alicante, E-03560 / Comunidad Valenciana ♿ 📶 (CC€17) iD 39 B1

- ▲ Costa Blanca***
- 🏠 C./Convento 143, N332 km 120,5
- 🗓 1 Jan - 31 Dec
- ☎ +34 965-630670
- @ info@campingcostablanca.com

1 ABDEJMNOQRT	AX 6
2 AOSVXY	ABDE**FGH** 7
3 A**KQ**	ABCDEFJNQRSTU 8
4 BDILO**PR**	AJL 9
5 ADEFGHJKLM**O**	ABDGHIJL**P**VW 10
6-25A CEE	❶ €33.25
1,1ha 66**T**(40-80m²) 36**P**	❷ €42.95

🗺 AP7 exit 67. Right at 1st roundabout after toll booths, 2nd right, 3rd roundabout straight on, right at 4th roundabout. Follow campsite signs.

💬 Small-scale campsite. Spotlessly clean toilets, very tidy grounds. Agreeable ambiance and friendly staff who will be happy to help you get your caravan onto the pitch (can be difficult for larger caravans). Located between Benidorm and Alicante. Close to beach (800m), swimming in lovely pool (open all year).

CC 1/1-25/3 1/4-13/7 31/8-31/12

🗺 N 38°26'10'' W 0°23'17''

www.eurocampings.co.uk/106694

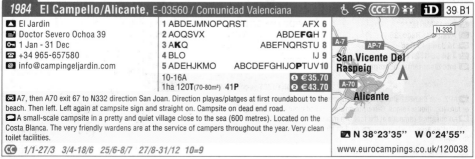

1984 El Campello/Alicante, E-03560 / Comunidad Valenciana ♿ 📶 (CC€17) 👫 iD 39 B1

- ▲ El Jardin
- 🏠 Doctor Severo Ochoa 39
- 🗓 1 Jan - 31 Dec
- ☎ +34 965-657580
- @ info@campingeljardin.com

1 ABDEJMNOPQRST	AFX 6
2 AOQSVX	ABDE**FGH** 7
3 A**KQ**	ABEFNQRSTU 8
4 BLO	IJ 9
5 ADEHJKMO	ABCDEFGHIJO**P**TUV 10
10-16A	❶ €35.70
1ha 120**T**(70-80m²) 41**P**	❷ €43.70

🗺 A7, then A70 exit 67 to N332 direction San Joan. Direction playas/platges at first roundabout to the beach. Then left. Left again at campsite sign and straight on. Campsite on dead end road.

💬 A small-scale campsite in a pretty and quiet village close to the sea (600 metres). Located on the Costa Blanca. The very friendly wardens are at the service of campers throughout the year. Very clean toilet facilities.

CC 1/1-27/3 3/4-18/6 25/6-8/7 27/8-31/12 10=9

🗺 N 38°23'35'' W 0°24'55''

www.eurocampings.co.uk/120038

1985 El Saler/Valencia, E-46012 / Comunidad Valenciana   ♿ 📶 (CC€15)   32 B3

- ▲ Camping Valencia el Saler
- ✉ Carrera del Riu 552
- 🗓 1 Jan - 31 Dec
- ☎ +34 961-830212
- @ campingvalencia1981@hotmail.com

1 BDEJMNOPQRST	AFKMPQX	6
2 ABEGHORVX	ABDEFGH	7
3 ABEFKLQT	ABEFKNQRSTV	8
4 ABCDEFHOQY	ELV	9
5 ABDEFHKLNO	AHIJLPRV	10
10A CEE	❶ €27.50	
5OT(50-74m²) 67P	❷ €35.50	

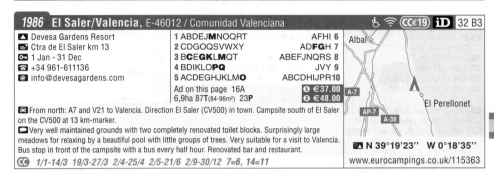

Valencia
Torrent

A-7

🏕 From north A7 and V21 to Valencia, in town take direction El Saler. On CV500 left on roundabout to CV5010, campsite on left after 300 metres. From south A7 before Valencia to Albufera and El Saler on CV500, take exit on El Saler roundabout. Site after 200 metres.
💬 Campsite with 50 camping pitches, reasonably quiet location 7 km from Valencia centre, which is easily accessible by bus or bike. About 200 metres from the sea and near nature park Albufera.
CC 1/1-8/7 26/8-31/12

📍 N 39°23'16'' W 0°19'55''
www.eurocampings.co.uk/118697

1986 El Saler/Valencia, E-46012 / Comunidad Valenciana   ♿ 📶 (CC€19) iD   32 B3

- ▲ Devesa Gardens Resort
- ✉ Ctra de El Saler km 13
- 🗓 1 Jan - 31 Dec
- ☎ +34 961-611136
- @ info@devesagardens.com

1 ABDEJMNOQRT	AFHI	6
2 CDGOQSVWXY	ADFGH	7
3 BCEGKLMQT	ABEFJNQRS	8
4 BDIKLOPQ	JVY	9
5 ACDEGHJKLMO	ABCDHIJPR	10
Ad on this page 16A	❶ €37.00	
6,9ha 87T(84-96m²) 23P	❷ €48.00	

Albal

A-7

AP-7   A-38

El Perellonet

🏕 From north: A7 and V21 to Valencia. Direction El Saler (CV500) in town. Campsite south of El Saler on the CV500 at 13 km-marker.
💬 Very well maintained grounds with two completely renovated toilet blocks. Surprisingly large meadows for relaxing by a beautiful pool with little groups of trees. Very suitable for a visit to Valencia. Bus stop in front of the campsite with a bus every half hour. Renovated bar and restaurant.
CC 1/1-14/3 19/3-27/3 2/4-25/4 2/5-21/6 2/9-30/12 7=6, 14=11

📍 N 39°19'23'' W 0°18'35''
www.eurocampings.co.uk/115363

1987 Grau de Gandía, E-46730 / Comunidad Valenciana   ♿ 📶 (CC€19) iD   67b

- ▲ L'Alquería
- ✉ Avda del Grau, 142
- 🗓 1 Jan - 31 Dec
- ☎ +34 96-2840470
- @ lalqueria@lalqueria.com

1 ABCDEJMNOPQRT	ACFX	6
2 AHOQSVXY	ABDEFGH	7
3 AL	ABCDEFNQRSTUV	8
4 LOPRTUVY	FJL	9
5 ABCDEGHJKMO	ABDHILPRV	10
Ad on page 668 10A	❶ €42.40	
4,4ha 123T(70-80m²) 115P	❷ €51.60	

Tavernes De La
Valldigna   N-332

Ap-7

Gandía

Oliva

🏕 AP7, exit 60 to N332. After 3.1 km turn onto N337. Then take the first right on each of the four roundabouts. Campsite 300 metres on the left.
💬 Campsite under various types of trees. Lovely swimming pool with plenty of deck chairs, covered and heated out of season. Cycle routes to the beach, the town and the surrounding area and also guided cycle tours in the winter months. No dogs on the dangerous breeds list and no dogs weighing more than 10 kg.
CC 1/1-28/3 3/4-30/6 1/9-20/12 7=6, 14=11

📍 N 38°59'10'' W 0°9'49''
www.eurocampings.co.uk/106678

1988 Guardamar del Segura/Alicante, E-03140 / Comunidad Valenciana 🛁 🛜 ✿ (CC€19) iD 39 B2

- 🏕 Marjal Guardamar Camping & Resort*****
- 🚫 Ctra N332 km 73,4
- 📅 1 Jan - 31 Dec
- ☎ +34 96-5484945
- @ reservas@marjal.com

1 ABDE**JM**NOPQRST	ACDHIQRSTV**X** 6	
2 ACGQRSVWX	ABDE**FGH** 7	
3 BCDEF**IKLM**QRT	ABCDEFHJNPQRSTUV 8	
4 BCDE**FH**ILN**O**P**QRS**TU**XYZ**	BEIJLVZ 9	
5 ACDEFGHIJKLM**O**	ABCDEHIM**NOP**VYZ 10	
16A	➊ €67.00	
4ha 120**T**(90m²) 90**P**	➋ €87.00	

🗺 A70, exit 72. From the N332 turn off at roundabout between the villages of La Marina and Guardamar. Campsite clearly signposted.

🛏 A spacious campsite with large pitches. Sunny in winter and in the early and late seasons. Large outdoor swimming pool and heated indoor pool. Lovely sunny terrace. Wifi and fitness facilities included in the price. Excursions to Elche (palm gardens), Alicante and Guardamar.

(CC) 1/1-28/3 2/4-14/6 9/9-31/10 4/11-27/12

📍 N 38°6'36'' W 0°39'18''

www.eurocampings.co.uk/109480

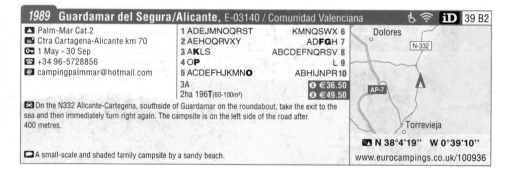

1989 Guardamar del Segura/Alicante, E-03140 / Comunidad Valenciana 🛁 🛜 iD 39 B2

- 🏕 Palm-Mar Cat.2
- 🚫 Ctra Cartagena-Alicante km 70
- 📅 1 May - 30 Sep
- ☎ +34 96-5728856
- @ campingpalmmar@hotmail.com

1 ADEJMNOQRST	KMNQSWX 6	
2 AEHOQRVXY	AD**FGH** 7	
3 A**K**LS	ABCDEFNQRSV 8	
4 O**P**	L 9	
5 ACDEFHJKMN**O**	ABHIJNPR 10	
3A	➊ €36.50	
2ha 196**T**(60-100m²)	➋ €49.50	

🗺 On the N332 Alicante-Cartegena, southside of Guardamar on the roundabout, take the exit to the sea and then immediately turn right again. The campsite is on the left side of the road after 400 metres.

🛏 A small-scale and shaded family campsite by a sandy beach.

📍 N 38°4'19'' W 0°39'10''

www.eurocampings.co.uk/100936

1990 Jávea/Alicante, E-03730 / Comunidad Valenciana 🛁 🛜 (CC€19) iD 67b

- 🏕 El Naranjal
- 🚫 Cami dels Morers 15
- 📅 1 Jan - 31 Dec
- ☎ +34 96-5792989
- @ info@campingelnaranjal.com

1 ACDEJMNOPQRT	A**X** 6	
2 QSVXY	ABDE**FGH** 7	
3 A**IK**LMNQ	ABEFJNRSV 8	
4 BDILO**PQR**Z	JL 9	
5 ADEFGHJKM**NO**	ABDGHIJ**P**R 10	
10A	➊ €34.85	
A100 2,3ha 164**T**(30-60m²) 31**P**	➋ €46.45	

🗺 AP7, exit 62 to the N332. Exit Jávea. Enter Jávea. Drive straight on at roundabout. At Arenal-Platges and Cap de la Nao signs turn right. Then follow signs.

🛏 Very well maintained campsite with excellent and clean toilet facilities. 3 km from the centre of Jávea, but just 600 metres from a shopping area with small restaurants, bars, beach and promenade. Modern amenities for campers.

(CC) 1/1-26/3 3/4-8/7 27/8-31/12

📍 N 38°46'14'' E 0°10'55''

www.eurocampings.co.uk/112079

1991 Jávea/Alicante, E-03730 / Comunidad Valenciana

🅰 Jávea Cat.1
📧 Camino de la Fontana, 10
🕐 1 Jan - 31 Dec
☎ +34 96-5791070
@ info@campingjavea.es

1 ABDEJMNOPQRST	AF**X** 6
2 GQRSVWXY	ABDE**FG** 7
3 AE**KLMQ**	ABCDEFJKNQRSTUV 8
4 BILO	JL 9
5 ABDEFGHJKMN**O**	ABCDHIJ**P**R**Z**10

Ad on this page 8-16A   ❶ €36.15
A50 2,5ha 193T(40-80m²) 13P   ❷ €47.15

🅰 AP7, exit 62 naar N332. Exit Jávea. Drive into Jávea. Straight on at roundabout. Follow signs Arenal/Platges and Cap de la Nao. After McDonalds, Euromarkt take bridge across (dried up) river. Sharp right onto side road. Follow campsite signs.

💬 Situated next to an orange tree plantation. View of the Montgo Mountain and the historic town centre of Jávea. Cycling to the local supermarket, village or beach (El Arenal about 2.5 km).

CC 1/1-27/3   2/4-6/7   27/8-31/12

Dénia
Gata De Gorgos   Jávea
Ap-7   N-332

📷 N 38°47'1''   E 0°10'20''
www.eurocampings.co.uk/106735

Spain

1992 La Marina/Alicante, E-03194 / Comunidad Valenciana

🅰 La Marina Camping & Resort*****
📧 Avenida de la Alegría s/n
🕐 1 Jan - 31 Dec
☎ +34 96-5419200
@ info@lamarinaresort.com

1 ABDE**JM**NOPRST	AEFHI**X** 6
2 ORSTUVWXY	ABDE**FGH** 7
3 BC**EKLMQSTU**	ABCDEFHJNPQRSTUV 8
4 BDILMO**PQRSTUVWXYZ**	JLU 9
5 ACDEFGHJKLM**O**	ABEGHIJLM**N**PRYZ10

Ad on page 670   16A CEE   ❶ €70.00
7ha 438T(70-120m²) 64P   ❷ €82.00

🅰 A70, exit 72 Santa Pola to N332. Site is on the N332 Alicante-Cartagena, 2 km south of La Marina. Clearly signposted from here on.

💬 A well-maintained and lively site with plenty of amenities for pampered campers. Perfect for families with children. The animation team organises games and water recreation. The swimming pools and site are well-supervised. A real holiday atmosphere for everyone. Shows during the weekend and disco for older children.

Urbanización Monte y Mar
N-332
AP-7

📷 N 38°7'47''   W 0°38'59''
www.eurocampings.co.uk/100935

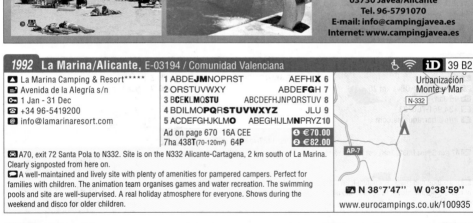

1993 La Vall de Laguar/Alicante, E-03791 / Comunidad Valenciana

🅰 Vall de Laguar
📧 Carrer Sant Antoni, 24
🕐 1 Jan - 31 Dec
☎ +34 96-5584590
@ info@campinglaguar.com

1 ABDEG**JM**NOPQRT	AF 6
2 FOQRSUVX	BE**FGH** 7
3	ABEFJNQRSTUV 8
4 FO	JL 9
5 DHJKMN**O**	ABCDHIJPRV10

6A   ❶ €30.60
A350 1,7ha 39T(50-120m²) 21P   ❷ €43.00

🅰 AP7, exit 62 direction Ondara/Valencia (N332). On Ondara bypass find CV731 towards Orba-Benidoleig-Vall de Laguar. In Campell follow campsite signs.

💬 A small, peacefully located terraced campsite with lovely views of the village, the Montgo mountain and the sea (about 10 km as the crow flies). A place to relax and stay for a long time. A good base for walking in the mountains. Very friendly, helpful management.

CC 1/1-15/3   9/4-14/7   1/9-4/10   15/10-31/12

Pego   El Verger
Pedreguer
AP-7

📷 N 38°46'36''   W 0°6'19''
www.eurocampings.co.uk/112503

1994 Mareny de Barraquetes/Sueca, E-46410 / Comunidad Valenciana ♿ 📶 (CC€15) iD 32 B3

🏕 Barraquetes
🚩 Ctra Nazaret-Oliva km 25
🗓 15 Jan - 15 Dec
☎ +34 961-760723
@ info@barraquetes.com

1 ABDE**JM**NOPQRST	AFH	6
2 BOQVXY	AD**FG**	7
3 AEM	AEFNORSTV	8
4 BIO	EJ	9
5 ABDGHJKMO	AFGHIJ**P**SX	10
20A		❶ €33.00
A50 3,7ha 113**T**(40-65m²) 99**P**		❷ €44.00

🚗 A7 exit Sueca N332. Then exit to Perelló/Mareny de Barraquetes. Then follow campsite signs.

💬 Relaxation and space. For nature lovers: the beach and Albufera nature reserve with a wide variety of native trees and plants. Rice fields and picturesque villages in the area.

(CC) 15/1-15/6 8/9-14/12 7=5, 14=10

Benifaió
A-38
Sueca
AP-7
Cullera

📍 N 39°14'31'' W 0°15'50''

www.eurocampings.co.uk/110239

1995 Moncofa, E-12593 / Comunidad Valenciana 📶 (CC€15) 32 B3

🏕 Los Naranjos****
🚩 Cami de Cabres
🗓 1 Jan - 31 Dec
☎ +34 964-580337
@ info@campinglosnaranjos.com

1 BDEJMNOPQRST	AFKMNOPQSUW	6
2 AEHJRSVY	ABDE**FG**H	7
3 BCELQ	ABCDEFIJKLMNRSTUV	8
4 BCDFHNO**P**	DEJKLV	9
5 ABDEFGHKLMN**O**	AFHIJO**P**TUV	10
10A CEE		❶ €33.40
185**T**(60-130m²) 66**P**		❷ €45.80

🚗 N340 exit Moncofa. AP-7 exit 49 Moncofa, A7 exit Vall d'Uxo and then Moncofa, in Moncofa right onto ring road and follow signs.

💬 Medium-sized campsite, 300 metres from a sandy and pebble beach. 2 km from Moncofa.

(CC) 1/1-28/3 10/4-24/6 10/9-31/12 11=10, 21=19, 30=27

La Vall d'Uixó
AP-7
A-7

Sagunto

📍 N 39°46'53'' W 0°8'56''

www.eurocampings.co.uk/115214

1996 Moncofa/Castellón, E-12593 / Comunidad Valenciana ⊗ ♿ 🛜 (CC€17) 32 B3

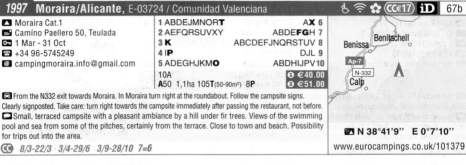

- 🏕 Camping Mon Mar Cat.2
- ✉ Camino Serratelles s/n
- 📅 1 Jan - 31 Dec
- ☎ +34 964-588592
- @ monmarcamping@gmail.com

1 BCDEHKNOPRST	AFIKMNPQS 6
2 AEHJOSVXY	ABDEFGH 7
3 BCDELMQ	ABCDEFJNQRSTUV 8
4 ABDHIO	JL 9
5 ABDEFHJKLMNO	ABDFGHIJOPR 10

6-10A ❶ €28.00
2ha 110T(70m²) 37P ❷ €46.00

🚗 A7 exit 49 direction Moncofa. In Moncofa follow 'Camping Mon Mar' signs. A7 exit 283 Moncofa. Then follow 'Camping Mon Mar' signs. On the N340 exit Moncofa between 950 and 953 km-markers. In Moncofa follow 'Camping Mon Mar' signs.

💬 Ideal for Valencia (45 km) with monuments, science park, modern architecture, aquarium, museums, botanical garden, festivals, opera! Cycling. Orange plantations and vineyards. Visit the underwater caves at San Josep.

🏕 N 39°48'31" W 0°7'40"

(CC) 1/1-27/3 9/4-29/6 3/9-31/12 7=6, 10=8, 20=15, 30=22 www.eurocampings.co.uk/111688

1997 Moraira/Alicante, E-03724 / Comunidad Valenciana ♿ 🛜 ❀ (CC€17) iD 67b

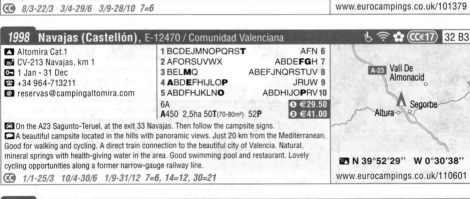

- 🏕 Moraira Cat.1
- ✉ Camíno Paellero 50, Teulada
- 📅 1 Mar - 31 Oct
- ☎ +34 96-5745249
- @ campingmoraira.info@gmail.com

1 ABDEJMNORT	AX 6
2 AEFQRSUVXY	ABDEFGH 7
3 K	ABCDEFJNQRSTUV 8
4 IP	DJL 9
5 ADEGHJKMO	ABDHIJPV 10

10A ❶ €40.00
A50 1,1ha 105T(50-90m²) 8P ❷ €51.00

🚗 From the N332 exit towards Moraira. In Moraira turn right at the roundabout. Follow the campsite signs. Clearly signposted. Take care: turn right towards the campsite immediately after passing the restaurant, not before.

💬 Small, terraced campsite with a pleasant ambiance by a hill under fir trees. Views of the swimming pool and sea from some of the pitches, certainly from the terrace. Close to town and beach. Possibility for trips out into the area.

🏕 N 38°41'9" E 0°7'10"

(CC) 8/3-22/3 3/4-29/6 3/9-28/10 7=6 www.eurocampings.co.uk/101379

1998 Navajas (Castellón), E-12470 / Comunidad Valenciana ♿ 🛜 ❀ (CC€17) 32 B3

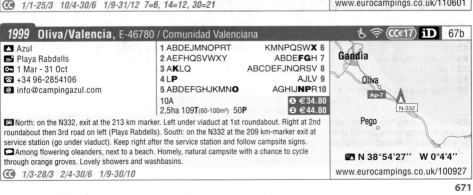

- 🏕 Altomira Cat.1
- ✉ CV-213 Navajas, km 1
- 📅 1 Jan - 31 Dec
- ☎ +34 964-713211
- @ reservas@campingaltomira.com

1 BCDEJMNOPQRST	AFN 6
2 AFORSUVWX	ABDEFGH 7
3 BELMQ	ABEFJNQRSTUV 8
4 ABDEFHIJLOP	JRUW 9
5 ABDFHJKLNO	ABDHIJOPRV 10

6A ❶ €29.50
A450 2,5ha 50T(70-80m²) 52P ❷ €41.00

🚗 On the A23 Sagunto-Teruel, at the exit 33 Navajas. Then follow the campsite signs.

💬 A beautiful campsite located in the hills with panoramic views. Just 20 km from the Mediterranean. Good for walking and cycling. A direct train connection to the beautiful city of Valencia. Natural, mineral springs with health-giving water in the area. Good swimming pool and restaurant. Lovely cycling opportunities along a former narrow-gauge railway line.

🏕 N 39°52'29" W 0°30'38"

(CC) 1/1-25/3 10/4-30/6 1/9-31/12 7=6, 14=12, 30=21 www.eurocampings.co.uk/110601

1999 Oliva/Valencia, E-46780 / Comunidad Valenciana ♿ 🛜 (CC€17) iD 67b

- 🏕 Azul
- ✉ Playa Rabdells
- 📅 1 Mar - 31 Oct
- ☎ +34 96-2854106
- @ info@campingazul.com

1 ABDEJMNOPRT	KMNPQSWX 6
2 AEFHQSVWXY	ABDEFGH 7
3 AKLQ	ABCDEFJNQRSV 8
4 LP	AJLV 9
5 ABDEFGHJKMNO	AGHIJNPR 10

10A ❶ €34.80
2,5ha 109T(60-100m²) 50P ❷ €44.80

🚗 North: on the N332, exit at the 213 km marker. Left under viaduct at 1st roundabout. Right at 2nd roundabout then 3rd road on left (Playa Rabdells). South: on the N332 at the 209 km-marker exit at service station (go under viaduct). Keep right after the service station and follow campsite signs.

💬 Among flowering oleanders, next to a beach. Homely, natural campsite with a chance to cycle through orange groves. Lovely showers and washbasins.

🏕 N 38°54'27" W 0°4'4"

(CC) 1/3-28/3 2/4-30/6 1/9-30/10 www.eurocampings.co.uk/100927

2000 Oliva/Valencia, E-46780 / Comunidad Valenciana ♿ 🛜 (CC€17) iD 67b

- 🏕 Eurocamping
- Partida Rabdells s/n
- 📅 1 Jan - 31 Dec
- ☎ +34 96-2854098
- @ info@eurocamping-es.com

1 ABDE**JM**NOPRST	KMNPQSW**X 6**	
2 ACEFHQRSVWXY	ABDE**FG**H 7	
3 A**K**Q	ABCDEFJNQRSV 8	
4 BDLO**P**	EIJL 9	
5 ABDEFHJKLM**O**	ABCDHIJL**PR**10	
6-10A	❶ €38.75	
4,5ha 299**T**(70-120m²) 30**P**	❷ €45.80	

🅩 From the north: on the N332, at the km-marker 210, turn towards the sea (across the viaduct). From the south: on the N332, at the km-marker 209, turn right. Signposted before and at the roundabout. Follow campsite signs.
🗨 A campsite right on sandy beach. Ideal for beach lovers. Very clean grounds and excellent toilet facilities. Very accessible for caravans and motorhomes. Reception closed between 2:00 and 4:00 pm.
ⓒⓒ *1/1-28/3 9/4-30/6 1/9-31/12*

Gandia
Oliva
AP-7
N-332
Els Poblets

📷 N 38°54'22'' W 0°4'2''

www.eurocampings.co.uk/110055

2001 Oliva/Valencia, E-46780 / Comunidad Valenciana ♿ 🛜 (CC€19) iD 67b

- 🏕 Kiko Park Cat.1
- C/. Assagador de Carro, 2
- 📅 1 Jan - 31 Dec
- ☎ +34 96-2850905
- @ kikopark@kikopark.com

1 ADE**JM**NOPQRST	ABFGKMNPQRST**XYZ** 6	
2 AEHOQRSVWXY	ABDE**FG**H 7	
3 F**K**	ABCDEFJNQRSTUV 8	
4 LO**RSTUVYZ**	ILMV 9	
5 ACDFGHJLM**O**	ABCDGHIJ**NP**RXY10	
Ad on this page 16A CEE	❶ €61.90	
2,9ha 170**T**(60-110m²) 31**P**	❷ €73.30	

🅩 Motorway AP7, exit 61. Take the N332 to Oliva. Turn left at the first roundabout/traffic lights. Then follow 'Platges' and campsite signs.
🗨 An international, floral campsite situated right next to the sea with a lovely sandy beach, perfect restaurant, large terrace and a tropical bar with sea views. Cycling and walking opportunities in the area. Enlarged with a lovely swimming pool and wellness centre. Also take-away meals.
ⓒⓒ *1/1-27/3 3/4-14/6 1/9-31/12*

Gandia
Oliva
Ap-7
N-332
Pego

📷 N 38°55'58'' W 0°5'51''

www.eurocampings.co.uk/101610

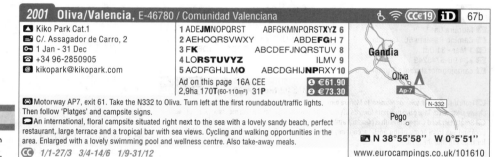

2002 Oliva/Valencia, E-46780 / Comunidad Valenciana ♿ 🛜 (CC€19) iD 67b

- 🏕 Olé****
- Pda. Aigua Morta s/n
- 📅 1 Jan - 31 Dec
- ☎ +34 96-2857517
- @ camping-ole@camping-ole.com

1 ADE**JM**NOPQRS**T**	AKMNQSW**X** 6	
2 EFHQSVWXY	ABDE**FG**H 7	
3 AE**K**Q	ABCDEFJNQRSTUV 8	
4 BDILO**P**	GIJL 9	
5 ACDFGHJKLMN**O**	ABCDGHIJ**PR**10	
6A	❶ €44.70	
4,2ha 314**T**(50-90m²) 56**P**	❷ €55.70	

🅩 When approaching from the north: on the N332 at km-marker 210 turn towards the sea (over the viaduct). When approaching from the south: on the N332 at km-marker 209 turn right. Signposted before and at the roundabout. Follow campsite signs.
🗨 A campsite right on the beach with fine white sand. Extensive views of the sea and beach. Great for beach walkers. Cycling opportunities. Excursions to Denia and inland.
ⓒⓒ *1/1-28/3 3/4-30/6 1/9-31/12*

Gandia
Oliva
AP-7
Els Poblets
N-332

📷 N 38°53'40'' W 0°3'13''

www.eurocampings.co.uk/106682

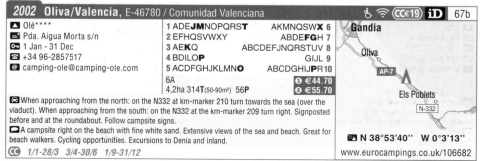

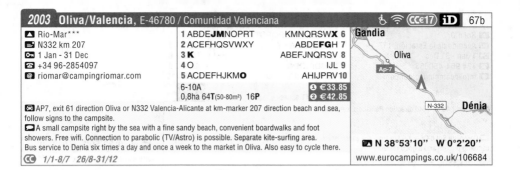

2003 Oliva/Valencia, E-46780 / Comunidad Valenciana ♿ 🛜 (CCE17) iD 67b

- ▲ Rio-Mar★★★
- 🚌 N332 km 207
- 📅 1 Jan - 31 Dec
- ☎ +34 96-2854097
- @ riomar@campingriomar.com

1 ABDE**JM**NOPRT	KMNQRSW**X** 6
2 ACEFHQSVWXY	ABDE**FGH** 7
3 **K**	ABEFJNQRSV 8
4 O	IJL 9
5 ACDEFHJKM**O**	AHIJPRV 10

6-10A ❶ €33.85
0,8ha 64T(50-80m²) 16P ❷ €42.85

Gandia

Oliva

Ap-7

N-332 **Dénia**

🔷 AP7, exit 61 direction Oliva or N332 Valencia-Alicante at km-marker 207 direction beach and sea, follow signs to the campsite.

🔷 A small campsite right by the sea with a fine sandy beach, convenient boardwalks and foot showers. Free wifi. Connection to parabolic (TV/Astro) is possible. Separate kite-surfing area. Bus service to Denia six times a day and once a week to the market in Oliva. Also easy to cycle there.

ⒸⒸ 1/1-8/7 26/8-31/12

🏕 N 38°53'10'' W 0°2'20''

www.eurocampings.co.uk/106684

2004 Oropesa del Mar (Castellón), E-12594 / Comunidad Valenciana ♿ 🛜 (CCE15) 66b

- ▲ Didota S.L. Cat.1
- 🚌 Avda Barcelona / Vereda Didota s/n
- 📅 1 Jan - 31 Dec
- ☎ +34 964-319551
- @ info@campingdidota.es

| 1 BCDEJMNOPRST AEFGKMNOPQRSTUVWX 6 |
2 AEHOQRSVXY	ABDE**FGH** 7
3 BCLQ	ABCDEFGIJKNQRSV 8
4 ABCDFHILOR**UY**	JLRUVW 9
5 ABDEFKLM**O**	ABDGHIJMNPRZ 10

6-10A ❶ €45.00
1,6ha 144T(90-120m²) 53P ❷ €50.55

N-340

Oropesa Del Mar

Ap-7

Benicàssim

🔷 A7, exit 45. Or on the N340 Tarragona-Valencia turn off at 999.2 km sign towards the sea. Follow camping signs (about 1 km).

🔷 A beautiful campsite by the beach. Lovely outdoor swimming pools, heated indoor pool with bubble bath and jacuzzi. Pitches with plenty of sun, pitches in summer with shade. Good restaurant and renovated toilet facilities. Plenty of opportunities in the low season for dance evenings with live music, flamenco and Spanish lessons.

ⒸⒸ 1/1-9/7 27/8-31/12 7=6, 15=12, 30=22, 45=30

🏕 N 40°7'16'' E 0°9'30''

www.eurocampings.co.uk/106725

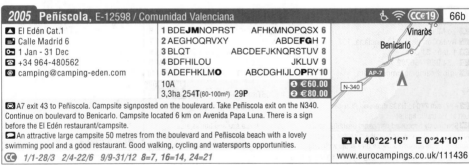

2005 Peñíscola, E-12598 / Comunidad Valenciana ♿ 🛜 (CCE19) 66b

- ▲ El Edén Cat.1
- 🚌 Calle Madrid 6
- 📅 1 Jan - 31 Dec
- ☎ +34 964-480562
- @ camping@camping-eden.com

1 BDE**JM**NOPRST	AFHKMNOPQSX 6
2 AEGHOQRVXY	ABDE**FGH** 7
3 BLQT	ABCDEFJKNQRSTUV 8
4 BDFHILOU	JKLUV 9
5 ADEFHKLM**O**	ABCDGHIJLO**P**RY 10

10A ❶ €60.00
3,3ha 254T(60-100m²) 29P ❷ €80.00

Vinaròs

Benicarló

AP-7

N-340

🔷 A7 exit 43 to Peñíscola. Campsite signposted on the boulevard. Take Peñíscola exit on the N340. Continue on boulevard to Benicarlo. Campsite located 6 km on Avenida Papa Luna. There is a sign before the El Edén restaurant/campsite.

🔷 An attractive large campsite 50 metres from the boulevard and Peñíscola beach with a lovely swimming pool and a good restaurant. Good walking, cycling and watersports opportunities.

ⒸⒸ 1/1-28/3 2/4-22/6 9/9-31/12 8=7, 16=14, 24=21

🏕 N 40°22'16'' E 0°24'10''

www.eurocampings.co.uk/111436

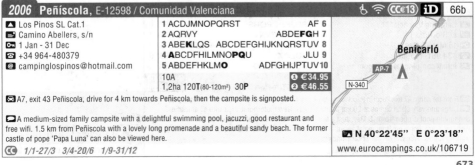

2006 Peñíscola, E-12598 / Comunidad Valenciana ♿ 🛜 (CCE13) iD 66b

- ▲ Los Pinos SL Cat.1
- 🚌 Camino Abellers, s/n
- 📅 1 Jan - 31 Dec
- ☎ +34 964-480379
- @ campinglospinos@hotmail.com

| 1 ACDJMNOPQRST | AF 6 |
| 2 AQRVY | ABDE**FGH** 7 |
| 3 ABE**K**LQS ABCDEFGHIJKNQRSTUV 8 |
| 4 **A**BCDFHILMNO**PQ**U | JLU 9 |
| 5 ABDEFHKLM**O** | ADFGHIJPTUV 10 |

10A ❶ €34.95
1,2ha 120T(80-120m²) 30P ❷ €46.55

Benicarló

AP-7

N-340

🔷 A7, exit 43 Peñíscola, drive for 4 km towards Peñíscola, then the campsite is signposted.

🔷 A medium-sized family campsite with a delightful swimming pool, jacuzzi, good restaurant and free wifi. 1.5 km from Peñíscola with a lovely long promenade and a beautiful sandy beach. The former castle of pope 'Papa Luna' can also be viewed here.

ⒸⒸ 1/1-27/3 3/4-20/6 1/9-31/12

🏕 N 40°22'45'' E 0°23'18''

www.eurocampings.co.uk/106719

Spain

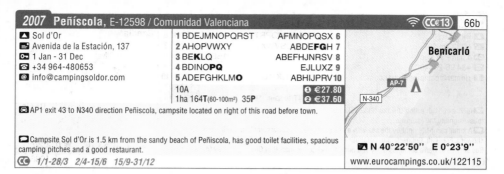

2007 Peñíscola, E-12598 / Comunidad Valenciana 📶 (CC€13) 66b

- ▲ Sol d'Or
- ✉ Avenida de la Estación, 137
- 🗓 1 Jan - 31 Dec
- ☎ +34 964-480653
- @ info@campingsoldor.com

1 BDEJMNOPQRST	AFMNOPQSX	6
2 AHOPVWXY	ABDE**FGH**	7
3 BE**KL**Q	ABEFHJNRSV	8
4 BDINO**PQ**	EJLUXZ	9
5 ADEFGHKLM**O**	ABHIJPRV	10
10A	❶ €27.80	
1ha 164**T**(60-100m²) 35**P**	❷ €37.60	

🚗 AP1 exit 43 to N340 direction Peñiscola, campsite located on right of this road before town.

💬 Campsite Sol d'Or is 1.5 km from the sandy beach of Peñiscola, has good toilet facilities, spacious camping pitches and a good restaurant.

CC 1/1-28/3 2/4-15/6 15/9-31/12

Benicarló

AP-7 N-340

⛺ N 40°22'50'' E 0°23'9''

www.eurocampings.co.uk/122115

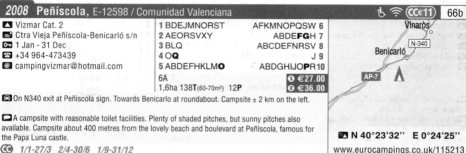

2008 Peñíscola, E-12598 / Comunidad Valenciana ♿ 📶 (CC€11) 66b

- ▲ Vizmar Cat. 2
- ✉ Ctra Vieja Peñiscola-Benicaló s/n
- 🗓 1 Jan - 31 Dec
- ☎ +34 964-473439
- @ campingvizmar@hotmail.com

1 BDEJMNORST	AFKMNOPQSW	6
2 AEORSVXY	ABDE**FGH**	7
3 BLQ	ABCDEFNRSV	8
4 O**Q**	J	9
5 ABDEFHKLM**O**	ABDGHIJO**PR**	10
6A	❶ €27.00	
1,6ha 138**T**(60-70m²) 12**P**	❷ €36.00	

🚗 On N340 exit at Peñiscola sign. Towards Benicarlo at roundabout. Campsite ± 2 km on the left.

💬 A campsite with reasonable toilet facilities. Plenty of shaded pitches, but sunny pitches also available. Campsite about 400 metres from the lovely beach and boulevard at Peñiscola, famous for the Papa Luna castle.

CC 1/1-27/3 2/4-30/6 1/9-31/12

Vinaròs

N-340

Benicarló

AP-7

⛺ N 40°23'32'' E 0°24'25''

www.eurocampings.co.uk/115213

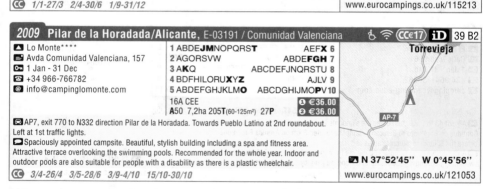

2009 Pilar de la Horadada/Alicante, E-03191 / Comunidad Valenciana ♿ 📶 (CC€17) iD 39 B2

- ▲ Lo Monte****
- ✉ Avda Comunidad Valenciana, 157
- 🗓 1 Jan - 31 Dec
- ☎ +34 966-766782
- @ info@campinglomonte.com

1 ABDE**JM**NOPQRS**T**	AEF**X**	6
2 AGORSVW	ABDE**FGH**	7
3 A**K**Q	ABCDEFJNQRSTU	8
4 BDFHILORU**XYZ**	AJLV	9
5 ABDEFGHJKLM**O**	ABCDGHIJMO**P**V	10
16A CEE	❶ €36.00	
A50 7,2ha 205**T**(60-125m²) 27**P**	❷ €36.00	

🚗 AP7, exit 770 to N332 direction Pilar de la Horadada. Towards Pueblo Latino at 2nd roundabout. Left at 1st traffic lights.

💬 Spaciously appointed campsite. Beautiful, stylish building including a spa and fitness area. Attractive terrace overlooking the swimming pools. Recommended for the whole year. Indoor and outdoor pools are also suitable for people with a disability as there is a plastic wheelchair.

CC 3/4-26/4 3/5-28/6 3/9-4/10 15/10-30/10

Torrevieja

AP-7

⛺ N 37°52'45'' W 0°45'56''

www.eurocampings.co.uk/121053

2010 Playa de Puçol, E-46530 / Comunidad Valenciana 📶 (CC€15) 32 B3

- ▲ Camping Valencia***
- ✉ c/ Rio Turia 1
- 🗓 15 Mar - 9 Dec
- ☎ +34 961-465806
- @ info@campingvalencia.com

1 BDJKNOPQRST	AFHKMPQ	6
2 AEHORSVXY	ABDE**FG**	7
3 BLMQT	ABEFNQRSTU	8
4 BDLO**X**	EJLV	9
5 ABDEHKLM**O**	ABGHIJ**NO**PSV	10
10A	❶ €40.00	
6ha 320**T**(70-80m²) 163**P**	❷ €48.00	

🚗 From the north: A7 exit Puçol in Puçol follow the signs. From Valencia: V21 exit Puçol then follow the signs.
💬 Large and very clean campsite 20 km from Valencia. New motorhome area with all amenities. Swimming pool is open from 18 May. Just a few metres from the beautiful beach of Puzol, certified with the international environmental award 'Blue Flag'. Family-friendly and in a quiet area. Cycling and walking routes. Free wifi on the whole campsite.

CC 15/3-15/6 10/9-8/12 7=6, 14=12, 30=20

Sagunto

AP-7

A-7

Benimàmet

⛺ N 39°36'4'' W 0°16'15''

www.eurocampings.co.uk/112247

Spain

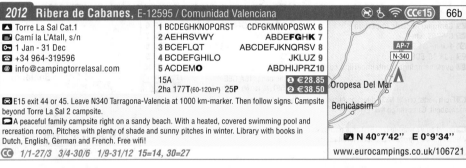

2011 Puçol/Valencia, E-46530 / Comunidad Valenciana ♿ 📶 (CC€15) iD 32 B3

- ▲ Puzol Cat.2
- 🏖 Playa de Puçol
- 📅 15 Jan - 16 Dec
- ☎ +34 961-421527
- @ campingpuzol@gmail.com

1 ADEJMNOPRST	AFHMNWX 6
2 AEGHORVWXY	ABDE**FGH** 7
3 BLOQ	ABEFJNQRSTUV 8
4 BDFHIO	EJ 9
5 ABDK	ABFGHIJL**NPR**10
10A	❶ €33.35
3ha 70**T**(60-70m²) 130**P**	❷ €42.00

🅿 On the A7 exit Puçol; on N340 exit Puçol then follow signs to Playa and campsite.

💬 A campsite 20 km from Valencia; little by little being reorganised and renovated for touring campers. There is a separate section with adequate amenities for these tourists. Lovely swimming pool from mid-June. About 150 metres from the Mediterranean with a fine sandy beach.

CC 15/1-1/7 1/9-15/12 7=6, 14=12, 30=21

Sagunto
Burjassot

📍 N 39°36'20" W 0°16'8"
www.eurocampings.co.uk/110244

2012 Ribera de Cabanes, E-12595 / Comunidad Valenciana ⊗ ♿ 📶 (CC€15) 66b

- ▲ Torre La Sal Cat.1
- 🏖 Camí la L'Atall, s/n
- 📅 1 Jan - 31 Dec
- ☎ +34 964-319596
- @ info@campingtorrelasal.com

1 BCDEGHKNOPQRST	CDFGKMNOPQSWX 6
2 AEHRSVWY	ABDE**FGH**K 7
3 BCEFLQT	ABCDEFJKNQRSV 8
4 BCDEFGHILO	JKLUZ 9
5 ACDEM**O**	ABDHIJPRZ10
15A	❶ €28.85
2ha 177**T**(60-120m²) 25**P**	❷ €38.50

🅿 E15 exit 44 or 45. Leave N340 Tarragona-Valencia at 1000 km-marker. Then follow signs. Campsite beyond Torre La Sal 2 campsite.

💬 A peaceful family campsite right on a sandy beach. With a heated, covered swimming pool and recreation room. Pitches with plenty of shade and sunny pitches in winter. Library with books in Dutch, English, German and French. Free wifi!

CC 1/1-27/3 3/4-30/6 1/9-31/12 15=14, 30=27

Oropesa Del Mar
Benicàssim

📍 N 40°7'42" E 0°9'34"
www.eurocampings.co.uk/106721

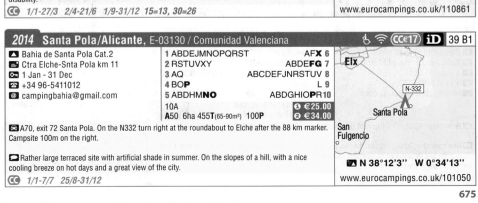

2013 Ribera de Cabanes, E-12595 / Comunidad Valenciana ♿ 📶 (CC€19) 66b

- ▲ Torre la Sal 2 Cat.1
- 🏖 Avda Camí l'Atall 44
- 📅 1 Jan - 31 Dec
- ☎ +34 964-319567
- @ camping@torrelasal2.com

1 BCDEJMNOPRST	ACDEFGHIKMNPQSW**X** 6
2 AEHJRSVXY	ABDE**FGH** 7
3 BCDE**IKLMO**PQRST	ABCDEFIJKNQRSTV 8
4 ABDFHILMNO**RSTUXZ**	EJUWZ 9
5 ACDEFGHKLM**O**	ABCDHIJMPRZ10
10A	❶ €56.70
9ha 517**T**(60-140m²) 113**P**	❷ €72.70

🅿 On the A7 Barcelona-Valencia take exit 45. On the N340 km-marker 998 or 1000. Signposted.
💬 A large residential campsite with beautiful, new toilet facilities and many other amenities: indoor and outdoor swimming pools, heated in winter. Covered car park, tennis and multisports grounds. Fitness, sauna and jacuzzi. Good cycling opportunities. Free wifi! Also well equipped for people with a disability.

CC 1/1-27/3 2/4-21/6 1/9-31/12 15=13, 30=26

Oropesa Del Mar
Benicàssim

📍 N 40°7'40" E 0°9'32"
www.eurocampings.co.uk/110861

2014 Santa Pola/Alicante, E-03130 / Comunidad Valenciana ♿ 📶 (CC€17) iD 39 B1

- ▲ Bahia de Santa Pola Cat.2
- 🏖 Ctra Elche-Snta Pola km 11
- 📅 1 Jan - 31 Dec
- ☎ +34 96-5411012
- @ campingbahia@gmail.com

1 ABDEJMNOPQRST	AF**X** 6
2 RSTUVXY	ABDE**FG** 7
3 AQ	ABCDEFJNRSTUV 8
4 BO**P**	L 9
5 ABDHM**NO**	ABDGHIO**PR**10
10A	❶ €25.00
A50 6ha 455**T**(65-90m²) 100**P**	❷ €34.00

🅿 A70, exit 72 Santa Pola. On the N332 turn right at the roundabout to Elche after the 88 km marker. Campsite 100m on the right.

💬 Rather large terraced site with artificial shade in summer. On the slopes of a hill, with a nice cooling breeze on hot days and a great view of the city.

CC 1/1-7/7 25/8-31/12

Elx
Santa Pola
San Fulgencio

📍 N 38°12'3" W 0°34'13"
www.eurocampings.co.uk/101050

Spain

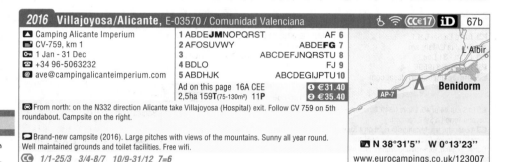

2015 Valencia, E-46012 / Comunidad Valenciana   32 B3

- ▲ Coll Vert Cat. 2
- ✉ Ctra del Riu, nr. 486 Pinedo
- 🅿 16 Jan - 15 Dec
- ☎ +34 96-1830036
- @ info@collvertcamping.com

1	ACDEJMNOPRST	AFHKMNOPQRST	6
2	AEHOPRVXY	ABDE**FGH**	7
3	BE**KL**Q	ABEFJNQRSV	8
4	BDFHLO	J	9
5	ABDEFGHK**O**	ABDEFGHIL**NOP**RV	10
10A			
2,4ha 80T(40-80m²) 103P		❶ €33.35	
		❷ €42.00	

🗺 From N: A7 and V21 dir. Valencia, follow El Saler signs. On CV500 1. roundabout go 3/4 of the way round and exit on CV5010. Site 300 metres on left. From S: A7 before Valencia dir. Albufera and El Saler on the CV500, turn off at El Saler roundabout, site 200m on left.

🚲 6 km from Valencia and 300m from a wide sandy beach and l'Albufera nature park. Go to Valencia by cycle path or by bus. If you don't mind some surrounding noise, you will not be disappointed.

ⓒ 16/1-14/7 1/9-14/12 7=6, 14=12, 30=21

Valencia
Torrent

🗺 N 39°23'47'' W 0°19'58''

www.eurocampings.co.uk/117748

2016 Villajoyosa/Alicante, E-03570 / Comunidad Valenciana   67b

- ▲ Camping Alicante Imperium
- ✉ CV-759, km 1
- 🅿 1 Jan - 31 Dec
- ☎ +34 96-5063232
- @ ave@campingalicanteimperium.com

1	ABDE**JM**NOPQRST	AF	6
2	AFOSUVWY	ABDE**FG**	7
3		ABCDEFJNQRSTU	8
4	BDLO	FJ	9
5	ABDHJK	ABCDEGIJPTU	10
Ad on this page 16A CEE		❶ €31.40	
2,5ha 159T(75-130m²) 11P		❷ €35.40	

🗺 From north: on the N332 direction Alicante take Villajoyosa (Hospital) exit. Follow CV 759 on 5th roundabout. Campsite on the right.

🚲 Brand-new campsite (2016). Large pitches with views of the mountains. Sunny all year round. Well maintained grounds and toilet facilities. Free wifi.

ⓒ 1/1-25/3 3/4-8/7 10/9-31/12 7=6

L'Albir
Benidorm

🗺 N 38°31'5'' W 0°13'23''

www.eurocampings.co.uk/123007

2017 Villajoyosa/Alicante, E-03570 / Comunidad Valenciana   67b

- ▲ Camping El Torres
- ✉ Calle Ilici 29, Playa El Torres
- 🅿 1 Jan - 31 Dec
- ☎ +34 965-995077
- @ info@campingeltorres.com

1	ABDE**JM**NOPQRST	AFK**N**PQSW**X**	6
2	AEFGHSTVWXY	ABDE**FGH**	7
3	A**K**Q	ABEFJNQRSTU	8
4	BDILO	JMR	9
5	ABDEFHJKLM**O**	ABCDHIJ**P**TU	10
Ad on page 677 10-16A		❶ €33.50	
2ha 114T(55-115m²) 5P		❷ €41.50	

🗺 From the N: N332 exit Villajoyosa (Hospital). Left at 3rd roundabout. Follow campsite signs.

🚲 New campsite (2014), right on the beach. Lots of sun in winter, artificial shade in summer. From every pitch and from the welcoming terrace there is a lovely view of the sea, and from the other side there is a view of the mountains.

ⓒ 9/4-17/6 16/9-30/9

Villajoyosa
Benidorm

🗺 N 38°30'57'' W 0°12'1''

www.eurocampings.co.uk/122140

Spain

Your campsite at the beach

Camping **El Torres** • Playa el torres •

Calle Ilici 29, Playa El Torres
03570 Villajoyosa/Alicante
Tel. 965-995077
GPS: N 38°30'57" W 0°12'01"
E-mail: info@campingeltorres.com
Internet: www.campingeltorres.com

2018   Villajoyosa/Alicante, E-03570 / Comunidad Valenciana   ♿ 🛜 (CC€17) iD   67b

🏕 Playa Paraíso Cat.2
✉ Paraíso, 66
📅 1 Jan - 31 Dec
☎ +34 966-851838
@ info@campingplayaparaiso.com

1	ABDEJMNOQR	AKPU	**6**
2	EJQSVWXY	ABDE**FG**	**7**
3	L	ABEFNQRSV	**8**
4	BDILO**PQ**	EMR	**9**
5	ABDEFGHJKMN**O**	ABCHIJPR	**10**

6-10A   ❶ €37.85
1,3ha 100**T**(40-60m²) 15**P**   ❷ €47.85

🚐 Campsite is on the old N332. Go through the town, and don't take new bypass around the town. So on N332 exit Villajoyosa. Campsite is at 136 kilometre-marker on the seaward side of the road.

💬 Small, family-run campsite right on the sea. Close to the colourful town of Villajoyosa. Spacious and lively outdoor seating area.

CC 1/1-28/3 2/4-8/7 26/8-31/12

🏕 N 38°29'59" W 0°14'57"
www.eurocampings.co.uk/106691

Map: Benidorm, AP-7, N-332, Playa Muchavista

2019   Villargordo del Cabriel, E-46317 / Comunidad Valenciana   ♿ 🛜 (CC€19) 🚻   32 A3

🏕 Kikopark Rural
✉ Ctra Embalse de Contreras km 3
📅 1 Jan - 31 Dec
☎ +34 96-2139082
@ rural@kikopark.com

1	BDE**JM**NOPQRST	AFNUVXY	**6**
2	ADGQRSUVXY	ABDE**FG**	**7**
3	BQ**R**	ABCDEFJNQRSTUV	**8**
4	ABCD**E**FHILO	FGJ	**9**
5	ABDEFHKL**NO**	ABDHIJLPR	**10**

10A CEE   ❶ €33.30
A800 2ha 76**T**(70-90m²) 72**P**   ❷ €45.30

🚐 A3, exit 255 towards Villargordo. Enter the village, turn right at T junction, campsite clearly signposted there. Another 3 km to the campsite.
💬 A campsite for peace and quiet. Views of the mountains and close to a large reservoir. Situated in a nature area with opportunities for walking, water sports, rafting, fishing, canoeing, hiking and mountain biking.

CC 1/1-27/3 3/4-14/6 1/9-31/12

🏕 N 39°33'8" W 1°28'28"
www.eurocampings.co.uk/111806

Map: Minglanilla, A-3, Villalpardo

2020   Xeraco, E-46770 / Comunidad Valenciana   🛜 (CC€15) iD   39 B1

🏕 San Vicente
✉ Avenida de la Mota 24
📅 1 Jan - 31 Dec
☎ +34 962-888188
@ info@campingsanvicente.com

1	ABDEILNOR	KPQ	**6**
2	EHNQSVXY	ABDE**FG**	**7**
3		ABEFNQRV	**8**
4	BILO	HJ	**9**
5	ABEFGHJKMO	ABCDHIJPS	**10**

Ad on page 678 5-10A   ❶ €29.75
0,5ha 42**T**(50-60m²) 21**P**   ❷ €39.95

🚐 AP7, exit 59 Favara to N332 direction Tavernes. On roundabout take CV603 and then CV605. Left after the bridge. Right on roundabout. Campsite is on left.

💬 Small campsite with small fields. Only suitable for tents, small caravans and small motorhomes. Right by the beach. Very easy-going atmosphere.

CC 1/1-27/3 2/4-20/6 3/9-31/12 7=6, 14=11

🏕 N 39°3'12" W 0°11'53"
www.eurocampings.co.uk/111116

Map: N-332, AP-7, Xeraco, A-38, Gandia

Spain

Aragon

Land of kings and conquerors

Aragon stretches from the Pyrenees to Valencia in the south, with an extremely diverse landscape: glaciers in the north, forests, verdant valleys with farmland, vineyards, arid plains, with gorges and rocky outcrops in between. Keep an eye out for the occasional tower: a reminder of the Moors who ruled here for three centuries.

Historically significant

Capital Saragossa, originally a Roman colony, has the largest city square in Europe, Plaza del Pilar. You'll be blown away by the Palacio de Aljaferia, built by the Moors in the 9th century, now a government complex. Saragossa is also a mecca for shopaholics, with as many as 13 different

shopping areas. You'll see striking Moorish-influenced Mudéjar architecture in the city of Turuel, and be sure to look out for the glazed tiles inventively used on the walls and steeples. Visit the town of Jaca, both a stop on the Camino de Santiago and a defensive city, and admire the pentagonal fort the Ciudadela.

From the mountains to the plains

You can still experience wilder, older Aragon at the Carnival of Bielsa (Huesca) in which participants wear costumes and horned headdresses. And it's easy to imagine yourself in another era at the castle at Loarre – the kids will get happily lost in the labyrinth of tunnels, dungeons and towers. All you need then is a dragon, and you won't be too far off with a visit to Dinopolis, one of the world's largest museums of palaeontology! For nature lovers and thrill-seekers, the forests, gorges, waterfalls and caves of Parque Natural Sierra y Canones de Guara are a guaranteed hit, and climbers flock to the Mallos de Riglos rock formations for their adrenaline fix.

Did you know ...?
The train station used in the film Casablanca was actually Estacion International Canfranc, located just 7 km from France.

Our tips

1. *Join a chocolate tour in Zaragoza. Go on. You know you want to*

2. *Visit El Pilar Cathedral, both a place of worship and a museum*

3. *An oasis in arid surroundings: Piedra Monastery and Nuevalos Gardens*

4. *The Moorish town of Albarracin and nearby El Rodeno*

5. *Admire art works of Aragon-born painter Francisco Goya in Saragossa*

Simple but not plain

Lamb, beef and dairy are abundant. Try Teruel ham, local olive oil, longaniza (sausage), rainbow trout, wild boar, truffles and wild mushrooms, with dark strong local red wines, followed by furtas de Aragon. Sample the local haggis known as cheireta, or hearty chilindrón, or go all out and try criadillas (lamb's testicles). Like garlic? Try Migas in Turuel: breadcrumbs with garlic, pork, sausage, and grapes.

2021 Albarracín/Teruel, E-44100 / Aragón   ♿ 🛜 (CC€17) | 32 A2

- 🏕 Ciudad de Albarracín**
- ✉ Camino de Gea s/n
- 🗓 9 Mar - 25 Nov
- ☎ +34 978-710197
- @ campingalbarracin5@hotmail.com

1 BDEJMNOPQRST	6
2 PVWXY	ABDEF 7
3 AE	ABEFNQRS 8
4 FHO	GJ 9
5 ABDEHJKMNO	ADHIJPTUV 10
10A	❶ €20.05
A1200 1,5ha 100T(70m²) 30P	❷ €26.65

🚗 From Teruel to Albarracín. Follow campsite signs in Albarracín.

💬 A quiet campsite on the edge of the 'most beautiful city in Spain' (classified historical heritage including Islam) and near an area with prehistoric rock paintings. Abundant fauna and flora. In July and August 1 Euro per person per day in the municipal open-air swimming pool.

CC 9/3-24/3 1/4-10/7 28/8-24/11

📍 N 40°24'43'' W 1°25'39''

Cella · Albarracín · A-1512 · Calomarde

www.eurocampings.co.uk/111580

2022 Alquézar, E-22145 / Aragón   🛜 (CC€17) | 24 B3

- 🏕 Alquézar
- ✉ Ctra Barbastro s/n
- 🗓 1 Jan - 31 Dec
- ☎ +34 974-318300
- @ camping@alquezar.com

1 BDEJMNOPQRST	AFU 6
2 FGPRUVWXY	ABDEFGK 7
3 BLS	ABEFNPQRSV 8
4 AEFHIO	EGJKU 9
5 ABEFHKLMNO	ABFGHIJPV 10
10A	❶ €27.90
1,5ha 120T(70-100m²) 28P	❷ €37.50

🚗 A22 Huesca-Barbastro. Take N240 west of Barbastro direction Barbastro. Then A1232 and A1233 to Alquézar. Follow campsite signs.

💬 A campsite for families and those who love walking, rafting, canyoning, escalade (rock climbing), etc. Located in the beautiful Sierra de Guara. Approx. 1 km from the medieval town of Alquézar with its castle (Christian and Moorish influences). UNESCO World Heritage Site (centuries-old rock drawings) and typical fauna.

CC 1/1-30/6 1/9-31/12

Alberuela de la Liena · Abiego · A-22

📍 N 42°9'53'' E 0°0'55''

www.eurocampings.co.uk/110781

2023 Alquézar, E-22145 / Aragón   🛜 (CC€17) | 24 B3

- 🏕 Rio Vero
- ✉ Puente de Colungo s/n
- 🗓 15 Mar - 31 Oct
- ☎ +34 974-318350
- @ info@campingriovero.com

1 BDEJMNOPQRST	JN 6
2 CKPUVWXY	ABDEF 7
3 AL	ABEFNRV 8
4 FHO	AEU 9
5 ACEFGHJKLMNO	ABDGHIJOV 10
Ad on this page 5A	❶ €25.50
A500 3ha 187T(70-100m²) 34P	❷ €34.10

🚗 From Barbastro A1233 direction Alquézar. Right A2205 direction Colungo. Follow campsite signs.

💬 A campsite in a wooded area of the Sierra de Guara national park and close to nearby canyons. Canyoning equipment can be hired at the campsite. The campsite is situated beside the Rio Vero river with opportunities for swimming. Guides for canyoning, escalade, via ferrata, ornithology, VTT (all-terrain bikes) and trekking.

CC 15/3-30/6 1/9-30/10 7=6

Alquézar · Abiego · N-240 · Castillazuelo

📍 N 42°9'7'' E 0°1'45''

www.eurocampings.co.uk/120835

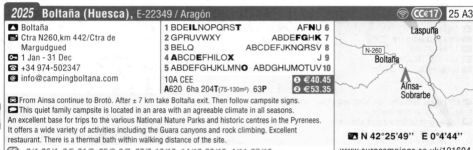

2024 Benasque (Huesca), E-22440 / Aragón

🔺 Aneto Cat.1
🚐 Ctra Barbastro Francia, km 100
📅 1/1 - 31/10, 1/12 - 31/12
☎ +34 974-551141
@ info@campinganeto.com

1	BDE**IL**NOPQRS**T**	ABFGJ**N**UV 6
2	CFGPUVWXY	ABDE**FG**IJ 7
3	B	ABCDEFJNQRS 8
4	**AB**EFHILO	FGIJ 9
5	ACDEFHJKLMN**O**	ABDHIJNOV 10
10A		❶ €36.40
A1237 6ha 200T(40-100m²) 91P		❷ €48.60

🚗 From Castejón take the Sos A139 direction Benasque. The campsite is on the left 3 km beyond Benasque.
💬 This family campsite offers relaxation, tranquillity and fresh mountain air. Starting point for various (mountain) walks, including in the rugged countryside. It has a swimming pool. The restaurant is open the week before Easter and during Holy Week.
ℂℂ 1/1-1/7 31/8-30/10 1/12-31/12

🔺 ⊚ CC€19 ♦♦ 25 A3

Benasque

📷 N 42°37'27'' E 0°32'39''

www.eurocampings.co.uk/108245

2025 Boltaña (Huesca), E-22349 / Aragón

🔺 Boltaña
🚐 Ctra N260,km 442/Ctra de Margudgued
📅 1 Jan - 31 Dec
☎ +34 974-502347
@ info@campingboltana.com

1	BDE**IL**NOPQRS**T**	AF**N**U 6
2	GPRUVWXY	ABDE**FGH**K 7
3	BELQ	ABCDEFJKNQRSV 8
4	**AB**CD**E**FHILO**X**	J 9
5	ABDEFGHJKLMN**O**	ABDGHIJMOTUV 10
10A CEE		❶ €40.45
A620 6ha 204T(75-130m²) 63P		❷ €53.35

🚗 From Ainsa continue to Broto. After ± 7 km take Boltaña exit. Then follow campsite signs.
💬 This quiet family campsite is located in an area with an agreeable climate in all seasons. An excellent base for trips to the various National Nature Parks and historic centres in the Pyrenees. It offers a wide variety of activities including the Guara canyons and rock climbing. Excellent restaurant. There is a thermal bath within walking distance of the site.
ℂℂ 2/4-26/4 2/5-21/6 25/6-8/7 27/8-10/10 14/10-30/10 4/11-27/12

⊚ CC€17 25 A3

Laspuña

N-260
Boltaña

Aínsa-Sobrarbe

📷 N 42°25'49'' E 0°4'44''

www.eurocampings.co.uk/101604

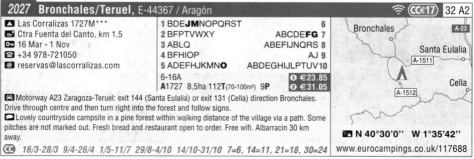

2026 Bonansa (Huesca), E-22486 / Aragón

🔺 Camping Baliera Cat.2
🚐 N260, km 355,5
📅 30/11 - 9/12, 26/12 - 28/10
☎ +34 974-554016
@ info@baliera.com

1	BDE**JM**NOPQRS**T**	AF**J**NUV 6
2	CGPVWXY	ABDE**FG**K 7
3	ABELQ	ABCDEFHJKNPQRSV 8
4	BFHILO**QR**	IJ 9
5	ABDGM**O**	AGHIJMNPTUV 10
5-10A		❶ €42.00
A925 5ha 173T(80-130m²) 46P		❷ €57.00

🚗 From Viella N230 dir. Pont de Suert. After about 3 km from Vilaller turn right dir. Castejón de Sos. After 2.5 km turn left at the forked road. Campsite immediately on the left.
💬 The campsite is located in the centre of the Isabena, Benasque, Aran and Boi valleys. It offers access to unusual and beautiful landscapes. Sample a mix of tradition and culture. Various activities all year: mountain sports, fishing, mushroom collecting in the autumn, skiing.
ℂℂ 1/1-14/7 1/9-27/10 30/11-8/12 26/12-31/12 7=6, 10=8, 15=12, 18=14

⊚ CC€19 25 A3

Taüll
La Vall De Boí
N-230
Bonansa
El Pont De Suert
N-260

📷 N 42°26'22'' E 0°41'56''

www.eurocampings.co.uk/106703

2027 Bronchales/Teruel, E-44367 / Aragón

🔺 Las Corralizas 1727M***
🚐 Ctra Fuenta del Canto, km 1,5
📅 16 Mar - 1 Nov
☎ +34 978-721050
@ reservas@lascorralizas.com

1	BDE**JM**NOPQRST	6
2	BFPTVWXY	ABCDE**FG** 7
3	ABLQ	ABEFIJNQRS 8
4	BFHIOP	AJ 9
5	ADEFHJKMN**O**	ABDEGHIJLPTUV 10
6-16A		❶ €23.85
A1727 8,5ha 112T(70-100m²) 9P		❷ €31.05

🚗 Motorway A23 Zaragoza-Teruel: exit 144 (Santa Eulalia) or exit 131 (Cella) direction Bronchales. Drive through centre and then turn right into the forest and follow signs.
💬 Lovely countryside campsite in a pine forest within walking distance of the village via a path. Some pitches are not marked out. Fresh bread and restaurant open to order. Free wifi. Albarracin 30 km away.
ℂℂ 16/3-28/3 9/4-26/4 1/5-11/7 29/8-4/10 14/10-31/10 7=6, 14=11, 21=18, 30=24

⊚ CC€17 32 A2

Bronchales A-23
Santa Eulalia
A-1511
Cella
A-1512

📷 N 40°30'0'' W 1°35'42''

www.eurocampings.co.uk/117688

Spain

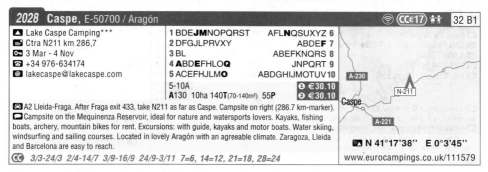

2028 Caspe, E-50700 / Aragón
📶 (CC€17) ♠♀ 32 B1

- 🏕 Lake Caspe Camping***
- 🚏 Ctra N211 km 286,7
- 📅 3 Mar - 4 Nov
- ☎ +34 976-634174
- @ lakecaspe@lakecaspe.com

1 BDE**JM**NOPQRST	AFL**N**QSUXYZ 6
2 DFGJLPRVXY	ABDE**F** 7
3 BL	ABEFKNQRS 8
4 **A**BD**E**FHLO**Q**	JNPQRT 9
5 ACEFHJLM**O**	ABDGHIJMOTUV 10

5-10A — ❶ €30.10
A130 10ha 140T(70-140m²) 55P — ❷ €30.10

🚗 A2 Lleida-Fraga. After Fraga exit 433, take N211 as far as Caspe. Campsite on right (286.7 km-marker).
💬 Campsite on the Mequinenza Reservoir, ideal for nature and watersports lovers. Kayaks, fishing boats, archery, mountain bikes for rent. Excursions: with guide, kayaks and motor boats. Water skiing, windsurfing and sailing courses. Located in lovely Aragón with an agreeable climate. Zaragoza, Lleida and Barcelona are easy to reach.
(CC) 3/3-24/3 2/4-14/7 3/9-16/9 24/9-3/11 7=6, 14=12, 21=18, 28=24

📍 N 41°17'38'' E 0°3'45''
www.eurocampings.co.uk/111579

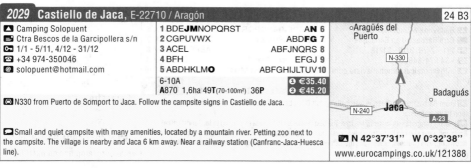

2029 Castiello de Jaca, E-22710 / Aragón
24 B3

- 🏕 Camping Solopuent
- 🚏 Ctra Bescos de la Garcipollera s/n
- 📅 1/1 - 5/11, 4/12 - 31/12
- ☎ +34 974-350046
- @ solopuent@hotmail.com

1 BDE**JM**NOPQRST	A**N** 6
2 CGPUVWX	ABD**FG** 7
3 ACEL	ABFJNQRS 8
4 BFH	EFGJ 9
5 ABDHKLM**O**	ABFGHIJLTUV 10

6-10A — ❶ €35.40
A870 1,6ha 49T(70-100m²) 36P — ❷ €45.20

🚗 N330 from Puerto de Somport to Jaca. Follow the campsite signs in Castiello de Jaca.

💬 Small and quiet campsite with many amenities, located by a mountain river. Petting zoo next to the campsite. The village is nearby and Jaca 6 km away. Near a railway station (Canfranc-Jaca-Huesca line).

📍 N 42°37'31'' W 0°32'38''
www.eurocampings.co.uk/121388

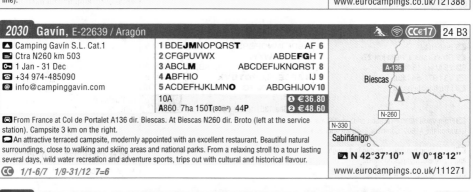

2030 Gavín, E-22639 / Aragón
🎿 📶 (CC€17) 24 B3

- 🏕 Camping Gavín S.L. Cat.1
- 🚏 Ctra N260 km 503
- 📅 1 Jan - 31 Dec
- ☎ +34 974-485090
- @ info@campinggavin.com

1 BDE**JM**NOPQRS**T**	AF 6
2 CFGPUVWX	ABDE**FG**H 7
3 ABCLM	ABCDEFIJKNQRST 8
4 **A**BFHIO	IJ 9
5 ACDEFHJKLMN**O**	ABDGHIJOV 10

10A — ❶ €36.80
A860 7ha 150T(80m²) 44P — ❷ €48.60

🚗 From France at Col de Portalet A136 dir. Biescas. At Biescas N260 dir. Broto (left at the service station). Campsite 3 km on the right.
💬 An attractive terraced campsite, modernly appointed with an excellent restaurant. Beautiful natural surroundings, close to walking and skiing areas and national parks. From a relaxing stroll to a tour lasting several days, wild water recreation and adventure sports, trips out with cultural and historical flavour.
(CC) 1/1-6/7 1/9-31/12 7=6

📍 N 42°37'10'' W 0°18'12''
www.eurocampings.co.uk/111271

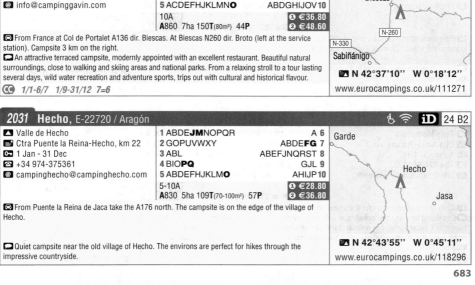

2031 Hecho, E-22720 / Aragón
♿ 📶 iD 24 B2

- 🏕 Valle de Hecho
- 🚏 Ctra Puente la Reina-Hecho, km 22
- 📅 1 Jan - 31 Dec
- ☎ +34 974-375361
- @ campinghecho@campinghecho.com

1 ABDE**JM**NOPQR	A 6
2 GOPUVWXY	ABDE**FG** 7
3 ABL	ABEFJNQRST 8
4 BIO**PQ**	GJL 9
5 ABDEFHJKLM**O**	AHIJP 10

5-10A — ❶ €28.80
A830 5ha 109T(70-100m²) 57P — ❷ €36.80

🚗 From Puente la Reina de Jaca take the A176 north. The campsite is on the edge of the village of Hecho.

💬 Quiet campsite near the old village of Hecho. The environs are perfect for hikes through the impressive countryside.

📍 N 42°43'55'' W 0°45'11''
www.eurocampings.co.uk/118296

Spain

2032 La Puebla de Castro, E-22435 / Aragón ⊚ (CC€17) 25 A3

- 🏕 Lago Barasona Cat. 1
- 🚍 Ctra Barbastro-Graus/N123a, km 25
- 🗓 1 Mar - 31 Oct
- ☎ +34 974-545148
- @ info@lagobarasona.com

1	BDEJMNOPQRST	AFLNQSWX 6
2	DFGIKPUVWXY	ABDEFGH 7
3	ABEFILMS	ABCDEFIJKNQRST 8
4	BCDFHLORTUV	EIJQRTUV 9
5	ABDEFGHJLMNO	ABDGHIJOTUVZ 10

6A CEE
A550 30ha 180T(70-120m²) 99P

❶ €43.20
❷ €55.40

📖 From Aínsa A138 direction Barbastro. About 8 km before Barbastro turn left towards N123 Benabara/Graus. Take the 123a to Graus at intersection. Campsite 2.4 km on the left. Follow the loop.
💬 A friendly family campsite on several levels. Good base for interesting sights with remnants of several cultures. Located on a lake with a beach and a meadow. Set in the foothills of the Pyrenees with many natural parks. Various watersports options.

CC 1/3-30/6 1/9-30/10

📌 N 42°8'32'' E 0°18'51''
www.eurocampings.co.uk/101373

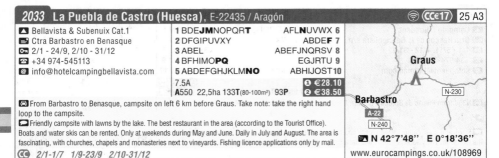

2033 La Puebla de Castro (Huesca), E-22435 / Aragón ⊚ (CC€17) 25 A3

- 🏕 Bellavista & Subenuix Cat.1
- 🚍 Ctra Barbastro en Benasque
- 🗓 2/1 - 24/9, 2/10 - 31/12
- ☎ +34 974-545113
- @ info@hotelcampingbellavista.com

1	BDEJMNOPQRT	AFLNUVWX 6
2	DFGIPUVXY	ABDEF 7
3	ABEL	ABEFJNQRSV 8
4	BFHIMOPQ	EGJRTU 9
5	ABDEFGHJKLMNO	ABHIJOST 10

7.5A
A550 22,5ha 133T(80-100m²) 93P

❶ €28.10
❷ €38.50

📖 From Barbastro to Benasque, campsite on left 6 km before Graus. Take note: take the right hand loop to the campsite.
💬 Friendly campsite with lawns by the lake. The best restaurant in the area (according to the Tourist Office). Boats and water skis can be rented. Only at weekends during May and June. Daily in July and August. The area is fascinating, with churches, chapels and monasteries next to vineyards. Fishing licence applications only by mail.

CC 2/1-1/7 1/9-23/9 2/10-31/12

📌 N 42°7'48'' E 0°18'36''
www.eurocampings.co.uk/108969

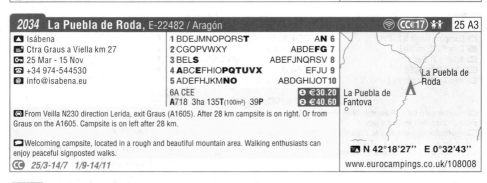

2034 La Puebla de Roda, E-22482 / Aragón ⊚ (CC€17) ♥♥ 25 A3

- 🏕 Isábena
- 🚍 Ctra Graus a Viella km 27
- 🗓 25 Mar - 15 Nov
- ☎ +34 974-544530
- @ info@isabena.eu

1	BDEJMNOPQRST	AN 6
2	CGOPVWXY	ABDEFG 7
3	BELS	ABEFJNQRSV 8
4	ABCEFHIOPQTUVX	EFJU 9
5	ADEFHJKMNO	ABDGHIJOT 10

6A CEE
A718 3ha 135T(100m²) 39P

❶ €30.20
❷ €40.60

📖 From Veilla N230 direction Lerida, exit Graus (A1605). After 28 km campsite is on right. Or from Graus on the A1605. Campsite is on left after 28 km.

💬 Welcoming campsite, located in a rough and beautiful mountain area. Walking enthusiasts can enjoy peaceful signposted walks.

CC 25/3-14/7 1/9-14/11

📌 N 42°18'27'' E 0°32'43''
www.eurocampings.co.uk/108008

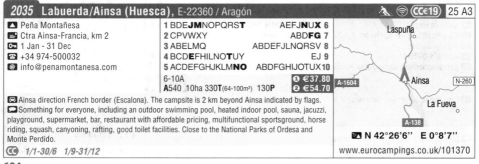

2035 Labuerda/Ainsa (Huesca), E-22360 / Aragón 🎿 ⊚ (CC€19) 25 A3

- 🏕 Peña Montañesa
- 🚍 Ctra Ainsa-Francia, km 2
- 🗓 1 Jan - 31 Dec
- ☎ +34 974-500032
- @ info@penamontanesa.com

1	BDEJMNOPQRST	AEFJNUX 6
2	CPVWXY	ABDFG 7
3	ABELMQ	ABDEFJLNQRSV 8
4	BCDEFHILNOTUY	EJ 9
5	ACDEFGHJKLMNO	ABDFGHIJOTUX 10

6-10A
A540 10ha 330T(64-100m²) 130P

❶ €37.80
❷ €54.70

📖 Ainsa direction French border (Escalona). The campsite is 2 km beyond Ainsa indicated by flags.
💬 Something for everyone, including an outdoor swimming pool, heated indoor pool, sauna, jacuzzi, playground, supermarket, bar, restaurant with affordable pricing, multifunctional sportsground, horse riding, squash, canyoning, rafting, good toilet facilities. Close to the National Parks of Ordesa and Monte Perdido.

CC 1/1-30/6 1/9-31/12

📌 N 42°26'6'' E 0°8'7''
www.eurocampings.co.uk/101370

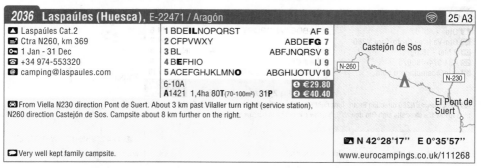

2036 Laspaúles (Huesca), E-22471 / Aragón

🔼 Laspaúles Cat.2
🚍 Ctra N260, km 369
🗓 1 Jan - 31 Dec
☎ +34 974-553320
@ camping@laspaules.com

1	BDEILNOPQRST	AF	6
2	CFPVWXY	ABDEFG	7
3	BL	ABFJNQRSV	8
4	BEFHIO	IJ	9
5	ACEFGHJKLMNO	ABGHIJOTUV	10

6-10A | | ❶ €29.80
A1421 1,4ha 80T(70-100m²) 31P | | ❷ €40.40

📷 From Viella N230 direction Pont de Suert. About 3 km past Vilaller turn right (service station), N260 direction Castejón de Sos. Campsite about 8 km further on the right.

💬 Very well kept family campsite.

🅿 N 42°28'17" E 0°35'57"
www.eurocampings.co.uk/111268

25 A3

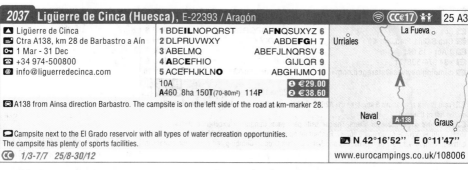

2037 Ligüerre de Cinca (Huesca), E-22393 / Aragón

🔼 Ligüerre de Cinca
🚍 Ctra A138, km 28 de Barbastro a Aín
🗓 1 Mar - 31 Dec
☎ +34 974-500800
@ info@liguerredecinca.com

1	BDEILNOPQRST	AFNQSUXYZ	6
2	DLPRUVWXY	ABDEFGH	7
3	ABELMQ	ABEFJLNQRSV	8
4	ABCEFHIO	GIJLQR	9
5	ACEFHJKLNO	ABGHIJMO	10

10A | | ❶ €29.00
A460 8ha 150T(70-80m²) 114P | | ❷ €38.60

📷 A138 from Ainsa direction Barbastro. The campsite is on the left side of the road at km-marker 28.

💬 Campsite next to the El Grado reservoir with all types of water recreation opportunities. The campsite has plenty of sports facilities.

CC 1/3-7/7 25/8-30/12

🅿 N 42°16'52" E 0°11'47"
www.eurocampings.co.uk/108006

25 A3

2038 Morillo de Tou/Ainsa, E-22395 / Aragón

🔼 Morillo de Tou
🚍 Ctra A138 Barbastro-Ainsa, km 41,8
🗓 1 Mar - 31 Dec
☎ +34 974-500793
@ info@morillodetou.com

1	BDEJMNOPQRST	AN	6
2	DOPRUVWXY	ABDEF	7
3	BELQ	ABEFNQRT	8
4	ABCDEFHIKOP	FGIJQRTU	9
5	ABDEFHJKLO	ABFGHIJPT	10

10A | | ❶ €30.00
54T(60-70m²) 121P | | ❷ €39.30

📷 Campsite on the A138 between Barbastro and Ainsa in Morillo de Tou.

💬 The campsite is located in the Morillo de Tou holiday centre, a reconstructed village in the Aragon Pyrenees and close to national parks and centres full of art, culture and history.

CC 1/3-5/7 24/8-31/12 7=6, 14=11

🅿 N 42°22'31" E 0°9'11"
www.eurocampings.co.uk/122062

25 A3

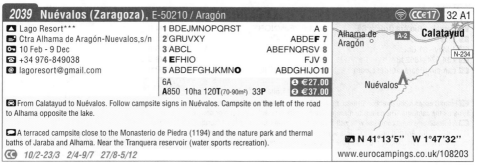

2039 Nuévalos (Zaragoza), E-50210 / Aragón

🔼 Lago Resort***
🚍 Ctra Alhama de Aragón-Nuevalos,s/n
🗓 10 Feb - 9 Dec
☎ +34 976-849038
@ lagoresort@gmail.com

1	BDEJMNOPQRST	A	6
2	GRUVXY	ABDEF	7
3	ABCL	ABEFNQRSV	8
4	EFHIO	FJV	9
5	ABDEFGHJKMNO	ABDGHIJO	10

6A | | ❶ €27.00
A850 10ha 120T(70-90m²) 33P | | ❷ €37.00

📷 From Calatayud to Nuévalos. Follow campsite signs in Nuévalos. Campsite on the left of the road to Alhama opposite the lake.

💬 A terraced campsite close to the Monasterio de Piedra (1194) and the nature park and thermal baths of Jaraba and Alhama. Near the Tranquera reservoir (water sports recreation).

CC 10/2-23/3 2/4-9/7 27/8-5/12

🅿 N 41°13'5" W 1°47'32"
www.eurocampings.co.uk/108203

32 A1

Spain

2040 Oto (Huesca), E-22370 / Aragón 24 B3

- ⛺ Oto
- 🏢 Oto-Valle de Broto-Ctra N260
- 📅 3 Mar - 15 Oct
- ☎ +34 974-486075
- @ info@campingoto.com

1 BDEJMNOPQRT	AFJ**N** 6
2 CGPVXY	ABDE**FG**H 7
3 BE	ACEFJNQRS V 8
4 **AE**FHIO	9
5 ABDEHJKLMN**O**	AFGHIJOTV 10
6A	❶ €24.50
A890 4ha 248T(70-100m²) 125P	❷ €33.70

From Biescas N260 direction Broto. Turn right 50 metres after the service station in Broto, then follow the campsite sign Oto downhill. Narrow passage and narrow bridge.

Family campsite with various options for nature lovers.

N 42°35'50'' W 0°7'52''

www.eurocampings.co.uk/110668

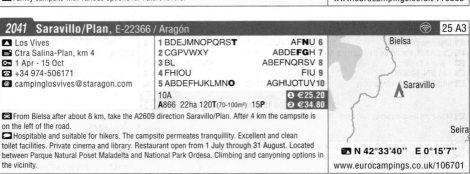

2041 Saravillo/Plan, E-22366 / Aragón 25 A3

- ⛺ Los Vives
- 🏢 Ctra Salina-Plan, km 4
- 📅 1 Apr - 15 Oct
- ☎ +34 974-506171
- @ campinglosvives@staragon.com

1 BDEJMNOPQRS**T**	AFN**U** 6
2 CGPVWXY	ABDE**FG**H 7
3 BL	ABEFNQRS V 8
4 FHIOU	FI**U** 9
5 ABDEFHJKLMN**O**	AGHIJOTUV 10
10A	❶ €25.20
A866 22ha 120T(70-100m²) 15P	❷ €34.80

From Bielsa after about 8 km, take the A2609 direction Saravillo/Plan. After 4 km the campsite is on the left of the road.

Hospitable and suitable for hikers. The campsite permeates tranquillity. Excellent and clean toilet facilities. Private cinema and library. Restaurant open from 1 July through 31 August. Located between Parque Natural Poset Maladeta and National Park Ordesa. Climbing and canyoning options in the vicinity.

N 42°33'40'' E 0°15'7''

www.eurocampings.co.uk/106701

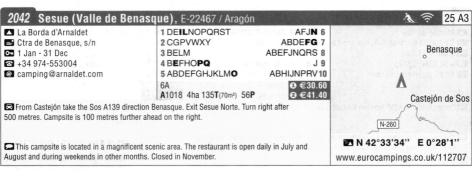

2042 Sesue (Valle de Benasque), E-22467 / Aragón 25 A3

- ⛺ La Borda d'Arnaldet
- 🏢 Ctra de Benasque, s/n
- 📅 1 Jan - 31 Dec
- ☎ +34 974-553004
- @ camping@arnaldet.com

1 DE**IL**NOPQRST	AFJ**N** 6
2 CGPVWXY	ABDE**FG** 7
3 BELM	ABEFJNQRS 8
4 **B**EFHO**PQ**	J 9
5 ABDEFGHJKLM**O**	ABHIJNPRV 10
6A	❶ €30.60
A1018 4ha 135T(70m²) 56P	❷ €41.40

From Castejón take the Sos A139 direction Benasque. Exit Sesue Norte. Turn right after 500 metres. Campsite is 100 metres further ahead on the right.

This campsite is located in a magnificent scenic area. The restaurant is open daily in July and August and during weekends in other months. Closed in November.

N 42°33'34'' E 0°28'1''

www.eurocampings.co.uk/112707

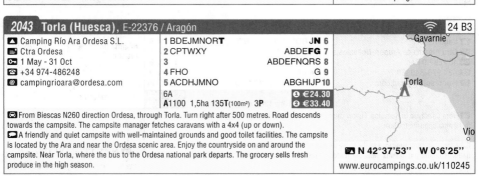

2043 Torla (Huesca), E-22376 / Aragón 24 B3

- ⛺ Camping Río Ara Ordesa S.L.
- 🏢 Ctra Ordesa
- 📅 1 May - 31 Oct
- ☎ +34 974-486248
- @ campingrioara@ordesa.com

1 BDEJMNOR**T**	**JN** 6
2 CPTWXY	ABDE**FG** 7
3	ABDEFNQRS 8
4 FHO	G 9
5 ACDHJMNO	ABGHIJP 10
6A	❶ €24.30
A1100 1,5ha 135T(100m²) 3P	❷ €33.40

From Biescas N260 direction Ordesa, through Torla. Turn right after 500 metres. Road descends towards the campsite. The campsite manager fetches caravans with a 4x4 (up or down).

A friendly and quiet campsite with well-maintained grounds and good toilet facilities. The campsite is located by the Ara and near the Ordesa scenic area. Enjoy the countryside on and around the campsite. Near Torla, where the bus to the Ordesa national park departs. The grocery sells fresh produce in the high season.

N 42°37'53'' W 0°6'25''

www.eurocampings.co.uk/110245

Spain

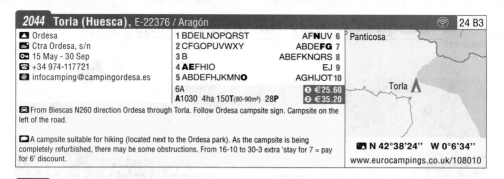

2044 Torla (Huesca), E-22376 / Aragón — 24 B3

- Ordesa
- Ctra Ordesa, s/n
- 15 May - 30 Sep
- +34 974-117721
- infocamping@campingordesa.es

1 BDEILNOPQRST	AFNUV 6
2 CFGOPUVWXY	ABDEFG 7
3 B	ABEFKNQRS 8
4 AEFHIO	EJ 9
5 ABDEFHJKMNO	AGHIJOT 10
6A	❶ €25.60
A1030 4ha 150T(80-90m²) 28P	❷ €35.20

From Biescas N260 direction Ordesa through Torla. Follow Ordesa campsite sign. Campsite on the left of the road.

A campsite suitable for hiking (located next to the Ordesa park). As the campsite is being completely refurbished, there may be some obstructions. From 16-10 to 30-3 extra 'stay for 7 = pay for 6' discount.

◪ N 42°38'24'' W 0°6'34''

www.eurocampings.co.uk/108010

Panticosa / Torla

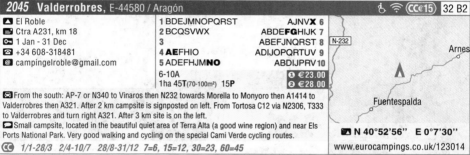

2045 Valderrobres, E-44580 / Aragón — 32 B2

- El Roble
- Ctra A231, km 18
- 1 Jan - 31 Dec
- +34 608-318481
- campingelroble@gmail.com

1 BDEJMNOPQRST	AJNVX 6
2 BCQSVWX	ABDEFGHIJK 7
3	ABEFJNQRST 8
4 AEFHIO	ADIJOPQRTUV 9
5 ADEFHJMNO	ABDIJPRV 10
6-10A	❶ €23.00
1ha 45T(70-100m²) 15P	❷ €28.00

From the south: AP-7 or N340 to Vinaros then N232 towards Morella to Monyoro then A1414 to Valderrobres then A321. After 2 km campsite is signposted on left. From Tortosa C12 via N2306, T333 to Valderrobres and turn right A321. After 3 km site is on the left.

Small campsite, located in the beautiful quiet area of Terra Alta (a good wine region) and near Els Ports National Park. Very good walking and cycling on the special Cami Verde cycling routes.

ℂℂ 1/1-28/3 2/4-10/7 28/8-31/12 7=6, 15=12, 30=23, 60=45

◪ N 40°52'56'' E 0°7'30''

www.eurocampings.co.uk/123014

N-232 / Arnes / Fuentespalda

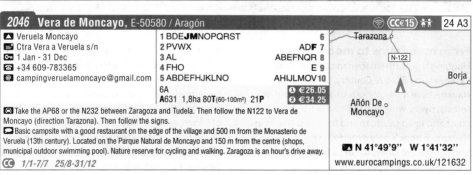

2046 Vera de Moncayo, E-50580 / Aragón — 24 A3

- Veruela Moncayo
- Ctra Vera a Veruela s/n
- 1 Jan - 31 Dec
- +34 609-783365
- campingveruelamoncayo@gmail.com

1 BDEJMNOPQRST	6
2 PVWX	ADF 7
3 AL	ABEFNQR 8
4 FHO	E 9
5 ABDEFHJKLNO	AHIJLMOV 10
6A	❶ €26.05
A631 1,8ha 80T(60-100m²) 21P	❷ €34.25

Take the AP68 or the N232 between Zaragoza and Tudela. Then follow the N122 to Vera de Moncayo (direction Tarazona). Then follow the signs.

Basic campsite with a good restaurant on the edge of the village and 500 m from the Monasterio de Veruela (13th century). Located on the Parque Natural de Moncayo and 150 m from the centre (shops, municipal outdoor swimming pool). Nature reserve for cycling and walking. Zaragoza is an hour's drive away.

ℂℂ 1/1-7/7 25/8-31/12

◪ N 41°49'9'' W 1°41'32''

www.eurocampings.co.uk/121632

Tarazona / N-122 / Borja / Añón De Moncayo

From mountains to moonscape

Hugging the northern Iberian coast and the Pyrenees, the Basque Country, La Rioja and Navarre have it all: glorious beaches, mountains, forests, rivers, wine, art and … desert. Leave the coast and head south, to arid Bardenas Reales in Navarre, Europe's only desert. Or stay in the north and admire the vineyards of La Rioja, or explore the mountainy villages of the Basque country. Did you know you can take the ferry from Portsmouth to Bilbao?

Highlights and historic cities

You'll have heard of Pamplona, in Navarra, where the infamous bull-running takes place. Take a more sedate approach and explore the 16th century fortifications, the Gothic Santa Maria le Real Cathedral and the collections of the Museo de Navarra. Logrono in La Rioja also has

a Gothic Cathedral: the Cathedral of Santa Maria la Redonda, surrounded by labyrinthine streets. Check out some of the pintxo bars. Locals relax, cycle, walk, fish, picnic or sunbathe in Parc del Ebro, and there's a nice view over Logrono. Think of Bilbao, and the silver Guggenheim Museum immediately comes to mind. Check out Euskal Museum for Basque history, and climb up Begona Basilica that overlooks the old town. Bilbao has undergone renewal in recent decades, but you'll find there's still a lot going on in the old part.

Incredible nature

Cyclists, hikers, swimmers and outdoor enthusiasts generally are spoiled for choice here. Walk through the Urdaibai conservation area, or follow the Ieza Gorge or the Roman Road along the Iregua valley. Walkers are in their element in the Sierra de Cebollera Nature Park with forests

comes straight from the barrel before it is being
bottled, this is called Txotx. Food is delicious
everywhere, but local foodies head for marina
area in Hondarribia.

and waterfalls. Wander the special routes at the
lakes at Leurtza, or venture underground into the
caves at Zugarramurdi, Mendukilo or Urdax.

¡Buen provecho!

Naturally there is Rioja wine, but have you ever
heard of Txakoli wine? It's delicious with pintxo,
the snacks served in bars, but for a more filling
meal, try Marmitako, a stew with tuna. Check
out the Basque region's Sagardotegi: this type of
restaurant has a set menu, and cider. The cider

Our tips

1. *Visit San Sebastian and go to the beach or make a boat trip on the river*
2. *Cross the man-made bridge to the isle of San Juan de Gaztelugatxe*
3. *Take in a game of Zesta Punta or Jai Alai, similar to racquetball*
4. *Check out the Logrono Harvest Festival, with wine, music, fireworks and food*
5. *Explore the dungeons and towers of the mediaeval Javier Castle*

2047 Acedo, E-31282 / Navarra — 24 A2

- ▲ Acedo Cat.1 ****
- ✉ Ctra Los Arcos s/n
- 🔓 10 Jan - 17 Dec
- ☎ +34 948-521351
- @ info@campingacedo.com

1 ABDJMNOPQRS**T**	AF 6
2 ABFGOPRVWXY	ABDE**FGH**IJ 7
3 BEL	ABCDEFKNQRSV 8
4 BDEFHIO**PU**	FJU 9
5 ACDEFHJKLMN**O**	BGHIJ**N**PVZ10

15A
A500 8,5ha 250T(70-90m²) 69P

❶ €27.00
❷ €37.40

🔲 N111 Pamplona-Logroño. Follow direction Acedo in Los Arcos. Campsite signposted here.

💬 Charming family campsite with an excellent restaurant. Nicely located near the route to Santiago and Urbasa nature park.

📍 N 42°39'40'' W 2°15'3''
www.eurocampings.co.uk/112075

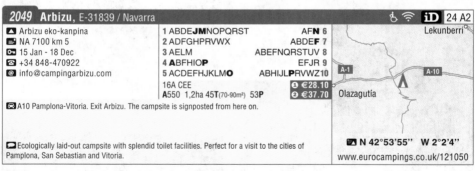

2048 Alsasua, E-31809 / Navarra — 24 A2

- ▲ Urbasa
- ✉ Ctra Estella-Olazagutia, km 30
- 🔓 15 Mar - 1 Dec
- ☎ +34 948-395223
- @ info@campingurbasa.com

1 ADE**JM**NOPQRST	6
2 ABGNPTWXY	ABDE 7
3 A**G**	ABEFJNQRV 8
4 **E**FGHIKO**PQ**	FGJU 9
5 ABDEFHJKL**NO**	ABGHIJMORVW10

6-10A
A900 8,8ha 300T(70-100m²) 27P

❶ €32.85
❷ €43.35

🔲 AP10 Pamplona-Vitoria. In Alsasua direction Urbasa. The campsite is 8 km further up the mountain.

💬 A quiet campsite in a stunning nature park. Perfect operating base for walks and cycle rides. A spacious campsite with no marked out pitches.

📍 N 42°51'6'' W 2°10'23''
www.eurocampings.co.uk/111885

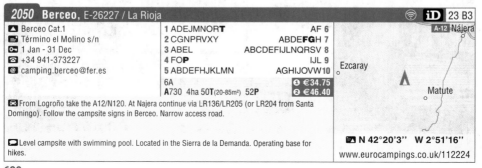

2049 Arbizu, E-31839 / Navarra — 24 A2

- ▲ Arbizu eko-kanpina
- ✉ NA 7100 km 5
- 🔓 15 Jan - 18 Dec
- ☎ +34 848-470922
- @ info@campingarbizu.com

1 ABDE**JM**NOPQRST	AF**N** 6
2 ADFGHPRVWX	ABDE**F** 7
3 AELM	ABEFNQRSTUV 8
4 **A**BFHIO**P**	EFJR 9
5 ACDEFHJKLM**O**	ABHIJL**P**RVWZ10

16A CEE
A550 1,2ha 45T(70-90m²) 53P

❶ €28.10
❷ €37.70

🔲 A10 Pamplona-Vitoria. Exit Arbizu. The campsite is signposted from here on.

💬 Ecologically laid-out campsite with splendid toilet facilities. Perfect for a visit to the cities of Pamplona, San Sebastian and Vitoria.

📍 N 42°53'55'' W 2°2'4''
www.eurocampings.co.uk/121050

2050 Berceo, E-26227 / La Rioja — 23 B3

- ▲ Berceo Cat.1
- ✉ Término el Molino s/n
- 🔓 1 Jan - 31 Dec
- ☎ +34 941-373227
- @ camping.berceo@fer.es

1 ADEJMNOR**T**	AF 6
2 CGNPRVXY	ABDE**FG**H 7
3 ABEL	ABCDEFIJLNQRSV 8
4 FO**P**	IJL 9
5 ABDEFHJKLMN	AGHIJOVW10

6A
A730 4ha 50T(20-85m²) 52P

❶ €34.75
❷ €46.40

🔲 From Logroño take the A12/N120. At Najera continue via LR136/LR205 (or LR204 from Santa Domingo). Follow the campsite signs in Berceo. Narrow access road.

💬 Level campsite with swimming pool. Located in the Sierra de la Demanda. Operating base for hikes.

📍 N 42°20'3'' W 2°51'16''
www.eurocampings.co.uk/112224

Spain

2051 Castañares de Rioja, E-26240 / La Rioja ♿ 📶 iD 23 B2

- 🏔 De la Rioja Cat.1a
- 📧 Ctra Haro-Sto. Domingo km 8,5
- 📅 20 Jan - 12 Dec
- ☎ +34 941-300174
- @ info@campingdelarioja.es

1 ABDEJMNOPRS**T**	AF **6**
2 ACGPVWXY	ABDE**FG**H **7**
3 ABELM	ABCEFJNQRSTUV **8**
4 FHIMO**PQ**	JL **9**
5 ABDFHJKM**NO**	ABGHIK**N**P **10**

4-6A   ❶ €37.55
A600 4ha 100**T**(60-90m²) 406**P**   ❷ €51.20

🚻 From Logroño take the N232 or AP18. Exit Haro. Direction San Domingo, the campsite is on the LR111 before Castañares.

💬 A campsite with many permanent pitches in the Rioja wine area. With a swimming pool.

📷 N 42°31'49''   W 2°55'18''

www.eurocampings.co.uk/109905

2052 Erratzu, E-31714 / Navarra ♿ 📶 iD 24 A2

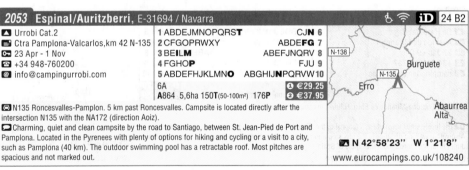

- 🏔 Baztan Camping Cat. 1
- 📧 Ctra Francia s/n
- 📅 15 Mar - 1 Nov
- ☎ +34 948-453133
- @ campingbaztan@campingbaztan.com

1 AD**JM**NOPQRST	AF**JN 6**
2 BCGPRVY	ABDE**FG 7**
3 BL**MOQ**	ABEFNQRSTV **8**
4 BFHIO**P**	IJK **9**
5 ACDEFHJKMN**O**	ABGHIJPRW **10**

10A   ❶ €35.90
A270 4ha 145**T**(100m²) 48**P**   ❷ €43.10

🚻 N121 from Hendaye direction Pamplona, in Mugaire direction Erratzu. Follow the 'Francia' signs in the centre. The campsite is located about 100 metres outside the village on the right.

💬 A quiet campsite with marked out pitches and surrounded by hedges. With a nice swimming pool and restaurant. Options for mountain hikes in the vicinity.

📷 N 43°10'51''   W 1°27'5''

www.eurocampings.co.uk/112498

2053 Espinal/Auritzberri, E-31694 / Navarra ♿ 📶 iD 24 B2

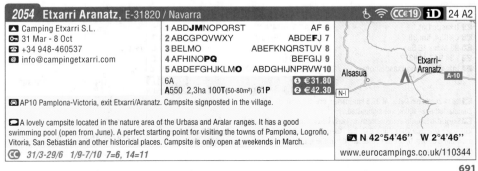

- 🏔 Urrobi Cat.2
- 📧 Ctra Pamplona-Valcarlos,km 42 N-135
- 📅 23 Apr - 1 Nov
- ☎ +34 948-760200
- @ info@campingurrobi.com

1 ABDEJMNOPQRS**T**	C**JN 6**
2 CFGOPRWXY	ABDE**FG 7**
3 BE**ILM**	ABEFJNQRV **8**
4 FGHO**P**	FJU **9**
5 ABDEFHJKLMN**O**	ABGHIJ**N**PQRVW **10**

6A   ❶ €29.25
A864 5,6ha 150**T**(50-100m²) 176**P**   ❷ €37.95

🚻 N135 Roncesvalles-Pamplon. 5 km past Roncesvalles. Campsite is located directly after the intersection N135 with the NA172 (direction Aoiz).

💬 Charming, quiet and clean campsite by the road to Santiago, between St. Jean-Pied de Port and Pamplona. Located in the Pyrenees with plenty of options for hiking and cycling or a visit to a city, such as Pamplona (40 km). The outdoor swimming pool has a retractable roof. Most pitches are spacious and not marked out.

📷 N 42°58'23''   W 1°21'8''

www.eurocampings.co.uk/108240

2054 Etxarri Aranatz, E-31820 / Navarra ♿ 📶 Ⓒ€19 iD 24 A2

- 🏔 Camping Etxarri S.L.
- 📅 31 Mar - 8 Oct
- ☎ +34 948-460537
- @ info@campingetxarri.com

1 ABD**JM**NOPQRST	AF **6**
2 ABCGPQVWXY	ABDE**F**J **7**
3 BELMO	ABEFKNQRSTUV **8**
4 AFHINO**PQ**	BEFGIJ **9**
5 ABDEFGHJKLM**O**	ABDGHIJNPRVW **10**

6A   ❶ €31.80
A550 2,3ha 100**T**(50-80m²) 61**P**   ❷ €42.30

🚻 AP10 Pamplona-Victoria, exit Etxarri/Aranatz. Campsite signposted in the village.

💬 A lovely campsite located in the nature area of the Urbasa and Aralar ranges. It has a good swimming pool (open from June). A perfect starting point for visiting the towns of Pamplona, Logroño, Vitoria, San Sebastián and other historical places. Campsite is only open at weekends in March.

ⒸⒸ 31/3-29/6   1/9-7/10 7=6, 14=11

📷 N 42°54'46''   W 2°4'46''

www.eurocampings.co.uk/110344

Spain

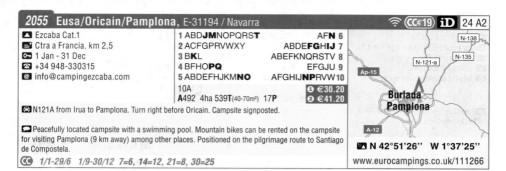

2055 Eusa/Oricain/Pamplona, E-31194 / Navarra — (Ce19) iD 24 A2

- ▲ Ezcaba Cat.1
- ◻ Ctra a Francia, km 2,5
- ◷ 1 Jan - 31 Dec
- ☎ +34 948-330315
- @ info@campingezcaba.com

1 ABDJMNOPQRST	AFN 6
2 ACFGPRVWXY	ABDEFGHIJ 7
3 BKL	ABEFKNQRSTV 8
4 BFHOPQ	EFGJU 9
5 ABDEFHJKMNO	AFGHIJNPRVW 10

10A
A492 4ha 539T(40-70m²) 17P

❶ €30.20
❷ €41.20

N121A from Irua to Pamplona. Turn right before Oricain. Campsite signposted.

Peacefully located campsite with a swimming pool. Mountain bikes can be rented on the campsite for visiting Pamplona (9 km away) among other places. Positioned on the pilgrimage route to Santiago de Compostela.

CC 1/1-29/6 1/9-30/12 7=6, 14=12, 21=8, 30=25

N 42°51'26'' W 1°37'25''

www.eurocampings.co.uk/111266

2056 Gorliz, E-48630 / Pais Vasco — iD 23 B2

- ▲ Arrien
- ◻ Uresaranse Bidea s/n
- ◷ 1 Mar - 31 Oct
- ☎ +34 946-771911
- @ recepcion@campinggorliz.com

1 ABDEJMNORT	KMNOPQSWXYZ 6
2 EGOPRUWXY	ABDEFGH 7
3 AK	ABCDEFKNRSTV 8
4 FHO	J 9
5 ACDEFHJKLMNO	AFGHIJLNOQRVW 10

6A
A50 2ha 150T(40-160m²) 60P

❶ €37.55
❷ €48.10

Coming from Bilbao direction Getxo/Plencia/Gorliz. The campsite is signposted in Gorliz. Campsite is next to the football field.

Basic campsite, perfectly located for a visit to Bilbao. with a metro station at 2 km and a quiet beach at 500 metres.

N 43°25'6'' W 2°56'15''

www.eurocampings.co.uk/113512

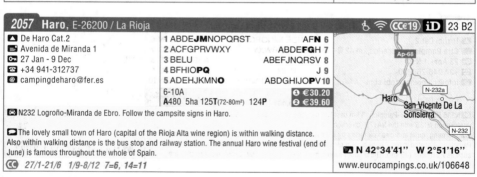

2057 Haro, E-26200 / La Rioja — (Ce19) iD 23 B2

- ▲ De Haro Cat.2
- ◻ Avenida de Miranda 1
- ◷ 27 Jan - 9 Dec
- ☎ +34 941-312737
- @ campingdeharo@fer.es

1 ABDEJMNOPQRST	AFN 6
2 ACFGPRVWXY	ABDEFGH 7
3 BELU	ABEFJNQRSV 8
4 BFHIOPQ	J 9
5 ADEHJKMNO	ABDGHIJOPV 10

6-10A
A480 5ha 125T(72-80m²) 124P

❶ €30.20
❷ €39.60

N232 Logroño-Miranda de Ebro. Follow the campsite signs in Haro.

The lovely small town of Haro (capital of the Rioja Alta wine region) is within walking distance. Also within walking distance is the bus stop and railway station. The annual Haro wine festival (end of June) is famous throughout the whole of Spain.

CC 27/1-21/6 1/9-8/12 7=6, 14=11

N 42°34'41'' W 2°51'16''

www.eurocampings.co.uk/106648

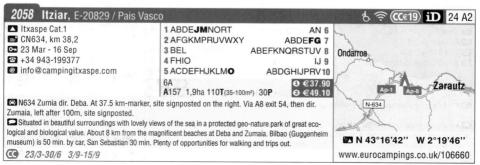

2058 Itziar, E-20829 / Pais Vasco — (Ce19) iD 24 A2

- ▲ Itxaspe Cat.1
- ◻ CN634, km 38,2
- ◷ 23 Mar - 16 Sep
- ☎ +34 943-199377
- @ info@campingitxaspe.com

1 ABDEJMNORT	AN 6
2 AFGKMPRUVWXY	ABDEFG 7
3 BEL	ABEFKNQRSTUV 8
4 FHIO	IJ 9
5 ACDEFHJKLMO	ABDGHIJPRV 10

6A
A157 1,9ha 110T(35-100m²) 30P

❶ €37.90
❷ €49.10

N634 Zumia dir. Deba. At 37.5 km-marker, site signposted on the right. Via A8 exit 54, then dir. Zumaia, left after 100m, site signposted.

Situated in beautiful surroundings with lovely views of the sea in a protected geo-nature park of great ecological and biological value. About 8 km from the magnificent beaches at Deba and Zumaia. Bilbao (Guggenheim museum) is 50 min. by car, San Sebastian 30 min. Plenty of opportunities for walking and trips out.

CC 23/3-30/6 3/9-15/9

N 43°16'42'' W 2°19'46''

www.eurocampings.co.uk/106660

Spain

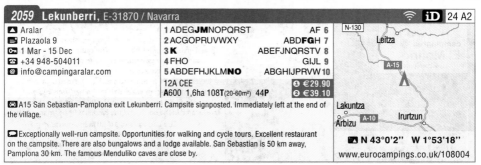

2059 Lekunberri, E-31870 / Navarra ⏚ iD 24 A2

- 🏔 Aralar
- 🏠 Plazaola 9
- 📅 1 Mar - 15 Dec
- ☎ +34 948-504011
- @ info@campingaralar.com

1 ADEGJMNOPQRST	AF	6
2 ACGOPRUVWXY	ABDFGH	7
3 K	ABEFJNQRSTV	8
4 FHO	GIJL	9
5 ABDEFHJKLMNO	ABGHIJPRVW	10
12A CEE	❶ €29.90	
A600 1,6ha 108T(20-60m²) 44P	❷ €39.10	

🚗 A15 San Sebastian-Pamplona exit Lekunberri. Campsite signposted. Immediately left at the end of the village.

💬 Exceptionally well-run campsite. Opportunities for walking and cycle tours. Excellent restaurant on the campsite. There are also bungalows and a lodge available. San Sebastian is 50 km away, Pamplona 30 km. The famous Menduliko caves are close by.

📷 N 43°0'2'' W 1°53'18''

www.eurocampings.co.uk/108004

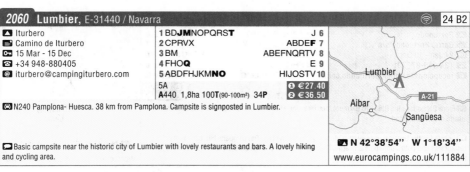

2060 Lumbier, E-31440 / Navarra 🛜 24 B2

- 🏔 Iturbero
- 🏠 Camino de Iturbero
- 📅 15 Mar - 15 Dec
- ☎ +34 948-880405
- @ iturbero@campingiturbero.com

1 BDJMNOPQRST	J	6
2 CPRVX	ABDEF	7
3 BM	ABEFNQRTV	8
4 FHOQ	E	9
5 ABDFHJKMNO	HIJOSTV	10
5A	❶ €27.40	
A440 1,8ha 100T(90-100m²) 34P	❷ €36.50	

🚗 N240 Pamplona- Huesca. 38 km from Pamplona. Campsite is signposted in Lumbier.

💬 Basic campsite near the historic city of Lumbier with lovely restaurants and bars. A lovely hiking and cycling area.

📷 N 42°38'54'' W 1°18'34''

www.eurocampings.co.uk/111884

2061 Mendexa, E-48289 / Pais Vasco ♿ 🛜 24 A2

- 🏔 Leagi
- 🏠 Calle/Barrio Leagi, 4
- 📅 1 Mar - 1 Nov
- ☎ +34 946-842352
- @ leagi@campingleagi.com

1 BDEJMNORT	AF	6
2 FGNPVWXY	ABDEFG	7
3 BDELU	ABEFNQSV	8
4 BCDFHOPQ	J	9
5 ABDFHJKLO	ABGHIJORVW	10
5A	❶ €36.10	
A175 5ha 280T(30-60m²) 43P	❷ €49.10	

🚗 A8 San Sebastian-Bilbao, exit Gernika. After Gernika BI2238 to Lekeitio. Then direction Mendexa, the campsite is signposted from here on.

💬 Well-maintained campsite with a lovely view of the sea. With a fine restaurant and water playground for the children.

📷 N 43°21'8'' W 2°29'38''

www.eurocampings.co.uk/113192

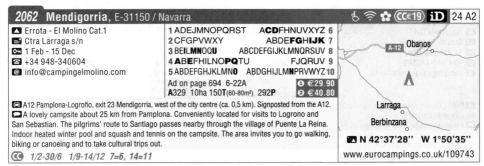

2062 Mendigorria, E-31150 / Navarra ♿ 🛜 ✿ CC€19 iD 24 A2

- 🏔 Errota - El Molino Cat.1
- 🏠 Ctra Larraga s/n
- 📅 1 Feb - 15 Dec
- ☎ +34 948-340604
- @ info@campingelmolino.com

1 ADEJMNOPQRST	ACDFHNUVXYZ	6
2 CFGPVWXY	ABDEFGHIJK	7
3 BEILMNOQU	ABCDEFGIJKLMNQRSUV	8
4 ABEFHILNOPQTU	FJQRUV	9
5 ABDEFGHJKLMNO	ABDGHIJLMNPRVWYZ	10
Ad on page 694 6-22A	❶ €29.90	
A329 10ha 150T(60-80m²) 292P	❷ €40.80	

🚗 A12 Pamplona-Logroño, exit 23 Mendigorria, west of the city centre (ca. 0,5 km). Signposted from the A12.

💬 A lovely campsite about 25 km from Pamplona. Conveniently located for visits to Logrono and San Sebastian. The pilgrims' route to Santiago passes nearby through the village of Puente La Reina. Indoor heated winter pool and squash and tennis on the campsite. The area invites you to go walking, biking or canoeing and to take cultural trips out.

CC 1/2-30/6 1/9-14/12 7=6, 14=11

📷 N 42°37'28'' W 1°50'35''

www.eurocampings.co.uk/109743

Spain

Errota - El Molino Cat.1

The environs are perfect for sports, such as canoeing, mountain biking or hiking tours. **The campsite has an indoor heated winter swimming pool** and options for tennis, squash, horseback riding, etc. There are various cultural highlights and events nearby, such as the road of St. Jacob, the castle route, mediaeval route, Roman ruins, regional festivals, a visit to a winery, etc. The Pyrenees and Irati forest are located in the north, and the Bardenas Reales in the south.

Ctra Larraga s/n, 31150 Mendigorria
Tel. 948-340604 • Fax 948-340082
E-mail: info@campingelmolino.com
Internet: www.campingelmolino.com

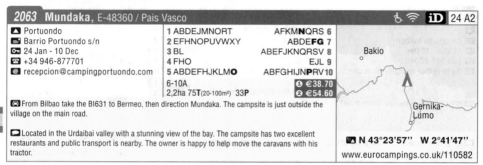

2063 Mundaka, E-48360 / Pais Vasco   24 A2

- 🏕 Portuondo
- ✉ Barrio Portuondo s/n
- 🗓 24 Jan - 10 Dec
- ☎ +34 946-877701
- @ recepcion@campingportuondo.com

1 ABDEJMNORT	AFKM**N**QRS 6
2 EFHNOPUVWXY	ABDE**FG** 7
3 BL	ABEFJKNQRSV 8
4 FHO	EJL 9
5 ABDEFHJKLM**O**	ABFGHIJN**P**RV 10
6-10A	❶ €38.70
2,2ha 75**T**(20-100m²) 33**P**	❷ €54.60

🚗 From Bilbao take the BI631 to Bermeo, then direction Mundaka. The campsite is just outside the village on the main road.

💬 Located in the Urdaibai valley with a stunning view of the bay. The campsite has two excellent restaurants and public transport is nearby. The owner is happy to help move the caravans with his tractor.

Bakio

Gernika-Lumo

📍 **N 43°23'57" W 2°41'47"**

www.eurocampings.co.uk/110582

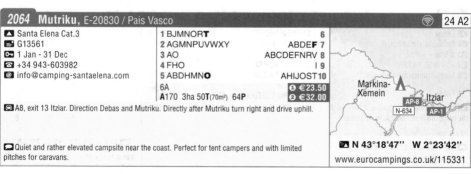

2064 Mutriku, E-20830 / Pais Vasco   24 A2

- 🏕 Santa Elena Cat.3
- 🗺 G13561
- 🗓 1 Jan - 31 Dec
- ☎ +34 943-603982
- @ info@camping-santaelena.com

1 BJMNOR**T**	6
2 AGMNPUVWXY	ABDE**F** 7
3 AO	ABCDEFNRV 8
4 FHO	I 9
5 ABDHMN**O**	AHIJOST 10
6A	❶ €23.50
A170 3ha 50**T**(70m²) 64**P**	❷ €32.00

🚗 A8, exit 13 Itziar. Direction Debas and Mutriku. Directly after Mutriku turn right and drive uphill.

💬 Quiet and rather elevated campsite near the coast. Perfect for tent campers and with limited pitches for caravans.

Markina-Xemein

Itziar
AP-8
N-634   AP-1

📍 **N 43°18'47" W 2°23'42"**

www.eurocampings.co.uk/115331

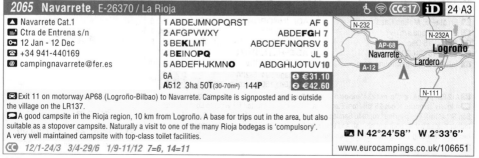

2065 Navarrete, E-26370 / La Rioja   24 A3

- 🏕 Navarrete Cat.1
- ✉ Ctra de Entrena s/n
- 🗓 12 Jan - 12 Dec
- ☎ +34 941-440169
- @ campingnavarrete@fer.es

1 ABDEJMNOPQRST	AF 6
2 AFGPVWXY	ABDE**FG**H 7
3 BE**K**LMT	ABCDEFJNQRSV 8
4 B**E**INO**PQ**	JL 9
5 ABDEFHJKMN**O**	ABDGHIJOTUV 10
6A	❶ €31.10
A512 3ha 50**T**(30-70m²) 144**P**	❷ €42.60

🚗 Exit 11 on motorway AP68 (Logroño-Bilbao) to Navarrete. Campsite is signposted and is outside the village on the LR137.

💬 A good campsite in the Rioja region, 10 km from Logroño. A base for trips out in the area, but also suitable as a stopover campsite. Naturally a visit to one of the many Rioja bodegas is 'compulsory'. A very well maintained campsite with top-class toilet facilities.

🆑 12/1-24/3   3/4-29/6   1/9-11/12   7=6, 14=11

N-232   N-232A
AP-68   **Logroño**
Navarrete   Lardero
A-12
N-111

📍 **N 42°24'58" W 2°33'6"**

www.eurocampings.co.uk/106651

Spain

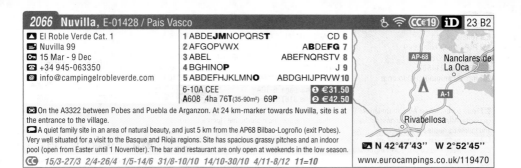

2066 Nuvilla, E-01428 / Pais Vasco   ♿ 🛜 (CC€19) iD 23 B2

- ▲ El Roble Verde Cat. 1
- 🏕 Nuvilla 99
- 📅 15 Mar - 9 Dec
- ☎ +34 945-063350
- @ info@campingelrobleverde.com

1 ABDE**JM**NOPQRST	CD	6
2 AFGOPVWX	AB**D**E**FG**	7
3 ABEL	ABEFNQRSTV	8
4 BGHINO**P**	J	9
5 ABDEFHJKLMN**O**	ABDGHIJPRVW	10
6-10A CEE	❶ €31.50	
A608 4ha 76T(35-90m²) 69**P**	❷ €42.50	

🚗 On the A3322 between Pobes and Puebla de Arganzon. At 24 km-marker towards Nuvilla, site is at the entrance to the village.

💬 A quiet family site in an area of natural beauty, and just 5 km from the AP68 Bilbao-Logroño (exit Pobes). Very well situated for a visit to the Basque and Rioja regions. Site has spacious grassy pitches and an indoor pool (open from Easter until 1 November). The bar and restaurant are only open at weekends in the low season.

CC 15/3-27/3 2/4-26/4 1/5-14/6 31/8-10/10 14/10-30/10 4/11-8/12 11=10

N 42°47'43'' W 2°52'45''

www.eurocampings.co.uk/119470

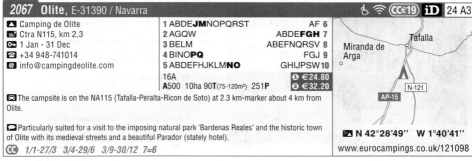

2067 Olite, E-31390 / Navarra   ♿ 🛜 (CC€19) iD 24 A3

- ▲ Camping de Olite
- 🏕 Ctra N115, km 2,3
- 📅 1 Jan - 31 Dec
- ☎ +34 948-741014
- @ info@campingdeolite.com

1 ABDE**JM**NOPQRST	AF	6
2 AGQW	ABDE**FGH**	7
3 BELM	ABEFNQRSV	8
4 BINO**PQ**	FGJ	9
5 ABDEFHJKLM**NO**	GHIJPSW	10
16A	❶ €24.80	
A500 10ha 90T(75-120m²) 251**P**	❷ €32.20	

🚗 The campsite is on the NA115 (Tafalla-Peralta-Ricon de Soto) at 2.3 km-marker about 4 km from Olite.

💬 Particularly suited for a visit to the imposing natural park 'Bardenas Reales' and the historic town of Olite with its medieval streets and a beautiful Parador (stately hotel).

CC 1/1-27/3 3/4-29/6 3/9-30/12 7=6

N 42°28'49'' W 1°40'41''

www.eurocampings.co.uk/121098

Spain

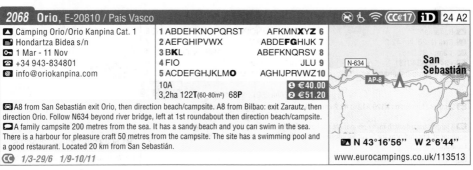

2068 Orio, E-20810 / Pais Vasco   ⊗ ♿ 🛜 (CC€17) iD 24 A2

- ▲ Camping Orio/Orio Kanpina Cat. 1
- 🏕 Hondartza Bidea s/n
- 📅 1 Mar - 11 Nov
- ☎ +34 943-834801
- @ info@oriokanpina.com

1 ABDEHKNOPQRST	AFKMN**XYZ**	6
2 AEFGHIPVWX	ABDE**FG**HIJK	7
3 B**KL**	ABEFKNQRSV	8
4 FIO	JLU	9
5 ACDEFGHJKLM**O**	AGHIJPRVWZ	10
10A	❶ €40.00	
3,2ha 122T(60-80m²) 68**P**	❷ €51.20	

🚗 A8 from San Sebastián exit Orio, then direction beach/campsite. A8 from Bilbao: exit Zarautz, then direction Orio. Follow N634 beyond river bridge, left at 1st roundabout then direction beach/campsite.
💬 A family campsite 200 metres from the sea. It has a sandy beach and you can swim in the sea. There is a harbour for pleasure craft 50 metres from the campsite. The site has a swimming pool and a good restaurant. Located 20 km from San Sebastián.

CC 1/3-29/6 1/9-10/11

N 43°16'56'' W 2°6'44''

www.eurocampings.co.uk/113513

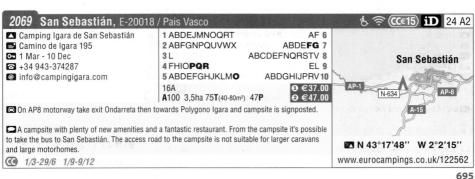

2069 San Sebastián, E-20018 / Pais Vasco   ♿ 🛜 (CC€15) iD 24 A2

- ▲ Camping Igara de San Sebastián
- 🏕 Camino de Igara 195
- 📅 1 Mar - 10 Dec
- ☎ +34 943-374287
- @ info@campingigara.com

1 ABDEJMNOQRT	AF	6
2 ABFGNPQUVWX	ABDE**FG**	7
3 L	ABCDEFNQRSTV	8
4 FHIO**PQR**	EL	9
5 ABDEFGHJKLM**O**	ABDGHIJPRV	10
16A	❶ €37.00	
A100 3,5ha 75T(40-80m²) 47**P**	❷ €47.00	

🚗 On AP8 motorway take exit Ondarreta then towards Polygono Igara and campsite is signposted.

💬 A campsite with plenty of new amenities and a fantastic restaurant. From the campsite it's possible to take the bus to San Sebastián. The access road to the campsite is not suitable for larger caravans and large motorhomes.

CC 1/3-29/6 1/9-9/12

N 43°17'48'' W 2°2'15''

www.eurocampings.co.uk/122562

2070 San Sebastián, E-20008 / Pais Vasco
♿ 🛜 (CC€19) iD 24 A2

- 🏕 Igueldo Cat.1
- 🏠 P. Padre Orkolaga 69
- 🗓 1 Jan - 31 Dec
- ☎ +34 943-214502
- @ info@campingigueldo.com

1	ABDE**J**MNOPQRS**T**	AF 6
2	AFGOPRUVWXY	ABDE**FG** 7
3	B**KL**	ABCDEFKNQRSTUV 8
4	FHO**P**	EJL 9
5	ABDEFHJKLM**NO**	ABDFGHIJ**N**PRVZ 10

Ad on this page 6-10A ❶ €40.80
A200 5ha 316T(20-70m²) 35P ❷ €50.40

San Sebastián

🚗 From border follow A8. Exit Ondarreta, dir. San Sebastián centre. On coast follow Monte Igueldo to campsite. Attention: SatNav chooses route unsuitable for caravans and motorhomes. Ignore this route and follow campsite signs.

💬 Large, well maintained campsite, excellent toilet facilities. Bus to San Sebastián stops in front of the campsite. Site has a welcoming bar and restaurant. Beautiful view of the surroundings and a new swimming pool in 2016.

(CC) 1/1-29/6 1/9-30/12 7=6

📍 N 43°18'48'' W 2°1'45''

www.eurocampings.co.uk/106658

2071 Santo Domingo de la Calzada, E-26257 / La Rioja
⛷ ♿ 🛜 (CC€19) iD 23 B3

- 🏕 Bañares****
- 🏠 Ctra N120, km 42,2
- 🗓 1 Jan - 31 Dec
- ☎ +34 941-340131
- @ info@campingbanares.es

1	ABDEGJMNOPQRS**T**	AF 6
2	AFGPRVWXY	ABDE**FG**H 7
3	BE**KLMN**Q	ABEFJNQRSTUV 8
4	**AB**EHINO**PQ**	JL 9
5	ACDEFHJKLM**O**	ADFGHIJ**N**PTZ 10

5-10A ❶ €33.35
A648 20ha 250T(70m²) 461P ❷ €45.85

Santo Domingo De La Calzada

🚗 Campsite located on N120/A12 at 42.2 km-marker near Santo Domingo de la Calzada.

💬 A large campsite with many permanent pitches, a lovely swimming pool and plenty of play equipment. Located near the beautiful village of Santo Domingo de la Calzada on the pilgrims' route to Santiago.

(CC) 1/1-29/6 1/9-30/12 7=6

📍 N 42°26'28'' W 2°54'55''

www.eurocampings.co.uk/113667

2072 Sunbilla, E-31791 / Navarra
♿ 🛜 iD 24 A2

- 🏕 Ariztigain
- 🏠 Añerdi Auzoa,11
- 🗓 15 Jan - 15 Dec
- ☎ +34 948-450540
- @ info@campingariztigain.com

1	ABDEJMNOPQRT	6
2	BFGNOPUVWXY	ABDE**F** 7
3	BT	ABEFNQRV 8
4	FHIO	AELUVW 9
5	ABDEFHJKLMN**O**	GHIJORW 10

6-16A ❶ €29.90
A140 1,8ha 200T(60-100m²) 38P ❷ €40.50

Lesaka

🚗 N121A Irun-Pamplona exit Sunbilla, the campsite is signposted here.

💬 Quiet campsite located between oak forests and 0.6 km from Sunbilla. The swimming pool in the village (10 minutes on foot) is free.

📍 N 43°10'27'' W 1°40'20''

www.eurocampings.co.uk/113520

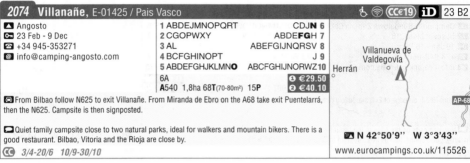

2073 Villafranca, E-31330 / Navarra
🚿 📶 (CC€19) 🚹🚺 iD 24 A3

🔺 Bardenas
🚏 Ctra NA-660 PK 13.4
📅 10 Jan - 21 Dec
☎ +34 948-846191
@ info@campingbardenas.com

1 ABDE**JM**NOPQRST	A 6
2 AFGPVWXY	ABDE**FG**H 7
3 BELM**QRU**	ABEFNQRSTUV 8
4 **AB**E**F**HIO**PR**	FIJU 9
5 ABDEFHJKLMN**O**	ABDGHIJLOSVZ 10

12A
A287 3ha 50**T**(70-105m²) 43**P**

❶ €27.00
❷ €37.00

🚗 From AP15 Pamplona-Zaragoza, take exit 29. Then towards Villafranca, campsite 1500 metres south of Villafranca.

💬 Campsite located on a main road with excellent toilet facilities. Bardenas nature reserve (walking, cycling) is 18 km away. Bodegas, gastronomy and plenty of culture in the area, including the castles of Olite and Marcilla.

CC 10/1-27/3 2/4-13/7 1/9-20/12 7=6, 14=12

📍 N 42°15'48" W 1°44'19"
www.eurocampings.co.uk/120361

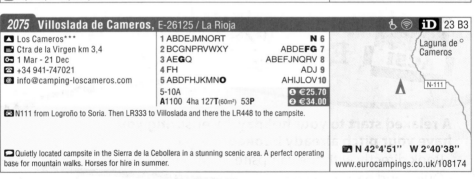

2074 Villanañe, E-01425 / Pais Vasco
🚿 📶 (CC€19) iD 23 B2

🔺 Angosto
📅 23 Feb - 9 Dec
☎ +34 945-353271
@ info@camping-angosto.com

1 ABDEJMNOPQRT	CDJ**N** 6
2 CGOPWXY	ABDE**FG**H 7
3 AL	ABEFGIJNQRSV 8
4 BCFGHINOPT	J 9
5 ABDEFGHJKLMN**O**	ABCFGHIJNORWZ 10

6A
A540 1,8ha 68**T**(70-80m²) 15**P**

❶ €29.50
❷ €40.10

🚗 From Bilbao follow N625 to exit Villanañe. From Miranda de Ebro on the A68 take exit Puentelarrá, then the N625. Campsite is then signposted.

💬 Quiet family campsite close to two natural parks, ideal for walkers and mountain bikers. There is a good restaurant. Bilbao, Vitoria and the Rioja are close by.

CC 3/4-20/6 10/9-30/10

📍 N 42°50'9" W 3°3'43"
www.eurocampings.co.uk/115526

2075 Villoslada de Cameros, E-26125 / La Rioja
🚿 📶 iD 23 B3

🔺 Los Cameros***
🚏 Ctra de la Virgen km 3,4
📅 1 Mar - 21 Dec
☎ +34 941-747021
@ info@camping-loscameros.com

1 ABDEJMNORT	**N** 6
2 BCGNPRVWXY	ABDE**FG** 7
3 AE**G**Q	ABEFJNQRV 8
4 FH	ADJ 9
5 ABDFHJKMN**O**	AHIJLOV 10

5-10A
A1100 4ha 127**T**(60m²) 53**P**

❶ €25.70
❷ €34.00

🚗 N111 from Logroño to Soria. Then LR333 to Villoslada and there the LR448 to the campsite.

💬 Quietly located campsite in the Sierra de la Cebollera in a stunning scenic area. A perfect operating base for mountain walks. Horses for hire in summer.

📍 N 42°4'51" W 2°40'38"
www.eurocampings.co.uk/108174

2076 Zarautz, E-20800 / Pais Vasco
🚿 📶 (CC€19) 🚹🚺 iD 24 A2

🔺 Gran Camping Zarautz Cat.2
🚏 Monte Talai-Mendi
📅 1 Jan - 31 Dec
☎ +34 943-831238
@ info@grancampingzarautz.com

1 ABDEJMNOPQRS**T**	6
2 AFGPRUVWXY	ABDE**FG** 7
3 AB**K**	ABEFJNQRSV 8
4 FO**P**	L 9
5 ACDEFGHJKLMN**O**	ABDFGHIJL**N**ORVYZ 10

Ad on page 698 6-10A
A126 5ha 440**T**(60-90m²) 110**P**

❶ €31.50
❷ €41.20

🚗 Coming from France take A8 San Sebastián-Bilbao, exit 38 Zarautz. Straight ahead at first roundabout, campsite signposted.

💬 A beautifully located campsite with lovely views of Zarautz Bay. An ideal starting point for trips out to San Sebastián, Bilbao and Pamplona. Many opportunities for walking and mountain-biking in the area.

CC 1/1-29/6 16/9-30/12 7=6

📍 N 43°17'22" W 2°8'45"
www.eurocampings.co.uk/106659

Spain

Zarautz is a famous water sports location with 2 km of beach, which is perfect for surfing. Options for paragliding. A visit to the hinterland is an absolute must. The location of the campsite is perfect for a visit to San Sebastian, Bilbao and Pamplona.

**Monte Talai-Mendi, 20800 Zarautz
Tel. 943-831238
E-mail: info@grancampingzarautz.com
Internet: www.grancampingzarautz.com**

2077 Zumaia, E-20750 / Pais Vasco

♿ 📶 (CC€19) iD | 24 A2

🏕 Camping & Bungalows Zumaia Cat.1
📧 Basusta bidea, 16
📅 19 Jan - 16 Dec
☎ +34 943-860475
@ info@campingzumaia.com

1	ABDE**JM**NOPQRS**T**	AF 6
2	AFGOPQSUVW	ABDE**FG** 7
3	ABL	ABEFKNQRSTV 8
4	**A**BFHIO	JL 9
5	ABDEFHJKL**O**	ABDGHIJO**P**RVWY 10

10A
2,2ha 109**T**(35-70m²) 24**P**

❶ €37.00
❷ €49.00

🅿 From N634, on edge of Zumaia, follow direction station. Campsite is then signposted.

📝 New campsite on the edge of the beautiful coastal town of Zumaia. Many options for walking nearby, good connection by bus and train to Zarautz and San Sebastián.

CC 19/1-5/7 27/8-15/12

🗺 N 43°17'23'' W 2°14'51''

www.eurocampings.co.uk/122504

Spain

698

Cantabria

Green and verdant northern Spain

Like neighbouring Asturias, Cantabria is green and verdant, so don't be surprised if you get caught in the odd shower. You'll see the benefits as you travel into the mountains! Being one of Spain's autonomous regions and provinces, Cantabria is bordered to the east and south by Basque province Biskaje, Castilia and León. UK visitors can travel to Santander, the capital, by ferry from Plymouth or Portsmouth – handy!

Earliest inhabitants

The earliest traces of humans have been found in Cantabria, and the region has many caves, painted with vivid depictions of animals that once roamed the land. Today the main city is Santander, and you can learn about that era in the city's Museum of Prehistory and Archaeology.

Walk around the Gothic Cathedral Nuestra Senora de la Asuncon and descend into the 12th-century crypt, or head to Paredo Gardens and Promenade for some fresh air. Another seaport town is Castro Urdiales, where you'll find plenty to admire in the pedestrianised Old Town, and the kids can let off steam on the impressive beaches.

Day trips

You'll feel like you're in a fairy tale on the cobbled streets of Santillana de Mar, with mediaeval towers and mansions with wooden balconies. For the kids, Santillana zoo has bisons, bears, wolves, deer and lynx – so everyone's happy. Historic Potes is an excellent base for exploring the Picos de Europa Massif, and if you come on a Monday, you could stock up for a picnic at the local market. Just outside of Potes is Santo Toribio monastery, an important stop along the Camino de Santiago. Follow the Camaleno valley to Fuente Dé and take the cable car at Mirador de

Our tips

1. *El Caprichio in Camillas is the only building by Gaudi outside of Catalonia*

2. *Love your food? Be sure to visit Mercado de la Ezperanza, Santander*

3. *Explore Saja-Besaya Nature Park, with deciduous forest, eagles, wolves, bears and deer*

4. *Happy feet: locals wear Albarcas, wooden shoes with feet, to walk through mountain meadows*

5. *Check out La Vijanera, the Winter Carnival in Silió, where the characters are in costume*

El Cable – and bring your camera and raingear. If it's raining, visit the De Monte Castillo caves: marvel at the vivid paintings of wild animals and the incredible stalactites and stalagmites.

Soul food

Need a good solid meal? Have some Cocido Montañes (stew with pork, beans and kale), followed by either Sobao (cake flavoured with anise), or Quesada pasiega (a rich pudding). Sample some Orujo liqueur, or enjoy refreshing local cider. Locals also enjoy crustaceans and shellfish.

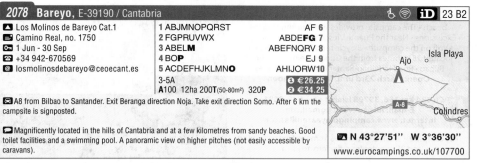

2078 Bareyo, E-39190 / Cantabria — 23 B2

- Los Molinos de Bareyo Cat.1
- Camino Real, no. 1750
- 1 Jun - 30 Sep
- ☎ +34 942-670569
- @ losmolinosdebareyo@ceoecant.es

1	ABJMNOPQRST	AF 6
2	FGPRUVWX	ABDE**FG** 7
3	ABEL**M**	ABEFNQRV 8
4	BO**P**	EJ 9
5	ACDEFHJKLMN**O**	AHIJORW 10

3-5A ❶ €26.25
A100 12ha 200**T**(50-80m²) 320**P** ❷ €34.25

A8 from Bilbao to Santander. Exit Beranga direction Noja. Take exit direction Somo. After 6 km the campsite is signposted.

Magnificently located in the hills of Cantabria and at a few kilometres from sandy beaches. Good toilet facilities and a swimming pool. A panoramic view on higher pitches (not easily accessible by caravans).

N 43°27'51" W 3°36'30"
www.eurocampings.co.uk/107700

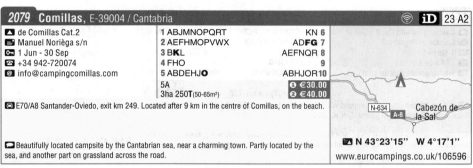

2079 Comillas, E-39004 / Cantabria — 23 A2

- de Comillas Cat.2
- Manuel Norièga s/n
- 1 Jun - 30 Sep
- ☎ +34 942-720074
- @ info@campingcomillas.com

1	ABJMNOPQRT	KN 6
2	AEFHMOPVWX	AD**FG** 7
3	B**KL**	AEFNQR 8
4	FHO	9
5	ABDEHJ**O**	ABHJOR 10

5A ❶ €30.00
3ha 250**T**(50-65m²) ❷ €40.00

E70/A8 Santander-Oviedo, exit km 249. Located after 9 km in the centre of Comillas, on the beach.

Beautifully located campsite by the Cantabrian sea, near a charming town. Partly located by the sea, and another part on grassland across the road.

N 43°23'15" W 4°17'1"
www.eurocampings.co.uk/106596

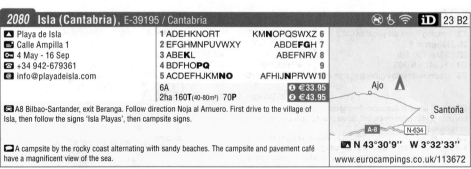

2080 Isla (Cantabria), E-39195 / Cantabria — 23 B2

- Playa de Isla
- Calle Ampilla 1
- 4 May - 16 Sep
- ☎ +34 942-679361
- @ info@playadeisla.com

1	ADEHKNORT	KM**N**OPQSWXZ 6
2	EFGHMNPUVWXY	ABDE**FG**H 7
3	ABE**KL**	ABEFNRV 8
4	BDFHO**PQ**	9
5	ACDEFHJKM**NO**	AFHIJ**N**PRVW 10

6A ❶ €33.95
2ha 160**T**(40-80m²) 70**P** ❷ €43.95

A8 Bilbao-Santander, exit Beranga. Follow direction Noja al Arnuero. First drive to the village of Isla, then follow the signs 'Isla Playas', then campsite signs.

A campsite by the rocky coast alternating with sandy beaches. The campsite and pavement café have a magnificent view of the sea.

N 43°30'9" W 3°32'33"
www.eurocampings.co.uk/113672

2081 Islares, E-39798 / Cantabria — 23 B2

- Playa Arenillas Cat.2
- Cu 634 km 156
- 23 Mar - 30 Sep
- ☎ +34 942-863152
- @ luis.cueva62@gmail.com

1	BDEHKNOPQRST	KNPQSXYZ 6
2	AEFGHOPVWX	ABDE**FG**H 7
3	BEL	AEFNQRSV 8
4	FHO**P**	AUV 9
5	ABDEFHJKLMN**O**	ABDHIJ**P**RW 10

Ad on page 702 6A ❶ €30.60
1,7ha 120**T**(50-70m²) 126**P** ❷ €39.80

A8 Bilbao to Santander exit 156 in the direction of Islares. Signposted here.

A friendly and appropriate welcome. Close to a sandy beach. 100 metres from the bus to Bilbao. Watersports opportunities. Ideal for enjoyable trips out into the surroundings. All information about Bilbao (35 km away) is available at the campsite.

CC 23/3-5/7 24/8-29/9

N 43°24'13" W 3°18'37"
www.eurocampings.co.uk/106622

Spain

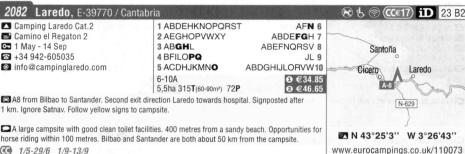

2082 Laredo, E-39770 / Cantabria ⊗ ♿ 🛜 (CC€17) iD 23 B2

🏕 Camping Laredo Cat.2
✉ Camino el Regaton 2
📅 1 May - 14 Sep
☎ +34 942-605035
@ info@campinglaredo.com

1 ABDEHKNOPQRST	AF**N** 6
2 AEGHOPVWXY	ABDE**FGH** 7
3 AB**GHL**	ABEFNQRSV 8
4 BFILO**PQ**	JL 9
5 ACDHJKMN**O**	ABDGHIJLORVW 10

6-10A ❶ €34.85
5,5ha 315**T**(60-90m²) 72**P** ❷ €46.65

🚗 A8 from Bilbao to Santander. Second exit direction Laredo towards hospital. Signposted after 1 km. Ignore Satnav. Follow yellow signs to campsite.

💬 A large campsite with good clean toilet facilities. 400 metres from a sandy beach. Opportunities for horse riding within 100 metres. Bilbao and Santander are both about 50 km from the campsite.
CC 1/5-29/6 1/9-13/9

📷 N 43°25'3'' W 3°26'43''
www.eurocampings.co.uk/110073

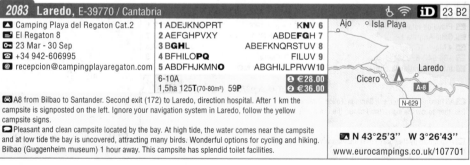

2083 Laredo, E-39770 / Cantabria ♿ 🛜 iD 23 B2

🏕 Camping Playa del Regaton Cat.2
✉ El Regaton 8
📅 23 Mar - 30 Sep
☎ +34 942-606995
@ recepcion@campingplayaregaton.com

1 ADEJKNOPRT	K**N**V 6
2 AEFGHPVXY	ABDE**FGH** 7
3 B**GHL**	ABEFKNQRSTUV 8
4 BFHILO**PQ**	FILUV 9
5 ABDFHJKMN**O**	ABGHIJLPRVW 10

6-10A ❶ €28.00
1,5ha 125**T**(70-80m²) 59**P** ❷ €36.00

🚗 A8 from Bilbao to Santander. Second exit (172) to Laredo, direction hospital. After 1 km the campsite is signposted on the left. Ignore your navigation system in Laredo, follow the yellow campsite signs.

💬 Pleasant and clean campsite located by the bay. At high tide, the water comes near the campsite and at low tide the bay is uncovered, attracting many birds. Wonderful options for cycling and hiking. Bilbao (Guggenheim museum) 1 hour away. This campsite has splendid toilet facilities.

📷 N 43°25'3'' W 3°26'43''
www.eurocampings.co.uk/107701

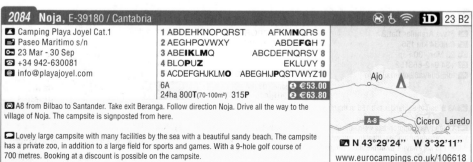

2084 Noja, E-39180 / Cantabria ⊗ ♿ 🛜 iD 23 B2

🏕 Camping Playa Joyel Cat.1
✉ Paseo Maritimo s/n
📅 23 Mar - 30 Sep
☎ +34 942-630081
@ info@playajoyel.com

1 ABDEHKNOPQRST	AFKM**N**QRS 6
2 AEGHPQVWXY	ABDE**FGH** 7
3 ABE**IKLMQ**	ABCDEFNQRSV 8
4 BLO**PUZ**	EKLUVY 9
5 ACDEFGHJKLM**O**	ABEGHIJ**P**QSTVWYZ 10

6A ❶ €53.00
24ha 800**T**(70-100m²) 315**P** ❷ €63.80

🚗 A8 from Bilbao to Santander. Take exit Beranga. Follow direction Noja. Drive all the way to the village of Noja. The campsite is signposted from here.

💬 Lovely large campsite with many facilities by the sea with a beautiful sandy beach. The campsite has a private zoo, in addition to a large field for sports and games. With a 9-hole golf course of 700 metres. Booking at a discount is possible on the campsite.

📷 N 43°29'24'' W 3°32'11''
www.eurocampings.co.uk/106618

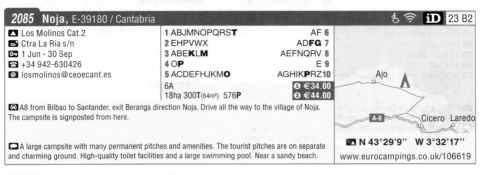

2085 Noja, E-39180 / Cantabria
    23 B2

- ▲ Los Molinos Cat.2
- ▤ Ctra La Ria s/n
- ☞ 1 Jun - 30 Sep
- ☎ +34 942-630426
- @ losmolinos@ceoecant.es

1 ABJMNOPQRS**T**	AF 6
2 EHPVWX	AD**FG** 7
3 ABE**KLM**	AEFNQRV 8
4 O**P**	E 9
5 ACDEFHJKM**O**	AGHIK**P**RZ 10
6A	❶ €34.00
18ha 300T(64m²) 576P	❷ €44.00

🚗 A8 from Bilbao to Santander, exit Beranga direction Noja. Drive all the way to the village of Noja. The campsite is signposted from here.

💬 A large campsite with many permanent pitches and amenities. The tourist pitches are on separate and charming ground. High-quality toilet facilities and a large swimming pool. Near a sandy beach.

📌 N 43°29'9'' W 3°32'17''
www.eurocampings.co.uk/106619

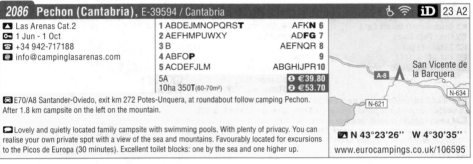

2086 Pechon (Cantabria), E-39594 / Cantabria
    23 A2

- ▲ Las Arenas Cat.2
- ☞ 1 Jun - 1 Oct
- ☎ +34 942-717188
- @ info@campinglasarenas.com

1 ABDEJMNOPQRS**T**	AF**KN** 6
2 AEFHMPUWXY	AD**FG** 7
3 B	AEFNQR 8
4 ABFO**P**	9
5 ACDEFJLM	ABGHIJPR 10
5A	❶ €39.80
10ha 350T(60-70m²)	❷ €53.70

🚗 E70/A8 Santander-Oviedo, exit km 272 Potes-Unquera, at roundabout follow camping Pechon. After 1.8 km campsite on the left on the mountain.

💬 Lovely and quietly located family campsite with swimming pools. With plenty of privacy. You can realise your own private spot with a view of the sea and mountains. Favourably located for excursions to the Picos de Europa (30 minutes). Excellent toilet blocks: one by the sea and one higher up.

📌 N 43°23'26'' W 4°30'35''
www.eurocampings.co.uk/106595

2087 Potes, E-39570 / Cantabria
    23 A2

- ▲ La Viorna Cat.1
- ▤ Car. Santo Toribio
- ☞ 24 Mar - 1 Nov
- ☎ +34 942-732021
- @ info@campinglaviorna.com

1 ABDEILNOPQR**T**	AF 6
2 FPUVXY	ABDE**FG**H 7
3 ABQ	ABEFKNQRS 8
4 AEFHO**PQ**	FL 9
5 ABDHJKLMN**O**	ABDGHIJLOR 10
6A	❶ €29.55
A400 1,9ha 110T(70m²) 1P	❷ €39.65

🚗 1 km past Potes, direction Fuente Dé, turn left to Santo Toribio.
💬 Lovely campsite with excellent amenities. The pitches at this terraced campsite have grass and shade. Large swimming pool. Most suitable as starting point for various walks and excursions. Plenty of information about the region available at the reception. Excellent restaurant, appetising menus of the day. Magnificent views of the mountain peaks of the Picos.
CC 24/3-29/6 1/9-31/10

📌 N 43°9'16'' W 4°38'37''
www.eurocampings.co.uk/106599

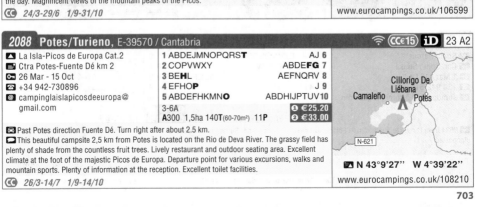

2088 Potes/Turieno, E-39570 / Cantabria
    23 A2

- ▲ La Isla-Picos de Europa Cat.2
- ▤ Ctra Potes-Fuente Dé km 2
- ☞ 26 Mar - 15 Oct
- ☎ +34 942-730896
- @ campinglaislapicosdeeuropa@
  gmail.com

1 ABDEJMNOPQRS**T**	AJ 6
2 COPVWXY	ABDE**FG** 7
3 BE**HL**	AEFNQRV 8
4 EFHO**P**	J 9
5 ABDEFHKMN**O**	ABDHIJPTUV 10
3-6A	❶ €25.20
A300 1,5ha 140T(60-70m²) 11P	❷ €33.00

🚗 Past Potes direction Fuente Dé. Turn right after about 2.5 km.
💬 This beautiful campsite 2,5 km from Potes is located on the Rio de Deva River. The grassy field has plenty of shade from the countless fruit trees. Lively restaurant and outdoor seating area. Excellent climate at the foot of the majestic Picos de Europa. Departure point for various excursions, walks and mountain sports. Plenty of information at the reception. Excellent toilet facilities.
CC 26/3-14/7 1/9-14/10

📌 N 43°9'27'' W 4°39'22''
www.eurocampings.co.uk/108210

Spain

2089 Ruiloba, E-39527 / Cantabria

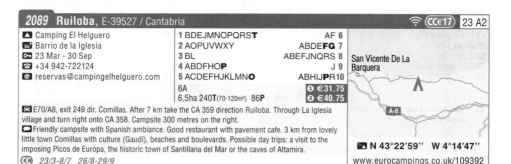

🏕 Camping El Helguero
🏠 Barrio de la Iglesia
📅 23 Mar - 30 Sep
☎ +34 942-722124
@ reservas@campingelhelguero.com

1 BDEJMNOPQRS**T**	AF 6
2 AOPUVWXY	ABDE**FG** 7
3 BL	ABEFJNQRS 8
4 ABDFHO**P**	J 9
5 ACDEFHJKLMN**O**	ABHIJ**P**R 10
6A	❶ €31.75
6,5ha 240**T**(70-120m²) 86**P**	❷ €40.75

🛈 E70/A8, exit 249 dir. Comillas. After 7 km take the CA 359 direction Ruiloba. Through La Iglesia village and turn right onto CA 358. Campsite 300 metres on the right.
💬 Friendly campsite with Spanish ambiance. Good restaurant with pavement cafe. 3 km from lovely little town Comillas with culture (Gaudí), beaches and boulevards. Possible day trips: a visit to the imposing Picos de Europa, the historic town of Santillana del Mar or the caves of Altamira.
Ⓒ 23/3-8/7 26/8-29/9

🛜 (CC€17) 23 A2

San Vicente De La Barquera

📷 N 43°22'59'' W 4°14'47''

www.eurocampings.co.uk/109392

2090 S. Vicente de la Barquera, E-39540 / Cantabria

🏕 Caravaning Oyambre Cat.1
🏠 Finca Peña Gerra
📅 3 Mar - 21 Oct
☎ +34 942-711461
@ camping@oyambre.com

1 ABDEJMNOPQRST	AF 6
2 GHOPUVWX	ABD**FG**H 7
3 BE**K**	ABEFNQRSV 8
4 O**P**	GJ 9
5 ABDEFJKLMN	ABHIJPR 10
Ad on this page 10A	❶ €30.15
4ha 128**T**(20-120m²) 102**P**	❷ €41.65

🛈 E70/A8 Santander-Oviedo, exit km-marker 264 S. Vicente de la Barquera, then N634 for 3 km to Comillas exit on the Ctra La Revilla-Comillas (CA 131) between km-markers 27 and 28.
💬 A luxury campsite in one of the nature parks of Cantabria. You can go on excursions from the campsite in all weather conditions. Culture (Gaudi in Comillas), nature (dunes, sea, Picos de Europa), history (caves of Altamira in Santillana del Mar). Fine campsite restaurant.
Ⓒ 3/3-29/6 1/9-20/10

♿ 🛜 (CC€19) iD 23 A2

San Vicente De La Barquera

N-634

📷 N 43°23'42'' W 4°20'17''

www.eurocampings.co.uk/110440

2091 Somo, E-39150 / Cantabria

🏕 Somo Parque***
🏠 Car. Somo Suesa
📅 1 Mar - 15 Dec
☎ +34 942-510309
@ somoparque@somoparque.com

1 ADEJMNOPQRST	6
2 AGHOPRVWXY	AD**F** 7
3 AB**K**	ABEFNQRTUV 8
4 FHINO**PQ**	EJL 9
5 ADHN**O**	ABHIJLORV 10
6A	❶ €21.60
2,5ha 130**T**(60-90m²) 88**P**	❷ €27.00

🛈 N634 from Laredo to Santander. At Solares exit direction Somo. After Suesa, the campsite is signposted.

💬 Quiet campsite at 1.5 km from the sea. This is where the boat to Santander departs.

🛜 iD 23 B2

Santander

Camargo

A-8

📷 N 43°26'46'' W 3°43'38''

www.eurocampings.co.uk/106620

Galicia

Land of a thousand rivers

With the Atlantic Ocean to the west and Portugal to the south, the Celtic past is still very much alive in Galicia. Locals speak the Galego language, and the gaita, or Iberian bagpipe, is played at local events. Named after the Celtic tribe that lived here before the Romans, Galicia was also ruled by Asturias, and later Castile and Leon. You'll see cliffs and long sea inlets on the Atlantic coast, and surfers are drawn to the region's beaches. Travel inland and upriver, and be charmed by the rivers, forests, gorges and mountains of Galicia.

Historic cities and towns

Did you know that Santiago de Compostella cathedral is so important in Spain that they've put it on their Eurocent coins? This majestic cathedral has been a pilgrimage destination for centuries. Soak up the Old Town's atmosphere at one of the many cafés, and explore Alameda Park. Castillo de San Antón in A Coruña is now a museum and nearby Santa Maria Park is ideal for Galician rainy days - with an Aquarium, Science Museum, and Planetarium, sure to keep the kids happy.

Places to go

Walk the Roman city walls of Lugo and visit the Interpretive Centre in Plaza de Campo. Near Lugo is the pre-Roman village Castro de Viladonga and Roman Temple of Santa Eulalia de Bóveda. History buffs also appreciate harbour town Ferrol: the home port of the Spanish Armada. Enjoy great views from Jardines de Herrera, including the two castles on either side of the harbour entrance. Nature lovers can chill in Fragas do Eume, where hiking trails take you past a Honey Museum! With kayaking, boating,

horse-riding, and a fun Adventure Park, there's something for everyone. And the best beach in the world, according to The Guardian, is on what the Romans called the 'Islands of the Gods', in the Galician Atlantic Islands National Park: Rodas Beach.

Food glorious food
Here the humble scallop is a symbol of Saint James. And do you believe you cannot make queimade, the regional brandy, unless you cast a spell on it? Try Pulpo á feira or Empanada, or caldo, churrasco, filloas or Padron peppers. Finish with San Simón tart, if you can.

Our tips
1. Love feeling pampered? Check out the hot water springs in Ourense
2. Look out for Horreos – storage sheds built off the ground
3. Check out the Arde Lucus Roman festival in Lugo
4. Explore the Vigo Museum of Contemporary Art
5. Visit Celtic fortress Castro de Barona

2092 Aldán/Cangas, E-36945 / Galicia ⊗ 🛜 iD 21 B2

- 🏕 Aldán
- ✉ Apartado 127
- ⛅ 24/3 - 1/4, 1/6 - 30/9
- ☎ +34 986-329468
- @ info@campingaldan.com

1 ABHKNOPRT	KNQS 6
2 EFGHOPUVWXY	AD**FG**H 7
3 BELM	AEFNQRS 8
4 FO	JKL 9
5 ACDEFHJKLM**NO**	ABGHIJL**N**PTUV10
6A	❶ €34.00
A65 2,5ha 186T(60-80m²) 4P	❷ €45.40

🚗 From Santiago-Vigo (exit Cangas) and motorway (no toll) to Aldan. One more kilometre. The campsite is clearly signposted.

📖 A beautiful campsite with a friendly reception. Located by a large bay on a peninsula. Dolmens and interesting small churches nearby. With an information stand at reception. Beautiful and friendly space with a fireplace for colder days.

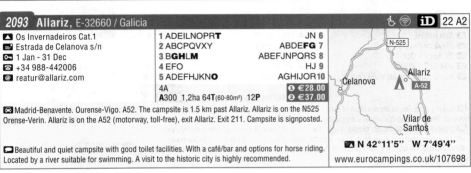

🏕 N 42°17'12'' W 8°48'53''

www.eurocampings.co.uk/109430

2093 Allariz, E-32660 / Galicia ♿ 🛜 iD 22 A2

- 🏕 Os Invernadeiros Cat.1
- ✉ Estrada de Celanova s/n
- ⛅ 1 Jan - 31 Dec
- ☎ +34 988-442006
- @ reatur@allariz.com

1 ADEILNOPR**T**	JN 6
2 ABCPQVXY	ABDE**FG** 7
3 B**GHLM**	ABEFJNPQRS 8
4 EFO	HJ 9
5 ADEFHJKN**O**	AGHIJOR10
4A	❶ €28.00
A300 1,2ha 64T(60-80m²) 12P	❷ €37.00

🚗 Madrid-Benavente. Ourense-Vigo. A52. The campsite is 1.5 km past Allariz. Allariz is on the N525 Orense-Verin. Allariz is on the A52 (motorway, toll-free), exit Allariz. Exit 211. Campsite is signposted.

📖 Beautiful and quiet campsite with good toilet facilities. With a café/bar and options for horse riding. Located by a river suitable for swimming. A visit to the historic city is highly recommended.

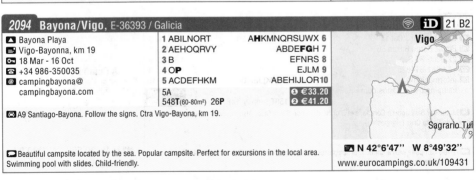

🏕 N 42°11'5'' W 7°49'4''

www.eurocampings.co.uk/107698

2094 Bayona/Vigo, E-36393 / Galicia 🛜 iD 21 B2

- 🏕 Bayona Playa
- ✉ Vigo-Bayonna, km 19
- ⛅ 18 Mar - 16 Oct
- ☎ +34 986-350035
- @ campingbayona@
  campingbayona.com

1 ABILNORT	A**H**KMNQRSUWX 6
2 AEHOQRVY	ABDE**FG**H 7
3 B	EFNRS 8
4 O**P**	EJLM 9
5 ACDEFHKM	ABEHIJLOR10
5A	❶ €33.20
548T(60-80m²) 26P	❷ €41.20

🚗 A9 Santiago-Bayona. Follow the signs. Ctra Vigo-Bayona, km 19.

📖 Beautiful campsite located by the sea. Popular campsite. Perfect for excursions in the local area. Swimming pool with slides. Child-friendly.

🏕 N 42°6'47'' W 8°49'32''

www.eurocampings.co.uk/109431

2095 Cangas del Morrazo, E-36940 / Galicia ⊗ 🛜 iD 21 B2

- 🏕 Limens Cat.2
- ✉ Playa de Limens s/n
- ⛅ 15 Mar - 15 Sep
- ☎ +34 986-304055
- @ administracion@campinglimens.com

1 ADEHKNOPRT	KMNOPQSW 6
2 AEFGHOPQRUVXY	AD**F** 7
3 B	AFNQRS 8
4 FHIO	JKLR 9
5 ADHMN**O**	ABHIJOTUV10
4-6A	❶ €34.70
0,7ha 51T(60-80m²) 17P	❷ €46.50

🚗 Direction Vigo/Pontevedra. Exit Cangas, AP9 direction Cangas. Camping is clearly signposted.

📖 A campsite located on an estuary. Plenty of opportunities for watersports. Well located as a base for historical visits around the area.

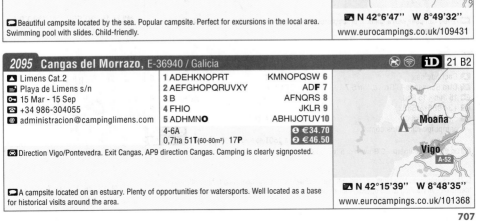

🏕 N 42°15'39'' W 8°48'35''

www.eurocampings.co.uk/101368

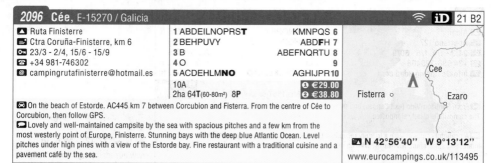

2096 Cée, E-15270 / Galicia 📶 iD 21 B2

🅰 Ruta Finisterre
🏕 Ctra Coruña-Finisterre, km 6
📅 23/3 - 2/4, 15/6 - 15/9
☎ +34 981-746302
@ campingrutafinisterre@hotmail.es

1 ABDEILNOPRS**T**	KMNPQS **6**
2 BEHPUVY	ABD**FH 7**
3 B	ABEFNQRTU **8**
4 O	**9**
5 ACDEHLM**NO**	AGHIJPR **10**

10A ❶ € 29.00
2ha 64**T**(60-80m²) 8**P** ❷ € 38.80

📷 On the beach of Estorde. AC445 km 7 between Corcubion and Fisterra. From the centre of Cée to Corcubion, then follow GPS.
💬 Lovely and well-maintained campsite by the sea with spacious pitches and a few km from the most westerly point of Europe, Finisterre. Stunning bays with the deep blue Atlantic Ocean. Level pitches under high pines with a view of the Estorde bay. Fine restaurant with a traditional cuisine and a pavement café by the sea.

🌐 **N 42°56'40'' W 9°13'12''**
www.eurocampings.co.uk/113495

2097 Foz, E-27780 / Galicia ♿ 📶 CC€13 iD 22 A1

🅰 San Rafael
🏕 Playa de Peizas
📅 27 Apr - 1 Oct
☎ +34 982-132218
@ info@campingsanrafael.com

1 ADEILNORT	KMNQSXYZ **6**
2 AEHPVWXY	ABD**F 7**
3 B	AEFNQRT **8**
4 AEFO**P**	M **9**
5 ABDHK**NO**	ABGHIJLOPRV **10**

6A ❶ € 21.05
1,2ha 100**T**(60-80m²) ❷ € 28.65

📷 Coming from Foz, in the direction of Ferrol N642, turn right to Playa de Peizas. From Ferrol towards Foz roundabout. Campsite signposted.
💬 Located in Playa de Peizás, close to Foz in the centre of Losta de Lugo, an area full of recreation with many opportunities for fishing, (water)sports, walking and more. 3 km from San Martin de Mondoñedo, 2 km from the ruins of Castro de Fazouro and 15 km from Playa de las Catedrales.
CC 27/4-9/7 27/8-30/9

🌐 **N 43°35'16'' W 7°16'56''**
www.eurocampings.co.uk/107750

2098 La Coruña (Sta Cruz), E-15179 / Galicia 📶 21 B1

🅰 Los Manzanos Cat.1
🏕 Emilia Pardo Bazan 65
📅 22 Mar - 30 Sep
☎ +34 981-614825
@ informacion@
  campinglosmanzanos.com

1 BDEGJMNOPRS**T**	A **6**
2 ABHPRWXY	AB**FG 7**
3 A	AEFNQ **8**
4 IO	J **9**
5 ABDFGHKLMN**O**	AGHIJLOPR **10**

9A CEE ❶ € 31.70
26,5ha 150**T**(50-80m²) 14**P** ❷ € 41.70

📷 Motorway Santiago-La Coruña, exit 3 or N6 direction Santa Cruz. Also via Sada or Bergondo direction Santa Cruz (signposted).

💬 Lovely campsite with architectural sculptures. Well-maintained. Friendly, family ambiance. Excellent restaurant.

🌐 **N 43°20'55'' W 8°20'8''**
www.eurocampings.co.uk/110546

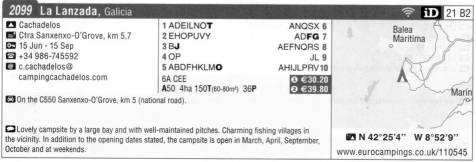

2099 La Lanzada, Galicia 📶 iD 21 B2

🅰 Cachadelos
🏕 Ctra Sanxenxo-O'Grove, km 5,7
📅 15 Jun - 15 Sep
☎ +34 986-745592
@ c.cachadelos@
  campingcachadelos.com

1 ADEILNO**T**	ANQSX **6**
2 EHOPUVY	AD**FG 7**
3 B**J**	AEFNQRS **8**
4 OP	JL **9**
5 ABDFHKLM**O**	AHIJLPRV **10**

6A CEE ❶ € 30.20
A50 4ha 150**T**(60-80m²) 36**P** ❷ € 39.80

📷 On the C550 Sanxenxo-O'Grove, km 5 (national road).

💬 Lovely campsite by a large bay and with well-maintained pitches. Charming fishing villages in the vicinity. In addition to the opening dates stated, the campsite is open in March, April, September, October and at weekends.

🌐 **N 42°25'4'' W 8°52'9''**
www.eurocampings.co.uk/110545

2100   Louro, E-15291 / Galicia   ✆ 🛜 (CC€17) ♟ 🆔 21 B2

🔼 A' Vouga
🚏 Ctra Muros-Finisterre, km 3
📅 16 Mar - 15 Oct
☎ +34 981-826115
@ avouga@hotmail.es

1 ADEJMNORST	KNPQS	6
2 EHKMOPVWX	ABDE**FGH**	7
3	ABEFNQT	8
4 AFO		9
5 ADFHKLMN**O**	ABGHIJNPTUVW	10
Ad on this page 10A	❶ €34.00	
1,5ha 70T	❷ €38.00	

🏕 Campsite on the Santiago-Noia-Muros-Louro road. 3 km beyond Muros. Well signposted.
💬 A small level site on the beach. Easily accessed, 500m from the village centre of Louro. 3 km from Muros. Bus stop in front of the campsite, which gets you to Santiago in 1 hour and 45 minutes. Very spacious, excellent and pleasant restaurant with typical Galician dishes and panoramic views of the sea. Dolphins can be seen from the terrace. Motorbike riders welcome.
CC 16/3-30/6   18/8-14/10   10=8

AC-550   Muros
Porto Do Son

🧭 N 42°45'39''   W 9°3'44''
www.eurocampings.co.uk/119317

Camping A' Vouga
The perfect place to really relax.

www.campingvouga.wix.com/a-vouga

Small-scale, flat campsite by the beach. Easily accessible and 500m from the village centre. Bus stop in front of the campsite, where a bus will take you to Santiago in two hours. Very spacious, pleasant and with a fine seafood restaurant overlooking the sea. You can spot dolphins in the sea from the pavement café. Motorcyclists are welcome.

Ctra Muros-Finisterre, km 3
15291 Louro • Tel. en fax 981-826115
E-mail: avouga@hotmail.es

Spain

2101   Louro/Muros, E-15291 / Galicia   ✆ 🛜 (CC€19) 🆔 21 B2

🔼 San Francisco Cat.1
📅 23 Mar - 16 Sep
☎ +34 981-826148
@ info@campingsanfrancisco.com

1 ABDEJMNOPRST	KMPQS	6
2 EHKMP	ABD**FG**	7
3 AEM	ABEFHNPQRT	8
4 IOQ		9
5 ABCDFHKL**O**	ABHIJOTUV	10
10A CEE	❶ €29.00	
A50 74T(60-80m²)	❷ €37.80	

🏕 Campsite is on the road Santiago-Noia-Muros-Louro.
💬 San Francisco campsite is located in the small village of Louro, in a beautiful area with trees, sea and mountains. With walking paths, architectural sights, petroglyphs, and just 200m from the beach. The campsite has all the facilities you could need on holiday. You can exercise and relax in a peaceful, pleasant atmosphere in direct contact with nature.
CC 23/3-30/6   2/7-8/7   26/8-15/9

Muros
Porto Do Son

🧭 N 42°45'44''   W 9°4'20''
www.eurocampings.co.uk/110541

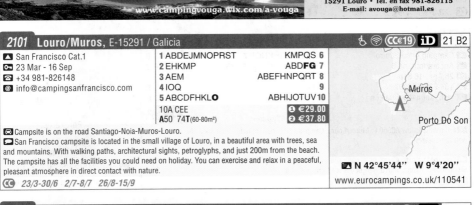

2102   Malpica, E-15113 / Galicia   ✆ 🛜 🆔 21 B1

🔼 Sisargas Cat.1
🚏 Ctra Carballo-Malpica, km 12,5
📅 15 Jun - 10 Sep
☎ +34 981-721702
@ info@campingsisargas.com

1 ADE**JM**NOPRT	AMNOP	6
2 HPWXY	ABDEF**G**	7
3 ABCG**HLM**	ABCEFNQRS	8
4 FHO**P**	FJU	9
5 ABDEFKMN**O**	AHIJOSTV	10
10A	❶ €28.60	
1,5ha 150T(max 60m²) 11P	❷ €37.80	

🚗 A55 from La Coruna. At Carballo direction Malpica, km 14. Campsite is clearly signposted.

💬 Quiet and well-maintained family campsite. Easily accessible. Swimming pool and options for tennis. Good restaurant.

Ponteceso
Carballo

🧭 N 43°17'48''   W 8°48'37''
www.eurocampings.co.uk/111894

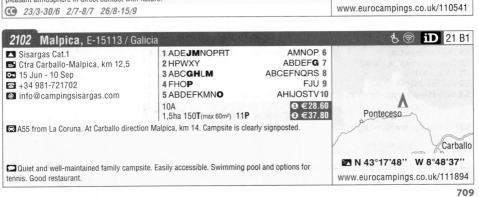

2103 Mougas/Oia, E-36309 / Galicia

🛖 Mougas
🏠 As Mariñas, 20B
📅 1 Apr - 15 Sep
☎ +34 986-385011
@ campingmougas@campingmougas.es

1 ABDEILNOPRST	AN 6
2 EFMOPUVWX	ADFGH 7
3 BE	AEFKNQRSV 8
4 AEFHIOPQ	BEGJ 9
5 ABDEFHJLMNO	ABGHIPSTV 10
10-16A	❶ €28.90
22ha 96T(60-80m²) 31P	❷ €37.30

🚗 Motorway A9 Vigo-Baiona C550 direction Guardia km 156. Campsite is signposted.

💬 A well-maintained and easily accessible campsite, perfect for excursions in the vicinity. Large pitches, located by the sea and with a swimming pool and restaurant.

Comesaña
Gondomar

📍 N 42°5'11'' W 8°53'28''
www.eurocampings.co.uk/110536

21 B2

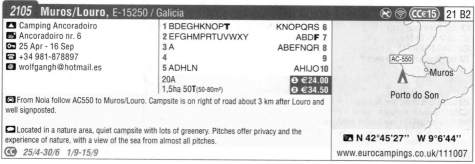

2104 Mougas/Oia, E-36309 / Galicia

🛖 O Muiño Cat.1
🏠 C550 km 158
📅 23 Mar - 14 Oct
☎ +34 986-361600
@ info@campingmuino.com

1 ADEILNOPQRT	AFNP 6
2 AEFGMOPUVWX	ABDFGH 7
3 ABEMNQ	ABFKNQRST 8
4 ABDEFHIMOP	AELV 9
5 ACDEFHJKNO	ABGHIPRV 10
6-10A CEE	❶ €33.80
2,2ha 65T(50-80m²) 39P	❷ €42.80

🚗 C550 Baiona-La Guardia as far as km-marker 26. Motorway Vigo-Baiona-a, Guardia. Campsite well signposted.

💬 A really beautiful, well run, level campsite by the sea with a lovely swimming pool. Every comfort is provided. The campsite is only open at the weekend (including Friday) from October up to and including March.

CC 23/3-9/7 1/9-13/10 7=6

Nigrán
Tomiño

📍 N 42°3'51'' W 8°53'30''
www.eurocampings.co.uk/106533

21 B2

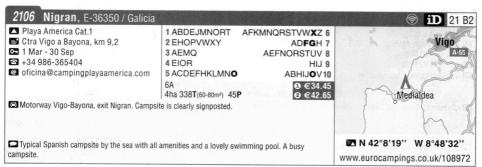

2105 Muros/Louro, E-15250 / Galicia

🛖 Camping Ancoradoiro
🏠 Ancoradoiro nr. 6
📅 25 Apr - 16 Sep
☎ +34 981-878897
@ wolfgangh@hotmail.es

1 BDEGHKNOPT	KNOPQRS 6
2 EFGHMPRTUVWXY	ABDF 7
3 A	ABEFNQR 8
4	9
5 ADHLN	AHIJO 10
20A	❶ €24.00
1,5ha 50T(50-80m²)	❷ €34.50

🚗 From Noia follow AC550 to Muros/Louro. Campsite is on right of road about 3 km after Louro and well signposted.

💬 Located in a nature area, quiet campsite with lots of greenery. Pitches offer privacy and the experience of nature, with a view of the sea from almost all pitches.

CC 25/4-30/6 1/9-15/9

AC-550
Muros
Porto do Son

📍 N 42°45'27'' W 9°6'44''
www.eurocampings.co.uk/111007

21 B2

2106 Nigran, E-36350 / Galicia

🛖 Playa America Cat.1
🏠 Ctra Vigo a Bayona, km 9,2
📅 1 Mar - 30 Sep
☎ +34 986-365404
@ oficina@campingplayaamerica.com

1 ABDEJMNORT	AFKMNQRSTVWXZ 6
2 EHOPVWXY	ADFGH 7
3 AEMQ	AEFNORSTUV 8
4 EIOR	HIJ 9
5 ACDEFHKLMNO	ABHIJOV 10
6A	❶ €34.45
4ha 338T(60-80m²) 45P	❷ €42.65

🚗 Motorway Vigo-Bayona, exit Nigran. Campsite is clearly signposted.

💬 Typical Spanish campsite by the sea with all amenities and a lovely swimming pool. A busy campsite.

Vigo
A-55
Medialdea

📍 N 42°8'19'' W 8°48'32''
www.eurocampings.co.uk/108972

21 B2

Spain

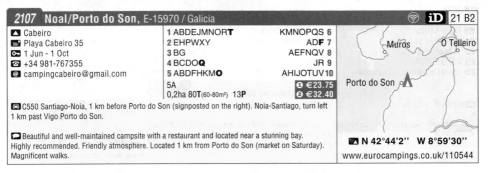

2107 Noal/Porto do Son, E-15970 / Galicia — 21 B2

- ▲ Cabeiro
- 🏕 Playa Cabeiro 35
- 🗓 1 Jun - 1 Oct
- ☎ +34 981-767355
- @ campingcabeiro@gmail.com

1 ABDEJMNOR**T**	KMNOPQS 6
2 EHPWXY	AD**F** 7
3 BG	AEFNQV 8
4 BCDO**Q**	JR 9
5 ABDFHKM**O**	AHIJOTUV 10
5A	❶ €23.75
0,2ha 80**T**(60-80m²) 13**P**	❷ €32.40

🚗 C550 Santiago-Noia, 1 km before Porto do Son (signposted on the right). Noia-Santiago, turn left 1 km past Vigo Porto do Son.

💬 Beautiful and well-maintained campsite with a restaurant and located near a stunning bay. Highly recommended. Friendly atmosphere. Located 1 km from Porto do Son (market on Saturday). Magnificent walks.

◪ N 42°44'2'' W 8°59'30''
www.eurocampings.co.uk/110544

2108 O Grove, E-36989 / Galicia — 21 B2

- ▲ Muiñeira
- 🏕 Playa Raeiros, 38
- 🗓 1 Mar - 15 Oct
- ☎ +34 986-738404
- @ info@campingmuineira.es

1 ACDGJMNOPRST	KMNOPQSVWX 6
2 ABEFHMPVWXY	ABDE**FG**HJK 7
3 ABF**K**	ABEFNQRS 8
4 **A**FGHOP	AGLMRV 9
5 ABDFHKMN**O**	ABFHIJLNOV 10
10A	❶ €34.10
0,7ha 80**T**(60-100m²) 4**P**	❷ €45.10

🚗 From AG-41 direction O Grove, follow PO-317 direction San Vincente do Grove. Once you reach the coast, the campsite is on the left.

💬 A campsite on a peninsula with spacious pitches, a view of the sea and near a sandy beach. Nice restaurant with a lovely pavement café higher than the campsite. The nearest large town is Sanxenxo.

◪ N 42°27'36'' W 8°53'38''
www.eurocampings.co.uk/113193

2109 O Grove/San Vicente, E-36988 / Galicia — 21 B2

- ▲ Playa Paisaxe II
- 🏕 Playa de Area Grande
- 🗓 1 Apr - 12 Oct
- ☎ +34 986-738331
- @ info@campingplayapaisaxe.com

1 ABDEILNOR**T**	AKMNPQSWX 6
2 AEHOPVWXY	ABD**F**H 7
3 ABEJM	ABEFNRS 8
4 OPQ	J 9
5 ABDEFHKN**O**	AGHIJPTUV 10
10A	❶ €29.40
4ha 200**T**(60-80m²) 20**P**	❷ €39.40

🚗 A9 Vigo-Pontevedra. Exit Pontevedra/O'Grove. Campsite is clearly signposted.

💬 Rural campsite with lovely swimming pool and new restaurant. With a pavement café and located by typical Gallego villages. Located 100 metres from the sea.

◪ N 42°28'29'' W 8°55'31''
www.eurocampings.co.uk/112214

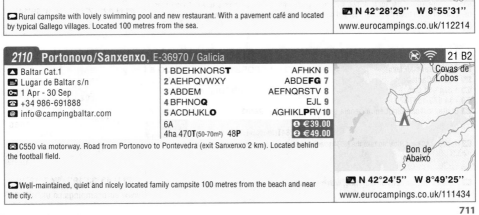

2110 Portonovo/Sanxenxo, E-36970 / Galicia — 21 B2

- ▲ Baltar Cat.1
- 🏕 Lugar de Baltar s/n
- 🗓 1 Apr - 30 Sep
- ☎ +34 986-691888
- @ info@campingbaltar.com

1 BDEHKNORS**T**	AFHKN 6
2 AEHPQVWXY	ABDE**FG** 7
3 ABDEM	AEFNQRSTV 8
4 BFHNO**Q**	EJL 9
5 ACDHJKL**O**	AGHIKL**P**RV 10
6A	❶ €39.00
4ha 470**T**(50-70m²) 48**P**	❷ €49.00

🚗 C550 via motorway. Road from Portonovo to Pontevedra (exit Sanxenxo 2 km). Located behind the football field.

💬 Well-maintained, quiet and nicely located family campsite 100 metres from the beach and near the city.

◪ N 42°24'5'' W 8°49'25''
www.eurocampings.co.uk/111434

Spain

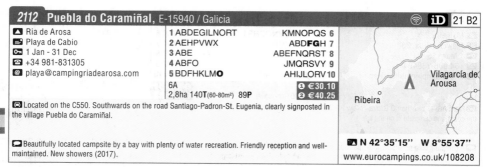

2111 Portonovo/Sanxenxo, E-36970 / Galicia

  ♿ 🛜 (CC€17) iD 21 B2

- ▲ Paxariñas Cat.2
- 🛏 Paxariñas 34
- ⚙ 15 Mar - 15 Oct
- ☎ +34 986-723055
- @ info@campingpaxarinas.com

1 ADEILNOPQRST	KMNQX 6
2 AEHMOPTUVX	ABDE**FG** 7
3 ABL	ABEFNRST 8
4 BO	IJLV 9
5 ACDEFHJL**NO**	ABFGHIJLPRV 10

10A   ❶ €33.20
2ha 205T(60-80m²) 82P   ❷ €43.40

🏨 Hotel and campsite complex face the sea. (C550). The entrance is on the bend. Clearly signposted.

💬 A beautifully located campsite on two large bays with beautiful sandy beaches, easily accessible for motorhomes. Reaches down to the sea with all amenities at the hotel complex. A convenient starting point for visits in the area and the special bathing resort Sanxenxo.

(CC) 15/3-1/7   1/9-14/10   8=7, 15=12

Marín

Bueu

📍 N 42°23'32'' W 8°50'39''

www.eurocampings.co.uk/101084

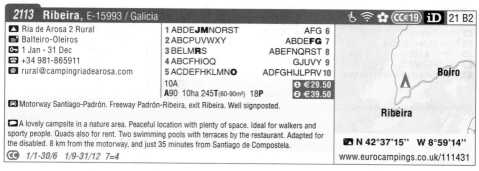

2112 Puebla do Caramiñal, E-15940 / Galicia

  🛜 iD 21 B2

- ▲ Ria de Arosa
- 🛏 Playa de Cabio
- ⚙ 1 Jan - 31 Dec
- ☎ +34 981-831305
- @ playa@campingriadearosa.com

1 ABDEGILNORT	KMNOPQS 6
2 AEHPVWX	ABD**FGH** 7
3 ABE	ABEFNRST 8
4 ABFO	JMQRSVY 9
5 BDFHKLM**O**	AHIJLORV 10

6A   ❶ €30.10
2,8ha 140T(60-80m²) 89P   ❷ €40.25

🏨 Located on the C550. Southwards on the road Santiago-Padron-St. Eugenia, clearly signposted in the village Puebla do Caramiñal.

💬 Beautifully located campsite by a bay with plenty of water recreation. Friendly reception and well-maintained. New showers (2017).

Vilagarcía de Arousa

Ribeira

📍 N 42°35'15'' W 8°55'37''

www.eurocampings.co.uk/108208

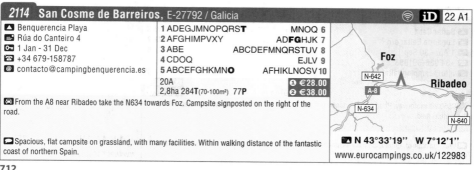

2113 Ribeira, E-15993 / Galicia

  ♿ 🛜 ⚙ (CC€19) iD 21 B2

- ▲ Ria de Arosa 2 Rural
- 🛏 Balteiro-Oleiros
- ⚙ 1 Jan - 31 Dec
- ☎ +34 981-865911
- @ rural@campingriadearosa.com

1 ABDE**JM**NORST	AFG 6
2 ABCPUVWXY	ABDE**FG** 7
3 BELM**RS**	ABEFNRST 8
4 ABCFHIOQ	GJUVY 9
5 ACDEFHKLMN**O**	ADFGHIJLPRV 10

10A
A90 10ha 245T(60-90m²) 18P   ❶ €29.50
        ❷ €39.50

🏨 Motorway Santiago-Padrón. Freeway Padrón-Ribeira, exit Ribeira. Well signposted.

💬 A lovely campsite in a nature area. Peaceful location with plenty of space. Ideal for walkers and sporty people. Quads also for rent. Two swimming pools with terraces by the restaurant. Adapted for the disabled. 8 km from the motorway, and just 35 minutes from Santiago de Compostela.

(CC) 1/1-30/6   1/9-31/12   7=4

Boiro

Ribeira

📍 N 42°37'15'' W 8°59'14''

www.eurocampings.co.uk/111431

2114 San Cosme de Barreiros, E-27792 / Galicia

  🛜 iD 22 A1

- ▲ Benquerencia Playa
- 🛏 Rúa do Canteiro 4
- ⚙ 1 Jan - 31 Dec
- ☎ +34 679-158787
- @ contacto@campingbenquerencia.es

1 ADEGJMNOPQRS**T**	MNOQ 6
2 AFGHIMPVXY	AD**FG**HJK 7
3 ABE	ABCDEFMNQRSTUV 8
4 CDOQ	EJLV 9
5 ABCEFGHKMN**O**	AFHIKLNOSV 10

20A   ❶ €28.00
2,8ha 284T(70-100m²) 77P   ❷ €38.00

🏨 From the A8 near Ribadeo take the N634 towards Foz. Campsite signposted on the right of the road.

💬 Spacious, flat campsite on grassland, with many facilities. Within walking distance of the fantastic coast of northern Spain.

Foz

N-642

A-8

Ribadeo

N-634

N-640

📍 N 43°33'19'' W 7°12'1''

www.eurocampings.co.uk/122983

2115 San Vicente do Mar, E-36988 / Galicia 🤶 iD 21 B2

- 🔺 O'Espiño Cat. 2
- 📧 Lanzada San Vicente do Mar
- 🔾 1 Jan - 31 Dec
- ☎ +34 986-738365
- @ info@campingoespino.com

1 ADEILNOPRST	KMNQSXZ 6
2 AEFHPUVWXY	ABD**F**H 7
3	AEFKNQRSTUV 8
4 FHO	9
5 ABDEHJN**O**	HIJORV 10
6A	❶ €28.10
2,1ha 110**T**(60-80m²) 90**P**	❷ €37.30

🚗 From C550 to Sanxenxo-O' Grove direction San Vicente. By car (no toll) via Couro-Sanxenxo Rua Rapida-O'Grove-Lanzada-San Vicente do Mar. Signposted.

💬 Lovely, small and well-maintained campsite. Friendly service and clean toilet facilities. Beautiful peninsula with lovely beaches. Quiet location (weekends are busier, in August in particular).

🗺 N 42°27'42'' W 8°55'5''

www.eurocampings.co.uk/111008

2116 San Vicente do Mar, E-36988 / Galicia 🤶 iD 21 B2

- 🔺 Siglo XXI Cat. 1
- 📧 Rua do Barrosa
- 🔾 7/4 - 17/4, 1/6 - 30/9
- ☎ +34 986-738100
- @ info@campingsiglo21.com

1 ABDEILNOR**T**	AFKMNQSWX 6
2 EHOPVWX	ABD**F** 7
3 AE**I**	ABCEFLMNQRTUV 8
4 O**P**	L 9
5 BCDFHKLM**O**	AGHIJPTUV 10
5A	❶ €37.00
A60 1,6ha 124**T**(60-80m²) 70**P**	❷ €48.00

🚗 Motorway Pontevedra-Santiago, exit O'Grove 25 km.

💬 Charming campsite with toilet facilities on each pitch; highly recommended. Quietly located by the beach. Good restaurant.

🗺 N 42°27'17'' W 8°55'32''

www.eurocampings.co.uk/111432

Spain

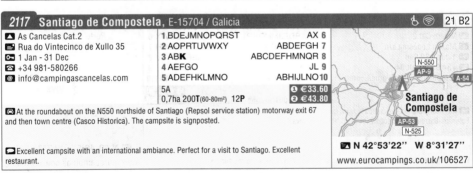

2117 Santiago de Compostela, E-15704 / Galicia ♿ 🤶 21 B2

- 🔺 As Cancelas Cat.2
- 📧 Rua do Vintecinco de Xullo 35
- 🔾 1 Jan - 31 Dec
- ☎ +34 981-580266
- @ info@campingascancelas.com

1 BDEJMNOPQRST	AX 6
2 AOPRTUVWXY	ABDEFGH 7
3 AB**K**	ABCDEFHMNQR 8
4 AEFGO	JL 9
5 ADEFHKLMNO	ABHIJLNO 10
5A	❶ €33.60
0,7ha 200**T**(60-80m²) 12**P**	❷ €43.80

🚗 At the roundabout on the N550 northside of Santiago (Repsol service station) motorway exit 67 and then town centre (Casco Historica). The campsite is signposted.

💬 Excellent campsite with an international ambiance. Perfect for a visit to Santiago. Excellent restaurant.

🗺 N 42°53'22'' W 8°31'27''

www.eurocampings.co.uk/106527

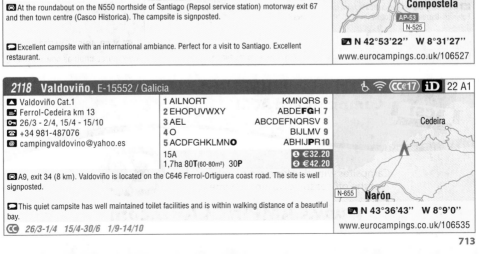

2118 Valdoviño, E-15552 / Galicia ♿ 🤶 (CC€17) iD 22 A1

- 🔺 Valdoviño Cat.1
- 📧 Ferrol-Cedeira km 13
- 🔾 26/3 - 2/4, 15/4 - 15/10
- ☎ +34 981-487076
- @ campingvaldovino@yahoo.es

1 AILNOR**T**	KMNQRS 6
2 EHOPUVWXY	ABDE**FG**H 7
3 AEL	ABCDEFNQRSV 8
4 O	BIJLMV 9
5 ACDFGHKLMN**O**	ABHIJ**PR**10
15A	❶ €32.20
1,7ha 80**T**(60-80m²) 30**P**	❷ €42.20

🚗 A9, exit 34 (8 km). Valdoviño is located on the C646 Ferrol-Ortiguera coast road. The site is well signposted.

💬 This quiet campsite has well maintained toilet facilities and is within walking distance of a beautiful bay.

CC 26/3-1/4 15/4-30/6 1/9-14/10

🗺 N 43°36'43'' W 8°9'0''

www.eurocampings.co.uk/106535

2119 Vilanova de Arousa, E-36620 / Galicia 📶 iD 21 B2

- 🏕 Playa Paisaxe I
- 📧 Playa de O Terròn, 16
- 📅 7 Apr - 30 Sep
- ☎ +34 986-554656
- @ info@campingplayapaisaxe.com

1 ADEILNORT	AKMNO 6
2 AEHOP	ABD**F**H 7
3 A**KL**	ABEFNRST 8
4 OP**Q**	J 9
5 ABDEFHKMN**O**	AHIJPRV 10
10A	❶ €34.00
1,3ha 130T(60-80m²) 45**P**	❷ €44.00

🅰 AP/9 Pontevedra-O'Grove-Vigo-Pontevedra. Pontevedra-Cambados-Villanova. (Clearly signposted).

Vilagarcía de Arousa
Ribeira

📷 N 42°33'6'' W 8°50'2''

💬 Lovely campsite by the sea. International ambiance. Easily accessible, lovely swimming pool.

www.eurocampings.co.uk/112213

2120 Villagarcia de Arosa, E-36600 / Galicia ♿ 📶 21 B2

- 🏕 Río Ulla Cat. 2a
- 📧 Bamio
- 📅 25 Mar - 16 Sep
- ☎ +34 986-505430
- @ campingrioulla@galicia.com

1 BJMNOPQRST	AFKNQRSXY 6
2 AEFHPVWXY	ABD**FG**H 7
3 BELM	AEFNQRST 8
4 FHINOR	IJLRV 9
5 ABDFHJKMN**O**	AGHIJLMPTUV 10
10A CEE	❶ €28.10
1ha 83T(60-80m²) 42**P**	❷ €37.10

🅰 Located on Po 548 Santiago-Cesures-Villagarcia direction Bamio, km 14. Clearly signposted in Villagarcia de Arosa.

Lestrove
N-550
AP-9
Vilagarcía de Arousa

💬 Beautiful and well-maintained campsite by the sea, with a swimming pool. Perfect operating base for a visit to the region. Just 35 km from Santiago. Perfect for motorhomes. Magnificent for windsurfers and kite surfers.

📷 N 42°38'4'' W 8°45'35''

www.eurocampings.co.uk/110543

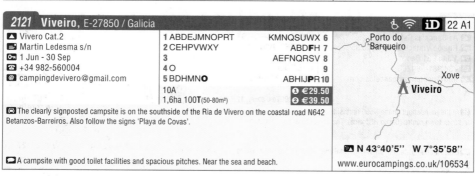

2121 Viveiro, E-27850 / Galicia ♿ 📶 iD 22 A1

- 🏕 Vivero Cat.2
- 📧 Martin Ledesma s/n
- 📅 1 Jun - 30 Sep
- ☎ +34 982-560004
- @ campingdevivero@gmail.com

1 ABDEJMNOPRT	KMNQSUWX 6
2 CEHPVWXY	ABD**F**H 7
3	AEFNQRSV 8
4 O	9
5 BDHMN**O**	ABHIJ**PR**10
10A	❶ €29.50
1,6ha 100T(50-80m²)	❷ €39.50

🅰 The clearly signposted campsite is on the southside of the Ria de Vivero on the coastal road N642 Betanzos-Barreiros. Also follow the signs 'Playa de Covas'.

Porto do Barqueiro
Xove
Viveiro

💬 A campsite with good toilet facilities and spacious pitches. Near the sea and beach.

📷 N 43°40'5'' W 7°35'58''

www.eurocampings.co.uk/106534

Spain

Asturias

Coste Verde

Located on the north coast of Spain between the Cantabrian Mountains and Cantabrian Sea, Asturias is Spain's best-kept secret. This verdant, mountainous region with a glorious coastline has a rocky streak – unlike most of Spain, it was never really conquered by either the Romans or the Moors, and today remains autonomous.

Distinctly Asturian

Today you see a distinctly Asturian pre-Romanesque architecture, and two examples of this are in Oviedo: the Santa María de Naranco church and San Miguel de Lillo palace, as well as the Foncalada, built by Asturian kings. Wander further through Oviedo and see ornate Baroque façades and elegant Art Nouveau buildings, and take a break along La Escandalera. Coastal

city Gijón is the largest of Asturias, and many industrial buildings have been converted – the Railway Museum is a classic example, and sure to appeal to train enthusiasts. Gijón's museums suit every taste: Contemporary Art and Culture, Campa Torres Archaeological Park, and an International Bagpipe Museum. All this and great beaches too!

Day trips and places to visit

Spend a day at the beach and explore the rock pools at low tide, or cycle along the coastline. Visit the Jurassic Museum of Asturias, make sure you take a selfie with the kids and a T-rex in the Museum gardens. Explore the depths of the earth in the Mining Museum in El Entrego, or take a look around the Bustiello Mining Village Interpretation Centre.

Head for the mountains: molar-shaped Picu Urriellu in Picos de Europa National Park glows orange in the evening sun, and you might spot some wildlife: chamois, golden eagles, buzzards,

Our tips

1. See great contemporary architecture at the Niermeyer Centre in Aviles
2. Go canoeing in Ubiñas-la-Mesa and walking in Cangas de Onis
3. Follow the coastal road between Pendueles and Llianes for amazing scenery
4. Visit the Altamira Caves and see art made during Palaeolithic times
5. Join the procession and dance until dawn during Las Fiestas de Camen in Luanco

vultures, even bears and wolves. Covadonga, just inside Picos de Europa, is where Virgin Mary blessed Asturian Christian forces with a well-timed signal to attack and defeat Spain's Moorish conquerors in the Battle of Covadonga. You can still visit the cave.

What to eat and drink

Sit down to a meal of Fabada Asturiana, a stew of pork and beans, or try some morzilla or black pudding, and you already know spicy chorizo. What about some cabrales blue cheese? Try it with some local wine, or some Asturian cider. Or go to the El Gaitero Cider Factory in Villaviciosa.

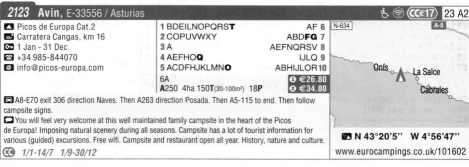

2122 Arenas de Cabrales (Asturias), E-33554 / Asturias ⟨wifi⟩ 23 A2

- ▲ Naranjo de Bulnes C.B. Cat.2
- ⌾ 23 Mar - 30 Sep
- ☎ +34 985-846578
- @ campingnaranjodebulnes@gmail.com

1	BDEILNOPRT		6
2	COPUVWXY	ABDFGH	7
3	A	AEFNQRS	8
4	HO	FJ	9
5	ABDEFJK	ABHIJNOR	10
6A		❶ €32.00	
A135 3ha 211T(25-90m²) 24P		❷ €43.20	

🔲 Route Panes-Cangas de Onis, 20 km from Panes, 35 km from Cangas. Located on the N6312.

💬 Campsite in the Picos de Europa, near trails and with proper amenities for an active holiday.

San Roque del Acebal

Sotres

◼ N 43°18'1''   W 4°48'11''

www.eurocampings.co.uk/106598

2123 Avin, E-33556 / Asturias ♿ ⟨wifi⟩ (CC€17) 23 A2

- ▲ Picos de Europa Cat.2
- 🚍 Carratera Cangas, km 16
- ⌾ 1 Jan - 31 Dec
- ☎ +34 985-844070
- @ info@picos-europa.com

1	BDEILNOPQRST	AF	6
2	COPUVWXY	ABDFG	7
3	A	AEFNQRSV	8
4	AEFHOQ	IJLQ	9
5	ACDFHJKLMNO	ABHIJLOR	10
6A		❶ €26.80	
A250 4ha 150T(30-100m²) 18P		❷ €34.80	

🔲 A8-E70 exit 306 direction Naves. Then A263 direction Posada. Then A5-115 to end. Then follow campsite signs.

💬 You will feel very welcome at this well maintained family campsite in the heart of the Picos de Europa! Imposing natural scenery during all seasons. Campsite has a lot of tourist information for various (guided) excursions. Free wifi. Campsite and restaurant open all year. History, nature and culture.

ⓒⓒ 1/1-14/7 1/9-30/12

Onís   La Salce

Cabrales

◼ N 43°20'5''   W 4°56'47''

www.eurocampings.co.uk/101602

Spain

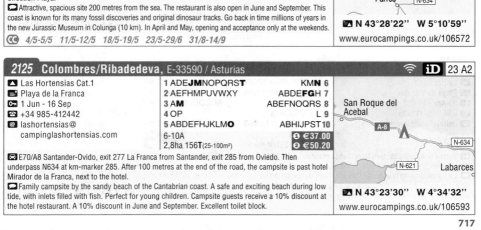

2124 Caravia/Prado, E-33344 / Asturias ⟨wifi⟩ (CC€19) iD 23 A1

- ▲ Arenal de Morís Cat.1
- 🚍 El Ponton
- ⌾ 4/5-6/5,11/5-13/5,18/5-20/5
- ☎ +34 985-853097
- @ camoris@desdeasturias.com

1	ABDEJMNOPQRST	AKMNQSWX	6
2	AEHKPRTUVW	ADFGH	7
3	BLM	AEFNQRTU	8
4	OP	I	9
5	ACDEFHIJKMN	ABFHIJOR	10
10A		❶ €35.85	
6ha 260T(50-150m²) 51P		❷ €44.65	

🔲 E70/A8 Santander-Oviedo. Exit 330. Direction Caravia, then N632 between 16 and 15 km posts direction Playa.

💬 Attractive, spacious site 200 metres from the sea. The restaurant is also open in June and September. This coast is known for its many fossil discoveries and original dinosaur tracks. Go back in time millions of years in the new Jurassic Museum in Colunga (10 km). In April and May, opening and acceptance only at the weekends.

ⓒⓒ 4/5-5/5 11/5-12/5 18/5-19/5 23/5-29/6 31/8-14/9

Ribadesella

Parres

◼ N 43°28'22''   W 5°10'59''

www.eurocampings.co.uk/106572

2125 Colombres/Ribadedeva, E-33590 / Asturias ⟨wifi⟩ iD 23 A2

- ▲ Las Hortensias Cat.1
- 🚍 Playa de la Franca
- ⌾ 1 Jun - 16 Sep
- ☎ +34 985-412442
- @ lashortensias@
  campinglashortensias.com

1	ADEJMNOPQRST	KMN	6
2	AEFHMPUVWXY	ABDEFGH	7
3	AM	ABEFNOQRS	8
4	OP	L	9
5	ABDEFHJKLMO	ABHIJPST	10
6-10A		❶ €37.00	
2,8ha 156T(25-100m²)		❷ €50.20	

🔲 E70/A8 Santander-Ovido, exit 277 La Franca from Santander, exit 285 from Oviedo. Then underpass N634 at km-marker 285. After 100 metres at the end of the road, the campsite is past hotel Mirador de la Franca, next to the hotel.

💬 Family campsite by the sandy beach of the Cantabrian coast. A safe and exciting beach during low tide, with inlets filled with fish. Perfect for young children. Campsite guests receive a 10% discount at the hotel restaurant. A 10% discount in June and September. Excellent toilet block.

San Roque del Acebal

Labarces

◼ N 43°23'30''   W 4°34'32''

www.eurocampings.co.uk/106593

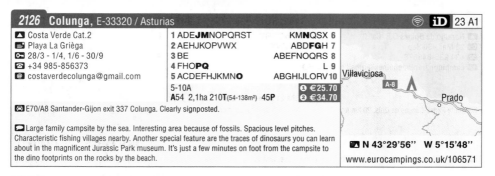

2126 Colunga, E-33320 / Asturias

⌃ 23 A1

- ⛰ Costa Verde Cat.2
- 🏖 Playa La Grièga
- ⊟ 28/3 - 1/4, 1/6 - 30/9
- ☎ +34 985-856373
- @ costaverdecolunga@gmail.com

1 ADE**JM**NOPQRST	KMN**QSX** 6
2 AEHJKOPVWX	ABD**FGH** 7
3 BE	ABEFNOQRS 8
4 FHO**PQ**	L 9
5 ACDEFHJKMN**O**	ABGHIJLORV 10
5-10A	❶ €25.70
A54 2,1ha 210**T**(54-138m²) 45**P**	❷ €34.70

🚫 E70/A8 Santander-Gijon exit 337 Colunga. Clearly signposted.

💬 Large family campsite by the sea. Interesting area because of fossils. Spacious level pitches. Characteristic fishing villages nearby. Another special feature are the traces of dinosaurs you can learn about in the magnificent Jurassic Park museum. It's just a few minutes on foot from the campsite to the dino footprints on the rocks by the beach.

📍 N 43°29'56" W 5°15'48"

www.eurocampings.co.uk/106571

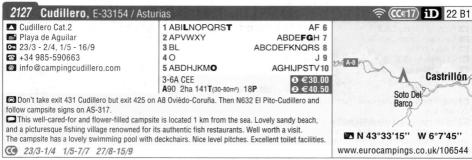

2127 Cudillero, E-33154 / Asturias

⌃ (CC€17) 22 B1

- ⛰ Cudillero Cat.2
- 🏖 Playa de Aguilar
- ⊟ 23/3 - 2/4, 1/5 - 16/9
- ☎ +34 985-590663
- @ info@campingcudillero.com

1 ABI**L**NOPQRS**T**	AF 6
2 APVWXY	ABDE**FG**H 7
3 BL	ABCDEFKNQRS 8
4 O	J 9
5 ABDHJKM**O**	AGHIJPSTV 10
3-6A CEE	❶ €30.00
A90 2ha 141**T**(30-80m²) 18**P**	❷ €40.50

🚫 Don't take exit 431 Cudillero but exit 425 on A8 Oviedo-Coruña. Then N632 El Pito-Cudillero and follow campsite signs on AS-317.

💬 This well-cared-for and flower-filled campsite is located 1 km from the sea. Lovely sandy beach, and a picturesque fishing village renowned for its authentic fish restaurants. Well worth a visit. The campsite has a lovely swimming pool with deckchairs. Nice level pitches. Excellent toilet facilities.

CC 23/3-1/4 1/5-7/7 27/8-15/9

📍 N 43°33'15" W 6°7'45"

www.eurocampings.co.uk/106544

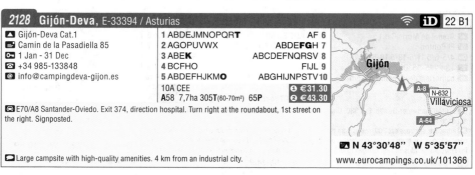

2128 Gijón-Deva, E-33394 / Asturias

⌃ 22 B1

- ⛰ Gijón-Deva Cat.1
- 🏖 Camin de la Pasadiella 85
- ⊟ 1 Jan - 31 Dec
- ☎ +34 985-133848
- @ info@campingdeva-gijon.es

1 ABDEJMNOPQR**T**	AF 6
2 AGOPUVWX	ABDE**FG**H 7
3 ABE**K**	ABCDEFNQRSV 8
4 BCFHO	FIJL 9
5 ABDEFHJKM**O**	ABGHIJNPSTV 10
10A CEE	❶ €31.30
A58 7,7ha 305**T**(60-70m²) 65**P**	❷ €43.30

🚫 E70/A8 Santander-Oviedo. Exit 374, direction hospital. Turn right at the roundabout, 1st street on the right. Signposted.

💬 Large campsite with high-quality amenities. 4 km from an industrial city.

📍 N 43°30'48" W 5°35'57"

www.eurocampings.co.uk/101366

2129 Llanes/Vidiago, E-33597 / Asturias

⌃ (CC€19) 23 A2

- ⛰ La Paz Cat.1
- 🏖 Playa de Vidiago
- ⊟ 23 Apr - 14 Oct
- ☎ +34 985-411235
- @ delfin@campinglapaz.com

1 BDE**JM**NOPQRT	K**N**PQS 6
2 AEFHMNOPUVWXY	ABDE**FG**H 7
3 A**K**Q	ABCDEFNQRSV 8
4 AFHO**PQ**	L 9
5 ACDEFJKLMN**O**	ABDGHIJOR 10
10-16A	❶ €38.00
1,1ha 432**T**(40-90m²)	❷ €50.50

🚫 Motorway A8 exit 285, then from Ovieda roundabout dir. N634 Unguera, 2nd roundabout Playa de Vidiago from Santander, exit Playa de Vidiago, site.

💬 A terraced site with fine views of the sea. Picos de Europa (30 min). Caravans towed to and from the pitch. Not much shade on the side facing the sea. Enjoy a beautiful sunset in the restaurant. Due to big differences in high and low tides you have wonderful wide beaches. Good renovated toilet facilities.

CC 23/4-29/6 1/9-13/10

📍 N 43°23'59" W 4°39'11"

www.eurocampings.co.uk/100914

2130 Luarca, E-33700 / Asturias

 🚹 🛜 **iD** 22 B1

- ◮ Los Cantiles Cat.1
- ▣ Los Cantiles
- ☷ 1 Jan - 31 Dec
- ☎ +34 985-640938
- @ cantiles@campingloscantiles.com

1 ABJMNOPQRST	6
2 AEFMOPUVWXY	ABDEFGH 7
3 L	ABEFKNOQRSV 8
4 O	F 9
5 BDNO	AFGHJNOSTV 10

3-6A   ❶ €23.55
A70 2,3ha 72T(65-90m²) 7P   ❷ €31.95

🅿 A8 Oviedo-A Coruña exit km 460. Follow direction Luarca and turn right at the service station. Follow the signs. Do not follow SatNav.

💬 Lovely and well-maintained campsite with hydrangeas and a view of the sea. Dutch manager. Nearby a friendly town. Daily fish market in Luarca. Options for cooking and staying in accommodation in early and late season.

📷 N 43°32'57''   W 6°31'28''

www.eurocampings.co.uk/106545

2131 Perlora/Candás, E-33491 / Asturias

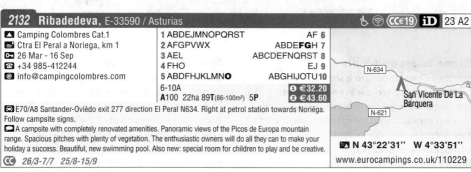

 🛜 22 B1

- ◮ Perlora s.l. Cat.2
- ▣ Perán s/n
- ☷ 19 Jan - 9 Dec
- ☎ +34 985-870048
- @ recepcion@campingperlora.com

1 BDILOPRT	KMNOPQ 6
2 AEHJKMOPUVW	ABDEFG 7
3 M	ABNQR 8
4 NO	9
5 ABDEHIJMNO	ABHIKO 10

6-10A CEE   ❶ €27.50
1,4ha 85T(55-65m²) 30P   ❷ €36.30

🅿 E70/A8 exit 397 Candás/Luarca. AS110 Perán-Perlora. Exit AS110 Luarca. AS118 direction Perlora, follow the campsite signs.

💬 From this medium-sized campsite you can walk to a typical Spanish town via the boulevard. Beautifully located on the rocky coast. Well-maintained toilet facilities.

📷 N 43°35'2''   W 5°45'22''

www.eurocampings.co.uk/115260

2132 Ribadedeva, E-33590 / Asturias

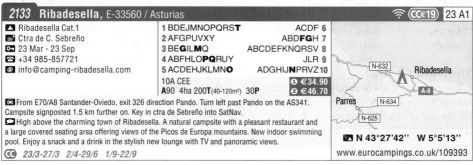

 🚹 🛜 **CC€19** **iD** 23 A2

- ◮ Camping Colombres Cat.1
- ▣ Ctra El Peral a Noriega, km 1
- ☷ 26 Mar - 16 Sep
- ☎ +34 985-412244
- @ info@campingcolombres.com

1 ABDEJMNOPQRST	AF 6
2 AFGPVWX	ABDEFGH 7
3 AEL	ABCDEFNQRST 8
4 FHO	EJ 9
5 ABDFHJKLMNO	ABGHIJOTU 10

6-10A   ❶ €32.20
A100 22ha 89T(86-100m²) 5P   ❷ €43.60

🅿 E70/A8 Santander-Oviedo exit 277 direction El Peral N634. Right at petrol station towards Noriega. Follow campsite signs.

💬 A campsite with completely renovated amenities. Panoramic views of the Picos de Europa mountain range. Spacious pitches with plenty of vegetation. The enthusiastic owners will do all they can to make your holiday a success. Beautiful, new swimming pool. Also new: special room for children to play and be creative.

ⒸⒸ 26/3-7/7   25/8-15/9

📷 N 43°22'31''   W 4°33'51''

www.eurocampings.co.uk/110229

2133 Ribadesella, E-33560 / Asturias

 🛜 **CC€19** 23 A1

- ◮ Ribadesella Cat.1
- ▣ Ctra de C. Sebreño
- ☷ 23 Mar - 23 Sep
- ☎ +34 985-857721
- @ info@camping-ribadesella.com

1 BDEJMNOPQRST	ACDF 6
2 AFGPUVXY	ABDFGH 7
3 BEGILMQ	ABCDEFKNQRSV 8
4 ABFHLOPQRUY	JLR 9
5 ACDEHJKLMNO	ADGHIJNPRVZ 10

10A CEE   ❶ €34.90
A90 4ha 200T(40-120m²) 30P   ❷ €46.70

🅿 From E70/A8 Santander-Oviedo, exit 326 direction Pando. Turn left past Pando on the AS341. Campsite signposted 1.5 km further on. Key in ctra de Sebreño into SatNav.

💬 High above the charming town of Ribadesella. A natural campsite with a pleasant restaurant and a large covered seating area offering views of the Picos de Europa mountains. New indoor swimming pool. Enjoy a snack and a drink in the stylish new lounge with TV and panoramic views.

ⒸⒸ 23/3-27/3   2/4-29/6   1/9-22/9

📷 N 43°27'42''   W 5°5'13''

www.eurocampings.co.uk/109393

Stone boars and bulls

You might be surprised to learn that Castile and Leon are two regions in one, located to the east of Portugal, and bordering Madrid, the Spanish capital. Geographical labels aside, it's a captivating region: dominated by a high plateau of mountains, crossed with rivers and forests, historic towns and cities. The Romans left their mark too: not just the aqueduct at Segovia, but also the mines at Las Médulas. You're also sure to come across a verracos, a megalithic stone sculpture of a boar or a bull.

The Devil's Bridge

Legend has it that the Segovia aqueduct was built by the devil in one night, in exchange for the soul of a young woman – but he didn't get her because the sun rose before he was finished! By contrast, Madrid is a much younger city, dating from the 9th century, and its great prosperity from the discovery and colonisation of the Americas helped create the Palacio Real, Botanical Gardens and the Palacio de Villenueva, now the Prado Museum. Explore Madrid's numerous art museums, then take a break in the the Parque del Buen Retiro, or check out San Miguel market. Walk around the University city of Salamanca and see all kinds of architectural styles: Romanesque, Renaissance, Moorish, Baroque, Art Nouveau and 20th century, many near Plaza Mayor. Note: here, tapas are 'pinchos'.

¡Vamonos!

Sierra de Atapuerca, where prehistoric human remains and fossils have been found, is sure to fascinate your budding young scientist, while the

Did you know ...?
The famous Snow White castle in the Disney movie was inspired by Alcázar castle in Segovia.

And that Sobrino de Botín, the oldest restaurant in the world, is located in Madrid? Tuck into veal and lamb dishes with chickpeas and lentils, or savour suckling pig, washed down with Toro wines from Zamora, followed by yemas, which are sugared egg yolks.

wild goats, Iberian Imperial eagles and buzzards in Sierra de Gredos appeal to animal lovers. Las Hoces del rio Duraton has it all: a series of gorges for thrill-seekers, and for bird-watchers there are griffons and Egyptian vultures, golden eagles and peregrine falcons, while history buffs can explore the hermitage of San Frutos, the caves with Bronze Age engravings, or the Sepúlveda architectural complex.

Celebrate food

Did you know that Madrid hosts a Festival of Gastronomy in February every year?

Our tips

1. Visit the Cathedral and the Museum of Human Evolution in Burgos
2. Walk to San Bartolome's Hermitage in Canon Del Rio Lobos, built by Templars
3. See the mediaeval city walls of Avila, and learn about Saint Teresa
4. Check out the mysterious chambers of the Valporquero caves
5. Explore the beautiful hilltop village of Pedraza

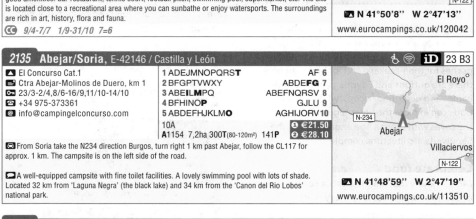

2134 Abejar, E-42146 / Castilla y León

 🚲 🛜 (CC€19) iD 23 B3

- 🏔 Urbion
- 🏕 Ctra Soria-Burgos, N234
- 📅 23 Mar - 1 Nov
- ☎ +34 646-243349
- @ info@campingurbion.com

1 ADE**JM**NOPQRS**T**	AF**N**QSXY	6
2 BDFGIPTWXY	ABD**E**F	7
3 BELM	ABEFJNQRSV	8
4 ABFHIO**P**	JRTU	9
5 ABDEFHJKLM**O**	AGHIJLOVW	10
10A		❶ €32.20
A1200 15ha 500T(120m²) 52P		❷ €42.80

🗺 From Soria take the N234 dir. Burgos, in Abejar towards Molinos on the CL117, campsite 4 km on the right.
💬 A spacious campsite for a wonderful, relaxing stay in beautiful natural surroundings. The site has good amenities: bar-restaurant, tennis court, football pitch, swimming pool, supermarket, etc. The site is located close to a recreational area where you can sunbathe or enjoy watersports. The surroundings are rich in art, history, flora and fauna.

CC 9/4-7/7 1/9-31/10 7=6

🗺 N 41°50'8'' W 2°47'13''

www.eurocampings.co.uk/120042

2135 Abejar/Soria, E-42146 / Castilla y León

 🚲 🛜 iD 23 B3

- 🏔 El Concurso Cat.1
- 🏕 Ctra Abejar-Molinos de Duero, km 1
- 📅 23/3-2/4,8/6-16/9,11/10-14/10
- ☎ +34 975-373361
- @ info@campingelconcurso.com

1 ADEJMNOPQRS**T**	AF	6
2 BFGPTVWXY	ABDE**FG**	7
3 ABE**IL**M**PQ**	ABEFNQRSV	8
4 BFHINO**P**	GJLU	9
5 ABDEFHJKLM**O**	AGHIJORV	10
10A		❶ €21.50
A1154 7,2ha 300T(80-120m²) 141P		❷ €28.10

🗺 From Soria take the N234 direction Burgos, turn right 1 km past Abejar, follow the CL117 for approx. 1 km. The campsite is on the left side of the road.

💬 A well-equipped campsite with fine toilet facilities. A lovely swimming pool with lots of shade. Located 32 km from 'Laguna Negra' (the black lake) and 34 km from the 'Canon del Rio Lobos' national park.

🗺 N 41°48'59'' W 2°47'19''

www.eurocampings.co.uk/113510

2136 Aranjuez (Madrid), E-28300 / Madrid

 🚲 🛜 (CC€19) iD 31 B2

- 🏔 Camping Internacional Aranjuez Cat.1
- 🏕 C/ Soto del Rebollo s/n
- 📅 1 Jan - 31 Dec
- ☎ +34 91-8911395
- @ info@campingaranjuez.com

1 ABDEJMNOPQRST	AFI**NUX**	6
2 ACPQVWXY	ABDE**FGH**	7
3 BE**GK**LQS	ABCDEFJNQRSTUV	8
4 BCDLO	GIJLR	9
5 ACDEFGHJKLM**N**O	ABCDEGHIJ**NO**PTU	10
Ad on this page 16A CEE		❶ €38.00
A600 3ha 147T(35-110m²) 65P		❷ €50.00

🗺 From Madrid A4 exit 37 Aranjuez Norte. Turn left after 8 km before Aranjuez and follow camping signs. From the south exit 52, then straight through the town. On the left next to 'La Rana Verde'. Follow campsite signs.
💬 Friendly, helpful staff. Site is located on the River Tajo. Plenty of vegetation. 42 km from Madrid, 40 km from Toledo. A lovely palace at Aranjuez. Gardens, avenues, fountains, flowers and plenty of walks. Trains to the heart of Madrid.

CC 1/1-27/3 2/4-25/4 2/5-27/6 2/9-31/12 7=6, 14=11

🗺 N 40°2'32'' W 3°35'58''

www.eurocampings.co.uk/106630

Spain

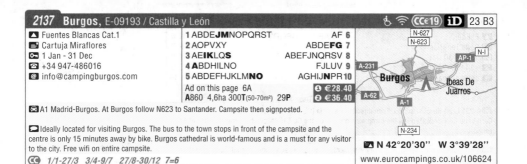

2137 Burgos, E-09193 / Castilla y León ♿ 🛜 (CC€19) iD 23 B3

- 🔺 Fuentes Blancas Cat.1
- 📧 Cartuja Miraflores
- 🗓 1 Jan - 31 Dec
- ☎ +34 947-486016
- @ info@campingburgos.com

1 ABDE**JM**NOPQRST	AF **6**
2 AOPVXY	ABDE**FG** **7**
3 AE**IKL**Q**S**	ABEFJNQRSV **8**
4 **A**BDHILNO	FJLUV **9**
5 ABDEFHJKLM**NO**	AGHIJ**N**PR **10**

Ad on this page 6A ❶ € 28.40
A860 4,6ha 300**T**(50-70m²) 29**P** ❷ € 36.40

🚗 A1 Madrid-Burgos. At Burgos follow N623 to Santander. Campsite then signposted.

💬 Ideally located for visiting Burgos. The bus to the town stops in front of the campsite and the centre is only 15 minutes away by bike. Burgos cathedral is world-famous and is a must for any visitor to the city. Free wifi on entire campsite.

CC 1/1-27/3 3/4-9/7 27/8-30/12 7=6

📍 N 42°20'30'' W 3°39'28''
www.eurocampings.co.uk/106624

This campsite is located 3 km from the centre of Burgos, a World Heritage City, and the Parque Natural de Fuentes Blancas. The campsite provides various amenities for the 300 pitches: a restaurant, bar, recreation room, free wifi throughout the entire grounds, a swimming pool and sports facilities. Entertainment in summer for all ages.

Cartuja Miraflores, 09193 Burgos
Tel. and fax 947-486016
E-mail: info@campingburgos.com
Internet: www.campingburgos.com

Spain

2138 Cabrerizos/Salamanca, E-37193 / Castilla y León ♿ 🛜 (CC€17) 🚻 iD 30 B1

- 🔺 Don Quijote***
- 📧 Ctra Aldealengua km 1,930
- 🗓 1 Mar - 31 Oct
- ☎ +34 923-209052
- @ info@campingdonquijote.com

1 ABDEILNOPQRS**T**	AFJNQX **6**
2 CHPQRVXY	ABDE**FG**H **7**
3 B	ABEFGINQR **8**
4 BHOP**Q**	JL **9**
5 ABCDEFHJKLN**O**	ABDGHIJPVW **10**

10A CEE ❶ € 23.65
A800 6ha 86**T**(70-100m²) 21**P** ❷ € 32.15

🚗 When entering Salamanca from any direction: follow the signs to Plaza de España, then follow the signs to Aldealengua village. The campsite is 4 km on the right from Plaza de España.
💬 Campsite close to the river and Salamanca, a town with plenty of sights. Friendly family campsite with different types of pitches available. A beautiful cycling/walking path runs along the river to the town. Renovated toilet facilities (2016).

CC 1/3-11/7 29/8-30/10 7=6, 14=11

📍 N 40°58'30'' W 5°36'11''
www.eurocampings.co.uk/100921

2139 Candelario/Salamanca, E-37710 / Castilla y León ⊗ ♿ 🛜 iD 30 B2

- 🔺 5 Castaños Cat.2
- 📧 Ctra de la Sierra s/n
- 🗓 14 Apr - 30 Sep
- ☎ +34 923-413204
- @ profetur@candelariohotel.com

1 ABDHKNORT	AFN **6**
2 BFGPQRSUVY	ABDE**F** **7**
3 A	ABFNQRS **8**
4 O	GJ **9**
5 ADEFHJKLMO	AHIJOR **10**

5-10A CEE ❶ € 24.65
A1167 1,6ha 54**T**(min 54m²) 71**P** ❷ € 33.00

🚗 Driving on N630 take one of the exits to Bejar. Follow the road to Candelario. Before the church and two telephone boxes in Candelario turn right, follow campsite signs.

💬 Beautiful mountain campsite in a perfect area for hikes in the mountains. The campsite has many shaded pitches and is mainly suitable for tent campers and smaller motorhomes and caravans.

📍 N 40°21'47'' W 5°45'1''
www.eurocampings.co.uk/101375

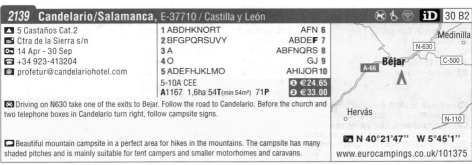

2140 Carrión de los Condes, E-34120 / Castilla y León 📶 iD 23 A3

- 🏕 El Edén
- ✉ Calle Tenerías 11
- 📅 1 Apr - 30 Oct
- ☎ +34 667-317891
- @ ciudaddecarrion@hotmail.com

1 ABJKNOPQRT	N	6
2 ACNPRWXY	ABDF	7
3	ABEFNPQRT	8
4 O	BD	9
5 ADHJKMNO	ABHIJPRW	10
6A CEE	❶ €19.80	
2ha 55T(80-140m²) 7P	❷ €26.40	

🗺 A-231 Leon-Burgos, exit 85. Then direction Palencia (CL-615). At second roundabout direction Carrión de los Condes. Follow the campsite signs. Or on the CL-615 follow the campsite signs at 1st roundabout.

💬 A campsite by the river in an old city with plenty of history nearby. Extensive information at the campsite. With a reasonably priced restaurant.

Carrión de los Condes
A-231 N-120

📷 N 42°20'9" W 4°36'16"

www.eurocampings.co.uk/115351

2141 Castrojeriz, E-09110 / Castilla y León 📶 CC€19 iD 23 A3

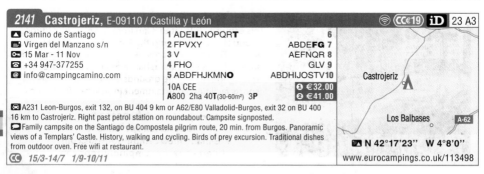

- 🏕 Camino de Santiago
- ✉ Virgen del Manzano s/n
- 📅 15 Mar - 11 Nov
- ☎ +34 947-377255
- @ info@campingcamino.com

1 ADEILNOPQRT		6
2 FPVXY	ABDEFG	7
3 V	AEFNQR	8
4 FHO	GLV	9
5 ABDFHJKMNO	ABDHIJOSTV	10
10A CEE	❶ €32.00	
A800 2ha 40T(30-60m²) 3P	❷ €41.00	

🗺 A231 Leon-Burgos, exit 132, on BU 404 9 km or A62/E80 Valladolid-Burgos, exit 32 on BU 400 16 km to Castrojeriz. Right past petrol station on roundabout. Campsite signposted.

💬 Family campsite on the Santiago de Compostela pilgrim route, 20 min. from Burgos. Panoramic views of a Templars' Castle. History, walking and cycling. Birds of prey excursion. Traditional dishes from outdoor oven. Free wifi at restaurant.

CC 15/3-14/7 1/9-10/11

Castrojeriz
Los Balbases A-62

📷 N 42°17'23" W 4°8'0"

www.eurocampings.co.uk/113498

2142 Ciudad Rodrigo/Salamanca, E-37500 / Castilla y León ♿ 📶 iD 30 A1

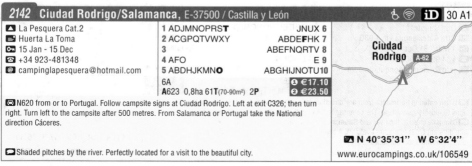

- 🏕 La Pesquera Cat.2
- ✉ Huerta La Toma
- 📅 15 Jan - 15 Dec
- ☎ +34 923-481348
- @ campinglapesquera@hotmail.com

1 ADJMNOPRST	JNUX	6
2 ACGPQTVWXY	ABDEFHK	7
3	ABEFNQRTV	8
4 AFO	E	9
5 ABDHJKMNO	ABGHIJNOTU	10
6A	❶ €17.10	
A623 0,8ha 61T(70-90m²) 2P	❷ €23.50	

🗺 N620 from or to Portugal. Follow campsite signs at Ciudad Rodrigo. Left at exit C326; then turn right. Turn left to the campsite after 500 metres. From Salamanca or Portugal take the National direction Cáceres.

💬 Shaded pitches by the river. Perfectly located for a visit to the beautiful city.

Ciudad Rodrigo A-62

📷 N 40°35'31" W 6°32'4"

www.eurocampings.co.uk/106549

2143 El Escorial/Madrid, E-28280 / Madrid ♿ 📶 CC€19 iD 31 A2

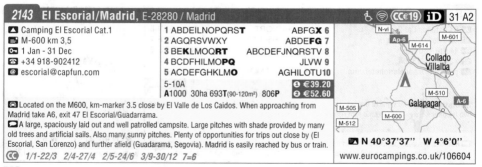

- 🏕 Camping El Escorial Cat.1
- ✉ M-600 km 3,5
- 📅 1 Jan - 31 Dec
- ☎ +34 918-902412
- @ escorial@capfun.com

1 ABDEILNOPQRST	ABFGX	6
2 AGQRSVWXY	ABDEFG	7
3 BEKLMOQRT	ABCDEFJNQRSTV	8
4 BCDFHILMOPQ	JLVW	9
5 ACDEFGHKLMO	AGHILOTU	10
5-10A	❶ €39.20	
A1000 30ha 693T(90-120m²) 806P	❷ €52.60	

🗺 Located on the M600, km-marker 3.5 close by El Valle de Los Caidos. When approaching from Madrid take A6, exit 47 El Escorial/Guadarrama.

💬 A large, spaciously laid out and well patrolled campsite. Large pitches with shade provided by many old trees and artificial sails. Also many sunny pitches. Plenty of opportunities for trips out close by (El Escorial, San Lorenzo) and further afield (Guadarama, Segovia). Madrid is easily reached by bus or train.

CC 1/1-22/3 2/4-27/4 2/5-24/6 3/9-30/12 7=6

N-vi M-601 M-614 Ap-6
Collado Villalba
M-510 A-6
Galapagar
M-505 M-600 M-512

📷 N 40°37'37" W 4°6'0"

www.eurocampings.co.uk/106604

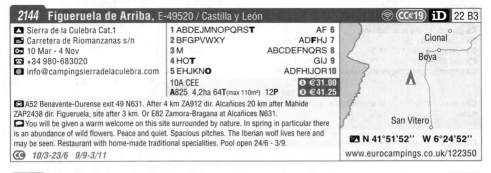

2144 Figueruela de Arriba, E-49520 / Castilla y León ⓢ CC€19 iD 22 B3

- ▲ Sierra de la Culebra Cat.1
- ⌂ Carretera de Riomanzanas s/n
- ◓ 10 Mar - 4 Nov
- ☎ +34 980-683020
- @ info@campingsierradelaculebra.com

1 ABDEJMNOPQRS**T**	AF	6
2 BFGPVWXY	AD**F**HJ	7
3 M	ABCDEFNQRS	8
4 HO**T**	GIJ	9
5 EHJKN**O**	ADFHIJOR	10
10A CEE	❶ €31.00	
A825 4,2ha 64**T**(max 110m²) 12**P**	❷ €41.25	

🚗 A52 Benavente-Ourense exit 49 N631. After 4 km ZA912 dir. Alcañices 20 km after Mahide ZAP2438 dir. Figueruela, site after 3 km. Or E82 Zamora-Bragana at Alcañices N631.

💬 You will be given a warm welcome on this site surrounded by nature. In spring in particular there is an abundance of wild flowers. Peace and quiet. Spacious pitches. The Iberian wolf lives here and may be seen. Restaurant with home-made traditional specialities. Pool open 24/6 - 3/9.

ⓒⓒ 10/3-23/6 9/9-3/11

▲ N 41°51'52'' W 6°24'52''

www.eurocampings.co.uk/122350

2145 Galende/Zamora/Castilla y Leon, E-49361 / Castilla y León ♿ ⓢ CC€17 ♖♗ iD 22 A3

- ▲ El Folgoso Cat.2
- ⌂ Ctra Puebl. de Sanabr-S.M.de Castan
- ◓ 1 Mar - 30 Sep
- ☎ +34 980-626774
- @ info@campingelfolgoso.com

1 ABDJMNOPQRST	LNQSX	6
2 BDHKOPQRTUY	ABDE**F**	7
3 A	ABEFHNQRV	8
4 FO**Q**	ABQ	9
5 ABDEFHKL**NO**	AGHIJO	10
6A	❶ €25.20	
A1000 13ha 500**T** 169**P**	❷ €32.80	

🚗 Via A52 exit Benavente/Puebla 79. Towards Ribadelago via ZA104. Follow arrows to El Folgoso.

💬 A campsite located in the woods of a nature park and beside the Lago de Sanabria. The campsite has good-quality clean toilet facilities, a beach for sunbathing and a lake for non-motorised water recreation.

ⓒⓒ 1/3-14/7 1/9-29/9

▲ N 42°7'52'' W 6°42'7''

www.eurocampings.co.uk/106543

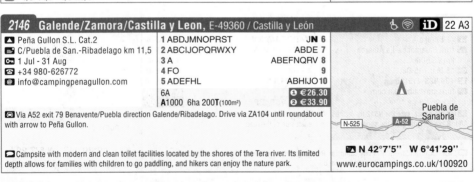

2146 Galende/Zamora/Castilla y Leon, E-49360 / Castilla y León ♿ ⓢ iD 22 A3

- ▲ Peña Gullon S.L. Cat.2
- ⌂ C/Puebla de San.-Ribadelago km 11,5
- ◓ 1 Jul - 31 Aug
- ☎ +34 980-626772
- @ info@campingpenagullon.com

1 ABDJMNOPRST	J**N**	6
2 ABCIJOPQRWXY	ABDE	7
3 A	ABEFNQRV	8
4 FO		9
5 ADEFHL	ABHIJO	10
6A	❶ €26.30	
A1000 6ha 200**T**(100m²)	❷ €33.90	

🚗 Via A52 exit 79 Benavente/Puebla direction Galende/Ribadelago. Drive via ZA104 until roundabout with arrow to Peña Gullon.

💬 Campsite with modern and clean toilet facilities located by the shores of the Tera river. Its limited depth allows for families with children to go paddling, and hikers can enjoy the nature park.

▲ N 42°7'5'' W 6°41'29''

www.eurocampings.co.uk/100920

2147 Gargantilla del Lozoya/Madrid, E-28739 / Madrid ♿ ⓢ ❀ CC€19 iD 31 B1

- ▲ Monte Holiday Cat.1
- ⌂ C604-km 9
- ◓ 1 Jan - 31 Dec
- ☎ +34 918-695278
- @ monteholiday@monteholiday.com

1 ABDEJMNOPQRS**T**	ABFG	6
2 ABFGQRSTUVWXY	ABCDE**FG**HK	7
3 BEFL**MNQRU**V	ABEFJNQRSV	8
4 BD**E**FHILO**PQ**	BFJLRU	9
5 ABDEFGHJKLMN**O**	ABDGHIJMNPVZ	10
7A CEE	❶ €30.60	
A1200 30ha 125**T**(60-200m²) 324**P**	❷ €43.20	

🚗 From the A1 at the 69 km-marker exit towards Rascafria/Lozoya (M604). Turn off at the 8.8 km-marker (just after the tunnel) to the campsite (800 metres).

💬 Lovely, eco-conscious campsite with a view of the mountain (Sierra de Guadarama). Quiet, clean, good restaurant and pool. Pitches with real green grass all year (for an extra fee). Suitable for visiting Segovia and Madrid.

ⓒⓒ 1/1-27/3 2/4-26/4 2/5-21/6 24/6-28/6 1/7-5/7 26/8-31/12 7=6

▲ N 40°57'0'' W 3°43'46''

www.eurocampings.co.uk/109599

2148 Hoyocasero/Ávila, E-05123 / Castilla y León   iD 31 A2

- 🏕 Gredos Hoyocasero Camping
- L/Talleres 6
- 1/4-8,4,1/5-6/5,11/5-16/5
- ☎ +34 920-293150
- @ camping@gredoshoyocasero.com

1 ABDJMNOPQR**T**	A**F**N 6
2 BGPQRUVWXY	ABDE**F**K 7
3 AB	ABEFNQV 8
4 A**E**FHIO	ADJK 9
5 ABEFHIJKMNO	HIJOTUV 10
6-16A CEE	❶ €19.00
A1340 9ha 80**T** 12**P**	❷ €23.00

Follow the N502 from Ávila, turn left AV905 Venta del Obispo, Barraco, then follow the campsite sign.

Beautifully located in a wooded area with panoramic views. Basic toilet facilities. In the Gredos scenic area with plenty of options for hiking.

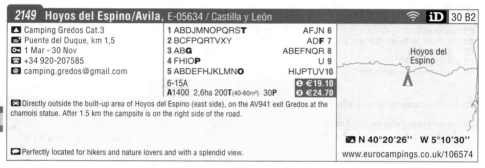

N-502

Hoyocasero

Villanueva de Ávila

◤ N 40°23'43''   W 4°58'46''

www.eurocampings.co.uk/122681

2149 Hoyos del Espino/Avila, E-05634 / Castilla y León   iD 30 B2

- 🏕 Camping Gredos Cat.3
- Puente del Duque, km 1,5
- 1 Mar - 30 Nov
- ☎ +34 920-207585
- @ camping.gredos@gmail.com

1 ABDJMNOPQRS**T**	A**F**JN 6
2 BCFPQRTVXY	AD**F** 7
3 AB**G**	ABEFNQR 8
4 FHIO**P**	U 9
5 ABDEFHJKLMN**O**	HIJPTUV 10
6-15A	❶ €19.10
A1400 2,6ha 200**T**(40-60m²) 30**P**	❷ €24.70

Directly outside the built-up area of Hoyos del Espino (east side), on the AV941 exit Gredos at the chamois statue. After 1.5 km the campsite is on the right side of the road.

Perfectly located for hikers and nature lovers and with a splendid view.

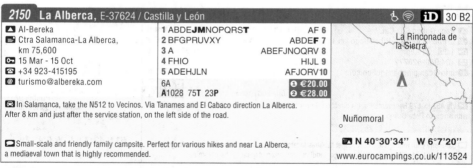

Hoyos del Espino

◤ N 40°20'26''   W 5°10'30''

www.eurocampings.co.uk/106574

2150 La Alberca, E-37624 / Castilla y León   ♿ iD 30 B2

- 🏕 Al-Bereka
- Ctra Salamanca-La Alberca, km 75,600
- 15 Mar - 15 Oct
- ☎ +34 923-415195
- @ turismo@albereka.com

1 ABDE**JM**NOPQRS**T**	A**F** 6
2 B**F**GPRUVXY	ABDE**F** 7
3 A	ABEFJNOQRV 8
4 FHIO	HIJL 9
5 ADEHJLN	A**F**JORV 10
6A	❶ €20.00
A1028 75**T** 23**P**	❷ €28.00

In Salamanca, take the N512 to Vecinos. Via Tanames and El Cabaco direction La Alberca. After 8 km and just after the service station, on the left side of the road.

Small-scale and friendly family campsite. Perfect for various hikes and near La Alberca, a mediaeval town that is highly recommended.

La Rinconada de la Sierra

Nuñomoral

◤ N 40°30'34''   W 6°7'20''

www.eurocampings.co.uk/113524

2151 La Cabrera (Madrid), E-28751 / Madrid   ♿ (CC€19) iD 31 B1

- 🏕 Pico de la Miel Cat.1
- Autovia A1, salida 57
- 1 Jan - 31 Dec
- ☎ +34 918-688082
- @ info@picodelamiel.com

1 ABDEJMNOQRT	A**F**X 6
2 AOQRSVWXY	ABDE**FG** 7
3 BE**KMN**OQ	ABEFJNQRTUV 8
4 BFILO**PQ**	JL 9
5 ACDEFHJKLM**O**	ABDHIJ**P** 10
10A CEE	❶ €35.50
A1025 30ha 75**T**(50-90m²) 325**P**	❷ €47.50

Campsite located about 1 km from the A1. From Burgos and Madrid exit 57. Follow campsite signs.

A campsite with a wide variety of trees, set at the foot of a beautiful mountain range, with a separate area for campers, and swimming pools. A trip out to the mountain villages and a tour along the valley are well worth the visit. Beautiful panoramic views in rural nature. Ideal also as an overnight stop on your way to Portugal and the south of Spain.

CC 1/1-29/6 31/8-31/12 7=6

M-610

A-1

Torrelaguna   Uceda

Venturada N-320

◤ N 40°51'30''   W 3°36'59''

www.eurocampings.co.uk/106628

2152 Mombeltrán/Avila, E-05410 / Castilla y León · ⬤ 🤟 📶 iD | 30 B2

- ▲ Prados Abiertos Cat.2
- 🚏 Ctra N502, km 72
- 🔑 1 Jan - 31 Dec
- ☎ +34 920-386061
- @ info@pradosabiertos.com

1 ADJMNOPRST	AFN	6
2 FGPQRSUVXY	ABDEFH	7
3 ABEGLOQR	ABEFNQRSTV	8
4 BFHOPQ	GJL	9
5 ABDEFHJKLMO	ABHIJLOPTU	10
4-10A	❶ €22.60	
A560 2ha 60T(60-140m²) 95P	❷ €30.20	

Arenas de San Pedro

N-502

🅰 From Mombeltrán follow the N502 direction Talavera. After 3.8 km at km-marker 72 at the right of the road.

💬 Campsite with plenty of shade. Well-maintained grounds and toilet facilities.

📍 N 40°13'52'' W 5°2'1''

www.eurocampings.co.uk/106577

2153 Nava de Francia/Salamanca, E-37659 / Castilla y León · ⬤ 🤟 📶 iD | 30 B2

- ▲ Sierra de Francia Cat.2
- 🚏 Salamanca km 73
- 🔑 1 Apr - 15 Sep
- ☎ +34 923-454081
- @ info@campingsierradefrancia.com

1 ABDJMNOPRST	AF	6
2 BCGOPQTVY	ABDEF	7
3 AB	ABEFNQRST	8
4 FHOQ	JV	9
5 ABDEFGHJKLNO	ABHIJORV	10
6A	❶ €23.75	
A1100 1,2ha 100T(65-80m²) 10P	❷ €32.85	

Morasverdes

Pinedas

🅰 From Salamanca take the N512 to Vecinos. Via Tamames en El Cabaco direction La Alberca. The campsite is 5 km after El Cabaco, to the right of the road.

💬 A campsite in a magnificent scenic area. Friendly management and clean toilet facilities. Perfect environs for a walk or bike ride starting from the campsite.

📍 N 40°31'18'' W 6°8'19''

www.eurocampings.co.uk/106550

Spain

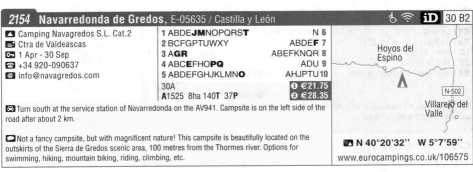

2154 Navarredonda de Gredos, E-05635 / Castilla y León · ⬤ 🤟 📶 iD | 30 B2

- ▲ Camping Navagredos S.L. Cat.2
- 🚏 Ctra de Valdeascas
- 🔑 1 Apr - 30 Sep
- ☎ +34 920-090637
- @ info@navagredos.com

1 ABDEJMNOPQRST	N	6
2 BCFGPTUWXY	ABDEF	7
3 AGR	ABEFKNQR	8
4 ABCEFHOPQ	ADU	9
5 ABDEFGHJKLMNO	AHJPTU	10
30A	❶ €21.75	
A1525 8ha 140T 37P	❷ €28.35	

Hoyos del Espino

N-502

Villarejo del Valle

🅰 Turn south at the service station of Navarredonda on the AV941. Campsite is on the left side of the road after about 2 km.

💬 Not a fancy campsite, but with magnificent nature! This campsite is beautifully located on the outskirts of the Sierra de Gredos scenic area, 100 metres from the Thormes river. Options for swimming, hiking, mountain biking, riding, climbing, etc.

📍 N 40°20'32'' W 5°7'59''

www.eurocampings.co.uk/106575

2155 Riaza/Segovia, E-40500 / Castilla y León · 🤟 📶 (CC€19) iD | 31 B1

- ▲ Riaza
- 🚏 Ctra de la Estación s/n
- 🔑 1 Jan - 31 Dec
- ☎ +34 921-550580
- @ info@camping-riaza.com

1 ABDEJMNOPQRST	AFX	6
2 ABGPQVWX	ABDEFG	7
3 AELMNOQ	ABEFJNQRSTU	8
4 FIO	EJ	9
5 ABDEFGHJKMNO	ABDHIJOPR	10
12A	❶ €33.20	
12ha 185T(96-144m²) 76P	❷ €44.80	

Boceguillas · Urbanización Prado Pinilla

A-1

Riaza

N-110

🅰 From Burgos A1, exit 104. From Madrid A1, exit 103, N110 dir. Riaza and Soria. Right at roundabout after 12 km. Campsite on the left, next to the 'Campo de Futbol'.

💬 Campsite close to the delightful village of Riaza. The villages offer many possibilities for trips out. The province of Segovia is renowned for its excellent food and wine. Restaurant on the campsite is closed on Tuesdays. Wintersports possible in La Pinilla (9 km) from December to March.

📍 N 41°16'10'' W 3°29'50''

www.eurocampings.co.uk/116853

CC 1/1-29/6 31/8-31/12 7=6

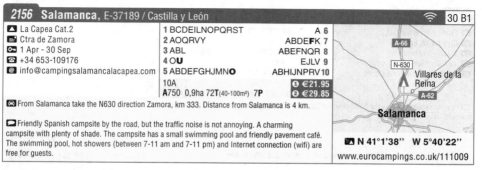

2156 Salamanca, E-37189 / Castilla y León — 30 B1

- △ La Capea Cat.2
- 🏕 Ctra de Zamora
- 🗓 1 Apr - 30 Sep
- ☎ +34 653-109176
- @ info@campingsalamancalacapea.com

1 BCDEILNOPQRST	A 6
2 AOQRVY	ABDE**F**K 7
3 ABL	ABEFNQR 8
4 O**U**	EJLV 9
5 ABDEFGHJMN**O**	ABHIJNPRV 10
10A	❶ €21.95
A750 0,9ha 72**T**(40-100m²) 7**P**	❷ €29.85

From Salamanca take the N630 direction Zamora, km 333. Distance from Salamanca is 4 km.

Friendly Spanish campsite by the road, but the traffic noise is not annoying. A charming campsite with plenty of shade. The campsite has a small swimming pool and friendly pavement café. The swimming pool, hot showers (between 7-11 am and 7-11 pm) and Internet connection (wifi) are free for guests.

N 41°1'38" W 5°40'22"

www.eurocampings.co.uk/111009

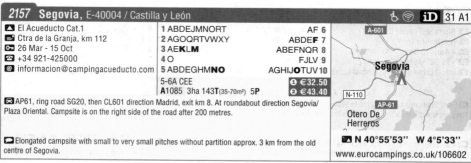

2157 Segovia, E-40004 / Castilla y León — iD 31 A1

- △ El Acueducto Cat.1
- 🏕 Ctra de la Granja, km 112
- 🗓 26 Mar - 15 Oct
- ☎ +34 921-425000
- @ informacion@campingacueducto.com

1 ABDEJMNORT	AF 6
2 AGOQRTVWXY	ABDE**F** 7
3 AE**KLM**	ABEFNQR 8
4 O	FJLV 9
5 ABDEGHM**NO**	AGHIJ**O**TUV 10
5-6A CEE	❶ €32.50
A1085 3ha 143**T**(35-70m²) 5**P**	❷ €43.40

AP61, ring road SG20, then CL601 direction Madrid, exit km 8. At roundabout direction Segovia/Plaza Oriental. Campsite is on the right side of the road after 200 metres.

Elongated campsite with small to very small pitches without partition approx. 3 km from the old centre of Segovia.

N 40°55'53" W 4°5'33"

www.eurocampings.co.uk/106602

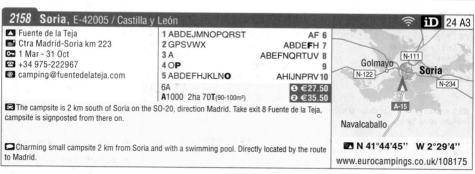

2158 Soria, E-42005 / Castilla y León — iD 24 A3

- △ Fuente de la Teja
- 🏕 Ctra Madrid-Soria km 223
- 🗓 1 Mar - 31 Oct
- ☎ +34 975-222967
- @ camping@fuentedelateja.com

1 ABDEJMNOPQRST	AF 6
2 GPSVWX	ABDE**FH** 7
3 A	ABEFNQRTUV 8
4 O**P**	9
5 ABDEFHJKLN**O**	AHIJNPRV 10
6A	❶ €27.50
A1000 2ha 70**T**(90-100m²)	❷ €35.50

The campsite is 2 km south of Soria on the SO-20, direction Madrid. Take exit 8 Fuente de la Teja, campsite is signposted from there on.

Charming small campsite 2 km from Soria and with a swimming pool. Directly located by the route to Madrid.

N 41°44'45" W 2°29'4"

www.eurocampings.co.uk/108175

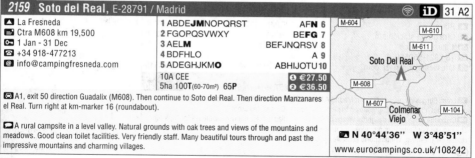

2159 Soto del Real, E-28791 / Madrid — iD 31 A2

- △ La Fresneda
- 🏕 Ctra M608 km 19,500
- 🗓 1 Jan - 31 Dec
- ☎ +34 918-477213
- @ info@campingfresneda.com

1 ABDE**JM**NOPQRST	AF**N** 6
2 FGOPQSVWXY	BE**FG** 7
3 AE**LM**	BEFJNQRSV 8
4 BDFHLO	A 9
5 ADEGHJKM**O**	ABHIJOTU 10
10A CEE	❶ €27.50
5ha 100**T**(60-70m²) 65**P**	❷ €36.50

A1, exit 50 direction Guadalix (M608). Then continue to Soto del Real. Then direction Manzanares el Real. Turn right at km-marker 16 (roundabout).

A rural campsite in a level valley. Natural grounds with oak trees and views of the mountains and meadows. Good clean toilet facilities. Very friendly staff. Many beautiful tours through and past the impressive mountains and charming villages.

N 40°44'36" W 3°48'51"

www.eurocampings.co.uk/108242

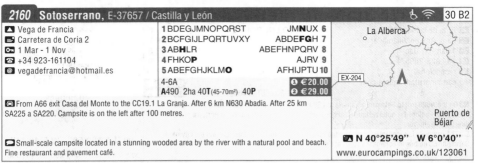

2160 Sotoserrano, E-37657 / Castilla y León
♿ 🛜 30 B2

- 🏕 Vega de Francia
- 🏢 Carretera de Coria 2
- 📅 1 Mar - 1 Nov
- ☎ +34 923-161104
- @ vegadefrancia@hotmail.es

1	BDEGJMNOPQRST	JMNUX	6
2	BCFGIJLPQRTUVXY	ABDEFGH	7
3	ABHLR	ABEFHNPQRV	8
4	FHKOP	AJRV	9
5	ABEFGHJKLMO	AFHIJPTU	10
4-6A		❶ €20.00	
A490	2ha 40T(45-70m²)	40P	❷ €29.00

🚗 From A66 exit Casa del Monte to the CC19.1 La Granja. After 6 km N630 Abadia. After 25 km SA225 to SA220. Campsite is on the left after 100 metres.

💬 Small-scale campsite located in a stunning wooded area by the river with a natural pool and beach. Fine restaurant and pavement café.

🧭 N 40°25'49'' W 6°0'40''

www.eurocampings.co.uk/123061

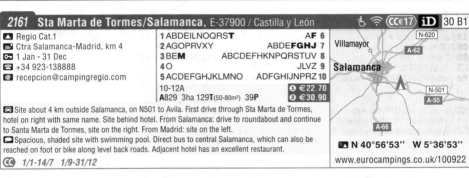

2161 Sta Marta de Tormes/Salamanca, E-37900 / Castilla y León
♿ 🛜 (CC€17) iD 30 B1

- 🏕 Regio Cat.1
- 🏢 Ctra Salamanca-Madrid, km 4
- 📅 1 Jan - 31 Dec
- ☎ +34 923-138888
- @ recepcion@campingregio.com

1	ABDEILNOQRST	AF	6
2	AGOPRVXY	ABDEFGHJ	7
3	BEM	ABCDEFHKNPQRSTUV	8
4	O	JLVZ	9
5	ACDEFGHJKLMNO	ADFGHIJNPRZ	10
10-12A		❶ €22.70	
A829	3ha 129T(50-80m²)	39P	❷ €30.90

🚗 Site about 4 km outside Salamanca, on N501 to Avila. First drive through Sta Marta de Tormes, hotel on right with same name. Site behind hotel. From Salamanca: drive to roundabout and continue to Santa Marta de Tormes, site on the right. From Madrid: site on the left.

💬 Spacious, shaded site with swimming pool. Direct bus to central Salamanca, which can also be reached on foot or bike along level back roads. Adjacent hotel has an excellent restaurant.

🆑 1/1-14/7 1/9-31/12

🧭 N 40°56'53'' W 5°36'53''

www.eurocampings.co.uk/100922

2162 Tordesillas, E-47100 / Castilla y León
♿ 🛜 iD 23 A3

- 🏕 El Astral Cat.1
- 🏢 Camino de Pollos, 8
- 📅 1 Jan - 31 Dec
- ☎ +34 983-770953
- @ info@campingelastral.es

1	ABDEJMNOPQRST	AF	6
2	ACGQRVXY	ABDEFG	7
3	BEIM	ABCDEFKNQRSV	8
4	BO	J	9
5	ABDEFHJKLMNO	ABGHIJOPTU	10
6-10A		❶ €33.80	
A700	3ha 150T(30-90m²)	37P	❷ €46.10

🚗 From A6 direction Tordesillas. Follow signs to 'Camping Parador Nacional'. Campsite is by the river.

💬 Well-equipped and clean campsite on a quiet location by a river and near a friendly town. It is on the route to Portugal and the hedged pitches have plenty of shade. A perfect operating base for a city trip to Salamanca, Valladolid and Zamora. The historic Tordesillas centre is near the campsite. A new grill restaurant that serves meat and fish specialities. Open all year.

🧭 N 41°29'44'' W 5°0'19''

www.eurocampings.co.uk/101606

2163 Villarcayo, E-09550 / Castilla y León
♿ 🛜 iD 23 B2

- 🏕 Camping Villarcayo
- 🏢 Ctra Burgos-Santoña, km 76
- 📅 1 Jan - 25 Dec
- ☎ +34 947-130281
- @ info@campingvillarcayo.com

1	ADEJMNOPQRST	AFN	6
2	CGOPVWXY	ABDEF	7
3		ABEFKNQRTV	8
4	IOPQ		9
5	ADEFHJKLMO	ABGHIJOSW	10
6A		❶ €22.00	
A595	2ha 170T(60-90m²)	16P	❷ €29.10

🚗 The campsite is north of the built-up area of Villarcayo on the road Burgos-Santoña at km-marker 76.

💬 Quiet stopover campsite about 600 metres from the centre of Villarcayo. The lovely municipal swimming pool is next to the campsite.

🧭 N 42°56'49'' W 3°34'9''

www.eurocampings.co.uk/121404

Spain

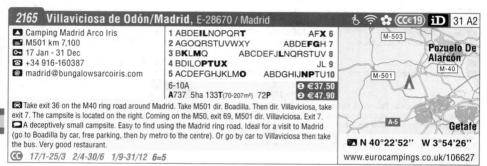

2164 Villares de la Reina/Salamanca, E-37184 / Castilla y León   CC€17 iD 30 B1

- Ruta de la Plata Cat.2
- Cam. Alto de Villamayor
- 1 Jan - 31 Dec
- +34 923-289574
- recepcion@
  campingrutadelaplata.com

1 ABCDILNOPQRST	A	6
2 AOPRTVXY	ABDEF	7
3 K	ABEFJNQR	8
4		9
5 ABDHJMNO	ABDIJOR	10
5A		❶ €23.60
A780 1,2ha 60T(60-80m²)		❷ €32.00

On the N620 exit to Salamanca/Zamora at 238 km-marker. Direction Salamanca then right immediately before 1st hotel restaurant under viaduct. Campsite on right. From Portugal exit 240 direction Villamayor.

The campsite is excellently located on the route to Southern Spain, Portugal and the city of Salamanca. The bus to Salamanca stops at the entrance.

CC 1/1-5/7 23/8-31/12 7=6

N 40°59'58" W 5°40'44"

www.eurocampings.co.uk/101608

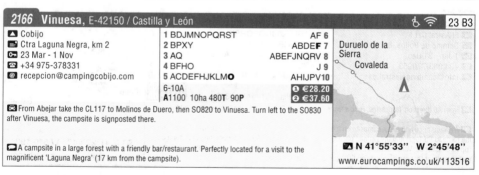

2165 Villaviciosa de Odón/Madrid, E-28670 / Madrid   CC€19 iD 31 A2

- Camping Madrid Arco Iris
- M501 km 7,100
- 17 Jan - 31 Dec
- +34 916-160387
- madrid@bungalowsarcoiris.com

1 ABDEILNOPQRT	AFX	6
2 AGOQRSTUVWXY	ABDEFGH	7
3 BKLMQ	ABCDEFJLNQRSTUV	8
4 BDILOPTUX	JL	9
5 ACDEFGHJKLMO	ABDGHIJNPTU	10
6-10A		❶ €37.50
A737 5ha 133T(70-207m²) 72P		❷ €47.90

Take exit 36 on the M40 ring road around Madrid. Take M501 dir. Boadilla. Then dir. Villaviciosa, take exit 7. The campsite is located on the right. Coming on the M50, exit 69, M501 dir. Villaviciosa. Exit 7.

A deceptively small campsite. Easy to find using the Madrid ring road. Ideal for a visit to Madrid (go to Boadilla by car, free parking, then by metro to the centre). Or go by car to Villaviciosa then take the bus. Very good restaurant.

CC 17/1-25/3 2/4-30/6 1/9-31/12 6=5

N 40°22'52" W 3°54'26"

www.eurocampings.co.uk/106627

2166 Vinuesa, E-42150 / Castilla y León   23 B3

- Cobijo
- Ctra Laguna Negra, km 2
- 23 Mar - 1 Nov
- +34 975-378331
- recepcion@campingcobijo.com

1 BDJMNOPQRST	AF	6
2 BPXY	ABDEF	7
3 AQ	ABEFJNQRV	8
4 BFHO	J	9
5 ACDEFHJKLMO	AHIJPV	10
6-10A		❶ €28.20
A1100 10ha 480T 90P		❷ €37.60

From Abejar take the CL117 to Molinos de Duero, then SO820 to Vinuesa. Turn left to the SO830 after Vinuesa, the campsite is signposted there.

A campsite in a large forest with a friendly bar/restaurant. Perfectly located for a visit to the magnificent 'Laguna Negra' (17 km from the campsite).

N 41°55'33" W 2°45'48"

www.eurocampings.co.uk/113516

The land of Don Quixote

'Cinematic' is the word that comes to mind as you travel through the sweeping steppes, thinly wooded areas, mountains and dry landscapes of Estremadura and Castile-La Mancha. Experience the intense colours of ripening cornfields dotted with trees, vineyards and olive groves on the hills, mediaeval villages and castles, and windmills, and the dry wind blowing over the wide open plains – this is the land of Don Quixote and El Greco.

Mérida and Toledo

Once a very important Roman city, the remains of the amphitheatre and aqueduct can still be seen in Mérida, the capital of Extremadura. Cross the river via the Puente Romano, and admire the Moorish Alcazar built on the city's Roman walls. Toledo, capital of Castile-La Mancha, was also in Roman and later Moorish hands, whose legacy lives on in the Bisagra city gate and the Mudéjar Sol city Gate. Afterwards, enjoy the lively square over a glass of wine at Plaza de Zocodover.

Intriguing routes to get you started

This sparsely populated region is crossed with great hiking and cycling trails, with interesting themes: there's the Route of the Black Villages, Route of the Saffron Fields, Route of the Castles, and naturally the Don Quixote trail. Hikers, birdwatchers and nature lovers are drawn to the River Tagus Nature Park where river rafting and tubing are also possible, but if a quieter day is more to your taste, many of the lakes are suitable for fishing. Or check out the bizarre rock formations of Callejones de Las Majadas, which resemble something out of a Dalí painting. Alternatively – take the kids to the beach on Orellana Lake, you're in Spain after all!

Our tips

1. *Be sure to visit Belmonte Castle, an intriguing mix of Gothic and Mudéjar design*

2. *Soak up quintessential southern Spain in the mediaeval village of Zafra, Estremadura*

3. *Marvel at the hanging houses of Cuenca, in Castile-La Mancha*

4. *See the windmills that typify Castile-La Mancha at Consuega and Compo de Criptana*

5. *Theatre festival at Almagro, Castile-La Mancha*

Celebrate cheese – and other delicacies

Everywhere you go you'll see delicious jamón de bellota or cured ham, but have you heard about the wonderful cheese? Try Manchego cheese, or sheep's cheese ripened in oil, and if you're really into cheeses, go to Trujillo in Extremadura in May for the National Cheese Fair. Other local dishes include El Frite (lamb stew), cachuela soup with liver and tripe, and Gazpacho Extremeno. Be sure to bring home some local honey and saffron, and sample the handmade marzipan Toledo.

2167 Aldeanueva de la Vera, E-10440 / Extremadura ⊗ ⛓ 🛜 `30 B2`

- ⛰ Yuste Cat.2
- 🏢 Ctra EX203 km 47
- 📅 1 Mar - 30 Sep
- ☎ +34 927-572522
- @ campingyuste@gmail.com

1	BHKNORS**T**	AN 6
2	FGPTXY	ABDE**F** 7
3	**M**	ABEFNQRV 8
4	AFHO**P**	9
5	ACDEFHJKLM**O**	HIJLORV 10
5A		❶ €25.50
A650 3ha 166**T**(60-80m²) 5**P**		❷ €37.70

🗺 The campsite is located on the EX203 Arenas-Plasencia, km 47. From Plasencia drive through the village of Aldeanueva, over the large bridge and take the first road to the right.

💬 Small, charming and shaded campsite overlooking a crevice and near a village. Dutch menu.

N-110 · Losar de la Vera · EX-203 · Jaraíz de la Vera · EX-392 · EX-119

🏕 N 40°7'36'' W 5°41'36''

www.eurocampings.co.uk/106555

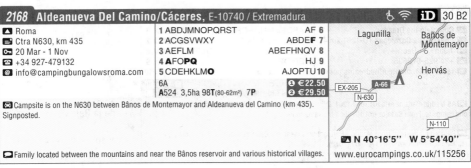

2168 Aldeanueva Del Camino/Cáceres, E-10740 / Extremadura ⛓ 🛜 `iD` `30 B2`

- ⛰ Roma
- 🏢 Ctra N630, km 435
- 📅 20 Mar - 1 Nov
- ☎ +34 927-479132
- @ info@campingbungalowsroma.com

1	ABDJMNOPQRST	AF 6
2	ACGSVWXY	ABDE**F** 7
3	AEFLM	ABEFHNQV 8
4	**A**FO**PQ**	HJ 9
5	CDEHKLM**O**	AJOPTU 10
6A		❶ €22.50
A524 3,5ha 98**T**(80-62m²) 7**P**		❷ €29.50

🗺 Campsite is on the N630 between Bãnos de Montemayor and Aldeanueva del Camino (km 435). Signposted.

Lagunilla · Baños de Montemayor · Hervás · EX-205 · A-66 · N-630 · N-110

💬 Family located between the mountains and near the Bãnos reservoir and various historical villages.

🏕 N 40°16'5'' W 5°54'40''

www.eurocampings.co.uk/115256

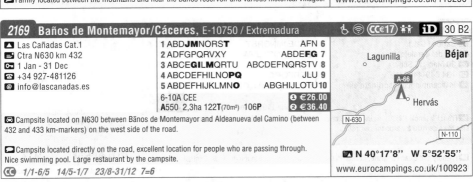

2169 Baños de Montemayor/Cáceres, E-10750 / Extremadura ⛓ 🛜 `CCe17` ♦♦ `iD` `30 B2`

- ⛰ Las Cañadas Cat.1
- 🏢 Ctra N630 km 432
- 📅 1 Jan - 31 Dec
- ☎ +34 927-481126
- @ info@lascanadas.es

1	ABD**JM**NORS**T**	AFN 6
2	ADFGPQRVXY	ABDE**FG** 7
3	ABCE**GILM**QRTU	ABCDEFNQRSTV 8
4	ABCDEFHILNO**PQ**	JLU 9
5	ABDEFHIJKLMN**O**	ABGHIJLOTU 10
6-10A CEE		❶ €26.00
A550 2,3ha 122**T**(70m²) 106**P**		❷ €36.40

🗺 Campsite located on N630 between Bãnos de Montemayor and Aldeanueva del Camino (between 432 and 433 km-markers) on the west side of the road.

💬 Campsite located directly on the road, excellent location for people who are passing through. Nice swimming pool. Large restaurant by the campsite.

Lagunilla · **Béjar** · A-66 · Hervás · N-630 · N-110

🅒🅒 1/1-6/5 14/5-1/7 23/8-31/12 7=6

🏕 N 40°17'8'' W 5°52'55''

www.eurocampings.co.uk/100923

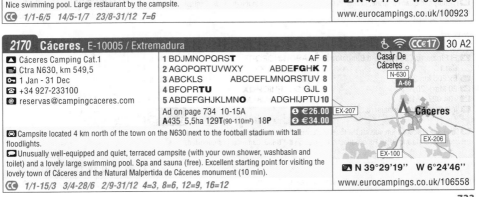

2170 Cáceres, E-10005 / Extremadura ⛓ 🛜 `CCe17` `30 A2`

- ⛰ Cáceres Camping Cat.1
- 🏢 Ctra N630, km 549,5
- 📅 1 Jan - 31 Dec
- ☎ +34 927-233100
- @ reservas@campingcaceres.com

1	BDJMNOPQRS**T**	AF 6
2	AGOPQRTUVWXY	ABDE**FGH K** 7
3	ABCKLS	ABCDEFLMNQRSTUV 8
4	BFOPR**TU**	GJL 9
5	ABDEFGHJKLMN**O**	ADGHIJPTU 10
Ad on page 734 10-15A		❶ €26.00
A435 5,5ha 129**T**(90-110m²) 18**P**		❷ €34.00

🗺 Campsite located 4 km north of the town on the N630 next to the football stadium with tall floodlights.

💬 Unusually well-equipped and quiet, terraced campsite (with your own shower, washbasin and toilet) and a lovely large swimming pool. Spa and sauna (free). Excellent starting point for visiting the lovely town of Cáceres and the Natural Malpertida de Cácenes monument (10 min).

Casar De Cáceres · N-630 · A-66 · **Cáceres** · EX-207 · EX-206 · EX-100

🅒🅒 1/1-15/3 3/4-28/6 2/9-31/12 4=3, 8=6, 12=9, 16=12

🏕 N 39°29'19'' W 6°24'46''

www.eurocampings.co.uk/106558

Cáceres Camping Cat.1

1st category campsite - bungalows
· Private/individual bathroom per pitch with
a shower and washbasin with hot water,
bathroom, laundry facilities and electricity
· Swimming pool for adults and children
· Green belts · Snack bar/restaurant
· Supermarket · Wifi · Launderette · Pavement
cafés · Children's entertainment · Bus stop
· Located in Cáceres, UNESCO world heritage city

Ctra N630, km 549,5, 10005 Cáceres
Tel. 927-233100
E-mail: reservas@campingcaceres.com
Internet: www.campingcaceres.com

2171 Cazalegas/Toledo, E-45683 / Castilla-La Mancha   ♿ 🛜 ((CC€17)) iD   31 A2

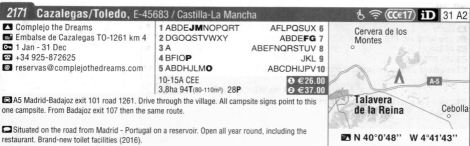

◤ Complejo the Dreams
🌊 Embalse de Cazalegas TO-1261 km 4
🔓 1 Jan - 31 Dec
☎ +34 925-872625
@ reservas@complejothedreams.com

1 ABDE**JM**NOPQRT	AFLPQSUX 6
2 DGOQSTVWXY	ABDE**FG** 7
3 A	ABEFNQRSTUV 8
4 BFIO**P**	JKL 9
5 ABDHJLM**O**	ABCDHIJPV 10
10-15A CEE	❶ €26.00
3,8ha 94**T**(80-110m²) 28**P**	❷ €37.00

🅰A5 Madrid-Badajoz exit 101 road 1261. Drive through the village. All campsite signs point to this one campsite. From Badajoz exit 107 then the same route.

🗨Situated on the road from Madrid - Portugal on a reservoir. Open all year round, including the restaurant. Brand-new toilet facilities (2016).

(CC) 1/1-30/6 1/9-31/12 8=7, 14=11

Cervera de los Montes

Talavera de la Reina   Cebolla

📷 N 40°0'48''   W 4°41'43''

www.eurocampings.co.uk/122596

2172 Cuacos de Yuste/Cáceres, E-10430 / Extremadura   ♿ 🛜   30 B2

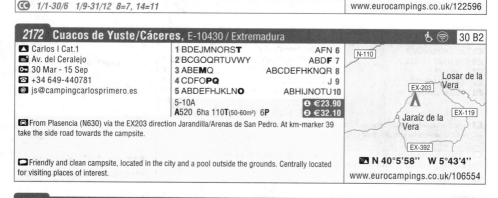

◤ Carlos I Cat.1
🌊 Av. del Ceralejo
🔓 30 Mar - 15 Sep
☎ +34 649-440781
@ js@campingcarlosprimero.es

1 BDEJMNORS**T**	AFN 6
2 BCGOQRTUVWY	ABD**F** 7
3 ABE**MQ**	ABCDEFHKNQR 8
4 CDFO**PQ**	J 9
5 ABDEFHJKLN**O**	ABHIJNOTU 10
5-10A	❶ €23.90
A520 6ha 110**T**(50-60m²) 6**P**	❷ €32.10

🅰From Plasencia (N630) via the EX203 direction Jarandilla/Arenas de San Pedro. At km-marker 39 take the side road towards the campsite.

🗨Friendly and clean campsite, located in the city and a pool outside the grounds. Centrally located for visiting places of interest.

N-110

Losar de la Vera

EX-203

EX-119

Jaraíz de la Vera

EX-392

📷 N 40°5'58''   W 5°43'4''

www.eurocampings.co.uk/106554

2173 Hervás/Cáceres, E-10700 / Extremadura   ♿ 🛜 iD   30 B2

◤ El Pinajarro Camping and Bungalows Cat.1
🌊 Ex 205 km 2,7
🔓 20 Mar - 20 Sep
☎ +34 927-481673
@ info@campingelpinajarro.com

1 ABD**IL**NOPQRT	AFN 6
2 ABGPQRVXY	ABDE**FHK** 7
3 ABEM	ABCDEFNQRS 8
4 **A**BCEFHIO**PQX**	AJL 9
5 ABDEFGHJKLMN**O**	AHIJLOTUV 10
5A	❶ €24.85
A650 2,2ha 120**T**(60-80m²) 16**P**	❷ €34.25

🅰Campsite is about 1 km outside the town of Hervás. Hervás is approx. 4 km from the N630 between Plasencia and Béjar. Follow direction Herras on the N630. Campsite is signposted.

🗨Charming and clean campsite. Lovely pavement café by the pool.

Lagunilla   Baños de Montemayor

Hervás

A-66

EX-205
N-630

N-110

📷 N 40°16'11''   W 5°52'49''

www.eurocampings.co.uk/106552

Spain

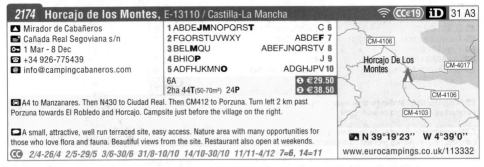

2174 Horcajo de los Montes, E-13110 / Castilla-La Mancha   📶 (CC€19) iD 31 A3

- 🔺 Mirador de Cabañeros
- 🏕 Cañada Real Segoviana s/n
- 📅 1 Mar - 8 Dec
- ☎ +34 926-775439
- @ info@campingcabaneros.com

1	ABDE**JM**NOPQRS**T**	C 6
2	FGORSTUVWXY	ABDE**F** 7
3	BEL**M**QU	ABEFJNQRSTV 8
4	BHIO**P**	J 9
5	ADFHJKMN**O**	ADGHJPV 10
6A		❶ €29.50
2ha 44**T**(50-70m²) 24**P**		❷ €38.50

🚗 A4 to Manzanares. Then N430 to Ciudad Real. Then CM412 to Porzuna. Turn left 2 km past Porzuna towards El Robledo and Horcajo. Campsite just before the village on the right.

💬 A small, attractive, well run terraced site, easy access. Nature area with many opportunities for those who love flora and fauna. Beautiful views from the site. Restaurant also open at weekends.

(CC) 2/4-26/4 2/5-29/5 3/6-30/6 31/8-10/10 14/10-30/10 11/11-4/12 7=6, 14=11

📍 N 39°19'23'' W 4°39'0''

www.eurocampings.co.uk/113332

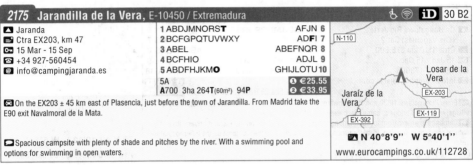

2175 Jarandilla de la Vera, E-10450 / Extremadura   ♿ 📶 iD 30 B2

- 🔺 Jaranda
- 🏕 Ctra EX203, km 47
- 📅 15 Mar - 15 Sep
- ☎ +34 927-560454
- @ info@campingjaranda.es

1	ABDJMNORS**T**	AFJN 6
2	BCFGPQTUVWXY	AD**F**I 7
3	ABEL	ABEFNQR 8
4	BCFHIO	ADJL 9
5	ABDFHJKM**O**	GHIJLOTU 10
5A		❶ €25.55
A700 3ha 264**T**(60m²) 94**P**		❷ €33.95

🚗 On the EX203 ± 45 km east of Plasencia, just before the town of Jarandilla. From Madrid take the E90 exit Navalmoral de la Mata.

💬 Spacious campsite with plenty of shade and pitches by the river. With a swimming pool and options for swimming in open waters.

📍 N 40°8'9'' W 5°40'1''

www.eurocampings.co.uk/112728

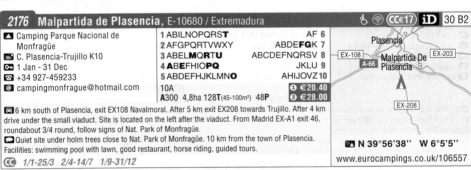

2176 Malpartida de Plasencia, E-10680 / Extremadura   ♿ 📶 (CC€17) iD 30 B2

- 🔺 Camping Parque Nacional de Monfragüe
- 🏕 C. Plasencia-Trujillo K10
- 📅 1 Jan - 31 Dec
- ☎ +34 927-459233
- @ campingmonfrague@hotmail.com

1	ABILNOPQRS**T**	AF 6
2	AFGPQRTVWXY	ABDE**FG**K 7
3	ABEL**MQRTU**	ABCDEFNQRSV 8
4	**AB**EFHIO**PQ**	JKLU 9
5	ABDEFHJKLMN**O**	AHIJOVZ 10
10A		❶ €20.40
A300 4,8ha 128**T**(45-100m²) 48**P**		❷ €28.00

🚗 6 km south of Plasencia, exit EX108 Navalmoral. After 5 km exit EX208 towards Trujillo. After 4 km drive under the small viaduct. Site is located on the left after the viaduct. From Madrid EX-A1 exit 46, roundabout 3/4 round, follow signs of Nat. Park of Monfragüe.

💬 Quiet site under holm trees close to Nat. Park of Monfragüe. 10 km from the town of Plasencia. Facilities: swimming pool with lawn, good restaurant, horse riding, guided tours.

(CC) 1/1-25/3 2/4-14/7 1/9-31/12

📍 N 39°56'38'' W 6°5'5''

www.eurocampings.co.uk/106557

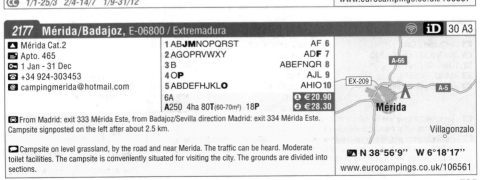

2177 Mérida/Badajoz, E-06800 / Extremadura   📶 iD 30 A3

- 🔺 Mérida Cat.2
- 🏕 Apto. 465
- 📅 1 Jan - 31 Dec
- ☎ +34 924-303453
- @ campingmerida@hotmail.com

1	AB**JM**NOPQRS**T**	AF 6
2	AGOPRVWXY	AD**F** 7
3	B	ABEFNQR 8
4	O**P**	AJL 9
5	ABDEFHJKL**O**	AHIO 10
6A		❶ €20.90
A250 4ha 80**T**(60-70m²) 18**P**		❷ €28.30

🚗 From Madrid: exit 333 Mérida Este, from Badajoz/Sevilla direction Madrid: exit 334 Mérida Este. Campsite signposted on the left after about 2.5 km.

💬 Campsite on level grassland, by the road and near Merida. The traffic can be heard. Moderate toilet facilities. The campsite is conveniently situated for visiting the city. The grounds are divided into sections.

📍 N 38°56'9'' W 6°18'17''

www.eurocampings.co.uk/106561

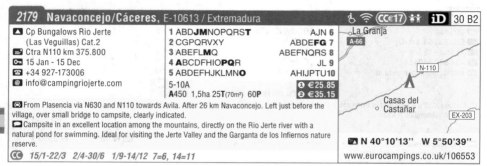

2178 Miajadas/Cáceres, E-10100 / Extremadura   30 B3

- ▲ EL 301 Cat.2
- ➡ Autovia de Extremadura km 301
- ⊙ 1 Jan - 31 Dec
- ☎ +34 927-347914
- @ camping301@hotmail.com

1 ABDJMNOQRS**T**	A 6
2 ACGPRVXY	ABDEK 7
3 AB	ABEFNQRSV 8
4 O	L 9
5 ABDEFHJKLN**O**	AHIJ10
6A CEE	❶ €24.00
A266 1ha 45**T**(70m²)	❷ €31.60

🏕 Campsite is on NV Madrid-Portugal, about 10 km southwest of Miajadas at km 301. Autovia de Extremadura at km 300 Via de Servicio.

🛏 The campsite is located by the busy Madrid-Badajoz road, but you are unaware of this on the campsite. Large swimming pool with sunbathing area. Toddlers' pool is open on Sundays. High-quality toilet facilities. Stopover campsite (± 300 km from Madrid).

🧭 N 39°5'45'' W 6°0'48''

www.eurocampings.co.uk/106559

2179 Navaconcejo/Cáceres, E-10613 / Extremadura   30 B2

- ▲ Cp Bungalows Rio Jerte (Las Veguillas) Cat.2
- ➡ Ctra N110 km 375.800
- ⊙ 15 Jan - 15 Dec
- ☎ +34 927-173006
- @ info@campingriojerte.com

1 ABDJ**JM**NOPQRS**T**	AJN 6
2 CGPQRVXY	ABDE**FG** 7
3 ABEF**LMQ**	ABEFNQRS 8
4 **A**BCDFHIO**PQ**R	JL 9
5 ABDEFHJKLMN**O**	AHIJPTU10
5-10A	❶ €25.85
A450 1,5ha 25**T**(70m²) 60**P**	❷ €35.15

🏕 From Plasencia via N630 and N110 towards Avila. After 26 km Navaconcejo. Left just before the village, over small bridge to campsite, clearly indicated.

🛏 Campsite in an excellent location among the mountains, directly on the Rio Jerte river with a natural pond for swimming. Ideal for visiting the Jerte Valley and the Garganta de los Infiernos nature reserve.

🧭 N 40°10'13'' W 5°50'39''

ⒸⒸ 15/1-22/3 2/4-30/6 1/9-14/12 7=6, 14=11

www.eurocampings.co.uk/106553

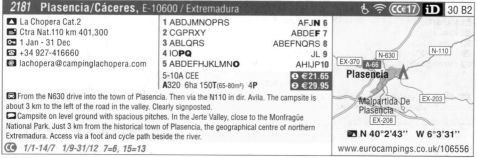

2180 Ossa de Montiel (Albacete), E-02611 / Castilla-La Mancha   31 B3

- ▲ Los Batanes Cat.1
- ➡ Ctra Lagunas de Ruidera km 8
- ⊙ 9 Feb - 4 Nov
- ☎ +34 926-699020
- @ camping@losbatanes.com

1 ABDE**JM**NOPQRS	AFLNP 6
2 BCDGQSVXY	ABDE**FGH** 7
3 BQU	ABCDEFIJNQRSTUV 8
4 BCDHLO	AJ 9
5 ABDEFHKM**O**	AGHIJLU10
6A	❶ €39.20
A800 8,5ha 255**T**(50-100m²) 48**P**	❷ €50.40

🏕 N IV. At Manzanares to N430 direction Albacete as far as Ruidera. Then right towards Lagunas de Ruidera. From Albacete to N430 also as far as Ruidera. Then left towards Lagunas de Ruidera. Campsite 8 km on the right.

🛏 Very well-run campsite with excellent toilet facilities. A lovely large swimming pool surrounded by a large sunbathing area, with some trees for shade. A good starting point for trips to various lakes and towns in a beautiful area with colourful rocks.

🧭 N 38°56'13'' W 2°50'51''

www.eurocampings.co.uk/111448

2181 Plasencia/Cáceres, E-10600 / Extremadura   30 B2

- ▲ La Chopera Cat.2
- ➡ Ctra Nat.110 km 401,300
- ⊙ 1 Jan - 31 Dec
- ☎ +34 927-416660
- @ lachopera@campinglachopera.com

1 ABDJMNOPRS	AF**JN** 6
2 CGPRXY	ABDE**F** 7
3 ABLQRS	ABEFNQRS 8
4 IO**PQ**	JL 9
5 ABDEFHJKLMN**O**	AHIJP10
5-10A CEE	❶ €21.65
A320 6ha 150**T**(65-80m²) 4**P**	❷ €29.95

🏕 From the N630 drive into the town of Plasencia. Then via the N110 in dir. Avila. The campsite is about 3 km to the left of the road in the valley. Clearly signposted.

🛏 Campsite on level ground with spacious pitches. In the Jerte Valley, close to the Monfragüe National Park. Just 3 km from the historical town of Plasencia, the geographical centre of northern Extremadura. Access via a foot and cycle path beside the river.

🧭 N 40°2'43'' W 6°3'31''

ⒸⒸ 1/1-14/7 1/9-31/12 7=6, 15=13

www.eurocampings.co.uk/106556

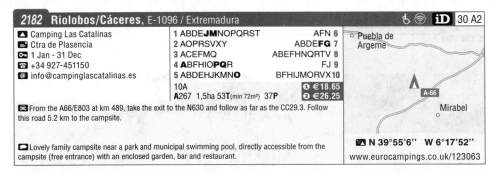

2182 Riolobos/Cáceres, E-1096 / Extremadura

 ♿ 🛜 **iD** 30 A2

- 🏔 Camping Las Catalinas
- 🚩 Ctra de Plasencia
- 📅 1 Jan - 31 Dec
- ☎ +34 927-451150
- @ info@campinglascatalinas.es

1 ABDE**JM**NOPQRST	AFN **6**	
2 AOPRSVXY	ABDE**FG 7**	
3 ACEFMQ	ABEFHNQRTV **8**	
4 ABFHIO**PQ**R	FJ **9**	
5 ABDEHJKMN**O**	BFHIJMORVX**10**	

10A
A267 1,5ha 53**T**(min 72m²) 37**P**

❶ €18.65
❷ €26.25

🚗 From the A66/E803 at km 489, take the exit to the N630 and follow as far as the CC29.3. Follow this road 5.2 km to the campsite.

💬 Lovely family campsite near a park and municipal swimming pool, directly accessible from the campsite (free entrance) with an enclosed garden, bar and restaurant.

Puebla de Argeme
Mirabel
A-66

📷 N 39°55'6'' W 6°17'52''
www.eurocampings.co.uk/123063

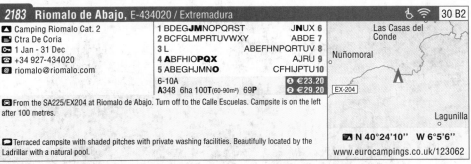

2183 Riomalo de Abajo, E-434020 / Extremadura

 ♿ 🛜 30 B2

- 🏔 Camping Riomalo Cat. 2
- 🚩 Ctra De Coria
- 📅 1 Jan - 31 Dec
- ☎ +34 927-434020
- @ riomalo@riomalo.com

1 BDEG**JM**NOPQRST	JNUX **6**	
2 BCFGLMPRTUVWXY	ABDE **7**	
3 L	ABEFHNPQRTUV **8**	
4 ABFHIO**PQX**	AJRU **9**	
5 ABEGHJMN**O**	CFHIJPTU**10**	

6-10A
A348 6ha 100**T**(60-90m²) 69**P**

❶ €23.20
❷ €29.20

🚗 From the SA225/EX204 at Riomalo de Abajo. Turn off to the Calle Escuelas. Campsite is on the left after 100 metres.

💬 Terraced campsite with shaded pitches with private washing facilities. Beautifully located by the Ladrillar with a natural pool.

Las Casas del Conde
Nuñomoral
EX-204
Lagunilla

📷 N 40°24'10'' W 6°5'6''
www.eurocampings.co.uk/123062

Spain

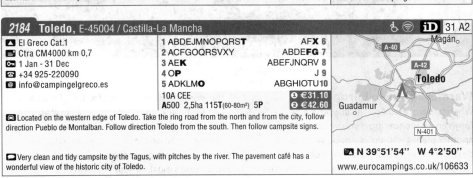

2184 Toledo, E-45004 / Castilla-La Mancha

 ♿ 🛜 **iD** 31 A2

- 🏔 El Greco Cat.1
- 🚩 Ctra CM4000 km 0,7
- 📅 1 Jan - 31 Dec
- ☎ +34 925-220090
- @ info@campingelgreco.es

1 ABDE**JM**NOPQRS**T**	AF**X 6**	
2 ACFGOQRSVXY	ABDE**FG 7**	
3 AE**K**	ABEFJNQRV **8**	
4 O**P**	J **9**	
5 ADKLM**O**	ABGHIOTU**10**	

10A CEE
A500 2,5ha 115**T**(60-80m²) 5**P**

❶ €31.10
❷ €42.60

🚗 Located on the western edge of Toledo. Take the ring road from the north and from the city, follow direction Pueblo de Montalban. Follow direction Toledo from the south. Then follow campsite signs.

💬 Very clean and tidy campsite by the Tagus, with pitches by the river. The pavement café has a wonderful view of the historic city of Toledo.

Magán
A-40
A-42
Toledo
Guadamur
N-401

📷 N 39°51'54'' W 4°2'50''
www.eurocampings.co.uk/106633

Andalusia

Warmest place in Europe

When you travel to Andalusia, you will be forgiven for wondering if you've landed on another planet – 'lunar' is a good word to describe some places. Bordering Portugal to the west and with the Rock of Gibraltar and the sea to the south, there are traces of Moorish history everywhere you look, in particular the seemingly impregnable hilltop fortresses that perch on cliff edges.

Historic cities

Walk around the Triana quarter in Seville and admire the distinctive blue and white tiles, and enjoy all types of local colour at the Mercado de Triana! Seville's Gothic Cathedral is the largest in

the world, and here's a fact for sci-fi fans: Plaza de Espana is a Star Wars location. Stroll around Cordoba's breathtaking Mezquite complex and see the Christian church, once a mosque, with its distinctive red and white patterned arches. Andalusia's most famous Moorish building is the Alhambra in Grenada – an evocative complex that's both a fort and a palace. View the Alhambra from Mirador de San Christobel, or get a taste of old Cordoba along the Carrera de Dallo walk by the river.

Mountains and coastline

As the only European region to have both an Atlantic and a Mediterranean coastline, Andalusian beaches are hugely popular – not just for swimming. Surfing, kitesurfing, windsurfing at Tarifa will keep adrenaline junkies happy, while the quiet beach of Bahia de Cadiz Nature Park appeals to walkers and cyclists. The incredible rock formations in El Torcal Nature Park draw hikers, climbers and photographers. Frigiliana, located near Almijara y Alhama Natural Park, Sierras de Tejeda, is considered the most beautiful village in Spain, and every year it hosts the Festival of Three Cultures, with music performances and a tapas route. The town is also conveniently close to several great hiking trails.

Food and drink of Andalusia
Try the local wines, and don't forget the sherry!

Jerez is the place to go for sherry bodegas. Try typical dishes such as Gazpacho, a cold light soup, olives, fried fish, white fish in vinegar, calamari, and pringa; a meat stew. Afterwards, sample alfajor, churros, or some of the delicious local fruit. Here locals tend to eat late, especially in summer.

Our tips

1. *Stroll around the beautiful mountain village of Pedroche, Sierra Morena*

2. *Visit the Museum of Dance in Seville to learn about Flamenco*

3. *Go underground and back in time in the caves at Nerja*

4. *Check out artworks by Malaga's most famous son, Picasso, in local museums*

5. *Bring the kids for a day at the beach on the Costa Del Sol*

2185 Alcalá de los Gazules, E-11180 / Andalucía ♿ 📶 CC€19 iD 37 A3

🔺 Los Gazules Cat.2
📧 Ctra de Patrite, km 4
🗓 1 Jan - 31 Dec
☎ +34 956-420486
@ info@campinglosgazules.com

1 ABDE**JM**NOPRST	AF 6
2 ACGPQVWX	ABDE**FG** 7
3 ABE**GQ**	ABEFNQR 8
4 FO**PQ**	J 9
5 ABDEFHJKM**O**	ABDHJL**O**TUV 10
10A	❶ €25.25
A93 40ha 140**T**(40-80m²) 50**P**	❷ €33.15

🚗 Between Jerez de la Frontera and Los Barrios via Ctra 381 to Alcalá de los Gazules. Exit 45 on the A381. Enter village. Follow road (not SatNav) into centre. Campsite signposted at end of road outside the town. Another 4 km.

💬 Set in beautiful countryside in the heart of the Los Alcornocales nature park. Perfectly suited to all types of outdoor activities. No traffic disturbance. Well equipped site with as much shade as you want. Affordable menus.

CC 1/1-24/3 1/4-14/7 1/9-31/12 7=6, 14=12

🗺 N 36°27'49'' W 5°39'53''

www.eurocampings.co.uk/110692

2186 Almayate (Málaga), E-29749 / Andalucía ⊗ ♿ 📶 CC€19 38 A3

🔺 Almayate Costa Cat.1
📧 Ctra N340a km 267
🗓 19 Jan - 15 Oct
☎ +34 952-556289
@ info@campingalmayatecosta.com

1 BDEHKNOPQRS**T**	AKMNOPQSW**X** 6
2 AEGHORVWY	ABDE**FG**K 7
3 BE**KLM**	ABCDEFNQRSV 8
4 **A**BCDIO	L 9
5 ACDEFHKLM**NO**	ABEHIJOPTUV 10
10A	❶ €36.30
3ha 234**T**(40-90m²) 8**P**	❷ €48.90

🚗 Located on the (old) coastal road N340a at km-marker 267. On Autovia A7 Málaga-Almería from Almería exit 272 to Torre del Mar. Continue direction Málaga. From Málaga exit Benejarafe/Chilches; continue towards Almería.

💬 Well maintained beachside campsite with excellent sanitation. Plenty of shade from trees. The campsite has a beautiful swimming pool.

CC 19/1-28/3 1/4-22/6 1/9-14/10

🗺 N 36°43'28'' W 4°8'5''

www.eurocampings.co.uk/101380

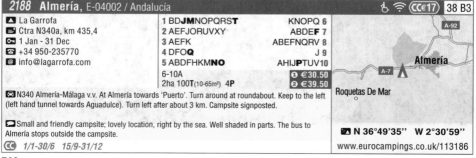

2187 Almayate (Málaga), E-29749 / Andalucía ⚲ ♿ 📶 CC€19 38 A3

🔺 FKK Camping Naturista Almanat
📧 Ctra N340, km 269
🗓 1 Jan - 31 Dec
☎ +34 952-556462
@ info@almanat.es

1 B**JM**NOPQRS**T**	AEKMNOPQSW**X** 6
2 AEGHJORVWXY	ABD**FG** 7
3 BE**GIKLQ**	ABCEFNQRTV 8
4 ABE**I**LO**T**	JLUV 9
5 ABDEHKLM**NO**	ABDGHIJ**P**RV 10
8-20A	❶ €37.90
2ha 240**T**(50-115m²) 18**P**	❷ €48.90

🚗 A7 Málaga-Motril, exit 272 Torre del Mar. In Torre del Mar keep in direction Málaga. Located on the N340a, at km-marker 269, just outside Torre del Mar, on the seaward side of the road. Signposted.

💬 Attractive naturist campsite located right by the sea with indoor and outdoor swimming pool. Restaurant by the beach.

CC 1/1-5/7 27/8-31/12

🗺 N 36°43'58'' W 4°6'52''

www.eurocampings.co.uk/110058

2188 Almería, E-04002 / Andalucía ♿ 📶 CC€17 38 B3

🔺 La Garrofa
📧 Ctra N340a, km 435,4
🗓 1 Jan - 31 Dec
☎ +34 950-235770
@ info@lagarrofa.com

1 BD**JM**NOPQRS**T**	KNOPQ 6
2 AEFJORUVXY	ABDE**F** 7
3 AEFK	ABEFNQRV 8
4 DFO**Q**	J 9
5 ABDFHKM**NO**	AHIJ**P**TUV 10
6-10A	❶ €30.50
2ha 100**T**(10-65m²) 4**P**	❷ €39.50

🚗 N340 Almería-Málaga v.v. At Almería towards 'Puerto'. Turn around at roundabout. Keep to the left (left hand tunnel towards Aguadulce). Turn left after about 3 km. Campsite signposted.

💬 Small and friendly campsite; lovely location, right by the sea. Well shaded in parts. The bus to Almería stops outside the campsite.

CC 1/1-30/6 15/9-31/12

🗺 N 36°49'35'' W 2°30'59''

www.eurocampings.co.uk/113186

2189 Almuñécar, E-18690 / Andalucía 🛜 38 A3

- 🔼 Tropical
- 🏕 Carretera N340, km 315,4
- 📅 1 Jan - 31 Dec
- ☎ +34 958-630322
- @ info@campingtropical.es

1 BD**JM**NO**T**		6
2 AFHJNORUVWY	ABD**FG**	7
3 AQS	ABEFNQRSV	8
4 FIO**T**	IJ	9
5 DEH	AHKPRV	10
12A	❶ €22.00	
A50 1ha 47**T**(25-55m²) 5**P**	❷ €28.00	

🚗 A7 exit Almuñécar-este. At roundabout direction Almuñécar. After 3 km the campsite is on the right. GPS is not always reliable. Campsite is signposted.

💬 Small and basic campsite. Suitable for small to medium motorhomes and small caravans.

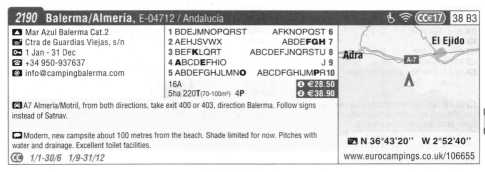

📍 N 36°44'18'' W 3°40'41''

www.eurocampings.co.uk/122191

2190 Balerma/Almería, E-04712 / Andalucía ♿ 🛜 CCe17 38 B3

- 🔼 Mar Azul Balerma Cat.2
- 🏕 Ctra de Guardias Viejas, s/n
- 📅 1 Jan - 31 Dec
- ☎ +34 950-937637
- @ info@campingbalerma.com

1 BDEJMNOPQRST	AFKNOPQST	6
2 AEHJSVWX	ABDE**FGH**	7
3 BEF**K**LQRT	ABCDEFJNQRSTU	8
4 **A**BCD**E**FHIO	J	9
5 ABDEFGHJLMN**O**	ABCDFGHIJMP**R**	10
16A	❶ €28.50	
5ha 220**T**(70-100m²) 4**P**	❷ €38.90	

🚗 A7 Almería/Motril, from both directions, take exit 400 or 403, direction Balerma. Follow signs instead of Satnav.

💬 Modern, new campsite about 100 metres from the beach. Shade limited for now. Pitches with water and drainage. Excellent toilet facilities.

CC 1/1-30/6 1/9-31/12

📍 N 36°43'20'' W 2°52'40''

www.eurocampings.co.uk/106655

2191 Beas de Granada, E-18184 / Andalucía ♿ 🛜 CCe19 38 A2

- 🔼 Alto de Viñuelas Cat. 2
- 🏕 Ctra Beas de Granada s/n
- 📅 1 Jan - 31 Dec
- ☎ +34 958-546023
- @ info@campingaltodevinuelas.com

1 BDEJMNOPQRST	AF	6
2 AFOPRUVWXY	ABDE**FG**H	7
3 LQ	ABEFNQRSV	8
4 FHO	JL	9
5 ADEFHKL**NO**	ABDGHIJP**R**V	10
10A	❶ €28.00	
A1100 1ha 48**T**(30-60m²) 5**P**	❷ €36.00	

🚗 A92 Granada-Almería/Murcia and vice versa, exit 256 direction Beas de Granada. Follow the signs.

💬 An unpretentious and peaceful campsite. Attractively laid out terraces. Lovely views of the Sierra Nevada. Good local cuisine. The bus to Granada stops outside the campsite. 2 euros charged for a trailer. More than one pet charged at 1 euro extra.

CC 1/1-14/7 1/9-31/12 7=6, 15=13

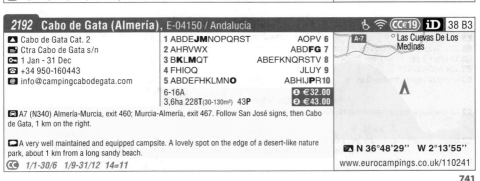

📍 N 37°13'29'' W 3°29'19''

www.eurocampings.co.uk/117802

2192 Cabo de Gata (Almería), E-04150 / Andalucía ♿ 🛜 CCe19 iD 38 B3

- 🔼 Cabo de Gata Cat. 2
- 🏕 Ctra Cabo de Gata s/n
- 📅 1 Jan - 31 Dec
- ☎ +34 950-160443
- @ info@campingcabodegata.com

1 ABDE**JM**NOPQRST	AOPV	6
2 AHRVWX	ABD**FG**	7
3 B**K**L**M**QT	ABEFKNQRSTV	8
4 FHIOQ	JLUY	9
5 ABDEFHKLMN**O**	ABHIJP**R**	10
6-16A	❶ €32.00	
3,6ha 228**T**(30-130m²) 43**P**	❷ €43.00	

🚗 A7 (N340) Almería-Murcia, exit 460; Murcia-Almería, exit 467. Follow San José signs, then Cabo de Gata, 1 km on the right.

💬 A very well maintained and equipped campsite. A lovely spot on the edge of a desert-like nature park, about 1 km from a long sandy beach.

CC 1/1-30/6 1/9-31/12 14=11

📍 N 36°48'29'' W 2°13'55''

www.eurocampings.co.uk/110241

Spain

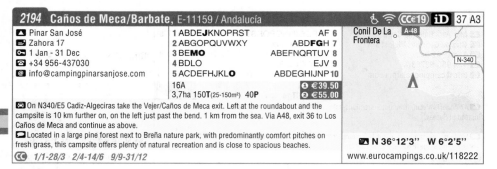

2193 Caños de Meca/Barbate, E-11159 / Andalucía ♿ 📶 iD 37 A3

- ▲ Caños de Meca Cat.1
- 🏠 Ctra Vejer-Los Caños, km 10
- 📅 23 Mar - 15 Oct
- ☎ +34 956-437120
- @ info@campingcm.com

1 ABDEGJKNOPRST	AFNOPQR	6
2 ABGHOQVXY	ABDE**FG**HK	7
3 AB**GL**	ABEFNQRSTUV	8
4 **A**BILO**PQ**UX	JLUVX	9
5 ACDEFHJKLM**O**	ABFHIJNPTUV	10
10A	❶ €44.00	
2ha 150**T**(50-120m²) 100**P**	❷ €49.20	

🚗 On N340/E5 Cadiz-Algeciras, take the exit Vejer/Los Caños de Meca near Barbate. Turn left at T-junction. 10 km after the exit the campsite is on the right, 800 metres from the sea.

💬 Child-friendly campsite with well-maintained toilet facilities and a swimming pool with seawater and a lift for the disabled. Almost entirely shaded with plenty of tent pitches. Very busy in the high season and during weekends. Lower prices except in July and August. This campsite is rather dominated by bungalows and tents.

Conil de la Frontera
A-48 N-340
Barbate

📷 N 36°12'7'' W 6°2'9''

www.eurocampings.co.uk/110242

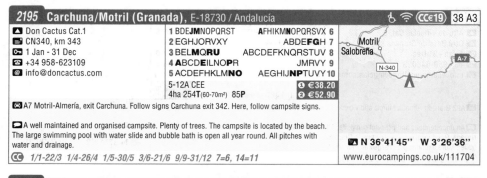

2194 Caños de Meca/Barbate, E-11159 / Andalucía ♿ 📶 (CCe19) iD 37 A3

- ▲ Pinar San José
- 🏠 Zahora 17
- 📅 1 Jan - 31 Dec
- ☎ +34 956-437030
- @ info@campingpinarsanjose.com

1 ABDE**J**KNOPRST	AF	6
2 ABGOPQUVWXY	ABD**F**FGH	7
3 BE**MO**	ABEFNQRTUV	8
4 BDLO	EJV	9
5 ACDEFHJKL**O**	ABDEGHIJNP	10
16A	❶ €39.50	
3,7ha 150**T**(25-150m²) 40**P**	❷ €55.00	

🚗 On N340/E5 Cadiz-Algeciras take the Vejer/Caños de Meca exit. Left at the roundabout and the campsite is 10 km further on, on the left just past the bend. 1 km from the sea. Via A48, exit 36 to Los Caños de Meca and continue as above.

💬 Located in a large pine forest next to Breña nature park, with predominantly comfort pitches on fresh grass, this campsite offers plenty of natural recreation and is close to spacious beaches.

Conil De La Frontera A-48
N-340

📷 N 36°12'3'' W 6°2'5''

(CC) 1/1-28/3 2/4-14/6 9/9-31/12

www.eurocampings.co.uk/118222

2195 Carchuna/Motril (Granada), E-18730 / Andalucía ♿ 📶 (CCe19) 38 A3

- ▲ Don Cactus Cat.1
- 🏠 CN340, km 343
- 📅 1 Jan - 31 Dec
- ☎ +34 958-623109
- @ info@doncactus.com

1 BDE**JM**NOPQRST	**A**FHIKMN**O**PQRSVX	6
2 EGHJORVXY	ABDE**FG**H	7
3 BEL**MQRU**	ABCDEFKNQRSTUV	8
4 **A**BCD**E**ILNO**P**R	JMRVY	9
5 ACDEFHKLM**NO**	AEGHIJ**N**PTUVY	10
5-12A CEE	❶ €38.20	
4ha 254**T**(60-70m²) 85**P**	❷ €52.90	

🚗 A7 Motril-Almería, exit Carchuna. Follow signs Carchuna exit 342. Here, follow campsite signs.

💬 A well maintained and organised campsite. Plenty of trees. The campsite is located by the beach. The large swimming pool with water slide and bubble bath is open all year round. All pitches with water and drainage.

Motril
Salobreña A-7
N-340

📷 N 36°41'45'' W 3°26'36''

(CC) 1/1-22/3 1/4-26/4 1/5-30/5 3/6-21/6 9/9-31/12 7=6, 14=11

www.eurocampings.co.uk/111704

2196 Cazalla de la Sierra, E-41370 / Andalucía 📶 37 B1

- ▲ La Fundición
- 🏠 Ctra Cazalla-San Nicolás del Puerto
- 📅 14 Mar - 3 Sep
- ☎ +34 955-954927
- @ info@campinglafundicion.es

1 BDEG**JM**NOPQRST	AFJ	6
2 BCFGPRSTVY	AD	7
3	BFNQRTU	8
4 FH	JU	9
5 ABDEFHJKLM**O**	ABCHIOTUZ	10
6-10A	❶ €29.00	
A435 22ha 90**T**(90-150m²) 7**P**	❷ €40.80	

🚗 The campsite is located between San Nicolas del Puerto and Cazalla de la Sierra on the SE7101 km 2.

💬 Spaciously laid out campsite in the La Sierra Norte de Sevilla nature park, surrounded by the Hueznar river and next to the Greenway with options for hiking and cycling. Open during the weekends from September through November.

Cazalla de la Sierra

📷 N 37°56'20'' W 5°41'6''

www.eurocampings.co.uk/122718

2197 Cazorla/Jaén, E-23470 / Andalucía � 38 B2

- 🏔 Puente de las Herrerías
- 🏢 Ctra Nacimiento Guadalquivir, km 2
- 📅 1 Apr - 15 Oct
- ☎ +34 953-727090
- @ puenteh@infonegocio.com

1 BDEJMNOQR**T**	AJ	6
2 BCGPRVY	AD**FG**	7
3 B**G**RU	ABEFNQR	8
4 BDFHI	GJ	9
5 ABDEFHLM**NO**	GHIKOTUV	10
6A	❶ €25.90	
A1000 10ha 120**T**(50-100m²) 30**P**	❷ €32.10	

🛣 Motorway Madrid-Córdoba v.v., exit 292. N322 direction Albacete. Approx. 10 km after Ubeda turn right direction Cazorla. Through Cazorla to small roundabout. Drive back approx. 20 metres, turn right uphill. Campsite after approx. 25 km.

💬 Large and basic campsite with plenty of trees and shade. Beautifully located in an extensive hilly and wooded nature park. Lovely hiking area. The campsite is reasonably accessible for caravans. The road there is long and winding, but with stunning views.

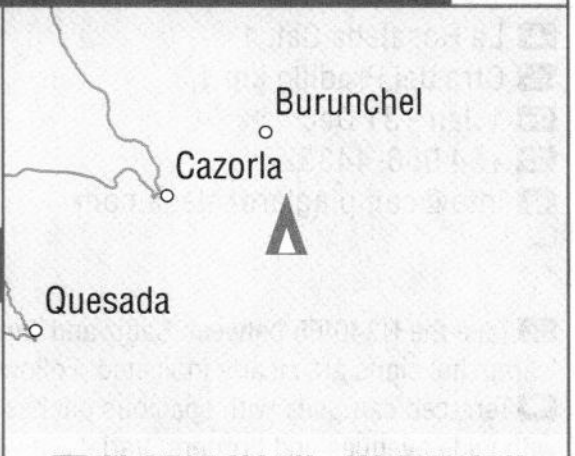

🧭 N 37°54'25'' W 2°56'8''

www.eurocampings.co.uk/111919

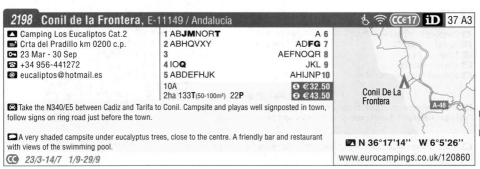

2198 Conil de la Frontera, E-11149 / Andalucía ♿ � (CC€17) iD 37 A3

- 🏔 Camping Los Eucaliptos Cat.2
- 🏢 Crta del Pradillo km 0200 c.p.
- 📅 23 Mar - 30 Sep
- ☎ +34 956-441272
- @ eucaliptos@hotmail.es

1 AB**JM**NOR**T**	A	6
2 ABHQVXY	AD**FG**	7
3	AEFNOQR	8
4 IO**Q**	JKL	9
5 ABDEFHJK	AHIJNP	10
10A	❶ €32.50	
2ha 133**T**(50-100m²) 22**P**	❷ €43.50	

🛣 Take the N340/E5 between Cadiz and Tarifa to Conil. Campsite and playas well signposted in town, follow signs on ring road just before the town.

💬 A very shaded campsite under eucalyptus trees, close to the centre. A friendly bar and restaurant with views of the swimming pool.

(CC) 23/3-14/7 1/9-29/9

🧭 N 36°17'14'' W 6°5'26''

www.eurocampings.co.uk/120860

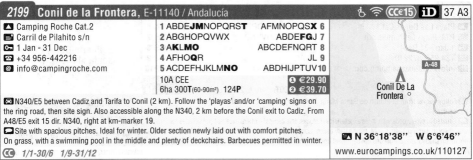

2199 Conil de la Frontera, E-11140 / Andalucía ♿ � (CC€15) iD 37 A3

- 🏔 Camping Roche Cat.2
- 🏢 Carril de Pilahito s/n
- 📅 1 Jan - 31 Dec
- ☎ +34 956-442216
- @ info@campingroche.com

1 ABDE**JM**NOPQRS**T**	AFMNOPQS**X**	6
2 ABGHOPQVWX	ABDE**FG**J	7
3 A**KLMO**	ABCDEFNQRT	8
4 AFHO**Q**R	JL	9
5 ACDEFHJKLM**NO**	ABDHIJPTUV	10
10A CEE	❶ €29.90	
6ha 300**T**(60-90m²) 124**P**	❷ €39.70	

🛣 N340/E5 between Cadiz and Tarifa to Conil (2 km). Follow the 'playas' and/or 'camping' signs on the ring road, then site sign. Also accessible along the N340, 2 km before the Conil exit to Cadiz. From A48/E5 exit 15 dir. N340, right at km-marker 19.

💬 Site with spacious pitches. Ideal for winter. Older section newly laid out with comfort pitches. On grass, with a swimming pool in the middle and plenty of deckchairs. Barbecues permitted in winter.

(CC) 1/1-30/6 1/9-31/12

🧭 N 36°18'38'' W 6°6'46''

www.eurocampings.co.uk/110127

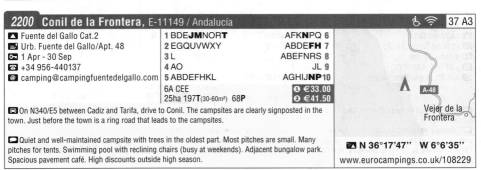

2200 Conil de la Frontera, E-11149 / Andalucía ♿ � 37 A3

- 🏔 Fuente del Gallo Cat.2
- 🏢 Urb. Fuente del Gallo/Apt. 48
- 📅 1 Apr - 30 Sep
- ☎ +34 956-440137
- @ camping@campingfuentedelgallo.com

1 BDE**JM**NOR**T**	AFK**N**PQ	6
2 EGQUVWXY	ABDE**FH**	7
3 L	ABEFNRS	8
4 AO	JL	9
5 ABDEFHKL	AGHIJ**NP**	10
6A CEE	❶ €33.00	
25ha 197**T**(30-60m²) 68**P**	❷ €41.50	

🛣 On N340/E5 between Cadiz and Tarifa, drive to Conil. The campsites are clearly signposted in the town. Just before the town is a ring road that leads to the campsites.

💬 Quiet and well-maintained campsite with trees in the oldest part. Most pitches are small. Many pitches for tents. Swimming pool with reclining chairs (busy at weekends). Adjacent bungalow park. Spacious pavement café. High discounts outside high season.

🧭 N 36°17'47'' W 6°6'35''

www.eurocampings.co.uk/108229

Spain

2201 Conil de la Frontera, E-11140 / Andalucía ⚹ 🛜 (CC€17) iD 37 A3

- ⛺ La Rosaleda Cat. 1
- 🏘 Ctra del Pradillo km 1,3
- 🗓 1 Jan - 31 Dec
- ☎ +34 956-443327
- @ info@campinglarosaleda.com

1 ABJKNOPQRS**T**	AOQ	6
2 GHPRUVWXY	ABD**EFG**H	7
3 BEF**KLMQR**	ABEFHKNQRSTUV	8
4 ABCD**EFHLOPQRTX**	JLVWZ	9
5 ACDEFHJKLM**O**	ABCDHIJNPTU	10
10A		
6ha 335**T**(72-150m²) 70**P**	❶ €39.50	
	❷ €50.70	

🚗 Take the N340/E5 between Cadiz and Tarifa to Conil (2 km). On the right the 'playas' and/or 'campsite' signs are clearly indicated. Follow signs. Campsite about 1 km on the right.
💬 Terraced campsite with spacious pitches screened by various types of tree. Beautifully landscaped with wide avenues and borders. Variety of winter entertainment. Barbecues permitted in the low season. Sauna and fitness room.
(CC) 1/1-21/6 10/9-31/12

Conil De La Frontera
A-48
📍 N 36°17'36'' W 6°5'44''
www.eurocampings.co.uk/111117

2202 Córdoba, E-14012 / Andalucía 🛜 37 B1

- ⛺ Camping M. 'El Brillante' Cat.2
- 🏘 Av. del Brillante 50
- 🗓 1 Jan - 31 Dec
- ☎ +34 957-403836
- @ elbrillante@campings.net

1 BJMNOPRS**T**	A	6
2 AGOQRUVXY	ABD**FG**H	7
3 **K**	ABEFNQRSV	8
4	L	9
5 BD**NO**	AFGHIKPTU	10
10A		
A300 2,6ha 108**T**(20-80m²)	❶ €32.50	
	❷ €40.50	

🚗 When entering the city of Córdoba follow direction 'Centro Ciudad'. Signs 'Parador Nacional'. Then signs Avenida El Brillante (green). Campsite on the right, behind white wall.

💬 Perfect for a visit to Córdoba. The pitches are rather small and the roads to the campsite provide limited manoeuvring space for large caravans.

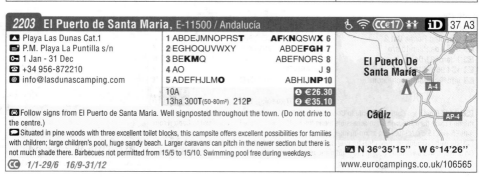

Villarrubia Córdoba A-4
N-432
A-45
📍 N 37°54'0'' W 4°47'14''
www.eurocampings.co.uk/106609

2203 El Puerto de Santa Maria, E-11500 / Andalucía ⚹ 🛜 (CC€17) ⚺ iD 37 A3

- ⛺ Playa Las Dunas Cat.1
- 🏘 P.M. Playa La Puntilla s/n
- 🗓 1 Jan - 31 Dec
- ☎ +34 956-872210
- @ info@lasdunascamping.com

1 ABDEJMNOPRS**T**	**AF**KNQSW**X**	6
2 EGHOQUVWXY	ABDE**FGH**	7
3 BE**KMQ**	ABEFNORS	8
4 AO	J	9
5 ADEFHJLM**O**	ABHIJ**NP**	10
10A		
13ha 300**T**(50-80m²) 212**P**	❶ €26.30	
	❷ €35.10	

🚗 Follow signs from El Puerto de Santa Maria. Well signposted throughout the town. (Do not drive to the centre.)
💬 Situated in pine woods with three excellent toilet blocks, this campsite offers excellent possibilities for families with children; large children's pool, huge sandy beach. Larger caravans can pitch in the newer section but there is not much shade there. Barbecues not permitted from 15/5 to 15/10. Swimming pool free during weekdays.
(CC) 1/1-29/6 16/9-31/12

El Puerto De Santa María
A-4
Cádiz AP-4
📍 N 36°35'15'' W 6°14'26''
www.eurocampings.co.uk/106565

2204 El Rocío, E-21750 / Andalucía ⚹ 🛜 ✿ (CC€19) iD 37 A2

- ⛺ La Aldea Cat.1
- 🏘 Ctra del Rocío, km 25
- 🗓 1 Jan - 31 Dec
- ☎ +34 959-442677
- @ info@campinglaaldea.com

1 ABDE**JM**NOPRT	A	6
2 GOPVWXY	ABDE**FG**	7
3 BE**GQ**	ABEFNQRTV	8
4 **A**HIO	JL	9
5 ACDEFHJLM**NO**	AHIJPR	10
10A		
6ha 200**T**(27-90m²) 85**P**	❶ €30.10	
	❷ €38.50	

🚗 E1/A49 Sevilla-Portugal. Exit 60 Almonte A483, this road becomes the A484 (new road). Follow El Rocio signs.
💬 Extremely well maintained site with large grassy pitches surrounded by hedges with shade. Swimming pool, attractive restaurant and air-conditioned recreational bar. Special seaside town near the famous Doñana natural area. CampingCard ACSI not accepted from 16/05 to 22/05 (La Romería de El Rocío).
(CC) 1/1-15/5 23/5-6/7 24/8-31/12 7=6, 14=11

Los Cabezudos
El Rocío
A-483
A-494
📍 N 37°8'29'' W 6°29'27''
www.eurocampings.co.uk/112253

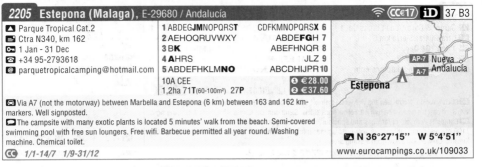

2205 Estepona (Malaga), E-29680 / Andalucía 📶 ⒸⒸ€17 📱iD 37 B3

- 🏕 Parque Tropical Cat.2
- 🏠 Ctra N340, km 162
- 📅 1 Jan - 31 Dec
- ☎ +34 95-2793618
- @ parquetropicalcamping@hotmail.com

1 ABDEG**JM**NOPQRS**T**	CDFKMNOPQRS**X** 6	
2 AEHOQRUVWXY	ABDE**FGH** 7	
3 B**K**	ABEFHNQR 8	
4 AHRS	JLZ 9	
5 ABDEFHKLM**NO**	ABCDHIJPR 10	
10A CEE	❶ €28.00	
1,2ha 71**T**(60-100m²) 27**P**	❷ €37.60	

🚗 Via A7 (not the motorway) between Marbella and Estepona (6 km) between 163 and 162 km-markers. Well signposted.
💬 The campsite with many exotic plants is located 5 minutes' walk from the beach. Semi-covered swimming pool with free sun loungers. Free wifi. Barbecue permitted all year round. Washing machine. Chemical toilet.
Ⓒ 1/1-14/7   1/9-31/12

🏔 **N 36°27'15''   W 5°4'51''**
www.eurocampings.co.uk/109033

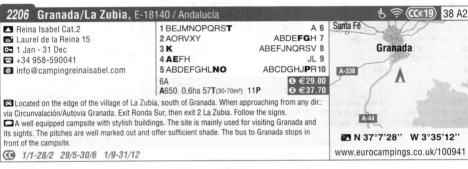

2206 Granada/La Zubia, E-18140 / Andalucía ♿ 📶 ⒸⒸ€19 38 A2

- 🏕 Reina Isabel Cat.2
- 🏠 Laurel de la Reina 15
- 📅 1 Jan - 31 Dec
- ☎ +34 958-590041
- @ info@campingreinaisabel.com

1 B**E**JMNOPQRS**T**	A 6	
2 AORVXY	ABDE**FGH** 7	
3 K	ABEFJNQRSV 8	
4 AEFH	JL 9	
5 ABDEFGHL**NO**	ABCDGHJ**P**R 10	
6A	❶ €29.00	
A650 0,6ha 57**T**(30-70m²) 11**P**	❷ €37.70	

🚗 Located on the edge of the village of La Zubia, south of Granada. When approaching from any dir.: via Circunvalación/Autovía Granada. Exit Ronda Sur, then exit 2 La Zubia. Follow the signs.
💬 A well equipped campsite with stylish buildings. The site is mainly used for visiting Granada and its sights. The pitches are well marked out and offer sufficient shade. The bus to Granada stops in front of the campsite.
Ⓒ 1/1-28/2   29/5-30/6   1/9-31/12

🏔 **N 37°7'28''   W 3°35'12''**
www.eurocampings.co.uk/100941

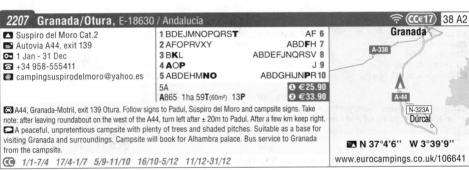

2207 Granada/Otura, E-18630 / Andalucía 📶 ⒸⒸ€17 38 A2

- 🏕 Suspiro del Moro Cat.2
- 🏠 Autovía A44, exit 139
- 📅 1 Jan - 31 Dec
- ☎ +34 958-555411
- @ campingsuspirodelmoro@yahoo.es

1 BDEJMNOPQRS**T**	AF 6	
2 AFOPRVXY	ABD**F**H 7	
3 B**KL**	ABEFJNQRSV 8	
4 AOP	J 9	
5 ABDEHM**NO**	ABDGHIJN**P**R 10	
5A	❶ €25.90	
A865 1ha 59**T**(60m²) 13**P**	❷ €33.90	

🚗 A44, Granada-Motril, exit 139 Otura. Follow signs to Padul, Suspiro del Moro and campsite signs. Take note: after leaving roundabout on the west of the A44, turn left after ± 20m to Padul. After a few km keep right.
💬 A peaceful, unpretentious campsite with plenty of trees and shaded pitches. Suitable as a base for visiting Granada and surroundings. Campsite will book for Alhambra palace. Bus service to Granada from the campsite.
Ⓒ 1/1-7/4   17/4-1/7   5/9-11/10   16/10-5/12   11/12-31/12

🏔 **N 37°4'6''   W 3°39'9''**
www.eurocampings.co.uk/106641

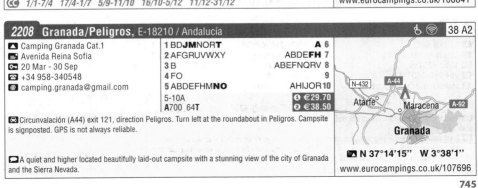

2208 Granada/Peligros, E-18210 / Andalucía ♿ 📶 38 A2

- 🏕 Camping Granada Cat.1
- 🏠 Avenida Reina Sofia
- 📅 20 Mar - 30 Sep
- ☎ +34 958-340548
- @ camping.granada@gmail.com

1 BD**JM**NOR**T**	**A** 6	
2 AFGRUVWXY	ABDE**FH** 7	
3 B	ABEFNQRV 8	
4 FO	9	
5 ABDEFHM**NO**	AHIJOR 10	
5-10A	❶ €29.70	
A700 64**T**	❷ €38.50	

🚗 Circunvalación (A44) exit 121, direction Peligros. Turn left at the roundabout in Peligros. Campsite is signposted. GPS is not always reliable.

💬 A quiet and higher located beautifully laid-out campsite with a stunning view of the city of Granada and the Sierra Nevada.

🏔 **N 37°14'15''   W 3°38'1''**
www.eurocampings.co.uk/107696

Spain

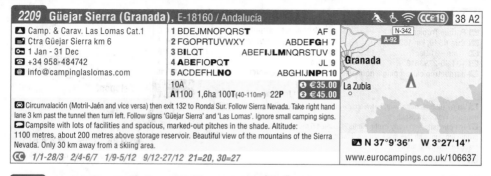

2209 Güejar Sierra (Granada), E-18160 / Andalucía

⬛ Camp. & Carav. Las Lomas Cat.1
📧 Ctra Güejar Sierra km 6
🗓 1 Jan - 31 Dec
☎ +34 958-484742
@ info@campinglaslomas.com

1	BDEJMNOPQRS**T**	AF 6
2	FGOPRTUVWXY	ABDE**FGH** 7
3	B**I**LQT	ABEF**IJLM**NQRSTUV 8
4	**ABE**FIO**PQT**	JL 9
5	ACDEFHL**NO**	ABGHIJ**NP**R10
10A		
A1100 1,6ha 100T(40-110m²) 22P		➊ €35.00
		➋ €45.00

🚗 Circunvalación (Motril-Jaén and vice versa) then exit 132 to Ronda Sur. Follow Sierra Nevada. Take right hand lane 3 km past the tunnel then turn left. Follow signs 'Güejar Sierra' and 'Las Lomas'. Ignore small camping signs.
💬 Campsite with lots of facilities and spacious, marked-out pitches in the shade. Altitude: 1100 metres, about 200 metres above storage reservoir. Beautiful view of the mountains of the Sierra Nevada. Only 30 km away from a skiing area.

CC 1/1-28/3 2/4-6/7 1/9-5/12 9/12-27/12 21=20, 30=27

N 37°9'36'' W 3°27'14''

www.eurocampings.co.uk/106637

38 A2

2210 Hinojos, E-21740 / Andalucía

⬛ Yelloh! Village Doñarrayan Park
📧 Ctra Hinojos a El Rocío 7 km
🗓 1/1 - 4/11, 5/12 - 31/12
☎ +34 959-027502
@ info@donarrayan-park.com

1	ABDEJMNOPQRST	A 6
2	BFGQVWXY	ABDE**FGH** 7
3	ABEQT	ABFNQRTUV 8
4	B**E**FHLO	ABCEKLVZ 9
5	ABDEFGHJLO	AFGHIJM**P**TU10
16A		
7ha 48T(100-120m²) 38P		➊ €33.00
		➋ €45.00

🚗 Follow E1/A49 Sevilla-Huelva. Take exit 34 Chucena/Hinojos. Via A481 to Hinojos. Take ring road A474 direction Almonte. After ± 500 metres left to Almoradux and ± 5 km to campsite.
💬 Beautiful campsite located in the woods in the heart of the Doñana National Park. Ideal for people seeking some peace and quiet, nature lovers, walkers and families with young children. Excellent amenities, swimming pool with lawn, restaurant and a small shop.

CC 1/1-22/3 7/4-2/6 16/6-30/6 1/9-3/11 5/12-31/12

N 37°14'30'' W 6°22'58''

www.eurocampings.co.uk/122581

37 A2

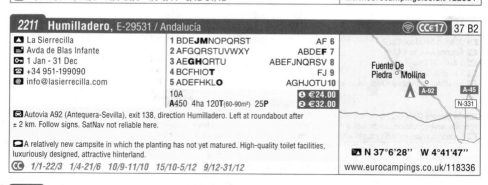

2211 Humilladero, E-29531 / Andalucía

⬛ La Sierrecilla
📧 Avda de Blas Infante
🗓 1 Jan - 31 Dec
☎ +34 951-199090
@ info@lasierrecilla.com

1	BDE**JM**NOPQRST	AF 6
2	AFGQRSTUVWXY	ABDE**F** 7
3	AE**GH**QRTU	ABEFJNQRSV 8
4	BCFHIO**T**	FJ 9
5	ADEFHKL**O**	AGHJOTU10
10A		
A450 4ha 120T(60-90m²) 25P		➊ €24.00
		➋ €32.00

🚗 Autovia A92 (Antequera-Sevilla), exit 138, direction Humilladero. Left at roundabout after ± 2 km. Follow signs. SatNav not reliable here.

💬 A relatively new campsite in which the planting has not yet matured. High-quality toilet facilities, luxuriously designed, attractive hinterland.

CC 1/1-22/3 1/4-21/6 10/9-11/10 15/10-5/12 9/12-31/12

N 37°6'28'' W 4°41'47''

www.eurocampings.co.uk/118336

37 B2

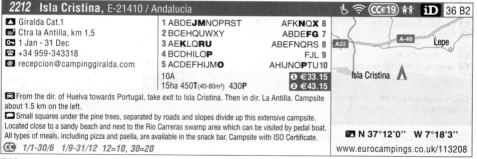

2212 Isla Cristina, E-21410 / Andalucía

⬛ Giralda Cat.1
📧 Ctra la Antilla, km 1,5
🗓 1 Jan - 31 Dec
☎ +34 959-343318
@ recepcion@campinggiralda.com

1	ABDE**JM**NOPRST	AFK**NQX** 6
2	BCEHQUWXY	ABDE**FG** 7
3	AE**KL**QRU	ABEFNQRS 8
4	BCDHILO**P**	FJL 9
5	ACDEFHIJM**O**	AHIJNOP**TU**10
10A		
15ha 450T(40-80m²) 430P		➊ €33.15
		➋ €43.15

🚗 From the dir. of Huelva towards Portugal, take exit to Isla Cristina. Then in dir. La Antilla. Campsite about 1.5 km on the left.
💬 Small squares over the pine trees, separated by roads and slopes divide up this extensive campsite. Located close to a sandy beach and next to the Rio Carreras swamp area which can be visited by pedal boat. All types of meals, including pizza and paella, are available in the snack bar. Campsite with ISO Certificate.

CC 1/1-30/6 1/9-31/12 12=10, 30=20

N 37°12'0'' W 7°18'3''

www.eurocampings.co.uk/113208

36 B2

2213 La Carlota/Córdoba, E-14100 / Andalucía ♿ 📶 37 B2

- ⛺ Carlos III
- 🚗 Ctra Madrid-Cadiz, km 430
- 📅 1 Jan - 31 Dec
- ☎ +34 957-300338
- @ camping@campingcarlosiii.com

1 BCDEJMNOPQRS**T**	AF 6
2 AGORVXY	ABDE**FG** 7
3 BE**GILMQ**	ABEFJNOQRV 8
4 BCFHNO**PQZ**	JL 9
5 ABDEFHKLM**NO**	AGHIJLOR 10
5-10A	➊ €27.70
A400 6ha 230**T**(65m²) 172**P**	➋ €36.70

🅿 Located between Córdoba and Sevilla, close to the village of La Carlota. On motorway N IV/E5 exit 432. Follow the signs.

💬 A level area with plenty of trees and shade. Areas with bungalows and annual pitches separated from touring pitches. With a large swimming pool and sunbathing area. Córdoba is approx. 25 km away and easily accessible via the Autovia.

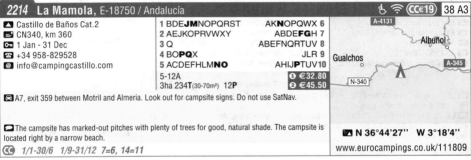

📷 N 37°40'58'' W 4°55'11''

www.eurocampings.co.uk/106581

2214 La Mamola, E-18750 / Andalucía ♿ 📶 CC€19 38 A3

- ⛺ Castillo de Baños Cat.2
- 🚗 CN340, km 360
- 📅 1 Jan - 31 Dec
- ☎ +34 958-829528
- @ info@campingcastillo.com

1 BDE**JM**NOPQRST	AK**N**OPQWX 6
2 AEJKOPRVWXY	ABDE**FG**H 7
3 Q	ABEFNQRTUV 8
4 BO**PQX**	JLR 9
5 ACDEFHLM**NO**	AHIJ**P**TUV 10
5-12A	➊ €32.80
3ha 234**T**(30-70m²) 12**P**	➋ €45.50

🅿 A7, exit 359 between Motril and Almeria. Look out for campsite signs. Do not use SatNav.

💬 The campsite has marked-out pitches with plenty of trees for good, natural shade. The campsite is located right by a narrow beach.

CC 1/1-30/6 1/9-31/12 7=6, 14=11

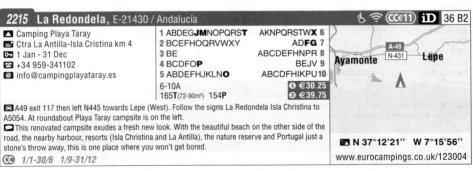

📷 N 36°44'27'' W 3°18'4''

www.eurocampings.co.uk/111809

2215 La Redondela, E-21430 / Andalucía ♿ 📶 CC€11 iD 36 B2

- ⛺ Camping Playa Taray
- 🚗 Ctra La Antilla-Isla Cristina km 4
- 📅 1 Jan - 31 Dec
- ☎ +34 959-341102
- @ info@campingplayataray.es

1 ABDEG**JM**NOPQRS**T**	AKNPQRSTW**X** 6
2 BCEFHOQRVWXY	AD**FG** 7
3 BE	ABCDEFHNPR 8
4 BCDFO**P**	BEJV 9
5 ABDEFHJKLN**O**	ABCDFHIKPU 10
6-10A	➊ €30.25
165**T**(72-90m²) 154**P**	➋ €39.75

🅿 A49 exit 117 then left N445 towards Lepe (West). Follow the signs La Redondela Isla Christina to A5054. At roundabout Playa Taray campsite is on the left.

💬 This renovated campsite exudes a fresh new look. With the beautiful beach on the other side of the road, the nearby harbour, resorts (Isla Christina and La Antilla), the nature reserve and Portugal just a stone's throw away, this is one place where you won't get bored.

CC 1/1-30/6 1/9-31/12

📷 N 37°12'21'' W 7°15'56''

www.eurocampings.co.uk/123004

2216 Laroles (Granada), E-18494 / Andalucía ♿ 📶 38 B2

- ⛺ Camping Alpujarras
- 🚗 Ctra A-337 (Chérin-La Calahora)
- 📅 1 Jan - 31 Dec
- ☎ +34 958-760231
- @ contacto@campingalpujarras.es

1 BDE**JM**NOQRT	AF 6
2 FGNPRUVXY	ABDE**FH**K 7
3 ALS	ABEFNQRV 8
4 **A**BEFHIORU	IJKL 9
5 ABDEFHJKLM**NO**	AHJPRV 10
10A CEE	➊ €22.00
A1150 1,4ha 52**T**(30-60m²) 12**P**	➋ €29.30

🅿 A7 Almería-Málaga v.v. exit 406 resp. 391 dir. Berja. In Berja dir. Alcolea until exit Chérin, then dir. Laroles. Via A92 Granada-Alméria, exit 312, Puerto de la Ragua (narrow road, alt. 2000 metres).

💬 Quietly located campsite with good toilet facilities. Perfect for summer and winter. Plenty of shade, beautifully laid-out with trees and plants. The campsite is located between the mountains and a perfect operating base for riding and hiking in the Sierra Nevada nature park. Discounts from September through June for longer stays.

📷 N 37°0'43'' W 3°0'44''

www.eurocampings.co.uk/111251

2217 Las Negras/Nijar (Almería), E-04116 / Andalucía   iD 38 B3

- Nautico la Caleta Cat.2
- Parque Natural Cabo de Gata
- 1 Jan - 31 Dec
- +34 950-525237
- info@campinglacaleta.com

1	ABJMNOPQRT	AKMNOPQSWX	6
2	EFHJMRVWX	ABDF	7
3	BQ	ABEFNR	8
4	FHR	JLRS	9
5	ACDEFHIKLMNO	ABCHIJPTU	10

10-16A   € 31.60
6,5ha 206T(50-85m²) 28P   € 43.20

Located in the Parque Natural Cabo de Gata. On motorway A7 (N340/E15) Lorca-Almeriá, exit 487 Campohermoso/Las Negras. Follow the signs to Las Negras and the campsite. Follow these instructions and not your navigation system.

A quietly located campsite surrounded by mountains, and directly by a small beach. With plenty of shade from the mats over the pitches.

N 36°52'21''   W 2°0'25''

www.eurocampings.co.uk/109034

2218 Los Escullos/Nijar (Almería), E-04118 / Andalucía   (CC€19) iD 38 B3

- Los Escullos Cat.1
- Parque Natural Cabo de Gata
- 1 Jan - 31 Dec
- +34 950-389811
- info@losesculloscabodegata.com

1	ABDEJMNOPQRST	ANOPQSTUVX	6
2	HJKMRUVWXY	ABDEFGH	7
3	BEFLMQRUV	ABEFNQRSV	8
4	ABCDEFGHILOQRSTU	BEJRSUV	9
5	ACDEFGHKLNO	ABCDGHIJPTUZ	10

16A   € 36.00
4,5ha 216T(40-80m²) 96P   € 47.80

Located in the Parque Natural Cabo de Gata. On the Autovia A7, exit 479 direction San José (AL 3108). Follow campsite signs.

A campsite with pitches shaded by trees or (in summer) by sun screens. About 1 km from the sea with beautiful bays. Situated in the very dry, desert-like park Cabo de Gata. The campsite has extras such as a sauna, fitness area, etc.

CC 1/1-30/6   1/9-31/12   7=6

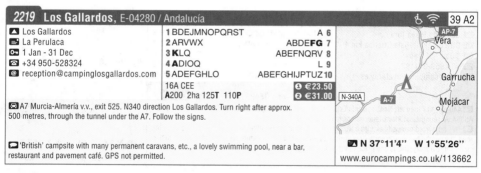

N 36°48'24''   W 2°4'53''

www.eurocampings.co.uk/108960

2219 Los Gallardos, E-04280 / Andalucía   39 A2

- Los Gallardos
- La Perulaca
- 1 Jan - 31 Dec
- +34 950-528324
- reception@campinglosgallardos.com

1	BDEJMNOPQRST	A	6
2	ARVWX	ABDEFG	7
3	KLQ	ABEFNQRV	8
4	ADIOQ	L	9
5	ADEFGHLO	ABEFGHIJPTUZ	10

16A CEE   € 23.50
A200 2ha 125T 110P   € 31.00

A7 Murcia-Almería v.v., exit 525. N340 direction Los Gallardos. Turn right after approx. 500 metres, through the tunnel under the A7. Follow the signs.

'British' campsite with many permanent caravans, etc., a lovely swimming pool, near a bar, restaurant and pavement café. GPS not permitted.

N 37°11'4''   W 1°55'26''

www.eurocampings.co.uk/113662

2220 Manilva, E-29691 / Andalucía   iD 37 B3

- La Bella Vista
- Crtra N340, km 142,8
- 1 Jan - 31 Dec
- +34 952-890020
- camping@campinglabellavista.com

1	ABDEJMNOPRST	AFKMNQSW	6
2	AEFHORSVWX	ABDEFG	7
3	AGHK	ABCDEFGIJKLMNQRSTUV	8
4	ADEHO	L	9
5	ABCDEFHLMNO	ABEGHIJNPTU	10

16-20A CEE   € 39.00
2,5ha 150T(38-76m²)   € 49.00

Coming from Malaga-Marbella the A340 becomes the A7 (not the motorway). In Manilva after Tinda service station (right), turn around on the roundabout. Campsite is on the right (after passing the service station again).

A beautifully laid out campsite with a lovely sandy beach. There is a playground and baby pool. Lovely swimming pool. All touring pitches are comfort pitches. The campsite organises various excursions. An 18-hole golf course 600 metres away. Splendid toilet facilities.

N 36°20'46''   W 5°14'11''

www.eurocampings.co.uk/121221

2221 Marbella, E-29604 / Andalucía   ♿ 🛜 (CC€19)   37 B3

- ◣ Cabopino
- 🚏 Ctra N340, km 194,7
- 📅 1 Jan - 31 Dec
- ☎ +34 952-850106
- @ info@campingcabopino.com

1	BDE**JM**NOPQRS**T**	ACDKMNQRSUVW**X**	6
2	AEGHOQRTUVXY	ABD**FG**H	7
3	BEF**K**LQRU	ABEF**K**LNQRSV	8
4	ABCDEILNO**PQR**T	JLMPRTVWXZ	9
5	ABDEFGHKL**O**	ABHIKLMO**P**TUY	10

10A

5ha 280**T**(50-80m²)   80**P**

❶ €37.50
❷ €50.50

🅿 The campsite is located close to the N340. From Fuengirola, at km 194.7, exit Cabopino. Site located on the right. From Marbella, at km 194.7, exit Cabopino. At the roundabout take the motorway. Campsite in front of you.
💬 A large, well-equipped campsite with spacious pitches. Some with minimal shade, others with plenty. The campsite is just a few hundred metres from the beach. Bus connections to Marbella.
CC   1/1-22/3   1/4-26/4   2/5-21/6   10/9-11/10   15/10-5/12   9/12-31/12

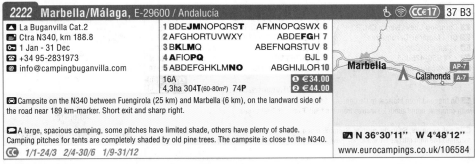

🖼 N 36°29'21''   W 4°44'35''
www.eurocampings.co.uk/108963

2222 Marbella/Málaga, E-29600 / Andalucía   ♿ 🛜 (CC€17)   37 B3

- ◣ La Buganvilla Cat.2
- 🚏 Ctra N340, km 188.8
- 📅 1 Jan - 31 Dec
- ☎ +34 95-2831973
- @ info@campingbuganvilla.com

1	BDE**JM**NOPQRS**T**	AFMNOPQSWX	6
2	AFGHORTUVWXY	ABD**FG**H	7
3	B**KL**MQ	ABEFNQRSTUV	8
4	**A**FIO**PQ**	BJL	9
5	ABDEFGHKLM**NO**	ABGHIJLOR	10

16A

4,3ha 304**T**(60-80m²)   74**P**

❶ €34.00
❷ €44.00

🅿 Campsite on the N340 between Fuengirola (25 km) and Marbella (6 km), on the landward side of the road near 189 km-marker. Short exit and sharp right.

💬 A large, spacious camping, some pitches have limited shade, others have plenty of shade. Camping pitches for tents are completely shaded by old pine trees. The campsite is close to the N340.
CC   1/1-24/3   2/4-30/6   1/9-31/12

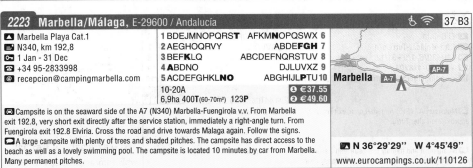

🖼 N 36°30'11''   W 4°48'12''
www.eurocampings.co.uk/106584

2223 Marbella/Málaga, E-29600 / Andalucía   ♿ 🛜   37 B3

- ◣ Marbella Playa Cat.1
- 🚏 N340, km 192,8
- 📅 1 Jan - 31 Dec
- ☎ +34 95-2833998
- @ recepcion@campingmarbella.com

1	BDE**J**MNOPQRS**T**	AFKM**N**OPQSWX	6
2	AEGHOQRVY	ABDE**FG**H	7
3	BEF**K**LQ	ABCDEFNQRSTUV	8
4	**A**BDNO	DJLUVXZ	9
5	ACDEFGHKL**NO**	ABGHIJL**P**TU	10

10-20A

6,9ha 400**T**(60-70m²)   123**P**

❶ €37.55
❷ €49.60

🅿 Campsite is on the seaward side of the A7 (N340) Marbella-Fuengirola v.v. From Marbella exit 192.8, very short exit directly after the service station, immediately a right-angle turn. From Fuengirola exit 192.8 Elviria. Cross the road and drive towards Malaga again. Follow the signs.
💬 A large campsite with plenty of trees and shaded pitches. The campsite has direct access to the beach as well as a lovely swimming pool. The campsite is located 10 minutes by car from Marbella. Many permanent pitches.

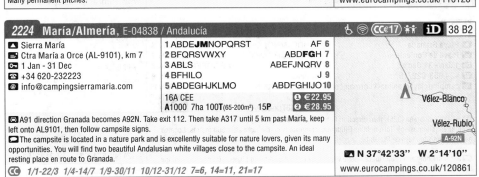

🖼 N 36°29'29''   W 4°45'49''
www.eurocampings.co.uk/110126

2224 María/Almería, E-04838 / Andalucía   ♿ 🛜 (CC€17) ⚞⚟ iD   38 B2

- ◣ Sierra María
- 🚏 Ctra María a Orce (AL-9101), km 7
- 📅 1 Jan - 31 Dec
- ☎ +34 620-232223
- @ info@campingsierramaria.com

1	ABDE**JM**NOPQRST	AF	6
2	BFQRSVWXY	ABD**FG**H	7
3	ABLS	ABEFJNQRV	8
4	BFHILO	J	9
5	ABDEGHJKLMO	ABDFGHIJO	10

16A CEE

A1000   7ha 100**T**(65-200m²)   15**P**

❶ €22.95
❷ €28.95

🅿 A91 direction Granada becomes A92N. Take exit 112. Then take A317 until 5 km past María, keep left onto AL9101, then follow campsite signs.
💬 The campsite is located in a nature park and is excellently suitable for nature lovers, given its many opportunities. You will find two beautiful Andalusian white villages close to the campsite. An ideal resting place en route to Granada.
CC   1/1-22/3   1/4-14/7   1/9-30/11   10/12-31/12   7=6, 14=11, 21=17

🖼 N 37°42'33''   W 2°14'10''
www.eurocampings.co.uk/120861

2225 Maro/Nerja (Málaga), E-29787 / Andalucía   📶 38 A3

- 🏕 Nerja Camping Cat.2
- 🛣 Ctra N340, km 297
- 📅 1/1 - 30/9, 1/11 - 31/12
- ☎ +34 952-529714
- @ info@nerjacamping.com

1 BJMNOPQR**T**	A**N**OPQ**X**	6
2 AHJMRTUVXY	AD**F**	7
3	ABEFNQRV	8
4 **E**FO	JL	9
5 ABDEFGHKM**NO**	ABHIJPTU	10
16A	❶ €32.45	
A150 0,7ha 45**T**(45-100m²) 4**P**	❷ €41.25	

🗺 Located on the N340a (Costa) between Almuñécar and Nerja, on the landside. On A7 exit 295, to N340a, then direction Motril. Campsite clearly signposted, turn left approx. 1 km after Maro.

💬 Small campsite with reasonable amenities. Most pitches have trees and shade. Well-occupied in winter, mainly with English guests. The campsite has its own water supply (a well).

📍 N 36°45'38''   W 3°50'4''
www.eurocampings.co.uk/106639

2226 Mojácar, E-04638 / Andalucía   📶 39 A2

- 🏕 Camping Cueva Negra Cat. 2
- 🛣 Ctra Mojácar-Carboneras
- 📅 1 Jan - 31 Dec
- ☎ +34 950-475855
- @ info@campingcuevanegra.es

1 BDE**JM**NOPQRST	AFKNOQS	6
2 EFHJMORSUVXY	AD**FGH**	7
3 B**KLMQ**	ABEFNQRTUV	8
4 **AE**F**TUV**	BGJ	9
5 ABDEFHKM**O**	ABCHIJ**PTU**	10
16A	❶ €36.60	
15ha 70**T**(60-100m²) 50**P**	❷ €45.95	

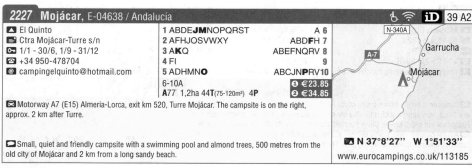

🗺 On the road from Mojácar to Carboneras, 1 km after Mojácar Playa, right side of the road. Sign with campsite name about 20 metres from the road. Exit is difficult to see.

💬 Small campsite. Spacious pitches. Swimming pool with 4 jacuzzis, covered with translucent material. The high pitches have a lovely view. Considerable discounts outside the high season (July-August).

📍 N 37°5'21''   W 1°51'24''
www.eurocampings.co.uk/115942

2227 Mojácar, E-04638 / Andalucía   ♿ 📶 iD 39 A2

- 🏕 El Quinto
- 🛣 Ctra Mojácar-Turre s/n
- 📅 1/1 - 30/6, 1/9 - 31/12
- ☎ +34 950-478704
- @ campingelquinto@hotmail.com

1 ABDE**JM**NOPQRST	A	6
2 AFHJOSVWXY	ABD**F**H	7
3 A**KQ**	ABEFNQRV	8
4 FI		9
5 ADHMN**O**	ABCJNP**R**V	10
6-10A	❶ €23.85	
A77 1,2ha 44**T**(75-120m²) 4**P**	❷ €34.85	

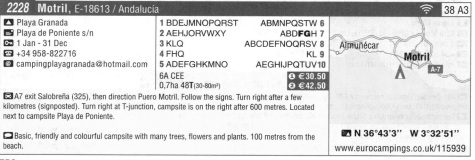

🗺 Motorway A7 (E15) Almeria-Lorca, exit km 520, Turre Mojácar. The campsite is on the right, approx. 2 km after Turre.

💬 Small, quiet and friendly campsite with a swimming pool and almond trees, 500 metres from the old city of Mojácar and 2 km from a long sandy beach.

📍 N 37°8'27''   W 1°51'33''
www.eurocampings.co.uk/113185

2228 Motril, E-18613 / Andalucía   📶 38 A3

- 🏕 Playa Granada
- 🛣 Playa de Poniente s/n
- 📅 1 Jan - 31 Dec
- ☎ +34 958-822716
- @ campingplayagranada@hotmail.com

1 BDEJMNOPQRST	ABMNPQSTW	6
2 AEHJORVWXY	ABD**FG**H	7
3 KLQ	ABCDEFNOQRSV	8
4 FHQ	KL	9
5 ADEFGHKMNO	AEGHIJPQTUV	10
6A CEE	❶ €30.50	
0,7ha 48**T**(30-80m²)	❷ €42.50	

🗺 A7 exit Salobreña (325), then direction Puero Motril. Follow the signs. Turn right after a few kilometres (signposted). Turn right at T-junction, campsite is on the right after 600 metres. Located next to campsite Playa de Poniente.

💬 Basic, friendly and colourful campsite with many trees, flowers and plants. 100 metres from the beach.

📍 N 36°43'3''   W 3°32'51''
www.eurocampings.co.uk/115939

2229 Motril/Granada, E-18600 / Andalucía ♿ 🛜 (CC€17) 38 A3

- 🔺 Playa de Poniente S.L. Cat.2
- 🏕 Playa de Poniente s/n
- 🗓 1 Jan - 31 Dec
- ☎ +34 958-820303
- @ info@campingplayadeponiente.com

1	BCDEJMNOPQRST	AKMNOPQRSTUVW**X**YZ 6
2	AEGHJOPQRVWXY	ABDE**FGH** 7
3	BE**GKLMNQ**	ABEFJKNQRSV 8
4	BCD**E**FHMO**PQR**	JLMQSTUVY 9
5	ABDEFHJKLMN**O**	ABDGHIJNPTUV 10
6-10A		❶ €33.15
3ha 202T(60-100m²)		❷ €45.95 64P

🚗 A7 exit Salobreña (325), then direction Puerto Motril. Follow the signs. After a few kilometres at sign turn right; then at T-junction turn right again. Campsite after about 500 metres.
💬 A good campsite for stopovers or as a base for visiting Granada, the Sierra Nevada and its southern edge (Alpujarras). Good toilet facilities. The campsite is in a quiet location and is close to the beach. Plenty of shade.
⏺ 1/1-27/3 1/4-30/6 1/9-31/12

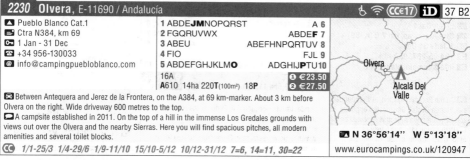

N 36°43'6'' W 3°32'46''
www.eurocampings.co.uk/106642

2230 Olvera, E-11690 / Andalucía ♿ 🛜 (CC€17) iD 37 B2

- 🔺 Pueblo Blanco Cat.1
- 🏕 Ctra N384, km 69
- 🗓 1 Jan - 31 Dec
- ☎ +34 956-130033
- @ info@campingpuebloblanco.com

1	ABDE**JM**NOPQRST	A 6
2	FGQRUVWX	ABDE**F** 7
3	ABEU	ABEFHNPQRTUV 8
4	FIO	FJL 9
5	ABDEFGHJKLM**O**	ADGHIJ**P**TU 10
16A		❶ €23.50
A610 14ha 220T(100m²)		❷ €27.50 18P

🚗 Between Antequera and Jerez de la Frontera, on the A384, at 69 km-marker. About 3 km before Olvera on the right. Wide driveway 600 metres to the top.
💬 A campsite established in 2011. On the top of a hill in the immense Los Gredales grounds with views out over the Olvera and the nearby Sierras. Here you will find spacious pitches, all modern amenities and several toilet blocks.
⏺ 1/1-25/3 1/4-29/6 1/9-11/10 15/10-5/12 10/12-31/12 7=6, 14=11, 30=22

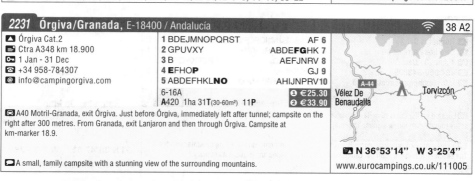

N 36°56'14'' W 5°13'18''
www.eurocampings.co.uk/120947

2231 Órgiva/Granada, E-18400 / Andalucía 🛜 38 A2

- 🔺 Órgiva Cat.2
- 🏕 Ctra A348 km 18.900
- 🗓 1 Jan - 31 Dec
- ☎ +34 958-784307
- @ info@campingorgiva.com

1	BDEJMNOPQRST	AF 6
2	GPUVXY	ABDE**FGH**K 7
3	B	AEFJNRV 8
4	**E**FHO**P**	GJ 9
5	ABDEFHKL**NO**	AHIJNPRV 10
6-16A		❶ €25.30
A420 1ha 31T(30-60m²)		❷ €33.90 11P

🚗 A40 Motril-Granada, exit Órgiva. Just before Órgiva, immediately left after tunnel; campsite on the right after 300 metres. From Granada, exit Lanjaron and then through Órgiva. Campsite at km-marker 18.9.
💬 A small, family campsite with a stunning view of the surrounding mountains.

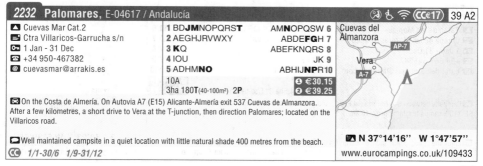

N 36°53'14'' W 3°25'4''
www.eurocampings.co.uk/111005

2232 Palomares, E-04617 / Andalucía 🦽 ♿ 🛜 (CC€17) 39 A2

- 🔺 Cuevas Mar Cat.2
- 🏕 Ctra Villaricos-Garrucha s/n
- 🗓 1 Jan - 31 Dec
- ☎ +34 950-467382
- @ cuevasmar@arrakis.es

1	BD**JM**NOPQRS**T**	AMNOPQSW 6
2	AEGHJRVWXY	ABDE**FGH** 7
3	**K**Q	ABEFKNQRS 8
4	IOU	JK 9
5	ADHM**NO**	ABHIJ**N**PR 10
10A		❶ €30.15
3ha 180T(40-100m²) 2P		❷ €39.25

🚗 On the Costa de Almería. On Autovia A7 (E15) Alicante-Almería exit 537 Cuevas de Almanzora. After a few kilometres, a short drive to Vera at the T-junction, then direction Palomares; located on the Villaricos road.
💬 Well maintained campsite in a quiet location with little natural shade 400 metres from the beach.
⏺ 1/1-30/6 1/9-31/12

N 37°14'16'' W 1°47'57''
www.eurocampings.co.uk/109433

2233 Pizarra/Álora, E-29560 / Andalucía — 37 B2

- ▲ Camping Park Pizarra
- 🚏 Ctra A7077, km 2
- 📅 1 Jan - 31 Dec
- ☎ +34 649-686087
- @ info@campingparkpizarra.com

1 B**JM**NOPQRS**T**		A 6
2 APRUWX		AD 7
3		AEFNQRV 8
4 FHO		HLW 9
5 DEGHJ		ABFGHIJOTUV 10
10-16A CEE		❶ €25.00
A150 1,7ha 47T(25-55m²) 1P		❷ €31.60

🚗 From Málaga, take the A357 direction Campillos. Exit Álora/Pizarra. A343 for a short while and then the A7077. Just before km 2 the campsite is signposted. GPS-coordinates approx. 1 km from campsite. Follow the signs from here.

💬 Basic campsite with clean toilet facilities and a swimming pool. Hilly environment. British owners. Charming bar and pavement café. Motor-friendly campsite.

📍 N 36°47'10'' W 4°43'8''
www.eurocampings.co.uk/122334

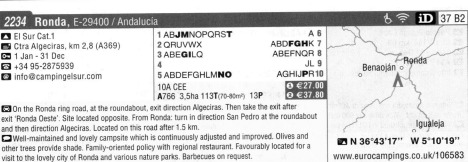

2234 Ronda, E-29400 / Andalucía — ♿ 📶 iD 37 B2

- ▲ El Sur Cat.1
- 🚏 Ctra Algeciras, km 2,8 (A369)
- 📅 1 Jan - 31 Dec
- ☎ +34 95-2875939
- @ info@campingelsur.com

1 AB**JM**NOPQRS**T**		A 6
2 QRUVWX		ABD**FGH**K 7
3 ABE**GIL**Q		ABEFNQR 8
4		JL 9
5 ABDEFGHLM**NO**		AGHIJ**PR** 10
10A CEE		❶ €27.00
A766 3,5ha 113T(70-80m²) 13P		❷ €37.80

🚗 On the Ronda ring road, at the roundabout, exit direction Algeciras. Then take the exit after exit 'Ronda Oeste'. Site located opposite. From Ronda: turn in direction San Pedro at the roundabout and then direction Algeciras. Located on this road after 1.5 km.

💬 Well-maintained and lovely campsite which is continuously adjusted and improved. Olives and other trees provide shade. Family-oriented policy with regional restaurant. Favourably located for a visit to the lovely city of Ronda and various nature parks. Barbecues on request.

📍 N 36°43'17'' W 5°10'19''
www.eurocampings.co.uk/106583

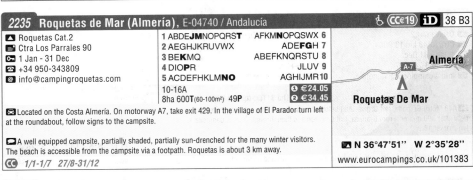

2235 Roquetas de Mar (Almería), E-04740 / Andalucía — ♿ CC€19 iD 38 B3

- ▲ Roquetas Cat.2
- 🚏 Ctra Los Parrales 90
- 📅 1 Jan - 31 Dec
- ☎ +34 950-343809
- @ info@campingroquetas.com

1 ABDE**JM**NOPQRS**T**	AFKM**N**OPQSWX 6
2 AEGHJKRUVWX	ADE**FG**H 7
3 BEK**M**Q	ABEFKNQRSTU 8
4 DIOP**R**	JLUV 9
5 ACDEFHKLM**NO**	AGHIJMR 10
10-16A	❶ €24.05
8ha 600T(60-100m²) 49P	❷ €34.45

🚗 Located on the Costa Almería. On motorway A7, take exit 429. In the village of El Parador turn left at the roundabout, follow signs to the campsite.

💬 A well equipped campsite, partially shaded, partially sun-drenched for the many winter visitors. The beach is accessible from the campsite via a footpath. Roquetas is about 3 km away.

CC 1/1-1/7 27/8-31/12

📍 N 36°47'51'' W 2°35'28''
www.eurocampings.co.uk/101383

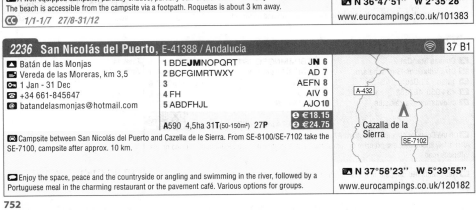

2236 San Nicolás del Puerto, E-41388 / Andalucía — 📶 37 B1

- ▲ Batán de las Monjas
- 🚏 Vereda de las Moreras, km 3,5
- 📅 1 Jan - 31 Dec
- ☎ +34 661-845647
- @ batandelasmonjas@hotmail.com

1 BDE**JM**NOPQRT	JN 6
2 BCFGIMRTWXY	AD 7
3	AEFN 8
4 FH	AIV 9
5 ABDFHJL	AJO 10
A590 4,5ha 31T(50-150m²) 27P	❶ €18.15
	❷ €24.75

🚗 Campsite between San Nicolás del Puerto and Cazella de le Sierra. From SE-8100/SE-7102 take the SE-7100, campsite after approx. 10 km.

💬 Enjoy the space, peace and the countryside or angling and swimming in the river, followed by a Portuguese meal in the charming restaurant or the pavement café. Various options for groups.

📍 N 37°58'23'' W 5°39'55''
www.eurocampings.co.uk/120182

Spain

752

2237 Santa Elena (Jaén), E-23213 / Andalucía ♿ 🛜 (CC€17) 38 A1

- 🏕 Despeñaperros Cat.1
- 🏠 Infanta Elena s/n
- 📅 1/1 - 23/12, 25/12 - 30/12
- ☎ +34 953-664192
- @ info@campingdespenaperros.com

1 BDEJMNOPQRST	AF	6
2 ABGORVXY	ABDF**H**	7
3 AE**G**	ABEFNQRSTUV	8
4 A**E**FHIO**P**	JL	9
5 ABDEFHKLM**NO**	AEGHIJL**N**PTUV	10
10A		
A750 4ha 112**T**(70-100m²) 36**P**	❶ €23.95 ❷ €32.05	

🚗 A4 Sevilla-Madrid, exit 259; Madrid-Sevilla, exit 257 or 258. Follow signs.

💬 Quiet wooded site conveniently located a short distance from the N IV/E5. Suitable for staying for some time to relax. Level grounds with sufficiently shaded pitches. The 'Batalla de Las Navas de Tolosa' museum in Sta Elena is most interesting. It shows a scene from a historical battle between the Christians and the Moors in 1212.

CC 1/1-24/3 2/4-15/6 15/9-22/12 25/12-29/12

🧭 N 38°20'36'' W 3°32'8''

www.eurocampings.co.uk/110060

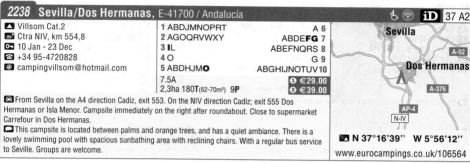

2238 Sevilla/Dos Hermanas, E-41700 / Andalucía ♿ 🛜 iD 37 A2

- 🏕 Villsom Cat.2
- 🏠 Ctra NIV, km 554,8
- 📅 10 Jan - 23 Dec
- ☎ +34 95-4720828
- @ campingvillsom@hotmail.com

1 ABDJMNOPRT	A	6
2 AGOQRVWXY	ABDE**FG**	7
3 I**L**	ABEFNQRS	8
4 O	G	9
5 ABDHJM**O**	ABGHIJNOTUV	10
7.5A		
2,3ha 180**T**(62-70m²) 9**P**	❶ €29.00 ❷ €39.00	

🚗 From Sevilla on the A4 direction Cadiz, exit 553. On the NIV direction Cadiz; exit 555 Dos Hermanas or Isla Menor. Campsite immediately on the right after roundabout. Close to supermarket Carrefour in Dos Hermanas.

💬 This campsite is located between palms and orange trees, and has a quiet ambiance. There is a lovely swimming pool with spacious sunbathing area with reclining chairs. With a regular bus service to Seville. Groups are welcome.

🧭 N 37°16'39'' W 5°56'12''

www.eurocampings.co.uk/106564

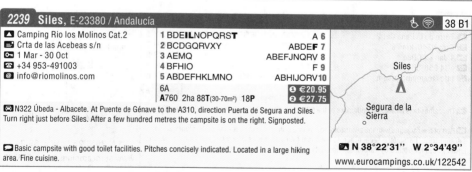

2239 Siles, E-23380 / Andalucía ♿ 🛜 38 B1

- 🏕 Camping Rio los Molinos Cat.2
- 🏠 Crta de las Acebeas s/n
- 📅 1 Mar - 30 Oct
- ☎ +34 953-491003
- @ info@riomolinos.com

1 BDE**I**LNOPQRS**T**	A	6
2 BCDGQRVXY	ABDE**F**	7
3 AEMQ	ABEFJNQRV	8
4 BFHIO	F	9
5 ABDEFHKLMNO	ABHIJORV	10
6A		
A760 2ha 88**T**(30-70m²) 18**P**	❶ €20.95 ❷ €27.75	

🚗 N322 Úbeda - Albacete. At Puente de Génave to the A310, direction Puerta de Segura and Siles. Turn right just before Siles. After a few hundred metres the campsite is on the right. Signposted.

💬 Basic campsite with good toilet facilities. Pitches concisely indicated. Located in a large hiking area. Fine cuisine.

🧭 N 38°22'31'' W 2°34'49''

www.eurocampings.co.uk/122542

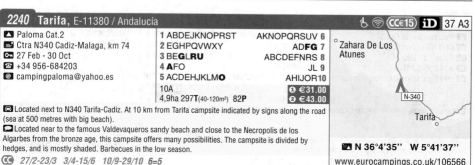

2240 Tarifa, E-11380 / Andalucía ♿ 🛜 (CC€15) iD 37 A3

- 🏕 Paloma Cat.2
- 🏠 Ctra N340 Cadiz-Malaga, km 74
- 📅 27 Feb - 30 Oct
- ☎ +34 956-684203
- @ campingpaloma@yahoo.es

1 ABDEJKNOPRST	AKNOPQRSUV	6
2 EGHPQVWXY	AD**FG**	7
3 BE**GLRU**	ABCDEFNRS	8
4 **A**FO	JL	9
5 ACDEHJKLM**O**	AHIJOR	10
10A		
4,9ha 297**T**(40-120m²) 82**P**	❶ €31.00 ❷ €43.00	

🚗 Located next to N340 Tarifa-Cadiz. At 10 km from Tarifa campsite indicated by signs along the road (sea at 500 metres with big beach).

💬 Located near to the famous Valdevaqueros sandy beach and close to the Necropolis de los Algarbes from the bronze age, this campsite offers many possibilities. The campsite is divided by hedges, and is mostly shaded. Barbecues in the low season.

CC 27/2-23/3 3/4-15/6 10/9-29/10 6=5

🧭 N 36°4'35'' W 5°41'37''

www.eurocampings.co.uk/106566

Spain

Spain

2241 Tarifa, E-11380 / Andalucía   ♿ 📶 37 A3

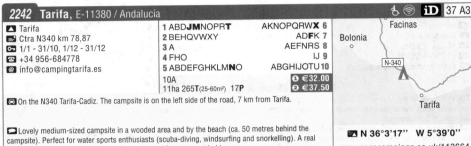

- 🏕 Rio Jara Cat.2
- 🏠 Ctra N340, km 81
- 🕐 1 Jan - 31 Dec
- ☎ +34 956-680570
- @ campingriojara@terra.com

1 BDJMNOPRST	KMNPQRSTX 6
2 EFHPQVWX	ABDFG 7
3 AG	AEFNRS 8
4 AIOQ	L 9
5 ACDEFGHKMO	AHIJPRY 10

10A
3ha 264T(50-100m²)

❶ €35.50
❷ €45.00

🅿 On the N340 Tarifa-Cadiz. The campsite is on the left side of the road, 3 km from Tarifa.

💬 This 'southernmost campsite in Europe' mainly has hedged pitches. The varied planting ensures some shade. With direct access to the large sandy beach for swimmers. Special rates outside of July/August up to 40%. Barbecue in winter. Entertainment programmes in winter. Public transport in July and August!

📍 N 36°2'33'' W 5°37'49''
www.eurocampings.co.uk/106569

2242 Tarifa, E-11380 / Andalucía   ♿ 📶 iD 37 A3

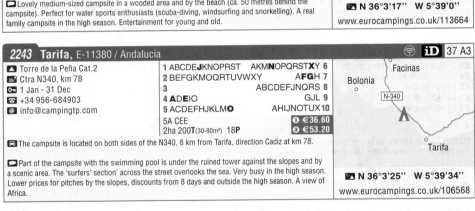

- 🏕 Tarifa
- 🏠 Ctra N340 km 78,87
- 🕐 1/1 - 31/10, 1/12 - 31/12
- ☎ +34 956-684778
- @ info@campingtarifa.es

1 ABDJMNOPRT	AKNOPQRWX 6
2 BEHQVWXY	ADFK 7
3 A	AEFNRS 8
4 FHO	IJ 9
5 ABDEFGHKLMNO	ABGHIJOTU 10

10A
11ha 265T(25-60m²) 17P

❶ €32.00
❷ €37.50

🅿 On the N340 Tarifa-Cadiz. The campsite is on the left side of the road, 7 km from Tarifa.

💬 Lovely medium-sized campsite in a wooded area and by the beach (ca. 50 metres behind the campsite). Perfect for water sports enthusiasts (scuba-diving, windsurfing and snorkelling). A real family campsite in the high season. Entertainment for young and old.

📍 N 36°3'17'' W 5°39'0''
www.eurocampings.co.uk/113664

2243 Tarifa, E-11380 / Andalucía   📶 iD 37 A3

- 🏕 Torre de la Peña Cat.2
- 🏠 Ctra N340, km 78
- 🕐 1 Jan - 31 Dec
- ☎ +34 956-684903
- @ info@campingtp.com

1 ABCDEJKNOPRST	AKMNOPQRSTXY 6
2 BEFGKMOQRTUVWXY	AFGH 7
3	ABCDEFJNQRS 8
4 ADEIO	GJL 9
5 ACDEFHJKLMO	AHIJNOTUX 10

5A CEE
2ha 200T(30-80m²) 18P

❶ €36.60
❷ €53.20

🅿 The campsite is located on both sides of the N340, 8 km from Tarifa, direction Cadiz at km 78.

💬 Part of the campsite with the swimming pool is under the ruined tower against the slopes and by a scenic area. The 'surfers' section across the street overlooks the sea. Very busy in the high season. Lower prices for pitches by the slopes, discounts from 8 days and outside the high season. A view of Africa.

📍 N 36°3'25'' W 5°39'34''
www.eurocampings.co.uk/106568

2244 Tarifa/Cádiz, E-11380 / Andalucía   ♿ 📶 CCE17 iD 37 A3

- 🏕 Valdevaqueros Cat.2
- 🏠 Ctra N340, km 75,5
- 🕐 1 Jan - 31 Dec
- ☎ +34 956-684174
- @ info@campingvaldevaqueros.com

1 ABDEJMNOPRST	AFKNQRSTWX 6
2 EGHPVWXY	ABDFG 7
3 BMO	ABCDEFLMNQRTUV 8
4 AEFHO	AIJLV 9
5 ACDEFGHJKLMO	AFGHIJLMNOTUV 10

6A CEE
5ha 324T(50-100m²) 53P

❶ €32.00
❷ €43.00

🅿 Located by the N340 Tarifa-Cadiz. Campsite is signposted 9 km from Tarifa towards Cadiz on the right.

💬 A campsite with individual connections and spacious, marked-out pitches. Shade for caravans and tents. Barbecues permitted outside the summer months.

CC 1/1-3/4 8/4-30/6 1/9-31/12 7=6, 14=12, 21=18, 28=24

📍 N 36°4'9'' W 5°40'49''
www.eurocampings.co.uk/106567

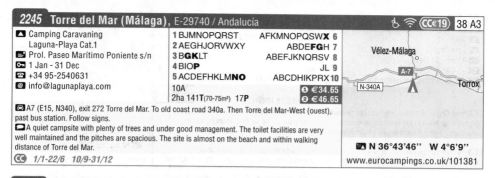

2245 Torre del Mar (Málaga), E-29740 / Andalucía   ♿ 📶 (CC€19)   38 A3

🔺 Camping Caravaning
Laguna-Playa Cat.1
📧 Prol. Paseo Marítimo Poniente s/n
📅 1 Jan - 31 Dec
☎ +34 95-2540631
@ info@lagunaplaya.com

1	BJMNOPQRST	AFKMNOPQSW**X**	6
2	AEGHJORVWXY	ABDE**FG**H	7
3	B**GK**LT	ABEFJKNQRSV	8
4	BIO**P**	JL	9
5	ACDEFHKLM**NO**	ABCDHIKPRX	10
10A		❶ €34.65	
2ha 141T(70-75m²) 17P		❷ €46.65	

🚗 A7 (E15, N340), exit 272 Torre del Mar. To old coast road 340a. Then Torre del Mar-West (ouest), past bus station. Follow signs.
💬 A quiet campsite with plenty of trees and under good management. The toilet facilities are very well maintained and the pitches are spacious. The site is almost on the beach and within walking distance of Torre del Mar.
CC 1/1-22/6 10/9-31/12

www.eurocampings.co.uk/101381

N 36°43'46" W 4°6'9"

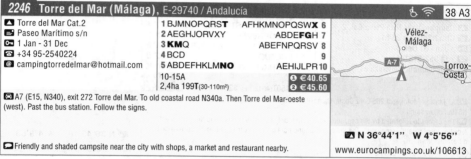

2246 Torre del Mar (Málaga), E-29740 / Andalucía   ♿ 📶   38 A3

🔺 Torre del Mar Cat.2
📧 Paseo Marítimo s/n
📅 1 Jan - 31 Dec
☎ +34 95-2540224
@ campingtorredelmar@hotmail.com

1	BJMNOPQRS**T**	AFHKMNOPQSW**X**	6
2	AEGHJORVXY	ABDE**FG**H	7
3	**KM**Q	ABEFNPQRSV	8
4	BCD		9
5	ABDEFHKLM**NO**	AEHIJLPR	10
10-15A		❶ €40.65	
2,4ha 199T(30-110m²)		❷ €45.60	

🚗 A7 (E15, N340), exit 272 Torre del Mar. To old coastal road N340a. Then Torre del Mar-oeste (west). Past the bus station. Follow the signs.

💬 Friendly and shaded campsite near the city with shops, a market and restaurant nearby.

www.eurocampings.co.uk/106613

N 36°44'1" W 4°5'56"

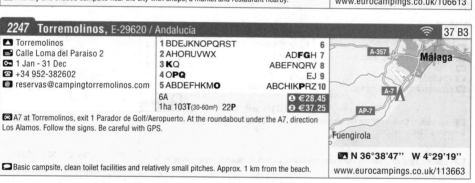

2247 Torremolinos, E-29620 / Andalucía   📶   37 B3

🔺 Torremolinos
📧 Calle Loma del Paraiso 2
📅 1 Jan - 31 Dec
☎ +34 952-382602
@ reservas@campingtorremolinos.com

1	BDEJKNOPQRST		6
2	AHORUVWX	AD**FG**H	7
3	**K**Q	ABEFNQRV	8
4	O**PQ**	EJ	9
5	ABDEFHKM**O**	ABCHIK**P**RZ	10
6A		❶ €28.45	
1ha 103T(30-60m²) 22P		❷ €37.25	

🚗 A7 at Torremolinos, exit 1 Parador de Golf/Aeropuerto. At the roundabout under the A7, direction Los Alamos. Follow the signs. Be careful with GPS.

💬 Basic campsite, clean toilet facilities and relatively small pitches. Approx. 1 km from the beach.

www.eurocampings.co.uk/113663

N 36°38'47" W 4°29'19"

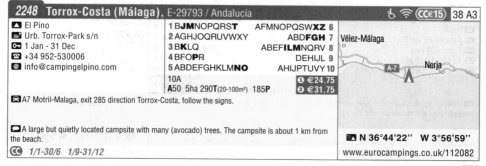

2248 Torrox-Costa (Málaga), E-29793 / Andalucía   ♿ 📶 (CC€15)   38 A3

🔺 El Pino
📧 Urb. Torrox-Park s/n
📅 1 Jan - 31 Dec
☎ +34 952-530006
@ info@campingelpino.com

1	B**JM**NOPQRS**T**	AFMNOPQSW**XZ**	6
2	AGHJOQRUVWXY	ABD**FGH**	7
3	B**KL**Q	ABEF**ILM**NQRV	8
4	BFO**P**R	DEHIJL	9
5	ABDEFGHKLM**NO**	AHIJPTUVY	10
10A		❶ €24.75	
A50 5ha 290T(20-100m²) 185P		❷ €31.75	

🚗 A7 Motril-Malaga, exit 285 direction Torrox-Costa, follow the signs.

💬 A large but quietly located campsite with many (avocado) trees. The campsite is about 1 km from the beach.
CC 1/1-30/6 1/9-31/12

www.eurocampings.co.uk/112082

N 36°44'22" W 3°56'59"

Spain

2249 Trevélez, E-18417 / Andalucía   38 A2

- 🏕 Trevélez
- 🛏 Ctra Órgiva-Trevélez, km 32,5
- 📅 1 Jan - 31 Dec
- ☎ +34 958-858735
- @ info@campingtrevelez.com

1 BDEGJMNOPQRS**T**	A 6
2 BFOPRUWXY	ABDE**F** 7
3 L	ABEFNQRV 8
4 **A**BCDEFHO	AJL 9
5 ABDFHKLMN**O**	ABHJNORV 10

4A   ❶ €23.05
A1560   1,3ha 100**T**(5-50m²)   11**P**   ❷ €29.35

🚗 From Órgiva direction Trevélez. The campsite is on the left, just before Trevélez (km 32.5). Signposted. Road to the campsite is winding, continually uphill. Easy for motorhomes, some experience and sufficient engine power required for caravans.

🛏 Elevated campsite (over 1500 metres) at the Alpujarra side of Sierra Nevada. Located on a mountain slope, approx. 20 minutes on foot from Trevélez. Lovely hiking area, possibly with a guide.

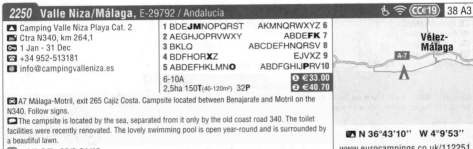

Capileira

Jorairátar

📍 N 36°59'30" W 3°16'15"

www.eurocampings.co.uk/117202

2250 Valle Niza/Málaga, E-29792 / Andalucía   38 A3

- 🏕 Camping Valle Niza Playa Cat. 2
- 🛏 Ctra N340, km 264,1
- 📅 1 Jan - 31 Dec
- ☎ +34 952-513181
- @ info@campingvalleniza.es

1 BDE**JM**NOPQRST	AKMNQRWXYZ 6
2 AEGHJOPRVWXY	ABDE**FK** 7
3 BKLQ	ABCDEFHNQRSV 8
4 BDFHOR**XZ**	EJVX**Z** 9
5 ABDEFHKLMN**O**	ABDFGHIJ**P**RV 10

6-10A   ❶ €33.00
2,5ha 150**T**(40-120m²)   32**P**   ❷ €40.70

🚗 A7 Málaga-Motril, exit 265 Cajiz Costa. Campsite located between Benajarafe and Motril on the N340. Follow signs.

🛏 The campsite is located by the sea, separated from it only by the old coast road 340. The toilet facilities were recently renovated. The lovely swimming pool is open year-round and is surrounded by a beautiful lawn.

CC 1/1-8/7   26/8-31/12

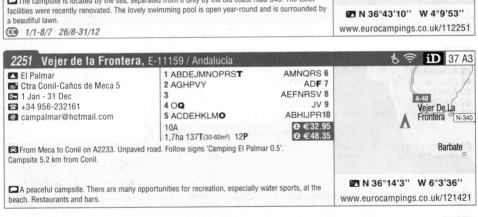

Vélez-Málaga

A-7

📍 N 36°43'10" W 4°9'53"

www.eurocampings.co.uk/112251

2251 Vejer de la Frontera, E-11159 / Andalucía   37 A3

- 🏕 El Palmar
- 🛏 Ctra Conil-Caños de Meca 5
- 📅 1 Jan - 31 Dec
- ☎ +34 956-232161
- @ campalmar@hotmail.com

1 ABDEJMNOPRS**T**	AMNQRS 6
2 AGHPVY	AD**F** 7
3	AEFNRSV 8
4 O**Q**	JV 9
5 ACDEHKLM**O**	ABHIJPR 10

10A   ❶ €32.95
1,7ha 137**T**(30-60m²)   12**P**   ❷ €48.35

🚗 From Meca to Conil on A2233. Unpaved road. Follow signs 'Camping El Palmar 0.5'. Campsite 5.2 km from Conil.

🛏 A peaceful campsite. There are many opportunities for recreation, especially water sports, at the beach. Restaurants and bars.

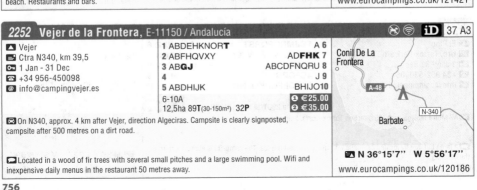

A-48

Vejer De La Frontera   N-340

Barbate

📍 N 36°14'3" W 6°3'36"

www.eurocampings.co.uk/121421

2252 Vejer de la Frontera, E-11150 / Andalucía   37 A3

- 🏕 Vejer
- 🛏 Ctra N340, km 39,5
- 📅 1 Jan - 31 Dec
- ☎ +34 956-450098
- @ info@campingvejer.es

1 ABDEHKNOR**T**	A 6
2 ABFHQVXY	AD**FHK** 7
3 AB**GJ**	ABCDFNQRU 8
4	J 9
5 ABDHIJK	BHIJO 10

6-10A   ❶ €25.00
12,5ha 89**T**(30-150m²)   32**P**   ❷ €35.00

🚗 On N340, approx. 4 km after Vejer, direction Algeciras. Campsite is clearly signposted, campsite after 500 metres on a dirt road.

🛏 Located in a wood of fir trees with several small pitches and a large swimming pool. Wifi and inexpensive daily menus in the restaurant 50 metres away.

Conil De La Frontera

A-48

Barbate   N-340

📍 N 36°15'7" W 5°56'17"

www.eurocampings.co.uk/120186

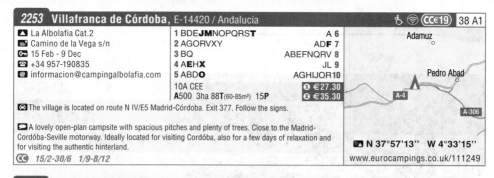

2253 Villafranca de Córdoba, E-14420 / Andalucía   ♿ ⊛ (CC€19) | 38 A1

- 🏕 La Albolafia Cat.2
- ✉ Camino de la Vega s/n
- 📅 15 Feb - 9 Dec
- ☎ +34 957-190835
- @ informacion@campingalbolafia.com

1 BDE**JM**NOPQRS**T**	A	6
2 AGORVXY	AD**F**	7
3 BQ	ABEFNQRV	8
4 A**E**H**X**	JL	9
5 ABD**O**	AGHIJOR	10
10A CEE	❶ €27.30	
A500 3ha 88**T**(60-85m²) 15**P**	❷ €35.30	

🅿 The village is located on route N IV/E5 Madrid-Córdoba. Exit 377. Follow the signs.

💬 A lovely open-plan campsite with spacious pitches and plenty of trees. Close to the Madrid-Cordóba-Seville motorway. Ideally located for visiting Cordóba, also for a few days of relaxation and for visiting the authentic hinterland.

CC 15/2-30/6 1/9-8/12

Adamuz

Pedro Abad

📍 N 37°57'13'' W 4°33'15''

www.eurocampings.co.uk/111249

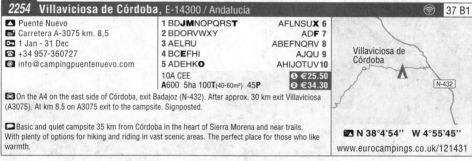

2254 Villaviciosa de Córdoba, E-14300 / Andalucía   ⊛ | 37 B1

- 🏕 Puente Nuevo
- ✉ Carretera A-3075 km. 8,5
- 📅 1 Jan - 31 Dec
- ☎ +34 957-360727
- @ info@campingpuentenuevo.com

1 BD**JM**NOPQRS**T**	AFLNSU**X**	6
2 BDORVWXY	AD**F**	7
3 AELRU	ABEFNQRV	8
4 BC**E**FHI	AJQU	9
5 ADEHK**O**	AHIJOTUV	10
10A CEE	❶ €25.50	
A600 5ha 100**T**(40-60m²) 45**P**	❷ €34.30	

🅿 On the A4 on the east side of Córdoba, exit Badajoz (N-432). After approx. 30 km exit Villaviciosa (A3075). At km 8.5 on A3075 exit to the campsite. Signposted.

💬 Basic and quiet campsite 35 km from Córdoba in the heart of Sierra Morena and near trails. With plenty of options for hiking and riding in vast scenic areas. The perfect place for those who like warmth.

Villaviciosa de Córdoba

📍 N 38°4'54'' W 4°55'45''

www.eurocampings.co.uk/121431

2255 Viñuela, E-29712 / Andalucía   ⊛ (CC€17) | 38 A2

- 🏕 Presa La Viñuela Cat. 2
- ✉ Ctra A356, km 30
- 📅 1 Jan - 31 Dec
- ☎ +34 952-554562
- @ campingpresalavinuela@hotmail.com

1 BDE**JM**NOPQRST	AN	6
2 FGRUVXY	ABDE**FG**	7
3 L	ABEFNQRTU	8
4 O	J	9
5 ABDKL	ABDEGHIJPTU	10
10A	❶ €26.00	
A400 1ha 39**T**(60-70m²) 13**P**	❷ €34.00	

🅿 N340, A7, exit 272 (e.g. Vélez-Malaga-La Viñuela). Follow A356 past La Viñuela. Campsite just past km 30. Indicated.

💬 Small, peaceful campsite with good amenities and an excellent restaurant. Beautiful view of the lake and mountains.

CC 1/1-14/7 1/9-31/12 7=6

Zafarraya

Colmenar

Moclinejo

📍 N 36°52'26'' W 4°11'10''

www.eurocampings.co.uk/117998

2256 Yunquera, E-29410 / Andalucía   ⊛ iD | 37 B3

- 🏕 Sierra de las Nieves Cat.2
- ✉ Cam.For.Sierra d/l Nieves
- 📅 1 Jan - 31 Dec
- ☎ +34 95-2482754
- @ info@campingsierradelasnieves.com

1 ABD**JM**NOPRS**T**	A**F**P	6
2 GQUVWX	A**C**D**FGH**IJK	7
3 E**G**LM**RU**	ABCDEFNQTU	8
4 **E**FHINO	FJKV	9
5 ADEHKLM**NO**	ABHKLPRV	10
10A CEE	❶ €22.00	
A800 50ha 30**T**(60-100m²) 32**P**	❷ €28.00	

🅿 On the N344 just outside Yunquera, direction El Burgo and Ronda. Follow the signs 'sports complex' at roundabout and bus station. Turn left to Sierra de las Nieves.

💬 A campsite located in a scenic area with magnificent Pinsapo pines (perfect for walks). Group excursions and hikes are held (min. 10 people). Clean toilet facilities. Suitable for groups and youngsters. Limited shade on the campsite. Open during weekends and holidays during the low season.

Casarabonela

Yunquera

Guaro

📍 N 36°44'9'' W 4°55'37''

www.eurocampings.co.uk/107699

Spain

Murcia

Land of contrasts

Did you know that Murcia, in the south-east corner of Spain, has 170 km of Mediterranean coastline? The great weather ensures the long beaches, pretty bays and salt marshes of the coast are generally busy; but inland, the orchards, olive groves, vineyards, farms, forests and towns of Murcia are much quieter.

Students and sardines

Experience the atmosphere of the lively university city of Murcia, with its tall belfry and striking Baroque-fronted cathedral. Find out how Murcians lived in the Monteaugudo Visitor Centre, located in the castle, or bring the kids to the Science and Water Museum. Escape the heat of the day at Plaza de la Flores, and in the evening, do what locals do and walk down riverside Paseo de Malecón to watch the sun set at Glorieta de Espanisa Square. Murcia City hosts the Burial of the Sardine festival, which started out as something of a student joke, and which takes place immediately after Easter.

So much to do!

Spend a day in Cartagena, explore the ancient Punic wall, Roman theatre and bridge, and for insights into more recent history, check out the Museum of the Spanish Civil War. Murcia has plenty for nature lovers: there's the salty lagoon of Mar Menor, and Macizo de Revolcadores and the Sabinar forest in Moratalla are a mecca for

Did you know ...?
In Murcia, there is a thing called snow well, used for storing snow in the mountains to supply ice to people in the surrounding area in summer.

climbers and hikers. For daredevils, check out Canon de Almadenes; not only are there caves and cave paintings, but the canyon is hugely popular for rafting, canyoning, birdwatching and hiking as well– and there's a zipline! For a great family day, go to Raphael de la Cerda Adventure Park, with a swimming pool, labyrinth, walking among treetops and paintball.

Delicious dishes

When in Murcia, try Zarangollo (scrambled eggs with courgette, onion and potato), or Pisto Murciano (aubergines, tomatoes, peppers, onions, olive oil and salt). Rice is also a staple, so sample Arroz al Calero, (fish, tomatoes, olive oil). Want something a little lighter? Try Ensalada Murciana (tomato, tuna, fresh onion, boiled eggs, and black olives). If you have room afterwards, try typical dessert Paparojotes (battered and fried lemon leaves), or Calatrava Bread Pudding.

Our tips

1. *Like making things? Bring the kids to some pottery workshops in Tolana*
2. *Spend the day at one of the region's great beaches*
3. *Visit the lost city of Begastri, near Cehegín*
4. *Bring your camera and get some shots of the bizarre Mazarrón landscape*
5. *Explore the fabulous castle of Lorca, dubbed the Fortress of the Sun*

2257 Águilas, E-30880 / Murcia   ♿ 🛜 CCє17 iD 39 A2

- ▲ Bellavista*
- 🏕 Ctra de Vera, km 3
- 🗓 1 Jan - 31 Dec
- ☎ +34 968-449151
- @ info@campingbellavista.com

1 ABDE**JM**NOPQRS**T**	AKNOPQRST 6
2 AEHORVWXY	ABDE**FGH** 7
3 ALQ	ABEFNQRSTUV**V** 8
4 BCDFIOQU	EJ 9
5 ABDEGHJLMO	ABCDFHIJMN**N**PV 10
10A CEE	❶ €34.20
1ha 65**T**(50-80m²) 11**P**	❷ €44.60

🗺 Located on route N332 from Águilas to Vera, km-marker 3.

💬 Small campsite with an eye for detail. Situated quite high up, giving some of the pitches wonderful sea views (250 metres). Many small bays in the area. Good restaurant next to the campsite. No credit cards or debit cards in the low season.

CC 1/1-15/2 26/2-28/3 2/4-30/6 1/9-31/12

N 37°23'31'' W 1°36'34''

www.eurocampings.co.uk/110778

2258 Águilas (Murcia), E-30889 / Murcia   🛜 CCє17 iD 39 A2

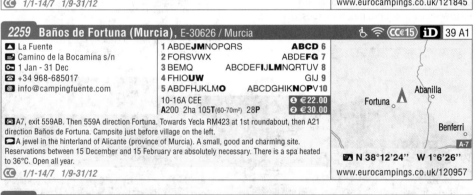

- ▲ La Quinta Bella
- 🏕 Finca El Charcon 31
- 🗓 1 Jan - 31 Dec
- ☎ +34 968-438535
- @ jonathan@quintabella.com

1 ABDEFJMNOPQRST	A 6
2 ACRSVWX	BDE**FG** 7
3 **KQ**	ABCDEFNQRTUV 8
4	9
5 ABDEFGHJKM**O**	ABCDFGHIJM**P**R 10
10-16A CEE	❶ €20.00
A600 14ha 43**T**(125-225m²) 30**P**	❷ €28.00

🗺 AP7, exit 878. On 1st roundabout direction Los Arejos RM-D24. Right at campsite sign after 2.9 km. Campsite is on right after 1.9 km.

💬 New campsite (2015), small-scale, large pitches. Rural location. Lots of sun. Very friendly, helpful management.

CC 1/1-14/7 1/9-31/12

N 37°27'14'' W 1°38'43''

www.eurocampings.co.uk/121845

2259 Baños de Fortuna (Murcia), E-30626 / Murcia   ♿ 🛜 CCє15 iD 39 A1

- ▲ La Fuente
- 🏕 Camino de la Bocamina s/n
- 🗓 1 Jan - 31 Dec
- ☎ +34 968-685017
- @ info@campingfuente.com

1 ABDE**JM**NOPQRS	**ABCD** 6
2 FORSVWX	ABDE**FG** 7
3 BEMQ	ABCDEF**IJLM**NQRTUV 8
4 FHIO**UW**	GIJ 9
5 ABDFHJKLM**O**	ABCDGHIK**N**OPV 10
10-16A CEE	❶ €22.00
A200 2ha 105**T**(60-70m²) 28**P**	❷ €30.00

🗺 A7, exit 559AB. Then 559A direction Fortuna. Towards Yecla RM423 at 1st roundabout, then A21 direction Baños de Fortuna. Campsite just before village on the left.

💬 A jewel in the hinterland of Alicante (province of Murcia). A small, good and charming site. Reservations between 15 December and 15 February are absolutely necessary. There is a spa heated to 36°C. Open all year.

CC 1/1-14/7 1/9-31/12

N 38°12'24'' W 1°6'26''

www.eurocampings.co.uk/120957

2260 Baños de Fortuna (Murcia), E-30626 / Murcia   ♿ 🛜 iD 39 A1

- ▲ Las Palmeras
- 🏕 Calle Camping s/n
- 🗓 1 Jan - 31 Dec
- ☎ +34 968-686095
- @ info@campinglaspalmeras.eu

1 ABDE**JM**NOPRST	6
2 ORSVWX	ABDEF 7
3 Q	ABEFNQRTUV 8
4 FO	9
5 ADEFGHJKLM	ABHIJ**P**R 10
10A	❶ €15.00
A221 2ha 73**T**(60-80m²) 8**P**	❷ €18.50

🗺 A-7, exit 559 AB. Then 559A direction Fortuna (RM-423). Then direction Yeala (C-3223). Then RM-A21 to Baños de Fortuna. Follow the campsite signs from here on.

💬 Quietly located medium campsite 3 km from Fortuna. Well-maintained.

N 38°12'20'' W 1°6'38''

www.eurocampings.co.uk/113660

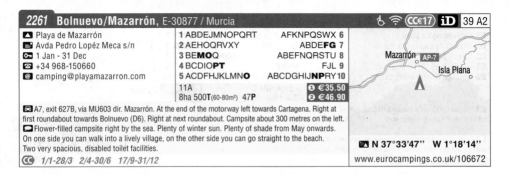

2261 Bolnuevo/Mazarrón, E-30877 / Murcia

♿ 🛜 CC€17 iD 39 A2

- 🏕 Playa de Mazarrón
- 📧 Avda Pedro Lopéz Meca s/n
- 🔓 1 Jan - 31 Dec
- ☎ +34 968-150660
- @ camping@playamazarron.com

1 ABDEJMNOPQRT	AFKNPQSWX	6
2 AEHOQRVXY	ABDE**FG**	7
3 BE**MOQ**	ABEFNQRSTU	8
4 BCDIO**PT**	FJL	9
5 ACDFHJKLMN**O**	ABCDGHIJ**NP**RY	10
11A	❶ €35.50	
8ha 500T(60-80m²) 47P	❷ €46.90	

Mazarrón AP-7 · Isla Plana

🚗 A7, exit 627B, via MU603 dir. Mazarrón. At the end of the motorway left towards Cartagena. Right at first roundabout towards Bolnuevo (D6). Right at next roundabout. Campsite about 300 metres on the left. 💬 Flower-filled campsite right by the sea. Plenty of winter sun. Plenty of shade from May onwards. On one side you can walk into a lively village, on the other side you can go straight to the beach. Two very spacious, disabled toilet facilities.

🗺 N 37°33'47" W 1°18'14"

CC 1/1-28/3 2/4-30/6 17/9-31/12

www.eurocampings.co.uk/106672

2262 El Berro/Alhama de Murcia, E-30848 / Murcia

🛜 CC€17 iD 39 A2

- 🏕 Sierra Espuña
- 📧 C/Juan Bautista s/n
- 🔓 1 Jan - 31 Dec
- ☎ +34 968-668038
- @ camping@campingsierraespuna.com

1 ABDE**JM**NOQRST	A	6
2 FRSTUVWXY	ABD**FG**	7
3 ABEIL**M**QU	ABEFJNQRSTV	8
4 BFHO**P**	J	9
5 DEHMN**O**	ABCDFGHIJLPVZ	10
6A	❶ €25.00	
A640 2ha 47T(45-80m²) 26P	❷ €33.60	

C-3315 · Librilla · Alhama De Murcia A-7 · N-340A

🚗 A7 Murcia-Granada, exit 627 Alhama de Murcia. Direction Mula on C3315. 2nd exit El Berro C25 (1st exit unsuitable). Follow signs at beginning of village. Don't go through village. Assistance available if required. Call in advance! 💬 A small, good campsite. Village and campsite are located in an area of natural beauty. A swimming pool with a lawn, the terrace for a drink, a small restaurant. You won't want to leave!

🗺 N 37°53'17" W 1°29'35"

CC 1/1-23/3 3/4-14/7 1/9-31/12 7=6

www.eurocampings.co.uk/110626

2263 El Portús/Cartagena, E-30393 / Murcia

🧖 ♿ 🛜 CC€19 iD 39 A2

- 🏕 Naturista 'El Portús'*
- 📧 Ctra Canteras-El Portús s/n
- 🔓 1 Jan - 31 Dec
- ☎ +34 968-553052
- @ elportus@elportus.com

1 ABDE**JM**NOPQRS**T**	ABEFGKQSW**X**	6
2 AEFGHJMOQRSTUVWX	ABDE**FG**	7
3 AL**MQ**	ABEFJNQRSTU	8
4 FO**PQRTUXYZ**	E	9
5 ACDEGHJKLM**O**	ABCDGHIJ**NP**RZ	10
6A	❶ €39.50	
10ha 350T(60-120m²) 140P	❷ €50.50	

Ap-7 · **Cartagena** · La Azohía

🚗 Located on the bay of El Portús, south-west of Cartagena. In Cartagena follow the signs Mazarrón N332 as far as Canteras/El Portús exit. After Canteras turn left towards El Portús. Follow campsite signs. 💬 Naturist campsite. Located on a bay with its own beach, surrounded by beautiful countryside. The restaurant, bar and supermarket are located higher up, from where there are stunning views. Indoor and outdoor swimming pool, spa and wellness area.

🗺 N 37°35'11" W 1°4'4"

CC 1/1-22/6 11/9-31/12

www.eurocampings.co.uk/100932

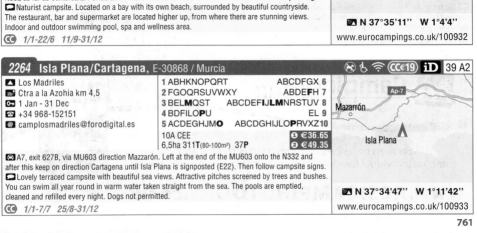

2264 Isla Plana/Cartagena, E-30868 / Murcia

🚫 ♿ 🛜 CC€19 iD 39 A2

- 🏕 Los Madriles
- 📧 Ctra a la Azohia km 4,5
- 🔓 1 Jan - 31 Dec
- ☎ +34 968-152151
- @ camplosmadriles@forodigital.es

1 ABHKNOPQRT	ABCDFGX	6
2 FGOQRSUVWXY	ABDE**FH**	7
3 BEL**MQ**ST	ABCDEF**IJLM**NRSTUV	8
4 BDFILO**PU**	EL	9
5 ACDEGHJM**O**	ABCDGHIJLO**P**RVXZ	10
10A CEE	❶ €36.65	
6,5ha 311T(80-100m²) 37P	❷ €49.35	

Ap-7 · Mazarrón · Isla Plana

🚗 A7, exit 627B, via MU603 direction Mazzarón. Left at the end of the MU603 onto the N332 and after this keep on direction Cartagena until Isla Plana is signposted (E22). Then follow campsite signs. 💬 Lovely terraced campsite with beautiful sea views. Attractive pitches screened by trees and bushes. You can swim all year round in warm water taken straight from the sea. The pools are emptied, cleaned and refilled every night. Dogs not permitted.

🗺 N 37°34'47" W 1°11'42"

CC 1/1-7/7 25/8-31/12

www.eurocampings.co.uk/100933

Spain

2265 La Manga del Mar Menor, E-30385 / Murcia

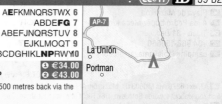 39 B2

- Caravaning La Manga
- Autovía de La Manga, salida 11
- 1 Jan - 31 Dec
- +34 968-563019
- lamanga@caravaning.es

1 ABDE**JM**NOPQRST	A**E**FKMNQRSTWX	6
2 AEHOQSTVWX	ABDE**FG**	7
3 BEI**K**LMOQ	ABEFJNQRSTUV	8
4 BDILO**PQRT**	EJKLMOQT	9
5 ACDEFGHJKLM**O**ABCDGHIKL**NP**RWY		**10**

Ad on this page 10A CEE   ❶ €34.00
32ha 950T(84-110m²) 553P   ❷ €43.00

La Unión

Portman

AP7, exit 800 to La Manga MU-312, exit 11. Across the viaduct and drive 500 metres back via the parallel road. Clearly signposted.

A good, extended campsite with pitches separated by hedges. Restaurant, bar and outdoor seating area by the sea with a beach and palms. In winter swimming in a heated indoor pool.

CC 1/1-30/6   1/9-31/12

🔲 N 37°37'30''   W 0°44'37''

www.eurocampings.co.uk/108232

Camping Caravaning La Manga

A true paradise between two seas with perfect temperatures all year.
Located on the banks of Mar Menor and the Mediterranean Sea with a white
sandy beach. Large pitches with water and electricity (6 kWh per day included,
more consumption for a fee). Tennis courts, crazy golf, pétanque, etc.
all included in the price. Discounts up to 50% on the prices in the low season
(not during Semana Santa).

**An indoor heated swimming pool in winter, jacuzzi, gym, sauna, internet
and wireless internet (wifi).**

**Autovía de La Manga, salida 11 (exit 11)
30385 La Manga del Mar Menor • Tel. 968-563019 • Fax 968-563426
E-mail: lamanga@caravaning.es • Internet: www.caravaning.es**

2266 Puerto de Mazarrón (Murcia), E-30860 / Murcia

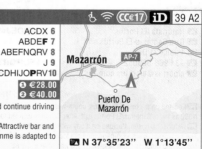 39 A2

- Las Torres
- Ctra N332 km 26
- 1 Jan - 31 Dec
- +34 968-595225
- info@campinglastorres.com

1 ABDE**JM**NOQR	ACDX	6
2 GOQRSVWXY	ABDE**F**	7
3 ALM	ABEFNQRV	8
4 IO**PQ**	J	9
5 ABDEFHJKM**O**	ABCDHIJO**P**RV	**10**

16A   ❶ €28.00
5ha 210T(70m²) 43P   ❷ €40.00

Mazarrón   AP-7

Puerto De
Mazarrón

A7 exit 627B via MU603 direction Mazarrón. Left at end of MU603 onto N332 and continue driving until 26 km-marker.

The region has a favourable climate, especially in winter. Very helpful managers. Attractive bar and restaurant run by 2 charming Spanish ladies. Spanish cuisine. Entertainment programme is adapted to suit winter, and indoor swimming in a heated pool.

CC 1/1-15/6   15/9-31/12

🔲 N 37°35'23''   W 1°13'45''

www.eurocampings.co.uk/108962

Spain

Viana do Castelo

Braga

Guimarães

Bragança

Vila Real

Porto

Miranda do Douro

Mogadouro

NORTHERN PORTUGAL

Aveiro

768

Viseu

Guarda

Atlantic Ocean

SPAIN

Coimbra

Fundão

Leiria

Castelo Branco

Plasencia

Caldas da Rainha

Santarém

Portalegre

Cáceres

Sintra

784

LISBOA

Mérida

Setúbal

Évora

Badajoz

SOUTHERN PORTUGAL

Beja

Odemira

Portimão

Lagos

Loulé

Huelva

Sevilla

Albufeira

Faro

CS-WEU

General
Portugal is a member of the EU. The capital city is Lisbon.

Time
The time in Portugal is the same as in London.

Language
Portuguese, but you will usually get by in English or French.

Crossing
To get to Portugal, you can choose to make the crossing through France, and drive from there, or you could take the ferry to Santander or Bilbao in Spain, and then drive on to Portugal. Check out page 36 for more information on ferry crossings.

Currency
The currency in Portugal is the euro. Approximate exchange rates September 2017: € 1 = £ 0.92.

Most bank branches in Portugal have automated cash points, Multibanco, as well as most large supermarkets and the main shopping areas in most towns or cities. You can buy/exchange Euros very easily at Cambios (Bureaux de Change or Change Shops), which are open seven days a week in the main tourist areas.

Credit cards
You can pay by credit card in many places. VISA, Mastercard and American Express cards are widely accepted.

(Mobile) phones
The mobile network works well throughout Portugal except in remote areas. There is a 4G network for mobile internet.

Wifi, internet
You can use wifi networks at many public locations, often for free.

Opening times/Public holidays
Banks
Banks are open Monday to Friday until 3:00 pm.

Shops (including pharmacies)
Generally open until 7:00 pm on weekdays.
Many shops have a siesta from 1:00 pm to
3:00 pm. On Saturdays shops are open until
1:00 pm. Pharmacies have the same opening
hours and have a siesta from 1:00 pm to 3:00 pm.

Post
Post offices (correios) are normally open on
weekdays until 6:00 pm.

Public holidays
New Year's Day, 13 February (Mardi Gras), Good
Friday, Easter Sunday, 25 April (Revolution
Remembrance Day), 1 May (Labour Day),
31 May (Corpus Christi), 10 June (Portugal Day),
15 August (The Assumption), 5 October (Republic
Day), All Saints, 1 December (Independence
Day), 8 December (Immaculate Conception) and
Christmas Day.

Roads and traffic
Traffic regulations
Remember, all traffic in Portugal drives on
the right and overtakes on the left! Headlight
deflectors are advisable to prevent annoying
oncoming drivers. If you are from Britain you will
need to attach a GB sticker to the rear, unless
your number plate incorporates a GB identifier.
If you go to Portugal by car, make sure that
you have the correct documents with you. See
page 18. Furthermore, it is advisable to have the
following items in your car in Portugal:
- Reflective jackets: one for each occupant, these
  must be kept inside the vehicle within easy
  reach.
- Warning triangle: compulsory in every vehicle
  with 4 wheels or more.
- Spare glasses: Drivers who wear glasses or
  contact lenses are advised to have spare
  glasses in their car.

Traffic coming from the right has priority. On
narrow roads, the car that can move over most
easily has to give way. Traffic on a roundabout
(coming from the left!) has priority over traffic
entering it. In built-up areas stopping and
parking is only permitted where indicated
or partly on the pavement in the direction of
the traffic. You may not stop on bridges and
in tunnels and you must use a phone hands-
free. The maximum permitted alcohol level is
0.5 promille.

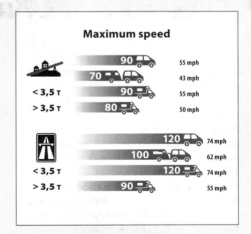

Take note: transporting bikes on a bicycle carrier
on the back of a car is not forbidden, but the
Portuguese government advises against it. You
are permitted to carry them on a roof rack on the
car, or on a bike rack on the back of your caravan

or motorhome. The bike must not protrude on the sides and must not protrude for more than 45 cm at the back.

Road network
Portugal uses the metric system, so distances are measured in kilometres (km) and speeds in kilometres per hour (km/h). 1 mile = 1.609 km and 1 km = 0.621 mile.
You are advised not to drive outside the towns during darkness. The ACP operates a breakdown service on all roads. To receive help you must have breakdown insurance. Emergency phones are located every 4 km on main roads. On other roads you should call 707509510.

Maximum permitted measurements of combined length
Height 4 metres, width 2.55 metres and maximum length 18.75 metres (of which the trailer is 12 metres maximum).

Fuel
Unleaded petrol, LPG and diesel are available almost everywhere. You can often pay by credit card.

Filling stations
Filling stations are usually open between 7:00 am and 10:00 pm.

Charging stations
Most charging stations are located in and around Lisbon. The network of public charging stations does not fully cover the whole country yet. Thus, it is definitely advisable to plan your trip carefully. For the exact location of charging stations check websites like ▶ *www.chargemap.com* ◀,

▶ *www.plugsurfing.com* ◀ or
▶ *openchargemap.org* ◀

Toll

You must pay a toll on various roads in Portugal. You can pay cash but on a number of routes you can only pay electronically. There are no barriers on these roads but your car will be registered as you enter. You can recognise these roads by the signs 'Electronic toll only'. You can buy a Toll Service card from an Easy Toll Welcome Point. This card is valid for 3 or 5 days. Another possibility is Easytoll. This is an automatic payment via credit card (MasterCard or Visa) which is registered together with your car number plate. You will need to register (free) at the border. You will receive a ticket that is valid for 30 days. You can also buy a pre-paid card (Toll card). You can purchase this at post offices, tourist offices and Easy Toll sales points. You will find more information on

▶ *www.visitportugal.com* ◀ and search for 'electronic tolls'.

Emergency number

112: the national emergency number for fire, police and ambulance.

Camping

Portugal has its own classification system for campsites. Campsites are categorised by 1 to 4 stars in proportion to their infrastructure and services, or simply as 'rural'. In this last category the campsite is part of a farm. You are recommended to reserve in high season.

Practical

- Make sure you have a world adaptor for electrical equipment.
- Tap water is of good quality. If in doubt you can drink bottled (mineral) water.

Mouth of the Douro

Can you imagine sailing from the Atlantic into the mouth of the river Douro in Northern Portugal? So many did: Celtic, pre-Celtic, Carthaginians, Romans, Moorish invaders ... and left behind a legacy of fortress towns, terraced hills and vineyards. Today the rabelo boats that transported the port wine from the wineries are replaced with modern barges, but it doesn't take a lot of imagination to slip back into the days of the great seafarers and explorers.

Oporto near the sea

Vibrant, colourful Oporto has so much to see! Wander around Sé, the cathedral on Pena Ventose Hill, where the open terrace has great views. Stroll down to Ribeira, the riverside quarter full of bars and cafés. Shopaholics go to Rua de Santa Catarina, and afterwards, take a break

in the shaded Crystal Palace Gardens. Visit the Serralves Museum of Contemporary art, and later on follow the river out to the beaches, where the kids will be fascinated by Sea Life, the aquarium right beside Praia Internacional beach.

Other places and activities

There are two places in Coimbra worth considering: Fado Ao Centro, the cultural centre dedicated to Portuguese Fado music, and Portugal dos Penquenitos – a park with miniature Portuguese monuments, adorable! For adrenaline junkies, the beaches near Oporto offer kitesurfing, surfing, and bodyboarding. Or head inland to Montesinho Nature Park to hike or ride a mountainbike or horse through the forest, where you might spot wolves, golden eagles, otters, boars and falcons. Learn about fossils in Arouca Geopark, visit traditional villages, or hike to

wrapped in lean cured ham) delicious with a glass of vino verde! Try a pasteis de nátas – be careful though, one is never enough!

waterfalls and see herds of goats. And for water sports enthusiasts there's rafting, canoeing and kayaking on Paiva River.

Bom apetite!

After a day in the mountains, a Francesinha – a meat sandwich covered with melted cheese and doused in tomato sauce –, with fries, served with beer – hits the spot. You might prefer something lighter like caldo verde (soup with potato, chorizo and cabbage), or Trutas con presunto (fried trout

Our tips

1. *Visit the spectacular Bom Jesus do Monte, near Braga and marvel at the ornate stairway*
2. *Go on a Douro river cruise through the wine-growing region*
3. *Visit a port warehouse on the Douro, across from Ribeira in Oporto*
4. *Relax in the thermal waters of Chaves, Trás-os-Montes*
5. *Go back in time in wild and romantic Agra, in the Serra da Cabreira region*

2267 Âncora/Gelfa, P-4910-012 / Viana do Castelo

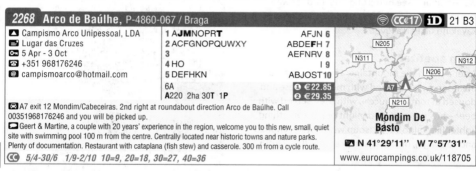

♿ 📶 **iD** 21 B3

🏕 Sereia da Gelfa**
📧 EN13, km 80,3
📅 1 Feb - 15 Dec
☎ +351 258401496
@ sereiadagelfa@gmail.com

1 ABD**JM**NOPR**T**	**AF**H	6
2 ABGHMOPQWXY	AD**F**	7
3 AE**M**	A**F**L**NRV**	8
4 IO**Q**	DJ	9
5 ADEH	AHIKLOST	10
6A	🔵 €27.40	
7ha 200**T**(50m²) 307**P**	🔵 €31.20	

🚗 A28 exit 27 Moledo/V.P.d'Âncora. Take N13 direction V.D. Castelo. Follow 'Parque de Campismo' signs. Campsite 800 metres past Intermarché on the N13.

💬 A busy residential campsite. Touring pitches can be found in and at the edge of a forest of spruce trees. Well-maintained toilet facilities. Leisure pool, pub and restaurant next to the site. A 15-minute walk will take you to the lovely beach.

Caminha
Vilar De Mouros

📍 N 41°47'47'' W 8°51'39''

www.eurocampings.co.uk/106371

2268 Arco de Baúlhe, P-4860-067 / Braga

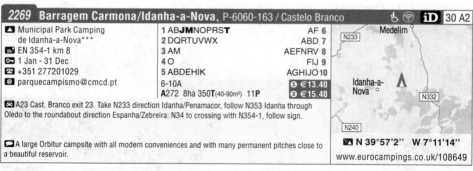

📶 **(CC€17)** **iD** 21 B3

🏕 Campismo Arco Unipessoal, LDA
📧 Lugar das Cruzes
📅 5 Apr - 3 Oct
☎ +351 968176246
@ campismoarco@hotmail.com

1 A**JM**NOPR**T**	**AF**J**N**	6
2 ACFGNOPQUWXY	ABDE**F**H	7
3	AE**F**N**RV**	8
4 HO	I	9
5 DEFHKN	ABJOST	10
6A	🔵 €22.85	
A220 2ha 30**T** 1**P**	🔵 €29.35	

🚗 A7 exit 12 Mondim/Cabeceiras. 2nd right at roundabout direction Arco de Baúlhe. Call 00351968176246 and you will be picked up.

💬 Geert & Martine, a couple with 20 years' experience in the region, welcome you to this new, small, quiet site with swimming pool 100 m from the centre. Centrally located near historic towns and nature parks. Plenty of documentation. Restaurant with cataplana (fish stew) and casserole. 300 m from a cycle route.

CC 5/4-30/6 1/9-2/10 10=9, 20=18, 30=27, 40=36

Mondim De Basto

📍 N 41°29'11'' W 7°57'31''

www.eurocampings.co.uk/118705

2269 Barragem Carmona/Idanha-a-Nova, P-6060-163 / Castelo Branco

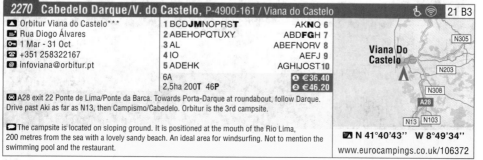

♿ 📶 **iD** 30 A2

🏕 Municipal Park Camping de Idanha-a-Nova***
📧 EN 354-1 km 8
📅 1 Jan - 31 Dec
☎ +351 277201029
@ parquecampismo@cmcd.pt

1 AB**JM**NOPRS**T**	AF	6
2 DQRTUVWX	ABD	7
3 AM	AE**F**N**RV**	8
4 O	FIJ	9
5 ABDEHIK	AGHIJO	10
6-10A	🔵 €13.40	
A272 8ha 350**T**(40-90m²) 11**P**	🔵 €15.40	

🚗 A23 Cast. Branco exit 23. Take N233 direction Idanha/Penamacor, follow N353 Idanha through Oledo to the roundabout direction Espanha/Zebreira: N34 to crossing with N354-1, follow sign.

💬 A large Orbitur campsite with all modern conveniences and with many permanent pitches close to a beautiful reservoir.

Medelim

Idanha-a-Nova

📍 N 39°57'2'' W 7°11'14''

www.eurocampings.co.uk/108649

2270 Cabedelo Darque/V. do Castelo, P-4900-161 / Viana do Castelo

♿ 📶 21 B3

🏕 Orbitur Viana do Castelo***
📧 Rua Diogo Álvares
📅 1 Mar - 31 Oct
☎ +351 258322167
@ infoviana@orbitur.pt

1 BCD**JM**NOPRS**T**	AK**NQ**	6
2 ABEHOPQTUXY	ABD**FG**H	7
3 AL	ABE**F**N**RV**	8
4 IO	AE**F**J	9
5 ADEHK	AGHIJOST	10
6A	🔵 €36.40	
2,5ha 200**T** 46**P**	🔵 €46.20	

🚗 A28 exit 22 Ponte de Lima/Ponte da Barca. Towards Porta-Darque at roundabout, follow Darque. Drive past Aki as far as N13, then Campismo/Cabedelo. Orbitur is the 3rd campsite.

💬 The campsite is located on sloping ground. It is positioned at the mouth of the Rio Lima, 200 metres from the sea with a lovely sandy beach. An ideal area for windsurfing. Not to mention the swimming pool and the restaurant.

Viana Do Castelo

📍 N 41°40'43'' W 8°49'34''

www.eurocampings.co.uk/106372

Portugal

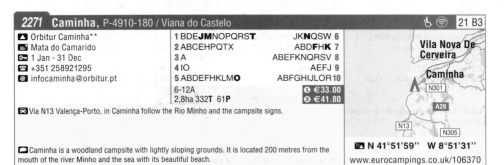

2271 Caminha, P-4910-180 / Viana do Castelo

  ♿ 🛜   21 B3

- ⛺ Orbitur Caminha**
- 🏕 Mata do Camarido
- 📅 1 Jan - 31 Dec
- ☎ +351 258921295
- @ infocaminha@orbitur.pt

1 BDE**JM**NOPQRS**T**	JK**N**QSW	6
2 ABCEHPQTX	ABD**FHK**	7
3 A	ABEFKNQRSV	8
4 IO	AEFJ	9
5 ABDEFHKLM**O**	ABFGHIJLOR	10
6-12A	❶ €33.00	
2,8ha 332**T** 61**P**	❷ €41.80	

🚗 Via N13 Valença-Porto, in Caminha follow the Rio Minho and the campsite signs.

💬 Caminha is a woodland campsite with lightly sloping grounds. It is located 200 metres from the mouth of the river Minho and the sea with its beautiful beach.

📍 N 41°51'59" W 8°51'31"

www.eurocampings.co.uk/106370

2272 Casfreires/Sátão, P-3560-043 / Viseu

  ♿ 🛜 (CC€17) iD   30 A1

- ⛺ Quinta Chave Grande
- 🏕 Rua do Barreiro 462
- 📅 15 Mar - 31 Oct
- ☎ +351 232665552
- @ info@chavegrande.com

1 ADE**JM**NOPR**T**	AF**N**	6
2 COPQRTUWXY	ABD**FG**H	7
3 AL**MQ**	ABEFHNR	8
4 AB**E**FHIO	ADEJ	9
5 ADFHJM**NO**	AGJMOPSTV	10
Ad on this page 6A CEE	❶ €24.00	
A700 9,5ha 180**T**(100-150m²) 6**P**	❷ €31.00	

🚗 A25 dir. Viseu, exit 19 direction Sátão. Then IP5 exit 17 Sátão. Stay on N229 to Sátão (Ferreira de Aves), when nearing Sátão follow arrow 'Campismo 12 km', from here switch off SatNav but follow arrows 'Campismo' to campsite.

💬 Located in the evergreen and sunny inlands of Central Portugal. Beautiful campsite in a green valley with magnificent views. Very spacious pitches and a lovely big swimming pool which uses salt instead of chlorine.

📍 N 40°49'22" W 7°41'46"

www.eurocampings.co.uk/108942

CC 15/3-14/7 1/9-30/10 10=9

This magnificent campsite is located in the ever sunny and green interior of Central Portugal. We speak Dutch, French and English.
This campsite is beautifully located in a natural and untouched valley and has a magnificent view. The pitches are very spacious and there is a wonderful large swimming pool, in addition to various mapped-out footpaths. 40 km from a high-quality golf course.

GPS: N 40°49'22" W 7°41'46"

**Rua do Barreiro 462, 3560-043 Casfreires/Sátão
Tel. 232665552 • E-mail: info@chavegrande.com
Internet: www.chavegrande.com**

Portugal

2273 Coimbra, P-3030-011 / Coimbra

  ♿ 🛜 (CC€17) iD   29 B2

- ⛺ AR Puro Camping Coimbra****
- 🏕 Rua da Escola
- 📅 1 Jan - 31 Dec
- ☎ +351 239086902
- @ coimbra@cacampings.com

1 ABCDE**JM**NOPQRS**T**	A**F**	6
2 AOPTUWX	AD**FG**H	7
3 AFI**K**	ABEFHNPQRV	8
4 A**E**IO**QRTZ**	JL	9
5 ADEFHJKMNO	AGHK**N**ORV	10
12A	❶ €23.65	
7ha 750**T**(40-100m²) 6**P**	❷ €26.05	

🚗 A1 exit 13 take IP3 to Coimbra-Viseu to exit 8, take IC2 towards Coimbra-Lisboa (not towards centre). Follow IC2, A31 signs to Campismo past Coimbrashopping and Leroy to Rua de Escola.

💬 City campsite in Coimbra. Good facilities. Bus 38 stops close to the campsite for a visit to the city. Discount 1/1 - 31/5 and 1/9 - 31/12, 7 days for price of 6, 14 days for price of 11.

📍 N 40°11'20" W 8°23'59"

www.eurocampings.co.uk/117240

CC 1/1-14/7 1/9-31/12

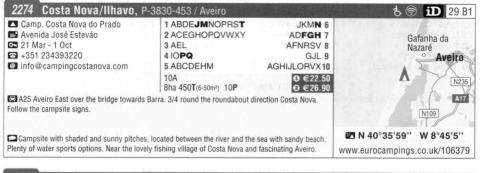

2274 Costa Nova/Ilhavo, P-3830-453 / Aveiro

🏕 Camp. Costa Nova do Prado
📧 Avenida José Estevão
📅 21 Mar - 1 Oct
☎ +351 234393220
@ info@campingcostanova.com

1 ABDE**J**MNOPRS**T**	JKM**N**	6
2 ACEGHOPQVWXY	AD**FGH**	7
3 AEL	AFNRSV	8
4 IO**PQ**	GJL	9
5 ABCDEHM	AGHIJLORVX	10
10A	❶ €22.50	
8ha 450**T**(6-50m²) 10**P**	❷ €26.90	

🚗 A25 Aveiro East over the bridge towards Barra. 3/4 round the roundabout direction Costa Nova. Follow the campsite signs.

💬 Campsite with shaded and sunny pitches, located between the river and the sea with sandy beach. Plenty of water sports options. Near the lovely fishing village of Costa Nova and fascinating Aveiro.

📍 N 40°35'59'' W 8°45'5''
www.eurocampings.co.uk/106379

29 B1

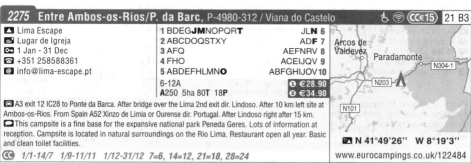

2275 Entre Ambos-os-Rios/P. da Barc, P-4980-312 / Viana do Castelo

🏕 Lima Escape
📧 Lugar de Igreja
📅 1 Jan - 31 Dec
☎ +351 258588361
@ info@lima-escape.pt

1 BDEG**J**MNOPQR**T**	JL**N**	6
2 ABCDOQSTXY	AD**F**	7
3 AFQ	AEFNRV	8
4 FHO	ACEIJQV	9
5 ABDEFHLMN**O**	ABFGHIJOV	10
6-12A	❶ €28.90	
A250 5ha 80**T** 18**P**	❷ €34.90	

🚗 A3 exit 12 IC28 to Ponte da Barca. After bridge over the Lima 2nd exit dir. Lindoso. After 10 km left site at Ambos-os-Rios. From Spain A52 Xinzo de Limia or Ourense dir. Portugal. After Lindoso right after 15 km.

💬 This campsite is a fine base for the expansive national park Peneda Geres. Lots of information at reception. Campsite is located in natural surroundings on the Rio Lima. Restaurant open all year. Basic and clean toilet facilities.

CC 1/1-14/7 1/9-11/11 1/12-31/12 7=6, 14=12, 21=18, 28=24

📍 N 41°49'26'' W 8°19'3''
www.eurocampings.co.uk/122484

21 B3

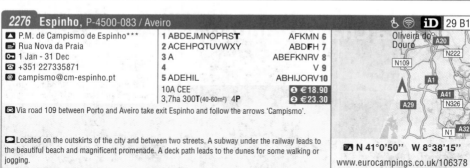

2276 Espinho, P-4500-083 / Aveiro

🏕 P.M. de Campismo de Espinho***
📧 Rua Nova da Praia
📅 1 Jan - 31 Dec
☎ +351 227335871
@ campismo@cm-espinho.pt

1 ABDE**J**MNOPRS**T**	AFKM**N**	6
2 ACEHPQTUVWXY	ABD**FH**	7
3 A	ABEFKNRV	8
4	V	9
5 ADEHIL	ABHIJORV	10
10A CEE	❶ €18.90	
3,7ha 300**T**(40-60m²) 4**P**	❷ €23.30	

🚗 Via road 109 between Porto and Aveiro take exit Espinho and follow the arrows 'Campismo'.

💬 Located on the outskirts of the city and between two streets. A subway under the railway leads to the beautiful beach and magnificent promenade. A deck path leads to the dunes for some walking or jogging.

📍 N 41°0'50'' W 8°38'15''
www.eurocampings.co.uk/106378

29 B1

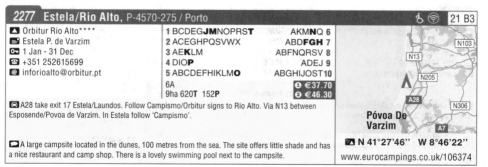

2277 Estela/Rio Alto, P-4570-275 / Porto

🏕 Orbitur Rio Alto****
📧 Estela P. de Varzim
📅 1 Jan - 31 Dec
☎ +351 252615699
@ inforioalto@orbitur.pt

1 BCDEG**J**MNOPRS**T**	AKM**N**Q	6
2 ACEGHPQSVWX	ABD**FGH**	7
3 AE**KLM**	ABFNQRSV	8
4 DIO**P**	ADEJ	9
5 ABCDEFHIKLM**O**	ABGHIJOST	10
6A	❶ €37.70	
9ha 620**T** 152**P**	❷ €46.30	

🚗 A28 take exit 17 Estela/Laundos. Follow Campismo/Orbitur signs to Rio Alto. Via N13 between Esposende/Povoa de Varzim. In Estela follow 'Campismo'.

💬 A large campsite located in the dunes, 100 metres from the sea. The site offers little shade and has a nice restaurant and camp shop. There is a lovely swimming pool next to the campsite.

📍 N 41°27'46'' W 8°46'22''
www.eurocampings.co.uk/106374

21 B3

Portugal

2278 Foz do Arelho, P-2500-516 / Leiria

🔺 Orbitur Foz do Arelho**
📧 Rua Maldonado Freitas
📅 1 Jan - 31 Dec
☎ +351 262978683
@ infofozarelho@orbitur.pt

1 ACDE**JM**NOPQRS**T**	AF	6
2 ABHOQTUVWXY	ABD**FGK**	7
3 A	ABEFKNORSV	8
4 IO**P**	AEFJ	9
5 ABCDEFHJK	AGHIJOS	10
6 A	❶ €38.60	
7ha 500**T**(80-125m²) 84**P**	❷ €46.40	

🗺 From the A8 take exit 19 towards the coast, left before the bay. Well signposted in the village.

💬 The campsite is located on a large sloping terrain in a peaceful setting, not far from the lagoon, with plenty of opportunities for water sports.

🔝 N 39°25'50" W 9°12'4"
www.eurocampings.co.uk/111706

São Martinho Do Porto

🛜 iD 29 A2

2279 Fundão, P-6230 / Castelo Branco

🔺 Fundatur S.A.*
📧 Quinta do Convento
📅 1 Jan - 31 Dec
☎ +351 275753118
@ campismofundao@gmail.com

1 ABJMNOPR**T**	AF	6
2 ABPQRTUWXY	ABD**FG**	7
3 ALU	AEFKNQRV	8
4 IO**Q**	DFU	9
5 ABDEFHJKN	ABHIJPSTV	10
6-10A	❶ €13.00	
A571 2,5ha 150**T**(50-100m²) 14**P**	❷ €16.20	

🗺 Take the IP2 from Fundão to Castel Branco, exit 'Fundão Sul'. From the centre follow the arrows to Camping and Campismo. Pay attention: steep entrance.

💬 Nice and small terraced campsite with plenty of trees. Located outside the city. Friendly reception. Good restaurant. With various marked out walking tours and mountain bike circuits. The park has options for tree climbing for kids and adults (adventure park).

🔝 N 40°7'55" W 7°30'43"
www.eurocampings.co.uk/106409

Paul
Silvares **Fundão**
N238

♿ 🛜 iD 30 A2

2280 Gafanha da Boa Hora/Vagos, P-3840-254 / Aveiro

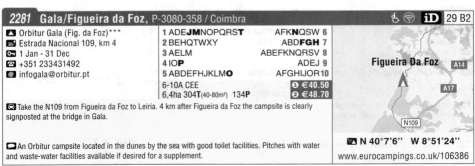

🔺 Orbitur Vagueira***
📧 Rua do Parque Campismo
📅 1 Jan - 31 Dec
☎ +351 234797526
@ infovagueira@orbitur.pt

1 BCDE**JM**NOPRS**T**	AF	6
2 ABHOPQVWXY	ABD**FGH**	7
3 ACEL**M**	ABEFKNQRS	8
4 IOQR	EFJ	9
5 ABDEFHKLM**O**	ABFGHIJOPRVW	10
6A CEE	❶ €32.30	
12ha 250**T**(80-125m²) 77**P**	❷ €39.90	

🗺 Take N109 from Aveiro to Figuero da Foz. In Vagos to Vagueira. Campsite located in front of the village.

💬 A family campsite located in pine woods with good amenities including Internet services. The campsite is located 1,500 m from the sea and 1 kilometre from Vagueira. You can observe wild grey herons on the beaches of Vagueira and Areão.

🔝 N 40°33'28" W 8°44'41"
www.eurocampings.co.uk/106381

Aveiro
Ílhavo
N109
A17

♿ 🛜 29 B1

2281 Gala/Figueira da Foz, P-3080-358 / Coimbra

🔺 Orbitur Gala (Fig. da Foz)***
📧 Estrada Nacional 109, km 4
📅 1 Jan - 31 Dec
☎ +351 233431492
@ infogala@orbitur.pt

1 ADE**JM**NOPQRS**T**	AFK**N**QSW	6
2 BEHQTWXY	ABD**FGH**	7
3 AELM	ABEFKNQRSV	8
4 IO**P**	ADEJ	9
5 ABDEFHJKLM**O**	AFGHIJOR	10
6-10A CEE	❶ €40.50	
6,4ha 304**T**(40-80m²) 134**P**	❷ €48.70	

🗺 Take the N109 from Figueira da Foz to Leiria. 4 km after Figueira da Foz the campsite is clearly signposted at the bridge in Gala.

💬 An Orbitur campsite located in the dunes by the sea with good toilet facilities. Pitches with water and waste-water facilities available if desired for a supplement.

🔝 N 40°7'6" W 8°51'24"
www.eurocampings.co.uk/106386

Figueira Da Foz A14
A17
N109

♿ 🛜 iD 29 B2

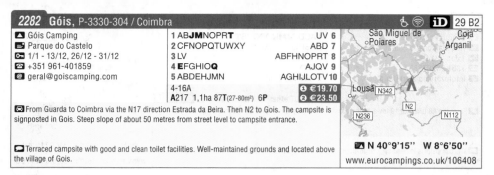

2282 Góis, P-3330-304 / Coimbra
🛗 ⊚ **iD** 29 B2

- 🏕 Góis Camping
- 🏘 Parque do Castelo
- 🗓 1/1 - 13/12, 26/12 - 31/12
- ☎ +351 961-401859
- @ geral@goiscamping.com

1 AB**JM**NOPR**T**	UV	**6**
2 CFNOPQTUWXY	ABD	**7**
3 LV	ABFHNOPRT	**8**
4 **E**FGHIO**Q**	AJQV	**9**
5 ABDEHJMN	AGHIJLOTV	**10**

4-16A   ❶ €19.70
A217 1,1ha 87**T**(27-80m²) 6**P**   ❷ €23.50

🚗 From Guarda to Coimbra via the N17 direction Estrada da Beira. Then N2 to Gois. The campsite is signposted in Gois. Steep slope of about 50 metres from street level to campsite entrance.

💬 Terraced campsite with good and clean toilet facilities. Well-maintained grounds and located above the village of Gois.

São Miguel de Poiares   Coja   Arganil
Lousã N342   N2
N236   N112

🏕 N 40°9'15'' W 8°6'50''

www.eurocampings.co.uk/106408

2283 Gondesende/Bragança, P-5300-561 / Bragança
🛗 ⊚ ✿ (CC€13) **iD** 22 A3

- 🏕 Cepo Verde***
- 🏘 Lugar da Vinha do Santo
- 🗓 1 Mar - 31 Oct
- ☎ +351 273999371
- @ cepoverde@montesinho.com

1 ABDE**JM**NOPQRS**T**	**A**	**6**
2 ABFGOPQTUVY	ABD**FG**HI	**7**
3 AL	ABEFNRSV	**8**
4 **B**EFO	FGJ	**9**
5 ADEFLMN**O**	AFHIJLM**O**STVW	**10**

6A   ❶ €18.50
A788 3ha 50**T**(15-60m²) 21**P**   ❷ €22.70

🚗 A4 exit Vinhais/Bragança (N103). 2nd exit at roundabout to Bragana/Vinhais via IP4. After 7 km exit right to N103 Bragana Oeste/Vinhais and Campismo. Follow signs.
💬 Enjoy the relaxed atmosphere in this wooded terraced campsite in the Montesinho nature park. Birdsong will help you to enjoy the beautiful panorama. Nearby you will discover typical villages such as Gimonde, Babe, Guadramil. Minor roads traverse the Montesinho Nature Park.

(CC) 1/3-7/7 25/8-30/10 7=6, 14=12, 21=18, 28=24

Vinhais N103   N103-7
Bragança   A4
N206

🏕 N 41°50'56'' W 6°51'41''

www.eurocampings.co.uk/116874

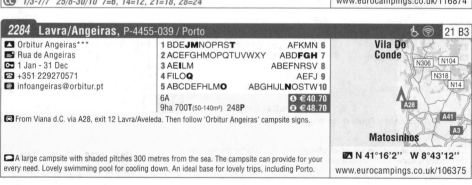

2284 Lavra/Angeiras, P-4455-039 / Porto
🛗 ⊚ 21 B3

- 🏕 Orbitur Angeiras***
- 🏘 Rua de Angeiras
- 🗓 1 Jan - 31 Dec
- ☎ +351 229270571
- @ infoangeiras@orbitur.pt

1 BDE**JM**NOPRS**T**	AFKMN	**6**
2 ACEFGHMOPQTUVWXY	ABD**FGH**	**7**
3 AE**I**LM	ABEFNRSV	**8**
4 FILO**Q**	AEFJ	**9**
5 ABCDEFHLM**O**	ABGHIJL**N**OSTW	**10**

6A   ❶ €40.70
9ha 700**T**(50-140m²) 248**P**   ❷ €48.70

🚗 From Viana d.C. via A28, exit 12 Lavra/Aveleda. Then follow 'Orbitur Angeiras' campsite signs.

💬 A large campsite with shaded pitches 300 metres from the sea. The campsite can provide for your every need. Lovely swimming pool for cooling down. An ideal base for lovely trips, including Porto.

Vila Do Conde   N306   N104
N318   N14
A28
A41
Matosinhos   A3

🏕 N 41°16'2'' W 8°43'12''

www.eurocampings.co.uk/106375

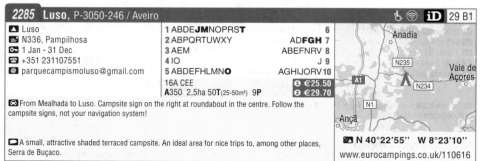

2285 Luso, P-3050-246 / Aveiro
🛗 ⊚ **iD** 29 B1

- 🏕 Luso
- 🏘 N336, Pampilhosa
- 🗓 1 Jan - 31 Dec
- ☎ +351 231107551
- @ parquecampismoluso@gmail.com

1 ABDE**JM**NOPRS**T**		**6**
2 ABPQRTUWXY	AD**FGH**	**7**
3 AEM	ABEFNRV	**8**
4 **I**O	J	**9**
5 ABDEFHLMN**O**	AGHIJORV	**10**

16A CEE   ❶ €25.50
A350 2,5ha 50**T**(25-50m²) 9**P**   ❷ €29.70

🚗 From Mealhada to Luso. Campsite sign on the right at roundabout in the centre. Follow the campsite signs, not your navigation system!

💬 A small, attractive shaded terraced campsite. An ideal area for nice trips to, among other places, Serra de Buçaco.

Anadia
N235   Vale de Açores
A1   N234
N1
Ança

🏕 N 40°22'55'' W 8°23'10''

www.eurocampings.co.uk/110616

Portugal

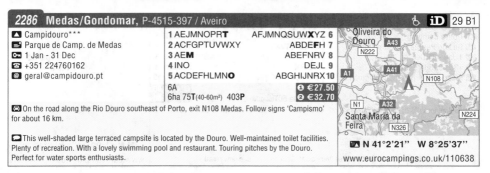

2286 Medas/Gondomar, P-4515-397 / Aveiro

♿ **iD** 29 B1

- ▲ Campidouro***
- 🏕 Parque de Camp. de Medas
- 📅 1 Jan - 31 Dec
- ☎ +351 224760162
- @ geral@campidouro.pt

1	AEJMNOPR**T**	AFJMNQSUW**X**YZ	6
2	ACFGPTUVWXY	ABDE**F**H	7
3	AE**M**	ABEFNRV	8
4	INO	DEJL	9
5	ACDEFHLMN**O**	ABGHIJNRX	10

6A
6ha 75T(40-60m²) 403P

❶ € 27.50
❷ € 32.70

📖 On the road along the Rio Douro southeast of Porto, exit N108 Medas. Follow signs 'Campismo' for about 16 km.

💬 This well-shaded large terraced campsite is located by the Douro. Well-maintained toilet facilities. Plenty of recreation. With a lovely swimming pool and restaurant. Touring pitches by the Douro. Perfect for water sports enthusiasts.

📌 **N 41°2'21" W 8°25'37"**

www.eurocampings.co.uk/110638

2287 Melo/Gouveia, P-6290-122 / Guarda

♿ 🛜 **iD** 30 A1

- ▲ Quinta das Cegonhas
- 🏕 Nabainhos
- 📅 1 Jan - 31 Dec
- ☎ +351 238745886
- @ cegonhas@cegonhas.com

1	AB**J**MNOPR**T**	AF	6
2	FOPRTUWXY	ABDE**FIJ**	7
3	I**L**SV	ABEFHNQRV	8
4	ABCEFGHIO**X**	ADGIJ	9
5	ADEHJK**N**	ABGJMNPTUW	10

10A
A580 3ha 50T(150-160m²) 8P

❶ € 23.00
❷ € 28.30

📖 E80, exit 36, direction Aveiro/Guarda north. A25 exit 26, then N17 direction Coimbra as far as km-marker 114, direction Melo, then follow the signs for 3 km.

💬 Quinta das Cegonhas; a rural estate for storks. Serre de Estrela nature park. Terraced campsite with spacious and no marked pitches. Easily accessible. Hospitable reception. Walks, yoga, massage, wifi and swimming pool. Daily menus and snacks are served.

📌 **N 40°31'15" W 7°32'30"**

www.eurocampings.co.uk/108945

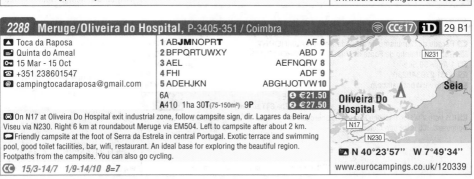

2288 Meruge/Oliveira do Hospital, P-3405-351 / Coimbra

🛜 **CC€17** **iD** 29 B1

- ▲ Toca da Raposa
- 🏕 Quinta do Ameal
- 📅 15 Mar - 15 Oct
- ☎ +351 238601547
- @ campingtocadaraposa@gmail.com

1	AB**J**MNOPR**T**	AF	6
2	BFPQRTUWXY	ABD	7
3	AEL	AEFNQRV	8
4	FHI	ADF	9
5	ADEHJKN	ABGHJOTVW	10

6A
A410 1ha 30T(75-150m²) 9P

❶ € 21.50
❷ € 27.50

📖 On N17 at Oliveira Do Hospital exit industrial zone, follow campsite sign, dir. Lagares da Beira/Viseu via N230. Right 6 km at roundabout Meruge via EM504. Left to campsite after about 2 km.

💬 Friendly campsite at the foot of Serra da Estrela in central Portugal. Exotic terrace and swimming pool, good toilet facilities, bar, wifi, restaurant. An ideal base for exploring the beautiful region. Footpaths from the campsite. You can also go cycling.

CC 15/3-14/7 1/9-14/10 8=7

📌 **N 40°23'57" W 7°49'34"**

www.eurocampings.co.uk/120339

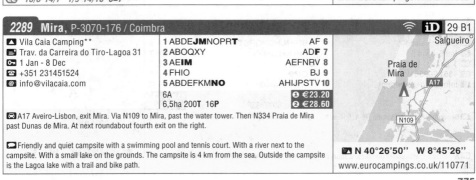

2289 Mira, P-3070-176 / Coimbra

🛜 **iD** 29 B1

- ▲ Vila Caia Camping**
- 🏕 Trav. da Carreira do Tiro-Lagoa 31
- 📅 1 Jan - 8 Dec
- ☎ +351 231451524
- @ info@vilacaia.com

1	ABDE**J**MNOPR**T**	AF	6
2	ABOQXY	AD**F**	7
3	AE**IM**	AEFNRV	8
4	FHIO	BJ	9
5	ABDEFKMN**O**	AHIJPSTV	10

6A
6,5ha 200T 16P

❶ € 23.20
❷ € 28.60

📖 A17 Aveiro-Lisbon, exit Mira. Via N109 to Mira, past the water tower. Then N334 Praia de Mira past Dunas de Mira. At next roundabout fourth exit on the right.

💬 Friendly and quiet campsite with a swimming pool and tennis court. With a river next to the campsite. With a small lake on the grounds. The campsite is 4 km from the sea. Outside the campsite is the Lagoa lake with a trail and bike path.

📌 **N 40°26'50" W 8°45'26"**

www.eurocampings.co.uk/110771

Portugal

2290 Miranda do Douro, P-5210-212 / Bragança   22 B3

- Douro Camping
- Rua do Parque de Campismo
- 1 Jan - 31 Dec
- +351 925642243
- reservas.dourocamping@gmail.com

1 ADEJMNOPR	**AE** 6	
2 FGRUWXY	ADFGH 7	
3 A	ABEFNQSTU 8	
4 ORX	AJW 9	
5 ABEFGHK	AFGHJOV 10	
10-16A	❶ €15.00	
A60 2ha 50**T**(60-100m²) 13**P**	❷ €17.00	

Via Bragança (E82), direction Zamora N122. Before Zamora direction Miranda de Douro. (ZA324/N218)

Family campsite with good toilet facilities. Very quiet. Comfortable bungalow rental.

N218   **Miranda do Douro**

N 41°29'34'' W 6°17'2''

www.eurocampings.co.uk/110691

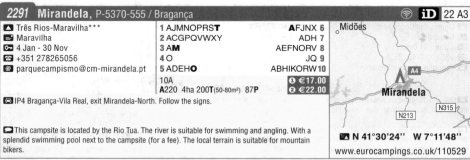

2291 Mirandela, P-5370-555 / Bragança   22 A3

- Três Rios-Maravilha***
- Maravilha
- 4 Jan - 30 Nov
- +351 278265056
- parquecampismo@cm-mirandela.pt

1 AJMNOPRS**T**	**A**FJNX 6	
2 ACGPQVWXY	ADH 7	
3 A**M**	AEFNORV 8	
4 O	JQ 9	
5 ADEH**O**	ABHIKORW 10	
10A	❶ €17.00	
A220 4ha 200**T**(50-80m²) 87**P**	❷ €22.00	

IP4 Bragança-Vila Real, exit Mirandela-North. Follow the signs.

This campsite is located by the Rio Tua. The river is suitable for swimming and angling. With a splendid swimming pool next to the campsite (for a fee). The local terrain is suitable for mountain bikers.

Midões   A4   **Mirandela**   N213   N315

N 41°30'24'' W 7°11'48''

www.eurocampings.co.uk/110529

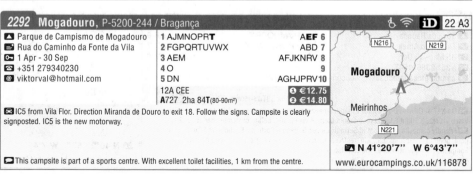

2292 Mogadouro, P-5200-244 / Bragança   22 A3

- Parque de Campismo de Mogadouro
- Rua do Caminho da Fonte da Vila
- 1 Apr - 30 Sep
- +351 279340230
- viktorval@hotmail.com

1 AJMNOPR**T**	**AEF** 6	
2 FGPQRTUVWX	ABD 7	
3 AEM	AFJKNRV 8	
4 O	9	
5 DN	AGHJPRV 10	
12A CEE	❶ €12.75	
A727 2ha 84**T**(80-90m²)	❷ €14.80	

IC5 from Vila Flor. Direction Miranda de Douro to exit 18. Follow the signs. Campsite is clearly signposted. IC5 is the new motorway.

This campsite is part of a sports centre. With excellent toilet facilities, 1 km from the centre.

N216   N219   **Mogadouro**   Meirinhos   N221

N 41°20'7'' W 6°43'7''

www.eurocampings.co.uk/116878

2293 Nazaré, P-2450-148 / Leiria   29 A2

- Orbitur Valado***
- Nat 8-5 km 9
- 1 Jan - 31 Dec
- +351 262561111
- infovalado@orbitur.pt

1 BDE**IL**NOPQRS**T**	A 6	
2 ABOQTUWXY	ABD**FGH** 7	
3 ALM	ABEFNRS 8	
4 O**PQ**	EJ 9	
5 ABDEHJM**O**	ABFHJOST 10	
6-10A	❶ €40.50	
A66 7ha 503**T** 33**P**	❷ €48.30	

Between Nazaré and Valado N8-4. Follow the sign and arrows to Orbitur campsite.

A quiet campsite under the trees, a short distance from the sea and the village. Excellent toilet facilities and swimming pool.

N356   Nazaré   A8   N242   São Martinho Do Porto   N8   N8-6   N1

N 39°35'53'' W 9°3'22''

www.eurocampings.co.uk/106354

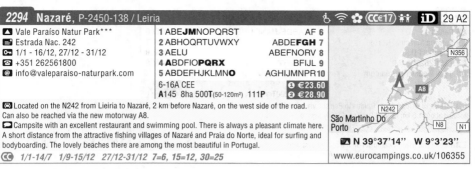

2294 Nazaré, P-2450-138 / Leiria

♿ 🛜 ✿ (CC€17) 🚻 **iD** 29 A2

- ⛰ Vale Paraíso Natur Park***
- 🚏 Estrada Nac. 242
- 🔓 1/1 - 16/12, 27/12 - 31/12
- ☎ +351 262561800
- @ info@valeparaiso-naturpark.com

1 ABE**JM**NOPQRST	AF **6**
2 ABHOQRTUVWXY	ABDE**FGH** 7
3 AELU	ABEFNORV **8**
4 ABDFIO**PQRX**	BFIJL **9**
5 ABDEFHJKLMN**O**	AGHIJMNPR**10**
6-16A CEE	❶ €23.60
A145 8ha 500**T**(50-120m²) 111**P**	❷ €28.90

🚗 Located on the N242 from Lieiria to Nazaré, 2 km before Nazaré, on the west side of the road. Can also be reached via the new motorway A8.
🏕 Campsite with an excellent restaurant and swimming pool. There is always a pleasant climate here. A short distance from the attractive fishing villages of Nazaré and Praia do Norte, ideal for surfing and bodyboarding. The lovely beaches there are among the most beautiful in Portugal.
(CC) 1/1-14/7 1/9-15/12 27/12-31/12 7=6, 15=12, 30=25

🅿 N 39°37'14'' W 9°3'23''
www.eurocampings.co.uk/106355

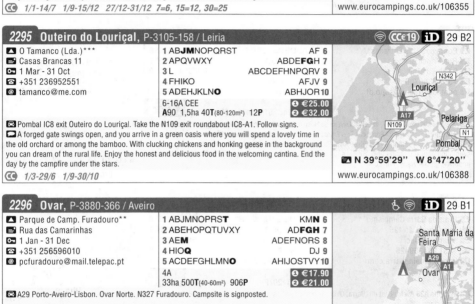

2295 Outeiro do Louriçal, P-3105-158 / Leiria

🛜 (CC€19) **iD** 29 B2

- ⛰ O Tamanco (Lda.)***
- 🚏 Casas Brancas 11
- 🔓 1 Mar - 31 Oct
- ☎ +351 236952551
- @ tamanco@me.com

1 AB**JM**NOPQRST	AF **6**
2 APQVWXY	ABDE**FGH** 7
3 L	ABCDEFHNPQRV **8**
4 FHIKO	AFJV **9**
5 ADEHJKLN**O**	ABHJOR**10**
6-16A CEE	❶ €25.00
A90 1,5ha 40**T**(80-120m²) 12**P**	❷ €32.00

🚗 Pombal IC8 exit Outeiro do Louriçal. Take the N109 exit roundabout IC8-A1. Follow signs.
🏕 A forged gate swings open, and you arrive in a green oasis where you will spend a lovely time in the old orchard or among the bamboo. With clucking chickens and honking geese in the background you can dream of the rural life. Enjoy the honest and delicious food in the welcoming cantina. End the day by the campfire under the stars.
(CC) 1/3-29/6 1/9-30/10

🅿 N 39°59'29'' W 8°47'20''
www.eurocampings.co.uk/106388

2296 Ovar, P-3880-366 / Aveiro

♿ 🛜 **iD** 29 B1

- ⛰ Parque de Camp. Furadouro**
- 🚏 Rua das Camarinhas
- 🔓 1 Jan - 31 Dec
- ☎ +351 256596010
- @ pcfuradouro@mail.telepac.pt

1 ABJMNOPRS**T**	KMN **6**
2 ABEHOPQTUVXY	AD**FGH** 7
3 AE**M**	ADEFNORS **8**
4 HIO**Q**	DJ **9**
5 ACDEFGHLMN**O**	AHIJOSTVY**10**
4A	❶ €17.90
33ha 500**T**(40-60m²) 906**P**	❷ €21.00

🚗 A29 Porto-Aveiro-Lisbon. Ovar Norte. N327 Furadouro. Campsite is signposted.

🏕 High-quality campsite in a pine forest with free choice of pitch. Good toilet facilities. Numerous options for recreation, 300 metres from the sea with a sandy beach. The campsite charges administration costs (2.73 Euros for the 1st night).

🅿 N 40°52'37'' W 8°40'10''
www.eurocampings.co.uk/100911

2297 Peniche, P-2520-206 / Leiria

29 A2

- ⛰ Parque de Camp. Mun. de Peniche**
- 🚏 Av. Mons Manuel Bastos
- 🔓 1 Jan - 31 Dec
- ☎ +351 262789696
- @ campismo-peniche@sapo.pt

1 BDEJMNOPQRS**T**	KMNOQS **6**
2 EHOQRTUW	AD 7
3 AM	AFKNR **8**
4 IO	L **9**
5 ABDEFHIJKMN**O**	AGHIJST**10**
4A	❶ €13.70
12,6ha 1000**T**(50-100m²) 400**P**	❷ €16.70

🚗 A8 exit Óbidos. From Óbidos to Peniche via the IP6. Turn right at first roundabout before Peniche. Follow the campsite signs.

🏕 A large beach campsite in the dunes, next to a swimming paradise, with moderate/reasonable toilet facilities. Many permanent pitches. New bar-restaurant with good price/quality ratio.

🅿 N 39°21'14'' W 9°21'39''
www.eurocampings.co.uk/110516

Portugal

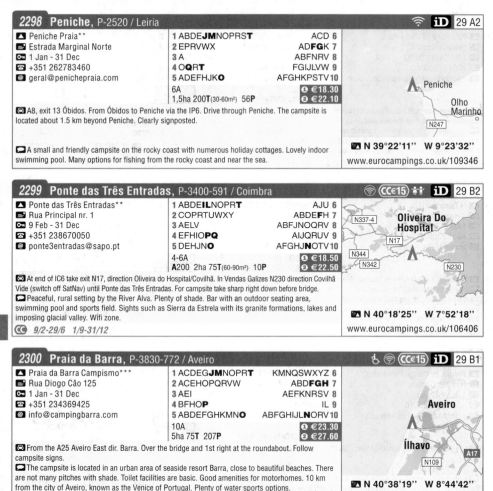

2298 Peniche, P-2520 / Leiria
🛜 iD 29 A2

- 🏕 Peniche Praia**
- 📧 Estrada Marginal Norte
- 📅 1 Jan - 31 Dec
- ☎ +351 262783460
- @ geral@penichepraia.com

1	ABDE**JM**NOPRS**T**	ACD **6**
2	EPRVWX	AD**FGK** 7
3	A	ABFNRV 8
4	O**QRT**	FGIJLVW 9
5	ADEFHJK**O**	AFGHKPSTV 10
6A		❶ €18.30
1,5ha 200T(30-60m²) 56P		❷ €22.10

🅰 A8, exit 13 Óbidos. From Óbidos to Peniche via the IP6. Drive through Peniche. The campsite is located about 1.5 km beyond Peniche. Clearly signposted.

💬 A small and friendly campsite on the rocky coast with numerous holiday cottages. Lovely indoor swimming pool. Many options for fishing from the rocky coast and near the sea.

📍 N 39°22'11'' W 9°23'32''

www.eurocampings.co.uk/109346

2299 Ponte das Três Entradas, P-3400-591 / Coimbra
🛜 (CC€15) ⚤ iD 29 B2

- 🏕 Ponte das Três Entradas**
- 📧 Rua Principal nr. 1
- 📅 9 Feb - 31 Dec
- ☎ +351 238670050
- @ ponte3entradas@sapo.pt

1	ABDE**IL**NOPR**T**	AJU **6**
2	COPRTUWXY	ABDEFH 7
3	AELV	ABFJNOQRV 8
4	EFHIO**PQ**	AIJQRUV 9
5	DEHJN**O**	AFGHJ**N**OTV 10
4-6A		❶ €18.50
A200 2ha 75T(60-90m²) 10P		❷ €22.50

🅰 At end of IC6 take exit N17, direction Oliveira do Hospital/Covilhã. In Vendas Galizes N230 direction Covilhã Vide (switch off SatNav) until Ponte das Três Entradas. For campsite take sharp right down before bridge.
💬 Peaceful, rural setting by the River Alva. Plenty of shade. Bar with an outdoor seating area, swimming pool and sports field. Sights such as Sierra da Estrela with its granite formations, lakes and imposing glacial valley. Wifi zone.

(CC) 9/2-29/6 1/9-31/12

📍 N 40°18'25'' W 7°52'18''

www.eurocampings.co.uk/106406

2300 Praia da Barra, P-3830-772 / Aveiro
♿ 🛜 (CC€15) iD 29 B1

- 🏕 Praia da Barra Campismo***
- 📧 Rua Diogo Cão 125
- 📅 1 Jan - 31 Dec
- ☎ +351 234369425
- @ info@campingbarra.com

1	ACDEG**JM**NOPR**T**	KMNQSWXYZ **6**
2	ACEHOPQRVW	ABD**FGH** 7
3	AEI	AEFKNRSV 8
4	BFHO**P**	IL 9
5	ABDEFGHKMN**O**	ABFGHIJL**N**ORV 10
10A		❶ €23.30
5ha 75T 207P		❷ €27.60

🅰 From the A25 Aveiro East dir. Barra. Over the bridge and 1st right at the roundabout. Follow campsite signs.
💬 The campsite is located in an urban area of seaside resort Barra, close to beautiful beaches. There are not many pitches with shade. Toilet facilities are basic. Good amenities for motorhomes. 10 km from the city of Aveiro, known as the Venice of Portugal. Plenty of water sports options.

(CC) 1/1-14/7 1/9-31/12

📍 N 40°38'19'' W 8°44'42''

www.eurocampings.co.uk/112687

2301 Praia de Mira, P-3070-752 / Coimbra
♿ 🛜 iD 29 B1

- 🏕 Mira Lodge Park
- 📧 Rua da Estrada Florestal
- 📅 1 Jan - 31 Dec
- ☎ +351 231480040
- @ info@miralodgepark.pt

1	ABCDEG**JM**NOPQRS	ABMNQRSTUVWXYZ **6**
2	ADFGHIJQRVWXY	ABDE**FG**HIJK 7
3	AEF**GLMQ**	ABCDEFGH**I**KNQRSTUV 8
4	ABCDEFHIJLNOP**QR**	ACJKR 9
5	ABDEFHJKLMN**O**	AFHIJLMPQRV**N** 10
10A		❶ €20.30
88T(100m²) 21P		❷ €20.30

🅰 A17, exit 11. Follow the signs 'Mira Lodge Park'.

💬 Spaciously laid out campsite with swimming pool, bar and restaurant. Near the village and the sea. New toilet facilities (2017). Friendly personnel at reception.

📍 N 40°26'42'' W 8°47'49''

www.eurocampings.co.uk/123103

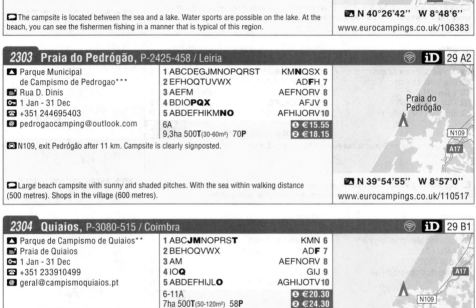

2302 Praia de Mira, P-3070-792 / Coimbra

♿ 📶 29 B1

- 🏕 Orbitur Mira**
- 🏤 Estrada Florestal 1-km 2
- 📅 1 Apr - 30 Sep
- ☎ +351 231471234
- @ infomira@orbitur.pt

1 BDEG**JM**NOPRS**T**	KM**N**QSTWX 6
2 ABCDEHOPQVWX	ABD**FGH** 7
3 A	ABEFKNRSV 8
4 BFHIO	AEJPQRT 9
5 ABDEFHKM**O**	ABFGHIJLPSTX 10
6A	❶ €38.60
3ha 280**T**(80-125m²) 47**P**	❷ €46.40

🚗 A17 Aveiro-Lisbon, exit Mira. N109 direction Mira, past water-tower. N334 to Praia de Mira. Past Dunas de Mira 1st right at roundabout direction Praia de Mira. Then follow arrows.

💬 The campsite is located between the sea and a lake. Water sports are possible on the lake. At the beach, you can see the fishermen fishing in a manner that is typical of this region.

Vagos
Mira

📷 N 40°26'42'' W 8°48'6''

www.eurocampings.co.uk/106383

2303 Praia do Pedrógão, P-2425-458 / Leiria

📶 **iD** 29 A2

- 🏕 Parque Municipal de Campismo de Pedrogao***
- 🏤 Rua D. Dinis
- 📅 1 Jan - 31 Dec
- ☎ +351 244695403
- @ pedrogaocamping@outlook.com

1 ABCDEGJMNOPQRST	KM**N**QSX 6
2 EFHOQTUVWX	AD**FH** 7
3 AEFM	AEFNORV 8
4 BDIO**PQX**	AFJV 9
5 ABDEFHIKM**NO**	AFHIJORV 10
6A	❶ €15.55
9,3ha 500**T**(30-60m²) 70**P**	❷ €18.15

🚗 N109, exit Pedrógão after 11 km. Campsite is clearly signposted.

💬 Large beach campsite with sunny and shaded pitches. With the sea within walking distance (500 metres). Shops in the village (600 metres).

Praia do Pedrógão

📷 N 39°54'55'' W 8°57'0''

www.eurocampings.co.uk/110517

2304 Quiaios, P-3080-515 / Coimbra

📶 **iD** 29 B1

- 🏕 Parque de Campismo de Quiaios**
- 🏤 Praia de Quiaios
- 📅 1 Jan - 31 Dec
- ☎ +351 233910499
- @ geral@campismoquiaios.pt

1 ABC**JM**NOPRS**T**	KMN 6
2 BEHOQVWX	AD**F** 7
3 AM	AEFNORV 8
4 IO**Q**	GIJ 9
5 ABDEFHIJL**O**	AGHIJOTV 10
6-11A	❶ €20.30
7ha 500**T**(50-120m²) 58**P**	❷ €24.30

🚗 EN109 Figuera da Foz-Aveiro, exit Praia de Quiaios. 5 km to the campsite after the village. Campsite well signposted.

💬 A pleasant, spacious campsite within walking distance of the sea. Large pitches on a firm level base divided by hedges. Hardly any pitches on the site have any shade.

Figueira Da Foz

📷 N 40°13'15'' W 8°53'5''

www.eurocampings.co.uk/109347

2305 S. Jacinto/Aveiro, P-3800-901 / Aveiro

♿ 29 B1

- 🏕 Orbitur S. Jacinto**
- 🏤 Estra Nat. 327
- 📅 1 Jun - 30 Sep
- ☎ +351 234838284
- @ infosjacinto@orbitur.pt

1 BDE**JM**NOPRS**T**	**N**QSWXZ 6
2 BDHPQXY	AD**FH** 7
3 A	ABEFNRV 8
4 O	EJ 9
5 ABDEFHM**O**	ABGHIJST 10
6A	❶ €33.10
2,5ha 250**T**(50-80m²) 11**P**	❷ €40.30

🚗 A29 Porto-Aveiro-Lisbon. Follow Ovar Norte N327 Furadouro. Stay on N327 S.Jacinto. Left Ria. Campsite signposted.

💬 A beautiful, clean campsite with many shaded pitches. Bordering on a nature park and the Lagune Ria. An ideal campsite for those seeking rest. The campsite provides for your every need. Excellent toilet facilities.

Murtosa
Aveiro

📷 N 40°42'10'' W 8°43'1''

www.eurocampings.co.uk/106380

2306 S. Martinho do Porto, P-2460-697 / Leiria
  (CC€15) iD 29 A2

- Colina do Sol***
- Serra dos Mangues
- 1/1 - 24/12, 26/12 - 31/12
- +351 262989764
- geral@colinadosol.org

1 ABDE**JM**NOPQR**T**	AF	6
2 AFHQRTUVWX	ABD**FGH**	7
3 AIL	ABEFNRV	8
4 **OPQ**	JV	9
5 ABDEFHJKMN	AGHJOST	10
6A	❶ €32.00	
10ha 400T(30-70m²) 180P	❷ €37.00	

Motorway A8 take exit 21 S. Martinho do Porto N242 towards S. Martinho do Porto. Avoid centre. Follow Nazare to Intermarché direction Nazare and camping sign. Campsite on the left after 500m.

Via a central road with tidy and organised permanent pitches, touring campers are welcome on the upper part of this campsite in the dunes, with both level and sloping pitches.

CC 1/1-30/6 1/9-23/12 26/12-31/12 7=6, 14=11

N 39°31'21'' W 9°7'23''

www.eurocampings.co.uk/101045

2307 Sao Pedro de Moel, P-2430 / Leiria
29 A2

- Orbitur S. Pedro de Moel***
- Rua Volta do Sete
- 1 Jan - 31 Dec
- +351 244599168
- infospedro@orbitur.pt

1 BDE**JM**NOPR**T**	AFHN	6
2 ABEHOQTWXY	ABD**FGH**	7
3 BLM	ABEFKNOQRS	8
4 BCDIO**PQ**	EJ	9
5 ABDEFHKM	AGHIJOR	10
6A	❶ €41.90	
7ha 400T(50-100m²) 154P	❷ €50.50	

From Leira via Marina Grande to Sao Pedro de Moel. Follow the signs 'Orbitur-camping'.

A campsite in the dunes with plenty of vegetation. High trees. Good toilet facilities, well equipped. An agreeable atmosphere and friendly management. Be prepared for sloping pitches.

N 39°45'29'' W 9°1'34''

www.eurocampings.co.uk/106353

2308 Sarzedo/Arganil, P-3300-432 / Coimbra
29 B2

- Camping Municipal Arganil**
- 1 Mar - 31 Oct
- +351 235205706
- camping@cm-arganil.pt

1 B**JM**NOPQRS**T**	JN	6
2 CFOPQRTUWXY	AD**FH**	7
3 **M**	ABEFKNOR	8
4 HO	JV	9
5 ABDEFHLMN**O**	AGHJPV	10
6-10A	❶ €12.50	
A200 3,5ha 120T(40-100m²) 10P	❷ €15.45	

The campsite is clearly signposted with arrows on the N342-4.

Flowerbeds, and friendly receptionists welcome guests for a quiet stay on a well-maintained campsite with ditto toilet facilities. New bar/restaurant complex. A magnificent route leads to Piódão. Protected rural area with an architectural style using slate.

N 40°14'30'' W 8°4'3''

www.eurocampings.co.uk/106407

2309 Terras de Bouro, P-4840-030 / Braga
  (CC€15) iD 21 B3

- Parque de Cerdeira***
- Rua de Cerdeira 400
- 1 Jan - 31 Dec
- +351 253351005
- info@parquecerdeira.com

1 ABDE**JM**NOPQRS**T**	**AFN**V	6
2 BGOPQRTUVY	ABD**FGH**	7
3 AEIM**RU**	ABEFJKNRSV	8
4 **AEF**GHIO**Q**	GJW	9
5 ABDEFHLMN**O**	ABGHIJOQRV	10
5-10A	❶ €30.00	
A697 6ha 200T(100m²) 16P	❷ €37.00	

Route 205-3 from Terras de Bouro to Campo do Gerês. Follow the signs to the campsite.

Wooded campsite located high up in the Parque National Penedal-Gerets. Ideal campsite for those who enjoy sports.

CC 1/1-30/6 1/9-31/12

N 41°45'47'' W 8°11'27''

www.eurocampings.co.uk/111465

Portugal

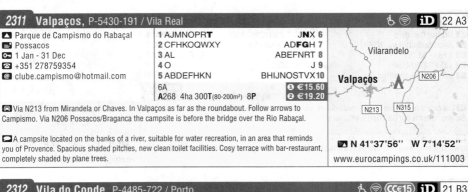

2310 Torreira, P-3870-340 / Aveiro

♿ 🛜 ✿ (CC€15) **iD** 29 B1

- 🏕 Torreira
- 🏠 Rua da Saudade
- 📅 1 Jan - 31 Dec
- ☎ +351 234838397
- @ info@torreiracamping.com

1	ACDG**JM**NOPQRS**T**	KM**X**	6
2	EHPQVWX	ADFGH	7
3	A	ABEFRSTV	8
4	FHIOQ	V	9
5	ABDEMNO	AFGHIJOSTV	10
12A		💶 €22.45	
200**T**(64m²) 50**P**		💶 €26.75	

🅰 From the A29 exit towards Ovar, then towards Furadouro, then road along river to Torreira. On entering Torreira at roundabout turn right. Campsite is signposted. Campsite is next to the water tower.

💬 Campsite is located in the residential part of Torreira, a village on a peninsula between the sea and Ria de Aveiro. Sandy beach nearby. Good toilet block. Limited number of shady pitches.

(CC) 1/1-14/7 1/9-31/12

🧭 N 40°45'44" W 8°42'10"

www.eurocampings.co.uk/121743

2311 Valpaços, P-5430-191 / Vila Real

♿ 🛜 **iD** 22 A3

- 🏕 Parque de Campismo do Rabaçal
- 🏠 Possacos
- 📅 1 Jan - 31 Dec
- ☎ +351 278759354
- @ clube.campismo@hotmail.com

1	A**J**MNOPR**T**	**J**N**X**	6
2	CFHKOQWXY	AD**FG**H	7
3	AL	ABEFNRT	8
4	O	J	9
5	ABDEFHKN	BHIJNOSTVX	10
6A		💶 €15.60	
A268 4ha 300**T**(80-200m²) 8**P**		💶 €19.20	

🅰 Via N213 from Mirandela or Chaves. In Valpaços as far as the roundabout. Follow arrows to Campismo. Via N206 Possacos/Bragança the campsite is before the bridge over the Rio Rabaçal.

💬 A campsite located on the banks of a river, suitable for water recreation, in an area that reminds you of Provence. Spacious shaded pitches, new clean toilet facilities. Cosy terrace with bar-restaurant, completely shaded by plane trees.

🧭 N 41°37'56" W 7°14'52"

www.eurocampings.co.uk/111003

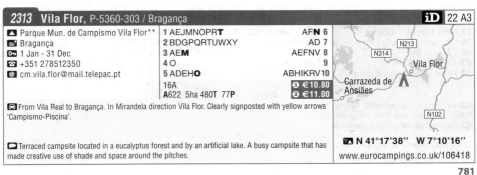

2312 Vila do Conde, P-4485-722 / Porto

♿ 🛜 (CC€15) **iD** 21 B3

- 🏕 Parque de Campismo Sol de Vila Chã***
- 🏠 Rua do Sol, 150 Vila Chã
- 📅 1 Jan - 31 Dec
- ☎ +351 229283163
- @ info@campingvilacha.pt

1	ADE**JM**NOPRS**T**	KNO	6
2	AEHOPWXY	ABD**FG**H	7
3	AELM	ABEFHKNORV	8
4	IO**Q**	DJL	9
5	ACDEHMN**O**	ABDGHIJOSTV	10
10A		💶 €19.90	
3ha 50**T**(80m²) 120**P**		💶 €23.70	

🅰 A28 exit Mindelo, then continue towards Vila Chã past Brico Outlet. At T-junction right to Vila Chã. Then immediately left. (Don't follow GPS and turn left, very narrow roads). Follow campsite signs.

💬 Located in a charming fishing village with a rocky and sandy beach. You can walk south from the fishing harbour along the coast via a wooden boardwalk. Good connections to Porto by metro from Povoa-Porto. Lovely new additional toilet block.

(CC) 1/1-7/7 1/9-31/12 7=6, 14=12, 21=18, 28=21

🧭 N 41°17'53" W 8°43'58"

www.eurocampings.co.uk/110700

2313 Vila Flor, P-5360-303 / Bragança

iD 22 A3

- 🏕 Parque Mun. de Campismo Vila Flor**
- 🏠 Bragança
- 📅 1 Jan - 31 Dec
- ☎ +351 278512350
- @ cm.vila.flor@mail.telepac.pt

1	AE**J**MNOPR**T**	AF**N**	6
2	BDGPQRTUWXY	AD	7
3	AE**M**	AEFNV	8
4	O		9
5	ADEH**O**	ABHIKRV	10
16A		💶 €10.80	
A622 5ha 480**T** 77**P**		💶 €11.00	

🅰 From Vila Real to Bragança. In Mirandela direction Vila Flor. Clearly signposted with yellow arrows 'Campismo-Piscina'.

💬 Terraced campsite located in a eucalyptus forest and by an artificial lake. A busy campsite that has made creative use of shade and space around the pitches.

🧭 N 41°17'38" W 7°10'16"

www.eurocampings.co.uk/106418

Portugal

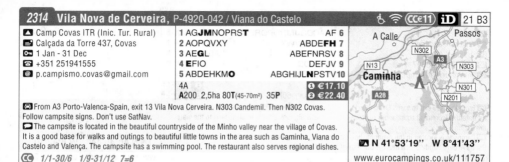

2314 Vila Nova de Cerveira, P-4920-042 / Viana do Castelo ♿ 🛜 ⓒⒺ11 🆔 21 B3

- 🏕 Camp Covas ITR (Inic. Tur. Rural)
- ✉ Calçada da Torre 437, Covas
- 🔓 1 Jan - 31 Dec
- ☎ +351 251941555
- @ p.campismo.covas@gmail.com

1 AG**JM**NOPRS**T**	AF	**6**
2 AOPQVXY	ABDE**FH**	**7**
3 AE**GL**	ABEFNRSV	**8**
4 **E**FIO	DEFJV	**9**
5 ABDEHKM**O**	ABGHIJL**N**PSTV	**10**
4A		❸ €17.10
A200 2,5ha 80**T**(45-70m²) 35**P**		❷ €22.40

🚗 From A3 Porto-Valenca-Spain, exit 13 Vila Nova Cerveira. N303 Candemil. Then N302 Covas. Follow campsite signs. Don't use SatNav.

💬 The campsite is located in the beautiful countryside of the Minho valley near the village of Covas. It is a good base for walks and outings to beautiful little towns in the area such as Caminha, Viana do Castelo and Valença. The campsite has a swimming pool. The restaurant also serves regional dishes.

ⓒⒸ 1/1-30/6 1/9-31/12 7=6

N 41°53'19" W 8°41'43"

www.eurocampings.co.uk/111757

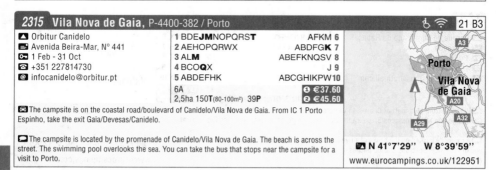

2315 Vila Nova de Gaia, P-4400-382 / Porto ♿ 🛜 21 B3

- 🏕 Orbitur Canidelo
- ✉ Avenida Beira-Mar, N° 441
- 🔓 1 Feb - 31 Oct
- ☎ +351 227814730
- @ infocanidelo@orbitur.pt

1 BDE**JM**NOPQRS**T**	AFKM	**6**
2 AEHOPQRWX	ABD**FGK**	**7**
3 AL**M**	ABEFKNQSV	**8**
4 BCO**Q**X	J	**9**
5 ABDEFHK	ABCGHIKPW	**10**
6A		❸ €37.60
2,5ha 150**T**(80-100m²) 39**P**		❷ €45.60

🚗 The campsite is on the coastal road/boulevard of Canidelo/Vila Nova de Gaia. From IC 1 Porto Espinho, take the exit Gaia/Devesas/Canidelo.

💬 The campsite is located by the promenade of Canidelo/Vila Nova de Gaia. The beach is across the street. The swimming pool overlooks the sea. You can take the bus that stops near the campsite for a visit to Porto.

N 41°7'29" W 8°39'59"

www.eurocampings.co.uk/122951

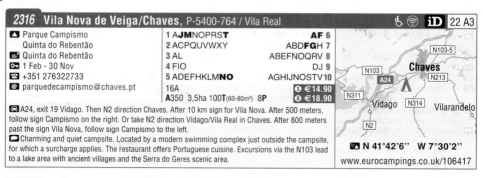

2316 Vila Nova de Veiga/Chaves, P-5400-764 / Vila Real ♿ 🛜 🆔 22 A3

- 🏕 Parque Campismo Quinta do Rebentão
- ✉ Quinta do Rebentão
- 🔓 1 Feb - 30 Nov
- ☎ +351 276322733
- @ parquedecampismo@chaves.pt

1 A**JM**NOPRS**T**	**AF**	**6**
2 ACPQUVWXY	ABD**FGH**	**7**
3 AL	ABEFNOQRV	**8**
4 FIO	DJ	**9**
5 ADEFHKLMN**O**	AGHIJNOSTV	**10**
16A		❸ €14.90
A350 3,5ha 100**T**(60-80m²) 8**P**		❷ €18.90

🚗 A24, exit 19 Vidago. Then N2 direction Chaves. After 10 km sign for Vila Nova. After 500 meters, follow sign Campismo on the right. Or take N2 direction Vidago/Vila Real in Chaves. After 800 meters past the sign Vila Nova, follow sign Campismo to the left.

💬 Charming and quiet campsite. Located by a modern swimming complex just outside the campsite, for which a surcharge applies. The restaurant offers Portuguese cuisine. Excursions via the N103 lead to a lake area with ancient villages and the Serra do Geres scenic area.

N 41°42'6" W 7°30'2"

www.eurocampings.co.uk/106417

2317 Vila Pouca de Aguiar, P-5450-101 / Vila Real ♿ 🛜 22 A3

- 🏕 Alvão Village Camping
- ✉ Lagoa da Falperra, Estrada Nacional
- 🔓 1 Jan - 31 Dec
- ☎ +351 259-419038
- @ geral@alvaovillagecamping.pt

1 BDE**JM**NOPQRS**T**	AF**N**	**6**
2 ABRWX	AD**FGH**	**7**
3 BC	ABCDEFNQRSV	**8**
4 FOQ**X**	J	**9**
5 ABDEFHKMNO	ABGHIJORV	**10**
6A		❸ €18.80
A700 2ha 52**T**(100m²) 12**P**		❷ €24.40

🚗 From Porto A7 and Chaves/Vila Real A24, take the exit Vila Pouca de Aguiar. Follow the signs 'Village & Camping' from there. It is another 4.5 km.

💬 Village and Camping Alvao exudes the ambiance of Roman times. The campsite and bungalows are surrounded by wooded poles (palisades) with watchtowers. All buildings have an exterior of abrasive rock, with all modern comforts inside. Opened in 2015. Lovely swimming pool and Roman playing equipment.

N 41°30'22" W 7°39'40"

www.eurocampings.co.uk/122785

Portugal

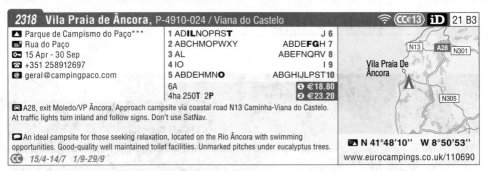

2318 Vila Praia de Âncora, P-4910-024 / Viana do Castelo 🛜 CC€13 iD 21 B3

- 🏕 Parque de Campismo do Paço***
- 🏠 Rua do Paço
- 📅 15 Apr - 30 Sep
- ☎ +351 258912697
- @ geral@campingpaco.com

1	ADILNOPRST	J 6
2	ABCHMOPWXY	ABDEFGH 7
3	AL	ABEFNQRV 8
4	IO	I 9
5	ABDEHMNO	ABGHIJLPST 10
6A		❸ €18.80
4ha 250T 2P		❷ €23.20

🚗 A28, exit Moledo/VP Âncora. Approach campsite via coastal road N13 Caminha-Viana do Castelo. At traffic lights turn inland and follow signs. Don't use SatNav.

💬 An ideal campsite for those seeking relaxation, located on the Rio Âncora with swimming opportunities. Good-quality well maintained toilet facilities. Unmarked pitches under eucalyptus trees.

CC 15/4-14/7 1/9-29/9

📍 N 41°48'10'' W 8°50'53''

www.eurocampings.co.uk/110690

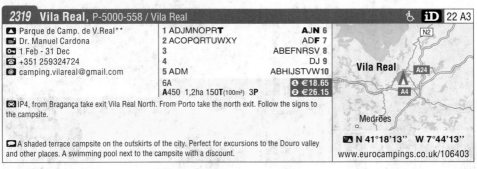

2319 Vila Real, P-5000-558 / Vila Real ♿ iD 22 A3

- 🏕 Parque de Camp. de V.Real**
- 🏠 Dr. Manuel Cardona
- 📅 1 Feb - 31 Dec
- ☎ +351 259324724
- @ camping.vilareal@gmail.com

1	ADJMNOPRT	AJN 6
2	ACOPQRTUWXY	ADF 7
3		ABEFNRSV 8
4		DJ 9
5	ADM	ABHIJSTVW 10
6A		❸ €18.65
A450 1,2ha 150T(100m²) 3P		❷ €26.15

🚗 IP4, from Bragança take exit Vila Real North. From Porto take the north exit. Follow the signs to the campsite.

💬 A shaded terrace campsite on the outskirts of the city. Perfect for excursions to the Douro valley and other places. A swimming pool next to the campsite with a discount.

📍 N 41°18'13'' W 7°44'13''

www.eurocampings.co.uk/106403

Portugal

Southern Portugal

The Land of Discovery

From lively Lisbon on the Tagus, through mountainous Alentejo and the Algarve with its golden beaches, southern Portugal both surprises and tantalises. Ruled by Celts, Romans, Arabs and Spaniards, the Portuguese themselves discovered so much of the known world. You've heard of Vasco da Gama, Ferdinand Magellan, Barthomeleu Dias, and Pedro Alvarez Cabral?

Lisbon – the old and the newer

You'll find capital Lisbon an intriguing mix of twisty little alleyways and a grid street system. Baixa and Avenida's street layout resulted from rebuilding after the 1755 earthquake and subsequent tsunami. Stroll around the shady squares and attractive cafés, and check out the eccentric Elevador de Santa Justa. Take a tram or walk up to the Alfama district, with its steep streets and beautiful Sao Jorge castle on the hilltop. Shop in Rua Garrett in the Bairro Alto district, and chill out later at the lovely Art Nouveau Café Brasileira, where there's often live music outside, or in Estrella Park.

Places to explore

Spend a day at Sintra, located on the edge of Sintra-Cascais Nature Park and visit the National Palace in the town. Look up: Castelo dos Mouros fort overlooks the town. A bus ride takes you through the forest to the beautiful Pena National Palace. Stop off at Evora, a town with Roman walls and winding narrow streets that remind you of an Arab souk. See the Roman temple

Did you know ...?
Sao Jorge castle has a camera obscura, where views of Lisbon are projected onto the walls inside of the Torre de Ulisses.

and aqueduct, and be enthralled or horrified in the chapel of bones in the Igreja Real de Sao Francisco church. Shake your own bones, and combine beach and music at MEO Sudoeste, the 4-day music festival at Zambujeira do Mar, and dance until dawn.

Soul food – and drink

Start a meal with petiscos: hearty snacks with bread. Alternatively, try sope de cacao: shark soup, or sopa de bacalhou: fish soup. Sopa de pedra is 'stone' soup – named after a fable about a travelling monk who tricked reluctant villagers into giving him ingredients to make a soup they all shared. Main dishes are: Porco a alentejana (pork with clams), salted fish, and grilled sardines are a great favourite. Portuguese cooking involves the use of spices like cinnamon, coriander, chili peppers and cloves.

Our tips

1. *Take the kids to Cascais or Estoril for a day at the beach*
2. *Visit the Escoural caves, and admire the 12,000 year old paintings*
3. *Go dolphin-watching from Setúbal – unforgettable!*
4. *Spend a day in Faro, and explore its souk-like warren of streets*
5. *Walk through Vale do Guadano National Park to the Pulo de Lobo waterfall*

2320 Aboboreiras/Tomar, P-2300-093 / Santarém

🛜 (CC€17) iD 29 B2

▲ Camping Pelinos-Tomar	1 ABJMNOPRT	A 6
🏠 Pelinos 77	2 ABOPQRTUWXY	ABDFGH 7
🕐 15 Mar - 1 Oct	3 L	ACEFGNQRSV 8
☎ +351 249301814	4 FO	9
@ info@campingpelinos.com	5 ADEHKN	ABCDJPTU10
	6A	❶ €20.50
	A186 1ha 30T(75-120m²)	❷ €26.50

🛣 IC9/IC3/A13, exit Tomar Norte. Left after 200m direction Aboboreiras. This is just before the petrol station. Follow campsite signs from here.

💬 Cosy terraced campsite with lively bar and pavement cafe. Easy-going, small and hospitable. Idyllic surroundings. Portuguese restaurant within walking distance. Extensive information folder for days out. Enthusiastic Dutch owners. Limited number of places.

© 15/3-2/6   1/9-30/9

🗺 N 39°38'18''   W 8°20'12''

www.eurocampings.co.uk/110782

2321 Albufeira, P-8200-555 / Faro

♿ 🛜 iD 36 A2

▲ Albufeira****	1 ADEJMNOPRST	AF 6
🏠 Estr. de Ferreiras	2 AGOPRTUWXY	ABDEFG 7
🕐 1 Jan - 31 Dec	3 BKM	ABCDEFNQRS 8
☎ +351 289587629	4 ABCDIMNOPQ	EJLUVW 9
@ geral@campingalbufeira.net	5 ACDEFGHILMNO	AGHIJNPRY10
	10A	❶ €26.80
	19ha 1400T 28P	❷ €30.80

🛣 On the N125 from Portimão to Faro. In Ferreiras take the N395 to Albufeira. After approx. 3 km the campsite is located on the left. Or on the IP1 exit Albufeira.

💬 Lovely campsite with various entertainment options. Varied planting and shade. Large swimming pools with sun terraces. Bar, restaurant and supermarket. Amenities open all year.

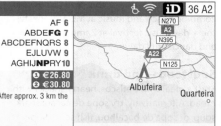

🗺 N 37°6'23''   W 8°15'12''

www.eurocampings.co.uk/106401

2322 Aldeia do Meco/Sesimbra, P-2970-063 / Setúbal

🛜 iD 29 A3

▲ Fetais Camping*	1 ADEILNOPQRT	AFX 6
🏠 Fetais/Rua da Fonte 4	2 HQRVWXY	ADFGH 7
🕐 1 Jan - 31 Dec	3 AEL	AEFNOQV 8
☎ +351 212682978	4 INOQ	J 9
@ geral@camping-fetais.com	5 ABDEFHJKMNO	AHIJNOSTV10
	6-10A	❶ €22.50
	A74 3ha 24T(60-90m²) 176P	❷ €27.50

🛣 On A2 exit direction Sesimbra. After 8 km direction Alfarim, then follow the campsite signs in Aldeia do Meco.

💬 Quietly located campsite with clean and basic toilet facilities between eucalyptus and various varieties of pine and spruce. Hedged pitches. In principle, the tourist part of the campsite has limited opening periods.

🗺 N 38°28'6''   W 9°10'29''

www.eurocampings.co.uk/106366

2323 Aljezur, P-8670-121 / Faro

♿ 🛜 iD 36 A2

▲ Campismo do Serrão***	1 ADEJMNOPQRST	AF 6
🏠 Herdade Serrão	2 GHMQRWXY	ABDF 7
🕐 1 Jan - 31 Dec	3 AEM	ABEFNOPRS 8
☎ +351 282990220	4 OXZ	IL 9
@ info@campingserrao.com	5 ABCDEFHIJLO	AGHIJNOSTVY10
	6A	❶ €25.00
	A112 10ha 800T 117P	❷ €30.50

🛣 On the IC4 (N120) from Lagos to Odemira, turn left 4 km past Aljezur. Clearly signposted from there on.

💬 Beautiful campsite with eucalyptus. Stunning environment. Lovely swimming pool. With hostel. Discounts in the low season.

🗺 N 37°20'22''   W 8°48'47''

www.eurocampings.co.uk/108652

2324 Alvito, P-7920-999 / Beja

    36 B1

- ▲ Markádia***
- ▣ Barragem de Odivelas/Ap. 17
- ☷ 1 Jan - 31 Dec
- ☎ +351 284-763141
- @ markadia@hotmail.com

1 ABDEJKNOPQRST	AFLNQSXY 6
2 DFGHRUWXY	ABDFGH 7
3 AEGIM	ABEFKNQRSV 8
4 FKO	ILMQT 9
5 ABEHLMNO	AHIJORV 10
16A	❶ €27.00
A112 10ha 150T 35P	❷ €33.00

Vila Nova da Baronia

N257   N258
N2
N259   N387

On the N2 at Odivelas take the N257 direction Alvito and Barragem/Odivelas and then follow Campisimo. Campsite is 15 km outside Alvito.

Located between the arms of a 1000 ha reservoir in a scenic area. Each spacious pitch has an (oak) tree to provide some shade. Dogs are permitted except in August, and in the low season. The restaurant is always open.

N 38°11'2" W 8°6'13"

www.eurocampings.co.uk/106392

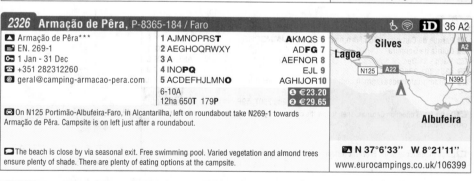

2325 Alvor Portimão, P-8500-053 / Faro

    36 A2

- ▲ Alvor***
- ▣ Estrada dos Montes
- ☷ 1 Jan - 31 Dec
- ☎ +351 282459178
- @ info@campingalvor.com

1 AJMNOPQRST	AF 6
2 AGHMOQRTUWXY	ABDFH 7
3 AKLQ	ABEFNORV 8
4 HIOPQ	EGHIJLV 9
5 ABDEFHJKNO	AGHIJPSTV 10
6-16A	❶ €24.00
4,5ha 400T 70P	❷ €30.00

A22
N125

Lagos   Portimão

Over two roundabouts by the white church on the N125 to Alvor (between Portimão-Lagos) then 1st exit. Campsite on the left, quite a way past the airport.

As it is divided into small terraces with plenty of shade, this large campsite always has a relaxed ambiance. Varied landscaping. Swimming pool with deckchairs close to the bar. Extra discount if staying 7 nights or more.

CC 1/1-1/7 1/9-31/12

N 37°8'6" W 8°35'26"

www.eurocampings.co.uk/106396

2326 Armação de Pêra, P-8365-184 / Faro

    36 A2

- ▲ Armação de Pêra***
- ▣ EN. 269-1
- ☷ 1 Jan - 31 Dec
- ☎ +351 282312260
- @ geral@camping-armacao-pera.com

1 AJMNOPRST	AKMQS 6
2 AEGHOQRWXY	ADFG 7
3 A	AEFNOR 8
4 INOPQ	EJL 9
5 ACDEFHJLMNO	AGHIJOR 10
6-10A	❶ €23.20
12ha 650T 179P	❷ €29.65

Silves
Lagoa   A2
N125   A22   N395

Albufeira

On N125 Portimão-Albufeira-Faro, in Alcantarilha, left on roundabout take N269-1 towards Armação de Pêra. Campsite is on left just after a roundabout.

The beach is close by via seasonal exit. Free swimming pool. Varied vegetation and almond trees ensure plenty of shade. There are plenty of eating options at the campsite.

N 37°6'33" W 8°21'11"

www.eurocampings.co.uk/106399

2327 Armação de Pêra/Alcantarilha, P-8365-908 / Faro

    36 A2

- ▲ Canelas***
- ▣ N-269-1
- ☷ 1 Jan - 31 Dec
- ☎ +351 282312612/3
- @ turismovel@mail.telepac.pt

1 AJMNOPQRS	AF 6
2 AGHOQRTUVWXY	ABDFGH 7
3 BM	ABEFKNQRV 8
4 DIOQ	IL 9
5 ACDEFHIJLMNO	AGHIJNORV 10
5-10A	❶ €23.00
6,9ha 430T(57-70m²) 98P	❷ €29.00

Silves
Lagoa   A2
N125   A22   N395

Albufeira

On the N125 from Portimão to Faro in Alcantarilha, turn left at the roundabout to the N269-1, direction Armação de Pêra. The campsite is on the right side of the road.

Well-maintained and quiet campsite. Special prices for guests spending winter. Varied planting to provide some shade. The marked out pitches are reserved and slightly more expensive. Swimming pool options and reclining chairs (for a fee in August).

N 37°7'9" W 8°21'4"

www.eurocampings.co.uk/106400

Portugal

2328 Barragem/Ortiga, P-6120-525 / Santarém

iD 29 B2

- Parque de Campismo de Ortiga
- Barragem de Belver
- 1 Jan - 31 Dec
- +351 241573464
- campismo@cm-macao.pt

1 ABDEGJMNOPQRS**T** L**N**XY 6
2 ADQRSTVWXY ABD**F** 7
3 ABEFKNQRV 8
4 FIO FQR 9
5 ABDN AHIJPSTV 10
10A CEE ❶ €21.30
A180 5ha 200T(25-50m²) 24P ❷ €23.70

A23 exit 12 Mação/Ortiga. Follow Ortiga to the left. Campsite is signposted further on.

Campsite located by the Teso reservoir and with a natural pool, water sports centre, restaurant and barbecue. No cars allowed by the tent or caravan in the high season.

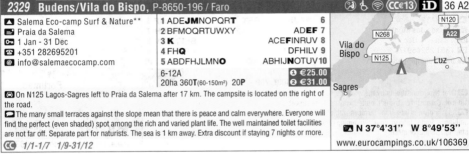

N 39°28'58'' W 8°0'11''
www.eurocampings.co.uk/113325

2329 Budens/Vila do Bispo, P-8650-196 / Faro

CC€13 iD 36 A2

- Salema Eco-camp Surf & Nature**
- Praia da Salema
- 1 Jan - 31 Dec
- +351 282695201
- info@salemaecocamp.com

1 ADE**JM**NOPQR**T** 6
2 BFMOQRTUWXY AD**EF** 7
3 **K** ACE**F**INRUV 8
4 FH**Q** DFHILV 9
5 ABDFHJLMN**O** ABHIJ**N**OTUV 10
6-12A ❶ €25.00
20ha 360T(60-150m²) 20P ❷ €31.00

On N125 Lagos-Sagres left to Praia da Salema after 17 km. The campsite is located on the right of the road.

The many small terraces against the slope mean that there is peace and calm everywhere. Everyone will find the perfect (even shaded) spot among the rich and varied plant life. The well maintained toilet facilities are not far off. Separate part for naturists. The sea is 1 km away. Extra discount if staying 7 nights or more.

1/1-1/7 1/9-31/12

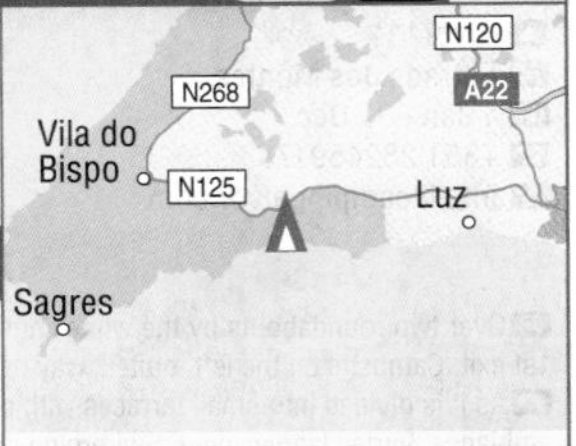

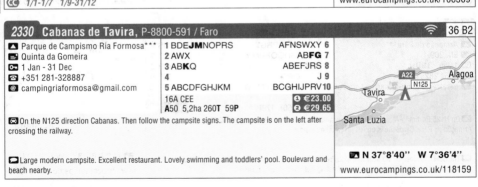

N 37°4'31'' W 8°49'53''
www.eurocampings.co.uk/106369

2330 Cabanas de Tavira, P-8800-591 / Faro

36 B2

- Parque de Campismo Ria Formosa***
- Quinta da Gomeira
- 1 Jan - 31 Dec
- +351 281-328887
- campingriaformosa@gmail.com

1 BDE**JM**NOPRS AFNSWXY 6
2 AWX AB**FG** 7
3 AB**K**Q ABEFJRS 8
4 J 9
5 ABCDFGHJKM BCGHIJPRV 10
16A CEE ❶ €23.00
A50 5,2ha 260T 59P ❷ €29.65

On the N125 direction Cabanas. Then follow the campsite signs. The campsite is on the left after crossing the railway.

Large modern campsite. Excellent restaurant. Lovely swimming and toddlers' pool. Boulevard and beach nearby.

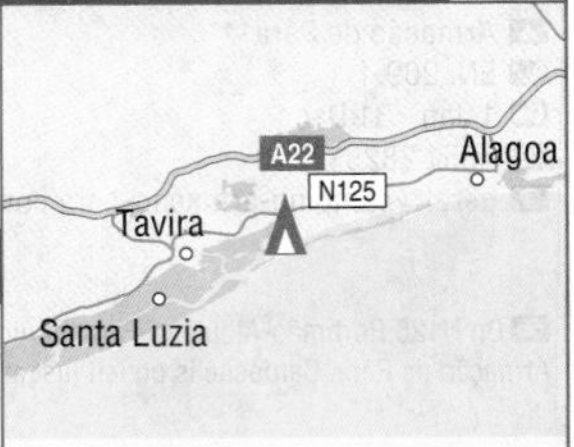

N 37°8'40'' W 7°36'4''
www.eurocampings.co.uk/118159

2331 Cascais/Guincho, P-2750-053 / Lisboa

iD 29 A3

- Orbitur Guincho**
- Lugar de Areia/EN 247-6
- 1 Jan - 31 Dec
- +351 214870450
- infoguincho@orbitur.pt

1 ABDE**JM**NOPQRS**T** AFQRS**X** 6
2 ABGHMOQTWXY ABD**FGHK** 7
3 A**GK**LM AEFNORSV 8
4 BCIO**Q** AFJLVXZ 9
5 ABDEFHIJKLM**O** ABGHIJOTU 10
6-10A ❶ €37.10
A70 7,7ha 600T(35-100m²) 387P ❷ €46.90

Via A5 direction Estoril to Cascais, at the end continue towards Cascais, after 500 metres follow the campsite signs at the roundabout.

Part of this campsite is only suitable for smaller camping equipment. Solid pitches for motor homes. The sea, 800 metres away, is much loved by surfers. Virtually the whole terrain is hidden under pine trees.

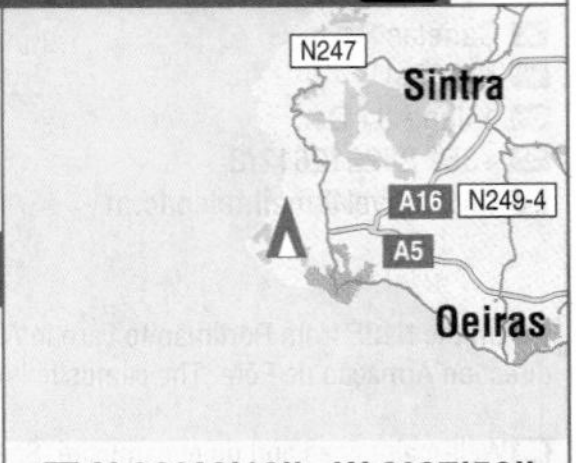

N 38°43'18'' W 9°27'59''
www.eurocampings.co.uk/106359

Portugal

2332 Costa de Caparica, P-2825-450 / Setúbal

                           🚲 📶 **iD** 29 A3

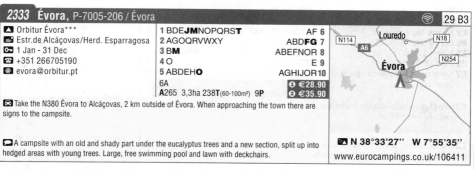

- ▲ Orbitur Costa de Caparica
- 🏢 Av. Afonso de Albuquerque
- 🔓 1 Jan - 31 Dec
- ☎ +351 212901366
- @ infocaparica@orbitur.pt

1 ACDE**JM**NOPQR**T**	KM**N**OPQSWX	6
2 AEHOQRVWXY	ABD**FGH**	7
3 AE**KL**M	ABEFNORV	8
4 BDINO**PQ**	ADEIJL	9
5 ABCDEFHJKM**O**	ABFGHIKORV	10
6A CEE	❶ €35.00	
5,7ha 250**T**(42-80m²) 184**P**	❷ €43.80	

🚗 Take exit Caparica on the A2/E4. Turn right after about 6 km, just before Costa da Caparica direction Trafaria. Campsite located on this bay. N377-1 after 2nd roundabout.

💬 A campsite where improvements are much in evidence. Many touring pitches are very sandy. The new part has virtually no shade. The older part under the pine trees is almost completely divided into pitches by hedges.

📷 N 38°39'14'' W 9°14'19''

www.eurocampings.co.uk/106363

2333 Évora, P-7005-206 / Évora

                           📶 29 B3

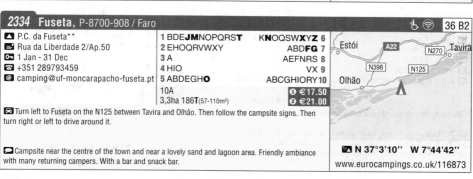

- ▲ Orbitur Évora***
- 🏢 Estr.de Alcáçovas/Herd. Esparragosa
- 🔓 1 Jan - 31 Dec
- ☎ +351 266705190
- @ evora@orbitur.pt

1 BDE**JM**NOPQRS**T**	AF	6
2 AGOQRVWXY	ABD**FG**	7
3 B**M**	ABEFNOR	8
4 O	E	9
5 ABDEH**O**	AGHIJOR	10
6A	❶ €28.90	
A265 3,3ha 238**T**(60-100m²) 9**P**	❷ €35.90	

🚗 Take the N380 Évora to Alcáçovas, 2 km outside of Évora. When approaching the town there are signs to the campsite.

💬 A campsite with an old and shady part under the eucalyptus trees and a new section, split up into hedged areas with young trees. Large, free swimming pool and lawn with deckchairs.

📷 N 38°33'27'' W 7°55'35''

www.eurocampings.co.uk/106411

2334 Fuseta, P-8700-908 / Faro

                         🚲 📶 36 B2

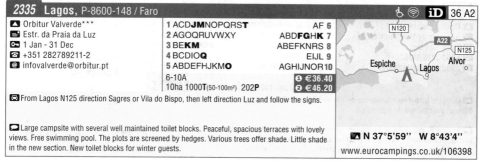

- ▲ P.C. da Fuseta**
- 🏢 Rua da Liberdade 2/Ap.50
- 🔓 1 Jan - 31 Dec
- ☎ +351 289793459
- @ camping@uf-moncarapacho-fuseta.pt

1 BDE**JM**NOPQRS**T**	K**N**OQSW**XYZ**	6
2 EHOQRVWXY	ABD**FG**	7
3 A	AEFNRS	8
4 HIO	VX	9
5 ABDEGH**O**	ABCGHIORY	10
10A	❶ €17.50	
3,3ha 186**T**(57-110m²)	❷ €21.00	

🚗 Turn left to Fuseta on the N125 between Tavira and Olhâo. Then follow the campsite signs. Then turn right or left to drive around it.

💬 Campsite near the centre of the town and near a lovely sand and lagoon area. Friendly ambiance with many returning campers. With a bar and snack bar.

📷 N 37°3'10'' W 7°44'42''

www.eurocampings.co.uk/116873

2335 Lagos, P-8600-148 / Faro

                         🚲 📶 **iD** 36 A2

- ▲ Orbitur Valverde***
- 🏢 Estr. da Praia da Luz
- 🔓 1 Jan - 31 Dec
- ☎ +351 282789211-2
- @ infovalverde@orbitur.pt

1 ACD**JM**NOPQRS**T**	AF	6
2 AGOQRUVWXY	ABD**FGH**K	7
3 BE**KM**	ABEFKNRS	8
4 BCDIO**Q**	EIJL	9
5 ABDEFHJKM**O**	AGHIJNOR	10
6-10A	❶ €36.40	
10ha 1000**T**(50-100m²) 202**P**	❷ €46.20	

🚗 From Lagos N125 direction Sagres or Vila do Bispo, then left direction Luz and follow the signs.

💬 Large campsite with several well maintained toilet blocks. Peaceful, spacious terraces with lovely views. Free swimming pool. The plots are screened by hedges. Various trees offer shade. Little shade in the new section. New toilet blocks for winter guests.

📷 N 37°5'59'' W 8°43'4''

www.eurocampings.co.uk/106398

Portugal

2336 Luz/Lagos, P-8600-109 / Faro

▲ Turiscampo****
🏠 E-N 125, km 17 - Espiche
☀ 1 Jan - 31 Dec
☎ +351 282789265
@ info@turiscampo.com

1 ADE**JL**NOPQRS**T**		AF	6
2 AGORTUVWXY	ABDE**FGH**		7
3 AE**KL**Q	ABCDEFJKNQRSV		8
4 ABCDLNOTUVX**Z**	EJLUVZ		9
5 ABDEFGHJLM**NO**	ABGHIJN**PRZ**		10
6-10A		❶ €45.30	
A80 7ha 258T(60-110m²) 140P		❷ €59.30	

Drive via the IP1/E1 or the N125 to Lagos and continue in the direction of Sagres. After exit Luz, continue on the N125. The campsite is located along this road, on the right, just after the traffic lights.
Turiscampo campsite with a Californian swimming pool. Luxurious toilet facilities. Individual toilet facilities available. Mild Algarve climate. Welcome all year round on a campsite with plenty of luxurious amenities.
CC 1/1-23/6 16/9-31/12

📷 N 37°6'5'' W 8°43'56''
www.eurocampings.co.uk/112387

36 A2

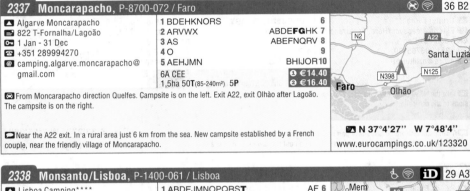

2337 Moncarapacho, P-8700-072 / Faro

▲ Algarve Moncarapacho
🏠 822 T-Fornalha/Lagoão
☀ 1 Jan - 31 Dec
☎ +351 289994270
@ camping.algarve.moncarapacho@gmail.com

1 BDEHKNORS		6	
2 ARVWX	ABDE**FG**HK		7
3 AS	ABEFNQRV		8
4 O		9	
5 AEHJMN	BHIJOR		10
6A CEE		❶ €14.40	
1,5ha 50T(85-240m²) 5P		❷ €16.40	

From Moncarapacho direction Quelfes. Campsite is on the left. Exit A22, exit Olhão after Lagoão. The campsite is on the right.

Near the A22 exit. In a rural area just 6 km from the sea. New campsite established by a French couple, near the friendly village of Moncarapacho.

📷 N 37°4'27'' W 7°48'4''
www.eurocampings.co.uk/123320

36 B2

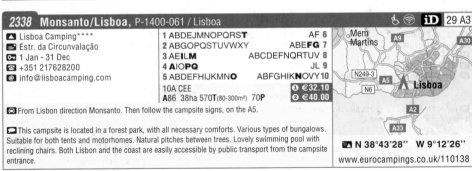

2338 Monsanto/Lisboa, P-1400-061 / Lisboa

▲ Lisboa Camping****
🏠 Estr. da Circunvalação
☀ 1 Jan - 31 Dec
☎ +351 217628200
@ info@lisboacamping.com

1 ABDEJMNOPQRS**T**		AF	6
2 ABGOPQSTUVWXY	ABE**FG**		7
3 AE**IL**M	ABCDEFNQRTUV		8
4 **A**IO**PQ**	JL		9
5 ABDEFHIJKMN**O**	ABFGHIK**NO**VY		10
10A CEE		❶ €32.10	
A86 38ha 570T(80-300m²) 70P		❷ €40.00	

From Lisbon direction Monsanto. Then follow the campsite signs, on the A5.

This campsite is located in a forest park, with all necessary comforts. Various types of bungalows. Suitable for both tents and motorhomes. Natural pitches between trees. Lovely swimming pool with reclining chairs. Both Lisbon and the coast are easily accessible by public transport from the campsite entrance.

📷 N 38°43'28'' W 9°12'26''
www.eurocampings.co.uk/110138

29 A3

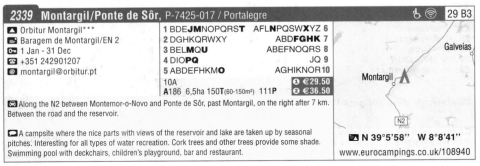

2339 Montargil/Ponte de Sôr, P-7425-017 / Portalegre

▲ Orbitur Montargil***
🏠 Baragem de Montargil/EN 2
☀ 1 Jan - 31 Dec
☎ +351 242901207
@ montargil@orbitur.pt

1 BDE**JM**NOPQRS**T**	AFL**N**PQSW**X**YZ		6
2 DGHKQRWXY	ABD**FGHK**		7
3 BEL**MQU**	ABEFNOQRS		8
4 DIO**PQ**	JQ		9
5 ABDEFHKM**O**	AGHIKNOR		10
10A		❶ €29.50	
A186 6,5ha 150T(60-150m²) 111P		❷ €36.50	

Along the N2 between Montemor-o-Novo and Ponte de Sôr, past Montargil, on the right after 7 km. Between the road and the reservoir.

A campsite where the nice parts with views of the reservoir and lake are taken up by seasonal pitches. Interesting for all types of water recreation. Cork trees and other trees provide some shade. Swimming pool with deckchairs, children's playground, bar and restaurant.

📷 N 39°5'58'' W 8°8'41''
www.eurocampings.co.uk/108940

29 B3

Portugal

2340 Odemira, P-7630-592 / Faro

⊗ 🛜 (CC€17) **iD** 36 A1

🔺 Campismo S. Miguel****
📧 EN 120
🔓 1 Jan - 31 Dec
☎ +351 926680611
@ camping.sao.miguel@mail.telepac.pt

1	ADEHKNOPRS**T**	**AF** 6
2	BGHMQTWX	ABDE**FG** 7
3	**AM**	ABEFNRV 8
4	IO**P**	DJ 9
5	ABDEFGHIJKN**O**	ABHIJ**NP**RY 10

6A   ❶ €32.50
7,5ha 460**T** 35**P**   ❷ €40.90

🚗 Campsite is 1.5 km before Odeceixe on EN120 (IC4) from Odemira to Lagos, on left. Campsite is well signposted.

💬 Campsite where the pitches are not marked out, with excellent amenities and recreational options. Swimming pool. Many shady spots under the spruce or eucalyptus trees. Sandy grounds.

CC   1/1-1/7   1/9-31/12

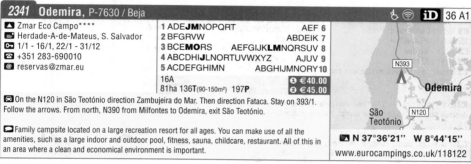

🖼 N 37°26'18"   W 8°45'20"

www.eurocampings.co.uk/108651

2341 Odemira, P-7630 / Beja

♿ 🛜 **iD** 36 A1

🔺 Zmar Eco Campo****
📧 Herdade-A-de-Mateus, S. Salvador
🔓 1/1 - 16/1, 22/1 - 31/12
☎ +351 283-690010
@ reservas@zmar.eu

1	ADE**JM**NOPQRT	AEF 6
2	BFGRVW	ABDEIK 7
3	BCE**MO**RS	AEFGIJK**LM**NQRSUV 8
4	ABCDHI**J**LNORTUVWXYZ	AJUV 9
5	ACDEFGHIMN	ABGHIJMNORY 10

16A   ❶ €40.00
81ha 136**T**(90-150m²) 197**P**   ❷ €45.00

🚗 On the N120 in São Teotónio direction Zambujeira do Mar. Then direction Fataca. Stay on 393/1. Follow the arrows. From north, N390 from Milfontes to Odemira, exit São Teotónio.

💬 Family campsite located on a large recreation resort for all ages. You can make use of all the amenities, such as a large indoor and outdoor pool, fitness, sauna, childcare, restaurant. All of this in an area where a clean and economical environment is important.

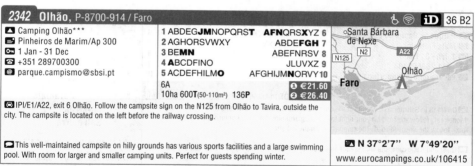

🖼 N 37°36'21"   W 8°44'15"

www.eurocampings.co.uk/118122

2342 Olhão, P-8700-914 / Faro

♿ 🛜 **iD** 36 B2

🔺 Camping Olhão***
📧 Pinheiros de Marim/Ap 300
🔓 1 Jan - 31 Dec
☎ +351 289700300
@ parque.campismo@sbsi.pt

1	ABDEG**JM**NOPQRS**T**	**AF**NQRS**X**YZ 6
2	AGHORSVWXY	ABDE**FGH** 7
3	BE**MN**	ABEFNRSV 8
4	**A**BCDFINO	JLUVXZ 9
5	ACDEFHILM**O**	AFGHIJM**N**ORVY 10

6A   ❶ €21.60
10ha 600**T**(50-110m²) 136**P**   ❷ €26.40

🚗 IPI/E1/A22, exit 6 Olhão. Follow the campsite sign on the N125 from Olhão to Tavira, outside the city. The campsite is located on the left before the railway crossing.

💬 This well-maintained campsite on hilly grounds has various sports facilities and a large swimming pool. With room for larger and smaller camping units. Perfect for guests spending winter.

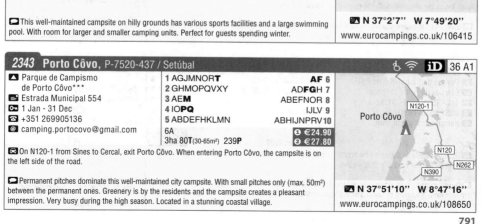

🖼 N 37°2'7"   W 7°49'20"

www.eurocampings.co.uk/106415

2343 Porto Côvo, P-7520-437 / Setúbal

♿ 🛜 **iD** 36 A1

🔺 Parque de Campismo
    de Porto Côvo***
📧 Estrada Municipal 554
🔓 1 Jan - 31 Dec
☎ +351 269905136
@ camping.portocovo@gmail.com

1	AGJMNOR**T**	**AF** 6
2	GHMOPQVXY	ADF**GH** 7
3	AE**M**	ABEFNOR 8
4	IO**PQ**	IJLV 9
5	ABDEFHKLMN	ABHIJNPRV 10

6A   ❶ €24.90
3ha 80**T**(30-65m²) 239**P**   ❷ €27.80

🚗 On N120-1 from Sines to Cercal, exit Porto Côvo. When entering Porto Côvo, the campsite is on the left side of the road.

💬 Permanent pitches dominate this well-maintained city campsite. With small pitches only (max. 50m²) between the permanent ones. Greenery is by the residents and the campsite creates a pleasant impression. Very busy during the high season. Located in a stunning coastal village.

🖼 N 37°51'10"   W 8°47'16"

www.eurocampings.co.uk/108650

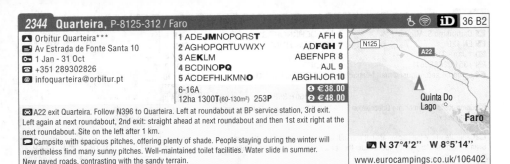

2344 Quarteira, P-8125-312 / Faro

🏕 Orbitur Quarteira***
✉ Av Estrada de Fonte Santa 10
🕐 1 Jan - 31 Oct
☎ +351 289302826
@ infoquarteira@orbitur.pt

1 ADE**JM**NOPQRS**T**		AFH **6**
2 AGHOPQRTUVWXY		AD**FGH 7**
3 AE**K**LM		ABEFNPR **8**
4 BCDINO**PQ**		AJL **9**
5 ACDEFHIJKMN**O**		ABGHIJOR**10**
6-16A	❶ €38.00	
12ha 1300**T**(60-130m²) 253**P**	❷ €48.00	

🗺 A22 exit Quarteira. Follow N396 to Quarteira. Left at roundabout at BP service station, 3rd exit. Left again at next roundabout, 2nd exit: straight ahead at next roundabout and then 1st exit right at the next roundabout. Site on the left after 1 km.

💬 Campsite with spacious pitches, offering plenty of shade. People staying during the winter will nevertheless find many sunny pitches. Well-maintained toilet facilities. Water slide in summer. New paved roads, contrasting with the sandy terrain.

⬛ N 37°4'2" W 8°5'14"

www.eurocampings.co.uk/106402

36 B2

2345 S. Teotónio/Odemira, P-7630-569 / Beja

🏕 Monte Carvalhal da Rocha
✉ Praïa do Carvalhal
🕐 1 Jan - 31 Dec
☎ +351 282947293
@ geral@montecarvalhaldarocha.com

1 ABDEJKNOPQRS**T**		**AFN 6**
2 FQUXY		AD**FH 7**
3 A		ABEFNR **8**
4 **EFO**Q**TVXY**		GIU **9**
5 ABDEGIJL**O**		AGHIJ**NOV**10
16A CEE	❶ €30.50	
4ha 250**T**(50m²) 25**P**	❷ €38.50	

🗺 On the N220 between S.Teotónio and Odeceixe, take exit Brejão. Keep right after the centre, direction Praia do Carvalhal. After approx. 2 km the campsite is on the right side of the road.

💬 Terraced and shaded campsite with plenty of options for relaxation and a large swimming pool. Near a fascinating beach by the Atlantic Ocean. Lovely trails.

⬛ N 37°29'43" W 8°47'12"

www.eurocampings.co.uk/118564

36 A1

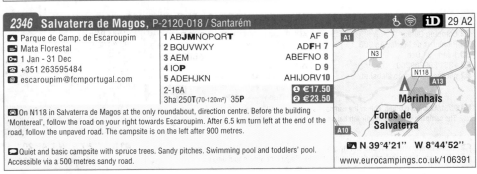

2346 Salvaterra de Magos, P-2120-018 / Santarém

🏕 Parque de Camp. de Escaroupim
✉ Mata Florestal
🕐 1 Jan - 31 Dec
☎ +351 263595484
@ escaroupim@fcmportugal.com

1 AB**JM**NOPQR**T**		AF **6**
2 BQUVWXY		AD**FH 7**
3 AEM		ABEFNO **8**
4 IO**P**		D **9**
5 ADEHJKN		AHIJORV**10**
2-16A	❶ €17.50	
3ha 250**T**(70-120m²) 35**P**	❷ €23.50	

🗺 On N118 in Salvaterra de Magos at the only roundabout, direction centre. Before the building 'Montereal', follow the road on your right towards Escaroupim. After 6.5 km turn left at the end of the road, follow the unpaved road. The campsite is on the left after 900 metres.

💬 Quiet and basic campsite with spruce trees. Sandy pitches. Swimming pool and toddlers' pool. Accessible via a 500 metres sandy road.

⬛ N 39°4'21" W 8°44'52"

www.eurocampings.co.uk/106391

29 A2

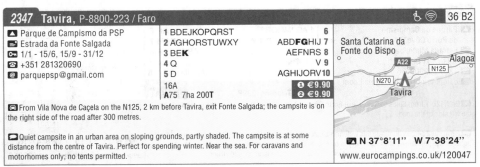

2347 Tavira, P-8800-223 / Faro

🏕 Parque de Campismo da PSP
✉ Estrada da Fonte Salgada
🕐 1/1 - 15/6, 15/9 - 31/12
☎ +351 281320690
@ parquepsp@gmail.com

1 BDEJKOPQRST		**6**
2 AGHORSTUWXY		ABD**FG**HIJ **7**
3 BE**K**		AEFNRS **8**
4 Q		V **9**
5 D		AGHIJORV**10**
16A	❶ €9.90	
A75 7ha 200**T**	❷ €9.90	

🗺 From Vila Nova de Caçela on the N125, 2 km before Tavira, exit Fonte Salgada; the campsite is on the right side of the road after 300 metres.

💬 Quiet campsite in an urban area on sloping grounds, partly shaded. The campsite is at some distance from the centre of Tavira. Perfect for spending winter. Near the sea. For caravans and motorhomes only; no tents permitted.

⬛ N 37°8'11" W 7°38'24"

www.eurocampings.co.uk/120047

36 B2

2348 Vila de Sagres, P-8650-998 / Faro

🛜 iD 36 A2

🔺 Orbitur Sagres**
📧 Cerro das Moitas
🔄 1 Jan - 31 Dec
☎ +351 282624371
@ infosagres@orbitur.pt

1	ADE**JM**NOPQRS**T**	**X** 6
2	BQSTUVWXY	AD**FGH** 7
3		ABEFNRV 8
4	BDHI**P**	AEFLV 9
5	ABCDEFHJKMN**O**	AFGHIJORV 10

6-10A   ❶ €33.50
7ha 550**T**(40-100m²) 24**P**   ❷ €41.90

N268

Vila Do Bispo

🔲 On the N268 from Vila do Bispo (9 km) to Sagres. In Sagres direction Cabo S. Vincente and follow the sign. After approx. 1 km the campsite is on the right of the road. Follow the signs.

🔲 A campsite set in a pine forest on very sandy grounds, but with about 70 paved driveways for motorhomes and heavier caravans. Mostly shaded areas with enclosed pitches for caravans.

📷 **N 37°1'22'' W 8°56'44''**
www.eurocampings.co.uk/101047

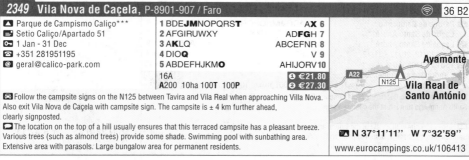

2349 Vila Nova de Caçela, P-8901-907 / Faro

🛜 36 B2

🔺 Parque de Campismo Caliço***
📧 Setio Caliço/Apartado 51
🔄 1 Jan - 31 Dec
☎ +351 281951195
@ geral@calico-park.com

1	BDE**JM**NOPQRS**T**	A**X** 6
2	AFGIRUWXY	AD**FGH** 7
3	A**KL**Q	ABCEFNR 8
4	DIO**Q**	V 9
5	ABDEFHJKM**O**	AHIJORV 10

16A   ❶ €21.80
A200 10ha 100**T** 100**P**   ❷ €27.30

A22
N125

Ayamonte

Vila Real de
Santo António

🔲 Follow the campsite signs on the N125 between Tavira and Vila Real when approaching Villa Nova. Also exit Vila Nova de Caçela with campsite sign. The campsite is ± 4 km further ahead, clearly signposted.

🔲 The location on the top of a hill usually ensures that this terraced campsite has a pleasant breeze. Various trees (such as almond trees) provide some shade. Swimming pool with sunbathing area. Extensive area with parasols. Large bungalow area for permanent residents.

📷 **N 37°11'11'' W 7°32'59''**
www.eurocampings.co.uk/106413

Portugal

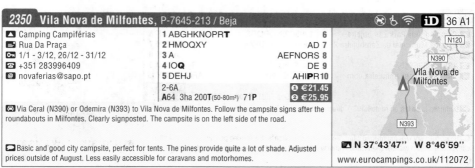

2350 Vila Nova de Milfontes, P-7645-213 / Beja

🚫 ♿ 🛜 iD 36 A1

🔺 Camping Campiférias
📧 Rua Da Praça
🔄 1/1 - 3/12, 26/12 - 31/12
☎ +351 283996409
@ novaferias@sapo.pt

1	ABGHKNOPR**T**	6
2	HMOQXY	AD 7
3	A	AEFNORS 8
4	IO**Q**	DE 9
5	DEHJ	AHI**P**R 10

2-6A   ❶ €21.45
A64 3ha 200**T**(50-80m²) 71**P**   ❷ €25.95

N120
N390

Vila Nova de
Milfontes

N393

🔲 Via Ceral (N390) or Odemira (N393) to Vila Nova de Milfontes. Follow the campsite signs after the roundabouts in Milfontes. Clearly signposted. The campsite is on the left side of the road.

🔲 Basic and good city campsite, perfect for tents. The pines provide quite a lot of shade. Adjusted prices outside of August. Less easily accessible for caravans and motorhomes.

📷 **N 37°43'47'' W 8°46'59''**
www.eurocampings.co.uk/112072

2351 Vila Nova de Milfontes, P-7645-300 / Beja

♿ 🛜 iD 36 A1

🔺 Camping Milfontes***
📧 Apartado 81
🔄 1 Jan - 31 Dec
☎ +351 283996104
@ reservas@campingmilfontes.com

1	ADJMNOPQRS**T**	A**F** 6
2	BHPQVWXY	ADE**FG**H 7
3	A	ABEFNORV 8
4	IO**PQ**	EJL 9
5	ACDEFHK**O**	AFGHIKPR 10

6A   ❶ €24.40
6,8ha 900**T**(30-100m²) 204**P**   ❷ €29.40

N120
N390

Vila Nova de
Milfontes

N393

🔲 On IP8 from the north or IC4 from the south. Via Cercal N390 or Odemira N393 to Vila Nova de Milfontes. Follow the campsite signs in Milfontes. Clearly signposted.

🔲 A campsite with plenty of shaded touring pitches. Guests are free to choose their pitch on part of the campsite. Pines in the old part and eucalyptus in the new. Good toilet facilities. Adjusted prices outside of August. A 10% discount on presentation of the ACSI Club ID.

📷 **N 37°43'55'' W 8°46'58''**
www.eurocampings.co.uk/106395

2352 Vila Nova de Milfontes, P-7645-017 / Beja

🏕 Orbitur Sitava Milfontes****
✉ Brejo da Zimbreira
📅 1 Jan - 31 Dec
☎ +351 283890100
@ infositavamilfontes@orbitur.pt

1 ABDEILNOPQRS**T**	**AF** 6
2 BHQTXY	ABD**FGH** 7
3 BEL**M**	ABEFNOR 8
4 BIO**Q**	FJL 9
5 ABCDEHIJKN**O**	AGHIJ**N**ORV 10
6A	➊ €35.00
A71 27ha 300T(40-80m²) 260P	➋ €39.10

🅡 N120 Odemira-Sines to Cercal, then N390 dir. Vila Nova de Milfontes, turn right before town to Port Covo. Signposted. Then another 4 km.

💬 A campsite under spruce trees with well maintained facilities. The site is located in a nature reserve.

N 37°46'48''   W 8°47'1''
www.eurocampings.co.uk/111988

36 A1

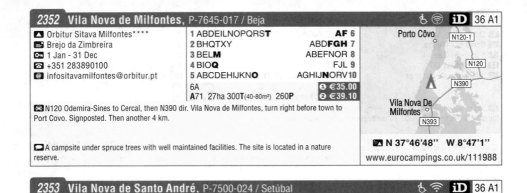

2353 Vila Nova de Santo André, P-7500-024 / Setúbal

🏕 Parque de Campismo
  Lagoa de Santo André**
✉ Lagoa de Santo André
📅 1/1 - 23/12, 26/12 - 31/12
☎ +351 269708550
@ s.andre@fcmportugal.com

1 ADG**JM**NOPQRS**T**	**NQX** 6
2 BDQSTVWXY	ABDE**FH** 7
3 AEFM	AEFNORV 8
4 FO	J 9
5 ABDHJKM**N**O	ABFGHIJ**P**RV 10
2-6A	➊ €17.50
18ha 600T(100m²) 107P	➋ €23.50

🅡 From Santiago do Cacém via N261 direction Santo André. Then follow the signs Lagoa de Santo André and turn left at the campsite sign.

💬 Large campsite with a view of the lagoon and near a vast sandy beach bordering the lagoon. Spruces provide shade in both free parts and divided terrain. Bird enthusiasts will have a wonderful time in this scenic area. Well-maintained amenities.

N 38°6'35''   W 8°47'14''
www.eurocampings.co.uk/113691

36 A1

2354 Zambujeira do Mar, Beja

🏕 Camping Villa Park Zambujeira
✉ Estrada Municipal da Zambujeira 2
📅 1 Jan - 31 Dec
☎ +351 283958407
@ info@campingzambujeira.com

1 ADEILNOPQRS	AF 6
2 EFGHORSUWX	AD**FGH** 7
3 AE**MO**	AEFK 8
4 IO**PQ**U	J 9
5 ABDEHJM	AFIJNPRVY 10
6-16A	➊ €27.75
A99 3,5ha 750T(70-100m²) 26P	➋ €34.65

🅡 Campsite is on left on route N393-1 directly after sign to Zambujeira do Mar, by a water-tower.

💬 Beautiful, very well maintained campsite with shaded pitches. Swimming pool and whirlpool filled with sea water and without chemicals. Within walking distance of the beach and a small historic town.
ⓒⓒ 1/1-15/6 13/9-31/12

N 37°31'33''   W 8°46'32''
www.eurocampings.co.uk/122668

36 A1

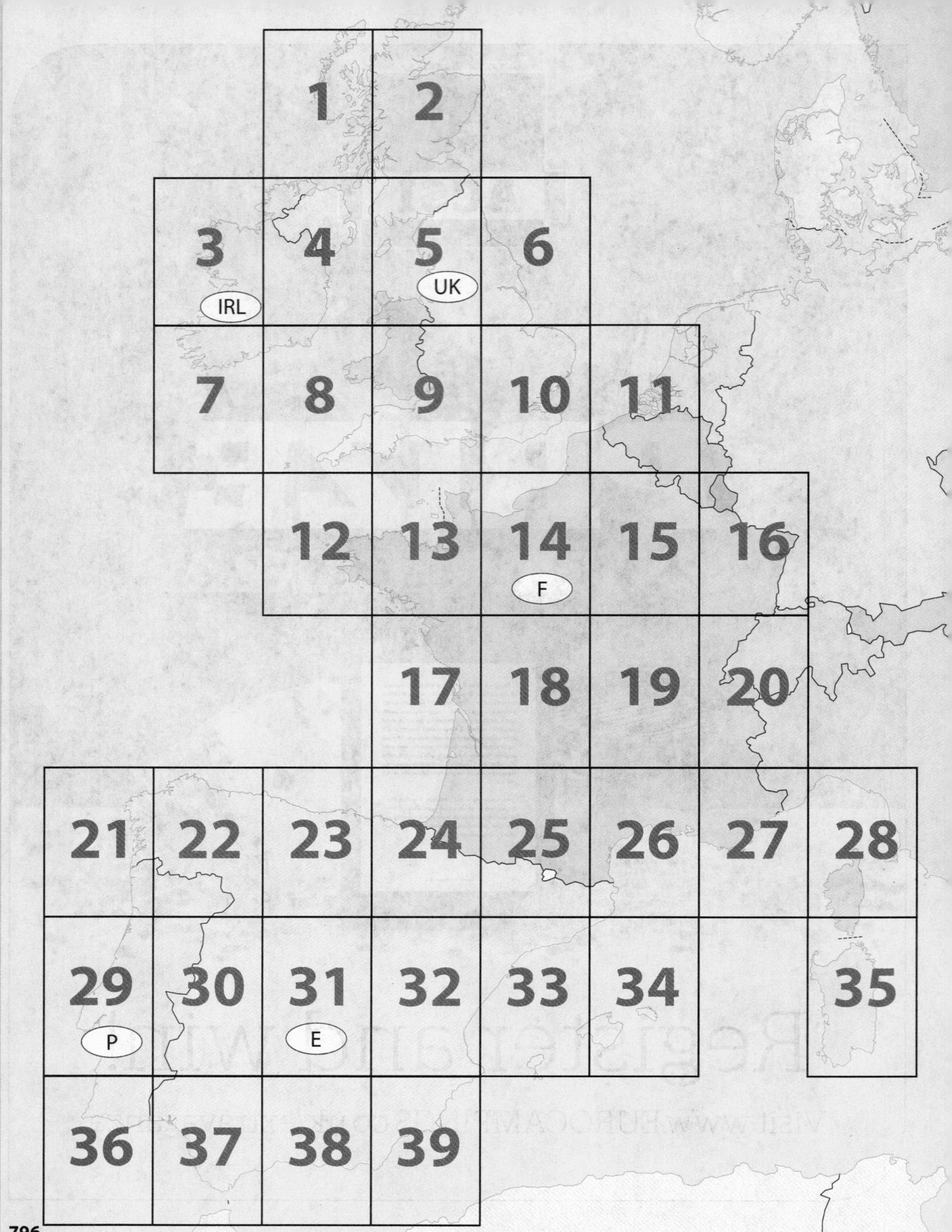
1
2
3
4
5
6
IRL
UK
7
8
9
10
11
12
13
14
15
16
F
17
18
19
20
21
22
23
24
25
26
27
28
29
30
31
32
33
34
35
P
E
36
37
38
39

Choose the area in which you are looking for a campsite on the general map of Europe on the left. Find the country map with the corresponding map number further on.

23 Adjacent to map on page 23.

B 1 Adjacent to the grid on the map.

A Red tent is a campsite.

A Blue tent is a campsite accepting CampingCard ACSI.

12 Each campsite has a number. You will find this number on the maps further on corresponding with each campsite.

Above the map of each campsite in this guide you will find the map and grid number on which the campsite is situated.

12 **Bude,** GB-EX23 9HJ / South West	🛶 🅰 🛶 ⅙ 🛜 ✿ (CC€19) 🚻 **iD** 8 B3
🔺 Wooda Farm Holiday Park*****	1 ADE**JM**NOPRS**T**	N 6
🔺 Poughill	2 EPSTVWX	ABDE**FGH**K 7

DETAIL ➡ 44 Detailed map on map number 44

All detailed maps in this guide:

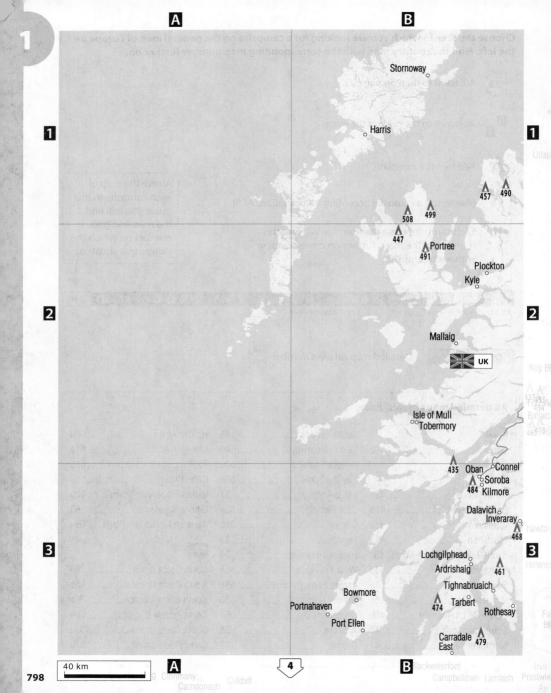

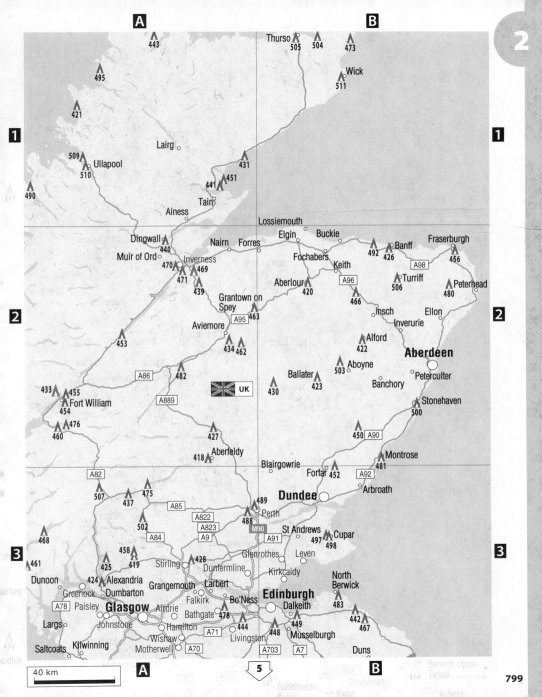

2

Thurso
505 504 473

Wick
511

443

495

421

1

Lairg

509 Ullapool
510

431

490

441 451

Tain

Alness

Lossiemouth

Dingwall
440

Elgin Buckie
Nairn Forres

Fraserburgh
492 Banff
426 A98 456

Muir of Ord
470 Inverness
471 469

439

Fochabers
Keith
A96

Turriff
506

Peterhead
480

Aberlour
420

466

Insch
Inverurie

Ellon

2

Grantown on
Spey
A95 463

Aviemore

453

434 462

Alford
422

Aberdeen

A86

482

Ballater
430 423

Aboyne
503

Peterculter

Banchory

433 455
Fort William
454

A889

UK

Stonehaven
500

460 476

427

450 A90

Aberfeldy
418

Blairgowrie

Montrose
481

A82

Forfar 452 A92

Arbroath

507

475

437

A85

489

Dundee

Perth
488

St Andrews
497 Cupar
498

502

A822
A823
M90

A84 A9 A91

Glenrothes

Leven

3

468

461

458
425 419

Stirling

428

Dunfermline

Kirkcaldy

North
Berwick

Dunoon

424 Alexandria
Greenock Dumbarton

Grangemouth
Larbert

Bo'Ness

Edinburgh
Dalkeith

483

A78 Paisley
Largs

Glasgow
Airdrie
Johnstone

Falkirk
Bathgate 478

Hamilton
A71

Livingston

444
448 449
Musselburgh

442
467

Saltcoats Kilwinning
Wishaw
Motherwell A70

A703 A7

Duns

40 km

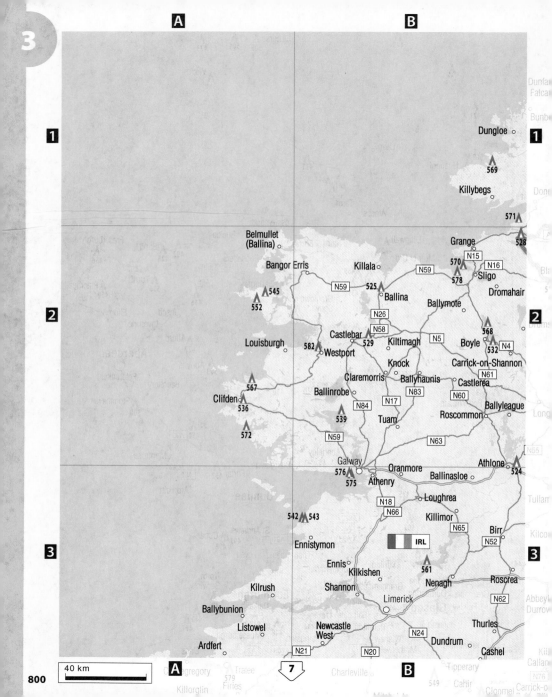

A **B**

1

Dungloe

△ 569

Killybegs

571 △

△ 528

Belmullet
(Ballina)

Grange
N15
2
570 △
578 △
Sligo

Bangor Erris

Killala

N59

Dromahair

N59

525 △
Ballina

Ballymote

△ 545
552 △

N26

N58

568 △

Castlebar

Kiltimagh

N5

Boyle

532 △ N4

582 △
Westport

529

Knock

Carrick-on-Shannon

N61

Louisburgh

Castlerea

Claremorris

Ballyhaunis

N60

567 △

Ballinrobe

N83

Clifden △
536

N84

N17

Tuam

Roscommon

Ballyleague

539 △

572 △

N59

N63

Galway

Oranmore

Athlone

N55

576 △
575

Athenry

Ballinasloe

524 △

Loughrea

N18

Tullam

N66

Killimor

542 △△ 543

N65

Birr

Ennistymon

N52

IRL

3

Ennis

Kilkishen

561 △

Roscrea

Kilrush

Shannon

Nenagh

N62

Limerick

Ballybunion

Thurles

Listowel

Newcastle
West

N24

Dundrum

Cashel

Ardfert

N21

N20

40 km

A **7** **B**

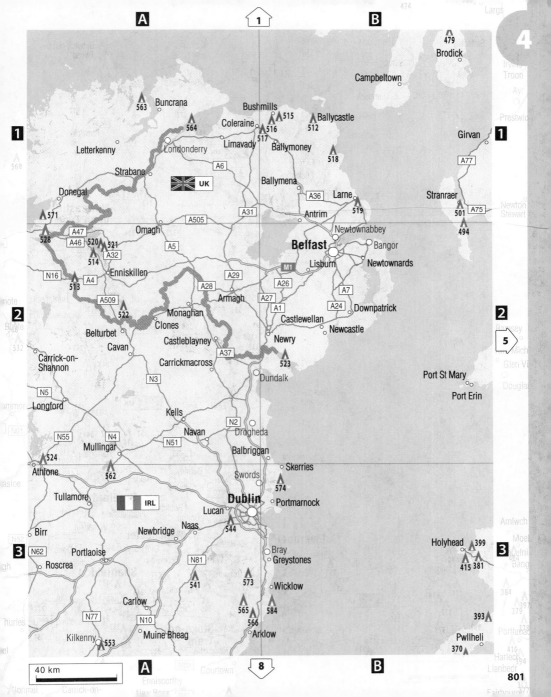

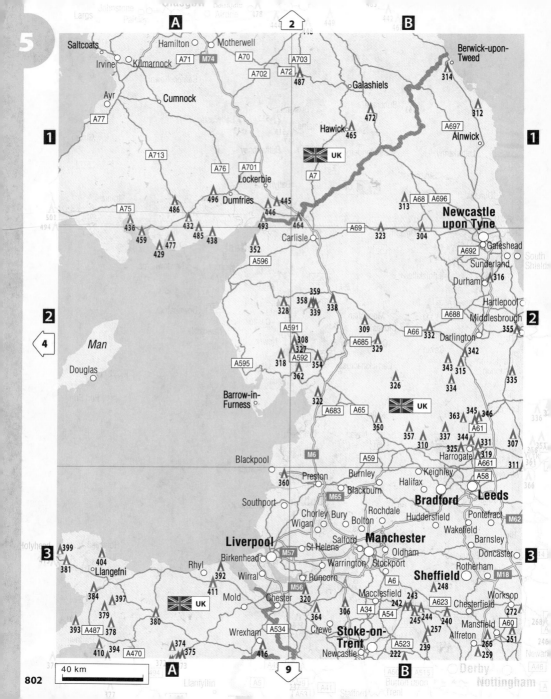

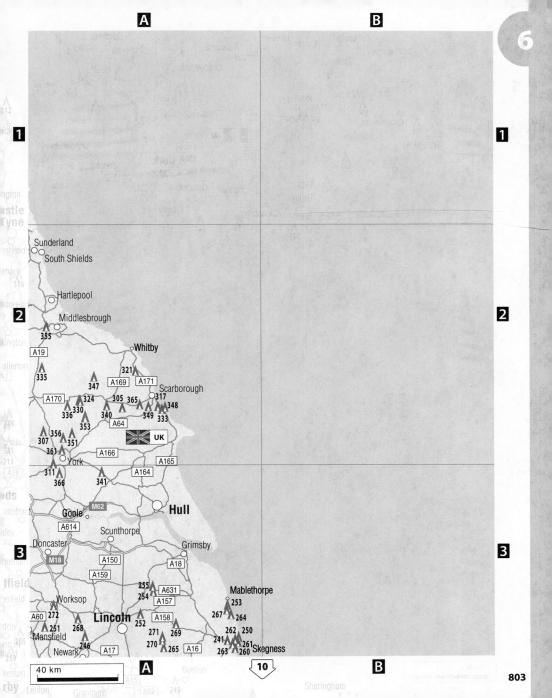

A

B

1

1

Sunderland
South Shields

Hartlepool

2

Middlesbrough

355

A19

Whitby

321
335
347   A169   A171
          Scarborough
A170   324   305 365 317
336 330   349   348
         340   333
     353

307 356
     351
361   A166
         York
311   A164
366   341

                    Hull
Goole   M62
A614
Scunthorpe
Doncaster   Grimsby
M18   A150   A18
     A159

255   A631   Mablethorpe
254   A157   253
Worksop   A158   267 264
A60 272   252   262 250
251 268   241 261
Mansfield   246   269   260 Skegness
Newark   A17   270 265 263
                        A16

2

3

UK

2

3

B

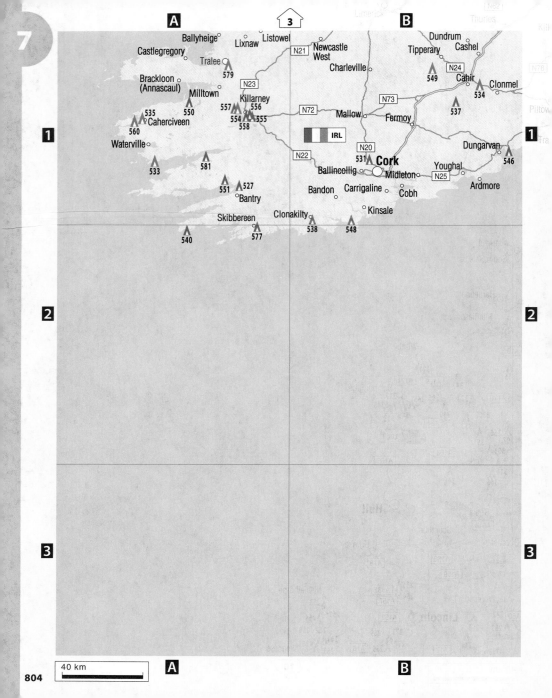

40 km

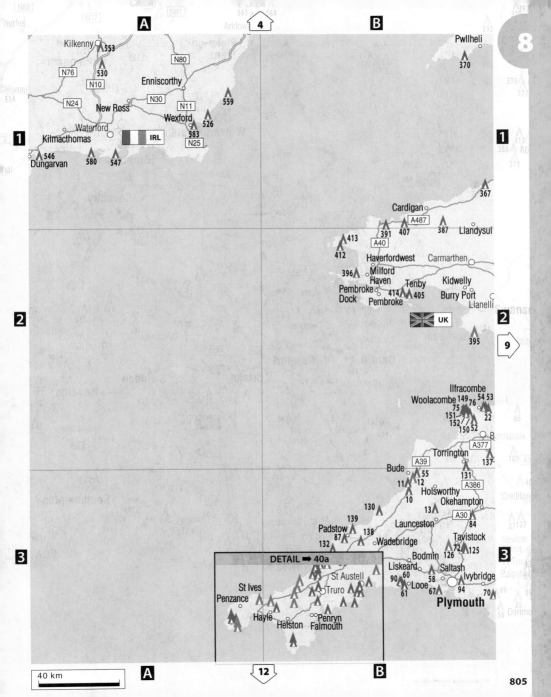

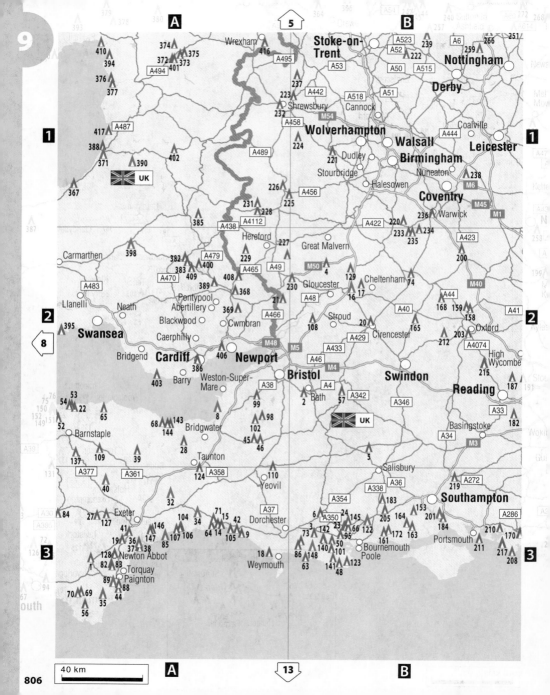

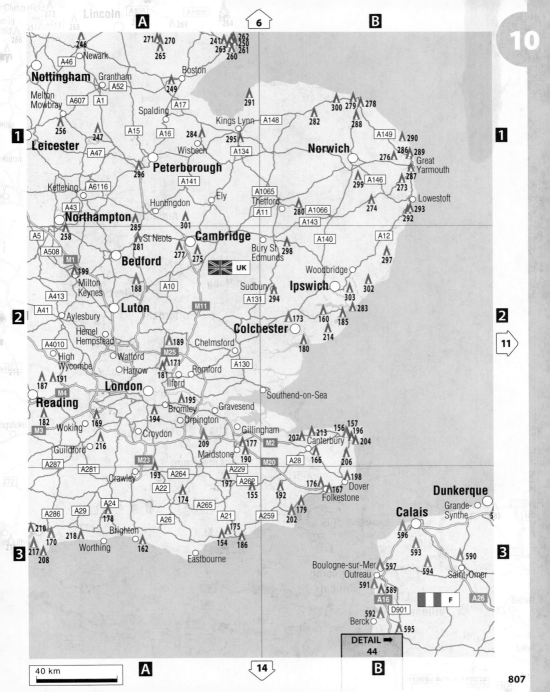

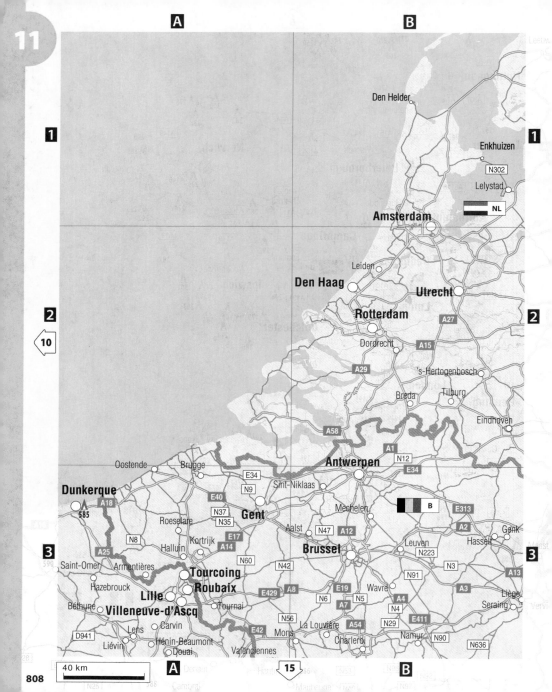

Den Helder

Enkhuizen

N302

Lelystad

NL

Leiden

Amsterdam

Den Haag

Utrecht

Rotterdam

A27

Dordrecht

A15

A29

's-Hertogenbosch

Breda

Tilburg

Eindhoven

A58

A1

N12

Oostende

Brugge

Antwerpen

E34

Dunkerque

E34

E40

N9

Sint-Niklaas

A18

585

Roeselare

Gent

Mechelen

E313

N37

B

Halluin

N35

Kortrijk

Aalst

N47

A12

Genk

N8

E17

Leuven

Hasselt

A2

Saint-Omer

Armentières

A14

Brussel

N223

A13

A25

N60

N91

N3

Hazebrouck

Tourcoing

N42

Liège

Béthune

Roubaix

E429

A8

E19

Wavre

A4

A3

Seraing

Lille

N6

N5

N4

Villeneuve-d'Ascq

Tournai

A7

E411

Lens

Carvin

N56

La Louvière

N29

Namur

N90

N636

D941

Liévin

Hénin-Beaumont

A54

Douai

Valenciennes

Mons

Charleroi

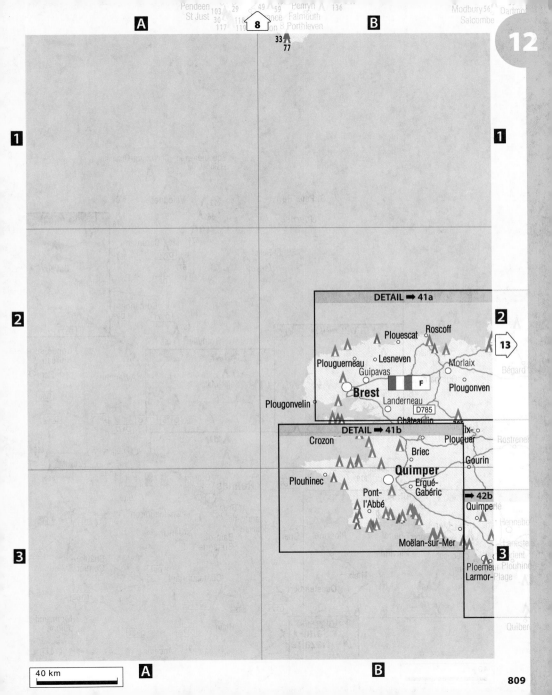

40 km

DETAIL ➡ 41a

Plouescat
Roscoff
Plouguerneau
Lesneven
Morlaix
Guipavas
Plougonven
Brest
F
Plougonvelin
Landerneau
D785
Châteaulin

DETAIL ➡ 41b

Crozon
Plouguer
Briec
Gourin
Quimper
Plouhinec
Ergué-
Gabéric
➡ 42b
Pont-
l'Abbé
Quimperlé
Moëlan-sur-Mer
Ploemeur
Plouhinec
Larmor-Plage

Pendeen 103
St Just 30
117 119

Penryn 136
Falmouth
Porthleven

Modbury 56
Salcombe
Dartmo

33
77

8

13

Bégard

Rostrenen

Hennebo
Lanester
Plouhine
Quiberon

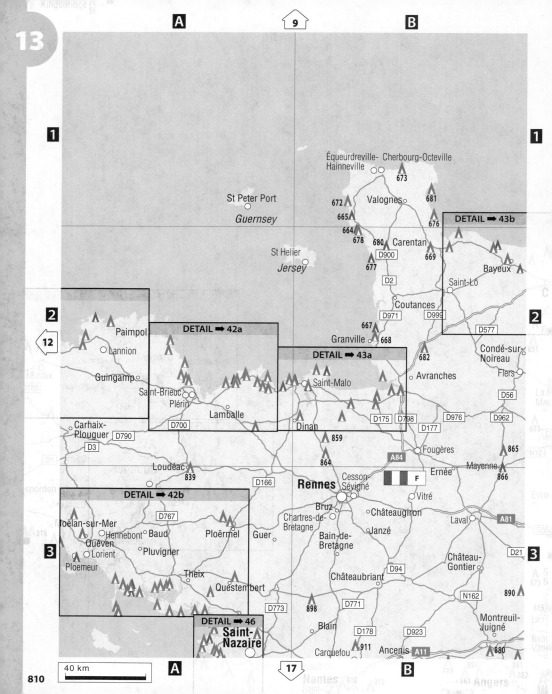

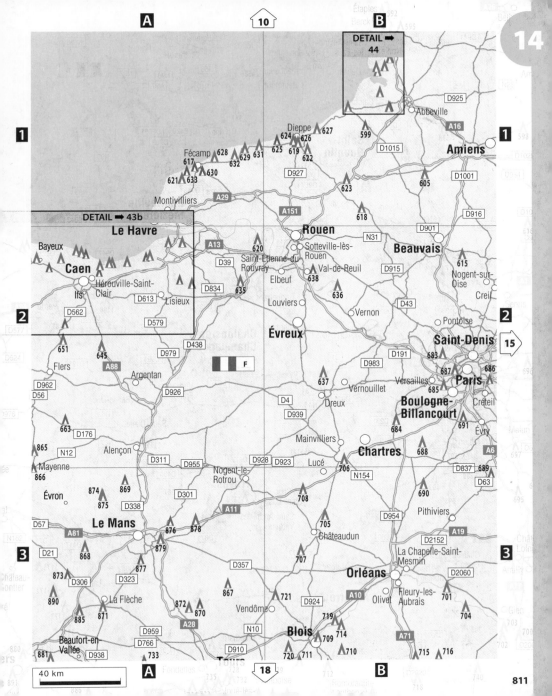

A · B

14

DETAIL ➡ 44

D925

Abbeville

A16

Dieppe 624 626 627

624 626 599

625 619 622 Amiens

Fécamp 628 D1015

617 629 631

632 630 623 D1001

621 633

605

Montivilliers A29 618 D916

DETAIL ➡ 43b 620 D901

Le Havre 638 Rouen N31 Beauvais 615

Bayeux A13 Saint-Étienne-du- Sotteville-lès- Nogent-sur-

Caen D39 Rouvray Rouen Oise

Hérouville-Saint- Elbeuf Val-de-Reuil D915 Creil

Ifs Clair Lisieux 635 638 D43

D613 636 Pontoise

D562 Louviers Saint-Denis 683 686

D834 687 685 Paris

D579 Vernon D191

651 D979 Évreux D983 Versailles 685

645 D438 637 684 Boulogne-

Flers A88 Vernouillet Billancourt 691

D962 Argentan Dreux 684 Évry

D56 D926 Mainvilliers 688 A6

663 D176 D4 Chartres D837 689

865 D939 706 D63

N12 Lucé 690

Mayenne Alençon D928 D923 N154 A19

866 D311 Nogent-le- 708 D954 Pithiviers

Évron 874 869 Rotrou 705 D2152

875 D301 La Chapelle-Saint- 690

D57 D338 Châteaudun Mesmin

A81 Le Mans 876 878 707 Orléans D2060

D21 879 D357 720 711 710 701

868 Fleury-les- 704

873 877 867 721 Aubrais

D306 D323 Vendôme D924 Olivet 719 714

890 La Flèche 872 870 A10 709

885 871 N10 715 716

Beaufort-en- A28 Blois A71

Vallée D959 733 720 711 709 710

881 D938 D766 D910

D57

40 km A · 18 · B

811

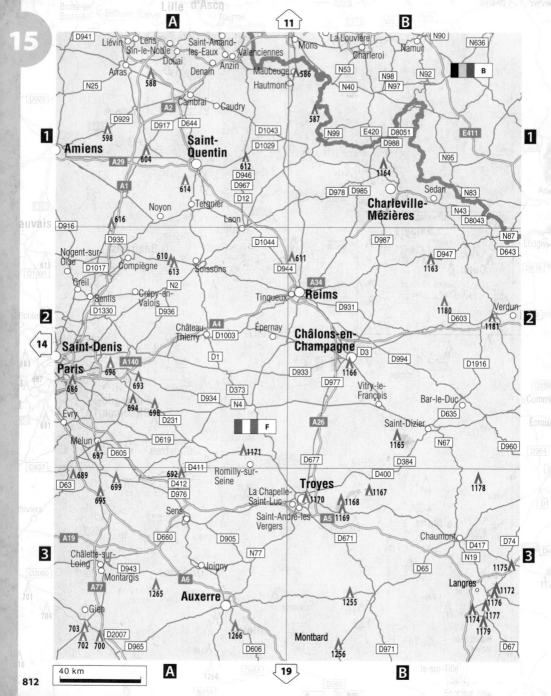

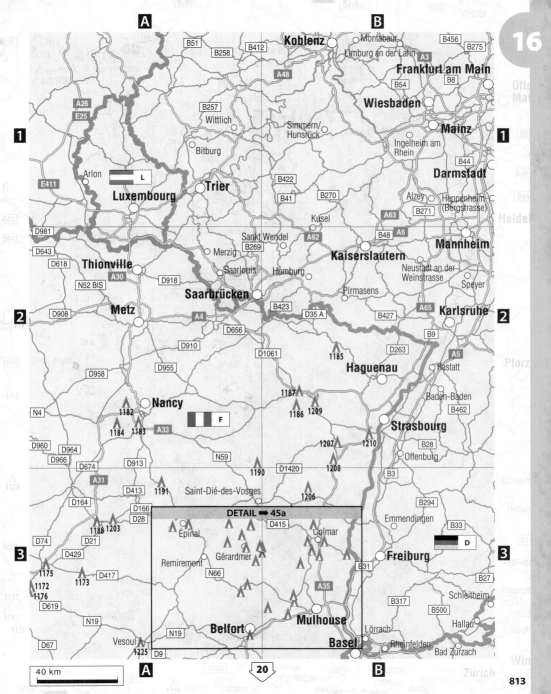

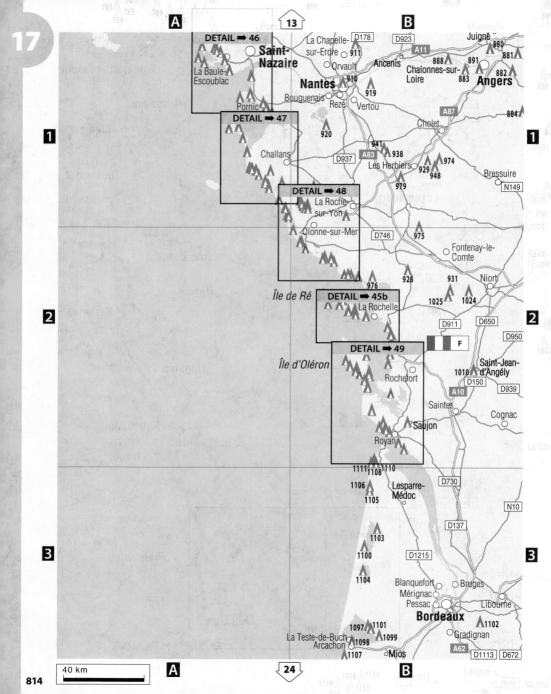

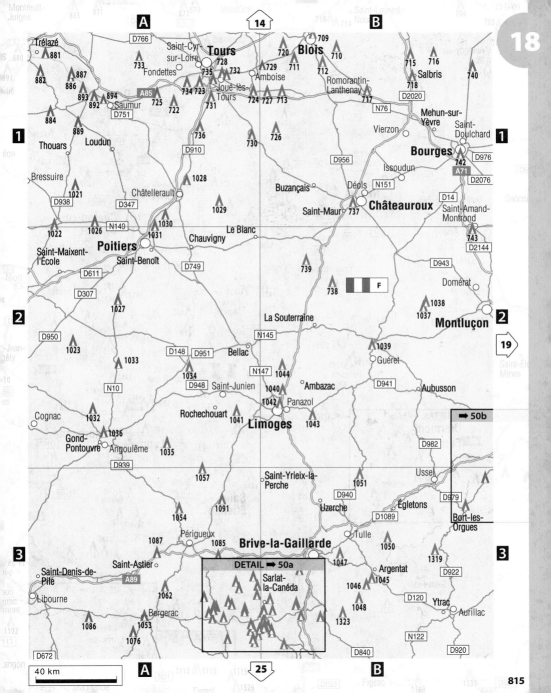

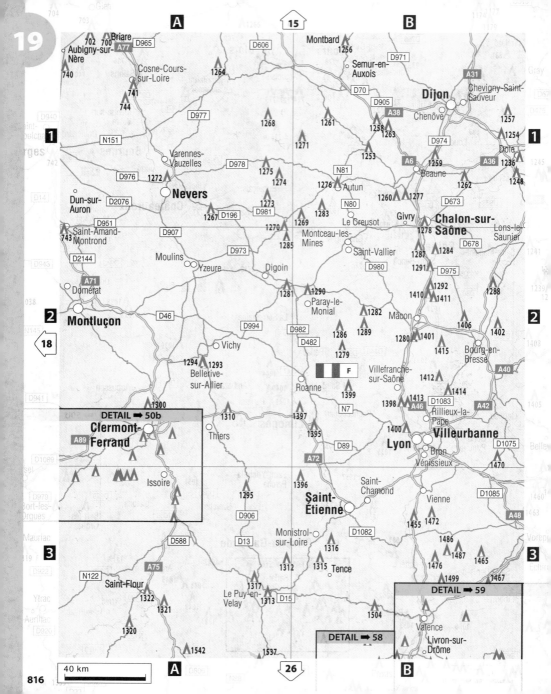

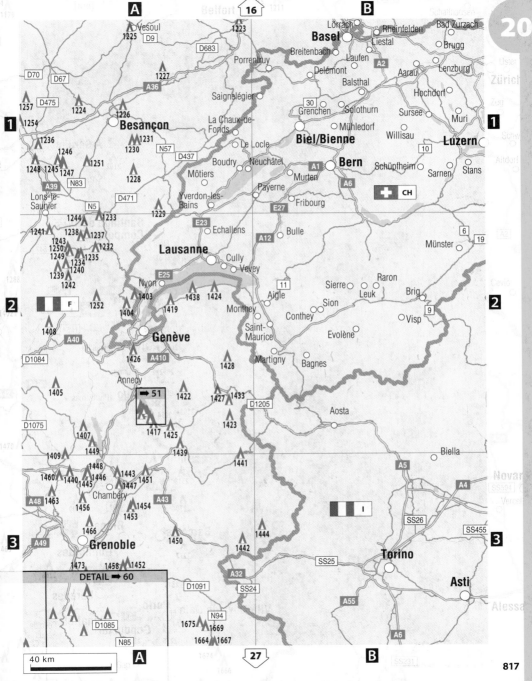

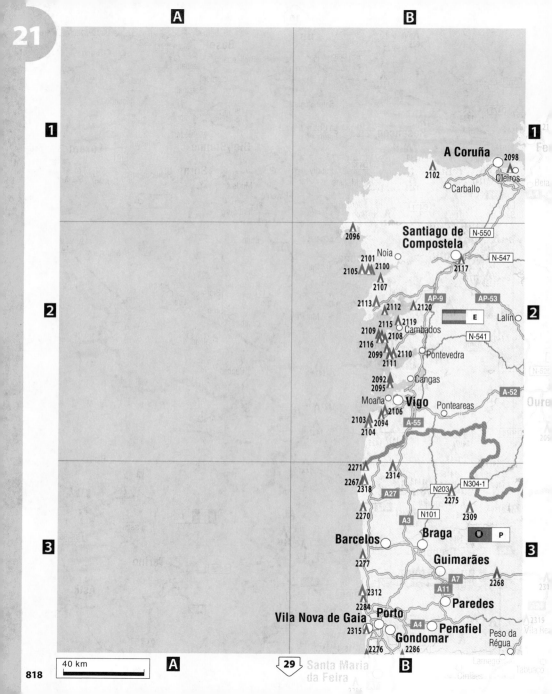

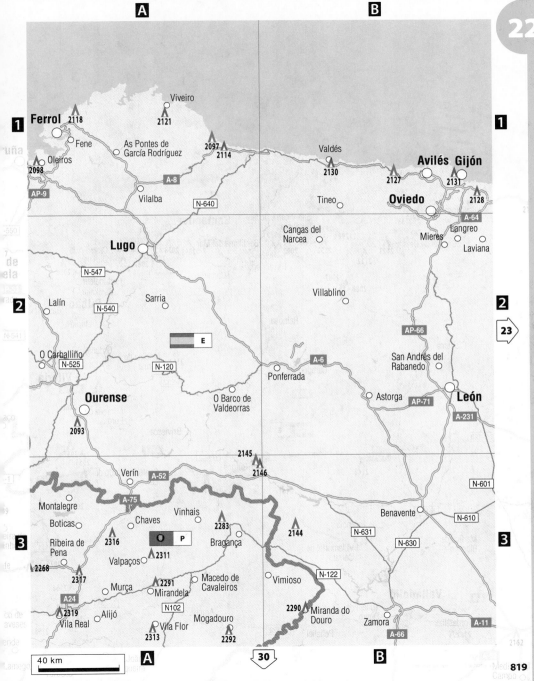

Viveiro
2121

Ferrol
2118
Fene
As Pontes de
García Rodríguez
2097
2114
Valdés
Avilés Gijón
2130
2127
2131
2128
Oleiros
2098
A-8
Oviedo
AP-9
Vilalba
N-640
Tineo
A-64
Langreo
Cangas del
Narcea
Mieres
Laviana
Lugo

N-547
Villablino
Lalín
Sarria
N-540
AP-66
E
O Carballiño
N-525
N-120
San Andrés del
Rabanedo
N-541
Ponferrada
A-6
Ourense
O Barco de
Valdeorras
Astorga
AP-71
León
2093
A-231
2145
2146
Verín
A-52
N-601
Montalegre
A-75
Benavente
N-610
Boticas
Chaves
Vinhais
N-631
N-630
2283

P
Bragança
2144
Ribeira de
Pena
2316
2311
2268
Valpaços
2317
Murça
2291
Macedo de
Cavaleiros
Vimioso
N-122
Mirandela
2290
Miranda do
Douro
A-24
2319
Alijó
N102
Zamora
A-11
Vila Real
Vila Flor
Mogadouro
2313
2292
A-66

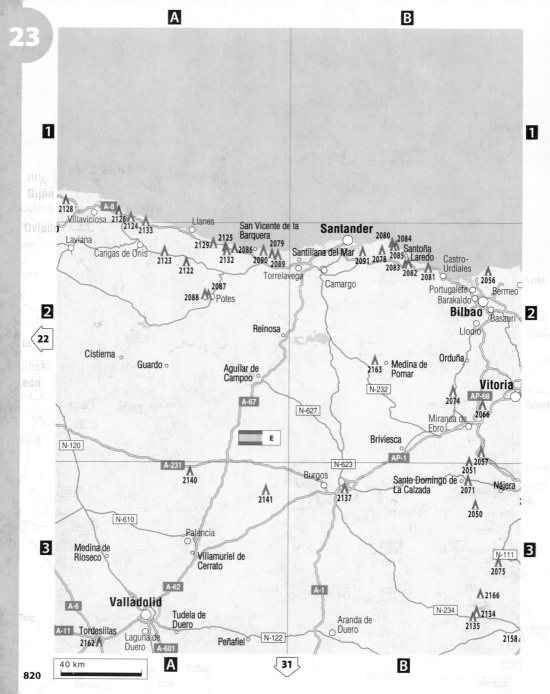

A   B

1   1

2131
Gijón
2128
Villaviciosa 2126
Laviana   2124 2133
Cangas de Onis
2123   Llanes
2122
2129   San Vicente de la
2125   Barquera
2132   2086
2090   2079
2089
2087
2088   Potes

Santillana del Mar   Santander
Torrelavega   2091 2078 2085 2082 2081
Camargo   2083
2080 2084
Santoña
Laredo
Castro-
Urdiales
2056
Portugalete   Bermeo
Barakaldo
Bilbao   Basauri
Llodio
Orduña
Vitoria
2074   AP-68
2066
Miranda de
Ebro

Cistierna   Guardo
Reinosa
Aguilar de
Campoo
A-67
N-627
E
N-232
2163   Medina de
Pomar

N-120
A-231
2140
2141
Burgos
N-623
AP-1
Briviesca
Santo Domingo de
La Calzada
2051
2071
2057
Nájera
2050

N-610
Palencia
Villamuriel de
Cerrato
2137

Medina de
Rioseco
A-62
N-234   N-111
2075

A-6
Valladolid
Tudela de
Duero
A-1
Aranda de
Duero
2166
2134
2135
2158

A-11   Tordesillas
2162
Laguna de
Duero
A-601
Peñafiel   N-122

40 km   A   31   B

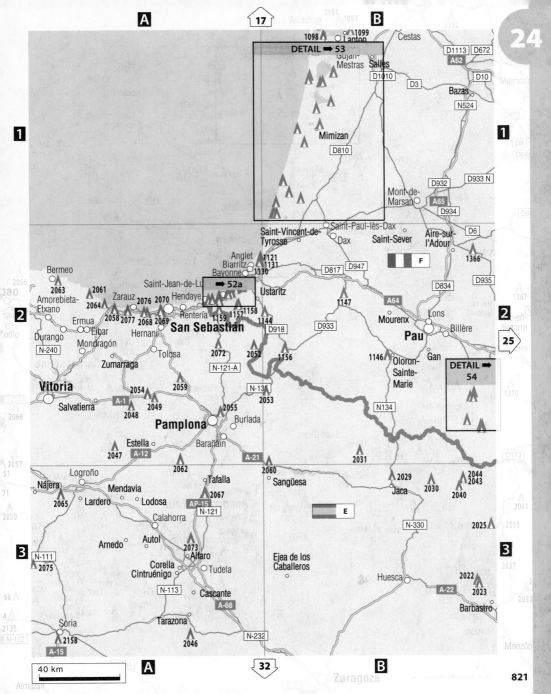

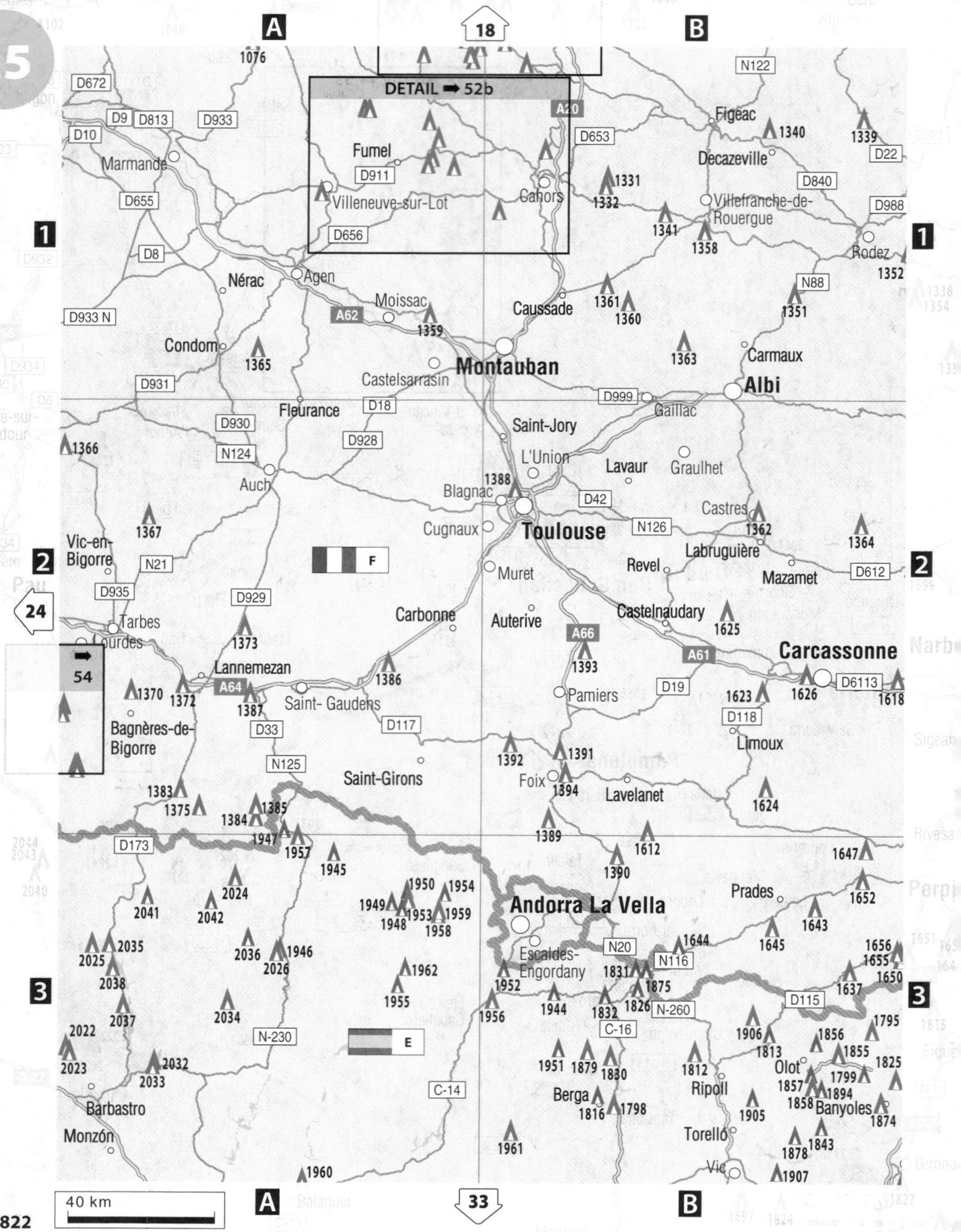

1076

D672
D9 D813 D933
D10
Marmande
D655
D8

1

N122
Figeac
1340 1339
Decazeville D22
D653 1331
Fumel 1332 Villefranche-de-
D911 Cahors Rouergue D988
Villeneuve-sur-Lot 1341 1358 Rodez
D656 1352

1

Nérac Agen
Moissac Caussade 1361 Carmaux
D933 N A62 1359 1360 N88 Albi
Condom 1365 1363 1351
Castelsarrasin Montauban D999 Gaillac
D931 Carmaux
Fleurance D18 Saint-Jory Lavaur Graulhet
D930 D928 L'Union Castres
N124 Blagnac 1388 D42 1362
Auch Cugnaux Toulouse N126 1364
1366 Muret Revel Labruguière D612
1367 Carbonne Auterive Mazamet

2

Vic-en-Bigorre N21 Castelnaudary A61 Carcassonne
D935 Tarbes 1373 Pamiers 1625 1623 1626 D6113 1618
Lourdes Lannemezan 1386 A66 D19
54 1370 1372 A64 1387 1393 D118 Limoux
Bagnères-de-Bigorre D33 D117 1392 1391 1624
N125 Saint-Girons Foix 1394 Lavelanet
1383 1375 1385 Saint-Gaudens
1384 1389 1612
D173 1947 1957 1390
1945

3

2041 2024 Andorra La Vella Prades 1647
2025 2035 2042 1950 1954 1652
2038 1949 1953 1959 1643
2037 2036 1946 1948 1958 Escaldes- 1645 1656 1655
2022 2034 2026 Engordany N20 N116 1644 1650
2023 2033 N-230 1962 1952 1831 1875 1637 1795
2032 1955 1956 1944 1832 1826 N-260 1906 1856 1825
C-14 1951 1879 1830 1812 Olot 1855
Barbastro C-16 Berga 1816 1798 Ripoll 1813 1857 1799 1894
Monzón 1961 Torelló 1905 1858 Banyoles
1960 Vic 1878 1843 1874
1907

40 km

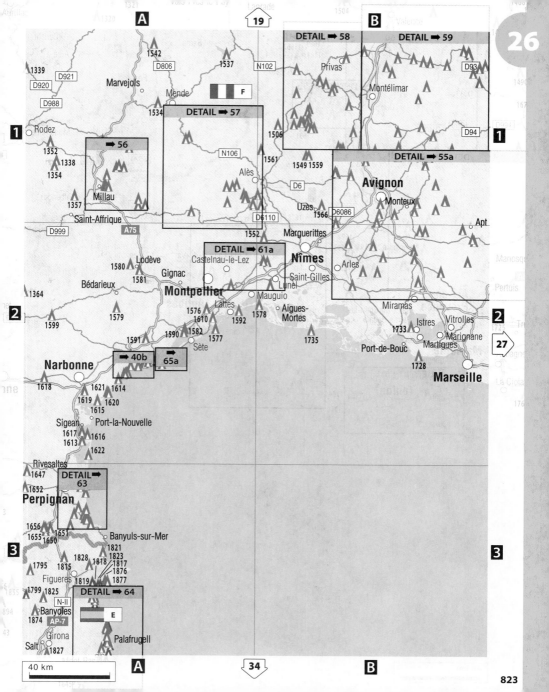

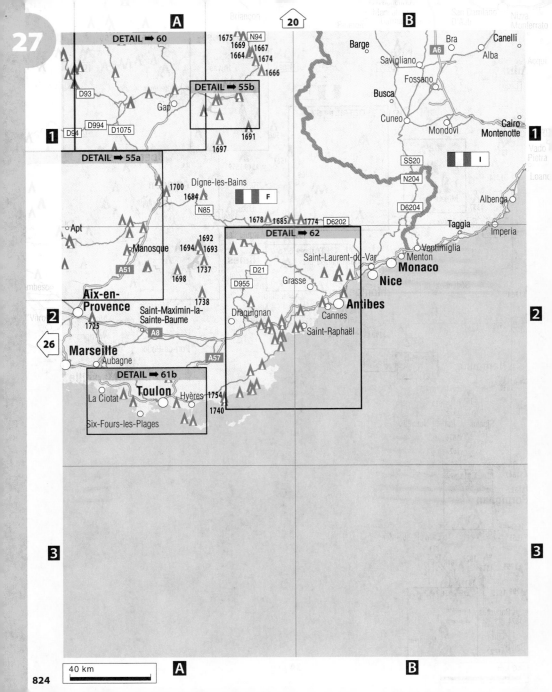

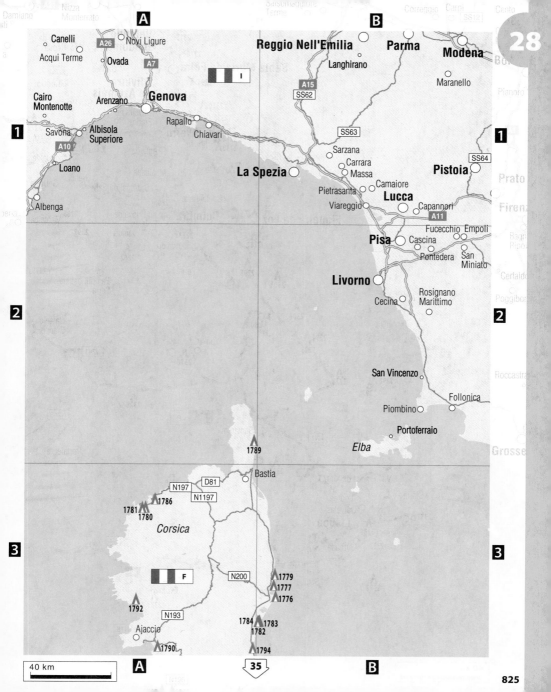

Canelli
Acqui Terme
Novi Ligure
A26
Ovada
A7
Cairo Montenotte
Arenzano
Genova
Savona
Albisola Superiore
Rapallo
Chiavari
A10
Loano
Albenga

Reggio Nell'Emilia
Parma
Modena
Langhirano
Maranello
A15
SS62
SS63
Sarzana
Carrara
Massa
SS64
La Spezia
Pistoia
Camaiore
Pietrasanta
Lucca
Viareggio
Capannori
A11
Fucecchio
Empoli
Pisa
Cascina
San Miniato
Pontedera
Livorno
Rosignano Marittimo
Cecina

San Vincenzo
Follonica
Piombino
Portoferraio
Elba

1789
Bastia
N197
D81
N1197
1781
1786
1780
Corsica
F
N200
1779
1777
1776
1792
N193
1784
1783
1782
Ajaccio
1794
1790

40 km

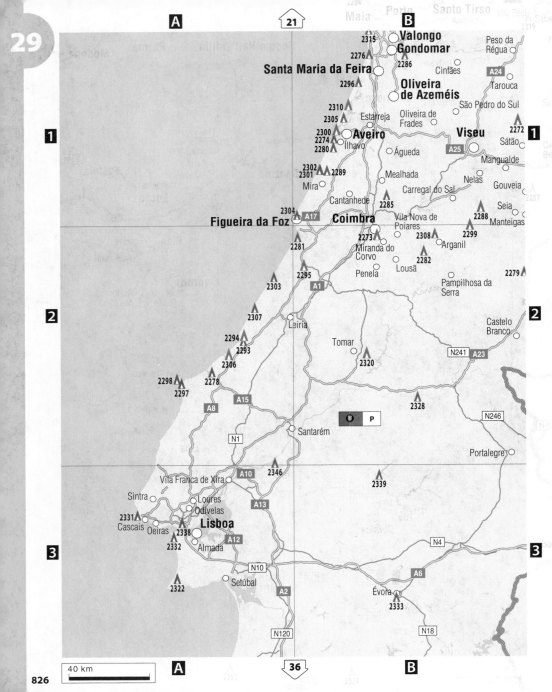

Maia · Porto · Santo Tirso

2315 ▲ **Valongo**
2276 ▲ **Gondomar**
2286

Peso da Régua

Santa Maria da Feira ○

2296 ▲

Oliveira de Azeméis

Cinfães

A24

Tarouca

2310 ▲
2305 ▲ Estarreja

Oliveira de Frades

São Pedro do Sul

1

2300 ▲ **Aveiro**
2274 ▲
2280 ▲ Ílhavo

Águeda

Viseu

2272 ▲
Sátão

A25

Mangualde

2302 ▲▲ 2289
2301 ▲
Mira ○

Mealhada

Nelas

Gouveia

Cantanhede ○

Carregal do Sal

2285 ▲

Seia

2288 ▲
Manteigas

2304 ▲
Figueira da Foz ○ A17

Coimbra ○

Vila Nova de Poiares

2281 ▲

2273 ▲
Miranda do Corvo

2308 ▲
Arganil

2299 ▲

2279 ▲

2295 ▲

Penela ○

2282 ▲
Lousã ○

Pampilhosa da Serra

2303 ▲

A1

2

2307 ▲

Leiria ○

Castelo Branco

2294 ▲
2293 ▲
2306 ▲

Tomar ○

2320 ▲

N241 A23

2298 ▲
2297 ▲

2278 ▲

A15

A8

2328 ▲

N246

Santarém ○

N1

Portalegre ○

Vila Franca de Xira ○
A10

2346 ▲

2339 ▲

Sintra ○

Loures ○
Odivelas ○

A13

2331 ▲
Cascais ○ Oeiras ○

2338 ▲
Lisboa ○

A12

N4

3

2332 ▲
Almada ○

N10

2322 ▲

Setúbal ○

A2

A6

Évora ○
2333 ▲

N120

N18

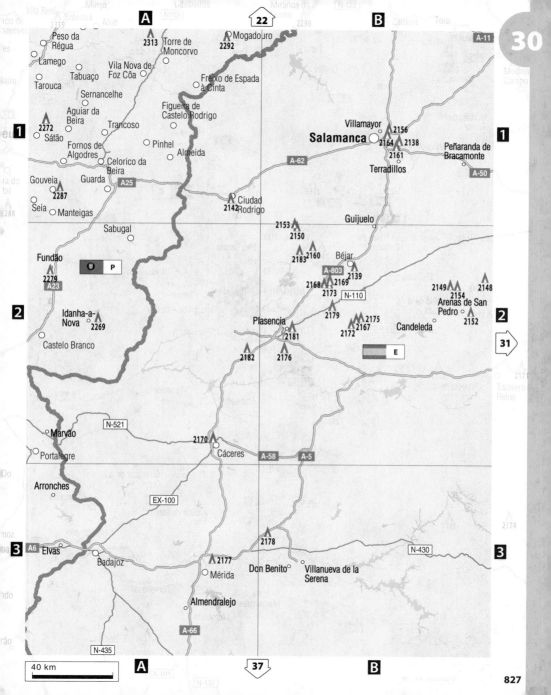

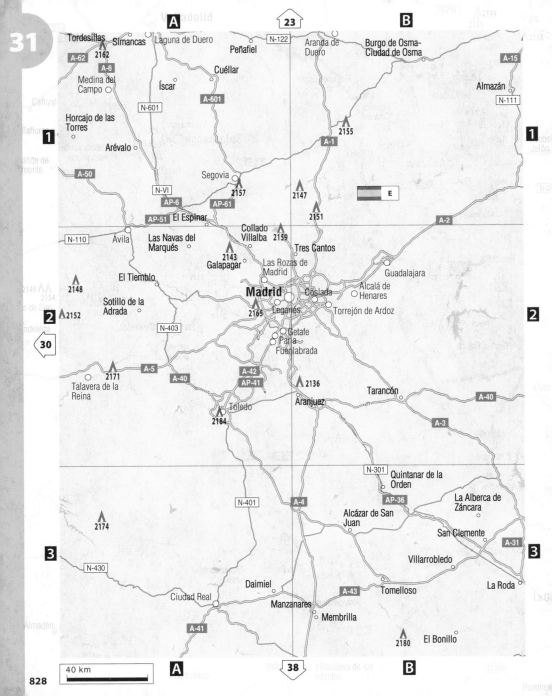

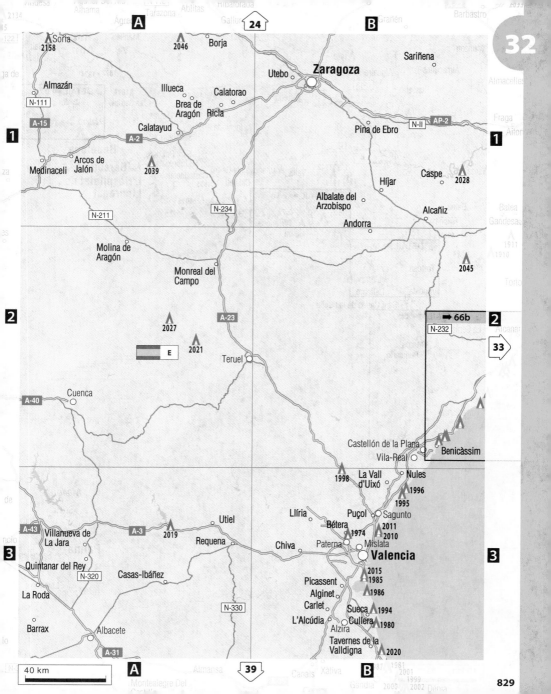

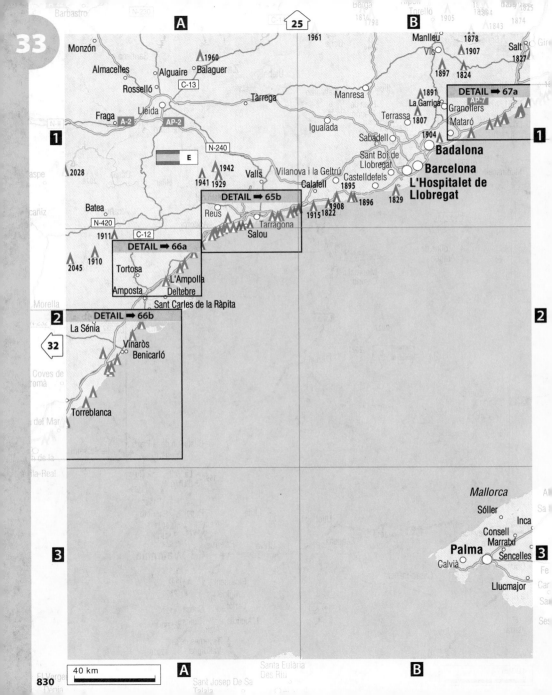

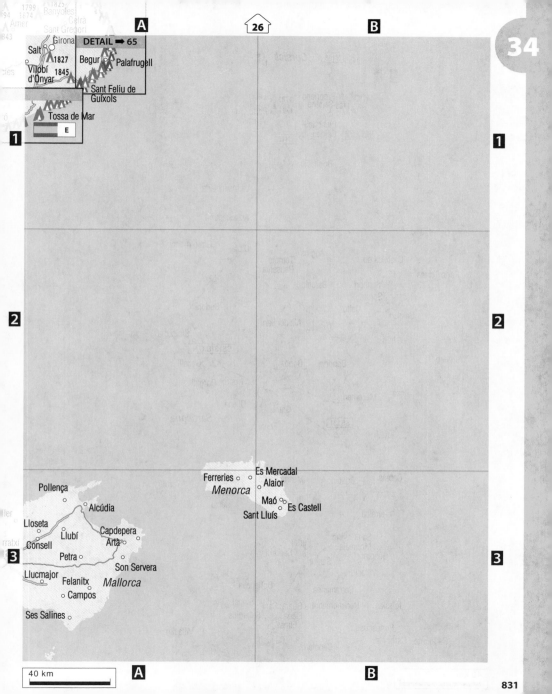

A

B

DETAIL ➡ 65

Girona
Salt
Vilobí
d'Onyar
1827
1845
Begur
Palafrugell
Sant Feliu de
Guíxols
Tossa de Mar
E

Banyoles
Amer
Sant Gregori

1

1

2

2

Pollença
Alcúdia
Lloseta
Llubí
Capdepera
Consell
Artà
Petra
Son Servera
Llucmajor
Felanitx
Mallorca
Campos
Ses Salines

Ferreries
Es Mercadal
Alaior
Menorca
Maó
Es Castell
Sant Lluís

3

3

40 km

A

B

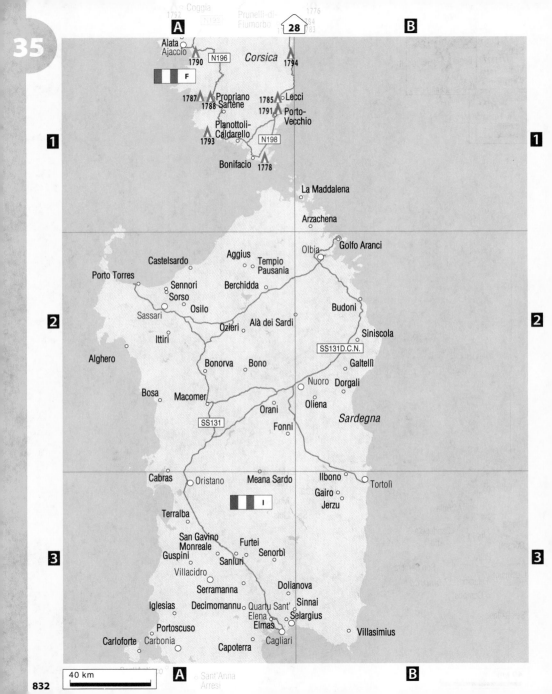

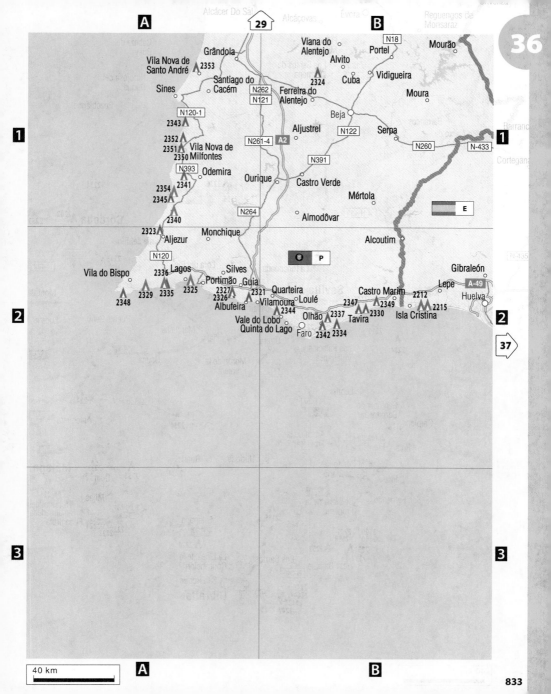

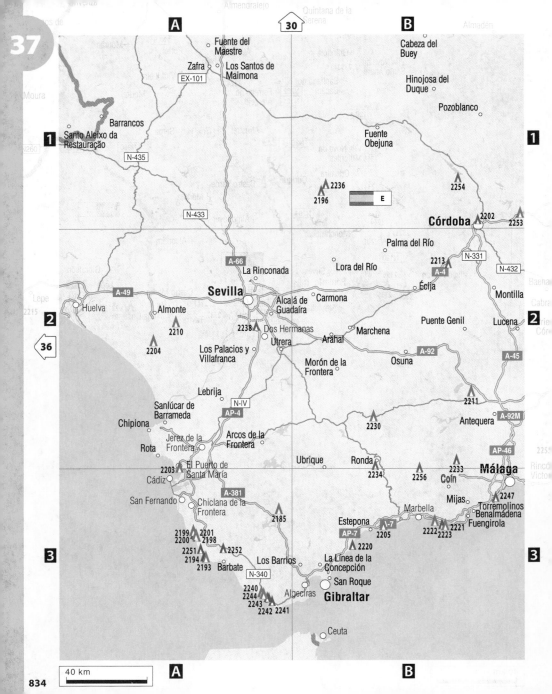

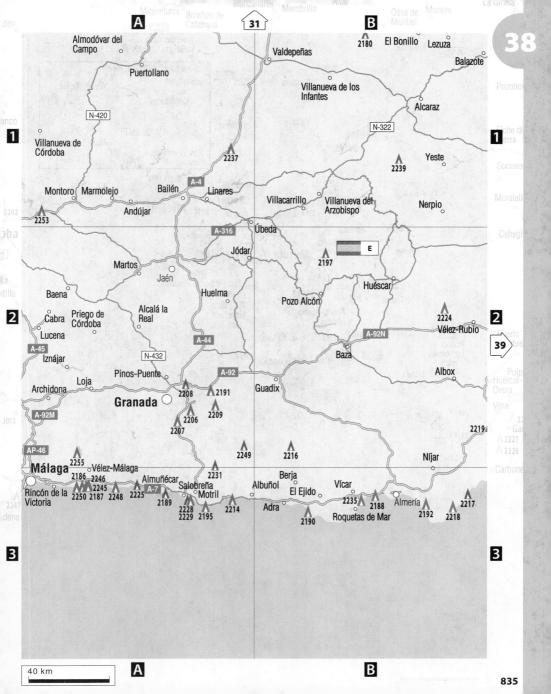

39

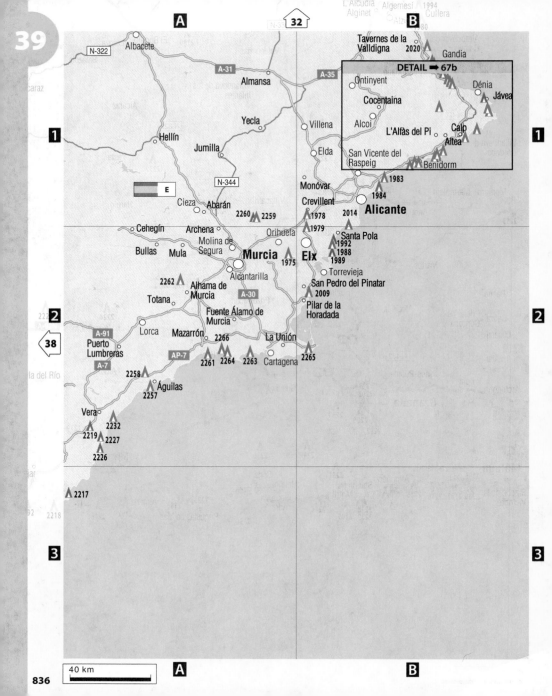

a Cornwall ➡ 8

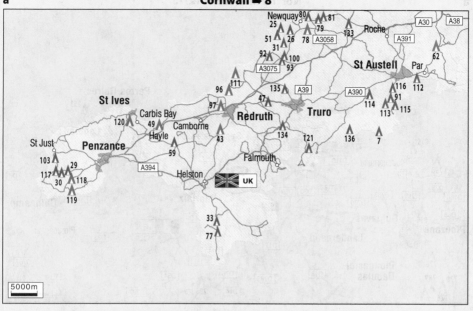

St Ives
Carbis Bay
Camborne
Redruth
Truro
St Austell
Par
Newquay
Roche
Penzance
St Just
Hayle
Helston
Falmouth

UK

5000m

b Valras-Plage/Vias-Plage ➡ 26

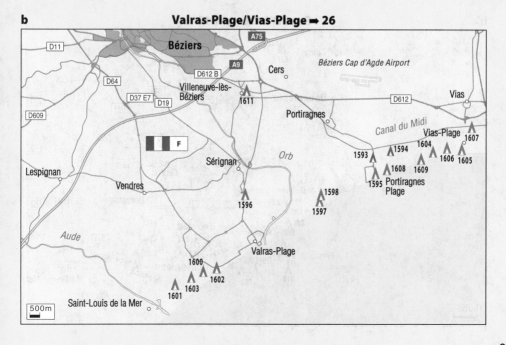

Béziers
Cers
Béziers Cap d'Agde Airport
Villeneuve-lès-Béziers
Vias
Portiragnes
Canal du Midi
Vias-Plage
F
Sérignan
Orb
Lespignan
Portiragnes Plage
Vendres
Aude
Valras-Plage
Saint-Louis de la Mer

500m

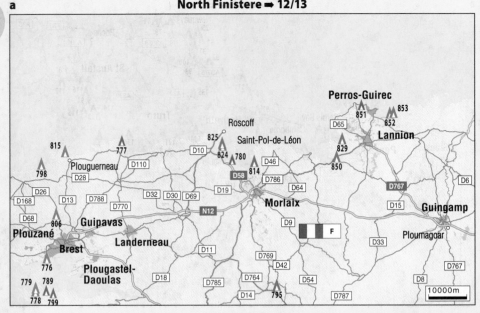

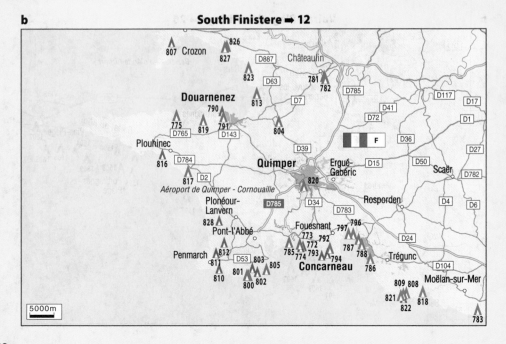

a

Côtes d'Armor ➡ 13

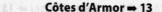

42

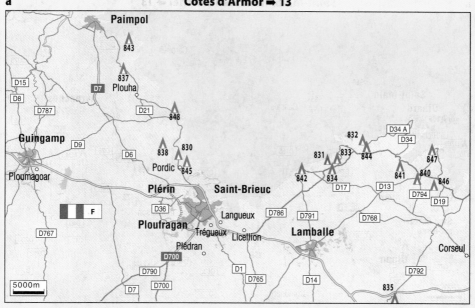

b

Morbihan ➡ 13

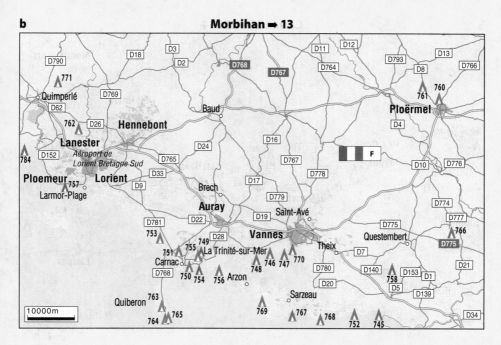

43

a — Saint-Malo/Mont Saint-Michel ➡ 13

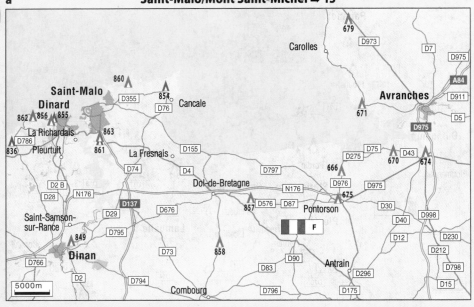

b — Calvados ➡ 13 / 14

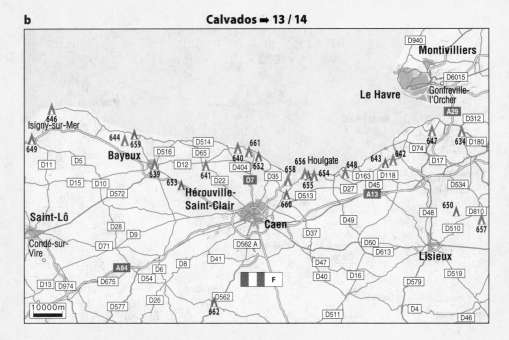

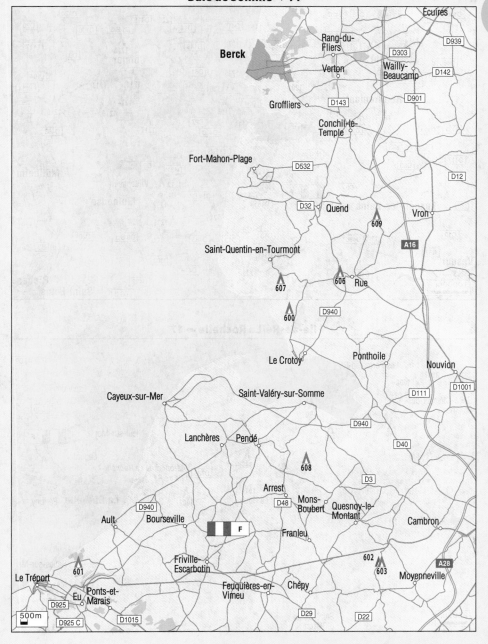

a

Vosges ➡ 16

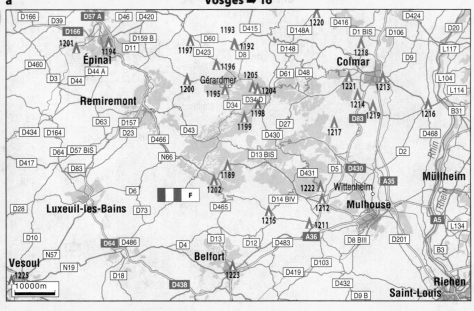

b

Ile-de-Ré/La Rochelle ➡ 17

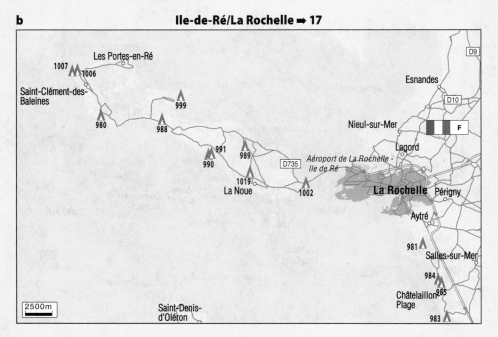

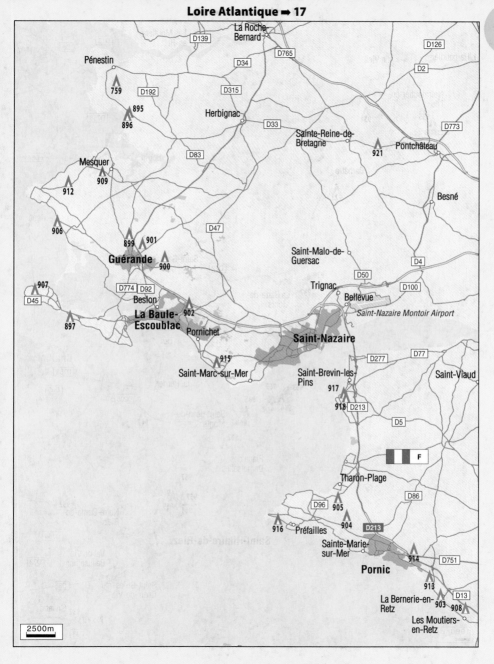

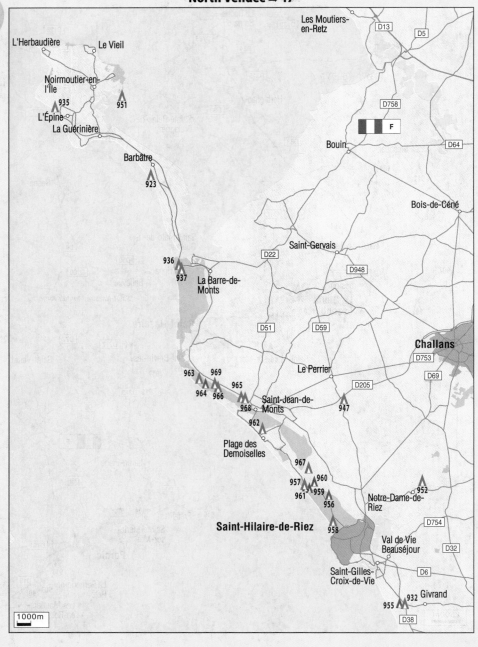

47

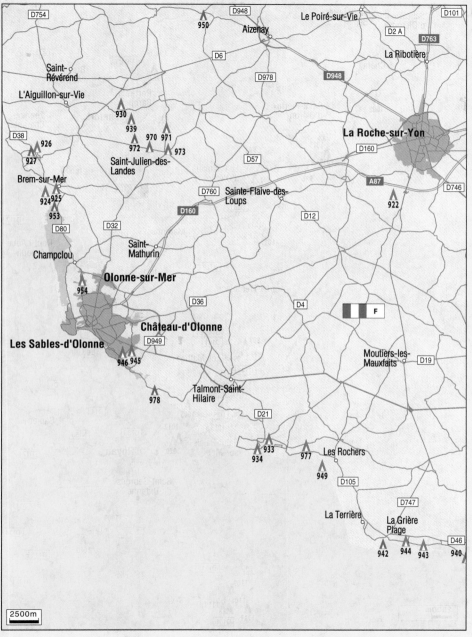

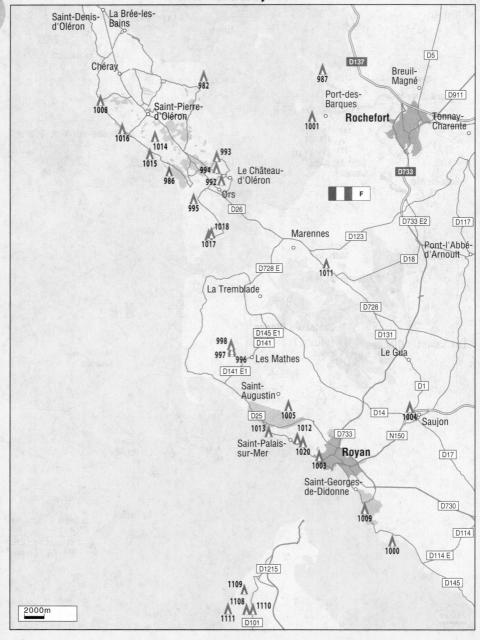

49

Saint-Denis-
d'Oléron

La Brée-les-
Bains

Chéray

982

1008

Saint-Pierre-
d'Oléron

1016

1014

1015

986

993

994

992

995

Le Château-
d'Oléron

Ors

D26

1018

1017

D728 E

Marennes

D123

1011

La Tremblade

D728

D145 E1
D141

998

997

996 Les Mathes

D141 E1

Saint-
Augustin

D25

1005

1013

1012

D733

1020

1003

Royan

Saint-Palais-
sur-Mer

Saint-Georges-
de-Didonne

1009

1000

D1215

1109

1108   1110

1111

D101

987

Port-des-
Barques

1001

D137

D5

Breuil-
Magné

D911

Rochefort

Tonnay-
Charente

D733

F

D733 E2

D117

D18

Pont-l'Abbé-
d'Arnoult

D131

Le Gua

D1

D14

1004

Saujon

N150

D17

D730

D114

D114 E

D145

2000m

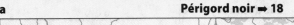

a — Périgord noir ➡ 18

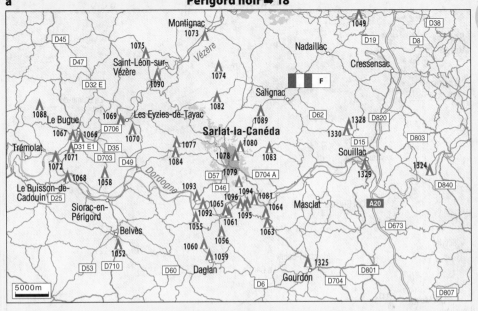

50

Montignac
1073

D45

1075

Saint-Léon-sur-Vézère

D47

D32 E

1090

1074

Nadaillac

D19

D8

D38

Cressensac

Salignac

F

1082

1088

Le Bugue

1069

Les Eyzies-de-Tayac

1089

D62

1328

D820

1067

1066

D706

1070

1330

Sarlat-la-Canéda

Souillac

D15

D803

Trémolat

D31 E1

D35

1077

1080

D840

1071

D703

1084

1078

1083

1324

1072

D49

Dordogne

1079

D704 A

1329

1068

1058

D57

D46

1094

1081

Masclat

A20

Le Buisson-de-Cadouin

D25

1093

1096

1064

Siorac-en-Périgord

1092

1065

1095

D673

1055

1061

D801

Belvès

1056

1063

D807

1060

1325

1052

1059

Gourdon

D53

D710

D60

Daglan

D6

D704

5000m

b — Puy-de-Dôme ➡ 18 / 19

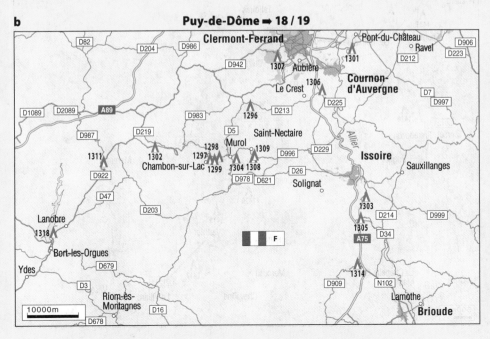

Clermont-Ferrand

D82

D204

D986

Pont-du-Château

Ravel

D906

D942

1301

D212

D223

1307

Aubière

Cournon-d'Auvergne

Le Crest

1306

D225

D7

D997

D1089

D2089

A89

D983

1296

D213

Aller

Saint-Nectaire

D987

D219

D5

Issoire

1311

1302

1298

Murol

1309

D996

D229

Sauxillanges

1297

1299

1304

1308

D26

Chambon-sur-Lac

D922

D978

D621

Solignat

Lanobre

D47

D203

1303

D214

D999

1318

1305

A75

D34

Bort-les-Orgues

D679

1314

Ydes

D3

D909

N102

Riom-ès-Montagnes

D16

Lamothe

10000m

D678

Brioude

F

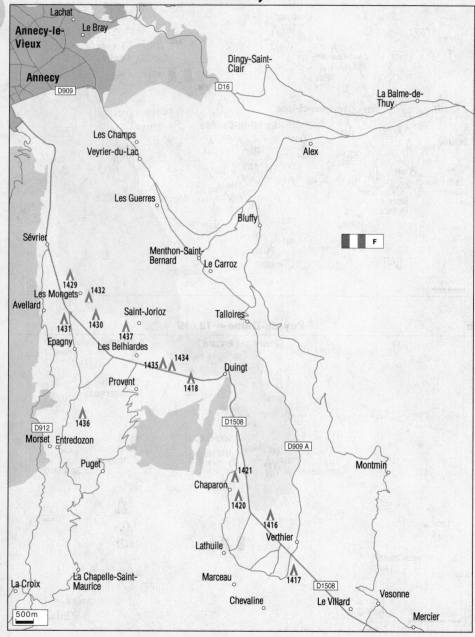

51

Lachat
Le Bray
Annecy-le-
Vieux
Annecy
D909

Dingy-Saint-
Clair
D16
La Balme-de-
Thuy

Les Champs
Veyrier-du-Lac
Alex

Les Guerres
Bluffy

Sévrier
Menthon-Saint-
Bernard
Le Carroz

1429
Les Mongets   1432
Avellard
1431   1430
Epagny
Saint-Jorioz
Talloires
1437
Les Belhiardes
1435 1434
Provent
1418
Duingt

1436
Morset Entredozon
D912
Puget
D1508
D909 A
Montmin

Chaparon
1421
1420
1416
Verthier
Lathuile

La Croix
La Chapelle-Saint-
Maurice
Marceau
1417
D1508
Vesonne
Chevaline
Le Villard
Mercier

F

500m

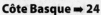

a — Côte Basque ➡ 24

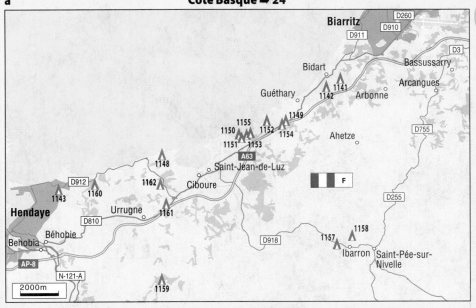

Biarritz
D260
D910
D911
D3
Bidart
Bassussarry
1141
Arcangues
Guéthary
1142
Arbonne
1149
D755
1155
1150
1152
1151 1153
1154
Ahetze
A63
1148
Saint-Jean-de-Luz
F
1162
Ciboure
D912
D255
1160
1143
1161
Hendaye
Urrugne
D810
D918
1158
Béhobie
1157
Behobia
Ibarron
Saint-Pée-sur-Nivelle
AP-8
N-121-A
2000m
1159

b — Quercy ➡ 25

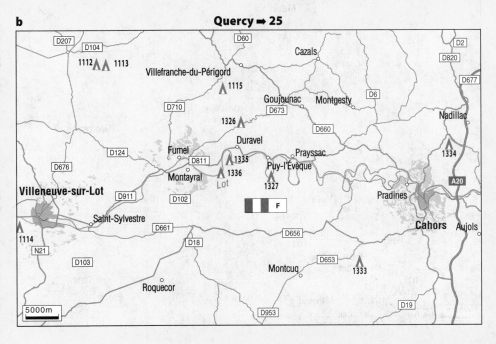

D207
D104
D60
Cazals
D2
1112   1113
D820
Villefranche-du-Périgord
D677
1115
D6
Goujounac
Montgesty
D710
D673
Nadillac
1326
D660
Duravel
Fumel
Prayssac
1335
Puy-l'Évêque
1334
D124
D811
1336
A20
D676
Montayral
1327
Lot
Villeneuve-sur-Lot
D911
D102
Pradines
Cahors
Saint-Sylvestre
F
D661
D656
Aujols
1114
N21
D18
D653
D103
Montcuq
1333
Roquecor
D19
5000m
D953

52

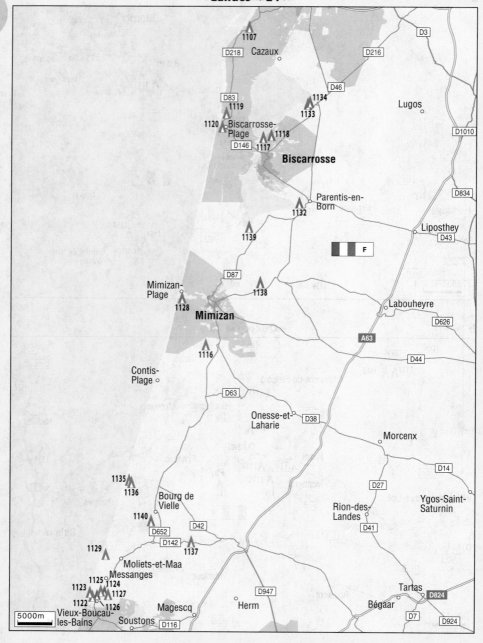

D3

D218   Cazaux   D216

1107

D46

D83   1134
1119   1133   Lugos

1120   Biscarrosse-
Plage   1118
D146   1117

Biscarrosse   D1010

D834

Parentis-en-
Born   Liposthey

1132   D43

1139

F

D87

Mimizan-   1138   Labouheyre
Plage

1128   D626

Mimizan   A63

D44

1116

Contis-
Plage

D63

Onesse-et-
Laharie   D38

Morcenx

D14

1135   D27
1136   Bourg de
Vielle   Ygos-Saint-
Saturnin

1140   Rion-des-
Landes

D652   D42   D41

D142

1129   1137

Moliets-et-Maa
1125   Messanges
1123   1124   Tartas   D824
1122   1127
1126
Vieux-Boucau-   Magescq   Herm   Bégaar
les-Bains
5000m   Soustons   D947   D7   D924
D116

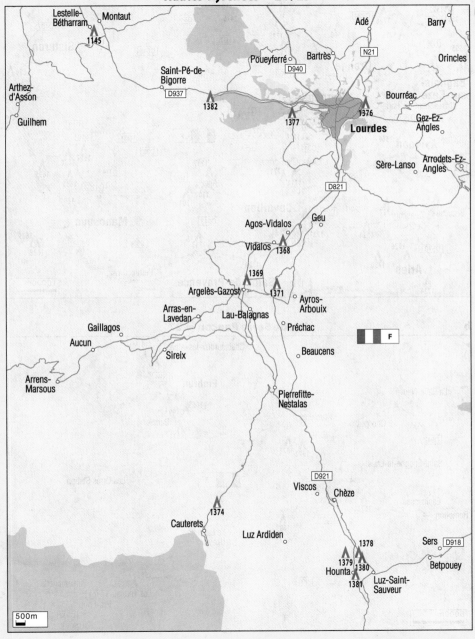

54

Lestelle-
Bétharram
Montaut
1145

Saint-Pé-de-
Bigorre
D937
1382

Poueyferré
D940
Bartrès
Adé
N21
Barry
Orincles

Arthez-
d'Asson
Guilhem

1377
1376
Bourréac
Gez-Ez-
Angles

Lourdes

Sère-Lanso
Arrodets-Ez-
Angles

D821

Agos-Vidalos
Géu
Vidalos
1368

1369

Argelès-Gazost
1371
Ayros-
Arbouix

Arras-en-
Lavedan
Lau-Balagnas
Préchac

Gaillagos
Beaucens

Aucun
Sireix

F

Arrens-
Marsous

Pierrefitte-
Nestalas

D921
Viscos
Chèze

1374

Cauterets
Luz Ardiden

Sers
D918
1378

1379
1380
Hounta
1381
Luz-Saint-
Sauveur
Betpouey

500m

a

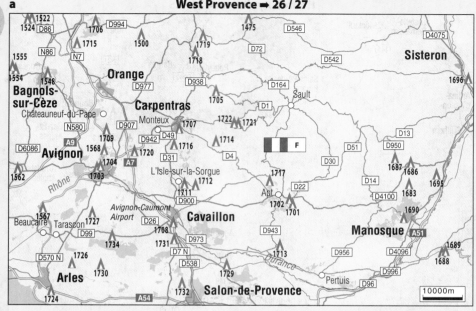

b Lac de Serre Ponçon ➡ 27

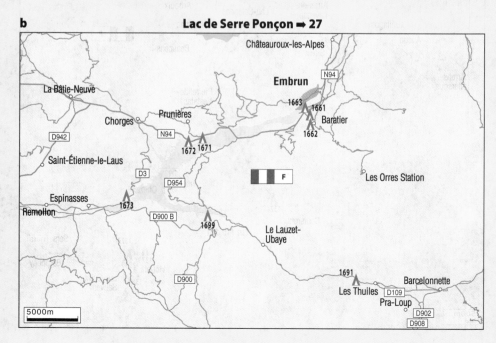

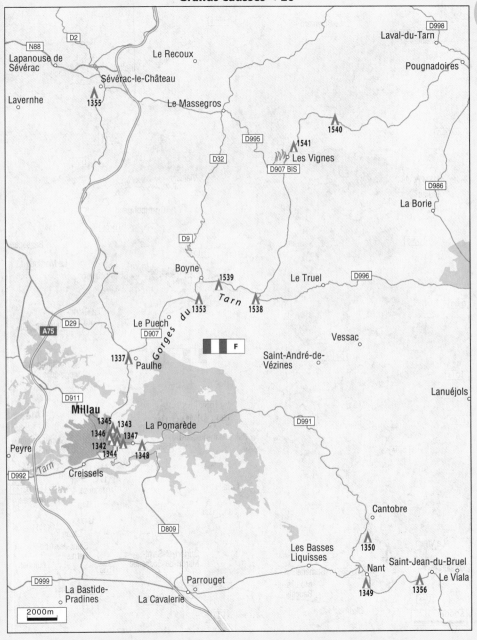

57

Saint-Étienne-du-Valdonnez

Le Bleymard

D901

Villefort

D907 BIS

D998

Vialas

D51

1536 1535
Florac

D906

Chamborigaud

1561
Bessèges

D983

N106

Le Martinet

D996

Le Collet-de-Dèze

Champclauson

La Grand-Combe

L'Habitarelle

D9

F

Saint-Martin-de-Valgalgues

D18

D269

Alès

D260

1565 1564 1560

Saint-Christol-lès-Alès

D986

Saint-Jean-du-Gard

D907

1543

1558

Montèze

Lasalle

1544
1546 1545
Anduze

Bagard

D24 D6110

Les Tavernes

1556

1550

1547

1551

Lézan

Le Vigan

Saint-Jean-de-Serres

Rochebelle

1557

D999

Sumène

Durfort-et-Saint-Martin-de-Sossenac

D35

Lédignan

D48

Moulès-et-Baucels

D982

5000m

Cazilhac

Sauve

D25

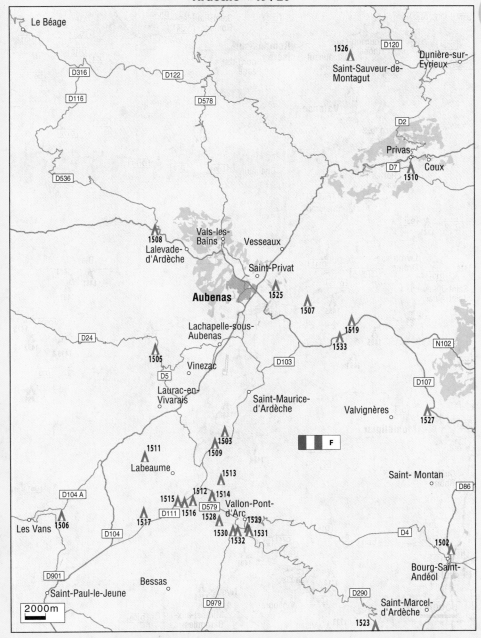

Le Béage

D316   D122

D116

D578

1526
Saint-Sauveur-de-
Montagut   D120   Dunière-sur-
Eyrieux

D2

D536   Privas
D7
1510   Coux

1508   Vals-les-
Bains   Vesseaux
Lalevade-
d'Ardèche   Saint-Privat

Aubenas   1525   1507

Lachapelle-sous-
Aubenas   1519
1533   N102

D24   1505   D103
D5   Vinezac
Laurac-en-
Vivarais   Saint-Maurice-
d'Ardèche   Valvignères   D107
1527

1511   1503
Labeaume   1509   F

1513   Saint- Montan

1515   1512 1514   D86
D104 A   D111 1516   D579   Vallon-Pont-
d'Arc   1528   1529
Les Vans   1506   1517   1530   1531
D104   1532   D4   1502

D901   Bessas   Bourg-Saint-
Andéol
Saint-Paul-le-Jeune   D290   Saint-Marcel-
d'Ardèche
2000m   D979
1523

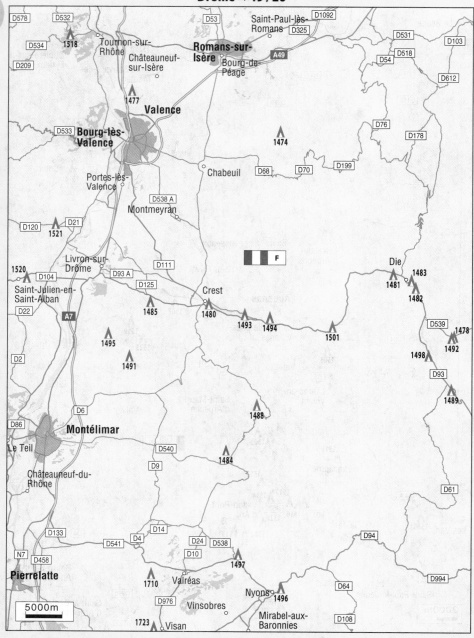

5000m

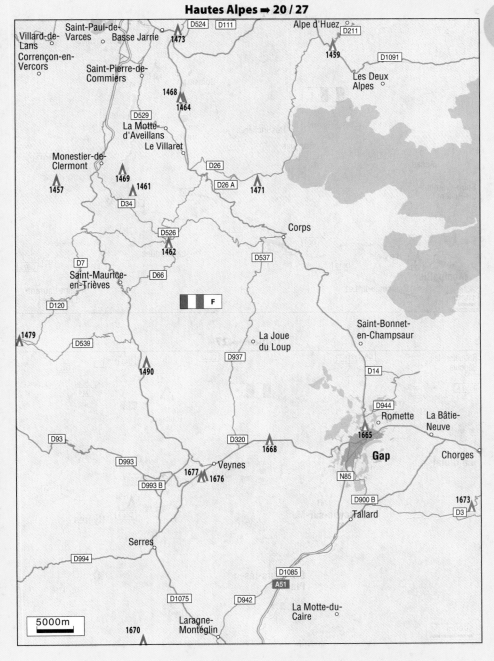

Montpellier ➡ 26

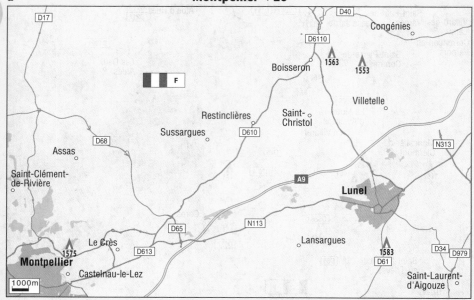

Toulon ➡ 27

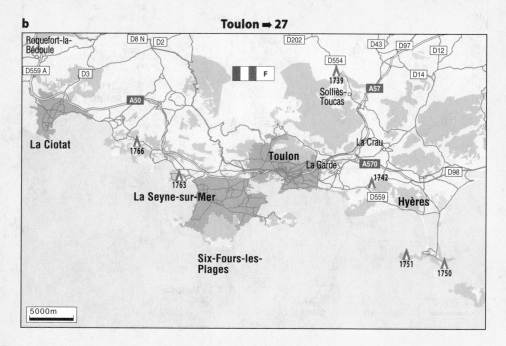

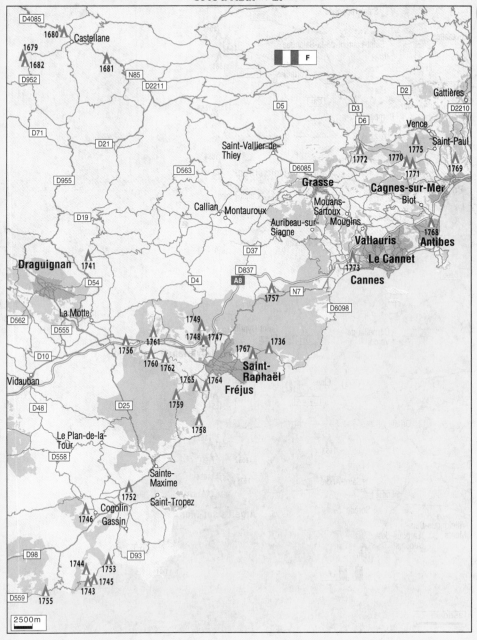

D4085
1680
1679
Castellane
1682
1681
D952
N85
D2211

F

D2
Gattières
D5
D3
D2210
D6
Vence
Saint-Paul
D71
1775
1772
1770
1769
D21
Saint-Vallier-de-
Thiey
1771
D563
D6085
Grasse
Cagnes-sur-Mer
D955
Biot
D19
Callian
Montauroux
Mouans-
Sartoux
Auribeau-sur-
Siagne
Mougins
Vallauris
1768
Antibes
D37
1741
D54
Draguignan
D4
D837
A8
Le Cannet
1773
N7
Cannes
1757
La Motte
D562
D6098
D555
1749
D10
1761
1748 1747
1736
1756
1767
Vidauban
1760 1762
Saint-
Raphaël
1765 1764
D48
D25
Fréjus
1759
1758
Le Plan-de-la-
Tour
D558
Sainte-
Maxime
1752
Saint-Tropez
Cogolin
1746
Gassin
D98
D93
1744
1753
1745
D559
1743
1755

2500m

63

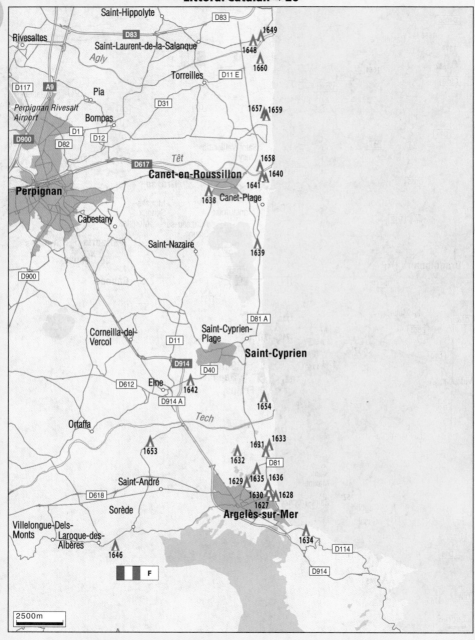

Saint-Hippolyte

D83

Rivesaltes

D83

Saint-Laurent-de-la-Salanque

Agly

1649
1648

1660

D117   A9

Pia

Torreilles

D11 E

Perpignan Rivesalt Airport

D31

1657 1659

Bompas

D900

D1

D82   D12

Têt

D617

1658
1640

Canet-en-Roussillon

Perpignan

1641

1638   Canet-Plage

Cabestany

Saint-Nazaire

1639

D900

Corneilla-del-Vercol

D81 A

Saint-Cyprien-Plage

D11

Saint-Cyprien

D914

D40

D612   Elne

1642

D914 A

1654

Tech

Ortaffa

1653

1631 1633

1632

D81

Saint-André

1629 1635 1636

D618

1630   1628

Sorède

1627

Argelès-sur-Mer

Villelongue-Dels-Monts

Laroque-des-Albères

1646

1634

D114

F

D914

2500m

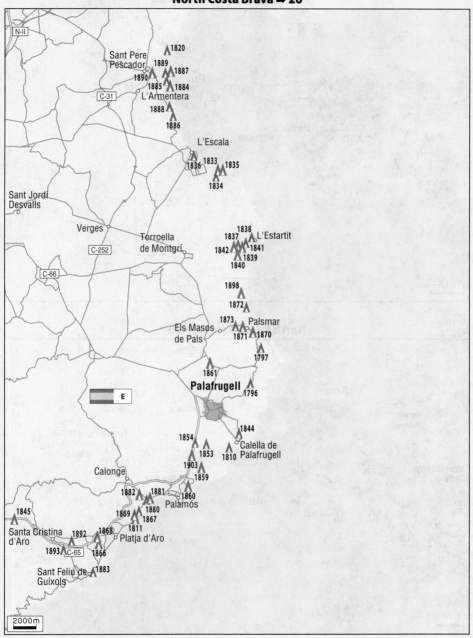

N-II

Sant Pere
Pescador
∧1820
1889
1887
1890
1885 1884
L'Armentera
1888
1886

C-31

L'Escala
1836 1833 1835
1834

Sant Jordi
Desvalls

Verges

Torroella
de Montgrí
C-252

C-66

1838
1837 L'Estartit
1842 1841
1839
1840

1898
1872
1873 Palsmar
Els Masos 1871 1870
de Pals
1797

1861
Palafrugell
1796

E

1844

1854
Calella de
1853 Palafrugell
1810
Calonge
1903
1859

1882 1881
1860
1869 1880 Palamós
1811 1867
1845
1892 1868
Santa Cristina
d'Aro 1866
1893 C-65
Platja d'Aro
Sant Feliu de 1883
Guíxols

2000m

a

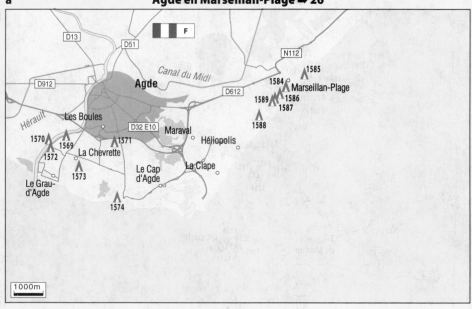

F

1000m

b

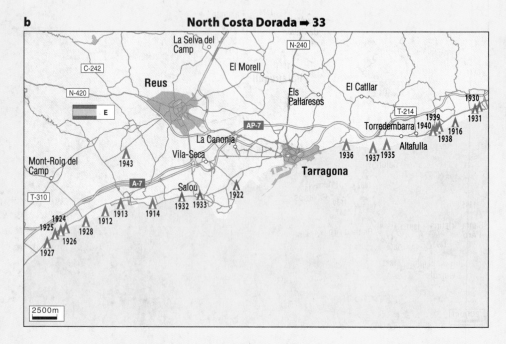

E

2500m

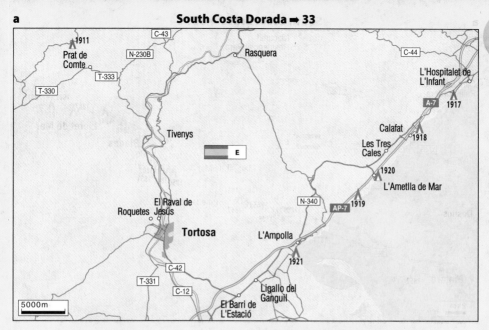

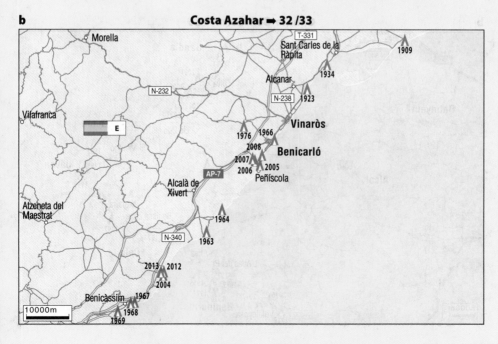

a South Costa Brava ➡ 33 / 34

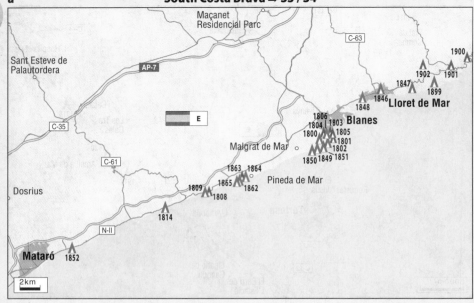

b Gandia-Benidorm ➡ 39

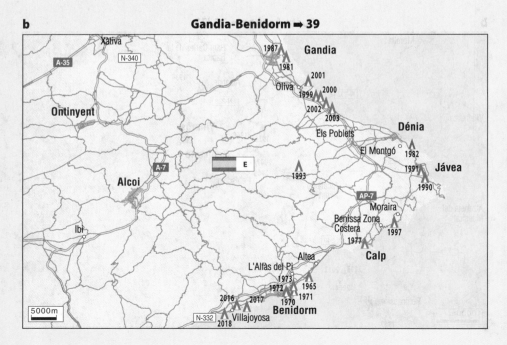

Advertisement index

Advertisement index

Place name index

A

B

D

F

H

Place name index

M

Q

R

S

W

Acknowledgements

2018 • 1st edition
Print run: 20.000
ACSI Campsite Guide is an ACSI initiative.
This ACSI Campsite Guide is a publication of
ACSI Publishing BV
PO Box 34, 6670 AA Zetten
The Netherlands
Telephone +31 (0)488 - 471434
Fax +31 (0)488 - 454210

Questions or comments?
For campers: *www.acsi.eu/customerservice*
For campsites: *www.acsi.eu/sales*

Printing
Westermann Druck GmbH
Braunschweig, Germany

ISBN: 978-94-92023-56-8

Editor-in-chief
Emily Venekant

Editorial staff
Mariska Adriaans, Richelle Alewijn, Suzanne Bas,
Jet Bouwmans, Peter Dellepoort, Rein Driessens,
Ellen Floor, Bobo Freeke, Rik Hoitink, Jasper de
Kinkelder, Seline Konings, Daniëlle Knobbout,
Marieke Krämer, Ton Oppers, Eric-Jan Rood,
Mariëlle Rouwenhorst-Küper, Thijs Saat, Esther
Schoonderbeek, Daniël Uleman, Lucia Velthuis

Translation
Vertaalbureau Noorderlicht BV, Den Haag
www.vertaalbureau-noorderlicht.nl

Maps
MapCreator BV, 5628 WB Eindhoven
mapcreator.eu/©Here/©Andes

ACSI office in Andelst